FOUNDATIONS OF MATHEMATICS

with Geometry, Trigonometry, and Statistics

Online Lessons

- Contain highly engaging and interactive videos that use cutting-edge Cloud Learning technologies.
- Break down math concepts into logical and intuitive steps that enhance the learning process.
- Prepare students for upcoming classes, labs, and quizzes through self-study lessons.
- Contain lessons that are self-paced and are excellent for visual learners.

Online Labs

- Contain a comprehensive test-bank of real-world problems, which may be used as an assessment tool.
- Break down every answer into dynamic, step-by-step solutions that include calculator methods of solving problems.
- Provide unlimited amount of practice through algorithmically generated problems.
- Contain numerous statistical tools to analyze students' strengths and weaknesses.

Vretta™

FOUNDATIONS OF MATHEMATICS

with Geometry, Trigonometry, and Statistics

Second Edition

Thambyrajah Kugathasan, *Seneca College*

Erin Kox, *Fanshawe College*

Vretta

ISBN 978-1-927737-12-5

Foundations of Mathematics with Geometry, Trigonometry, and Statistics, Second Edition

Textbook printed in Canada.

Authors: Thambyrajah Kugathasan and Erin Kox

Developmental and Copy Editors: Lakshmi Kugathasan and Arbane Miftari
Art Director: Aleksandar Vozarevic
Solution Manual Editors: Banpreet Singh, Rrezane Miftari, and Leo Han
Assistant Editor: Heather Bewley

Instructional Designers: Charles Anifowose and Ali Alavi
Test Bank and PowerPoint Editor: Arbane Miftari
Technology Systems: Zach Williams
Marketing Director: Lionel Loganathan

Expert Advice: TK Academic Consulting Inc.
Turning Technologies' Student Response System (Clickers) Integrated into PowerPoint Presentations
Online Resources: Vretta's Cloud Learning™ Technologies

Preface

Mathematics is for everyone.

Why is it so important to have a strong foundation in Mathematics? You simply cannot avoid its influence or impact on our culture and society in the 21st century. In fact, Mathematics has been critical in the development of civilizations throughout history. The way we organize and analyze our surroundings, from the most basic level to some of the most complex concepts and technologies related to Biology, Chemistry, Physics, Business, Finance and the Information Technology, stem from these foundations. Mathematics has played an integral part in influencing and shaping our lives.

Most importantly, Mathematics is vital to functioning in everyday life. Have you ever calculated the amount of tax on a purchase? Have you calculated amounts for ingredients in a recipe? Can you interpret player statistics displayed at sporting events? How much will a tank of gas cost for your car? Have you calculated your budget of living expenses in relation to your income? As a marketing or business professional, you may be responsible for devising product pricing strategies; as a human resource professional, you may be required to calculate payroll for employees; as a business manager, you may be responsible for ensuring cost efficiencies to maintain a profit; as a fashion designer, you may need to calculate amounts of material needed and related costs. These are just a few examples of the many ways in which foundational mathematics is necessary to succeed in today's world.

The Foundations of Mathematics resources have been built for students just like you: future professionals who will need strong foundational skills in the basics in order to succeed in daily life and your profession of choice.

Mathematics, with its diverse applications, attracts a broad range of students from varying disciplines, who learn best using different methods and styles. To optimize the learning experience, we have leveraged cutting-edge technologies and mediums of delivery available in the 21st century to provide students with highly immersive and engaging learning experiences. As each student has their own preferred learning style, our team has worked to give students access to innovative tools using diverse methods of teaching. Students have access to four distinct methods of learning: utilizing interactive online lessons, attempting tracked lab assessments, perusing student PowerPoints, and by learning via the e-textbook and textbook.

At Vretta, we believe that if you learn mathematics, you will live smarter and your success will be enhanced. As you embark on the journey of learning and mastering this important subject, we hope that the blended, hybrid resources for the Foundations of Mathematics will provide great value in helping you along the way.

Kuga, Erin, and Team Vretta

Brief Contents

Contents

Chapter 4
Ratios and Proportions

Chapter 5
Percents and Percent Changes

Chapter 6
Applications of Ratios and Percents

Chapter 7
Units of Measurement

Chapter 8
Basic Algebra

Chapter 9

Graphs and Systems of Linear Equations

Chapter 10

Basic Geometry

Chapter 11
Basic Trigonometry

Chapter 12
Basic Statistics and Probability

List of Tables and Exhibits

Tables

Exhibits

Acknowledgements

The authors and Vretta would like to thank the following professors for their detailed feedback on helping us update the Second Edition of the Foundations of Mathematics textbook and its accompanying online resources:

- Andrea Learmonth, Conestoga College
- Amy Hoang, Niagara College
- Beth Condino, Niagara College
- Gina Kerr, St. Lawrence College
- Irene Lee, Humber College
- Jenna Ritchie, Humber College
- Lisa Koster, Conestoga College
- Mary Richmond, Seneca College
- Melanie Christian, St. Lawrence College
- Nasim Naji, Centennial College
- Sean Saunders, Sheridan College
- Soobia Siddiqui, Fleming College

Resources

Textbook

Language and Illustrations The Foundations of Mathematics textbook has been carefully tailored keeping the student in mind. The language, along with the accompanying illustrations, are simple and straight-forward, while maintaining the levels of sophistication required to thoroughly prepare students for the next stage in their academic and professional careers.

Pedagogies and Learning Methods The Foundations of Mathematics textbook has been developed by incorporating numerous research-backed pedagogies and learning methods. These pedagogies have been developed and used for over 30 years, successfully with thousands of students across the country. The pedagogies have succeeded in simplifying critical mathematical concepts and significantly improving the retention of core concepts. Additionally, in order to cater to the varied learning student styles, the examples provide different methods of solving problems.

Calculator In addition to providing various methods to solve problems, the Foundations of Mathematics textbook contains instructions to solve problems using calculators, wherever applicable. The calculator instructions are designed using the actual images of the calculator keys, making it easy for students to follow the sequence of operations.

Exercises The Foundations of Mathematics textbook has over 3,000 exercises, review exercises, self-test exercises, as well as over 425 solved examples. The problems are designed to test students on real-world, practical applications and are presented in increasing levels of difficulty, with the most difficult problems being indicated by a dot (•). The problems are categorized into pairs of similar questions to provide professors with an opportunity to solve the even-numbered problems in class and assign the odd numbered problems as homework.

Solution Manuals

The Foundations of Mathematics resource includes solution manuals that are available online. All the problems in the end-of-section exercises, review exercises, and self-test exercises have been solved using detailed step-by-step methods. Instructors have access to Instructor Solution Manuals that contain solutions to all problems. Students have access to Student Solution Manuals that contain solutions to the odd problems for the end-of-section exercises and review exercises, and all problems for the self-test exercises. The manuals are available in MS Word format so that instructors can modify problems as per their requirement.

PowerPoint Presentations

The Foundations of Mathematics resource includes animated PowerPoint presentations (PPTs) that contain both the algebraic and calculator methods of solving problems. They are also designed to work with clickers to gauge student-understanding of concepts.
The following PPTs are available for use in this resource:

- Instructor PPTs contain answers to all questions that appear in a step-by-step animated form. These can only be viewed in the PPT slide-show mode.
- Student Handouts do not contain answers to problems. They can be printed out and provided to students for them to work through the problems in class. All students have access to the Student Handouts.
- Delayered PPTs are the same as Instructor PPTs, but they have no animations.

The PPTs have been provided in an open format for instructors to make changes to them as per their requirement.

Test Bank

A comprehensive test bank, of 3000+ problems in varying levels of difficulty, that covers all concepts in the textbook is provided for professors to use as a database for exercises, quizzes, cases, group projects, or assignments.

Online Lessons

The online lessons are created as a pre-study component for students. They contain pedagogies that are highly interactive and engaging, and which teach concepts in a very logical and intuitive way. These lessons are not PowerPoint presentations but are interactive movies that have been created to enrich and enhance the learning experience. Every frame is locked to ensure that students go through the lessons sequentially as they are designed to build on learning concepts in succession. The system automatically records students' progress and performance. Once students complete a lesson, the frame unlocks itself, allowing students to navigate back and forth through the lesson. Professors, on the other hand, have administrative access which allows them to navigate through the online lessons without any restrictions.

Online Labs

The online lab assessment system contains a rich comprehensive test bank of real-world problems that are algorithmically generated and that provide students with dynamic feedback on their responses. The labs can also be customized based on course requirements. A few of the customizable features include, previewing and selecting questions, setting the number of questions, setting and modifying start and due dates, opening, closing and re-opening labs, creating new labs and quizzes, and determining the weighting and number of attempts for each question.

Administrative Tools

The following administrative tools will provide professors with the ability to monitor overall class performance and individual student performance on online lessons and labs.

Performance Dashboard for Professors

The lesson performance dashboard provides professors with the average completion percentage per chapter, including a lesson-by-lesson percentage completed visualization for the entire class. The lab performance dashboard provides them with the average percentage mark on each lab for the class. Professors can also download or export individual grades for lessons and labs to a spreadsheet or to the college's course management system.

Performance Dashboard for Students

The lesson performance dashboard provides students with their chapter completion mark, including a lesson-by-lesson percentage completed visualization. The lab performance dashboard provides them with their lab percentage marks.

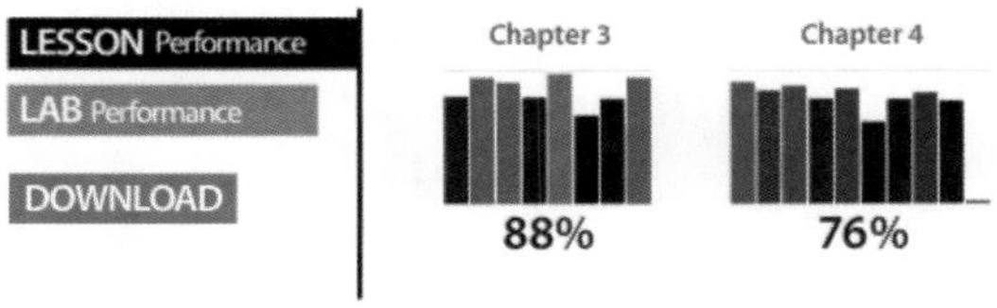

Lab Management System

The lab management system is provided for administrators or subject leaders to create new labs, quizzes and case studies, preview and select questions, set the number of questions, set and modify start and due dates, open, close and re-open labs, and determine the weighting and number of attempts for each question.

FOUNDATIONS OF MATHEMATICS

with Geometry, Trigonometry, and Statistics

Second Edition

Thambyrajah Kugathasan, *Seneca College*

Erin Kox, *Fanshawe College*

Vretta

1 WHOLE NUMBERS

Arithmetic is the elementary branch of mathematics that we use in everyday life. When we count, we use arithmetic; when we perform the simple operations of addition, subtraction, multiplication, and division, we use principles of arithmetic. We use arithmetic for everyday tasks such as buying, selling, estimating expenses, and checking bank balances. Arithmetic is woven into our general interaction with the real world, and as such, it forms the basis of all science, technology, engineering, and business. In this chapter, you will learn about mathematical operations involving whole numbers, including powers and roots of perfect squares.

LEARNING OBJECTIVES

- Identify whole numbers.
- Read, write, and round whole numbers correctly.
- Solve problems involving arithmetic operations, whole numbers, and signed numbers.
- Perform order of operations with whole numbers.
- Determine the lowest common multiple and highest common factor.

CHAPTER OUTLINE

1.1 | Understanding Whole Numbers

Introduction

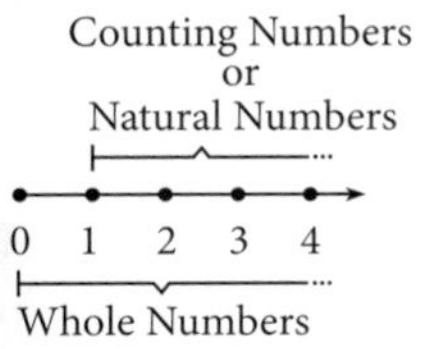

Whole numbers are simply the numbers 0, 1, 2, 3, 4.... They include all counting numbers, also known as natural numbers or positive integers (1, 2, 3, 4...), and zero (0).

All whole numbers are integers. However, whole numbers and integers are not the same because integers include counting numbers (positive integers) and their negatives (negative integers).

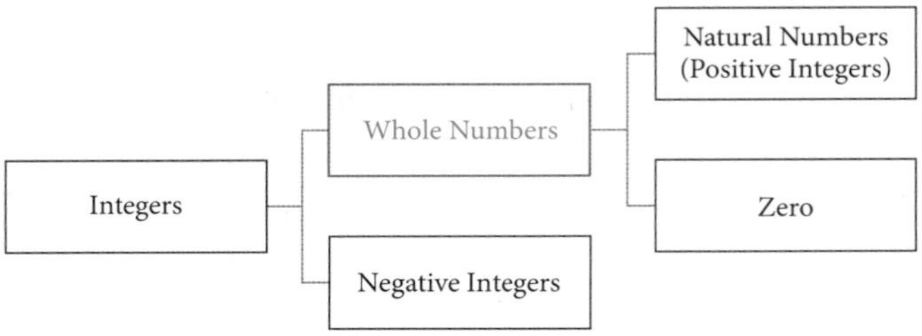

Place Value of Whole Numbers

All numbers can be made up using the digits **0, 1, 2, 3, 4, 5, 6, 7, 8, and 9**. Numbers may consist of one or more digits. When a number is written using the above digits, it is said to be in **standard form**.

For example, 7, 85, and 2,349 are examples of numbers in their standard form where 7 is a single- (one) digit number, 85 is a two-digit number, and 2,349 is a four-digit number.

The **position** of each digit in a whole number determines the **place value** for the digit.

Exhibit 1.1-a illustrates the place value of the ten digits in the whole number, 3,867,254,129. In this whole number, 4 occupies the 'thousands' place value and represents 4 thousand, or 4,000; whereas 7 occupies the 'millions' place value and represents 7 million, or 7,000,000.

We read and write numbers from the left to the right. A comma (or alternatively, a space) separates every three digits into groups, starting from the place value for 'ones', thereby making it easier to read a whole number.

The place value of 'ones' is 10^0 (= 1) and each position has a value 10 times the place value to its right, as shown in Table 1.1.

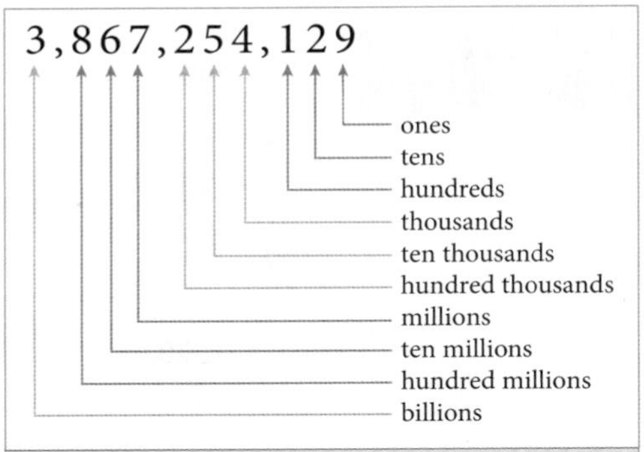

Exhibit 1.1-a Place Value of a Ten-Digit Whole Number

Table 1.1 **Place Value Chart of Whole Numbers**

10^9	10^8	10^7	10^6	10^5	10^4	10^3	10^2	10^1	10^0
1,000,000,000	100,000,000	10,000,000	1,000,000	100,000	10,000	1,000	100	10	1
Billions	Hundred millions	Ten millions	Millions	Hundred thousands	Ten thousands	Thousands	Hundreds	Tens	Ones

A number in **standard form** is separated into groups of three digits using commas. The vertical red lines in Table 1.1 denote the positions of the commas that separate the groups of three numbers, starting from the place value for 'ones'.

For example, the 10-digit whole number in Exhibit 1.1-a, written as 3,867,254,129, is represented in its standard form for writing numbers.

3	8	6	7	2	5	4	1	2	9

Numbers can be written in standard form and in expanded form using figures, or in word form.

For example, number 3,867,254,129 in standard form can be written in **expanded form**, as follows:

3,000,000,000 + 800,000,000 + 60,000,000 + 7,000,000 + 200,000

+ 50,000 + 4,000 + 100 + 20 + 9

Or

3 billion + 800 million + 60 million + 7 million + 200 thousand

+ 50 thousand + 4 thousand + 1 hundred + 2 tens + 9 ones

This can also be written in **word form**, as follows:

Three billion, eight hundred sixty-seven million, two hundred fifty-four thousand, one hundred twenty-nine.

Example 1.1-a **Identifying the Place Value of a Digit and the Amount it Represents**

What is the place value of the digit 5 in each of the following numbers and what amount does it represent?

(i) $2,543 (ii) $75,342 (iii) $6,521,890 (iv) $915,203,847

Solution

	(i) $2,543	(ii) $75,342	(iii) $6,521,890	(iv) $915,203,847
Place value of the digit 5:	Hundreds	Thousands	Hundred Thousands	Millions
Amount it represents:	$500	$5,000	$500,000	$5,000,000

Example 1.1-b **Identifying the Digit of a Number Given its Place Value**

In the number 5,320,948 identify the digit that occupies the following place values:

(i) Hundred thousands (ii) Ten thousands (iii) Thousands

(iv) Tens (v) Hundreds (vi) Millions

Solution

(i) 5,320,948 ↑ Hundred thousands

(ii) 5,320,948 ↑ Ten thousands

(iii) 5,320,948 ↑ Thousands

(iv) 5,320,948 ↑ Tens

(v) 5,320,948 ↑ Hundreds

(vi) 5,320,948 ↑ Millions

Example 1.1-c **Writing Numbers in Expanded Form**

Write the following numbers in expanded form:

(i) 698 (ii) 8,564 (iii) 49,005

(iv) 521,076 (v) 9,865,323 (vi) 43,583,621

Solution

(i) 698

600 + 90 + 8

(ii) 8,564

8,000 + 500 + 60 + 4

Solution
continued

(iii) 49,005

40,000 + 9,000 + 5

(iv) 521,076

500,000 + 20,000 + 1,000 + 70 + 6

(v) 9,865,323

9,000,000 + 800,000 + 60,000 + 5,000 + 300 + 20 + 3

(vi) 43,583,621

40,000,000 + 3,000,000 + 500,000 + 80,000 + 3,000 + 600 + 20 + 1

Reading and Writing Whole Numbers

To make it easier to read and write numbers, any number larger than three digits is separated into smaller groups of three digits, starting from the last digit of the number. Each group of these three digits has a name.

- The first group of 3 digits on the right is the "**Units**" group.
- The second group from the right is the "**Thousands**" group.
- The third group from the right is the "**Millions**" group.
- The fourth group from the right is the "**Billions**" group.
- The fifth group from the right is the "**Trillions**" group and so on, as shown in the following chart.

Trillions			Billions			Millions			Thousands			Units		
Hundreds	Tens	Ones	Hundreds	Tens	Ones	Hundreds	Tens	Ones	Hundreds	Tens	Ones	Hundreds	Tens	Ones

Follow these steps to write large numbers in word form:

Step 1: Start from the group furthest to the left and write the number formed by the digits in that group, followed by the name of the group.

Step 2: Moving to the next group (to the right), write the numbers formed by this next group, followed by its name. Continue to do this for each of the groups.

Step 3: For the last group (i.e., the group furthest to the right), write the numbers formed by the group; however, for this group, do not write the name of it.

Note: When a group contains all zeros, that group is never read or written.

Also, commas and hyphens are used when expressing numbers in word form.

- Commas (,) are used between the groups to separate them.
- Hyphens (-) are used to express the two digit numbers in each group;

  i.e., 21 to 29, 31 to 39, 41 to 49,...91 to 99.

For example, 2,835,197,000,642 expressed in word form using the above rules would be as follows:

Trillions			Billions			Millions			Thousands			Units		
Hundreds	Tens	Ones	Hundreds	Tens	Ones	Hundreds	Tens	Ones	Hundreds	Tens	Ones	Hundreds	Tens	Ones
		2	8	3	5	1	9	7	0	0	0	6	4	2
Two trillion,			eight hundred thirty-five billion,			one hundred ninety-seven million,						six hundred forty-two		

The word 'and' does not appear in the word form of whole numbers.

When writing the numbers in word form, the names of the groups remain in their singular form, irrespective of the number preceeding; i.e., hundred, thousand, million, billion, trillion, etc.

For example:

- Eight **hundred** thirty-five **billion.**
- One **hundred** ninety-seven **million.**

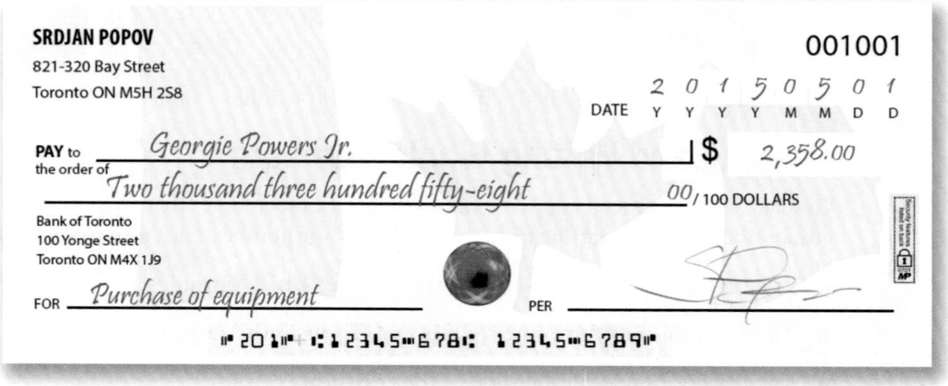

Exhibit 1.1-b Sample of a cheque showing a number expressed in its standard form and word form.

Example 1.1-d Writing Numbers in Word Form Given their Standard Form

Write the following numbers in word form:

(i)	743	(ii)	5,006	(iii)	15,017
(iv)	800,629	(v)	6,783,251	(vi)	52,630,042

Solution

(i)	743	Seven hundred forty-three.
(ii)	5,006	Five thousand, six.
(iii)	15,017	Fifteen thousand, seventeen.
(iv)	800,629	Eight hundred thousand, six hundred twenty-nine.
(v)	6,783,251	Six million, seven hundred eighty-three thousand, two hundred fifty-one.
(vi)	52,630,042	Fifty-two million, six hundred thirty thousand, forty-two.

Example 1.1-e Writing Numbers In Standard Form Given their Word Form

Write the following in standard form:

(i) Two hundred five

(ii) Six thousand, four

(iii) Thirty-five thousand, eight hundred twenty-five

(iv) Eight hundred thousand, five

(v) Two million, three hundred forty-two thousand, six hundred seventeen

(vi) Half of a million

(vii) Three-quarters of a billion

Solution

(i)	Two hundred five	205
(ii)	Six thousand, four	6,004
(iii)	Thirty-five thousand, eight hundred twenty-five	35,825
(iv)	Eight hundred thousand, five	800,005
(v)	Two million, three hundred forty-two thousand, six hundred seventeen	2,342,617
(vi)	Half of a million	$\frac{1}{2} \times 1{,}000{,}000 = 500{,}000$
(vii)	Three-quarters of a billion	$\frac{3}{4} \times 1{,}000{,}000{,}000 = 750{,}000{,}000$

Number Line

Whole numbers can be represented graphically as a point on a horizontal line, called the **number line**, as shown below.

The arrowhead at the end shows that the line continues indifinitely in that direction.

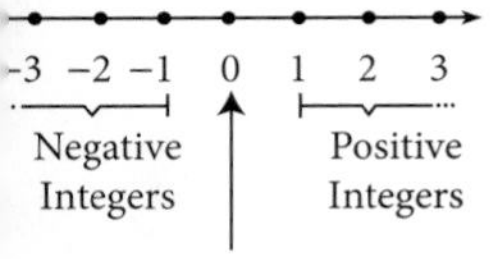

Zero is neither positive nor negative.

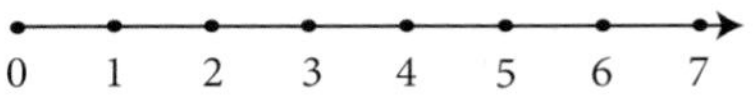

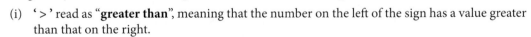

The smallest whole number is zero (0). It is not possible to find the largest whole number because for any given number, there will always be another number greater than that number.

Writing numbers on a number line helps in comparing and identifying numbers that are smaller or larger than other numbers. Numbers that lie to the left of a number on the number line are smaller than the numbers that lie to the right of that number, and vice versa.

For example,

- 6 is greater than 2 (or 2 is less than 6).

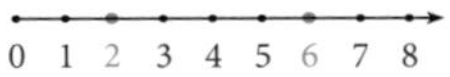

- 5 is less than 7 (or 7 is greater than 5).

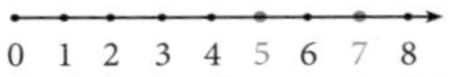

The signs used to show the relative position of two numbers (or quantities) are:

he signs < and > always point owards the smaller number.

(i) ' > ' read as "**greater than**", meaning that the number on the left of the sign has a value greater than that on the right.

For example, "6 is greater than 2" is written as $6 > 2$.

This is the same as "2 is less than 6" and written as $2 < 6$.

(ii) ' < ' read as "**less than**", meaning that the number on the left of the sign has a value less than that on the right.

For example, "5 is less than 7" is written as $5 < 7$.

This is the same as "7 is greater than 5" and written as $7 > 5$.

Example 1.1-f

Graphing Numbers on a Number Line and Using Signs to Show the Relative Positions of the Numbers

For each of the following, graph the numbers on a number line and place the correct sign, < or >, in the spaces between the numbers:

(i) 7 ☐ 11 ☐ 5 (ii) 11 ☐ 12 ☐ 5

(iii) 3 ☐ 5 ☐ 12 (iv) 12 ☐ 7 ☐ 3

Solution

(i) $7 < 11 > 5$

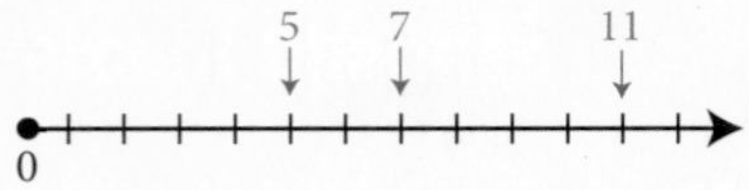

(ii) $11 < 12 > 5$

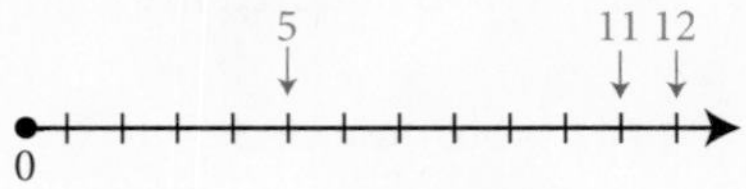

(iii) $3 < 5 < 12$

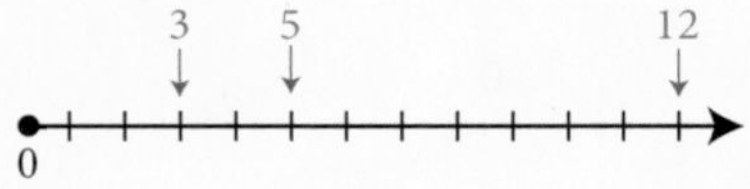

(iv) $12 > 7 > 3$

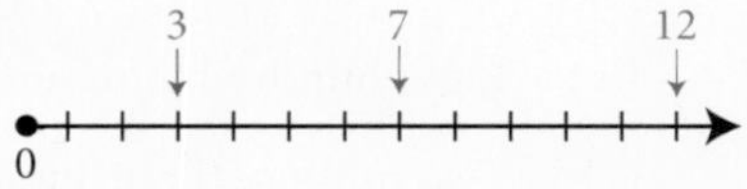

Example 1.1-g

Writing a Statement to Represent ">" or "<"

Write statements using the words "greater than" or "less than" for the following expressions:

(i) $24 > 22$ (ii) $36 < 39$ (iii) $9 > 0$ (iv) $0 < 5$

Solution

(i) $24 > 22$

24 is greater than 22 ***or*** 22 is less than 24.

(ii) $36 < 39$

36 is less than 39 ***or*** 39 is greater than 36.

(iii) $9 > 0$

9 is greater than 0 ***or*** 0 is less than 9.

(iv) $0 < 5$

0 is less than 5 ***or*** 5 is greater than 0.

Rounding Whole Numbers

Rounding numbers makes them easier to work with and easier to remember. Rounding changes some of the digits in a number but keeps its value close to the original. It is used in reporting large quantities or values that change often, such as population, income, expenses, etc.

For example, the population of Canada is approximately 33 million or Henry's car expense for this month is approximately $700.

The rounding of numbers also makes arithmetic operations faster and easier, especially when determining the exact answer is not required.

For example, if you are required to estimate the area of a rectangular plot of land that measures 114 m by 97 m, you would have to multiply 114×97, which would result in 11,058 m^2. However, rounding the measurements to the nearest ten can provide a quick estimate.

For example,

- Rounding 114 m to the nearest ten is 110 m.

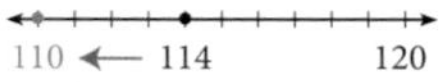

114 is closer to 110 than 120. Therefore, round down to 110.

- Rounding 97 m to the nearest ten is 100 m.

97 is closer to 100 than 90. Therefore, round up to 100.

This would result in an estimated area of $110 \times 100 = 11{,}000\ m^2$.

Rounding Whole Numbers to the Nearest Ten, Hundred, Thousand, etc.

Rounding whole numbers refers to changing the value of the whole number to the nearest ten, hundred, thousand, etc. It is also referred to as rounding whole numbers to multiples of 10, 100, 1,000, etc.

For example,

- Rounding a whole number to the nearest ten is the same as rounding it to a multiple of 10.
- Rounding a whole number to the nearest hundred is the same as rounding it to a multiple of 100.
- Rounding an amount to the nearest $10 refers to rounding the amount to a multiple of $10.

Follow these steps to round whole numbers:

Step 1: Identify the digit to be rounded (this is the place value for which the rounding is required).

Step 2: If the digit to the immediate right of the required rounding digit is less than 5 (0, 1, 2, 3, 4), do not change the value of the rounding digit.

If the digit to the immediate right of the required rounding digit is 5 or greater than 5 (5, 6, 7, 8, 9), increase the value of the rounding digit by one (round up by one number).

Step 3: After Step 2, change the value of all digits that are to the right of the rounding digit to 0.

Example 1.1-h

Rounding Numbers Using Number Line (Visual Method)

Round the following numbers to the indicated place value using a number line:

(i) 624 to the nearest ten (multiple of 10).

(ii) 150 to the nearest hundred (multiple of 100).

(iii) 1,962 to the nearest hundred (multiple of 100).

Solution

We can visualize these numbers on a number line to determine the nearest number:

(i) 624 to the nearest ten (multiple of 10).

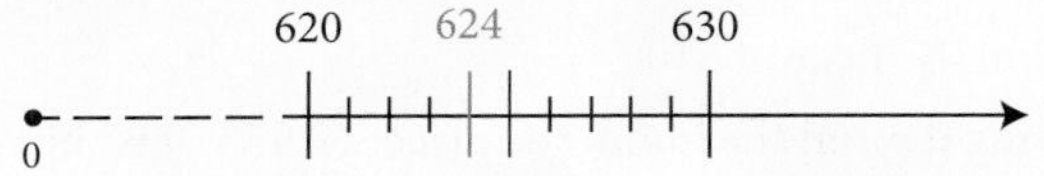

624 is closer to 620 than to 630.

Therefore, 624 rounded to the nearest ten is 620.

(ii) 150 to the nearest hundred (multiple of 100).

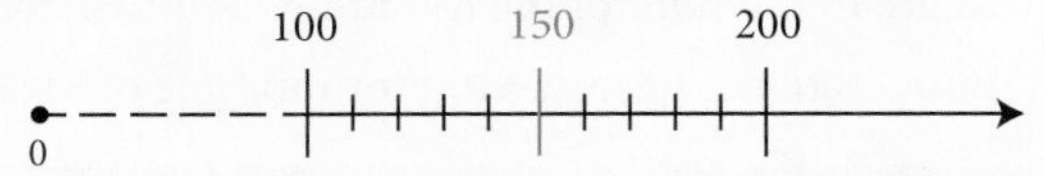

150 is exactly between 100 and 200. By convention, if a number is exactly in the middle, we round it up.

Therefore, 150 rounded to the nearest hundred is 200.

(iii) 1,962 to the nearest hundred (multiple of 100).

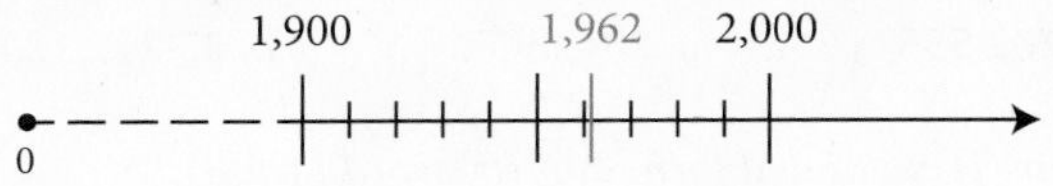

1,962 is closer to 2,000 than to 1,900.

Therefore, 1,962 rounded to the nearest hundred is 2,000.

Example 1.1-i

Rounding to Indicated Place Values

Round the following to the indicated place values:

(i) $568 to the nearest $10.

(ii) $795 to the nearest $10.

(iii) $5,643 to the nearest $100.

(iv) $19,958 to the nearest $100.

Solution

(i) Rounding $568 to the nearest $10.

Identify the rounding digit in the tens place: 568 (6 is the digit in the tens place).

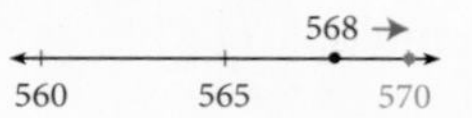

The digit to the immediate right of the rounding digit is 8, which is greater than 5; therefore, increase the value of the rounding digit by one, from 6 to 7, and change the value of the digits that are to the right of the rounding digit to 0, which will result in 570.

Therefore, $568 rounded to the nearest $10 (or multiple of 10) is $570.

(ii) Rounding $795 to the nearest $10.

Identify the rounding digit in the tens place: 795 (9 is the digit in the tens place).

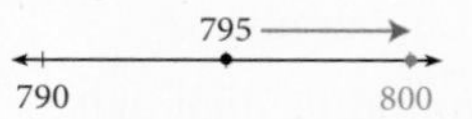

The digit to the immediate right of the rounding digit is 5; therefore, increase the value of the rounding digit by one, from 9 to 10. This is done by replacing the rounding digit 9 with 0, and increasing the next digit to its left by one, from 7 to 8. Change the value of the digits that are to the right of the rounding digit to 0, which will result in 800.

Therefore, $795 rounded to the nearest $10 (or multiple of 10) is $800.

(iii) Rounding $5,643 to the nearest $100.

Identify the rounding digit in the hundreds place: 5,643 (6 is the digit in the hundreds place).

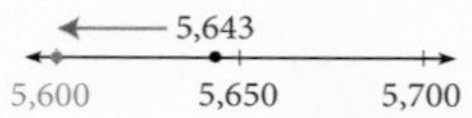

The digit to the immediate right of the rounding digit is 4, which is less than 5; therefore, do not change the value of the rounding digit, but change the value of the digits that are to the right of the rounding digit to 0, which will result in 5,600.

Therefore, $5,643 rounded to the nearest $100 (or multiple of $100) is $5,600.

(iv) Rounding $19,958 to the nearest $100.

Identify the rounding digit in the hundreds place: 19,958 (9 is the digit in the hundreds place).

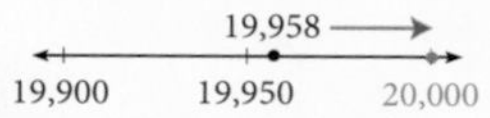

The digit to the immediate right of the rounding digit is 5; therefore, increase the value of the rounding digit by one, from 9 to 10. This is done by replacing the rounding digit 9 with 0 and increasing the next digit to its left by one. In this case it is 9, so increase again from 9 to 10. Replace that digit 9 with 0 and increase the number to its left by one, from 1 to 2. Change the value of the digits that are to the right of the rounding digit to 0, which will result in 20,000.

Therefore, $19,958 rounded to the nearest $100 (or multiple of $100) is $20,000.

1.1 | Exercises

Answers to odd-numbered problems are available at the end of the textbook.

For Problems 1 to 4, write (i) the place value of the underlined digit and (ii) the value it represents.

1. a. 4,7$\underline{9}$2 b. 5,$\underline{3}$52 c. 45,$\underline{7}$21
2. a. 7, $\underline{6}$28 b. 4,6$\underline{8}$7 c. $\underline{9}$4,083
3. a. 3$\underline{1}$9,526 b. 7,8$\underline{2}$5,500 c. 1$\underline{6}$,702,555
4. a. 20$\underline{4}$,095 b. 3$\underline{5}$,217,123 c. 4,$\underline{3}$85,207

For Problems 5 to 10, write the numbers in their (i) expanded form and (ii) word form.

5. a. 407 b. 2,056
6. a. 860 b. 7,805
7. a. 29,186 b. 464,448
8. a. 94,975 b. 684,137
9. a. 2,604,325 b. 15,300,604
10. a. 9,084,351 b. 23,006,045

For Problems 11 to 16, write the numbers in their (i) standard form and (ii) word form.

11. a. 600 + 70 + 9 b. 3,000 + 100 + 40 + 7
12. a. 400 + 50 + 6 b. 1,000 + 900 + 30 + 2
13. a. 2,000 + 600 + 5 b. 9,000 + 20 + 4
14. a. 5,000 + 300+1 b. 7,000 + 80 + 8
15. a. 40,000 + 900 + 90 b. 10,000 + 50 + 3
16. a. 60,000 + 700 + 80 b. 20,000 + 100 + 4

For Problems 17 to 24, write the numbers in their (i) standard form and (ii) expanded form.

17. a. Five hundred seventy
    b. Eight hundred three
18. a. One thousand five
    b. Seven thousand twenty

19. a. Eighty thousand, six hundred thirty

    b. Seventy-five thousand, twenty-five

20. a. Sixty-five thousand, two hundred forty-four

    b. Eight hundred thirty-three thousand, six hundred forty-one

21. a. Twelve million, four hundred fifty-two thousand, eight hundred thirty-two

    b. Thirty-two million, six hundred eighty-four thousand, two hundred fifty-six

22. a. Two billion, one thousand

    b. One billion, twenty-five thousand

23. a. One-eighth of a million

    b. Three-quarters of a million

24. a. Half of a billion

    b. One-tenth of a billion

For Problems 25 and 26, plot the numbers on a number line.

25. a. 14, 19, 15, 7 b. 12, 8, 17, 5 26. a. 18, 9, 6, 11 b. 4, 10, 7, 16

For Problems 27 and 28, place the correct sign '<' or '>' in the space between the numbers.

27. a. 7 ☐ 15 b. 19 ☐ 14 c. 0 ☐ 5 d. 19 ☐ 0

28. a. 12 ☐ 17 b. 8 ☐ 5 c. 17 ☐ 0 d. 0 ☐ 8

For Problems 29 and 30, express the relationship between numbers using the statement (i) "less than" and (ii) "greater than".

29. a. $6 < 9$ b. $18 > 11$ c. $5 < 11$ d. $11 > 0$

30. a. $4 < 7$ b. $16 > 7$ c. $10 < 16$ d. $0 < 4$

For Problems 31 to 34, arrange the numbers in order from smallest to largest.

31. a. 87; 108; 99; 103; 96 b. 159; 141; 108; 139; 167

32. a. 58; 129; 147; 49; 68 b. 836; 820; 805; 873; 875

33. a. 2,067; 2,040; 2,638; 2,533 b. 79,487; 79,534; 79,468; 78,812

34. a. 2,668; 2,630; 2,579; 2,759 b. 68,336; 69,999; 69,067; 68,942

For Problems 35 and 36, create the (i) smallest and (ii) largest possible numbers using all the given digits.

35. a. 9, 2, 5 b. 7, 9, 1, 8 c. 3, 5, 4, 8

36. a. 6, 1, 7 b. 9, 4, 8, 5 c. 4, 7, 2, 6, 5

For Problems 37 and 38, round the numbers to (i) nearest ten, (ii) nearest hundred, and (iii) nearest thousand.

37.

	Number	**Nearest Ten**	**Nearest Hundred**	**Nearest Thousand**
a.	425			
b.	1,645			
c.	53,562			
d.	235,358			

38.

	Number	Nearest Ten	Nearest Hundred	Nearest Thousand
a.	895			
b.	9,157			
c.	25,972			
d.	139,835			

For Problems 39 and 40, round the numbers to (i) nearest ten thousand, (ii) nearest hundred thousand, and (iii) nearest million.

39.

	Number	Nearest Ten Thousand	Nearest Hundred Thousand	Nearest Million
a.	875,555			
b.	1,656,565			
c.	3,368,850			
d.	4,568,310			

40.

	Number	Nearest Ten Thousand	Nearest Hundred Thousand	Nearest Million
a.	759,850			
b.	3,254,599			
c.	7,555,450			
d.	2,959,680			

1.2 | Arithmetic Operations with Whole Numbers

Addition of Whole Numbers

Addition can be done in any order and the sum will be the same.

A + B = B + A

For example,

9 + 5 = 14, and 5 + 9 = 14

This is known as the **commutative property** of addition.

Addition of whole numbers refers to combining two or more (finding the total or sum of) numbers and finding the answer.

When numbers are added, the numbers added are called **addend**. The result or answer is called the **total, sum, or amount**.

The symbol '+' denotes addition.

For example, 9 + 5 refers to adding 9 and 5.

$$\begin{array}{r} 9 \\ +\ 5 \\ \hline 14 \end{array}$$

Plus sign → +; 9 and 5 → Addend; 14 → Total, sum, or amount

Follow these steps to add one number to another number:

Step 1: Start by writing the numbers one under the other by aligning the place values (ones, tens, hundreds, etc.) of these numbers and drawing a horizontal line.

Step 2: Starting with the ones place value, add all the numbers in the 'ones' column. If their total is less than 10, write the total under the horizontal line. If the total is 10 or more, write the 'ones' digit of the total under the horizontal line and write the tens digit above the tens column. This is called 'carrying'.

Step 3: Add the numbers in the tens column followed by the hundreds column, etc., by following the same procedure for each column.

Example 1.2-a **Adding Whole Numbers**

Perform the following additions:

(i) 3,514 + 245

(ii) 8,578 + 3,982 + 564 + 92

Solution

(i) 3,514 + 245

Thousands	Hundreds	Tens	Ones
3	5	1	4
+	2	4	5
3	7	5	9

The sum of the digits in the **ones column** is 9 since 4 + 5 = 9. There are 9 ones, so we write 9 in the ones column below the horizontal line.

The sum of the digits in the **tens column** is 5 since 10 + 40 = 50. There are 5 tens, so we write 5 in the tens column below the horizontal line.

The sum of the digits in the **hundreds column** is 7 since 500 + 200 = 700. There are 7 hundreds, so we write 7 in the hundreds column below the horizontal line.

As only 3 is in the **thousands column**, the sum of the digits in the **thousands column** is 3. Write 3 in the thousands column below the horizontal line.

Therefore, adding 3,514 and 245 results in 3,759.

(ii) 8,578 + 3,982 + 564 + 92

	Ten Thousands	Thousands	Hundreds	Tens	Ones
		2	3	1	
		8	5	7	8
		3	9	8	2
			5	6	4
+				9	2
	1	3	2	1	6

The sum of the digits in the **ones column** is 16 since 8 + 2 + 4 + 2 = 16, which is 1 ten and 6 ones. Write 6 in the ones column and carry the 1 above the tens column.

The sum of the digits in the **tens column** is 31 since 1 + 7 + 8 + 6 + 9 = 31, which is 3 hundreds and 1 ten. Write 1 in the tens column and carry the 3 above the hundreds column.

The sum of the digits in the **hundreds column** is 22 since 3 + 5 + 9 + 5 = 22, which is 2 thousands and 2 hundreds. Write 2 in the hundreds column and carry the 2 above the thousands column.

The sum of the digits in the **thousands column** is 13 since 2 + 8 + 3 = 13, which is 1 ten-thousand and 3 thousands. Write 3 in the thousands column and 1 in the ten-thousands column for the final answer.

Therefore, adding 8,578, 3,982, 564, and 92 results in 13,216.

Subtraction of Whole Numbers

Subtraction of whole numbers refers to finding the difference between numbers. This is the reverse process of addition.

When numbers are subtracted, the number from which another number is subtracted is called the **minuend** and the number that is being subtracted is called the **subtrahend**. The result or answer is called the **difference**. The symbol '–' denotes subtraction.

For example, 8 – 5 refers to subtracting 5 from 8. This is read as 8 minus 5.

Subtraction should be done in the written order.

$A - B \neq B - A$

For example,

8 – 5 = 3, but 5 – 8 = –3

i.e., 5 – 8 gives the negative answer of 8 – 5.

	8 ⟵	Minuend
Minus sign ⟶	– 5 ⟵	Subtrahend
	3 ⟵	Difference

Follow these steps to subtract a number from another number:

Step 1: Start by writing the numbers one under the other by aligning the same place values (ones, tens, hundreds, etc.) of these numbers and drawing a horizontal line. Ensure that the number that is being subtracted from is in the top row and that the number that is being subtracted is below.

Step 2: Starting from the ones place value, subtract the bottom number from the top number. If the top digit is greater than the bottom digit, subtract the ones column and write the number under the line. If the top digit is smaller than the bottom digit, borrow one ten from the digit to the left of this top digit for an additional 10 ones. Add this to the ones digit on the top, find the difference, and write the difference under the horizontal line. This is called "borrowing".

Step 3: Subtract the numbers in the tens column, followed by the hundreds column, etc., and follow the same procedure for each column.

Example 1.2-b **Subtracting Whole Numbers**

Perform the following subtractions:

(i) Subtract 1,314 from 3,628 (ii) Subtract 789 from 8,357

Solution

(i) Subtract 1,314 from 3,628

	Thousands	Hundreds	Tens	Ones
	3	6	2	8
−	1	3	1	4
	2	3	1	4

The difference of the digits in the **ones column** is 4 since 8 – 4 = 4. There are 4 ones, so we write 4 in the ones column below the horizontal line.

The difference of the digits in the **tens column** is 1 since 20 – 10 = 10. There is 1 ten, so we write 1 in the tens column below the horizontal line.

The difference of the digits in the **hundreds column** is 3 since 600 – 300 = 300. There are 3 hundreds, so we write 3 in the hundreds column below the horizontal line.

The difference of the digits in the **thousands column** is 2 since 3,000 – 1,000 = 2,000. There are 2 thousands, so we write 2 in the thousands column below the horizontal line.

Therefore, subtracting 1,314 from 3,628 results in 2,314.

(ii) Subtract 789 from 8,357

	Thousands	Hundreds	Tens	Ones
		12	14	
	7	~~2~~	~~4~~	17
	~~8~~	~~3~~	~~5~~	~~7~~
−		7	8	9
	7	5	6	8

In the **ones column**, the ones digit on the top (7) is smaller than the ones digit on the bottom (9). Borrow one ten from the tens digit on the top row to get 17 ones. 17 – 9 = 8. Write 8 in the ones column.

In the **tens column**, the tens digit on the top (4) is smaller than the tens digit on the bottom (8). Borrow one hundred from the hundreds digit on the top row to get 14 tens. 14 – 8 = 6. Write 6 in the tens column.

In the **hundreds column**, the hundreds digit on the top (2) is smaller than the hundreds digit on the bottom (7). Borrow one thousand from the thousands digit on the top row to get 12 hundreds. 12 – 7 = 5. Write 5 in the hundreds column.

As only 7 is in the **thousands column**, write 7 in the thousands column below the horizontal line.

Therefore, subtracting 789 from 8,357 results in 7,568.

Multiplication of Whole Numbers

Multiplication can be done in any order and the product will be the same.

A × B = B × A

For example,

9 × 5 = 45, and 5 × 9 = 45

This is called the **commutative property** of multiplication.

Multiplication is the process of finding the product of two numbers. Multiplication of whole numbers can be thought of as repeated additions.

For example, 5 × 4 refers to repeatedly adding 5, four times. This is read as 'five times four'.

The symbol '×' denotes multiplication. This can also be written as 5 · 4 or (5)(4).

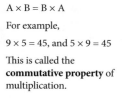

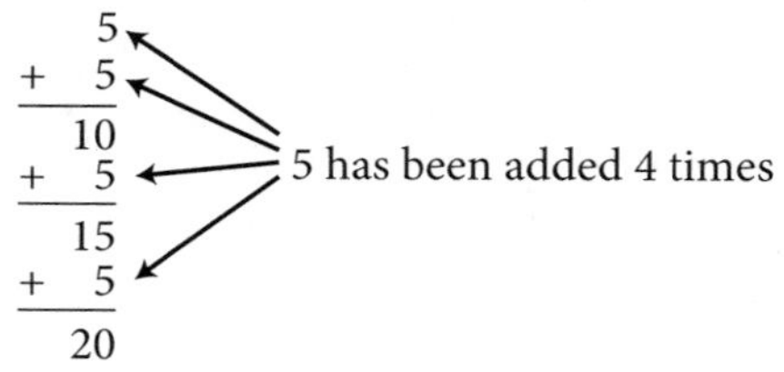

5 × 4 can be represented pictorially as:

x x x x x

x x x x x

x x x x x

x x x x x

In the example, "5 × 4", the size of the set is 5 and the number of times it is repeated is 4.

When numbers are multiplied the number that is multiplied (the size of the set) is called the **multiplier**, the number that indicates the number of times (the repetition) is called the **multiplicand**, the answer is called the **product**, and both the multiplier and multiplicand are called factors of the answer (product).

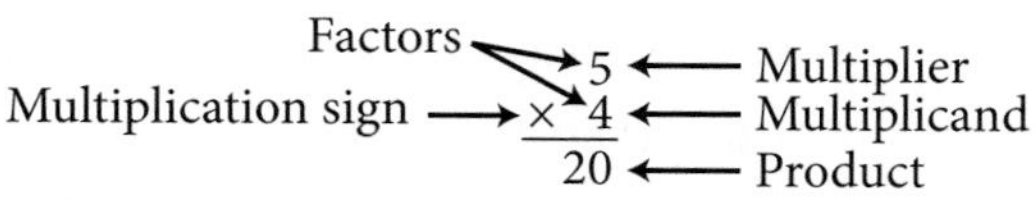

In this example, 5 and 4 are factors of 20.

Follow these steps to multiply one number by another number:

Step 1: Align the numbers and draw a horizontal line, as done for addition and subtraction.

Step 2: Starting from the first digit at the right of the multiplicand, multiply the multiplier by the digit and write the product below the line.

Step 3: Then multiply the multiplier by the multiplicand's next digit to the left and write the product below the first product, but one place to the left.

Step 4: Continue this procedure for multiplying the multiplier by all the digits of the multiplicand and add to get the answer.

The above steps for multiplying numbers are provided in detail in Example 1.2-c below.

Example 1.2-c

Multiplying Whole Numbers

Perform the following multiplication:

(i) Multiply 38 by 6 (ii) Multiply 36 by 24 (iii) Multiply 263 by 425

Solution

(i) Multiply 38 by 6

Hundreds	Tens	Ones
	4	
	3	8
×		6
2	2	8

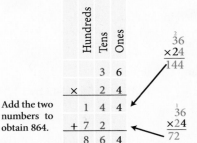

Multiplying 8 ones by 6 results in 48 ones. This is 4 tens and 8 ones.

Write 8 in the ones column and 4 above the tens column.

Multiplying 3 tens by 6 results in 18 tens. Add the 4 tens to 18 to obtain 22 tens. Write 22 in the tens and hundreds column.

Therefore, multiplying 38 by 6 results in 228.

(ii) Multiply 36 by 24

When multiplying one number by another, align the numbers by place value, similar to the way in addition and subtraction.

Hundreds	Tens	Ones
	3	6
×	2	4
1	4	4
+ 7	2	
8	6	4

Add the two numbers to obtain 864.

36
×24
144

Multiply 36 by 4 ones, as shown, to obtain 144.

36
×24
72

Multiply 36 by 2 tens. To do this, write a '0' under the ones column (you may omit the zero and leave it blank, as shown) and multiply 36 by 2 to obtain 72.

Therefore, multiplying 36 by 24 results in 864.

(iii) Multiply 263 by 425

Hundred thousands	Ten thousands	Thousands	Hundreds	Tens	Ones
			2	6	3
		×	4	2	5
		1	3	1	5
		5	2	6	
+ 1	0	5	2		
1	1	1	7	7	5

Add the three numbers to obtain 111,775

263
× 425
1315

Multiply 263 by 5 ones.

263
× 425
526

Multiply 263 by 2 tens.

263
× 425
1052

Multiply 263 by 4 hundreds.

Therefore, multiplying 263 by 425 results in 111,775.

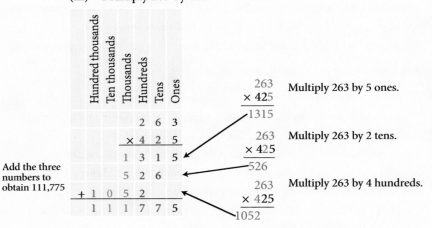

Division of Whole Numbers

Division should be done in the written order.

A ÷ B ≠ B ÷ A

For example,

$6 \div 2 = 3$, but $2 \div 6 = \frac{1}{3}$

i.e., 6 ÷ 2 gives the reciprocal of 2 ÷ 6.

Division is the process of determining how many times one number is contained in another. This is the inverse process of multiplication. When a larger number is divided by a smaller number, this division can be thought of as repeated subtractions.

For example, 20 ÷ 5 refers to repeatedly subtracting 5 from 20.

The symbol '÷' denotes division. This can also be written as $5\overline{)20}$. This is read as 'twenty divided by five'.

$$\begin{array}{r} 20 \\ -\ 5 \\ \hline 15 \\ -\ 5 \\ \hline 10 \\ -\ 5 \\ \hline 5 \\ -\ 5 \\ \hline 0 \end{array}$$

5 has been subtracted 4 times

0 No remainder

Therefore, 20 ÷ 5 = 4.

When dividing one number by another number, the number that is being divided is called the **dividend**, the number by which the dividend is divided is called the **divisor**. The answer is called the **quotient**. If the dividend cannot be divided evenly by the divisor, the number left over is called the **remainder**.

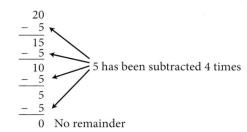

For example, 25 ÷ 7

$$\begin{array}{r} 3 \\ 7\overline{)25} \\ 21 \\ \hline 4 \end{array}$$

Divisor → 7; 3 ← Quotient; 25 ← Dividend; 4 ← Remainder

Dividend	=	Divisor	×	Quotient	+	Remainder
25	=	7	×	3	+	4

The steps to be followed in dividing numbers are provided in detail in Example 1.2-d.

Example 1.2-d **Dividing Whole Numbers**

Perform the following divisions and state the quotient and remainder:

(i) Divide 76 by 3 (ii) Divide 637 by 25 (iii) Divide 6,543 by 12

Solution

(i) Divide 76 by 3

$$\begin{array}{r} 25 \\ 3\overline{)76} \\ -6\downarrow \\ \hline 16 \\ -15 \\ \hline 1 \end{array}$$

7 can be divided by 3. Therefore, determine the number of multiples of 3 there are in 7.
There are two 3's in 7. Write 2 in the quotient area above 7.
Multiply 2 by 3 (= 6) and subtract this from 7. Write the remainder 1.
Bring down the 6 and determine the number of multiples of 3 there are in 16.
There are five 3's in 16. Write 5 in the quotient area above 6.
Multiply 5 by 3 (= 15) and subtract this from 16 to get the final remainder of 1.

Therefore, the quotient is 25 and the remainder is 1.

(ii) Divide 637 by 25

$$\begin{array}{r} 25 \\ 25\overline{)637} \\ -50\downarrow \\ \hline 137 \\ -125 \\ \hline 12 \end{array}$$

6 cannot be divided by 25. Therefore, determine the number of multiples of 25 there are in 63.
There are two 25's in 63. Write 2 in the quotient area above 3.
Multiply 2 by 25 (= 50) and subtract this from 63. Write the remainder 13.
Bring down 7 and determine the number of multiples of 25 there are in 137.
There are five 25's in 137. Write 5 in the quotient area above 7.
Multiply 5 by 25 (= 125) and subtract this from 137 to get the final remainder of 12.

Therefore, the quotient is 25 and the remainder is 12.

Solution *continued*

(iii) Divide 6,543 by 12

```
     545
12 | 6543
    -60
      54
     -48
       63
      -60
        3
```

6 cannot by divided by 12. Therefore, determine the number of multiples of 12 there are in 65.

There are five 12's in 65. Write 5 in the quotient area above 5.

Multiply 5 by 12 (= 60) and subtract this from 65. Write the remainder 5. Bring down 4 and determine the number of multiples of 12 there are in 54.

There are four 12's in 54. Write 4 in the quotient area above 4. Multiply 4 by 12 (= 48) and subtract this from 54 to get the remainder 6. Bring down 3 and determine the number of multiples of 12 there are in 63.

There are five 12's in 63. Write 5 in the quotient area above 3. Multiply 5 by 12 (= 60) and subtract this from 63 to get the final remainder of 3.

Therefore, the quotient is 545 and the remainder is 3.

Arithmetic Operations with Zero and One

Table 1.2-a Arithmetic Operations with Zero

Operation	Description	Examples
Addition	When 0 is added to a number, or when a number is added to 0, there will be no change to that number.	$25 + 0 = 25$ $0 + 25 = 25$
Subtraction	When 0 is subtracted from a number, there will be no change to that number.	$16 - 0 = 16$
	When a number is subtracted from 0, the answer will be the negative value of that number.	$0 - 16 = -16$
Multiplication	When 0 is multiplied by a number, or when a number is multiplied by 0, the answer will be 0.	$0 \times 35 = 0$ $35 \times 0 = 0$
Division	When 0 is divided by a number, the answer will be 0.	$0 \div 25 = 0$
	When a number is divided by 0, the answer is undefined.	$25 \div 0 =$ Undefined

Table 1.2-b Arithmetic Operations with One

Operation	Description	Examples
Addition	When 1 is added to a number, or when a number is added to 1, the answer will be 1 greater than that number.	$14 + 1 = 15$ $1 + 14 = 15$
Subtraction	When 1 is subtracted from a number, the answer will be 1 less than that number.	$10 - 1 = 9$
	When a number is subtracted from 1, the answer will be 1 more than the negative value of that number. (In the given example, the negative value of 10 is −10; i.e., one more than −10 = −10 + 1 = −9.)	$1 - 10 = -9$
Multiplication	When 1 is multiplied by a number, or when a number is multiplied by 1, there will be no change to that number.	$1 \times 12 = 12$ $12 \times 1 = 12$
Division	When 1 is divided by a number, the answer is the reciprocal of that number.	$1 \div 35 = \frac{1}{35}$
	When a number is divided by 1, there will be no change to that number.	$35 \div 1 = \frac{35}{1} = 35$

1.2 | Exercises

Answers to odd-numbered problems are available at the end of the textbook.

For the addition Problems 1 to 8, (i) estimate the answer by rounding each number to the nearest ten and (ii) calculate the exact answer.

1. a. 48 + 29 b. 38 + 95
2. a. 16 + 79 b. 69 + 47
3. a. 875 + 48 b. 574 + 79
4. a. 459 + 27 b. 356 + 65
5. a. 286 + 109 + 15 b. 839 + 645 + 27
6. a. 989 + 215 + 25 b. 798 + 237 +12
7. a. 195 + 459 + 8 b. 996 + 816 + 6
8. a. 896 + 642 + 9 b. 995 + 724 + 8

For the addition Problems 9 to 14, (i) estimate the answer by rounding each number to the nearest hundred and (ii) calculate the exact answer.

9. a. 745 + 668 b. 427 + 225
10. a. 357 + 245 b. 451 + 645
11. a. 1,883 + 5,466 b. 2,157 + 3,459
12. a. 6,950 + 2,367 b. 3,765 + 1,992
13. a. 2,635 + 372 + 1,524 b. 653 + 2,188 + 891
14. a. 1,650 + 1,647 + 875 +167 b. 3,869 + 1,967 + 550 + 745

For the subtraction Problems 15 to 22, (i) estimate the answer by rounding each number to the nearest ten and (ii) calculate the exact answer.

15. a. 62 – 25 b. 33 – 18
16. a. 43 – 27 b. 71 – 59
17. a. 208 – 79 b. 315 – 47
18. a. 327 – 28 b. 500 – 73
19. a. 767 – 159 b. 804 – 308
20. a. 904 – 629 b. 584 – 167
21. a. 8,302 – 7,244 b. 2,927 – 888
22. a. 9,185 – 6,728 b. 5,765 – 777

For the subtraction Problems 23 to 28, (i) estimate the answer by rounding each number to the nearest hundred and (ii) calculate the exact answer.

23. a. 946 – 452 b. 855 – 251
24. a. 868 – 745 b. 495 – 357
25. a. 2,950 – 2,275 b. 3,961 – 1,833
26. a. 2,955 – 1,350 b. 1,967 – 352
27. a. 3,513 – 2,846 b. 3,981 – 1,657
28. a. 7,676 – 3,969 b. 5,789 – 5,626

For the multiplication Problems 29 to 34, (i) estimate the answer by rounding each number to the nearest ten and (ii) calculate the exact answer.

29. a. 58 × 75 b. 63 × 59
30. a. 35 × 97 b. 95 × 71
31. a. 764 × 53 b. 799 × 68
32. a. 482 × 95 b. 755 × 55
33. a. 1,995 × 37 b. 2,150 × 59
34. a. 2,996 × 32 b. 2,995 × 38

For the division Problems 35 to 44, (i) estimate the answer by rounding each number to the nearest ten and (ii) perform the exact division and state the quotient and the remainder.

35. a. 78 ÷ 5 b. 36 ÷ 8
36. a. 69 ÷ 7 b. 85 ÷ 9
37. a. 86 ÷ 27 b. 78 ÷ 19
38. a. 59 ÷ 12 b. 95 ÷ 18
39. a. 654 ÷ 14 b. 396 ÷ 24
40. a. 777 ÷ 16 b. 255 ÷ 19
41. a. 2,578 ÷ 18 b. 1,225 ÷ 28
42. a. 2,097 ÷ 55 b. 1,795 ÷ 64
43. a. 3,004 ÷ 204 b. 6,501 ÷ 498
44. a. 3,875 ÷ 264 b. 5,195 ÷ 255

45. a. What amount is $65 less than $784? b. What amount is $35 more than $98?

46. a. What amount is $79 less than $487? b. What amount is $97 more than $52?

47. a. What amount is $515 increased by $847? b. What amount is $745 decreased by $125?

48. a. What amount is $745 increased by $1,274? b. What amount is $526 decreased by $346?

49. a. If there are 24 pens in a box, how many pens are there in 15 boxes?

    b. A wire of length 420 centimeters is to be cut into 35 - centimetre pieces. How many 35 - centimetre pieces can be cut?

50. a. If you save $125 every month, how much will you save in one year?

    b. If 8 people can be seated at a dinner table, how many tables are required to seat 280 people?

51. a. If you save $15 a week, how many weeks will it take you to save $675?

    b. If there are 16 chairs in a row, how many chairs are there in 22 rows?

52. a. If you work 25 hours per week, how many weeks will it take you to complete a job that requires 450 hours?

    b. If you earn $18 per hour, how much will you earn in a week in which you have worked 32 hours?

53. Mythili went to a bookstore and bought a dictionary. She gave the cashier a $100 note and received $47 as change. How much did the dictionary cost?
54. There were 744 students in a primary school. In May, after some students left to join another school, 576 students remained. How many students left for the other school?
55. Andy has $1,238 and Bill has $346 less than Andy. How much money do both of them have together?
56. A television costs $649 more than a DVD player. If the DVD player costs $235, how much will it cost to buy the TV and the DVD player?
57. Peter earns $18 per hour. If he worked 25 hours last week, calculate his earning for that week.
58. Sam's overtime rate is $37 per hour. If he worked 29 hours overtime last week, calculate his overtime pay for that week.
59. Earl wants to save $3,150. If he saves $75 per week, how many weeks will it take for him to achieve his goal?
60. How long will it take to travel 1,190 km at 85 km per hour?
61. A large group of students visited an exhibition on Friday. The first 275 students were given one free balloon each. 487 students were disappointed that they did not receive any balloons. How many students visited the exhibition?
62. There were 2,415 boys and 1,875 girls that attended a fair. The first 2,650 visitors to the fair received gifts. How many visitors did not receive gifts?

• 63. There were 450 passengers on a train. Half of them were men, 125 were children, and the rest were women. How many more men than women were there on the train?

• 64. Out of the 3,678 visitors at an art exhibition, 1,469 were men, 1,234 were women, and the rest were children. How many more adults than children went to the exhibition?

• 65. Aran had some money saved up. On his birthday, Aran's grandparents gave him $125. After spending $98 on toys and $75 on clothes, he had $115 remaining. What amount did Aran have in his savings before his birthday?

• 66. Girija had some biscuits. She ate 19 and gave 27 to her brother and 5 to her parents. She had 12 biscuits left. How many biscuits did Girija have originally?

• 67. There are 19 girls in a class of 43 students. 15 of the girls and 11 of the boys are wearing eye glasses.

    a. How many boys are there in the class?

    b. How many students do not wear eye glasses?

• 68. There are 22 players on a soccer field. 10 players are wearing blue and 2 are wearing green. The rest of the players are wearing red. How many players are wearing red?

1.3 | Factors and Multiples

Introduction

1 is a factor of every number and every number is a factor of itself.

Factors of a number are whole numbers that can divide the number evenly (with no remainder).

For example, to find factors of 12, divide the number 12 by 1, 2, 3, 4...; the numbers that divide 12 evenly are its factors.

We can also express factors of a number by showing how the product of two factors results in the number.

$12 = 1 \times 12$	$12 \div 1 = 12$
$12 = 2 \times 6$	$12 \div 2 = 6$
$12 = 2 \times 2 \times 3$	$12 \div 3 = 4$
$12 = 3 \times 4$	$12 \div 4 = 3$
	$12 \div 6 = 2$
	$12 \div 12 = 1$

Therefore, 1, 2, 3, 4, 6, and 12 are factors of 12.

Note: 5, 7, 8, 9, 10, and 11 will not divide 12 evenly. Therefore, they are not factors of 12.

Multiples of a number are the product of the number and the whole numbers (1, 2, 3, 4,...).

For example, multiples of 10:

10×1	10×2	10×3	10×4	10×5
10	20	30	40	50

Therefore, multiples of 10 are 10, 20, 30, 40, 50, etc.

Note: Multiples of a number can be divided by the number with no remainder.

Prime Numbers and Composite Numbers

A **prime number** is a whole number that has only two factors: 1 and the number itself; i.e., prime numbers can be divided only by 1 and the number itself.

For example, 7 is a prime number because it only has two factors: 1 and 7.

0 and 1 are neither prime numbers nor composite numbers.

A **composite number** is a whole number that has at least one factor other than 1 and the number itself; i.e., all whole numbers that are not prime numbers are composite numbers.

For example, 8 is a composite number because it has more than 2 factors: 1, 2, 4, and 8.

Example 1.3-a | **Identifying Prime Numbers**

Identify all the prime numbers less than 25.

Solution

All the prime numbers less than 25 are: 2, 3, 5, 7, 11, 13, 17, 19, and 23.

Example 1.3-b | **Identifying Composite Numbers**

Identify all the composite numbers less than 25.

Solution

All the composite numbers less than 25 are:

4, 6, 8, 9, 10, 12, 14, 15, 16, 18, 20, 21, 22, and 24.

Example 1.3-c **Finding Factors of Prime Numbers**

Find all the factors of 13.

Solution

1 and 13 are the only factors of 13.

Example 1.3-d **Finding All Factors of Composite Numbers**

Find all the factors of:

(i) 16 (ii) 20

Solution

(i) The factors of 16 are: 1, 2, 4, 8, and 16. (ii) The factors of 20 are: 1, 2, 4, 5, 10, and 20.

Example 1.3-e **Finding the Prime Factors of Composite Numbers**

Find all the prime factors of 24.

Solution

All the factors of 24 are: 2, 3, 4, 6, 8, 12, and 24.

Of the above factors, only 2 and 3 are prime numbers.

Therefore, the prime factors of 24 are 2 and 3.

Least or Lowest Common Multiple (LCM)

LCM is the smallest integer that is a common multiple of two or more numbers.

The **Lowest Common Multiple (LCM)** of two or more whole numbers is the smallest multiple that is common to those numbers. The LCM can be determined from one of the following methods:

Method 1: First, select the largest number and check to see if it is divisible by all the other numbers. If it divides, then the largest number is the LCM.

For example, in finding the LCM of 2, 3, and 12, the largest number 12 is divisible by the other numbers 2 and 3. Therefore, the LCM of 2, 3, and 12 is 12.

If the largest number is not divisible by the other numbers, then find a multiple of the largest number that is divisible by all the other numbers.

For example, in finding the LCM of 3, 5, and 10, the largest number 10 is not divisible by 3. Multiples of 10 are 10, 20, 30, 40... 30 is divisible by both 3 and 5. Therefore, the LCM of 3, 5, and 10 is 30.

If none of the multiples of the largest number are divisible by all the other numbers and if the numbers have no common factor, then the LCM of the numbers is the product of all the numbers.

For example, in finding the LCM of 2, 5, and 7, these numbers have no common factors. Therefore, the LCM of 2, 5, and 7, is $2 \times 5 \times 7 = 70$.

A number is divisible by 2 if the last digit of the number ends in a 0, 2, 4, 6, or 8.

A number is divisible by 3 if the sum of all the digits of a number is divisble by 3.

A number is divisible by 5 if the last digit of the number is a 0 or a 5.

Method 2: Step 1: Find the prime factors of each of the numbers using a factor tree and list the different prime numbers (creating a factor tree is shown in the example below).

Step 2: Count the number of times each different prime number appears in each of the factorizations.

Step 3: Find the largest of these counts for each prime number.

Step 4: List that prime number as many times as you counted it in Step 3. The LCM is the product of all the prime numbers listed.

Factor Tree

A factor tree helps to find all of the prime factors of a number. It also shows the number of times that each prime factor appears.

For example, creating a factor tree for number 24:

Step 1: Write 24. Draw two short lines down at diverging angles as shown.

Step 2: 24 is divisible by the first prime number 2; i.e. $24 = 2 \times 12$.

Write these factors at the end of the lines. Now 24 is at the top and 2×12 is the 2nd layer below it, as shown.

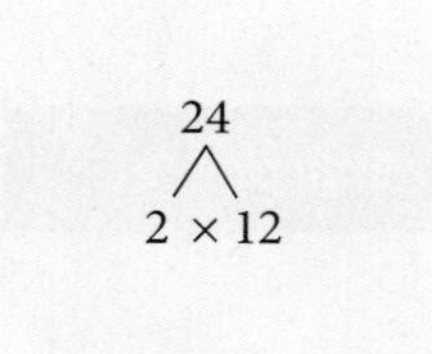

Step 3: Now, 12 is divisible by the prime number 2; i.e. $12 = 2 \times 6$.

Write these factors below 12; i.e. the 3rd layer is $2 \times 2 \times 6$, as shown.

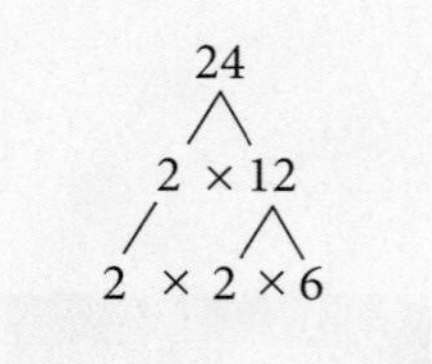

Step 4: Next, 6 is divisible by the prime number 2; i.e. $6 = 2 \times 3$.

Write the factor below 6; i.e. the 4th layer is $2 \times 2 \times 2 \times 3$.

Step 5: The factors at the 4th layer are all prime numbers and cannot be factored any more. Therefore, $24 = 2 \times 2 \times 2 \times 3$.

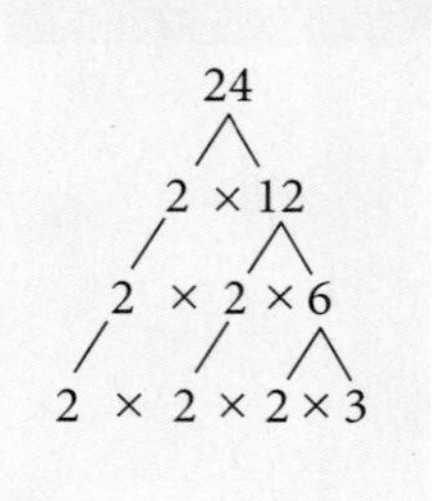

Note: It is not necessary to do every step starting with a prime number. You may start with any two factors that multiply together to get the number.

For example, $24 = 4 \times 6$

Then continue with the factor until you are left with only prime numbers, as shown. The answer will be same.

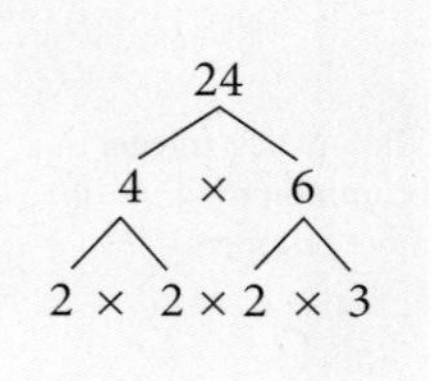

Example 1.3-f **Finding the Least Common Multiple**

Find the LCM of 9 and 15.

Solution

Method 1: The largest number, 15, is **not** divisible by 9.

Multiples of 15 are: 15, 30, 45...

45 is divisible by 9.

Therefore, the LCM of 9 and 15 is 45.

Method 2:

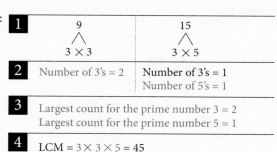

1	9 → 3 × 3	15 → 3 × 5
2	Number of 3's = 2	Number of 3's = 1 Number of 5's = 1
3	Largest count for the prime number 3 = 2 Largest count for the prime number 5 = 1	
4	LCM = $3 \times 3 \times 5 = 45$	

Example 1.3-g Finding the Least Common Multiple

Find the LCM of 3, 5, and 8.

Solution

Method 1: The largest number, 8, is ***not*** divisible by 3 and 5.

Multiples of 8 are: 16, 24, 32, 40, 48, 56, 64... None of the multiples listed above are divisible by 3 and 5.

Since 3, 5, and 8 have no common factors, the LCM is the product of all the numbers: $3 \times 5 \times 8 = 120$.

Therefore, the LCM of 3, 5, and 8 is 120.

Method 2:

1	3	5	8 / \\ 2 × 4 / / \\ 2 × 2 × 2
2	Number of 3's = 1	Number of 5's = 1	Number of 2's = 3
3	Largest count for the prime number 2 = 3 Largest count for the prime number 3 = 1 Largest count for the prime number 5 = 1		
4	LCM = $2 \times 2 \times 2 \times 3 \times 5 = 120$		

Example 1.3-h Finding the Least Common Multiple

Find the LCM of 3, 6, and 18.

Solution

Method 1: The largest number, 18, is divisible by both 6 and 3.

Therefore, the LCM of 3, 6, and 18 is 18.

Method 2:

1	3	6 / \\ 2 × 3	18 / \\ 2 × 9 / / \\ 2 × 3 × 3
2	Number of 3's = 1	Number of 2's = 1 Number of 3's = 1	Number of 2's = 1 Number of 3's = 2
3	Largest count for the prime number 2 = 1 Largest count for the prime number 3 = 2		
4	LCM = $2 \times 3 \times 3 = 18$		

Example 1.3-i

Finding the Least Common Multiple

Find the LCM of 24, 36, and 48.

Solution

Method 1: The largest number, 48, is divisible by 24 but **not** by 36.
Multiples of 48 are: 48, 96, 144, 192, 240, ...
144 is divisible by both 24 and 36.
Therefore, the LCM of 24, 36, and 48 is 144.

Method 2:

1

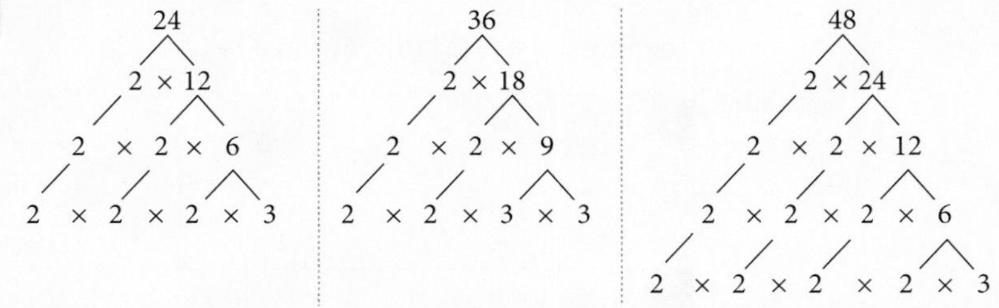

2

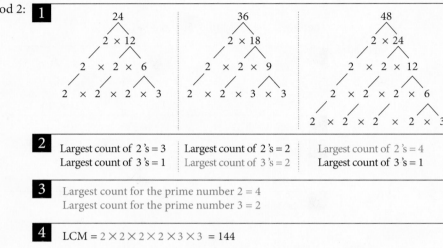

Largest count of 2's = 3 Largest count of 3's = 1	Largest count of 2's = 2 Largest count of 3's = 2	Largest count of 2's = 4 Largest count of 3's = 1

3 Largest count for the prime number 2 = 4
Largest count for the prime number 3 = 2

4 LCM = $2 \times 2 \times 2 \times 2 \times 3 \times 3 = 144$

Example 1.3-j

Finding the Least Common Multiple

Two flashing lights are turned on at the same time. One light flashes every 16 seconds and the other flashes every 20 seconds. How often will they flash together?

Solution

In this example, we are required to find the least common interval for both lights to flash together. Thereafter, both lights will continue to flash together at this interval (multiple).

Method 1: The largest number, 20, is ***not*** divisible by 16.

Multiples of 20 are: 20, 40, 60, 80,...

80 is divisble by 16. The LCM of 16 and 20 is 80.

Therefore, the two flashing lights will flash together every 80 seconds.

Method 2:

1

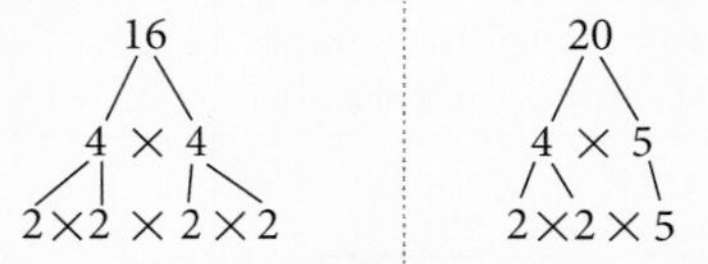

2

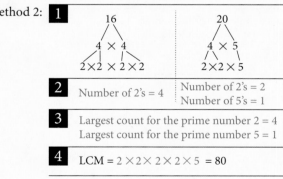

Number of 2's = 4	Number of 2's = 2 Number of 5's = 1

3 Largest count for the prime number 2 = 4
Largest count for the prime number 5 = 1

4 LCM = $2 \times 2 \times 2 \times 2 \times 5 = 80$

Therefore, the two flashing lights will flash together every 80 seconds.

Highest Common Factor (HCF)

HCF is the largest integer that divides the set of numbers without remainder.

The factors that are common to two or more numbers are called **common factors** of those numbers.

The **Highest Common Factor (HCF)** of two or more numbers is the largest common number that divides the numbers with no remainder. In other words, the HCF is the largest of all the common factors.

HCF can be determined from one of the following methods:

Method 1: First list all the factors of the number. Then select all the common factors of the numbers. The highest value of the common factors is the HCF.

For example, in finding the HCF of 12 and 18:

The factors of 12 are 1, 2, 3, 4, 6, and 12.

The factors of 18 are 1, 2, 3, 6, 9, and 18.

The common factors are 2, 3, and 6.

Therefore, the HCF is 6.

Method 2: First express each number as a product of prime numbers. Then identify the prime numbers that are common to all numbers. The product of these prime numbers is the HCF.

For example, in finding the HCF of 12 and 18:

Number	Prime Factors of:	
	2	3
12	2, 2	3
18	2	3, 3

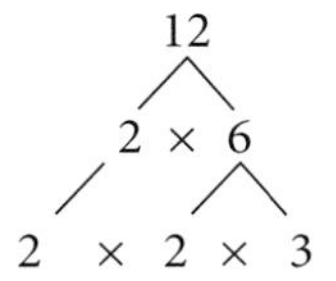

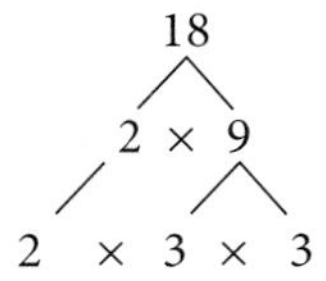

Therefore, HCF is $2 \times 3 = 6$.

Note: 1 is a factor that is common to all numbers but is not included in the list of common factors. If there are no common factors other than 1, then 1 is the highest common factor.

For example, 1 is the only common factor of 3, 5, 7, and 9.

Example 1.3-k **Finding the Highest Common Factor**

Find the HCF of 36 and 60.

Solution

Method 1: Factors of 36 are: 1, 2, 3, 4, 6, 9, 12, 18, and 36.

Factors of 60 are: 1, 2, 3, 4, 5, 6, 10, 12, 15, 20, 30, and 60.

The common factors are: 2, 3, 4, 6, and 12.

Therefore, the HCF is 12.

Method 2:

Number	Prime Factors of:		
	2	3	5
36	2, 2	3, 3	
60	2, 2	3	5

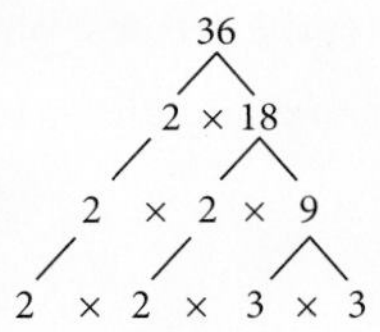

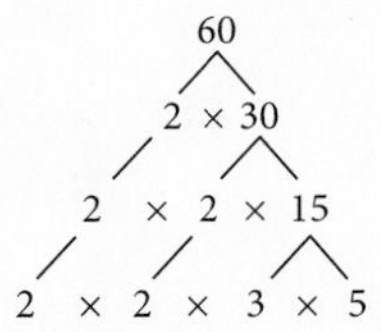

Therefore, HCF is $2 \times 2 \times 3 = 12$.

Example 1.3-l **Finding the Highest Common Factor**

Find the HCF of 72, 126, and 216.

Solution

Method 1: The factors of 72 are: 1, 2, 3, 4, 6, 8, 9, 12, 18, 24, 36, and 72.

The factors of 126 are: 1, 2, 3, 6, 7, 9, 14, 18, 21, 42, 63, and 126.

The factors of 216 are: 1, 2, 3, 4, 6, 8, 9, 12, 18, 24, 27, 36, 54, 72, 108, and 216.

The common factors are: 2, 3, 6, 9, and 18.

Therefore, the HCF is 18.

Solution *continued*

Method 2:

Number	Prime Factors of:		
	2	3	7
72	2, 2, 2	3, 3	
126	2	3, 3	7
216	2, 2, 2	3, 3, 3	

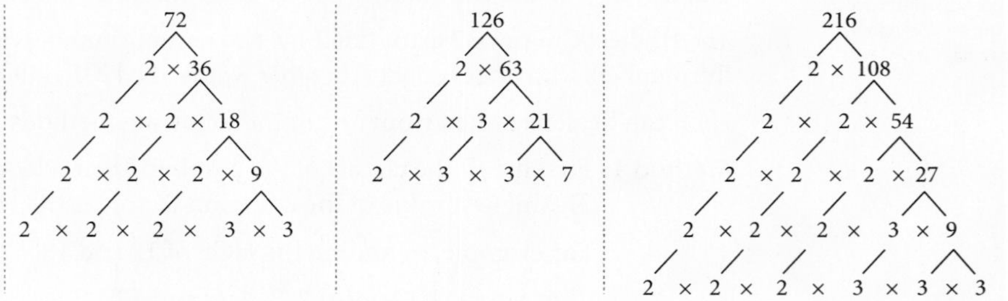

Therefore, HCF is $2 \times 3 \times 3 = 18$.

Example 1.3-m **Finding the Highest Common Factor**

Three pieces of timber with lengths 48 cm, 72 cm, and 96 cm are to be cut into smaller pieces of equal length without remainders.

(i) What is the greatest possible length of each piece?

(ii) How many pieces of such equal lengths are possible?

Solution

Method 1: Factors of 48 are: 2, 3, 4, 6, 8, 12, 16, 24, and 48,

Factors of 72 are: 2, 3, 4, 6, 8, 9, 12, 16, 18, 24, 36, and 72,

Factors of 96 are: 2, 3, 4, 6, 8, 12, 16, 24, 48, and 96,

The common factors are: 2, 3, 4, 6, 8, 12, 16, and 24.

Therefore, the HCF is 24.

Method 2:

Number	Prime Factors of:	
	2	3
48	2, 2, 2, 2	3
72	2, 2, 2	3, 3
96	2, 2, 2, 2, 2	3

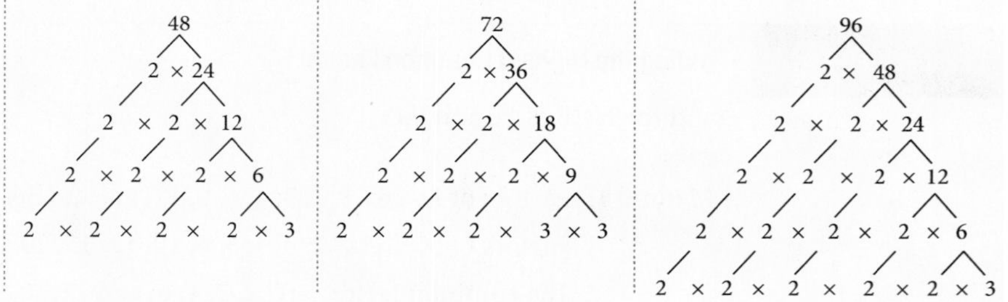

Therefore, the HCF $= 2 \times 2 \times 2 \times 3 = 24$.

(i) Therefore, the greatest possible length of equal piece is 24 cm.

(ii) Number of equal pieces is the number of multiples of 24 cm of each piece.

$$48 = 24 \times 2$$

$$72 = 24 \times 3$$

$$96 = 24 \times 4$$

Therefore, the number of equal pieces of 24 cm possible is $2 + 3 + 4 = 9$.

1.3 | Exercises

Answers to odd-numbered problems are available at the end of the textbook.

1. List all the prime numbers less than 20.
2. List all the prime numbers between 20 and 40.
3. List all the composite numbers greater than 10 and less than 30.
4. List all the composite numbers greater than 30 and less than 50.
5. Identify the prime numbers in the given sets of numbers: a. 13, 19, 36, 47, 49 b. 11, 14, 29, 35, 43
6. Identify the prime numbers in the given sets of numbers: a. 31, 39, 41, 59, 63 b. 23, 37, 45, 51, 53

For Problems 7 to 14, (i) find all the factors and (ii) list the prime factors of the numbers.

7. a. 15 b. 34
8. a. 18 b. 35
9. a. 64 b. 54
10. a. 56 b. 60
11. a. 21 b. 25
12. a. 30 b. 42
13. a. 36 b. 65
14. a. 40 b. 49

For Problems 15 to 18, find the first 6 multiples of the numbers.

15. a. 6 b. 8
16. a. 5 b. 12
17. a. 9 b. 10
18. a. 7 b. 15

For Problems 19 to 24, find the lowest common multiple (LCM) of each pair of the numbers.

19. a. 10, 15 b. 15, 18
20. a. 12, 16 b. 21, 36
21. a. 18, 24 b. 35, 45
22. a. 10, 25 b. 45, 60
23. a. 16, 64 b. 8, 60
24. a. 12, 90 b. 25, 30

For Problems 25 to 32, find the lowest common multiple (LCM) of the sets of numbers.

25. a. 2, 3, 8 b. 4, 9, 10
26. a. 8, 5, 12 b. 5, 15, 20
27. a. 10, 15, 25 b. 6, 27, 36
28. a. 4, 8, 40 b. 3, 16, 2
29. a. 14, 21, 28 b. 3, 18, 27
30. a. 4, 6, 21 b. 12, 28, 42
31. a. 24, 36, 12 b. 6, 15, 18
32. a. 5, 12, 15 b. 12, 40, 48

For Problems 33 to 38 find the (i) factors, (ii) common factors, and (iii) highest common factor (HCF) of each pair of numbers.

33. a. 15, 25 b. 18, 32
34. a. 14, 35 b. 8, 36
35. a. 18, 48 b. 32, 60
36. a. 16, 30 b. 36, 42
37. a. 25, 80 b. 40, 120
38. a. 35, 75 b. 24, 64

For Problems 39 to 44 find the (i) factors, (ii) common factors, and (iii) highest common factor (HCF) of the sets of numbers.

39. a. 8, 12, 15 b. 6, 15, 20
40. a. 6, 8, 10 b. 10, 15, 25
41. a. 12, 18, 24 b. 12, 30, 42
42. a. 24, 36, 40 b. 12, 36, 48
43. a. 40, 50, 80 b. 30, 75, 90
44. a. 50, 75, 125 b. 60, 90, 120
45. Two wires of lengths 96 cm and 160 cm are to be cut into pieces of equal length, without wastage. Find the greatest possible length of each piece.
46. Two ribbons of lengths 112 cm and 154 cm are to be cut into pieces of equal length, without wastage. Find the greatest possible length of each piece.
47. Tahrell has music lessons every 6th day and swimming lessons every 8th day. If he had music and swimming lessons on February 5th, on which date will he have both lessons again?

48. Enea has skating lessons every 8th day and ballet lessons every 10th day. If she had skating and ballet lessons on March 3rd, on which date will she have both lessons again?

- 49. Three wires measuring 18 m, 45 m, and 36 m are to be cut into pieces of equal length, without wastage. What is the maximum possible length of each piece?

- 50. A store has 54 green marbles, 72 yellow marbles, and 90 red marbles. The owner decides to package all the marbles into bags, such that each bag contained the same number of marbles. As well, each bag had to contain marbles of the same colour. Find the maximum possible number of marbles in each bag.

- 51. Three lights, red, blue, and green, flash at intervals of 15, 18, and 40 seconds, respectively. If they begin flashing at the same time, how long will it take (in minutes) until all 3 flash at the same time again?

- 52. Three bells ring simultaneously. If they ring at intervals of 24, 36, and 40 seconds, how long will it take (in minutes) until they ring together again?

1.4 | Powers, Square Roots, and Order of Operations

Powers of Whole Numbers

We learned that multiplication is a shorter way to write repeated additions of a number. Similarly, when a number is multiplied by itself repeatedly, we represent this repeated multiplication using **exponential notation.** In this section, we will learn about exponential notation and the positive powers of whole numbers.

When 2 is multiplied 5 times, in repeated multiplication, it is represented by:

$$2 \times 2 \times 2 \times 2 \times 2$$

1 raised to any power = 1

0 raised to any power = 0

However, when 2 is multiplied 100 times, it would be tedious to represent it using repeated multiplication. Instead, the exponential notation can be used.

When 2 is multiplied 5 times, it is represented as $\mathbf{2^5}$ using exponential notation. The whole representation is read as "2 raised to the power of 5" or "2 to the 5th power".

Base ⟶ 2^5 ⟵ Exponent

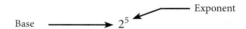

In the notation 2^5, 2 is called the **base** and 5 is called the **exponent**.

The base represents the number and the exponent represents the number of times the base is multiplied. The exponent is the number written in superscript to the right of the base number.

Example 1.4-a **Converting an Exponential Notation to Repeated Multiplication and Solving**

Expand 8^2 to show the repeated multiplication and simplify.

Solution

$$8^2 = \overbrace{8 \times 8}^{\text{Repeated Multiplication}} = 64$$

8^2: Exponential Notation; 64: Standard Notation

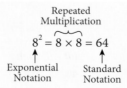

Example 1.4-b **Writing Repeated Multiplication in Exponential Form**

Express the repeated multiplication $9 \times 9 \times 9 \times 9 \times 9 \times 9$ in exponential form.

Solution

Number 9 is multiplied repeatedly 6 times.

The **base** is **9** and the **exponent** is **6**.

Therefore, $9 \times 9 \times 9 \times 9 \times 9 \times 9 = \mathbf{9^6}$.

Example 1.4-c

Evaluating Expressions by Writing in Standard Form

Express the following in standard form and then evaluate:

(i) 5×3^4 (ii) $2^3 \times 3^2$ (iii) $5^4 + 2^2$ (iv) $5^2 - 4^2$

Solution

(i) $5 \times 3^4 = 5 \times [\,3 \times 3 \times 3 \times 3\,] = 5 \times 81 = 405$

(ii) $2^3 \times 3^2 = [\,2 \times 2 \times 2\,] \times [\,3 \times 3\,] = 8 \times 9 = 72$

(iii) $5^4 + 2^2 = [\,5 \times 5 \times 5 \times 5\,] + [\,2 \times 2\,] = 625 + 4 = 629$

(iv) $5^2 - 4^2 = [\,5 \times 5\,] - [\,4 \times 4\,] = 25 - 16 = 9$

Example 1.4-d

Knowing One Power and Using it to Find Another Power of the Same Base

If $6^5 = 7{,}776$, find: (i) 6^6 (ii) 6^4

Solution

(i) $6^6 = 6 \times 6^5$ Using the property of powers (exponents),

$= 6 \times 7{,}776$

$= 46{,}656$

(ii) $6^5 = 6 \times 6^4$ Using the property of powers (exponents),

$7{,}776 = 6 \times 6^4$

$6^4 = \dfrac{7{,}776}{6}$

$= 1{,}296$

Table 1.4

Examples of Powers of Exponents of 2, 3, 4, and 5

Powers of 2		Powers of 3	Powers of 4	Powers of 5
$1^2 = 1$	$11^2 = 121$	$1^3 = 1$	$1^4 = 1$	$1^5 = 1$
$2^2 = 4$	$12^2 = 144$	$2^3 = 8$	$2^4 = 16$	$2^5 = 32$
$3^2 = 9$	$13^2 = 169$	$3^3 = 27$	$3^4 = 81$	$3^5 = 243$
$4^2 = 16$	$14^2 = 196$	$4^3 = 64$	$4^4 = 256$	$4^5 = 1{,}024$
$5^2 = 25$	$15^2 = 225$	$5^3 = 125$	$5^4 = 625$	$5^5 = 3{,}125$
$6^2 = 36$				
$7^2 = 49$				
$8^2 = 64$				
$9^2 = 81$				
$10^2 = 100$				

Roots of Perfect Squares

The square root of a number is one of two identical factors of that number.

Any whole number base with an exponent of 2 is called a perfect square. For example, 1, 4, 9, 16, 25, 36, 49, 64, 81, 100, ... are perfect squares.

$1^2 = 1$	$2^2 = 4$	$3^2 = 9$	$4^2 = 16$	$5^2 = 25$
$6^2 = 36$	$7^2 = 49$	$8^2 = 64$	$9^2 = 81$	$10^2 = 100$

Finding the root of a perfect square is the inverse of raising a number to the power of 2.

2 is the **square root** of 4 because $2^2 = 4$ or $2 \times 2 = 4$

5 is the **square root** of 25 because $5^2 = 25$ or $5 \times 5 = 25$

That is, a whole number multiplied by itself results in a perfect square. The number multiplied by itself to get that perfect square is called the square root of that perfect square.

For example,

16 is a **perfect square** because it has two identical factors of 4. i.e., $16 = 4 \times 4$

Therefore, 4 is the square root of 16.

The radical sign '$\sqrt{\ }$' indicates the root of a number (or expression). The square root of 16, using the radical sign, is represented by $\sqrt[2]{16}$, where 2 is the index. The index is written as a small number to the left of the radical symbol. It indicates which root is to be taken. For square roots, the index 2 does not need to be written as it is understood to be there; i.e. $\sqrt[2]{16}$ is written as $\sqrt{16}$.

Example 1.4-e **Finding the Square Root of Perfect Squares**

Find the square root of the following:

(i) $\sqrt{36}$

(ii) $\sqrt{81}$

(iii) $\sqrt{144}$

Solution

(i) $\sqrt{36} = \sqrt{6 \times 6}$ (Using $36 = 6 \times 6$)

$= 6$

(ii) $\sqrt{81} = \sqrt{9 \times 9}$ (Using $81 = 9 \times 9$)

$= 9$

(iii) $\sqrt{144} = \sqrt{12 \times 12}$ (Using $144 = 12 \times 12$)

$= 12$

Order of Operations for Whole Numbers

You have learned: addition, subtraction, multiplication, division, powers, and roots of whole numbers. In this section, you will learn the correct order (or sequence) for performing the combined arithmetic operations of whole numbers.

When there are no groupings (operations within brackets or a radical sign), the six arithmetic operations are performed in the following sequence:

1. Exponents (Powers) and Roots.
2. Division and Multiplication in order from left to right.
3. Addition and Subtraction in order from left to right.

Example 1.4-f Evaluating Expressions with Mixed Arithmetic Operations

Solve the following arithmetic expressions:

(i) $16 \div 2^2 + 44 - 3^3$ (ii) $12 \div 3 \times 2 + 5^2$

Solution

(i) $16 \div \mathbf{2^2} + 44 - \mathbf{3^3}$ Working on the exponents,

$= \mathbf{16 \div 4} + 44 - 27$ Dividing,

$= \mathbf{4 + 44} - 27$ Adding,

$= \mathbf{48 - 27}$ Subtracting,

$= 21$

(ii) $12 \div 3 \times 2 + \mathbf{5^2}$ Working on the exponent,

$= \mathbf{12 \div 3} \times 2 + 25$ Dividing,

$= \mathbf{4 \times 2} + 25$ Multiplying,

$= \mathbf{8 + 25}$ Adding,

$= 33$

Where there are groupings, the arithmetic operations within the groupings are to be evaluated first. Common symbols used for groupings are brackets ( ), [ ], { }, and $\sqrt{\ }$.

When there are groupings with more than one bracket, start with the innermost bracket, and move outwards to complete evaluating all expressions within the brackets by following the order of operations explained earlier.

Arithmetic expressions that contain multiple operations, with brackets, exponents, divisons, multiplications, additions, and subtractions, are performed in the following sequence:

1. Brackets
2. Exponents (Powers) and Roots
3. Division and Multiplication in order from left to right
4. Addition and Subtraction in order from left to right

The above Order of Operations, Brackets, Exponents, Divisions, Multiplications, Additions, and Subtractions, can be remembered by the acronym '**BEDMAS**'.

Example 1.4-g Evaluating by Finding the Square Roots

Evaluate the following:

(i) $\sqrt{49} + \sqrt{25}$ (ii) $\sqrt{64} - \sqrt{16}$ (iii) $\sqrt{4} \times \sqrt{9}$

Solution

(i) $\sqrt{49} + \sqrt{25}$ Working on the square root,

$= 7 + 5$ Adding,

$= 12$

(ii) $\sqrt{64} - \sqrt{16}$ Working on the square root,

$= 8 - 4$ Subtracting,

$= 4$

(iii) $\sqrt{4} \times \sqrt{9}$ Working on the square root,

$= 2 \times 3$ Multiplying,

$= 6$

Example 1.4-h Evaluating Expressions by Finding the Square Roots

Evaluate the following expressions:

(i) $5 \times \sqrt{121}$ (ii) $\sqrt{100} \div 5$ (iii) $35 + \sqrt{49} - \sqrt{9}$

Solution

(i) $5 \times \sqrt{121}$	Working on the square root,
$= 5 \times 11$	Multiplying,
$= 55$	
(ii) $\sqrt{100} \div 5$	Working on the square root,
$= 10 \div 5$	Dividing,
$= 2$	
(iii) $35 + \sqrt{49} - \sqrt{9}$	Working on the square root,
$= 35 + 7 - 3$	Adding and subtracting from left to right,
$= 39$	

Example 1.4-i Evaluating Expressions with Groupings

Solve the following arithmetic expressions:

(i) $4 \times 50 \div (8 - 3)^2 - 1$ (ii) $(100 - 3 \times 24) \div 2\,(6 - 3) \div 2$

(iii) $\sqrt{3^2 + 4^2} \times (7 - 4) + 2$ (iv) $35 \div 7 + \sqrt{4^2 + 9}$

(v) $4^2 - \sqrt{13^2 - 5^2} + 3^2\sqrt{25}$

Solution

(i) $4 \times 50 \div \mathbf{(8 - 3)}^2 - 1$	Working on the brackets,
$= 4 \times 50 \div \mathbf{5^2} - 1$	Working on the exponent,
$= \mathbf{4 \times 50} \div 25 - 1$	Dividing and multiplying from left to right,
$= \mathbf{200 \div 25} - 1$	
$= 8 - 1$	Subtracting,
$= 7$	
(ii) $(100 - \mathbf{3 \times 24}) \div 2\,\mathbf{(6 - 3)} \div 2$	Working on the **bolded** operations within the brackets first,
$= \mathbf{(100 - 72)} \div 2\,\mathbf{(3)} \div 2$	
$= \mathbf{28 \div 2} \times 3 \div 2$	Dividing and multiplying from left to right,
$= \mathbf{14 \times 3} \div 2$	
$= \mathbf{42} \div 2$	
$= \mathbf{21}$	
(iii) $\sqrt{\mathbf{3^2 + 4^2}} \times (7 - 4) + 2$	Working on the exponents,
$= \sqrt{\mathbf{9 + 16}} \times (7 - 4) + 2$	Adding within the radical,
$= \sqrt{\mathbf{25}} \times (7 - 4) + 2$	Working on the square root,
$= \mathbf{5 \times 3} + 2$	Multiplying,
$= 15 + 2$	Adding,
$= 17$	

Solution *continued*

(iv) $35 \div 7 + \sqrt{4^2 + 9}$ Evaluating the grouping within the radical sign,

$= 35 \div 7 + \sqrt{\mathbf{16 + 9}}$

$= 35 \div 7 + \sqrt{\mathbf{25}}$

$= 35 \div 7 + 5$ Dividing,

$= \mathbf{5 + 5}$ Adding,

$= 10$

(v) $4^2 - \sqrt{13^2 - 5^2} + 3^2\sqrt{25}$ Evaluating the grouping within the radical sign,

$= 4^2 - \sqrt{\mathbf{169 - 25}} + 3^2\sqrt{25}$

$= 4^2 - \sqrt{\mathbf{144}} + 3^2\sqrt{\mathbf{25}}$

$= \mathbf{4^2} - 12 + \mathbf{3^2} \times 5$ Working on the exponents,

$= 16 - 12 + \mathbf{9 \times 5}$ Multiplying,

$= \mathbf{16 - 12} + 45$ Adding and subtracting from left to right,

$= \mathbf{4 + 45}$

$= 49$

Example 1.4-j **Evaluating Expressions with More than One Bracket**

Evaluate the following:

(i) $4 \times 50 \div [(8-3)^2 - 5]$ (ii) $100 - 3\,[24 \div 2(6-3)] \div 2$ (iii) $[10^2 \times 4 + 50] \div [(8-3)^2 - 4^2]$

Solution

(i) $4 \times 50 \div [(\mathbf{8 - 3})^2 - 5]$ Working on the brackets,

$= 4 \times 50 \div [\mathbf{5^2} - 5]$ Working on the exponent and then subtracting within the brackets,

$= 4 \times 50 \div [\mathbf{25 - 5}]$

$= \mathbf{4 \times 50} \div 20$ Dividing and multiplying from left to right,

$= \mathbf{200 \div 20}$

$= 10$

(ii) $100 - 3[24 \div 2\,(\mathbf{6 - 3})] \div 2$ Dividing and multiplying from left to right within the brackets,

$= 100 - 3[\mathbf{24 \div 2} \times \mathbf{3}] \div 2$

$= 100 - 3[\mathbf{12 \times 3}] \div 2$

$= 100 - \mathbf{3 \times 36} \div 2$ Dividing and multiplying from left to right,

$= 100 - \mathbf{108 \div 2}$

$= \mathbf{100 - 54}$ Subtracting,

$= 46$

(iii) $[10^2 \times 4 + 50] \div [(\mathbf{8 - 3})^2 - 4^2]$ Working on the inner brackets,

$= [\mathbf{10^2} \times 4 + 50] \div [\mathbf{5^2 - 4^2}]$ Working on the exponents,

$= [\mathbf{100 \times 4} + 50] \div [25 - 16]$ Working on the outer brackets,

$= [400 + \mathbf{50}] \div 9$

$= \mathbf{450} \div 9$ Dividing,

$= 50$

1.4 | Exercises

Answers to odd-numbered problems are available at the end of the textbook.

For Problems 1 to 4, express the repeated multiplication in exponential notation.

1. a. $6 \times 6 \times 6 \times 6$ b. 12×12
2. a. $5 \times 5 \times 5$ b. $7 \times 7 \times 7 \times 7 \times 7$
3. a. $3 \times 3 \times 3 \times 3 \times 3 \times 3$ b. $9 \times 9 \times 9 \times 9$
4. a. $8 \times 8 \times 8 \times 8 \times 8$ b. $4 \times 4 \times 4 \times 4 \times 4$

For Problems 5 to 8, write the base and exponent for the powers.

5. a. 2^9 b. 5^7
6. a. 6^2 b. 10^9
7. a. 1^{20} b. 5^7
8. a. 7^5 b. 12^1

For Problems 9 and 10, express the powers in standard notation and then evaluate.

9. a. 10^6 b. 3^5
10. a. 2^8 b. 5^4
11. If $3^{10} = 59{,}049$, evaluate 3^9 and 3^{11}
12. If $5^8 = 390{,}625$, evaluate 5^7 and 5^9

For Problems 13 to 20, evaluate the expressions.

13. a. $4^2 \times 2^4$ b. $3^2 \times 2^3$
14. a. $5^2 \times 2^3$ b. $4^2 \times 3^3$
15. a. $(7 - 4)^2$ b. $(3 + 2)^3$
16. a. $(8 - 5)^3$ b. $(4 + 1)^2$
17. a. $2^3 + 3^3$ b. $5^2 - 4^2$
18. a. $5^2 + 6^2$ b. $8^2 - 6^2$
19. a. $6^2 \times 2 - 2$ b. $100 - 5^2 \times 3$
20. a. $5^2 \times 3 - 15$ b. $144 - 3^3 \times 4$

For Problems 21 to 32, evaluate the expressions.

21. a. $\sqrt{100} + \sqrt{25}$ b. $\sqrt{81} - \sqrt{16}$
22. a. $\sqrt{121} + \sqrt{36}$ b. $\sqrt{144} - \sqrt{9}$
23. a. $\sqrt{9 \times 16}$ b. $\sqrt{36 \times 49}$
24. a. $\sqrt{25 \times 64}$ b. $\sqrt{81 \times 121}$
25. a. $\sqrt{40 - 24}$ b. $\sqrt{75 - 11}$
26. a. $\sqrt{125 - 76}$ b. $\sqrt{48 - 23}$
27. a. $\sqrt{3^2 + 4^2}$ b. $\sqrt{13^2 - 5^2}$
28. a. $\sqrt{5^2 - 4^2}$ b. $\sqrt{12^2 + 5^2}$
29. a. $\sqrt{100 \div 25}$ b. $\sqrt{196 \div 4}$
30. a. $\sqrt{256 \div 4}$ b. $\sqrt{225 \div 25}$
31. a. $\sqrt{8^2}$ b. $\sqrt{20^2}$
32. a. $\sqrt{12^2}$ b. $\sqrt{45^2}$

For Problems 33 to 50, evaluate the expressions.

33. a. $5 \times 4 + 25 \div 25$ b. $64 \div 8 \times 2$
34. a. $7 \times 5 + 20 \div 4$ b. $36 \div 4 \times 9$
35. a. $100 \div 25 \times 4$ b. $18 \div 2 \times 3 + 5$
36. a. $80 \div 10 \times 8$ b. $50 \times 2 \times 5 + 10$
37. a. $32 \div 4 \div 2 \times 4$ b. $96 \div 12 \times 2 + 4$
38. a. $20 \div 4 \times 5 + 2$ b. $56 \div 4 \div 2 \times 5$
39. a. $5^2\sqrt{16} + 10 - 2$ b. $19 - 2^2\sqrt{9} + 3$
40. a. $40 - 3^2\sqrt{16} + 1$ b. $6^2\sqrt{25} + 16 - \sqrt{100}$
41. a. $(4 + 3)^2 - 5^2 + 2^3$ b. $6^2 + 2^3 - (12 - 8)^2$
42. a. $(9 - 6)^2 - 2^2 + 3^3$ b. $3^2 + 2^4 - (15 - 9)^2$
43. a. $12^2 - 5 \times 27 \div (5 - 2)^2 - 3$ b. $3^2[(9 - 6)^2 \div 9 + 7 - 4]$
44. a. $16 \div 8 \times 10^2 + (12 - 7)^2 \times 2$ b. $3^2[(12^2 + 8)^2 \div 4 + 6 - 2]$
45. a. $7 + (3\sqrt{49} - 1)^2$ b. $16 \div \sqrt{64} + \sqrt{10^2 - 6^2}$
46. a. $15 + (5\sqrt{9} - 8)^2$ b. $\sqrt{12^2 + 5^2} - 27 \div \sqrt{81}$
47. a. $[(20 \div 5) \times 8] \div (2^2 + 4)$ b. $(64 \div 8 \div 4)^2 + (3^2 + 6^0)$
48. a. $[(6^2 \div 4) \times 5] \div (2^2 + 5)$ b. $(81 \div 9 \div 3)^2 + (9^0 + 2^2)$
49. $[(11 - 2)^2 + 3] + (16 \div 2)^2$
50. $(20 \div 2)^2 + [(13 - 6) + 4^2]$

1 | Review Exercises

Answers to odd-numbered problems are available at the end of the textbook.

For Problems 1 and 2, write the answers in (i) expanded form and (ii) word form.

1. a. 7,502 b. 25,047 c. 620,025 d. 3,054,705

2. a. 9,024 b. 38,024 c. 405,037 d. 2,601,071

For Problems 3 and 4, write the the numbers in (i) standard form and (ii) expanded form.

3. a. Five thousand, six hundred seven
   b. Thirty-seven thousand, forty
   c. Four hundred eight thousand, one hundred five
   d. One million, seventy thousand, fifty-five

4. a. Nine thousand, nine hundred three
   b. Fifty nine thousand, three hundred three
   c. Seven hundred thousand, eight hundred eighty-eight
   d. Seven million, seventy six thousand, fifty-five

For Problems 5 and 6, insert the proper sign of ineqality (< or >) between each pair of numbers.

5. a. 167 ⬚ 176 b. 2,067 ⬚ 2,097 c. 79, 084 ⬚ 79,087 d. 162,555 ⬚ 162,507

6. a. 159 ⬚ 139 b. 1,838 ⬚ 1,868 c. 52,109 ⬚ 51,889 d. 379,847 ⬚ 397,487

For Problems 7 and 8, (i) estimate the answer by rounding each number to the nearest hundred and (ii) calculate the exact answer.

7. a. 3,495 + 276 + 85 b. 5,555 + 157 + 60 c. 7,836 – 655 d. 6,405 – 2,769

8. a. 8,655 + 348 + 75 b. 3,450 + 645 + 50 c. 5,245 – 876 d. 2,056 – 444

For Problems 9 and 10, perform the arithmetic operation.

9. a. 465×23 b. 365×24 c. $314 \div 5$ d. $2{,}524 \div 12$

10. a. 345×34 b. 237×25 c. $276 \div 6$ d. $4{,}783 \div 15$

For Problems 11 and 12, find the LCM of the numbers.

11. a. 12 and 20 b. 16 and 72 c. 16, 18, and 33

12. a. 16 and 40 b. 36 and 54 c. 8, 24, and 32

For Problems 13 and 14, find the HCF of the numbers.

13. a. 8 and 12 b. 42 and 48 c. 24, 30, and 32

14. a. 4 and 9 b. 40 and 72 c. 12, 16, and 60

For Problems 15 to 28, perform the arithmetic operations.

15. a. $6 + 8 - 6 \times 2 \div 4$ b. $15 - (7 - 5) \div 2$

16. a. $9 + 2 - 4 \times 3 \div 2$ b. $10 - (7 - 4) \div 3$

17. a. $12 - 2\,(9 - 6) + 10 \div 5 + 5$ b. $9 - 8\,(7 - 5) \div (6 + 2)$

18. a. $8 - 4\,(6 - 4) + 16 \div 4 + 4$ b. $10 - 4\,(9 - 7) \div (5 + 3)$

19. a. $8\,(7 + 3) + 6^2 \div 4$ b. $8^2 \div 4 - 6\,(5 - 3)$

20. a. $7\,(6 + 4) + 4^2 \div 2$ b. $9^2 \div 3\,(8 - 5) - 4\,(5 + 3)$

21. a. $24 \div 2^2 \times 3 + (5 - 2)^2$ b. $8\,(7 - 3)^2 \div 4 - 5$

22. a. $64 \div 2\,(8 - 4)^2 + 5^2$ b. $9\,(8 - 5) \div 3 + (7 - 4)^2$

23. a. $(16 + 4 \times 2) \div (4^2 - 8)$ b. $6^2 - 2\,[(6 - 3)^2 + 4]$

24. a. $(6 + 3 \times 2) \div (2^2 - 1)$ b. $8^2 - 3\,[(7 - 3)^2 + 2]$

25. a. $\sqrt{9} - (8 - 5) + 10 \div 5 + 7$
    b. $15 - 15(8 - 6) \div \sqrt{36} + 15$

26. a. $\sqrt{49} - 7(6 - 4) \div (5 - 3)$
    b. $\sqrt{16} + (10 - 7) + 20 \div 4 - 3$

27. a. $6^2 \div 9 + 6(5^2 - 2^2)$
    b. $3[(7 - 4)^2 + 4] - (2 + 3)^2$

28. a. $5(12^2 - 2^2) + 48 \div 4^2$
    b. $(6 + 2)^2 - 4[(12 - 9)^2 + 3]$

29. After Martha gave 175 stamps to her brother, she had 698 stamps left. How many stamps did she have at the beginning?

30. Amy spent \$349 and had \$167 left. How much did she have at the beginning?

31. Each ticket for a concert costs \$25. A total of \$35,000 was collected from ticket sales for Saturday and Sunday. If 550 tickets were sold on Saturday, how many were sold on Sunday?

32. A company manufactured printers for \$40 a unit. Over two weeks, \$46,000 was spent on manufacturing printers. If 500 printers were manufactured in the first week, how many printers were manufactured in the second week?

33. At a concert, 245 tickets were sold for \$125 each and 325 tickets were sold for \$68 each. How much money was collected altogether?

34. Susie held a bake sale. She sold 45 cookies for \$2 each and 63 brownies for \$3 each. How much money did she make altogether?

35. Allan and Babar have a total of \$2,550. Allan has \$800 more than Babar. How much money does each of them have?

36. Ayesha saved \$5,500 more than Beth. If they saved \$32,450 together, how much did each of them save?

• 37. An elevator can carry a maximum of 540 kg. Two workmen want to move 20 boxes of tiles, each weighing 24 kg. One of the workmen weighs 72 kg and the other weighs 65 kg. What is the largest number of boxes that can be carried in the elevator if both workmen are in it?

• 38. A delivery truck can carry a maximum of 2,000 kg. Two workmen want to move 100 planks of wood, each weighing 30 kg. One of the workmen weighs 85 kg and the other weighs 77 kg. What is the largest number of planks that can be carried by the truck if both workmen are in the truck?

• 39. Three balls of yarn measuring 24 metres, 60 metres, and 36 metres are to be cut into pieces of equal lengths, without wastage. What is the maximum possible length of each piece?

• 40. A store has 32 oranges, 48 bananas, and 72 apples. The owner decides to make fruit baskets each containing an equal number of fruits, without any left over. It was required that each basket have only one type of fruit in it. Find the maximum possible number of fruits in each basket.

• 41. Amy, Bob, and Cathy go for a swim every 3rd, 7th, and 14th day, respectively. If they met each other on a particular day at the pool, how many days later would they meet again?

• 42. Three gentlemen decided to go for a walk around a circular park. The first man takes 6 minutes, the second takes 10 minutes, and the third takes 8 minutes. If they start together, when will they meet again?

1 | Self-Test Exercises

Answers to all problems are available at the end of the textbook.

1. In the following, (i) estimate the answer by rounding each number to the nearest hundred, and (ii) calculate the exact answer.

   a. $3,950 + 2,540 + 709 + 65$

   b. $5,475 + 1,260 + 179 - 50$

   c. $1,274 \times 350$

   d. $6,650 \div 112$

For Problems 2 to 5 evaluate the expressions.

2. a. $4\,(10 + 2^3) \div 3$

   b. $5\,(3^2 - 4) + (5^2 - 4^2)$

   c. $(5 + 4)^2 \div (5 - 2)^3$

   d. $4\,[12 - (6 - 3)\,2] \div 12$

3. a. $3^2 - 5 + 4^2 \div 8$

   b. $8 + (8 \times 5 + 4) + 11 - 7$

   c. $(5 + 1)^2\,[(11 - 9)^2 - 6 \div 2]$

   d. $100 \div [5 \times 4 + (8 - 3)^2 + 5]$

4. a. $\sqrt{(12^2 \div 4)} + 3 \times 2^4$

   b. $\sqrt{(4^2 \times 5 + 1)} - \sqrt{3^2 + 4^2}$

   c. $16 \times 8 - (4^2 + 8) + \sqrt{(16 \div 4)^2}$

   d. $5(5^2 - 3^2) \div 4(5 - 3)$

5. a. $4(1 + 5)^2 \div [24 - (12 + 4)]$

   b. $(4 \times 8 - 4^2) \div \sqrt{10^2 - 6^2}$

   c. $[(12^2 - 4 \times 3) + 8] \div 7$

   d. $12^2 \div 4 - 3 \times 3^2$

6. Bob and Hari saved a total of \$7,650. If Bob saved 5 times as much as Hari, how much money do each of them have?

7. The number of toasters sold by a manufacturer of kitchen appliances over each of the 4 quarters of last year were 9,092, 9,108, 9,102, and 9,976. Calculate:

   a. The total number of toasters sold last year.

   b. The difference between the highest and the lowest number of toasters sold quarterly.

8. A truck can hold 1,275 cartons of milk. Each carton weighs 18 kg and the empty truck weighs 3,045 kg. Calculate the total weight of the truck when it is fully loaded with milk.

9. Lionel has a job that pays \$24 an hour for each regular working hour and \$36 hour for every hour of overtime that he works. Last week he worked 40 regular hours and 7 hours overtime. Calculate his pay for last week.

10. Caroline's take home pay for last year was \$48,750. Calculate her pay for each week. (Assume 1 year = 52 weeks).

11. A carpark has 9 rows and each row has 47 parking spaces. How many cars are in the carpark if there were 29 empty parking spaces?

12. On Thursday, there were 1,075 shoppers at the Eaton Centre, which was 368 more than that on Friday.

    a. How many shoppers were there on Friday?

    b. If on Saturday, there were 125 fewer shoppers at the Eaton Centre than on Friday. How many shoppers were there on Saturday?

- 13. 4,256 people visited the Toronto Zoo on Sunday. 1,968 were adults and the rest were children. How many more children than adults visited the zoo?
- 14. There were some passengers on a train as it left the station in Toronto. At the station in Kitchener, 94 passengers got off and 35 got on. At the station in London, 89 passengers got off and 125 got on. If there were now 194 passengers on board, how many passengers were on the train at the station in Toronto?
- 15. Four lights, red, blue, green, and yellow, flash at intervals of 12, 16, 18, and 21 seconds, respectively. If they begin flashing at the same time, when will they flash together again?
- 16. Four wires measuring 12 m, 18 m, 24 m, and 42 m are to be cut into pieces of equal lengths, without wastage. What is the maximum possible length of each piece?

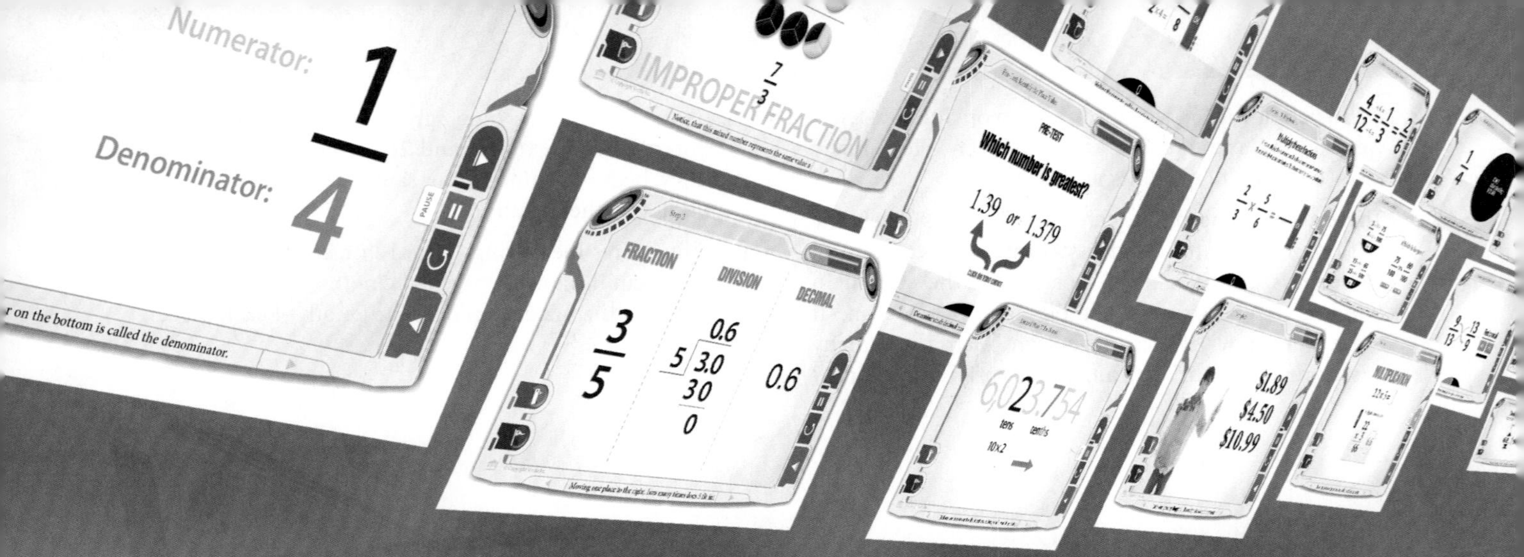

2 FRACTIONS AND DECIMALS

Fractions and decimal numbers are used to express numbers that are a portion of a whole number. Fractions are useful for understanding measurement, probability, and data. Decimal numbers are a type of fraction that has the denominator expressed in powers of ten. It is easier to read, write, and perform arithmetic operations with decimal numbers than with fractions. In addition, it is easier to determine the magnitude of numbers when they are expressed as decimal numbers rather than fractions. For example, it is easier to recognize that 7.75 , instead of its fractional form, $\frac{93}{12}$, lies between 7 and 8. In this chapter, we will learn about the different types of decimals and fractions and the methods to convert them from one form to the other. As well, we will learn to perform mathematical operations of fractions and decimal numbers combined with powers and square roots.

LEARNING OBJECTIVES

- Identify the types of fractions and perform computations with them.
- Read, write, and round decimal numbers.
- Solve problems involving fractions and decimal numbers.
- Determine the relationship between fractions and decimal numbers.
- Perform arithmetic operations combined with fractions and decimal numbers.

CHAPTER OUTLINE

2.1 | Fractions

Introduction

In the previous chapter, you learned about whole numbers and how to perform basic operations with whole numbers. However, measurements and calculations of quantities, values, amounts, etc., will not always be in whole numbers. Most of these involve portions of whole numbers and are represented by **fractions**. In this section, you will learn about fractions and how to perform basic mathematical operations with fractions.

If we divide one whole unit into several equal portions, then one or several of these equal portions can be represented by a fraction.

A fraction is composed of the following three parts:

1. **Numerator:** Representing the number of equal parts of a whole unit.
2. **Fraction bar:** Representing the division sign, meaning 'divided by'.
3. **Denominator:** Representing the total number of equal parts into which the whole unit is divided.

For example, $\frac{3}{8}$ is a fraction.

fraction bar → $\frac{3}{8}$ ← numerator, ← denominator

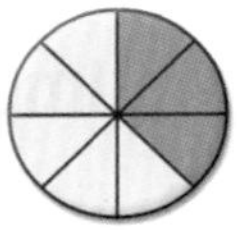

The **numerator** '**3**' indicates that the fraction represents 3 equal parts of a whole unit and the **denominator** '**8**' indicates that the whole unit is divided into 8 equal parts, as shown. The **fraction bar** indicates that the numerator '3' is divided by the denominator '8'.

In the above example, $\frac{3}{8}$ is read as "three divided by eight", "three-eighths", or "three over eight". All of these indicate that 3 is the numerator and that 8 is the denominator.

The numerator and denominator are referred to as the terms of the fraction. A **fraction** is another method of representing numbers, where one integer is divided by another non-zero integer.

A fraction where one integer is divided by another non-zero integer is called a **rational number**.

For example, $\frac{3}{2}, \frac{5}{2}, \frac{7}{1}, ...$ are rational numbers.

We know that 7 is an integer and also a whole number. Since 7 can be written as $\frac{7}{1}$ it is also a rational number.

The denominator of a fraction cannot be zero, since zero cannot represent a whole unit.

Fractions can be represented on a number line.

For example, $\frac{1}{2}$ is represented on a number line as:

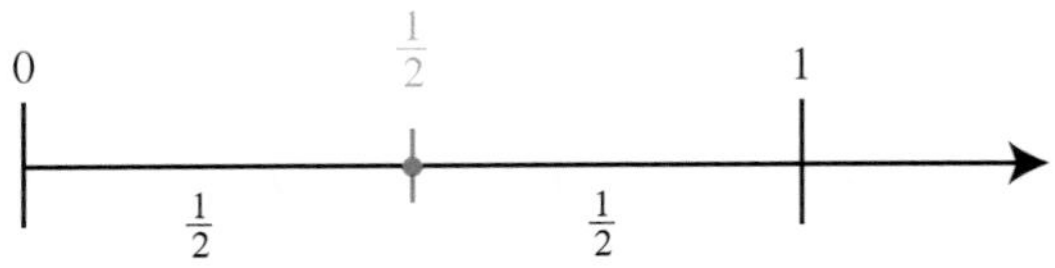

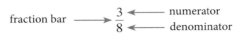

When one unit is divided into two equal portions, each portion represents one half of that unit, and is written as $\frac{1}{2}$.

Example 2.1-a

Number Line

Represent the following fractions on a number line:

(i) $\frac{2}{3}$ (ii) $\frac{3}{5}$

Solution

(i)

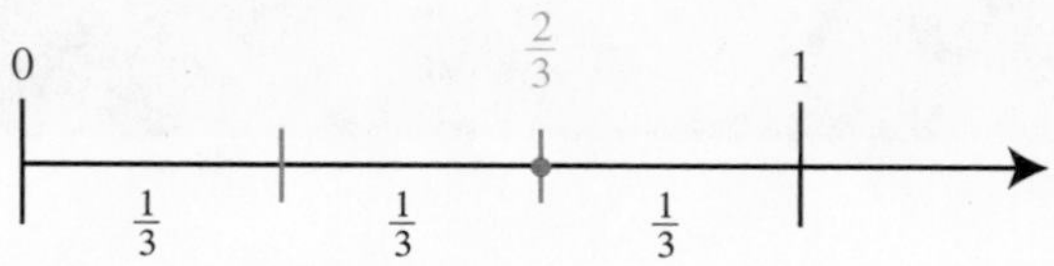

When one unit is divided into three equal portions, each portion represents one third of that unit. Two of such equal portions is two thirds and is written as $\frac{2}{3}$.

(ii)

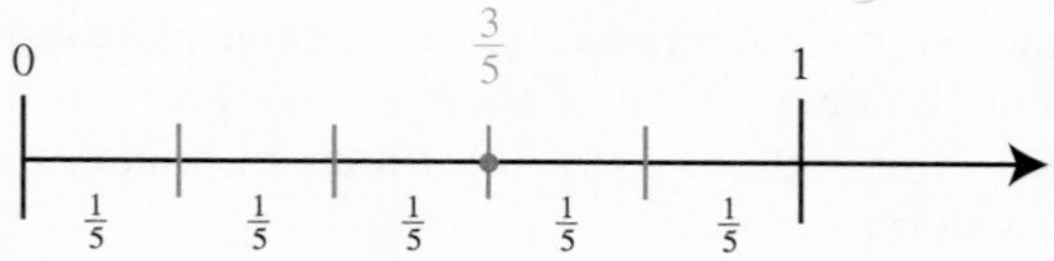

When one unit is divided into five equal portions, each portion represents one fifth of that unit. Three of such equal portions is three fifths and is written as $\frac{3}{5}$.

Proper Fractions

Fractions represent division. For example, $\frac{3}{5}$ is the same as $3 \div 5$.

A **proper fraction** is a fraction in which the numerator is less than the denominator.

For example,

$\frac{3}{8}$ is a proper fraction because the numerator, 3, is less than the denominator, 8.

Improper Fractions

An **improper fraction** is a fraction in which the numerator is greater than the denominator; i.e., the value of the entire fraction is more than 1.

For example,

$\frac{7}{4}$ is an improper fraction because the numerator 7 is greater than the denominator 4 (i.e., $7 > 4$, or $\frac{7}{4} > 1$).

Mixed Numbers (or Mixed Fractions)

A **mixed number** consists of both a whole number and a proper fraction, written side-by-side, which implies that the whole number and the proper fraction are added.

For example, $3\frac{5}{8}$ is a mixed number, where 3 is the whole number, and $\frac{5}{8}$ is the proper fraction.

$3\frac{5}{8}$ implies $3 + \frac{5}{8}$

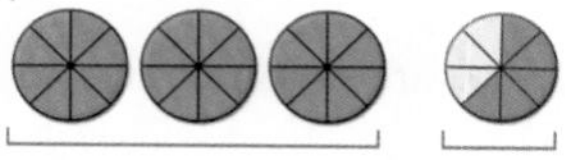

Complex Fractions

A **complex fraction** is a fraction in which one or more fractions are found in the numerator or denominator.

For example:

$\dfrac{1}{\left(\frac{3}{4}\right)}$ is a complex fraction because it has a fraction in the denominator.

$\dfrac{\left(\frac{2}{3}\right)}{6}$ is a complex fraction because it has a fraction in the numerator.

$\dfrac{\left(\frac{2}{5} + \frac{1}{4}\right)}{3}$ is a complex fraction because it has two fractions in the numerator.

$\dfrac{\left(\frac{5}{6}\right)}{\left(\frac{1}{8}\right)}$ is a complex fraction because it has a fraction in both the numerator and the denominator.

Relationship Between Mixed Numbers and Improper Fractions

Converting a Mixed Number to an Improper Fraction

Follow these steps to convert a mixed number to an improper fraction:	**Example:** **Convert $3\frac{5}{8}$ to an improper fraction.**
Step 1: Multiply the whole number by the denominator of the fraction and add this value to the numerator of the fraction.	$3(8)$ $24 + 5 = 29$
Step 2: The resulting answer will be the numerator of the improper fraction.	$\frac{29}{8}$
Step 3: The denominator of the improper fraction is the same as the denominator of the original fraction in the mixed number.	Therefore, $3\frac{5}{8} = \frac{29}{8}$.

$$3\frac{5}{8} = \frac{3(8)+5}{8} = \frac{29}{8}$$

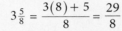

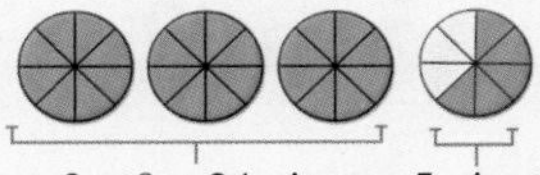

3 × 8 = 24 pieces 5 pieces

There is a total of 29 pieces, each piece being one-eighth in size.

Converting an Improper Fraction to a Mixed Number

Follow these steps to convert an improper fraction to a mixed number:	**Example:** **Convert $\frac{29}{8}$ to a mixed number.**
Step 1: Divide the numerator by the denominator.	$8\overline{)29}$ = 3 ← Quotient 24 5 ← Remainder
Step 2: The quotient becomes the whole number and the remainder becomes the numerator of the fraction.	
Step 3: The denominator of the mixed number is the same as the denominator of the original improper fraction.	Therefore, $\frac{29}{8} = 3\frac{5}{8}$.

Converting Fractions to their Equivalent Fractions

If two fractions reduced to their lowest terms are the same, then the two fractions are equivalent.

When both the numerator and denominator of a fraction are either multiplied by the same number or divided by the same number, the result is a new fraction called an **equivalent fraction**. Equivalent fractions imply that the old and new fractions have the same value.

That is, the same part (or portion) of a whole unit can be represented by different fractions.

For example,

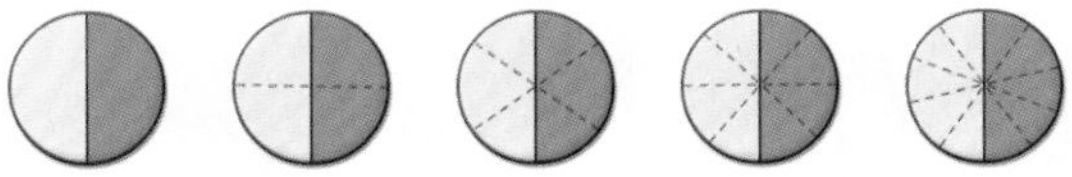

$\frac{1}{2}$ $\frac{2}{4}$ $\frac{3}{6}$ $\frac{4}{8}$ $\frac{5}{10}$

$\frac{1}{2}, \frac{2}{4}, \frac{3}{6}, \frac{4}{8}, \frac{5}{10}$, ... are equvalent fractions.

Example 2.1-b Finding Equivalent Fractions by Raising to Higher Terms

Find 2 equivalent fractions of $\frac{2}{5}$ by raising to higher terms.

Solution

$\frac{2}{5}$  (2 portions of 5 equal parts of the whole)

$\frac{2}{5} = \frac{2 \times 2}{5 \times 2}$ Multiplying both the numerator and denominator by 2,

$= \frac{4}{10}$ 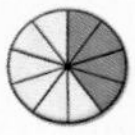 (4 portions of 10 equal parts of the whole)

$\frac{2}{5} = \frac{2 \times 3}{5 \times 3}$ Multiplying both the numerator and denominator by 3,

$= \frac{6}{15}$  (6 portions of 15 equal parts of the whole)

Therefore, $\frac{4}{10}$ and $\frac{6}{15}$ are equivalent fractions of $\frac{2}{5}$.

Example 2.1-c Finding Equivalent Fractions by Reducing to Lower Terms

Find 2 equivalent fractions of $\frac{12}{30}$ by reducing to lower terms.

Solution

$\frac{12}{30} = \frac{12 \div 3}{30 \div 3}$ Dividing both the numerator and denominator by 3,

$= \mathbf{\frac{4}{10}}$ This can be further reduced by dividing both the numerator and denominator by 2,

$= \frac{4 \div 2}{10 \div 2}$

$= \mathbf{\frac{2}{5}}$

$\frac{12}{30} = \frac{12 \div 6}{30 \div 6}$ Or, the lowest term can be found by dividing both the numerator and denominator of the original fraction, $\frac{12}{30}$, by 6,

$= \mathbf{\frac{2}{5}}$

Therefore, $\frac{4}{10}$ and $\frac{2}{5}$ are equivalent fractions of $\frac{12}{30}$.

Identifying Equivalent Fractions Using Cross Products

If the **cross products** of two fractions are equal, then the two fractions are equivalent fractions, and vice versa (i.e., if the fractions are equivalent, then their cross products are equal).

i.e., If $\frac{a}{b} = \frac{c}{d}$, then $a \times d = b \times c$

a × d and **b × c** are called cross products

For example, $\frac{3}{5}$ and $\frac{12}{20}$ are equivalent fractions because their cross products 3×20 and 5×12 are equal.

$$3 \times 20 = 5 \times 12$$

$$60 = 60$$

Example 2.1-d **Classifying Fractions as 'Equal' or 'Not Equal'**

Classify the pair of fractions as 'equal' or 'not equal' by using their cross products.

(i) $\frac{2}{5}$ and $\frac{12}{30}$ (ii) $\frac{5}{4}$ and $\frac{20}{12}$ (iii) $\frac{3}{8}$ and $\frac{9}{24}$

Solution

(i) $\frac{2}{5}$ and $\frac{12}{30}$

The cross products are 2×30 and 5×12.

$2 \times 30 = 60$

$5 \times 12 = 60$

The cross products are equal.

Therefore, the two fractions are equal.

(ii) $\frac{5}{4}$ and $\frac{20}{12}$

The cross products are 5×12 and 4×20.

$5 \times 12 = 60$

$4 \times 20 = 80$

The cross products are not equal.

Therefore, the two fractions are not equal.

(iii) $\frac{3}{8}$ and $\frac{9}{24}$

The cross products are 3×24 and 8×9.

$3 \times 24 = 72$

$8 \times 9 = 72$

The cross products are equal.

Therefore, the two fractions are equal.

Simplifying Fractions

Dividing both the numerator and denominator of a fraction by the same number, which results in an equivalent fraction, is called **reducing** or **simplifying** the fraction.

For example, we can simplify $\frac{16}{20}$ as shown:

Method 1: $\frac{16}{20} = \frac{16 \div 2}{20 \div 2}$

Dividing both the numerator and denominator by 2,

$= \mathbf{\frac{8}{10}}$

$$= \frac{8 \div 2}{10 \div 2}$$

Further dividing both the numerator and denominator by 2,

$$= \frac{4}{5}$$

Method 2: $\frac{16}{20} = \frac{16 \div 4}{20 \div 4} = \frac{4}{5}$

Dividing both the numerator and denominator of the original fraction $\frac{16}{20}$ by 4, the HCF of 16 and 20,

Therefore, $\frac{8}{10}$ and $\frac{4}{5}$ are reduced fractions of $\frac{16}{20}$.

Fractions in Lowest (or Simplest) Terms

A fraction in which the numerator and denominator have no factors in common (other than 1) is said to be a **fraction in its lowest (or simplest) terms.**

Any fraction can be **fully reduced** to its lowest terms by one of the following two methods:

Method 1: Dividing both the numerator and denominator by the highest common factor (HCF).

Method 2: Dividing by the common factors of the prime factors of the numerator and denominator.

Example 2.1-e **Reducing Fractions to their Lowest Terms**

Reduce the following fractions to their lowest terms.

(i) $\frac{40}{45}$ (ii) $\frac{54}{24}$

Solution

(i) $\frac{40}{45}$

Method 1: The factors of 40 are: 1, 2, 4, **5**, 8, 10, 20, and 40.

The factors of 45 are: 1, 3, **5**, 9, 15, and 45.

The HCF is 5.

Therefore, dividing the numerator and denominator by the HCF, 5, results in a fraction in its lowest terms:

$$\frac{40}{45} = \frac{40 \div 5}{45 \div 5} = \frac{8}{9}$$

Therefore, $\frac{40}{45}$ is equal to $\frac{8}{9}$ in its lowest term.

Method 2: Prime factors of 40 are: $2 \times 2 \times 2 \times 5$.

Prime factors of 45 are: $3 \times 3 \times 5$.

$$\frac{40}{45} = \frac{2 \times 2 \times 2 \times \cancel{5}^{1}}{3 \times 3 \times \cancel{5}_{1}} = \frac{8}{9}$$

Therefore, $\frac{40}{45}$ is equal to $\frac{8}{9}$ in its lowest term.

Solution
continued

(ii) $\frac{54}{24}$

Method 1: Factors of 54 are: 1, 2, 3, **6**, 9, 18, 27, and 54.

Factors of 24 are: 1, 2, 3, 4, **6**, 8, 12, and 24.

The HCF is 6.

Therefore, dividing the numerator and denominator by the HCF, 6, results in a fraction in its lowest terms:

$$\frac{54}{24} = \frac{54 \div 6}{24 \div 6} = \frac{9}{4}$$

Therefore, $\frac{54}{24}$ is equal to $\frac{9}{4}$ in its lowest term.

Method 2: Prime factors of 54 are: $2 \times 3 \times 3 \times 3$.

Prime factors of 24 are: $2 \times 2 \times 2 \times 3$.

$$\frac{54}{24} = \frac{{}^{1}\cancel{2} \times \cancel{3}^{1} \times 3 \times 3}{{}_{1}\cancel{2} \times 2 \times 2 \times \cancel{3}_{1}} = \frac{3 \times 3}{2 \times 2} = \frac{9}{4}$$

Therefore, $\frac{54}{24}$ is equal to $\frac{9}{4}$ in its lowest term.

Reciprocals of Fractions

Every non-zero real number has a reciprocal. Two numbers whose products are equal to 1 are called reciprocals of each other.

For example,

$\frac{2}{3}$ and $\frac{3}{2}$ are reciprocals of each other (because $\frac{2}{3} \times \frac{3}{2} = 1$).

When the numerator and denominator of a fraction are interchanged, the resulting fraction is known as the reciprocal of the original fraction.

For example,

5 and $\frac{1}{5}$ are reciprocals (5 can also be written as $\frac{5}{1}$).

Similarly, the reciprocal of $\frac{-2}{5}$ is $\frac{5}{-2} = -\frac{5}{2}$

The reciprocal of a number has the same sign as that number.

The reciprocal of a positive number is always positive and the reciprocal of a negative number is always negative.

Note:

(i) The reciprocal of a number is not the negative of that number.

(The reciprocal of $3 \neq -3$. The reciprocal of $3 = \frac{1}{3}$.)

(ii) The reciprocal of a fraction is not the equivalent fraction of that fraction.

(The reciprocal of $\frac{2}{5} \neq \frac{4}{10}$. The reciprocal of $\frac{2}{5} = \frac{5}{2}$.)

Table 2.1 **Examples of Numbers with their Negatives and Reciprocals**

When any number is multiplied by its reciprocal, the answer is always 1.

When any number is added to its opposite, the answer is always 0.

Number	5	−3	$\frac{2}{3}$	$-\frac{3}{8}$
Negative of the Number	−5	3	$-\frac{2}{3}$	$\frac{3}{8}$
Reciprocal of the Number	$\frac{1}{5}$	$-\frac{1}{3}$	$\frac{3}{2}$	$-\frac{8}{3}$

2.1 | Exercises

Answers to odd-numbered problems are available at the end of the textbook.

For Problems 1 to 6, classify the fractions as proper fractions, improper fractions, mixed numbers, or complex fractions.

1. a. $\frac{16}{35}$ b. $3\frac{2}{9}$
2. a. $15\frac{12}{13}$ b. $\frac{29}{30}$
3. a. $\frac{19}{16}$ b. $9\frac{7}{8}$
4. a. $\frac{21}{22}$ b. $\frac{52}{25}$
5. a. $4\frac{2}{5}$ b. $\frac{2\frac{1}{3}}{\frac{1}{8}}$
6. a. $\frac{15}{6\frac{1}{2}}$ b. $\frac{20}{75}$

For Problems 7 to 10, convert the mixed numbers to improper fractions.

7. a. $2\frac{2}{7}$ b. $3\frac{1}{8}$
8. a. $3\frac{2}{5}$ b. $7\frac{5}{8}$
9. a. $5\frac{4}{5}$ b. $6\frac{3}{4}$
10. a. $4\frac{3}{7}$ b. $9\frac{5}{6}$

For Problems 11 to 14, convert the improper fractions to mixed numbers.

11. a. $\frac{19}{7}$ b. $\frac{45}{8}$
12. a. $\frac{23}{7}$ b. $\frac{34}{3}$
13. a. $\frac{23}{3}$ b. $\frac{31}{6}$
14. a. $\frac{26}{4}$ b. $\frac{29}{5}$

For Problems 15 to 22, classify the pair of fractions as 'equal' or 'not equal' by first converting the mixed numbers to improper fractions.

15. $\frac{44}{5}$ and $8\frac{4}{5}$
16. $\frac{47}{8}$ and $5\frac{7}{8}$
17. $11\frac{5}{7}$ and $7\frac{5}{7}$
18. $\frac{41}{4}$ and $10\frac{3}{4}$
19. $\frac{54}{7}$ and $7\frac{5}{7}$
20. $\frac{17}{8}$ and $2\frac{3}{8}$
21. $\frac{37}{9}$ and $4\frac{1}{9}$
22. $\frac{45}{11}$ and $4\frac{3}{11}$

For Problems 23 to 30, classify the pair of fractions as 'equal' or 'not equal' by first converting the improper fractions to mixed numbers.

23. $\frac{15}{4}$ and $3\frac{1}{4}$
24. $\frac{43}{6}$ and $7\frac{5}{6}$
25. $\frac{18}{5}$ and $3\frac{3}{5}$
26. $\frac{45}{7}$ and $6\frac{3}{7}$
27. $3\frac{8}{9}$ and $\frac{35}{9}$
28. $\frac{34}{8}$ and $4\frac{1}{8}$
29. $\frac{41}{12}$ and $3\frac{5}{12}$
30. $7\frac{3}{9}$ and $\frac{67}{9}$

For Problems 31 to 36, (i) reduce the fractions to their lowest terms and (ii) write their reciprocals.

31. a. $\frac{32}{20}$ b. $\frac{48}{84}$
32. a. $\frac{44}{12}$ b. $\frac{42}{70}$
33. a. $\frac{56}{48}$ b. $\frac{84}{21}$
34. a. $\frac{75}{105}$ b. $\frac{144}{48}$
35. a. $\frac{36}{63}$ b. $\frac{60}{96}$
36. a. $\frac{132}{84}$ b. $\frac{54}{126}$

For Problems 37 to 44, classify the pair of fractions as 'equal' or 'not equal'.

37. $\frac{6}{12}$ and $\frac{15}{30}$
38. $\frac{6}{10}$ and $\frac{9}{15}$
39. $\frac{8}{10}$ and $\frac{15}{12}$
40. $\frac{12}{18}$ and $\frac{18}{27}$
41. $\frac{15}{12}$ and $\frac{36}{45}$
42. $\frac{35}{15}$ and $\frac{28}{12}$
43. $\frac{20}{25}$ and $\frac{24}{30}$
44. $\frac{16}{24}$ and $\frac{25}{30}$

For Problems 45 to 50, find the missing values.

45. a. $\frac{4}{9} = \frac{?}{27}$ b. $\frac{4}{9} = \frac{20}{?}$

46. a. $\frac{42}{36} = \frac{14}{?}$ b. $\frac{42}{36} = \frac{?}{30}$

47. a. $\frac{9}{12} = \frac{18}{?}$ b. $\frac{9}{12} = \frac{?}{4}$

48. a. $\frac{45}{75} = \frac{?}{25}$ b. $\frac{45}{75} = \frac{18}{?}$

49. a. $\frac{3}{2} = \frac{12}{?}$ b. $\frac{3}{2} = \frac{?}{12}$

50. a. $\frac{25}{15} = \frac{?}{3}$ b. $\frac{25}{15} = \frac{35}{?}$

For Problems 51 to 58, express the answer as a fraction reduced to its lowest terms.

51. What fraction of 1 year is 4 months?
52. What fraction of 1 hour is 25 minutes?
53. Karen cut a pizza into 16 equal slices and served 12 slices to her friends. What fraction of the pizza was served?
54. Out of 35 students in a math class, 15 received an 'A' in their final exam. What fraction of the students in the class received an 'A' grade?
55. In a survey of 272 people, 68 people responded 'yes' and the remaining responded 'no'. What fraction of the people responded 'no'?
56. In a finance math course with 490 students, 70 students failed the final exam. What fraction of the students passed the final exam in this course?
57. Out of the 480 units in a condominium tower, 182 are rented. What fraction of the units are not rented?
58. In a community of 6,000 people, 1,800 were 60 years or older. What fraction of the people were below the age of 60 years?

2.2 | Arithmetic Operations with Fractions

Least or Lowest Common Denominator (LCD)

The **Least** or **Lowest Common Denominator (LCD)** of a set of two or more fractions is the smallest whole number that is divisible by each of the denominators. It is the least common multiple (LCM) of the denominators of the fractions. There are two methods of finding the LCM as explained in Chapter 1, Section 1.3.

In performing addition and subtraction of fractions, it is necessary to find the equivalent fraction using the least common denominator. The best choice for a common denominator is the LCD, because it makes any further simplification easier.

Example 2.2-a **Finding the Least Common Denominator**

Find the LCD of $\frac{4}{9}$ and $\frac{7}{15}$.

Solution

The LCD of the fractions $\frac{4}{9}$ and $\frac{7}{15}$ is the same as the LCM of the denominators 9 and 15.

Using one of the methods you had learned in Chapter 1, Section 1.3:

Multiples of 9 are: 9, 18, 27, 36, 45, 54,...

45 is divisible by both 9 and 15.

Thus, the LCM of 9 and 15 is 45.

Therefore, LCD of $\frac{4}{9}$ and $\frac{7}{15}$ is 45.

It is best to convert a mixed number into an improper fraction before performing any basic arithmetic operations.

Comparing Fractions

Fractions can easily be compared when they have the same denominator. If they do not have the same denominator, find the LCD of the fractions, then convert them into equivalent fractions with that LCD as their denominator.

Example 2.2-b

Comparing Fractions

Which of the fractions, $\frac{5}{12}$ or $\frac{3}{8}$, is greater?

Solution

$\frac{5}{12}$ or $\frac{3}{8}$

Step 1: Since the fractions do not have the same denominator, we need to first find the LCD of the fractions, which is the same as the LCM of the denominators. The LCM of 12 and 8 is 24.

Step 2: Convert each of the fractions to its equivalent fraction with 24 as the denominator.

Step 3: To convert $\frac{5}{12}$ to its equivalent fraction with 24 as the denominator, multiply the denominator by 2 to obtain the LCD of 24 and multiply the numerator by 2 as well to maintain an equivalent fraction.

$$\frac{5}{12} = \frac{5 \times 2}{12 \times 2} = \frac{10}{24}$$

5 portions of 12 equal parts of a whole is equal to 10 portions of 24 equal parts of that whole.

Similarly, convert $\frac{3}{8}$ to an equivalent fraction with 24 as the denominator:

$$\frac{3}{8} = \frac{3 \times 3}{8 \times 3} = \frac{9}{24}$$

3 portions of 8 equal parts of a whole is equal to 9 portions of 24 equal parts of that whole.

Since the denominators are the same, we can now compare the numerators of the above to identify the greater fraction.

Since 10 > 9, it implies: $\frac{10}{24} > \frac{9}{24}$.

Therefore, $\frac{5}{12} > \frac{3}{8}$.

Addition of Fractions

The denominator of a fraction indicates the number of parts into which an item is divided. Therefore, addition of fractions requires that the denominators of every fraction be the same. If the demoninators are different, they must be made the same, by finding the LCD and changing each fraction to its equivalent fraction with that denominator. When the fractions are equivalent, add the numerators of each of the fractions. The resulting fraction will have the common denominator, and its numerator will be the sum of the numerators of the equivalent fractions.

Example 2.2-c

Adding Fractions That Have the Same Denominator

Add $\frac{2}{9}$ and $\frac{5}{9}$.

Solution

$\frac{2}{9} + \frac{5}{9}$

$= \frac{2 + 5}{9}$

$= \frac{7}{9}$

The denominators of the fractions are same. Adding the numerators, and writing the common denominator,

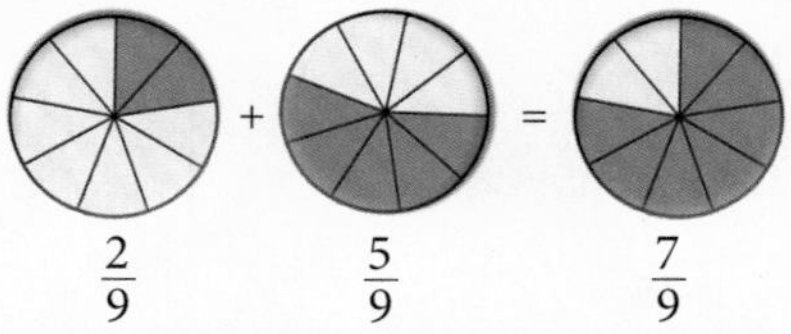

Therefore, the result from adding $\frac{2}{9}$ and $\frac{5}{9}$ is $\frac{7}{9}$.

Example 2.2-d **Adding Fractions That Have Different Denominators**

Add $\frac{3}{4}$ and $\frac{2}{3}$.

Solution

$\frac{3}{4} + \frac{2}{3}$ — The LCM of 4 and 3 is 12 (i.e., LCD = 12). Finding the equivalent fraction using the LCD of 12,

$= \frac{9}{12} + \frac{8}{12}$

$= \frac{9 + 8}{12}$ — Adding the numerators and writing the common denominator once,

$= \frac{17}{12}$ — Converting the improper fraction to a mixed number,

$= 1\frac{5}{12}$

Therefore, the result from adding $\frac{3}{4}$ and $\frac{2}{3}$ is $1\frac{5}{12}$.

Example 2.2-e **Adding Fractions That Have Different Denominators**

Add $3\frac{5}{6}$ and $\frac{4}{9}$.

Solution

Method 1:

$3\frac{5}{6} + \frac{4}{9}$ — Converting the mixed number to an improper fraction,

$= \frac{(3 \times 6) + 5}{6} + \frac{4}{9} = \frac{23}{6} + \frac{4}{9}$ — LCM of 6 and 9 is 18 (i.e. LCD = 18). Finding the equivalent fraction using the LCD of 18,

$= \frac{69}{18} + \frac{8}{18} = \frac{77}{18}$ — Converting the improper fraction to a mixed number,

$= 4\frac{5}{18}$

Therefore, the result from adding $3\frac{5}{6}$ and $\frac{4}{9}$ is $4\frac{5}{18}$.

Method 2:

$3\frac{5}{6} + \frac{4}{9}$ — Separating the whole number and the fractions,

$= 3 + \left(\frac{5}{6} + \frac{4}{9}\right)$ — LCM of 6 and 9 is 18 (i.e., LCD = 18), Finding the equivalent fractions using LCD of 18,

$= 3 + \left(\frac{15}{18} + \frac{8}{18}\right)$ — Adding the fractions,

$= 3 + \frac{23}{18}$ — Converting the improper fraction to a mixed number,

$= 3 + 1\frac{5}{18}$

$= 3 + 1 + \frac{5}{18}$ — Adding the whole numbers and then the fraction,

$= 4 + \frac{5}{18}$

$= 4\frac{5}{18}$

Therefore, the result from adding $3\frac{5}{6}$ and $\frac{4}{9}$ is $4\frac{5}{18}$.

Example 2.2-f **Adding Mixed Numbers**

Add (i) $2\frac{1}{6}$ and $4\frac{3}{4}$ (ii) $15\frac{2}{3}$ and $3\frac{3}{5}$.

Solution

(i) $2\frac{1}{6} + 4\frac{3}{4}$

LCM of 6 and 4 is 12 (i.e., LCD = 12). Finding the equivalent mixed number using LCD of 12,

$2\frac{2}{12} + 4\frac{9}{12}$

$= (2 + 4) + \left(\frac{2}{12} + \frac{9}{12}\right)$

Adding the whole number and the fractions,

$= 6\frac{11}{12}$

Therefore, the result from adding $2\frac{1}{6}$ and $4\frac{3}{4}$ is $6\frac{11}{12}$.

(ii) $15\frac{2}{3} + 3\frac{3}{5}$

LCM of 3 and 5 is 15 (i.e., LCD = 15). Finding the equivalent mixed number using LCD of 15,

$15\frac{10}{15} + 3\frac{9}{15}$

$= (15 + 3) + \left(\frac{10}{15} + \frac{9}{15}\right)$

Adding the whole numbers and then the fractions,

$= 18 + \frac{19}{15}$

Converting $\frac{19}{15}$ to a mixed number $= 1\frac{4}{15}$,

$= 18 + 1\frac{4}{15}$

Adding the whole numbers and then the fraction,

$= 19\frac{4}{15}$

Therefore, the result from adding $15\frac{2}{3}$ and $3\frac{3}{5}$ is $19\frac{4}{15}$.

Subtraction of Fractions

The process for subtraction of fractions is the same as that of addition of fractions. First, find a common denominator, then change each fraction to its equivalent fraction with the common denominator. The resulting fraction will have that denominator and its numerator will be the difference of the numerators of the original fractions.

Example 2.2-g **Subtracting Fractions That Have the Same Denonimators**

Subtract $\frac{3}{8}$ from $\frac{7}{8}$.

Solution

$\frac{7}{8} - \frac{3}{8}$

The denominators of the fractions are the same. Therefore, subtracting the numerators and writing the common denominator,

$= \frac{7-3}{8}$

$= \frac{4}{8} = \frac{\cancel{4}^{1}}{\cancel{8}_{2}}$

Reducing to lowest terms.

$= \frac{1}{2}$

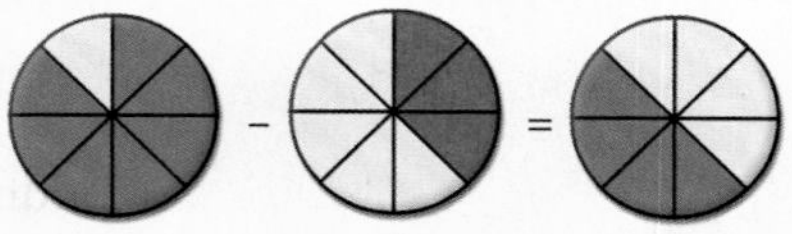

$\frac{7}{8}$ $\frac{3}{8}$ $\frac{4}{8} = \frac{1}{2}$

Therefore, the result from subtracting $\frac{3}{8}$ from $\frac{7}{8}$ is $\frac{1}{2}$.

Example 2.2-h

Subtracting Fractions that have Different Denominators

Subtract $\frac{2}{8}$ from $\frac{7}{10}$.

Solution

$\frac{7}{10} - \frac{2}{8}$ — LCM of 8 and 10 is 40 (i.e., LCD = 40). Finding the equivalent fractions using LCD of 40,

$= \frac{28}{40} - \frac{10}{40}$ — Subtracting numerators and writing the common denominator once,

$= \frac{28 - 10}{40}$

$= \frac{18}{40} = \frac{\cancel{18}^{9}}{\cancel{40}_{20}}$ — Reducing to lowest terms,

$= \frac{9}{20}$

Therefore, the result from subtracting $\frac{2}{8}$ from $\frac{7}{10}$ is $\frac{9}{20}$.

Example 2.2-i

Subtracting Mixed Numbers

Subtract $7\frac{2}{3}$ from $12\frac{1}{2}$.

Solution

Method 1:

$12\frac{1}{2} - 7\frac{2}{3}$ — Converting the mixed numbers to improper fractions,

$= \frac{(12 \times 2) + 1}{2} - \frac{(7 \times 3) + 2}{3}$

$= \frac{25}{2} - \frac{23}{3}$ — LCM of 2 and 3 is 6 (i.e., LCD = 6). Finding the equivalent fractions using the LCD of 6,

$= \frac{75}{6} - \frac{46}{6}$ — Subtracting,

$= \frac{75 - 46}{6}$

$= \frac{29}{6}$ — Converting the improper fraction to a mixed number,

$= 4\frac{5}{6}$

Therefore, the result from subtracting $7\frac{2}{3}$ from $12\frac{1}{2}$ is $4\frac{5}{6}$.

Method 2:

$12\frac{1}{2} - 7\frac{2}{3}$ — LCM of 2 and 3 is 6 (i.e., LCD = 6). Finding the equivalent mixed number using LCD of 6,

$= 12\frac{3}{6} - 7\frac{4}{6}$ — The fraction $\frac{4}{6}$ is greater than $\frac{3}{6}$. Therefore, we have to regroup the mixed number $12\frac{3}{6}$.

Regrouping $12\frac{3}{6} = 11 + \underbrace{1 + \frac{3}{6}} = 11 + \underbrace{\frac{6}{6} + \frac{3}{6}} = 11\frac{9}{6}$

$= 11\frac{9}{6} - 7\frac{4}{6}$ — Subtracting the fractions and then the whole numbers,

$= 4\,\frac{(9 - 4)}{6}$

$= 4\frac{5}{6}$

Therefore, the result from subtracting $7\frac{2}{3}$ from $12\frac{1}{2}$ is $4\frac{5}{6}$.

Multiplication of Fractions

When multiplying two or more fractions, first convert any mixed number to its improper fraction, then simply multiply the numerators together to get the new numerator and multiply the denominators together to get the new denominator.

Reduce as much as possible before multiplying the numerators together and the denominators together.

Express the final answer reduced to the lowest term and rewrite the improper fraction as a mixed number, if necessary.

Example 2.2-j **Multiplying Fractions**

Multiply:

(i) $\frac{3}{2} \times \frac{4}{11}$ (ii) $15 \times \frac{2}{5}$ (iii) $3\frac{1}{8} \times 2\frac{4}{5}$

Solution

(i) $\frac{3}{2} \times \frac{4}{11} = \frac{3}{\cancel{2}_1} \times \frac{\cancel{4}^2}{11}$ Reducing the fractions to lowest terms,

$= \frac{3}{1} \times \frac{2}{11}$ Multiplying the numerators together and denominators together to get a new fraction,

$= \frac{6}{11}$

Therefore, the result of $\frac{3}{2} \times \frac{4}{11}$ is $\frac{6}{11}$.

(ii) $15 \times \frac{2}{5} = \frac{\cancel{15}^3}{1} \times \frac{2}{\cancel{5}_1}$ Reducing the fractions to lowest terms,

$= \frac{3}{1} \times \frac{2}{1}$ Multiplying the numerators together and denominators together to get a new fraction,

$= \frac{6}{1} = 6$

Therefore, the result of $15 \times \frac{2}{5}$ is 6.

(iii) $3\frac{1}{8} \times 2\frac{4}{5}$ Converting the mixed numbers to improper fractions,

$= \frac{(3 \times 8) + 1}{8} \times \frac{(2 \times 5) + 4}{5}$

$= \frac{25}{8} \times \frac{14}{5} = \frac{^5\cancel{25}}{_4\cancel{8}} \times \frac{\cancel{14}^7}{\cancel{5}_1}$ Reducing to lowest terms,

$= \frac{5}{4} \times \frac{7}{1}$ Multiplying the numerators together and denominators together to get the new fraction,

$= \frac{35}{4}$ Converting the improper fraction to a mixed number,

$= 8\frac{3}{4}$

Therefore, the result of $3\frac{1}{8} \times 2\frac{4}{5}$ is $8\frac{3}{4}$.

Division of Fractions

When a fraction is inverted, the resulting fraction is called the 'reciprocal' of the original fraction.

When dividing fractions, as in multiplication, first convert any mixed numbers to its improper fractions. The division of fractions is done by multiplying the first fraction by the reciprocal of the second fraction. Then, follow the procedure used in multiplication to get the final result.

Note:

- *Dividing by 2 is the same as multiplying by the reciprocal of 2, which is* $\frac{1}{2}$.
- *When multiplying or dividing mixed numbers, it is incorrect to multiply or divide the whole number parts separately from the fractional parts to arrive at the answer.*

Example 2.2-k **Dividing Fractions**

Divide $\frac{15}{16}$ by $\frac{9}{20}$.

Solution

$\frac{15}{16} \div \frac{9}{20}$

$= \frac{15}{16} \times \frac{20}{9}$ Multiplying $\frac{15}{16}$ by the reciprocal of $\frac{9}{20}$, which is $\frac{20}{9}$,

$= \frac{{}^{5}\cancel{15}}{{}_{4}\cancel{16}} \times \frac{\cancel{20}^{5}}{\cancel{9}_{3}}$ Simplifying the numerator and the denominator,

$= \frac{25}{12}$ Converting the improper fraction to a proper fraction,

$= 2\frac{1}{12}$

Therefore, the result of $\frac{15}{16}$ divided by $\frac{9}{20}$ is $2\frac{1}{12}$.

Example 2.2-l **Dividing Mixed Numbers**

Divide $3\frac{3}{20}$ by $1\frac{4}{5}$.

Solution

$3\frac{3}{20} \div 1\frac{4}{5}$ Converting the mixed numbers to improper fractions,

$= \frac{63}{20} \div \frac{9}{5}$ Multiplying $\frac{63}{20}$ by the reciprocal of $\frac{9}{5}$, which is $\frac{5}{9}$,

$= \frac{63}{20} \times \frac{5}{9}$

$= \frac{{}^{7}\cancel{63}}{{}_{4}\cancel{20}} \times \frac{\cancel{5}^{1}}{\cancel{9}_{1}}$ Simplifying the numerators and the denominators,

$= \frac{7}{4}$

Therefore, the result of $3\frac{3}{20}$ divided by $1\frac{4}{5}$ is $\frac{7}{4}$.

Converting Complex Fractions into Proper or Improper Fractions

A complex fraction can be converted into a proper or an improper fraction by dividing the numerator by the denominator and then simplifying the expression.

For example,

$$\frac{\left(\frac{7}{2}\right)}{5} = \frac{7}{2} \div 5 = \frac{7}{2} \times \frac{1}{5} = \frac{7}{10}$$

$$\frac{8}{\left(\frac{9}{2}\right)} = 8 \times \left(\frac{2}{9}\right) = \frac{16}{9}$$

2.2 | Exercises

Answers to odd-numbered problems are available at the end of the textbook.

For Problems 1 to 8, identify the greater fraction in each pair.

1. $\frac{2}{5}$ or $\frac{3}{8}$
2. $\frac{4}{3}$ or $\frac{6}{5}$
3. $\frac{12}{15}$ or $\frac{35}{45}$
4. $\frac{5}{4}$ or $\frac{7}{6}$
5. $\frac{8}{7}$ or $\frac{13}{12}$
6. $\frac{5}{13}$ or $\frac{16}{39}$
7. $\frac{8}{9}$ or $\frac{39}{45}$
8. $\frac{3}{8}$ or $\frac{25}{48}$
9. Which of the following fractions are less than $\frac{2}{3}$?
   $\frac{5}{8}, \frac{6}{7}, \frac{3}{5}, \frac{7}{9}$
10. Which of the following fractions are greater than $\frac{3}{4}$?
   $\frac{4}{5}, \frac{7}{9}, \frac{5}{7}, \frac{9}{11}$

For Problems 11 to 18, perform the addition, reduce to lowest terms, and express the answer as a mixed number, whenever possible.

11. a. $\frac{5}{8} + \frac{7}{8}$ b. $\frac{7}{12} + \frac{9}{12}$
12. a. $\frac{5}{9} + \frac{7}{9}$ b. $\frac{7}{10} + \frac{9}{10}$
13. a. $\frac{9}{10} + \frac{1}{2}$ b. $\frac{21}{25} + \frac{7}{8}$
14. a. $\frac{3}{4} + \frac{1}{8}$ b. $\frac{35}{18} + \frac{3}{6}$
15. a. $\frac{4}{3} + \frac{5}{6}$ b. $12\frac{4}{3} + 5\frac{1}{3}$
16. a. $\frac{21}{13} + \frac{1}{3}$ b. $18\frac{5}{7} + 2\frac{2}{5}$
17. a. $9\frac{3}{4} + 6\frac{1}{6}$ b. $8\frac{2}{3} + 5\frac{3}{4}$
18. a. $11\frac{1}{4} + 5\frac{2}{3}$ b. $7\frac{1}{12} + 5\frac{3}{4}$

For Problems 19 to 24, perform the subtraction, reduce to lowest terms, and express the answer as a mixed number, whenever possible.

19. a. $\frac{2}{3} - \frac{1}{9}$ b. $\frac{9}{12} - \frac{3}{5}$
20. a. $\frac{1}{6} - \frac{1}{8}$ b. $\frac{19}{20} - \frac{8}{10}$
21. a. $\frac{5}{3} - \frac{3}{8}$ b. $16\frac{1}{8} - 1\frac{1}{2}$
22. a. $\frac{17}{9} - \frac{5}{6}$ b. $5\frac{2}{3} - 1\frac{5}{12}$
23. a. $8\frac{5}{6} - 5\frac{3}{9}$ b. $9\frac{2}{5} - 7\frac{3}{10}$
24. a. $8\frac{5}{12} - 4\frac{3}{6}$ b. $5\frac{5}{8} - 4\frac{5}{6}$

For Problems 25 to 30, perform the multiplication, reduce to lowest terms, and express the answer as a mixed number, whenever possible.

25. a. $\frac{16}{5} \times \frac{5}{4}$ b. $3 \times \frac{7}{9}$
26. a. $\frac{12}{5} \times \frac{25}{3}$ b. $\frac{6}{9} \times \frac{19}{12}$
27. a. $\frac{3}{8} \times \frac{5}{11}$ b. $9\frac{3}{5} \times 1\frac{29}{96}$
28. a. $\frac{4}{5} \times \frac{23}{9}$ b. $11\frac{4}{3} \times 1\frac{1}{74}$
29. a. $\frac{9}{38} \times \frac{19}{63}$ b. $2\frac{2}{9} \times 1\frac{1}{2}$
30. a. $\frac{15}{27} \times \frac{18}{45}$ b. $2\frac{7}{9} \times \frac{25}{45}$

For Problems 31 to 36, perform the division, reduce to lowest terms, and express the answer as a mixed number, whenever possible.

31. a. $\frac{2}{3} \div \frac{4}{9}$ b. $\frac{3}{8} \div 4$

32. a. $\frac{3}{5} \div \frac{3}{4}$ b. $\frac{1}{7} \div \frac{3}{5}$

33. a. $\frac{10}{15} \div \frac{3}{7}$ b. $23\frac{1}{2} \div 8\frac{13}{16}$

34. a. $\frac{8}{12} \div \frac{2}{4}$ b. $10\frac{1}{4} \div 2\frac{27}{48}$

35. a. $5\frac{1}{5} \div 13$ b. $18 \div 4\frac{4}{5}$

36. a. $5\frac{1}{4} \div 7$ b. $15 \div 3\frac{1}{3}$

For Problems 37 to 44, perform the indicated arithmetic operations, reduce to lowest terms, and express the answer as a mixed number, whenever possible.

37. a. $\frac{1}{10} + \frac{17}{100} + \frac{39}{1{,}000}$ b. $\frac{3}{5} + \frac{7}{10} + \frac{9}{15}$

38. a. $\frac{3}{10} + \frac{47}{100} + \frac{241}{1{,}000}$ b. $\frac{2}{3} + \frac{3}{4} + \frac{5}{8}$

39. a. $\frac{32}{100} - \frac{8}{1{,}000}$ b. $\frac{5}{8} + \frac{13}{16} - \frac{3}{4}$

40. a. $\frac{3}{10} - \frac{4}{1{,}000}$ b. $\frac{7}{12} + \frac{5}{6} - \frac{2}{3}$

41. a. $\left(2\frac{1}{6} + 1\frac{2}{3}\right) \div 5\frac{3}{4}$ b. $6\frac{5}{2} \div \left(2\frac{2}{5} + 2\right)$

42. a. $\left(5\frac{1}{4} + 2\frac{5}{6}\right) \div 1\frac{1}{2}$ b. $2\frac{2}{3} \div \left(1\frac{7}{15} + \frac{2}{3}\right)$

43. a. $10\frac{1}{2} \div 4\frac{1}{5} + \frac{9}{10} \times 2\frac{2}{5} - \frac{3}{4}$ b. $13\frac{3}{7} \times \frac{5}{94} + 6\frac{4}{5} \div \frac{4}{15} + 7\frac{1}{5}$

44. a. $7\frac{2}{3} \div 2\frac{1}{3} + \frac{3}{5} \times 4\frac{2}{3} - \frac{2}{5}$ b. $1\frac{7}{6} \div \frac{26}{45} + 3\frac{1}{4} \times 4\frac{1}{2} - \frac{3}{8}$

For Problems 45 to 66, express your answers as a proper fraction or a mixed number, where appropriate.

45. Peter spent $\frac{5}{12}$ of his money on rent and $\frac{1}{4}$ on food. What fraction of his money did he spend on rent and food?
46. Alan walked $\frac{3}{5}$ km to his friend's house and from there, he walked another $\frac{3}{4}$ km to his school. How far did Alan walk?
47. Last night, Amy spent $3\frac{1}{6}$ hours on her math project and $2\frac{3}{10}$ hours on her design project. How much time did she spend on both projects altogether?
48. A bag contains $2\frac{3}{5}$ kg of red beans and $1\frac{1}{8}$ kg of green beans. What is the total weight of the bag?
49. Thomas baked a $2\frac{1}{2}$ pound cake. He gave $1\frac{5}{8}$ pounds of it to his friend, Yan. How much was left?
50. Alexander bought $4\frac{2}{5}$ litres of milk and drank $1\frac{2}{3}$ litres of it. How much milk was left?
51. Sarah had $\frac{3}{4}$ kg of cheese. She used $\frac{2}{7}$ kg of the cheese while baking. How many kilograms of cheese was left?
52. Cassidy bought $\frac{5}{8}$ litres of olive oil and used $\frac{1}{3}$ litre of the oil while cooking. What quantity of olive oil was left?
53. David spent $\frac{7}{10}$ of his money on toys and $\frac{1}{3}$ of the remainder on food. What fraction of his money was spent on food?
54. Mary spent $\frac{2}{5}$ of her money on a school bag. She then spent $\frac{1}{3}$ of the remainder on shoes. What fraction of her money was spent on shoes?
55. After selling $\frac{2}{5}$ of its textbooks, a bookstore had 810 books left. How many textbooks were in the bookstore initially?

56. Rose travelled $\frac{3}{5}$ of her journey by car and the remaining 20 km by bus. How far did she travel by car?
57. Cheng can walk $5\frac{1}{4}$ km in $1\frac{1}{2}$ hours. How many kilometres can he walk in 1 hour?
58. $2\frac{3}{4}$ litres of juice weighs $4\frac{2}{3}$ kg. Find the weight (in kilograms) of 1 litre of juice.
59. A chain of length $\frac{7}{8}$ metres is cut into pieces measuring $\frac{1}{16}$ metres each. How many pieces are there?
60. A cake that weighs $\frac{2}{3}$ kg is cut into slices weighing $\frac{1}{12}$ kg each. How many slices are there?
61. A bottle of medicine contains 80 mg of medicine. Each dose of the medicine is $\frac{2}{5}$ mg. How many doses are there in the bottle?
62. A box of cereal contains 917 grams of cereal. How many bowls of cereal will there be if each serving is $32\frac{3}{4}$ grams?
63. Out of 320 bulbs, $\frac{1}{20}$ of the bulbs are defective. How many of them are not defective?
64. If $\frac{4}{15}$ of the 1,800 students enrolled for a mathematics course, how many students did not enroll for the course?
65. The product of two numbers is 9. If one number is $3\frac{3}{4}$, what is the other number?
66. If a wire that is $42\frac{3}{4}$ cm long is cut into several $2\frac{1}{4}$ cm equal pieces, how many pieces would exist?

2.3 | Decimal Numbers

Introduction

When a number is less than 1, it is usually expressed in its decimal form with 0 in its ones place. For example, .25 is expressed as 0.25.

Decimal numbers, decimal fractions, or decimals represent a part or a portion of a whole, similar to fractions that you had learned in previous sections.

Decimal numbers are used in situations that require more precision than which whole numbers can provide. We use decimal numbers more frequently in our daily lives than whole numbers - money is a good example: [5¢ = \$0.05, 10¢ = \$0.10, 25¢ = \$0.25].

A decimal number may have both a whole number portion and a decimal number portion. The decimal point (.) separates the whole number portion and the decimal number portion of a decimal number. The whole number portion of a decimal comprises of those digits to the left of the decimal point. The decimal portion is represented by the digits to the right of the decimal point. It represents a number less than 1.

For example,

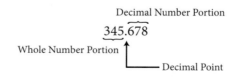

Decimal Number Portion

345.678

Whole Number Portion

Decimal Point

Fractions whose denominators are a power of 10 (such as 100, 1,000, etc.) are called decimal fractions.

For example, $\frac{3}{10}, \frac{7}{100}, \frac{9}{1{,}000}$, etc. are decimal fractions.

(0.3, 0.07, 0.009 are their equivalent decimal numbers)

The decimal number portion of 345.678 written as a decimal fraction: $\frac{678}{1{,}000}$.

When decimal numbers are expressed as a fraction using 10 or powers of 10, we do not reduce to their lowest terms.

For example, $\frac{678}{1{,}000}$ if reduced to $\frac{339}{500}$ is no longer expressed as a power of 10.

Similarly, $1.2 = 1\frac{2}{10}$

$$23.45 = 23\frac{45}{100}$$

$$75.378 = 75\frac{378}{1,000}$$

Every whole number can be written as a decimal number by placing a decimal point to the right of the units digits.

For example, 5 in **decimal form** is 5. or 5.0 or 5.00.

The number of decimal places in a decimal number depends on the number of digits writen to the right of the decimal point.

For example,

5.	No decimal place
5.0	One decimal place
5.00	Two decimal places
1.250	Three decimal places
2.0050	Four decimal places

Types of Decimal Numbers

There are three different types of decimal numbers.

(i) Non-repeating, terminating decimals numbers:

For example, 0.2, 0.3767, 0.86452

(ii) Repeating, non-terminating decimal numbers:

For example, 0.222222.... ($0.\overline{2}$), 0.255555.... ($0.2\overline{5}$), 0.867867.... ($0.\overline{867}$)

(iii) Non-repeating, non-terminating decimal numbers:

For example, 0.453740...., π (3.141592...), e (2.718281...)

Place Value of Decimal Numbers

The position of each digit in a decimal number determines the place value of the digit. Exhibit 2.3 illustrates the place value of the five-digit decimal number: 0.35796.

The place value of each digit as you move right from the decimal point is found by decreasing powers of 10. The first place to the right of the decimal point is the tenths place, the second place value is the hundredths place, and so on, as shown in Table 2.3.

Table 2.3 **Place Value Chart of Decimal Numbers**

$10^{-1} = \frac{1}{10}$	$10^{-2} = \frac{1}{100}$	$10^{-3} = \frac{1}{1,000}$	$10^{-4} = \frac{1}{10,000}$	$10^{-5} = \frac{1}{100,000}$
0.1	0.01	0.001	0.0001	0.00001
Tenths	Hundredths	Thousandths	Ten-thousandths	Hundred-thousandths

Example of the decimal number written in its **standard form**:

0.	3	5	7	9	6

The above can be written in **expanded form** as follows:

0.3 + 0.05 + 0.007 + 0.0009 + 0.00006

Or

3 tenths + 5 hundredths + 7 thousandths + 9 ten-thousandths + 6 hundred-thousandths

Or

$$\frac{3}{10}+\frac{5}{100}+\frac{7}{1,000}+\frac{9}{10,000}+\frac{6}{100,000} \qquad \left(0.35796 \text{ in decimal fraction is } \frac{35,796}{100,000}\right)$$

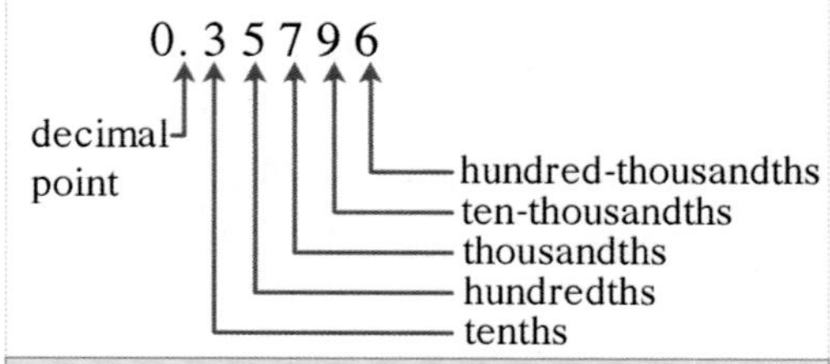

Exhibit 2.3 Place Value of a Five-Digit Decimal Number

0.3
0.05
0.007
0.0009
0.00006
0.35796

Reading and Writing Decimal Numbers

The word 'and' is used to represent the decimal point (.)

Follow these steps to read and write decimal numbers:

Step 1: Read or write the numbers to the left of a decimal point as a whole number.

Step 2: Read or write the decimal point as "and".

Step 3: Read or write the number to the right of the decimal point also as a whole number, but followed by the name of the place value occupied by the digit on the far right.

For example 745.023 is written in word form as:

Seven hundred forty-five and twenty-**three** thousandths

Whole Number Portion | Decimal Point | Decimal Portion

The last digit, three, ends in the thousandths place. Therefore, the decimal portion is $\frac{23}{1,000}$.

There are other ways of reading and writing decimal numbers as noted below.

(i) Use the word "point" to indicate the decimal point and thereafter, read or write each digit individually.

For example,

745.023 can also be read or written as: Seven hundred forty-five point zero, two, three.

(ii) Ignore the decimal point of the decimal number and read or write the number as a whole number and include the place occupied by the digit on the far right of the decimal number.

For example,

745.023 can also be read or written as: Seven hundred forty-five thousand, twenty-three thousandths. (i.e., $\frac{745,023}{1,000}$).

Note: The above two representations are not used in the examples and exercise questions within this chapter.

Use of Hyphens to Express Numbers in Word Form

- A hyphen (-) is used to express the two digit numbers, 21 to 29, 31 to 39, 41 to 49, … 91 to 99, in each group in their word form.
- A hyphen (-) is also used while expressing the place value portion of a decimal number, such as ten-thousandths, hundred-thousandths, ten-millionths, hundred-millionths, and so on.

The following examples illustrate the use of hyphens to express numbers in their word form:

0.893 Eight hundred ninety-three thousandths.

0.0506 Five hundred six ten-thousandths.

0.00145 One hundred forty-five hundred-thousandths.

Example 2.3-a Writing in Decimal Notation

Express the following in decimal notation:

(i) Two hundred and thirty-five hundredths

(ii) Three and seven tenths

(iii) Eighty-four thousandths

Solution

(i)

Whole Number Portion		Decimal Portion	
Two hundred	and	thirty-five <u>hundredths</u>	The last digit, five, ends in the hundredths place.
200	.	$\frac{35}{100} = 0.35$	

Therefore, the number is written in decimal form as **200.35**.

(ii)

Whole Number Portion		Decimal Portion	
Three	and	seven <u>tenths</u>	The last digit, seven, ends in the tenths place.
3	.	$\frac{7}{10}$	

Therefore, the number is written in decimal form as **3.7**.

(iii)

Whole Number Portion		Decimal Portion	
		Eighty-four <u>thousandths</u>	The last digit, four, ends in the thousandths place.
0	.	$\frac{84}{1{,}000} = 0.084$	

Therefore, the number is written in decimal form as **0.084**.

Example 2.3-b Writing Decimal Numbers in Word Form

Express the following decimal numbers in their word form:

(i) 23.125 (ii) 7.43

(iii) 20.3 (iv) 0.2345

Solution

(i) 23.125

The last digit, 5, is in the thousandths place.

$23\frac{125}{1{,}000}$

Twenty-three and one hundred twenty-five thousandths.

(ii) 7.43

The last digit, 3, is in the hundredths place.

$7\frac{43}{100}$

Seven and forty-three hundredths.

Solution
continued

(iii) 20.**3**

The last digit, 3, is in the tenths place.

$$20\frac{3}{10}$$

Twenty and three tenths.

(iv) 0.234**5**

The last digit, 5, is in the ten-thousandths place.

$$\frac{2,345}{10,000}$$

Two thousand three hundred forty-five ten-thousandths.

Rounding Decimal Numbers

Rounding Decimal Numbers to the Nearest Whole Number, Tenth, Hundredth, etc.

Rounding decimal numbers refers to changing the value of the decimal number to the nearest whole number, tenth, hundredth, thousandth, etc. It is also referred to as "rounding to a specific number of decimal places", indicating the number of decimal places that will be left when the rounding is complete.

For example,

- Rounding to the nearest whole number is the same as rounding without any decimals.
- Rounding to the nearest tenth is the same as rounding to one decimal place.
- Rounding to the nearest hundredth is the same as rounding to two decimal places.
- Rounding to the nearest cent refers to rounding the amount to the nearest hundredth or to two decimal places.

Follow these steps to round decimal numbers:

Step 1: Identify the digit to be rounded (this is the place value for which the rounding is required).

Step 2: If the digit to the immediate right of the identified rounding digit is less than 5 (0, 1, 2, 3, 4), do not change the value of the rounding digit.

If the digit to the immediate right of the identified rounding digit is 5 or greater than 5 (5, 6, 7, 8, 9), increase the value of the rounding digit by one (i.e., round up by one number).

Step 3: After Step 2, drop all digits that are to the right of the rounding digit.

Example 2.3-c **Rounding Decimal Numbers**

Round the following decimal numbers to the indicated place value:

(i) 268.143 to the nearest hundredth

(ii) $489.679 to the nearest cent

(iii) $39.9985 to the nearest cent

Solution

(i) Rounding 268.143 to the nearest hundredth:

4 is the rounding digit in the hundredths place: 268.143.

The digit to the immediate right of the rounding digit is less than 5; therefore, do not change the value of the rounding digit. Drop all of the digits to the right of the rounding digit. This will result in 268.14.

Therefore, 268.143 rounded to the nearest hundredth is 268.14.

Solution
continued

(ii) Rounding \$489.679 to the nearest cent:

7 is the rounding digit in the hundredths place: \$489.679.

The digit to the immediate right of the rounding digit is greater than 5; therefore, increase the value of the rounding digit by one, from 7 to 8, and drop all digits that are to the right of the rounding digit. This will result in \$489.68.

Therefore, \$489.679 rounded to the nearest cent is \$489.68.

(iii) Rounding \$39.9985 to the nearest cent:

9 is the rounding digit in the hundredths place: \$39.9985.

The digit to the immediate right of the rounding digit is greater than 5; therefore, increase the value of the rounding digit by one, from 9 to 10, carrying the one to the tenths place, then to the ones, and then to the tens, to increase 3 to 4. Finally, drop all digits that are to the right of the hundredths place. This will result in \$40.00

Therefore, \$39.9985 rounded to the nearest cent is \$40.00.

2.3 | Exercises

Answers to odd-numbered problems are available at the end of the textbook.

For Problems 1 to 8, express the numbers in decimal notation.

1. a. $\frac{6}{10}$ b. $\frac{7}{1,000}$
2. a. $\frac{9}{1,000}$ b. $\frac{41}{1,000}$
3. a. $\frac{12}{100}$ b. $\frac{29}{1,000}$
4. a. $\frac{75}{100}$ b. $\frac{3}{10}$
5. a. $7\frac{5}{10}$ b. $9\frac{503}{1,000}$
6. a. $9\frac{3}{10}$ b. $6\frac{207}{1,000}$
7. a. $\frac{367}{100}$ b. $\frac{2,567}{1,000}$
8. a. $\frac{475}{10}$ b. $\frac{2,972}{100}$

For Problems 9 to 24, write the numbers in word form to (i) decimal form and (ii) standard form.

9. Eighty-seven and two tenths
10. Thirty-five and seven tenths
11. Three and four hundredths
12. Nine and seven hundredths
13. Four hundred one ten-thousandths
14. Fifty-two and three hundred five thousandths
15. Eighty-nine and six hundred twenty-five ten-thousandths
16. Two hundred eight-thousandths
17. One thousand, seven hundred eighty-seven and twenty-five thousandths
18. Nine hundred eighty-seven and twenty hundredths
19. Four hundred twelve and sixty-five hundredths
20. Seven thousand, two hundred sixty and fifteen thousandths
21. One million, six hundred thousand and two hundredths
22. Six million, two hundred seventeen thousand and five hundredths
23. Twenty-three and five tenths
24. Twenty-nine hundredths

For Problems 25 to 32, express the decimal numbers in their word form.

25. a. 42.55 b. 734.125
26. a. 7.998 b. 12.77
27. a. 0.25 b. 9.5
28. a. 0.987 b. 311.2
29. a. 7.07 b. 15.002
30. a. 11.09 b. 9.006
31. a. 0.062 b. 0.054
32. a. 0.031 b. 0.073

33. Which of the following is the largest number?

    0.034, 0.403, 0.043, 0.304

34. Which of the following is the smallest number?

    1.014, 1.011, 1.104, 1.041

For Problems 35 to 42, round the numbers to one decimal place (nearest tenth).

35. 415.1654
36. 7.8725
37. 264.1545
38. 25.5742
39. 24.1575
40. 112.1255
41. 10.3756
42. 0.9753

Fo Problems 43 to 50, round the numbers to two decimal places (nearest hundredth, or nearest cent).

43. 14.3585
44. 0.0645
45. 181.1267
46. 19.6916
47. $16.775
48. $10.954
49. $9.987
50. $24.995

2.4 | Arithmetic Operations with Decimal Numbers

Addition of Decimal Numbers

Addition of decimal numbers (finding the **total** or **sum**) refers to combining numbers. It is similar to adding whole numbers.

Follow these steps to add one decimal number to another decimal number:

Step 1: Write the numbers one under the other by aligning the decimal points of these numbers.

Step 2: Add zeros to the right to have the same number of decimal places, if necessary, and draw a horizontal line.

Step 3: Starting from the right, add all the numbers in that column and continue towards the left.

- If the total is less than 10, write the total under the horizontal line.
- If the total is 10 or more, write the 'ones' digit of the total under the horizontal line and write the tens digit above the tens column.

Step 4: Follow this procedure for each column going from right to left. Write the decimal point in the answer.

Example 2.4-a **Adding Decimal Numbers**

Perform the following additions:

(i) 25.125 + 7.14

(ii) 741.87 + 135.456

(iii) 127 + 68.8 + 669.95

Solution

(i) 25.125 + 7.14

$$\begin{array}{r} \scriptstyle 1 \\ 25.125 \\ +7.140 \\ \hline 32.265 \end{array}$$

← Add a zero to match the number of decimal places.

Therefore, adding 25.125 and 7.14 results in 32.265.

(ii) 741.87 + 135.456

$$\begin{array}{r} \scriptstyle 11 \\ 741.870 \\ +135.456 \\ \hline 877.326 \end{array}$$

← Add a zero to match the number of decimal places.

Therefore, adding 741.87 and 135.456 results in 877.326.

(iii) 127 + 68.8 + 669.95

```
  1 2 1
  1 2 7 . 0 0  ←— Add two zeros to match the number of decimal places.
    6 8 . 8 0  ←— Add a zero to match the number of decimal places.
+ 6 6 9 . 9 5
  8 6 5 . 7 5
```

Therefore, adding 127, 68.8 and 669.95 results in 865.75.

Subtraction of Decimal Numbers

Subtraction of decimal numbers refers to finding the **difference** between decimal numbers. It is similar to subtracting whole numbers.

Follow these steps to subtract one decimal number from another decimal number:

Step 1: Write the numbers one under the other by aligning the decimal points of these numbers.

Step 2: Add zeros to the right to have the same number of decimal places, if necessary, and draw a horizontal line.

Step 3: Ensure that the number from which subtraction is indicated is written above the number that is being subtracted.

Step 4: Starting from the right, subtract the bottom number from the top number.

- If the top digit is greater than the bottom digit, subtract and write the difference under the line.
- If the top digit is smaller than the bottom digit, borrow from the digit to the left of this top digit, and add one to the digit on the top, then find the difference and write it under the horizontal line.

Step 5: Follow this procedure for each column going from right to left. Write the decimal point in the answer.

Example 2.4-b

Subtracting Decimal Numbers

Perform the following subtractions:

(i) Subtract 29.02 from 135.145

(ii) Subtract 38.7 from 457

Solution

(i) Subtract 29.02 from 135.145

```
   2 15
 1 3 5 . 1 4 5
-  2 9 . 0 2 0
 1 0 6 . 1 2 5
```

Therefore, subtracting 29.02 from 135.145 results in 106.125.

(ii) Subtract 38.7 from 457

```
     16
   4  6  10
   4 5 7 . 0
 -   3 8 . 7
   4 1 8 . 3
```

Therefore, subtracting 38.7 from 457 results in 418.3

Multiplication of Decimal Numbers

Multiplication of decimal numbers refers to finding the **product** of two decimal numbers.

Follow these steps to multiply one decimal number with another decimal number:

Step 1: Line up the numbers on the right without aligning the decimal points.

Step 2: Multiply the number assuming that there are no decimal points; i.e., multiply each digit on the top number by each digit in the bottom number and add the products, similar to the process of multiplying whole numbers.

Step 3: Count the total number of decimal places in the numbers that are being multiplied.

Step 4: Place the decimal point in the answer starting at the right and moving towards the left by the total number of decimal places counted.

Example 2.4-c **Multiplying Decimal Numbers**

Multiply 12.56 and 1.8.

Solution

$$\begin{array}{rl} 12.56 & \text{(2 Decimal places)} \\ \times \quad 1.8 & \text{(1 Decimal places)} \\ \hline 10048 & \\ 12560 & \\ \hline 22.608 & \text{(3 Decimal places)} \end{array}$$

(2 Decimal places) and (1 Decimal places): Total of 3 Decimals places

Therefore, multiplying 12.56 and 1.8 results in 22.608.

Division of Decimal Numbers

Division of decimal numbers is the process of determining how many times one decimal number is contained in another decimal number.

Follow these steps to divide a decimal number:

Step 1: If the divisor is not a whole number, convert it to a whole number by moving the decimal point to the right. Move the decimal point in the dividend by the same number of places.

Step 2: Divide by following a similar process to the process of dividing whole numbers.

- Add zeros to the right of the last digit of the dividend and keep dividing until no remainder or a repeating pattern shows up in the quotient.

Example 2.4-d **Dividing Decimal Numbers**

Perform the following divisions:

(i) Divide 8.25 by 0.6

(ii) Divide: 0.166 by 0.03

Solution

(i) Step 1: $8.25 \div 0.6$

Since the denominator contains one decimal place, move the decimal point by one decimal place to the right for both the numerator and the denominator,

$$= \frac{8.25}{0.6}$$

This is the same as multiplying both the numerator and denominator by 10.

$$= \frac{82.5}{6}$$

$$\frac{8.25 \times 10}{0.6 \times 10} = \frac{82.5}{6}$$

Step 2:

$$\begin{array}{r} 13.75 \\ 6\,\overline{)\,82.50} \\ -6 \\ \hline 22 \\ -18 \\ \hline 45 \\ -42 \\ \hline 30 \\ -30 \\ \hline 0 \end{array}$$

Position the decimal point within the quotient directly above the decimal point within the dividend.

30 ← Add a Zero

Therefore, when 8.25 is divided by 0.6, the quotient is 13.75 and the remainder is 0.

Solution *continued*

(ii) Step 1: $0.166 \div 0.03 = \frac{0.166}{0.03} = \frac{16.6}{3}$

Since the denominator contains two decimal places, move the decimal point by two decimal places to the right for both the numerator and the denominator.

This is the same as multiplying both the numerator and denominator by 100.

$$\frac{0.166 \times 100}{0.03 \times 100} = \frac{16.6}{3}$$

Step 2:

$$\begin{array}{r} 5.533 \\ 3\overline{)16.600} \\ -15 \\ \hline 16 \\ -15 \\ \hline 10 \\ -9 \\ \hline 10 \\ -9 \\ \hline 1 \end{array}$$

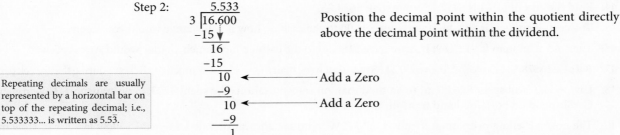

Position the decimal point within the quotient directly above the decimal point within the dividend.

Add a Zero

Add a Zero

Repeating decimals are usually represented by a horizontal bar on top of the repeating decimal; i.e., 5.533333... is written as $5.5\bar{3}$.

Therefore, when 0.166 is divided by 0.03, the quoitent is $5.5\bar{3}$ and the remainder is 1.

2.4 | Exercises

Answers to odd-numbered problems are available at the end of the textbook.

For Problems 1 to 8, perform the additions.

1. 927.896 + 659.50 + 128.649
2. 619.985 + 52.82 + 3.187
3. 74 + 129.258 + 0.32 + 666.015
4. 17 + 3.48 + 0.278 + 78.24
5. 292.454 + 121.69 + 65.3
6. 396.716 + 191.68 + 90.6
7. 948.684 + 15.17 + 0.717
8. 625.365 + 27.97 + 0.613

9. Find the sum of the following numbers:
Twenty and ninety-five hundredths, Two hundred and seventy-two thousandths , and Nineteen and nine tenths.

10. Find the sum of the following numbers:
Six and thirty-nine thousandths, Eighty and fourteen hundredths , and Sixteen and eight tenths.

For Problems 11 to 18, perform the subtractions.

11. 423.92 – 185.728
12. 9.555 – 7.18
13. 29.28 – 13.4
14. 15.7 – 7.92
15. 539.64 – 258.357
16. 848.62 – 495.476
17. 409.5 – 179.832
18. 475.3 – 281.375
19. Subtract three hundred five and thirty-nine hundredths from seven hundred twenty and four tenths.
20. Subtract eight hundred twenty and four hundredths from one thousand, one hundred one and six tenths.

For Problems 21 to 28, perform the multiplications.

21. 137.89 and 5.4
22. 189.945 and 6.3
23. 62.095 and 4.18
24. 92.74 and 3.25
25. 0.43 and 0.8
26. 0.59 and 0.9
27. 109.78 and 2.91
28. 145.75 and 3.74

For Problems 29 to 36, perform the divisions.

29. 67.78 by 9
30. 261.31 by 7
31. 732.6 by 8
32. 413.9 by 6
33. 14.6 by 0.6
34. 9.155 by 0.7
35. 3.1 by 0.25
36. 2.7 by 0.15

For Problems 37 to 44, formulate arithmetic expressions and evaluate.

37. Find the amount that is $248.76 less than $627.40.
38. Find the amount that is $45.27 less than $90.75.
39. Find the difference in the amounts $30.75 and $15.89.
40. Find the difference in the amounts $235.62 and $115.75.
41. Find the sum of $52.43 and $23.95.
42. Find the sum of $252.34 and $297.90.
43. Find the amount that is $38.89 more than $25.67.
44. Find the amount that is $412.78 more than $634.25.
45. The cost of an item is $88.46. If you gave $90.00 to the cashier, how much change would you receive?
46. The cost of an item is $125.69. If Arun gave $150.00 to the cashier, how much change would Arun receive?
47. Bill saved $578.50 this week. He saved $124.85 more last week than this week. How much did Bill save during the 2-week period?
48. Last week Carol spent $96.75 more on food than on transportation. She spent $223.15 on transport. How much did Carol spend on both food and transportation last week?
49. The normal selling price of an item is $237.75. When this item was on sale Dave paid $49.89 less for it. How much did Dave pay for that item?
50. A car driver filled gas when the odometer reading was 35,894.9 km. The odometer reading now is 39,894.4 km. How many kilometres did the driver travel, rounded to the nearest kilometre?
51. After spending $38.96 on toys and $1.75 on wrapping paper, Ann still had $45.75. How much money did Ann have initially?
52. After paying $515.09 for a car lease and $379.92 for property tax, my bank balance was $675.45. How much money did I have initially?
53. Simon bought a camera that was on sale for $799.99. He agreed to pay $70.35 every month for 12 months. How much more money than the sale price did Simon pay for the camera?
54. Andy bought a TV that was on sale for $2,249.95. He agreed to pay $130.45 every month for 18 months. How much more money than the sale price did Andy pay for the TV?
55. A salesperson earns a salary of $725.35 every week. During the past 3 weeks, he also received commissions of $375.68, $578.79, and $338.57. Calculate his total income for the past 3 weeks.
56. I leased a car on a 4-year term at $694.38 per month. At the end of the lease period, I paid an additional $18,458.74 to purchase the car. Find the total amount I paid for the car.
57. John bought 2 shirts at $20.95 each and 3 pairs of pants at $34.55 each. He gave $200 to the cashier. Calculate the balance he should receive from the cashier.
58. I bought 3 kg of walnuts at $8.69 per kg and 4 kg of almonds at $7.72 per kg. I gave the cashier a $100 bill. How much change should I receive from the cashier?
59. A string that measured 0.875 m was cut into pieces of 0.0625 m each. How many pieces did this result in?
60. A cake that weighed 0.82 kg was cut into slices that weighed 0.1025 kg each. How many slices did this result in?
61. Marion bought 3 dresses at $22.49 per dress and 2 pairs of shoes at $14.99 per pair. She gave a $100 bill to the cashier. What change should she expect to receive from the cashier?
62. Gilbert bought 2 kg of grapes at $3.29 per kg and 1.5 kg of strawberries at $5.99 per kg. He gave a $20 bill to the cashier. How much should he expect to receive in change from the cashier?

2.5 | Arithmetic Operations with Fractions and Decimal Numbers

Converting Decimal Numbers to Fractions

It is possible to convert **terminating** decimal numbers (e.g.: 0.275) and **repeating decimal numbers** (e.g.: 0.333333...) to fractions. However, there is no exact equivalent fraction for **non-repeating, non-terminating** decimal numbers (e.g.: 0.837508...).

Converting Terminating Decimal Numbers to Fractions

Any non-repeating, terminating decimal number can be converted to a fraction by following these steps:

Step 1: Count the number of decimal places.

Step 2: Move the decimal point by that many places to the right and divide the answer by 10-fold for every number of place moved; (i.e., if there is 1 decimal place, divide by 10, if 2 decimal places, divide by 100, if 3 decimal places, divide by 1,000, etc.)

This is the same as multiplying and dividing by 10-fold for every digit after the decimal point.

Step 3: Simplify (or reduce) the fraction.

Example 2.5-a

Converting Terminating Decimal Numbers to Fractions

Convert the following decimal numbers to their fractional equivalent:

(i) 3.75 (ii) 0.015

Solution

(i) Converting 3.75 to its fractional equivalent:

$= 3.75$

3.75 contains two decimal places. Therefore, move two decimal places to the right and divide by 100.

(This is the same as multiplying by 100 and dividing by 100: $\frac{3.75 \times 100}{100} = \frac{375}{100}$)

$= \frac{375}{100}$

Dividing by 25 and simplifying,

$= \frac{375^{\div 25}}{100_{\div 25}} = \frac{15}{4}$

Therefore, 3.75 converted to its fractional equivalent is $\frac{15}{4}$.

(ii) Converting 0.015 to its fractional equivalent:

$= 0.015$

0.015 contains three decimal places. Therefore, move three decimal places to the right. (This is the same as multiplying by 1,000 and dividing by 1,000:

$\frac{0.015 \times 1{,}000}{1{,}000} = \frac{15}{1{,}000}$)

$= \frac{15}{1{,}000}$

$= \frac{15 \div 5}{1{,}000 \div 5}$

Dividing by 5 and simplifying,

$= \frac{3}{200}$

Therefore, 0.015 converted to its fractional equivalent is $\frac{3}{200}$.

Converting Repeating Decimal Numbers to Fractions

Any repeating decimal number can be converted to a fraction by following the procedure given in the following examples.

Example 2.5-b **Converting Repeating Decimal Numbers to Fractions**

Convert 0.77777... to a fraction.

Solution

Let 0.7777777... be equal to a fraction x.

Therefore,

(a) $x = 0.777777... = 0.\overline{7}$ Multiplying both sides by 10,

(b) $10x = 7.777777... = 7.\overline{7}$

Subtracting (a) from (b) to obtain,

$$10x - x = 7.\overline{7} - 0.\overline{7}$$
$$9x = 7$$
$$x = \frac{7}{9}$$

Therefore, $0.777777... = \frac{7}{9}$.

Example 2.5-c **Converting Repeating Decimal Numbers to Fractions**

Convert 0.655555... to a fraction.

Solution

Let 0.655555... be equal to a fraction x.

Therefore,

(a) $x = 0.655555... = 0.6\overline{5}$ Multiplying both sides by 10,

(b) $10x = 6.555555... = 6.\overline{5}$ Multiplying both sides again by 10, since the repeating digit is in the hundredths place,

(c) $100x = 65.55555... = 65.\overline{5}$

Subtracting (b) from (c) to obtain,

$$100x - 10x = 65.\overline{5} - 6.\overline{5}$$
$$90x = 59$$
$$x = \frac{59}{90}$$

Therefore, $0.655555... = \frac{59}{90}$.

Example 2.5-d **Converting Repeating Decimal Numbers to Fractions**

Convert 0.353535... to a fraction.

Solution

Let 0.353535... be equal to a fraction x.

(a) $x = 0.353535... = 0.\overline{35}$ Multiplying both sides by 100,

(b) $100x = 35.3535... = 35.\overline{35}$

Subtract (a) from (b) to obtain,

$$100x - x = 35.\overline{35} - 0.\overline{35}$$
$$99x = 35$$
$$x = \frac{35}{99}$$

Therefore, $0.353535... = \frac{35}{99}$.

Rational Numbers can be represented by $\frac{a}{b}$.

Irrational Numbers cannot be represented by $\frac{a}{b}$,

where 'a' and 'b' are integers and $b \neq 0$.

From Examples 2.5-a to 2.5-d, you learned that it is possible to convert non-repeating, terminating decimal numbers (e.g., 0.015) and repeating decimal numbers (e.g., $0.6\overline{5}$) into fractions. Therefore, such decimal numbers are also called ***rational numbers****.*

It is not possible to convert non-repeating and non-terminating numbers (e.g., $\sqrt{2}$, π, 5.81271...) to fractions. Such decimal numbers are called ***irrational numbers****.*

These rational numbers and irrational (non-rational) numbers are called ***'Real Numbers'*** *in the number system.*

Converting Fractions to Decimal Numbers

Converting Proper and Improper Fractions to Decimal Numbers

A proper or improper fraction can be converted to its equivalent decimal number by dividing the numerator by the denominator, as shown in the following examples.

Example 2.5-e

Converting Proper and Improper Fractions to Decimal Numbers

Convert the following fractions to their decimal equivalents:

(i) $\frac{3}{8}$ (ii) $\frac{15}{11}$

Solution

(i) $\frac{3}{8}$

$= 3 \div 8$

$= 0.375$

$$\begin{array}{r} .375 \\ 8\overline{)3.000} \\ \underline{24} \\ 60 \\ \underline{56} \\ 40 \\ \underline{40} \\ 0 \end{array}$$

Therefore, 0.375 is the decimal equivalent of $\frac{3}{8}$.

(ii) $\frac{15}{11}$

$= 15 \div 11$

$= 1.3636....$

$= 1.\overline{36}$

$$\begin{array}{r} 1.36\overline{36} \\ 11\overline{)15.0000} \\ \underline{11} \\ 40 \\ \underline{33} \\ 70 \\ \underline{66} \\ 40 \\ \underline{33} \\ 70 \\ \underline{66} \\ 4 \end{array}$$

Therefore, $1.\overline{36}$ is the decimal equivalent of $\frac{15}{11}$.

Converting Mixed Numbers to Decimal Numbers

A mixed number can be converted to its decimal form by first converting it to an improper fraction, then dividing the numerator by the denominator, as shown in the following example.

Example 2.5-f

Converting Mixed Numbers to Decimal Numbers

Convert the following mixed numbers to their decimal number equivalents:

(i) $3\frac{5}{2}$ (ii) $11\frac{3}{7}$

Solution

(i) $3\frac{5}{2}$

$= \frac{3(2)+5}{2} = \frac{11}{2}$ Coverting to an improper fraction,

$= 5.5$

Therefore, the decimal number equivalent of $3\frac{5}{2}$ is 5.5.

(ii) $11\frac{3}{7}$

$= \frac{11(7)+3}{7} = \frac{80}{7}$ Coverting to an improper fraction,

$= 11.428571... = 11.43$

Therefore, the decimal number equivalent of $11\frac{3}{7}$ is 11.43.

Powers of Fractions and Decimal Numbers

Powers of fractions and decimal numbers are expressed the same way as whole numbers. The fractions and decimal numbers are usually writtten within brackets when they are raised to a power.

For example, $\left(\frac{2}{3}\right)^2$ is read as two-thirds squared.

Exponents indicate the number of times the base is to be multiplied.

This means that $\left(\frac{2}{3}\right)$ is used as a factor 2 times.

i.e., $\left(\frac{2}{3}\right)^2 = \frac{2}{3} \times \frac{2}{3} = \frac{4}{9}$

Similarily, $(0.12)^3$ is read as twelve hundredths raised to the power 3.

This means that (0.12) is used as a factor 3 times.

i.e., $(0.12)^3 = (0.12)\ (0.12)\ (0.12) = 0.001728$.

A mixed number that is raised to a power is evaluated by first converting it into an improper fraction and then following the same procedure explained earlier.

For example, $\left(1\frac{2}{3}\right)^4$ is evaluated by first converting $\left(1\frac{2}{3}\right)$ into an improper fraction form.

i.e., $\left(1\frac{2}{3}\right)^4 = \frac{1(3)+2}{3} = \left(\frac{5}{3}\right)^4$ Then, expand by using $\left(\frac{5}{3}\right)$ as a factor 4 times.

$= \left(\frac{5}{3}\right)\left(\frac{5}{3}\right)\left(\frac{5}{3}\right)\left(\frac{5}{3}\right)$

$= \frac{625}{81}$

Example 2.5-g **Evaluating Powers of Fractions and Decimal Numbers**

Evaluate the following powers:

(i) $\left(\frac{4}{5}\right)^4$ (ii) $\left(1\frac{1}{2}\right)^5$ (iii) $(1.12)^3$

Solution

(i) $\left(\frac{4}{5}\right)^4$ Expanding by using $\left(\frac{4}{5}\right)$ as a factor 4 times,

$= \left(\frac{4}{5}\right)\left(\frac{4}{5}\right)\left(\frac{4}{5}\right)\left(\frac{4}{5}\right) = \frac{256}{625}$

(ii) $\left(1\frac{1}{2}\right)^5$ Converting to an improper fraction,

$= \left(\frac{1 \times 2 + 1}{2}\right)^5$ Expanding by using $\left(\frac{3}{2}\right)$ as a factor 5 times,

Solution *continued*

$= \left(\frac{3}{2}\right)^5 = \left(\frac{3}{2}\right)\left(\frac{3}{2}\right)\left(\frac{3}{2}\right)\left(\frac{3}{2}\right)\left(\frac{3}{2}\right)$

$= \frac{243}{32}$ Coverting to a mixed number,

$= 7\frac{19}{32}$

(iii) $(1.12)^3$ Expanding by using (1.12) as a factor 3 times,

$= (1.12)\ (1.12)\ (1.12) = 1.404928$

Roots of Fractions and Decimal Numbers

In this section you will learn about the **square roots** of **fractions** and **decimals** that have exact roots.

Square roots of fractions are calculated the same way as the square roots of whole numbers, but the numerators and denominators are evaluated separately. The answers are expressed in simplified or reduced form.

For example, $\sqrt{\frac{9}{16}}$ is the same as $\frac{\sqrt{9}}{\sqrt{16}} = \frac{3}{4}$

$\sqrt{\frac{a}{b}}$ is equal to $\frac{\sqrt{a}}{\sqrt{b}}$

Finding roots of decimals becomes easy if the decimal number is converted to a fraction having an even power of ten; i.e., 100, 1,000, etc., and then following the procedure for finding the square roots of fractions.

For example, $\sqrt{0.25} = \sqrt{\frac{25}{100}} = \frac{\sqrt{25}}{\sqrt{100}} = \frac{5}{10} = \frac{1}{2}$ or 0.5

Example 2.5-h

Evaluating Square Roots of Fractions and Decimal Numbers

Evaluate the following square roots:

(i) $\sqrt{\frac{25}{144}}$ (ii) $\sqrt{0.49}$

Solution

(i) $\sqrt{\frac{25}{144}} = \frac{\sqrt{25}}{\sqrt{144}} = \frac{5}{12}$ (ii) $\sqrt{0.49} = \sqrt{\frac{49}{100}} = \frac{\sqrt{49}}{\sqrt{100}} = \frac{7}{10} = 0.7$

Combined Order of Operations

The Order of Operations (BEDMAS) learned in Chapter 1, Section 1.4, is also used in evaluating expressions with fractions and decimal numbers.

Follow these steps to evaluate expressions with fractions and decimal numbers:

Step 1: Evaluate the expressions within the grouping symbols: brackets and radical signs are grouping symbols.

Step 2: Evaluate powers and roots.

Step 3: Perform multiplcation and division in order from left to right.

Step 4: Perform addition and subtraction in order from left to right.

Note: For mutliplication, division, powers, and roots of mixed numbers, they must be converted to improper fractions before proceeding with the Order of Operations.

Example 2.5-i

Evaluating Expressions Using Order of Operations (BEDMAS)

Evaluate the following expressions:

(i) $\left(1\frac{1}{3}\right)^2 + \sqrt{\frac{5}{16} + \frac{20}{16}}$ (ii) $\left(\frac{2}{3}\right)^2 + \frac{1}{2}\left(4\frac{1}{2}\right)^2 \div \sqrt{81}$

(iii) $\left(\frac{4}{5}\right)^2 + \left(\frac{11}{9} + \sqrt{\frac{49}{81}}\right) \times \frac{3}{25}$ (iv) $\sqrt{1\frac{69}{100}} + \sqrt{0.09} + \sqrt{\frac{64}{25}}$

(v) $\left(1 + \frac{0.08}{4}\right)^2 - 1$

Solution

(i) $\left(1\frac{1}{3}\right)^2 + \sqrt{\frac{5}{16} + \frac{20}{16}}$

$= \left(\frac{4}{3}\right)^2 + \sqrt{\frac{25}{16}}$

$= \left(\frac{4}{3}\right)\left(\frac{4}{3}\right) + \frac{\sqrt{25}}{\sqrt{16}}$

$= \frac{16}{9} + \frac{5}{4}$

$= \frac{64 + 45}{36}$

$= \frac{109}{36}$

$= 3\frac{1}{36}$

(ii) $\left(\frac{2}{3}\right)^2 + \frac{1}{2}\left(4\frac{1}{2}\right)^2 \div \sqrt{81}$

$= \left(\frac{2}{3}\right)\left(\frac{2}{3}\right) + \frac{1}{2}\left(\frac{9}{2}\right)\left(\frac{9}{2}\right) \div 9$

$= \frac{4}{9} + \frac{81}{8} \times \frac{1}{9}$

$= \frac{4}{9} + \frac{9}{8}$

$= \frac{32 + 81}{72}$

$= \frac{113}{72}$

$= 1\frac{41}{72}$

(iii) $\left(\frac{4}{5}\right)^2 + \left(\frac{11}{9} + \sqrt{\frac{49}{81}}\right) \times \frac{3}{25}$

$= \left(\frac{4}{5}\right)^2 + \left(\frac{11}{9} + \frac{7}{9}\right) \times \frac{3}{25}$

$= \left(\frac{4}{5}\right)^2 + \frac{18}{9} \times \frac{3}{25}$

$= \left(\frac{4}{5}\right)\left(\frac{4}{5}\right) + 2 \times \frac{3}{25}$

$= \frac{16}{25} + \frac{6}{25}$

$= \frac{22}{25}$

(iv) $\sqrt{1\frac{69}{100}} + \sqrt{0.09} + \sqrt{\frac{64}{25}}$

$= \sqrt{\frac{169}{100}} + \sqrt{0.09} + \sqrt{\frac{64}{25}}$

$= \sqrt{\frac{169}{100}} + \sqrt{\frac{9}{100}} + \sqrt{\frac{64}{25}}$

$= \frac{\sqrt{169}}{\sqrt{100}} + \frac{\sqrt{9}}{\sqrt{100}} + \frac{\sqrt{64}}{\sqrt{25}}$

$= \frac{13}{10} + \frac{3}{10} + \frac{8}{5}$

$= \frac{13 + 3 + 16}{10}$

$= \frac{32}{10}$

$= \frac{16}{5} = 3\frac{1}{5}$

(v) $\left(1 + \frac{0.08}{4}\right)^2 - 1$

$= (1 + 0.02)^2 - 1$

$= (1.02)^2 - 1$

$= (1.02)(1.02) - 1$

$= 1.0404 - 1$

$= 0.0404$

Example 2.5-j **Evaluating Expressions by Using the Order of Operations (BEDMAS)**

Evaluate: $\frac{4}{2^3}\ [(0.5 \times 5^2 + 2.5)^2 \div 3^2] + \sqrt{25}$

Solution

$\frac{4}{2^3}\ [(0.5 \times 5^2 + 2.5)^2 \div 3^2] + \sqrt{25}$

$= \frac{4}{2^3}\ [(0.5 \times 25 + 2.5)^2 \div 3^2] + 5$

$= \frac{4}{2^3}\ [(12.5 + 2.5)^2 \div 3^2] + 5$

Solution
continued

$$= \frac{4}{2^3}\,[15^2 \div 3^2] + 5$$

$$= \frac{4}{2^3}\,[225 \div 9] + 5$$

$$= \frac{4}{2^3} \times 25 + 5$$

$$= \frac{4}{8} \times 25 + 5$$

$$= 0.5 \times 25 + 5$$

$$= 12.5 + 5$$

$$= 17.5$$

2.5 | Exercises

Answers to odd-numbered problems are available at the end of the textbook.

For Problems 1 to 8, convert the decimal numbers to proper fractions and the proper fractions to decimal numbers.

1.

	Decimal Number	Proper Fraction
a.	0.2	?
b.	?	$\frac{3}{4}$
c.	0.06	?

2.

	Decimal Number	Proper Fraction
a.	0.26	?
b.	?	$\frac{41}{50}$
c.	0.92	?

3.

	Decimal Number	Proper Fraction
a.	?	$\frac{9}{25}$
b.	0.004	?
c.	?	$\frac{7}{50}$

4.

	Decimal Number	Proper Fraction
a.	?	$\frac{16}{25}$
b.	0.225	?
c.	?	$\frac{19}{20}$

5.

	Decimal Number	Proper Fraction
a.	?	$\frac{1}{2}$
b.	0.4	?
c.	?	$\frac{3}{50}$

6.

	Decimal Number	Proper Fraction
a.	?	$\frac{13}{20}$
b.	0.425	?
c.	?	$\frac{14}{25}$

7.

	Decimal Number	Proper Fraction
a.	0.005	?
b.	?	$\frac{9}{25}$
c.	0.01	?

8.

	Decimal Number	Proper Fraction
a.	0.66	?
b.	?	$\frac{43}{50}$
c.	0.78	?

For Problems 9 to 12, convert the decimal numbers to improper fractions and the improper fractions to decimal numbers.

9.

	Decimal Number	Improper Fraction
a.	3.5	?
b.	?	$\frac{8}{5}$
c.	5.6	?

10.

	Decimal Number	Improper Fraction
a.	7.2	?
b.	?	$\frac{37}{5}$
c.	8.4	?

11.

	Decimal Number	Improper Fraction
a.	?	$\frac{101}{20}$
b.	6.8	?
c.	?	$\frac{11}{4}$

12.

	Decimal Number	Improper Fraction
a.	?	$\frac{107}{50}$
b.	4.8	?
c.	?	$\frac{22}{4}$

For Problem 13 to 16, convert the decimal numbers to mixed numbers and the mixed numbers to decimal numbers.

13.

	Decimal Number	Mixed Number
a.	2.25	?
b.	?	$1\frac{3}{4}$
c.	4.02	?

14.

	Decimal Number	Mixed Number
a.	5.04	?
b.	?	$12\frac{3}{5}$
c.	14.025	?

15.

	Decimal Number	Mixed Number
a.	?	$8\frac{7}{20}$
b.	16.005	?
c.	?	$15\frac{1}{2}$

16.

	Decimal Number	Mixed Number
a.	?	$3\frac{5}{8}$
b.	4.75	?
c.	?	$5\frac{9}{20}$

For Problems 17 to 20, convert the repeating decimal numbers to proper fractions and the proper fractions to repeating decimal numbers.

17.

	Decimal Number	Proper Fraction
a.	$0.\overline{6}$	?
b.	?	$\frac{23}{90}$
c.	$0.\overline{25}$	?

18.

	Decimal Number	Proper Fraction
a.	$0.\overline{27}$	?
b.	?	$\frac{4}{7}$
c.	$0.8\overline{3}$	?

19.

	Decimal Number	Proper Fraction
a.	?	$\frac{5}{11}$
b.	$0.\overline{2}$	?
c.	?	$\frac{2}{7}$

20.

	Decimal Number	Proper Fraction
a.	?	$\frac{5}{11}$
b.	0.75	?
c.	?	$\frac{2}{7}$

For Problems 21 to 30 evaluate the powers of the fractions.

21. a. $\left(\frac{3}{5}\right)^2$ b. $\left(\frac{6}{7}\right)^2$

22. a. $\left(\frac{3}{4}\right)^2$ b. $\left(\frac{2}{9}\right)^2$

23. a. $\left(\frac{3}{4}\right)^3$ b. $\left(\frac{5}{3}\right)^4$

24. a. $\left(\frac{2}{7}\right)^3$ b. $\left(\frac{6}{5}\right)^4$

25. a. $\left(1\frac{1}{3}\right)^2$ b. $\left(3\frac{1}{2}\right)^3$

26. a. $\left(2\frac{1}{4}\right)^2$ b. $\left(1\frac{2}{3}\right)^3$

27. a. $\left(\frac{3}{5}\right)^2\left(\frac{2}{3}\right)^3$ b. $\left(\frac{3}{4}\right)^3\left(\frac{1}{6}\right)^2$

28. a. $\left(\frac{5}{2}\right)^3\left(\frac{1}{3}\right)^2$ b. $\left(\frac{3}{8}\right)^2\left(\frac{4}{3}\right)^3$

29. a. $\left(\frac{1}{4}\right)^2 \div \left(\frac{1}{8}\right)^2$ b. $\left(\frac{5}{3}\right)^2 \div \left(\frac{10}{9}\right)^2$

30. a. $\left(\frac{1}{2}\right)^2 \div \left(\frac{1}{3}\right)^2$ b. $\left(\frac{2}{3}\right)^2 \div \left(\frac{4}{9}\right)^2$

For Problems 31 to 40 evaluate the roots of the fractions.

31. a. $\sqrt{\frac{1}{9}}$ b. $\sqrt{\frac{1}{49}}$

32. a. $\sqrt{\frac{1}{16}}$ b. $\sqrt{\frac{1}{36}}$

33. a. $\sqrt{\frac{4}{25}}$ b. $\sqrt{\frac{81}{16}}$

34. a. $\sqrt{\frac{36}{100}}$ b. $\sqrt{\frac{9}{49}}$

35. a. $\sqrt{\frac{100}{121}}$ b. $\sqrt{\frac{1}{100}}$

36. a. $\sqrt{\frac{144}{81}}$ b. $\sqrt{\frac{1}{10{,}000}}$

37. a. $\sqrt{\frac{5}{9}+\frac{4}{9}}$ b. $\sqrt{\frac{2}{25}+\frac{14}{25}}$

38. a. $\sqrt{\frac{15}{36}+\frac{10}{36}}$ b. $\sqrt{\frac{1}{16}+\frac{8}{16}}$

39. a. $\sqrt{3\frac{1}{16}}$ b. $\sqrt{6\frac{1}{4}}$

40. a. $\sqrt{1\frac{11}{25}}$ b. $\sqrt{1\frac{21}{100}}$

For Problems 41 to 44, evaluate the powers of the decimal numbers.

41. a. $(0.1)^3$ b. $(0.3)^2$

42. a. $(1.1)^3$ b. $(1.2)^3$

43. a. $(0.4)^2$ b. $(0.02)^3$

44. a. $(0.9)^2$ b. $(0.05)^3$

For Problems 45 to 50, evaluate the roots of the decimal numbers.

45. a. $\sqrt{0.25}$ b. $\sqrt{0.49}$

46. a. $\sqrt{0.36}$ b. $\sqrt{0.64}$

47. a. $\sqrt{1.21}$ b. $\sqrt{1.69}$

48. a. $\sqrt{2.56}$ b. $\sqrt{1.44}$

49. a. $\sqrt{0.01}$ b. $\sqrt{0.0049}$

50. a. $\sqrt{0.09}$ b. $\sqrt{0.0004}$

For Problems 51 to 64, evaluate the expressions.

51. a. $\left(\frac{3}{5}\right)^2 + \left(1\frac{1}{5}\right)\left(\sqrt{144}\right)$ b. $\left(\frac{2}{5}\right)^2 + \left(\frac{3}{2}\right)^3$

52. a. $\left(\frac{4}{7}\right)^2 + \sqrt{\frac{3}{9} + \frac{1}{9}}$ b. $\left(\frac{3}{8}\right)^2 + \left(\frac{1}{2}\right)^3$

53. a. $\sqrt{4\frac{21}{25}} \times \left(\frac{5}{3}\right)^2$ b. $\left(\frac{1}{4}\right)^2 \div \left(\frac{1}{8}\right)^2$

54. a. $\sqrt{1\frac{9}{16}} \times \left(\frac{4}{5}\right)^2$ b. $\left(\frac{1}{3}\right)^2 \div \left(\frac{1}{6}\right)^2$

55. a. $(1.3)^2 \times \sqrt{0.04}$ b. $(0.1)^3 \div \sqrt{\frac{1}{100}}$

56. a. $(0.01)^2 \times \sqrt{0.09}$ b. $(0.5)^3 \div \sqrt{\frac{1}{100}}$

57. $\left(\frac{5}{8}\right)^2 \div \frac{3}{16} + \frac{5}{12} \div 1\frac{2}{3}$

58. $\left(\frac{6}{7}\right)^2 \div 1\frac{5}{9} + \frac{5}{6} \div 4\frac{1}{2}$

59. $\sqrt{\frac{7}{9} - \frac{2}{3}} \div \left(\frac{1}{12} + \frac{1}{9}\right)$

60. $\left(\frac{5}{12} - \frac{3}{8}\right) \div \sqrt{\frac{4}{18} + \frac{1}{36}}$

61. $[0.8 - (7.2 - 6.5)] \div [3 \div (3.4 - 0.4)]$

62. $(9.9 \div 1.1) \div (8.1 \div 1.5) + (9.2 - 7.7 + 1.5)$

63. $(9.2 + 2.8)\ 0.25 \div (5.6 - 2.3 + 1.7)$

64. $(9.1 - 7.3)\ 0.5 \div (5.8 + 8.6 - 5.4)$

2 | Review Exercises

Answers to odd-numbered problems are available at the end of the textbook.

For Problems 1 and 2, find the missing values.

1. a. $\frac{6}{12} = \frac{?}{6} = \frac{24}{?}$ b. $\frac{12}{45} = \frac{?}{15} = \frac{16}{?}$

   c. $\frac{20}{25} = \frac{?}{5} = \frac{12}{?}$ d. $\frac{36}{48} = \frac{?}{36} = \frac{18}{?}$

2. a. $\frac{9}{15} = \frac{?}{45} = \frac{15}{?}$ b. $\frac{18}{27} = \frac{?}{18} = \frac{10}{?}$

   c. $\frac{21}{35} = \frac{?}{25} = \frac{12}{?}$ d. $\frac{12}{28} = \frac{?}{70} = \frac{15}{?}$

For Problems 3 and 4, place the appropriate symbol (<, >, =) between each of the fractions.

3. a. $\frac{24}{21}\ \square\ \frac{11}{5}$ b. $\frac{20}{44}\ \square\ \frac{6}{15}$

   c. $\frac{18}{45}\ \square\ \frac{16}{4}$ d. $\frac{15}{25}\ \square\ \frac{63}{105}$

4. a. $\frac{15}{18}\ \square\ \frac{30}{42}$ b. $\frac{21}{24}\ \square\ \frac{35}{40}$

   c. $\frac{40}{48}\ \square\ \frac{35}{42}$ d. $\frac{8}{38}\ \square\ \frac{12}{57}$

For Problems 5 and 6, change the improper fractions to mixed numbers in simplest form.

5. a. $\frac{15}{10}$ b. $\frac{39}{26}$

   c. $\frac{88}{12}$ d. $\frac{102}{9}$

6. a. $\frac{18}{8}$ b. $\frac{98}{12}$

   c. $\frac{88}{10}$ d. $\frac{48}{15}$

For Problems 7 and 8, reduce the fractions to their lowest terms.

7. a. $\frac{75}{345}$ b. $\frac{124}{48}$

   c. $\frac{70}{15}$ d. $\frac{292}{365}$

8. a. $\frac{36}{144}$ b. $\frac{68}{10}$

   c. $\frac{80}{12}$ d. $\frac{61}{366}$

For Problems 9 to 12, express the decimal numbers in their word form.

9. a. 0.5 b. 0.007

   c. 0.12 d. 0.029

10. a. 0.75 b. 0.3

    c. 0.008 d. 0.04

11. a. 32.04 b. 200.2

    c. 45,005.001 d. 1,005,071.25

12. a. 27.602 b. 470.5

    c. 32,010.07 d. 3,500,007.45

For Problems 13 and 14, perform the indicated arithmetic operations.

13. a. $478.82 + 85.847$ b. $65.09 - 24.987$

c. 54.37×1.46 d. $77.09 \div 8$

14. a. $716.03 + 49.936$ b. $15.71 - 3.509$

c. 15.71×3.26 d. $39.83 \div 9$

15. What is the difference between the smallest and the largest numbers of the following?

0.012, 0.201, 0.02, 0.102

16. What is the sum of the smallest and the largest numbers of the following?

0.041, 0.011, 0.014, 0.01

17. Which of the following is closest to 2?

2.011, 2.005, 1.996, 1.995

18. Which of the following is closest to 1?

2.011, 2.004, 1.997, 1.996

For Problems 19 and 20, convert the decimal numbers to proper fractions in lowest terms and the fractions to decimal numbers.

19.

	Decimal Number	Proper Fraction
a.	0.025	?
b.	?	$\frac{5}{8}$
c.	0.08	?
d.	?	$\frac{7}{25}$
e.	0.002	?
f.	?	$\frac{39}{50}$

20.

	Decimal Number	Proper Fraction
a.	0.06	?
b.	?	$\frac{23}{50}$
c.	0.075	?
d.	?	$\frac{27}{40}$
e.	0.004	?
f.	?	$\frac{17}{25}$

21. Find the total weight of three items that weigh $3\frac{2}{3}$ kg, $4\frac{1}{2}$ kg, and $5\frac{3}{8}$ kg.

22. I used $2\frac{1}{5}$ litres of paint for my bedroom, $1\frac{1}{4}$ litres for my study room, and $7\frac{1}{3}$ litres for my living room. How many litres of paint did I use for the three rooms?

23. Henry is $8\frac{1}{4}$ years old. Amanda is $2\frac{5}{12}$ years old. How many years younger is Amanda than Henry?

24. I purchased $12\frac{1}{3}$ hectares of land and sold $4\frac{2}{5}$ hectares. How many hectares do I now own?

25. A car can travel $8\frac{1}{4}$ km with one litre of gas. How many kilometres can it travel using $45\frac{3}{5}$ litres of gas?

26. Samantha can walk $5\frac{3}{8}$ km in one hour. How far can she walk in $4\frac{1}{3}$ hours?

27. Alisha and Beyonce saved a total of \$580. Two-fifth's of Alisha's savings equals \$144. How much did each of them save?

28. Andy and Bob had \$128. One-third of Bob's amount is \$25. How much did each of them have?

29. Lakshmi had \$2,675.68 in her chequing account. She deposited 2 cheques in the amounts of \$729.27 and \$72.05 and withdrew \$1,275.60. How much did she have in her account after the withdrawal?

30. George's car had 12.47 litres of gas at the start of his trip to the United States. He added the following quantities of gas during his trip: 34.25 litres, 15.2 litres, and 20.05 litres. At the end of the trip, there were 7.9 litres of gas left in the car. How much gas was used during the trip?

31. Barbie's hourly pay is \$23.07. If Barbie worked 37.75 hours last week, calculate her gross pay for last week.

32. Carol's overtime rate of pay is \$57.45 per hour. If Carol worked 12.5 hours overtime last week, calculate her gross overtime pay for last week.

33. Three-fourths of the number of boys at a school is equal to half of the number of girls. The school has 480 students in total. How many more girls are there than boys?

34. There are 3,400 spectators at a soccer match. Three-fifth's of the number of men equals six-seventh's of the number of women. How many spectators are women?

For Problems 35 to 46, evaluate the expressions.

35. $5 + \left(\frac{6}{10}\right)^3 + \sqrt{6^2 + 8^2}$

36. $\left(\frac{5}{7}\right)^2 \div 5 + \sqrt{3^2 + 4^2}$

37. $\sqrt{1.21} - (0.5)^2 + \sqrt{\frac{4}{25}}$

38. $\sqrt{0.81} - (0.2)^2 + \sqrt{\frac{9}{36}}$

39. $\left(\frac{1}{5}\right)^3 + \left(\frac{4}{25}\right)^2$

40. $\left(\frac{2}{3}\right)^3 + \left(\frac{2}{9}\right)^2$

41. $\left(\frac{5}{12}\right)^3 \left(\frac{4}{5}\right)^2$

42. $\left(\frac{4}{7}\right)^2 \left(\frac{1}{4}\right)^3$

43. $\left(2\frac{4}{5} - \frac{7}{10}\right) \div 2\frac{4}{5}$

44. $\left(2\frac{5}{8} + 1\frac{5}{12}\right) \div 1\frac{1}{2}$

45. $3\frac{1}{5} \div 2\left(\frac{3}{5} + \frac{1}{2}\right)$

46. $2\frac{2}{3} \div 3\left(\frac{4}{5} + 1\frac{5}{5}\right)$

2 | Self-Test Exercises

Answers to all problems are available at the end of the textbook.

1. Find the missing values:

   a. $\frac{8}{5} = \frac{?}{20} = \frac{24}{?}$ b. $\frac{12}{22} = \frac{6}{?} = \frac{?}{55}$

   c. $\frac{48}{72} = \frac{12}{?} = \frac{?}{144}$ d. $\frac{11}{12} = \frac{?}{72} = \frac{22}{?}$

2. Reduce the following fractions to their lowest terms:

   a. $\frac{225}{30}$ b. $\frac{156}{18}$

   c. $\frac{256}{144}$ d. $\frac{135}{825}$

3. Perform the indicated operations:

   a. $7\frac{2}{2} + 6\frac{1}{4}$ b. $5\frac{1}{3} - 3\frac{7}{15}$

   c. $\frac{3}{4} \times \frac{26}{27} \times \frac{9}{13}$ d. $2\frac{1}{4} \div \frac{3}{8}$

4. Perform the indicated operations:

   a. 0.165 + 10.8478 + 14.7 + 2.19
   b. 34.09 – 25.957
   c. 0.524 × 4.08
   d. 6.893 ÷ 3

5. Express the following numbers in word from:

   a. 0.004 b. 6.05

   c. 300.02 d. 7.071

6. Convert the decimal numbers to fractions:

	Decimal Number	Fraction
a.	0.625	?
b.	3.2	?
c.	3.4	?
d.	0.72	?
e.	2.3	?
f.	1.73	?

7. Convert the fractions to decimal numbers:

	Fraction	Decimal Number
a.	$\frac{7}{20}$	?
b.	$\frac{11}{5}$	?
c.	$1\frac{4}{5}$	?
d.	$\frac{8}{9}$	?
e.	$\frac{16}{15}$	?
f.	$2\frac{1}{3}$	?

8. On a certain map, 1 cm represents 125 km. How many km are represented by 4.75 cm? How many cm on the map will represent a distance of 4,725 km?

9. Henry took 3 days to make 69 deliveries. On the first day, he completed one-third of the deliveries. On the second day, he made 10 more deliveries than on the first day. How many deliveries did he make on the third day?

10. Kyle had $4,000 and gave half of it to Bob. Bob spent a quarter of the money he received from Kyle. How much money does Bob have left?

11. Niveda spent one-third of her money on a handbag and half of the remainder on shoes. What fraction of her money did she spend on shoes? If she has $40 left, how much did she spend?

12. Adrian's annual salary is $52,000. Calculate his hourly rate if he works 37.5 hours per week. (Hint: 1 year = 52 weeks)

13. An item in a store sells for $279.75. The same item is sold online for $245.99. How much cheaper is the item online?

14. The cost per day to rent a car is $24.45 plus $0.37 per kilometre driven. What would be the cost to rent a car for 5 days if Sally plans to drive 325.50 km?

15. I walked for $\frac{3}{4}$ hour at $5\frac{1}{2}$ km per hour and jogged for $\frac{1}{2}$ hour at 10 km per hour. What was the total distance that I covered?

For Problems 16 to 24, evaluate the expressions.

16. $\sqrt{0.0025} + \left(\frac{2}{5}\right)^2 - \sqrt{\frac{49}{16}}$

17. $\sqrt{\frac{81}{64}} - \left(\frac{5}{4}\right)^3 \div \left(\frac{25}{16}\right)^2 + \sqrt{7^2 + 24^2}$

18. $\sqrt{\frac{1}{9}} + \sqrt{\frac{4}{36}} - \left(\frac{2}{3}\right)^2$

19. $\left(\frac{3}{5}\right)^3\left(\frac{25}{6}\right)^2 + (\sqrt{0.25})\sqrt{100}$

20. $\sqrt{5^2 + 12^2} - (\sqrt{0.49})\sqrt{\frac{25}{144}}$

21. $\left(4\frac{9}{10} \div \frac{7}{15} \times 1\frac{3}{5}\right) \div 1\frac{9}{10}$

22. $3\frac{1}{2} \div 1\frac{2}{5} + \frac{9}{10} \times 2\frac{2}{5} - \frac{3}{4}$

23. $\left(3\frac{4}{15} + 2\frac{3}{5}\right) \times \left(\frac{5}{6} + \frac{1}{9}\right) - 1\frac{1}{2}$

24. $\left(\frac{1}{2} \times \frac{3}{4} + \frac{4}{5} \times \frac{5}{6}\right) - \left(\frac{1}{2} + 2\frac{7}{20}\right)$

3 OPERATIONS WITH EXPONENTS AND INTEGERS

An exponent is a notation that demonstrates the number of times a number or expression is multiplied by itself. It allows us to represent extremely large and extremely small numbers and perform arithmetic operations more easily than having to use the standard form of a number. For example, exponents are used in equations to calculate compound interest on loans and investments. Roots (or radicals) and exponents are the opposites of each other. If 3 raised to the power of 2 equals 9, then the square root of 9, $\sqrt{9}$, is 3. Fractional exponents simplify calculations involving radicals, such as square roots, cubic roots, etc. When we have expressions involving more than one operation, we follow rules for the operation, known as order of operations (BEDMAS). In this chapter, we will learn about the properties and rules associated with exponents, roots, fractional exponents, and signed numbers, perform calculations involving scientific notation, and round numbers using significant digits.

LEARNING OBJECTIVES

- Identify the types and properties of exponents.
- Perform arithmetic operations with exponents.
- Identify types of roots.
- Perform computations with roots and fractional exponents.
- Perform arithmetic operations with signed numbers.
- Apply rounding rules using significant digits.
- Perform calculations involving scientific notation.

CHAPTER OUTLINE

3.1 | Exponents

Introduction

In Section 1.4 (Chapter 1) and Section 2.5 (Chapter 2), you learned about powers and roots of whole numbers, fractions, and decimal numbers.

Recall that when a number is raised to a whole number exponent, we can think of it as a repeated multiplication. Power is a shorter way to indicate repeated multiplication, similar to how multiplication is a shorter way to indicate repeated addition. Powers are expressed using exponential notations.

For example, number 2 multiplied by itself 5 times, $2 \times 2 \times 2 \times 2 \times 2$, is written in exponential notation as $\mathbf{2^5}$:

2^5 ← exponent (5), base (2)

The whole representation, 2^5, is known as the power.

$$\underbrace{2^5}_{\text{Power using Exponents and Bases}} = \underbrace{2 \times 2 \times 2 \times 2 \times 2}_{\text{Repeated Multiplication}} = \underbrace{32}_{\text{Standard Notation}}$$

Similarly, the fraction $\left(\frac{4}{5}\right)$ multiplied by itself 4 times, $\left(\frac{4}{5}\right) \times \left(\frac{4}{5}\right) \times \left(\frac{4}{5}\right) \times \left(\frac{4}{5}\right)$, is written in exponential notation as $\left(\frac{4}{5}\right)^4$:

$\left(\frac{4}{5}\right)^4$ ← exponent (4), base $\left(\frac{4}{5}\right)$

The whole representation, $\left(\frac{4}{5}\right)^4$, is the power.

$$\left(\frac{4}{5}\right)^4 = \frac{4}{5} \times \frac{4}{5} \times \frac{4}{5} \times \frac{4}{5} = \frac{256}{625}$$

Similarily, the decimal number 1.2 multiplied by itself 3 times, $(1.2) \times (1.2) \times (1.2)$, is written in exponential notation as $(1.2)^3$:

$(1.2)^3$ ← exponent (3), base (1.2)

The whole representation, $(1.2)^3$, is the power.

$$(1.2)^3 = 1.2 \times 1.2 \times 1.2 = 1.728$$

Properties (Rules) of Exponents

The following properties of exponents, called the **rules** or **laws** of exponents, are used to simplify expressions that involve exponents.

Product of Powers (Product Rule)

When multiplying powers of the same bases, add the exponents.

To multiply powers with the same base, add their exponents.

For example, $7^5 \times 7^3$

$$= \underbrace{\underbrace{(7 \times 7 \times 7 \times 7 \times 7)}_{\text{5 Factors of 7}} \times \underbrace{(7 \times 7 \times 7)}_{\text{3 Factors of 7}}}_{\text{8 Factors of 7}}$$

$$= 7^{(5+3)} = 7^8 \quad \text{(Adding exponents)}$$

You will note that the resulting exponent, 8, is obtained by adding the exponents 5 and 3. That is, the exponents are added when powers with the same base are multiplied.

In general, for powers with base 'a' and exponents 'm' and 'n',

$$a^m \times a^n = a^{(m+n)}$$

Note: $a^m + a^n \neq a^{(m+n)}$

Example 3.1-a **Simplifying in Exponential Form Using the Product Rule**

Express the following as a single exponent:

(i) $2^3 \times 2^4 \times 2^2$ (ii) $\left(\frac{3}{5}\right)^6 \times \left(\frac{3}{5}\right)^2$ (iii) $(0.2)^3 \times (0.2)^2$

Solution

(i) $2^3 \times 2^4 \times 2^2$
$= 2^{(3+4+2)}$
$= 2^9$

(ii) $\left(\frac{3}{5}\right)^6 \times \left(\frac{3}{5}\right)^2$
$= \left(\frac{3}{5}\right)^{(6+2)} = \left(\frac{3}{5}\right)^8$

(iii) $(0.2)^3 \times (0.2)^2$
$= (0.2)^{(3+2)}$
$= (0.2)^5$

Quotient of Powers (Quotient Rule)

When dividing powers wtih the same bases, subtract the exponent of the denominator from that of the numerator.

To divide two powers with the same base, subtract their exponents.

For example, $4^7 \div 4^2 = \dfrac{\overbrace{4 \times 4 \times 4 \times 4 \times 4 \times 4 \times 4}^{\text{7 Factors of 4}}}{\underbrace{4 \times 4}_{\text{2 Factors of 4}}}$

$= \dfrac{4 \times 4}{4 \times 4} \times 4 \times 4 \times 4 \times 4 \times 4$

$= \underbrace{4 \times 4 \times 4 \times 4 \times 4}_{\text{5 Factors of 4}} = 4^{(7-2)} = 4^5$ (Subtracting exponents)

You will note that the resulting exponent, 5, can be obtained by subtracting the exponent of the denominator from the exponent of the numerator (7 – 2 = 5) since the powers have the same base.

In general, for any non-zero power with base 'a' and exponents 'm' and 'n',

$$\frac{a^m}{a^n} = a^{(m-n)}, \text{ where } a \neq 0$$

Note: am – an ≠ a(m – n)

Example 3.1-b **Simplifying in Exponential Form Using the Quotient Rule**

Express the following as a single exponent:

(i) $3^9 \div 3^5$ (ii) $\left(\frac{2}{3}\right)^6 \div \left(\frac{2}{3}\right)^4$ (iii) $(1.15)^5 \div (1.15)^2$

Solution

(i) $3^9 \div 3^5$
$= 3^{(9-5)}$
$= 3^4$

(ii) $\left(\frac{2}{3}\right)^6 \div \left(\frac{2}{3}\right)^4$
$= \left(\frac{2}{3}\right)^{(6-4)}$
$= \left(\frac{2}{3}\right)^2$

(iii) $(1.15)^5 \div (1.15)^2$
$= (1.15)^{(5-2)}$
$= (1.15)^3$

Power of a Product (Power of a Product Rule)

To find the **Power of a Product**, each factor of the product is raised to the indicated power.

For example, $(3 \times 5)^4 = (3 \times 5)\,(3 \times 5)\,(3 \times 5)\,(3 \times 5)$

$$= \underbrace{3 \times 3 \times 3 \times 3}_{\text{4 Factors of 3}} \times \underbrace{5 \times 5 \times 5 \times 5}_{\text{4 Factors of 5}}$$

$$= 3^4 \times 5^4$$

To raise the product of factors 'a' and 'b' to the power 'n', raise each factor to the nth power.

You will note from the result that each factor of the product is raised to the 4th power.

In general, if any product of numbers 'a' and 'b' are raised to a power 'n', then each number in the product is also raised to the same power,

$$(a \times b)^n = a^n \times b^n$$

Example 3.1-c **Simplifying in Exponential Form Using the Power of a Product Rule**

Express the following in expanded form using the Power of a Product Rule:

(i) $(8 \times 6)^3$ (ii) $\left(\frac{3}{5} \times \frac{2}{7}\right)^3$ (iii) $(1.12 \times 0.6)^3$

Solution

(i) $(8 \times 6)^3$
$= 8^3 \times 6^3$

(ii) $\left(\frac{3}{5} \times \frac{2}{7}\right)^3$
$= \left(\frac{3}{5}\right)^3 \times \left(\frac{2}{7}\right)^3$

(iii) $(1.12 \times 0.6)^3$
$= (1.12)^3 \times (0.6)^3$

Power of a Quotient (Power of a Quotient Rule)

This is similar to the power of a product rule. To find the **Power of a Quotient**, raise the numerator to the indicated power and divide by the denominator raised to the indicated power.

For example, $\left(\frac{5}{8}\right)^3 = \underbrace{\left(\frac{5}{8}\right) \times \left(\frac{5}{8}\right) \times \left(\frac{5}{8}\right)}_{\text{3 Factors of } \left(\frac{5}{8}\right)}$

$$= \frac{5 \times 5 \times 5}{8 \times 8 \times 8}$$ ← 3 factors of 5 (numerator); ← 3 factors of 8 (denominator)

$$= \frac{5^3}{8^3}$$

To raise a fraction to the power 'n', raise both the numerator and denominator to the nth power.

You will note from the result that the numerator and the denominator of the expression is raised to the power of 3.

In general, if any quotient with numerator 'a' and a non-zero denominator 'b' is raised to a power 'n', then the numerator 'a' and denominator 'b' are both raised to the same power,

$$\left(\frac{a}{b}\right)^n = \frac{a^n}{b^n}, \text{ where } b \neq 0$$

Example 3.1-d **Simplifying in Exponential Form Using Power of a Quotient Rule**

Express the following in expanded form using the Power of a Quotient Rule:

(i) $\left(\frac{7}{4}\right)^3$ (ii) $\left[\frac{\left(\frac{2}{3}\right)}{\left(\frac{3}{5}\right)}\right]^4$ (iii) $\left(\frac{1.05}{0.05}\right)^3$

Solution

(i) $\left(\frac{7}{4}\right)^3 = \frac{7^3}{4^3}$

(ii) $\left[\frac{\left(\frac{2}{3}\right)}{\left(\frac{3}{5}\right)}\right]^4 = \left(\frac{2}{3} \div \frac{3}{5}\right)^4 = \left(\frac{2}{3}\right)^4 \div \left(\frac{3}{5}\right)^4 = \frac{2^4}{3^4} \div \frac{3^4}{5^4}$

(iii) $\left(\frac{1.05}{0.05}\right)^3 = \frac{(1.05)^3}{(0.05)^3}$

Power of a Power (Power of a Power Rule)

To raise a power to a power, multiply the exponents.

In order to find the **Power of a Power** of a number, multiply the two exponents of the powers together to determine the new exponent of the power.

For example, $(9^3)^2$

$= (9^3) \times (9^3)$

$= (9 \times 9 \times 9) \times (9 \times 9 \times 9)$

$= 9 \times 9 \times 9 \times 9 \times 9 \times 9$

$= 9^6$, which is the same as $9^{(3 \times 2)}$

In general, to raise the power of a number, 'a' to a power 'm' and then to raise it to a power 'n' [i.e., $(a^m)^n$], raise the power of the number 'a' to the product of the power 'm' and 'n',

$$\boldsymbol{(a^m)^n = a^{mn}}$$

Example 3.1-e **Simplifying in Exponential Form Using Power of a Power Rule**

Solve the following:

(i) $(5^4)^3$ (ii) $\left[\left(\frac{3}{8}\right)^3\right]^2$ (iii) $[(1.04)^4]^2$

Solution

(i) $(5^4)^3 = 5^{(4 \times 3)} = 5^{12}$

(ii) $\left[\left(\frac{3}{8}\right)^3\right]^2 = \left(\frac{3}{8}\right)^{(3 \times 2)} = \left(\frac{3}{8}\right)^6 = \frac{3^6}{8^6}$

(iii) $[(1.04)^4]^2 = (1.04)^{(4 \times 2)} = (1.04)^8$

Example 3.1-f **Solving Expressions Using Power of a Power Rule, Product Rule, and Quotient Rule**

Solve the following:

(i) $(2^2)^3 \times 2^7 \div 2^9$ (ii) $7^5 \div (7^3)^2 \times 7^2$

Solution

(i) $(2^2)^3 \times 2^7 \div 2^9$

$= 2^6 \times 2^7 \div 2^9$

$= 2^{(6 + 7 - 9)}$

$= 2^4$

$= 16$

(ii) $7^5 \div (7^3)^2 \times 7^2$

$= 7^5 \div 7^6 \times 7^2$

$= 7^{(5 - 6 + 2)}$

$= 7^1$

$= 7$

Table 3.1-a summarizes the properties (rules) of exponents.

Table 3.1-a **Properties (Rules) of Exponents**

Property (Rule)	Rule in Exponential Form	Example
Product Rule	$a^m \times a^n = a^{(m+n)}$	$3^5 \times 3^4 = 3^{(5+4)} = 3^9$
Quotient Rule	$\frac{a^m}{a^n} = a^{(m-n)}$	$\frac{3^7}{3^4} = 3^{(7-4)} = 3^3$
Power of a Product Rule	$(a \times b)^n = a^n \times b^n$	$(3 \times 5)^2 = 3^2 \times 5^2$
Power of a Quotient Rule	$\left(\frac{a}{b}\right)^n = \frac{a^n}{b^n}$	$\left(\frac{3}{5}\right)^3 = \frac{3^3}{5^3}$
Power of a Power Rule	$(a^m)^n = a^{(m \times n)}$	$(3^2)^3 = 3^{2 \times 3} = 3^6$

Properties of Exponents and Bases of One and Zero

Table 3.1-b explains the properties of exponents and bases of one and zero.

Table 3.1-b **Exponents and Bases of One (1) and Zero (0)**

Property (Rule)	Description	Rule in Exponential Form	Example
Base 'a' Exponent 1	Any number of base 'a' raised to the exponent '1' equals the number itself.	$a^1 = a$	$8^1 = 8$
Base 'a' Exponent 0	Any non-zero number of base 'a' raised to the exponent '0' equals 1.	$a^0 = 1$	$8^0 = 1$
Base '1' Exponent 'n'	A base of '1' raised to any exponent 'n' equals 1.	$1^n = 1$	$1^5 = 1$
Base '0' Exponent 'n'	A base of '0' raised to any positive exponent 'n' equals 0.	$0^n = 0$	$0^5 = 0$
Base '0' Exponent '0'	A base of '0' raised to the exponent '0' is indeterminate (∞).	0^0 = indeterminate	0^0 = indeterminate

For Addition or Subtraction of Powers, there is no special rule for exponents with either the same or different bases. Evaluate each operation separately and then perform the addition or subtraction.

For example,

Addition of exponential expressions with the same base:

(i) $2^3 + 2^4$ Evaluating 2^3 and 2^4 separately, and then adding,

$= 8 + 16 = 24$

Addition of exponential expressions with different bases:

(ii) $2^2 + 3^3$ Evaluating 2^3 and 3^3 separately, and then adding,

$= 4 + 27 = 31$

Subtraction of exponential expressions with the same base:

(iii) $5^3 - 5^2$ Evaluating 5^3 and 5^2 separately, and then subtracting,

$= 125 - 25 = 100$

Subtraction of exponential expressions with different bases:

(iv) $4^3 - 2^3$ Evaluating 4^3 and 2^3 separately, and then subtracting,

$= 64 - 8 = 56$

There is also no special rule for the **product or quotient of powers having exponents of different bases.** Evaluate each operation separately and then perform the multipication or division.

For example,

Product of exponential expressions with different bases:

(i) $2^4 \times 3^2$ Evaluating 2^4 and 3^2 separately, and then multiplying,

$= 16 \times 9 = 144$

Quotient of exponential expressions with different bases:

(ii) $\frac{3^3}{2^4}$ Evaluating 3^3 and 2^4 separately, and then dividing,

$= \frac{27}{16} = 1.6875$

Example 3.1-g **Adding and Subtracting Powers**

Evaluate the following:

(i) $3^3 + 3^2$ (ii) $5^2 + 3^2$ (iii) $5^4 - 5^2$ (iv) $6^2 - 4^2$

Solution

(i) $3^3 + 3^2$

$= 27 + 9$

$= 36$

Note: $a^m + a^n \neq a^{(m+n)}$

$3^3 + 3^2 \neq 3^{(3+2)} \neq 3^5$

(ii) $5^2 + 3^2$

$= 25 + 9$

$= 34$

Note: $a^m + b^m \neq (a+b)^m$

$5^2 + 3^2 \neq (5+3)^2$

(iii) $5^4 - 5^2$

$= 625 - 25$

$= 600$

Note: $a^m - a^n \neq a^{(m-n)}$

$5^4 - 5^2 \neq (5)^{(4-2)}$

(iv) $6^2 - 4^2$

$= 36 - 16$

$= 20$

Note: $a^m - b^m \neq (a-b)^m$

$6^2 - 4^2 \neq (6-4)^2$

Example 3.1-h **Multiplying and Dividing Powers that have Exponents with Different Bases**

Evaluate the following:

(i) $5^3 \times 4^2$ (ii) $5^3 \div 3^2$ (iii) $9^2 \times 5^1$ (iv) $4^2 \times 5^0$

Solution

(i) $5^3 \times 4^2$

$= 125 \times 16$

$= 2{,}000$

(ii) $5^3 \div 3^2$

$= 125 \div 9$

$= \frac{125}{9}$

$= 13\frac{8}{9}$

(iii) $9^2 \times 5^1$

$= 81 \times 5$

$= 405$

(iv) $4^2 \times 5^0$

$= 16 \times 1$

$= 16$

Calculator Method for Solving Expressions with Exponents

The exponent key on different calculators can be identified by symbols such as [∧], [y^x], [x^y], etc.

In the following examples, '[∧]' will be used to to represent the exponential key.

Example 3.1-i **Solving Exponential Expressions**

Calculate: (i) 5^6 (ii) $\left(\frac{3}{2}\right)^3$ (iii) $(1.02)^4$

Solution

(i) 5^6

[5] [∧] [6] [=] 15625

↑ Exponent key

(ii) $\left(\frac{3}{2}\right)^3$

[3] [÷] [2] [=] [∧] [3] [=] 3.375

↑ Exponent key

(iii) $(1.02)^4$

[1.02] [∧] [4] [=] 1.082432

↑ Exponent key

3.1 | Exercises

Answers to odd-numbered problems are available at the end of the textbook.

For Problems 1 and 2, find the missing values.

1.

	Repeated Multiplication	Base	Exponent	Power (Exponential Notation)
a.	$7 \times 7 \times 7 \times 7$			
b.				9^5
c.		3	4	
d.	$\frac{2}{5} \times \frac{2}{5} \times \frac{2}{5} \times \frac{2}{5} \times \frac{2}{5} \times \frac{2}{5}$			
e.				$\left(\frac{5}{7}\right)^5$
f.		$\left(\frac{4}{7}\right)$	3	
g.	$(1.15) \times (1.15) \times (1.15) \times (1.15)$			
h.				$(1.6)^3$
i.		(1.25)	5	

2.

	Repeated Multiplication	Base	Exponent	Power (Exponential Notation)
a.	$2 \times 2 \times 2 \times 2 \times 2 \times 2 \times 2 \times 2$			
b.				6^7
c.		5	3	
d.	$\frac{2}{7} \times \frac{2}{7} \times \frac{2}{7} \times \frac{2}{7} \times \frac{2}{7}$			
e.				$\left(\frac{3}{8}\right)^4$
f.		$\left(\frac{2}{9}\right)$	4	
g.	$(2.5) \times (2.5) \times (2.5) \times (2.5) \times (2.5)$			
h.				$(1.1)^5$
i.		(0.75)	4	

Express Problems 3 to 22 as a single exponent and then evaluate using a calculator. Round the answer to two decimal places, wherever applicable.

3. $4^3 \times 4^6$
4. $5^5 \times 5^6$
5. $\left(\frac{1}{2}\right)^4 \left(\frac{1}{2}\right)^3$
6. $\left(\frac{2}{3}\right)^2 \left(\frac{2}{3}\right)^3$
7. $\left(\frac{5}{2}\right)^2 \left(\frac{5}{2}\right)^3$
8. $\left(\frac{5}{3}\right)^3 \left(\frac{5}{3}\right)^2$
9. $(3.25)^4 (3.25)^2$
10. $(0.75)^3 (0.75)^4$
11. $6^8 \div 6^3$
12. $3^7 \div 3^5$
13. $\left(\frac{2}{5}\right)^3 \div \left(\frac{2}{5}\right)^1$
14. $\left(\frac{3}{2}\right)^4 \div \left(\frac{3}{2}\right)^3$
15. $(1.4)^5 \div (1.4)^2$
16. $(3.25)^6 \div (3.25)^5$
17. $[(6)^2]^3$
18. $[(5)^3]^2$
19. $\left[\left(\frac{2}{3}\right)^4\right]^3$
20. $\left[\left(\frac{3}{4}\right)^4\right]^2$
21. $[(2.5)^2]^3$
22. $[(1.03)^3]^2$

Express Problems 23 to 34 as a power of the indicated base value.

23. 4^5 as a power of 2
24. 9^6 as a power of 3
25. $9(27)^2$ as a power of 3
26. $8(16)^2$ as a power of 2
27. $\frac{3^9 \times 3^2}{3^5}$ as a power of 3
28. $\frac{2^9 \times 2^1}{2^5}$ as a power of 2
29. $\frac{(2^5)^4}{4^6}$ as a power of 2
30. $\frac{(2^5)^4}{16^3}$ as a power of 2
31. $\frac{10^6}{10^0}$ as a power of 10
32. $\frac{3^7}{27}$ as a power of 3
33. $\frac{8^5}{8^3}$ as a power of 2
34. $\frac{5^6}{125}$ as a power of 5

Evaluate Problems 35 to 70.

35. $5^2 + 5^3$
36. $4^3 + 4^2$
37. $5^4 - 2^4$
38. $6^3 - 4^3$
39. $4^4 - 4^2$
40. $6^3 - 6^1$
41. $7^2 + 3^2$
42. $8^3 + 2^3$
43. $3^5 + 5^3$
44. $4^3 + 3^4$
45. $2^5 - 5^2$
46. $2^6 - 6^2$
47. $5^4 - 4^2$
48. $10^3 - 7^2$
49. $4^0 + 4^4$
50. $3^0 + 3^4$
51. $(5 \times 4)^3$
52. $(10 \times 2)^4$
53. $(1.25 \times 4)^4$
54. $(5 \times 0.8)^3$
55. $\left(\frac{2}{3} + 6\right)^5$
56. $\left(\frac{3}{5} + \frac{15}{15}\right)^3$
57. $3^4 + 3^2 + 3^0$
58. $4^2 + 4^4 + 4^0$
59. $2^4 + 3^4 - 1^4$
60. $3^3 + 2^3 - 1^3$
61. $\left(\frac{1}{2}\right)^3 + \left(\frac{1}{2}\right)^2 + \left(\frac{1}{2}\right)^0$
62. $\left(\frac{1}{5}\right)^2 + \left(\frac{1}{5}\right)^0 + \left(\frac{1}{5}\right)^4$
63. $(2.1)^2 + (2.1)^0$
64. $(3.2)^2 + (3.2)^1$
65. $4^3 \times 3^4$
66. $7^2 \times 2^2$
67. $6^4 \div 5^4$
68. $8^2 \div 7^2$
69. $(2 \times 3^2)^4$
70. $(5 \times 2^2)^3$

3.2 | Roots and Fractional Exponents

Roots

Roots are the inverse of exponents.

For example, the square of 2 (or raising 2 to the exponent 2) is 4; i.e., $2^2 = 4$. The inverse of squaring a number is finding the square root of that number. Therefore, the square root of 4 is 2.

Similarly, the square of 3 is 9; i.e., $3^2 = 9$. Therefore, the square root of 9 is 3.

Two types of notations may be used to represent the above. One is using the symbol '$\sqrt{\ }$', which represents a radical. The other is using fractional exponents.

For example, the square root of 9 can be represented as $\sqrt{9}$ in radical form, or as $9^{\frac{1}{2}}$ in fractional exponent form.

Square root of $9 = \sqrt{9} = 9^{\frac{1}{2}}$

We know that $9 = 3 \times 3 = 3^2$ Therefore, the square root (2nd root) of 9 is 3.

Similarly, $8 = 2 \times 2 \times 2 = 2^3$ Therefore, the cube root (3rd root) of 8 is 2.

$16 = 2 \times 2 \times 2 \times 2 = 2^4$ Therefore, the 4th root of 16 is 2.

A radical is an indicated root of a number (or expression).

$\sqrt[2]{9}$ indicates the 2nd root (square root) of 9. For square roots, the index 2 does not need to be written as it is understood to be there, i.e., $\sqrt[2]{9} = \sqrt{9}$.

$\sqrt[3]{8}$ indicates the 3rd root (cube root) of 8.

$\sqrt[4]{16}$ indicates the 4th root of 16.

$\sqrt[n]{a}$ refers to the nth root of a.

Radical sign

Index of the root → $\sqrt[n]{a}$ ← 'a' represents any positive number

The index is written as a small number on the left of the radical symbol. It indicates which root is to be taken. $\sqrt[3]{125}$ indicates the 3rd root or cube root of 125.

Perfect Roots

Roots of a whole number may not always be a whole number. A whole number is a perfect root if its root is also a whole number.

For example,

4 is a perfect square root of 16 because $4^2 = 16$; i.e., $\sqrt{16} = 4$

3 is a perfect cube root of 27 because $3^3 = 27$; i.e., $\sqrt[3]{27} = 3$

Table 3.2 **Examples of Perfect Roots**

Roots	1	2	3	4	5	6	7	8	9	10
Square Roots	$\sqrt{1}$	$\sqrt{4}$	$\sqrt{9}$	$\sqrt{16}$	$\sqrt{25}$	$\sqrt{36}$	$\sqrt{49}$	$\sqrt{64}$	$\sqrt{81}$	$\sqrt{100}$
Cube Roots	$\sqrt[3]{1}$	$\sqrt[3]{8}$	$\sqrt[3]{27}$	$\sqrt[3]{64}$	$\sqrt[3]{125}$	$\sqrt[3]{216}$	$\sqrt[3]{343}$	$\sqrt[3]{512}$	$\sqrt[3]{729}$	$\sqrt[3]{1{,}000}$
Fourth Roots	$\sqrt[4]{1}$	$\sqrt[4]{16}$	$\sqrt[4]{81}$	$\sqrt[4]{256}$	$\sqrt[4]{625}$	$\sqrt[4]{1{,}296}$	$\sqrt[4]{2{,}401}$	$\sqrt[4]{4{,}096}$	$\sqrt[4]{6{,}561}$	$\sqrt[4]{10{,}000}$

The Product Rule and the knowledge of Perfect Roots are used in simplifying square roots, cube roots, etc.

For Example,

(i) To simplify $\sqrt{12}$, 12 may be written as 4 × 3, a combination of two factors, where one of the factors, 4, is a perfect square.

i.e., $\sqrt{12} = \sqrt{4} \times \sqrt{3} = 2\sqrt{3}$

(ii) To simplify $\sqrt[3]{54}$, may be written as 54 as 27 × 2, a combination of two factors, where one of the factors, 27, is a perfect cube of 3.

i.e., $\sqrt[3]{54} = \sqrt[3]{27} \times (\sqrt[3]{2}) = 3(\sqrt[3]{2})$

Example 3.2-a

Finding Perfect Roots

Simplify using perfect roots of a number:

(i) $\sqrt{72}$ (ii) $\sqrt[3]{40}$

Solution

(i) $\sqrt{72}$

$= \sqrt{36} \times \sqrt{2}$ $72 = 36 \times 2$

$= 6\sqrt{2}$ 36 is a perfect square of 6.

(ii) $\sqrt[3]{40}$

$= \sqrt[3]{8} \times (\sqrt[3]{5})$ $40 = 8 \times 5$

$= 2(\sqrt[3]{5})$ 8 is a perfect cube of 2.

Fractional Exponents

Fractional exponents are easier to write than radical notations. As explained earlier, **square (or 2nd) root** is written as the power '$\frac{1}{2}$' in fractional exponent notation.

For example, $\sqrt{5} = 5^{\frac{1}{2}}$

Cube (or 3rd) root is written as the power '$\frac{1}{3}$' in fractional exponent notation.

For example, $\sqrt[3]{8} = 8^{\frac{1}{3}}$

The **fourth (4th) root** is written as the power '$\frac{1}{4}$' in fractional exponent notation.

For example, $\sqrt[4]{5^3} = (5^3)^{\frac{1}{4}} = 5^{\frac{3}{4}}$

An appropriate radical will "undo" an exponent.

For example,

$\sqrt{5^2} = (5^2)^{\frac{1}{2}} = 5$

$\sqrt[3]{7^3} = (7^3)^{\frac{1}{3}} = 7$

When entering a fractional exponents in a calculator, **brackets** must be used.

For example,

In order to evaluate $25^{\frac{2}{5}}$ brackets around $\frac{2}{5}$ must be used.

To evalute $25^{\frac{2}{5}}$ using a calculator, enter it as follows: it would be entered as;

Without the brackets, the operation will mean $(25)^2 \div 5$, which is incorrect.

Example 3.2-b

Evaluating Expressions with Fractional Exponents Using a Calculator

Solve the following:

(i) $15^{\frac{3}{2}}$ (ii) $\left(\frac{3}{5}\right)^{\frac{1}{4}}$ (iii) $(2.5)^{\frac{3}{7}}$

Solution

(i) $15^{\frac{3}{2}} =$ 15 ^ (3 ÷ 2) =

58.094750... $= 58.09$

(ii) $\left(\frac{3}{5}\right)^{\frac{1}{4}} =$ (3 ÷ 5) ^ (1 ÷ 4) =

0.880111... $= 0.88$

(iii) $(2.5)^{\frac{3}{7}} =$ (2.5) ^ (3 ÷ 7) =

1.480968... $= 1.48$

Arithmetic Operations with Fractional Exponents

All the rules of exponents Product Rule, Quotient Rule, Power of a Product Rule, Power of a Quotient Rule, Power of a Power Rule, etc. learned in Section 3.1 and as outlined in Table 3.1-a and Table 3.1-b are applicable to fractional exponents.

Example 3.2-c

Solving Expressions with Fractional Exponents Using the Product Rule

Simplify the following using the Product Rule to express in exponential form and then evaluate to two decimal places:

(i) $2^{\frac{1}{2}} \times 2^{\frac{1}{3}}$ (ii) $3^{\frac{3}{4}} \times 3^{\frac{9}{4}} \times 3^{0}$ (iii) $\left(\frac{3}{5}\right)^{\frac{7}{3}} \times \left(\frac{3}{5}\right)^{\frac{2}{3}}$

Solution

(i) $2^{\frac{1}{2}} \times 2^{\frac{1}{3}}$

$= 2^{\left(\frac{1}{2} + \frac{1}{3}\right)}$

$= 2^{\left(\frac{3+2}{6}\right)}$

$= 2^{\frac{5}{6}}$

$= 1.781797... = 1.78$

(ii) $3^{\frac{3}{4}} \times 3^{\frac{9}{4}} \times 3^{0}$

$= 3^{\left(\frac{3}{4} + \frac{9}{4} + 0\right)}$

$= 3^{\frac{12}{4}}$

$= 3^{3}$

$= 27.00$

(iii) $\left(\frac{3}{5}\right)^{\frac{7}{3}} \times \left(\frac{3}{5}\right)^{\frac{2}{3}}$

$= \left(\frac{3}{5}\right)^{\left(\frac{7+2}{3}\right)}$

$= \left(\frac{3}{5}\right)^{\frac{9}{3}}$

$= \left(\frac{3}{5}\right)^{3}$

$= 0.216 = 0.22$

Example 3.2-d

Solving Expressions with Fractional Exponents Using the Quotient Rule

Simplify the following using the Quotient Rule to express the answer in exponential form and then evaluate to two decimal places:

(i) $2^{\frac{4}{3}} \div 2^{\frac{2}{3}}$ (ii) $(1.2)^{\frac{5}{2}} \div (1.2)^{\frac{1}{2}}$ (iii) $\left(\frac{1}{3}\right)^{\frac{6}{4}} \div \left(\frac{1}{3}\right)^{\frac{3}{4}}$

Solution

(i) $2^{\frac{4}{3}} \div 2^{\frac{2}{3}}$

$= 2^{\left(\frac{4}{3} - \frac{2}{3}\right)}$

$= 2^{\left(\frac{4-2}{3}\right)}$

$= 2^{\frac{2}{3}}$

$= 1.587401... = 1.59$

(ii) $(1.2)^{\frac{5}{2}} \div (1.2)^{\frac{1}{2}}$

$(1.2)^{\left(\frac{5}{2} - \frac{1}{2}\right)}$

$= (1.2)^{\frac{4}{2}}$

$= (1.2)^2$

$= 1.44$

(iii) $\left(\frac{1}{3}\right)^{\frac{6}{4}} \div \left(\frac{1}{3}\right)^{\frac{3}{4}}$

$= \left(\frac{1}{3}\right)^{\left(\frac{6-3}{4}\right)}$

$= \left(\frac{1}{3}\right)^{\frac{3}{4}}$

$= 0.438691... = 0.44$

Example 3.2-e

Solving Expressions with Fractional Exponents Using the Power of a Product Rule

Simplify the following using the Power of a Product Rule to express the answer in exponential form and then evaluate to two decimal places:

(i) $(4^2 \times 3^2)^{\frac{1}{2}}$ (ii) $\left(7^2 \times \frac{1}{3^2}\right)^{\frac{1}{2}}$ (iii) $(2^6 \times 3^2)^{\frac{3}{2}}$

Solution

(i) $(4^2 \times 3^2)^{\frac{1}{2}}$

$= (4^2)^{\frac{1}{2}} \times (3^2)^{\frac{1}{2}}$

$= 4 \times 3$

$= 12.00$

(ii) $\left(7^2 \times \frac{1}{3^2}\right)^{\frac{1}{2}}$

$= \frac{(7^2)^{\frac{1}{2}}}{(3^2)^{\frac{1}{2}}}$

$= \frac{7}{3}$

$= 2.333333... = 2.33$

(iii) $(2^6 \times 3^2)^{\frac{3}{2}}$

$= (2^6)^{\frac{3}{2}} \times (3^2)^{\frac{3}{2}}$

$= 2^9 \times 3^3$

$= 512 \times 27$

$= 13{,}824.00$

Example 3.2-f

Solving Expressions with Fractional Exponents Using the Power of a Quotient Rule

Simplify the following using the Power of a Quotient Rule to express the answer in exponential form and then evaluate to two decimal places:

(i) $\left(\frac{4^2}{3^2}\right)^{\frac{1}{2}}$ (ii) $\left(\frac{5^3}{2^6}\right)^{\frac{1}{3}}$

Solution

(i) $\left(\frac{4^2}{3^2}\right)^{\frac{1}{2}}$

$= \frac{(4^2)^{\frac{1}{2}}}{(3^2)^{\frac{1}{2}}}$

$= \frac{4}{3}$

$= 1.333333... = 1.33$

(ii) $\left(\frac{5^3}{2^6}\right)^{\frac{1}{3}}$

$= \frac{5}{2^2}$

$= \frac{5}{4}$

$= 1.25$

Example 3.2-g

Solving Expressions with Fractional Exponents Using the Power of a Power Rule

Simplify the following using the Power of a Power Rule to express the answer in exponential form and then evaluate to two decimal places:

(i) $\left(6^{\frac{1}{2}}\right)^3$ (ii) $\left(18^{\frac{1}{3}}\right)^{\frac{1}{4}}$ (iii) $\left[\left(\frac{2}{3}\right)^3\right]^2$

Solution

(i) $\left(6^{\frac{1}{2}}\right)^3$

$= 6^{\left(\frac{1}{2}\times 3\right)}$

$= 6^{\frac{3}{2}}$

$= 14.696938...$

$= 14.70$

(ii) $\left(18^{\frac{1}{3}}\right)^{\frac{1}{4}}$

$= 18^{\left(\frac{1}{3}\times\frac{1}{4}\right)}$

$= 18^{\frac{1}{12}}$

$= 1.272348...$

$= 1.27$

(iii) $\left[\left(\frac{2}{3}\right)^3\right]^2$

$= \left(\frac{2}{3}\right)^{3\times 2}$

$= \left(\frac{2}{3}\right)^6$

$= \frac{2^6}{3^6}$

$= \frac{64}{729}$

$= 0.087791... = 0.09$

Example 3.2-h

Expressions in Radical Form

Express the following in radical form:

(i) $2^{\frac{5}{6}}$ (ii) $3^{\frac{2}{5}}$ (iii) $\left(\frac{2}{3}\right)^{\frac{3}{4}}$

Solution

(i) $2^{\frac{5}{6}}$

$= \sqrt[6]{2^5}$

(ii) $3^{\frac{2}{5}}$

$= \sqrt[5]{3^2}$

(iii) $\left(\frac{2}{3}\right)^{\frac{3}{4}}$

$= \sqrt[4]{\left(\frac{2}{3}\right)^3}$

Example 3.2-i

Solving Expressions with Fractional Exponents and Different Bases

Solve the following to two decimal places:

(i) $16^{\frac{1}{2}} + 8^{\frac{1}{2}}$ (ii) $25^{\frac{1}{2}} - 27^{\frac{1}{3}}$ (iii) $\left(\frac{7}{8}\right)^{\frac{1}{4}} - \left(\frac{2}{3}\right)^{\frac{1}{3}}$

(iv) $(5)^{\frac{1}{2}} \times (3)^{\frac{1}{2}}$ (v) $(2)^{\frac{3}{4}} \div (3)^{\frac{1}{2}}$ (vi) $5^{\left(2\frac{3}{4}\right)}$

Solution

(i) $16^{\frac{1}{2}} + 8^{\frac{1}{2}}$

$= 4 + 2.828427...$

$= 6.828427...$

$= 6.83$

(ii) $25^{\frac{1}{2}} - 27^{\frac{1}{3}}$

$= 5 - 3$

$= 2.00$

(iii) $\left(\frac{7}{8}\right)^{\frac{1}{4}} - \left(\frac{2}{3}\right)^{\frac{1}{3}}$

$= 0.967168... - 0.873580...$

$= 0.093587...$

$= 0.09$

(iv) $(5)^{\frac{1}{2}} \times (3)^{\frac{1}{2}}$

$= 2.236067... \times 1.732050...$

$= 3.872983...$

$= 3.87$

(v) $(2)^{\frac{3}{4}} \div (3)^{\frac{1}{2}}$

$= 1.681792... \div 1.732050...$

$= 0.970983...$

$= 0.97$

(vi) $5^{\left(2\frac{3}{4}\right)}$

$= 5^{\frac{11}{4}}$

$= 83.592538...$

$= 83.59$

Negative Exponents

In the exponential notation of a number, the base of the number may be raised to a negative exponent. When the exponent is negative, it is represented by a^{-n}. The negative exponent is the reciprocal of a positive exponent.

Positive Exponent: $a^n = a \times a \times a \times a \times a \times \ldots \times a$ (multiplication of 'n' factors of 'a')

Negative Exponent: $a^{-n} = \dfrac{1}{a^n} = \dfrac{1}{a \times a \times a \times a \times a \times \ldots \times a}$ (division of 'n' factors of 'a')

$$a^{-n} = \frac{1}{a^n},$$

$$\text{or } \frac{1}{a^{-n}} = a^n$$

Therefore, a^n and a^{-n} are reciprocals.

The properties (rules) of exponents in Section 3.1 of this chapter (summarized in Table 3.1-a) also apply to all negative exponents.

We use these properties to simplify negative exponents and then convert negative exponents to positive exponents.

Example 3.2-j **Using Properties of Exponents to Simplify Negative Exponents**

Simplify the following and express the answer with positive exponents (do not evaluate):

(i) $2^{-2} \times 2^{-3}$ (ii) $\dfrac{3^{-4}}{3^{-2}}$ (iii) $(3 \times 5)^{-2}$ (iv) $(3^{-2})^3$

Solution

(i) $2^{-2} \times 2^{-3}$ Using Product Rule,

$= 2^{-2+(-3)}$

$= 2^{-2-3}$

$= 2^{-5}$ Using Negative Exponent Rule,

$= \dfrac{1}{2^5}$

(ii) $\dfrac{3^{-4}}{3^{-2}}$ Using Quotient Rule,

$= 3^{-4-(-2)}$

$= 3^{-4+2}$

$= 3^{-2}$ Using Negative Exponent Rule,

$= \dfrac{1}{3^2}$

(iii) $(3 \times 5)^{-2}$ Using Power of a Product Rule,

$= 3^{-2} \times 5^{-2}$ Using Negative Exponent Rule,

$= \dfrac{1}{3^2} \times \dfrac{1}{5^2}$

(iv) $(3^{-2})^3$ Using Power of a Power Rule,

$= 3^{-2(3)}$

$= \dfrac{5^4}{3^4}$

$= 3^{-6}$ Using Negative Exponent Rule,

$= \dfrac{1}{3^6}$

Repeated Multiplication		Positive Exponential Notation
$5 \times 5 \times 5 \times 5$	=	5^4
$5 \times 5 \times 5$	=	5^3
5×5	=	5^2
5	=	5^1
1	=	5^0

Factors are divided by 5

If this pattern is continued further...

Exponents are reduced by 1

Repeated Division		Negative Exponential Notation
$\frac{1}{5}$	=	5^{-1}
$\frac{1}{5 \times 5}$	=	5^{-2}
$\frac{1}{5 \times 5 \times 5}$	=	5^{-3}

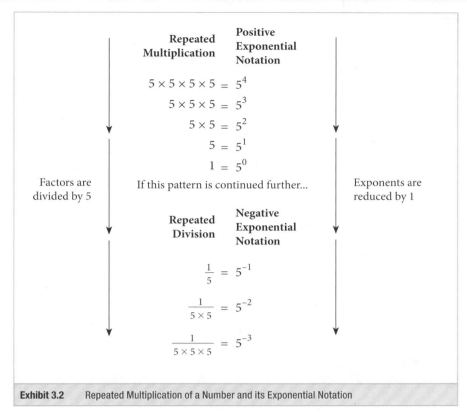

Exhibit 3.2 Repeated Multiplication of a Number and its Exponential Notation

Any positive number base with a negative exponent will always result in a positive answer. For example,

Negative Exponential Notation	Positive Exponential Notation	Repeated Division	Standard Notation
5^{-1}	$\frac{1}{5^1}$	$\frac{1}{5}$	$\frac{1}{5}$
5^{-2}	$\frac{1}{5^2}$	$\frac{1}{5 \times 5}$	$\frac{1}{25}$
5^{-3}	$\frac{1}{5^3}$	$\frac{1}{5 \times 5 \times 5}$	$\frac{1}{125}$

Fractions with Negative Exponents

When a fraction has a negative exponent, change the fraction to its reciprocal and drop the sign of the exponent. After this change, the number in the exponent indicates the number of times the numerator and denominator should be multiplied.

$$\left(\frac{a}{b}\right)^{-n} = \left(\frac{b}{a}\right)^{n}$$

For example,

$$\left(\frac{2}{5}\right)^{-3} = \left(\frac{5}{2}\right)^{3} = \left(\frac{5}{2}\right)\left(\frac{5}{2}\right)\left(\frac{5}{2}\right) = \frac{5 \times 5 \times 5}{2 \times 2 \times 2} = \frac{125}{8}$$

Note: The reciprocal of $\frac{2}{5}$ *is* $\frac{5}{2}$.

Example 3.2-k **Solving Fractions with Negative Exponents**

Solve the following: (i) $\left(\frac{5}{4}\right)^{-2} \times \left(\frac{2}{3}\right)^{-3}$ (ii) $\left(\frac{3}{5}\right)^{-3} \div \left(\frac{2}{75}\right)^{-2}$

Solution

(i) $\left(\frac{5}{4}\right)^{-2} \times \left(\frac{2}{3}\right)^{-3}$

$= \left(\frac{4}{5}\right)^{2} \times \left(\frac{3}{2}\right)^{3}$

$= \frac{4^2}{5^2} \times \frac{3^3}{2^3}$

$= \frac{16}{25} \times \frac{27}{8}$

$= \frac{2}{25} \times \frac{27}{1}$

$= \frac{54}{25}$

$= 2\frac{4}{25} = 2.16$

(ii) $\left(\frac{3}{5}\right)^{-3} \div \left(\frac{2}{75}\right)^{-2}$

$= \left(\frac{3}{5}\right)^{-3} \times \left(\frac{75}{2}\right)^{-2}$

$= \left(\frac{3}{5}\right)^{-3} \times \left(\frac{2}{75}\right)^{2}$

$= \frac{3^3}{5^3} \times \frac{2^3}{75^3}$

$= \frac{125}{27} \times \frac{4}{25}$

$= \frac{5}{27} \times \frac{4}{25}$

$= \frac{20}{27}$

3.2 | Exercises

Answers to odd-numbered problems are available at the end of the textbook.

Express Problems 1 to 4 in their radical form and evaluate.

1. a. $64^{\frac{1}{2}}$ b. $\left(\frac{25}{16}\right)^{\frac{1}{2}}$
2. a. $81^{\frac{1}{2}}$ b. $\left(\frac{8}{25}\right)^{\frac{1}{2}}$
3. a. $8^{\frac{1}{3}}$ b. $\left(\frac{27}{64}\right)^{\frac{1}{3}}$
4. a. $64^{\frac{1}{3}}$ b. $\left(\frac{125}{8}\right)^{\frac{1}{3}}$

Express Problems 5 to 14 in their fractional exponent form and then evaluate and round the answers to two decimal places wherever applicable.

5. a. $\sqrt{144}$ b. $\sqrt[3]{64}$
6. a. $\sqrt{81}$ b. $\sqrt[3]{125}$
7. a. $\sqrt{2^6}$ b. $\sqrt{40}$
8. a. $\sqrt{3^4}$ b. $\sqrt{50}$
9. a. $\sqrt{8} \times \sqrt{12}$ b. $\sqrt{7} \times \sqrt{14}$
10. a. $\sqrt{12} \times \sqrt{10}$ b. $\sqrt{9} \times \sqrt{27}$
11. a. $\sqrt[4]{25^2 \times 25^2}$ b. $\sqrt[4]{5^2 \times 25^3}$
12. a. $\sqrt[2]{3^4 \times 2^4}$ b. $\sqrt[6]{9^3 \times 27^4}$
13. a. $\sqrt{\frac{25}{49}}$ b. $\sqrt{\frac{64}{9}}$
14. a. $\sqrt{\frac{36}{64}}$ b. $\sqrt{\frac{24}{6}}$

Simplify Problems 15 to 24 by expressing them as single exponents (using the properties of exponents) and then evaluate and round the answers to two decimal places, wherever applicable.

15. a. $5^{\frac{1}{2}} \times 5^{\frac{3}{4}}$ b. $3^{\frac{7}{8}} \times 3^{\frac{5}{9}}$
16. a. $3^{\frac{1}{2}} \times 3^{\frac{1}{4}}$ b. $11^{\frac{3}{4}} \times 11^{\frac{2}{3}}$
17. a. $8^{\frac{4}{5}} \times 8^{\frac{2}{5}} \times 8^{\frac{1}{5}}$ b. $5^{\frac{1}{3}} \times 5^{\frac{1}{2}} \times 5^{0}$
18. a. $5^{\frac{4}{7}} \times 5^{\frac{4}{7}} \times 5^{\frac{6}{7}}$ b. $9^{\frac{5}{8}} \times 9^{\frac{2}{3}} \times 9^{0}$
19. a. $8^{\frac{1}{3}} \times 8^{\frac{2}{3}} \times 8^{1}$ b. $\frac{3^{\frac{8}{3}}}{3^{2}}$
20. a. $2^{\frac{2}{3}} \times 2^{\frac{1}{2}} \times 2^{1}$ b. $\frac{6^{\frac{7}{2}}}{6^{2}}$
21. a. $\frac{4^{\frac{5}{7}}}{4^{\frac{2}{7}}}$ b. $\left(3^{2}\right)^{\frac{1}{3}}$
22. a. $\frac{2^{\frac{4}{5}}}{2^{\frac{3}{5}}}$ b. $(10^3)^0$

23. a. $\left(12^{\frac{1}{2}}\right)^4$ b. $\left(7^{\frac{1}{4}}\right)^8$ 24. a. $\left(5^{\frac{2}{3}}\right)^6$ b. $\left(4^{\frac{2}{3}}\right)^6$

Evaluate Problems 25 to 32 and express the answers rounded to two decimal places wherever applicable.

25. a. $5^{\frac{1}{2}} + 7^{\frac{1}{2}}$ b. $16^{\frac{1}{2}} - 9^{\frac{1}{2}}$ 26. a. $125^{\frac{1}{3}} + 64^{\frac{1}{3}}$ b. $50^{\frac{1}{2}} - 40^{\frac{1}{2}}$

27. a. $5 \times 3^{\frac{1}{2}} + 2^{\frac{1}{2}}$ b. $(2^5)^{\frac{1}{2}} + (5^2)^{\frac{1}{5}}$ 28. a. $12 \times 10^{\frac{1}{2}} + 5^{\frac{1}{2}}$ b. $(3^4)^{\frac{1}{3}} + (4^3)^{\frac{1}{4}}$

29. a. $8^{\frac{1}{2}} \times 9^{\frac{1}{2}}$ b. $45^{\frac{1}{2}} \times 60^{\frac{1}{2}}$ 30. a. $6^{\frac{1}{2}} \times 3^{\frac{1}{2}}$ b. $24^{\frac{1}{2}} \times 75^{\frac{1}{2}}$

31. a. $\dfrac{5 + 4^{\frac{1}{2}}}{36^{\frac{1}{2}}}$ b. $\dfrac{10^{\frac{1}{2}} - 5^{\frac{1}{2}}}{25^{\frac{1}{2}}}$ 32. a. $\dfrac{6^{\frac{1}{2}} + 6^{\frac{1}{2}}}{9^{\frac{1}{2}}}$ b. $\dfrac{7 - 7^{\frac{1}{2}}}{4^{\frac{1}{2}}}$

Simplify Problems 33 to 42 by expressing them as single exponents (using the properties of exponents) and as a radical, then evaluate and round the answers to two decimal places, wherever applicable.

33. a. $6^{-\frac{5}{4}} \times 6^{\frac{3}{4}}$ b. $7^{\frac{4}{3}} \times 7^{-\frac{2}{3}}$ 34. a. $5^{\frac{4}{9}} \times 5^{-\frac{2}{9}}$ b. $3^{-\frac{6}{7}} \times 3^{\frac{2}{7}}$

35. a. $\dfrac{10^{-\frac{3}{5}} \times 10^{\frac{4}{5}}}{10^{\frac{2}{5}}}$ b. $\dfrac{2^{\frac{5}{7}} \times 2^{-\frac{6}{7}}}{2^{-\frac{8}{7}}}$ 36. a. $\dfrac{5^{\frac{2}{7}} \times 5^{\frac{4}{7}}}{5^{-\frac{6}{7}}}$ b. $\dfrac{3^{\frac{2}{3}} \times 3^{-\frac{4}{3}}}{3^{\frac{5}{3}}}$

37. a. $\dfrac{6^{-\frac{5}{9}} \times 6^0}{6^{-\frac{7}{9}}}$ b. $\dfrac{7^{\frac{7}{8}} \times 7^{\frac{8}{3}}}{7^2}$ 38. a. $\dfrac{9^{\frac{2}{5}} \times 9^0}{9^{-\frac{3}{5}}}$ b. $\dfrac{5^{\frac{5}{6}} \times 5^{\frac{2}{3}}}{5^2}$

39. a. $(5^{-2})^{\frac{4}{3}}$ b. $(6^{-\frac{1}{2}})^{-6}$ 40. a. $(4^{-2})^{\frac{5}{2}}$ b. $(2^{-\frac{4}{5}})^{-5}$

41. a. $(8^{-\frac{2}{3}})^{-6}$ b. $(7^{-\frac{1}{3}})^9$ 42. a. $(6^{-\frac{2}{3}})^{-3}$ b. $(3^{-\frac{4}{9}})^0$

Evaluate Problems 43 to 48 and express the answers rounded to two decimal places, wherever applicable.

43. a. $\dfrac{3^{-1}}{2^{-1}}$ b. $3^{-1} + 2^{-1}$ 44. a. $\dfrac{2^{-2}}{3^{-1}}$ b. $2^{-2} + 3^{-1}$

45. a. $3^{-1} \times 3^2 \times 3^{-2}$ b. $[2^{-3}]^{-1}$ 46. a. $5^{-2} \times 5^2 \times 5^3$ b. $[5^{-2}]^{-2}$

47. a. $\dfrac{2^{\frac{2}{5}} + 3^0 \times 2^{-1}}{\left(\frac{1}{2}\right)^{-1}}$ b. $2^{-2} + \dfrac{1}{2^{-1}}$ 48. a. $\dfrac{3^{-1} + 2 \times 3^{-1}}{\left(\frac{1}{3}\right)^{-1}}$ b. $3^{-2} + \dfrac{1}{3^{-1}}$

3.3 | Arithmetic Operations with Signed Numbers

Introduction

In the previous chapters, you learned that positive real numbers can be represented by points on a number line from zero to the right of the zero. That is, whole numbers, positive integers, and positive rational and irrational numbers can be represented on a number line from zero to the right of the zero.

Every positive number has a negative number known as its opposite. Zero, '0', is neither positive nor negative. The numbers that are to the left of the zero on the number line represent negative numbers. We use the negative sign, '–', to represent negative integers, and the positive sign, '+', to represent positive integers.

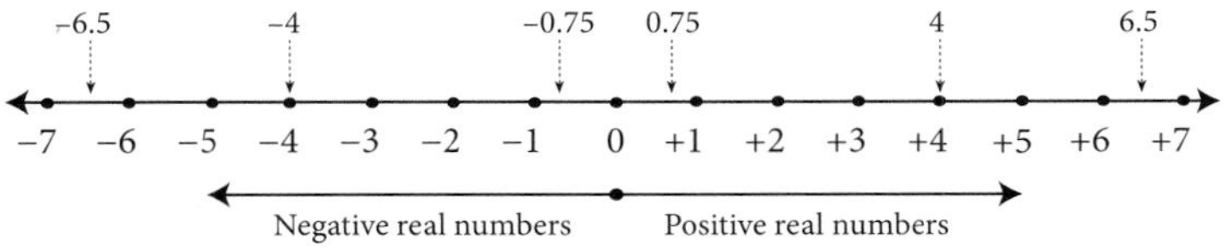

The arrowhead on either end shows that the line continues indifinitely in both the positive and negative directions.

Real numbers include all positive numbers and negative numbers.

Positive and negative numbers are referred to as signed numbers. Since numbers are naturally positive, when we read or write positive numbers, we usually omit the word **'positive'** or the positive sign (+). However, when the number is negative, we must read or write it as **'negative'** or include the negative sign (–). For example, '+ 7' is read as **'seven'** and is written as '7'. But '– 7' should be read as **'negative seven'** and should be written with the **'negative'** sign as '– 7'.

Two integers that are at equal distances from the origin and in opposite directions are called opposites.

Any positive number and its negative (opposite) will be at an equal distance from zero (origin) on the number line.

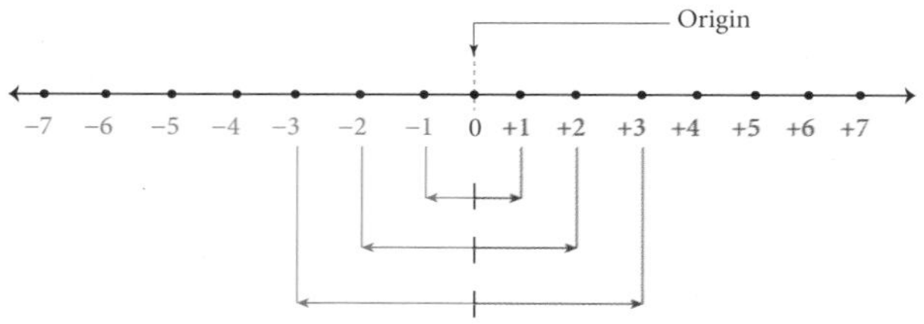

A negative number is the opposite of a positive number. For example, – 3 is the opposite of + 3.

Numbers that lie to the left of a number on the number line are smaller than the numbers that lie to the right of that number.

For example,

- 3 is greater than −2, i.e., $3 > -2$
- −3 is greater than −5, i.e., $-3 > -5$
- −5 is smaller than −4, i.e., $-5 < -4$
- −1 is smaller than 2 i.e., $-1 < 2$

Absolute Value

Absolute value is the magnitute of the number.

The absolute value of a number is its distance from the origin '0' on the number line. Since it is a distance, it is always positive and the direction does not matter.

For example, – 5 and +5 are 5 units from the origin '0'.

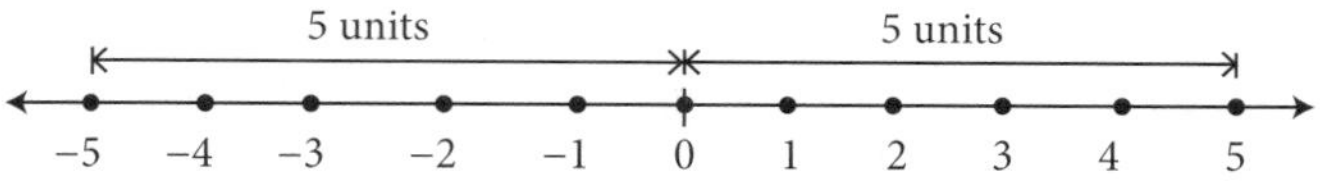

The absolute value of a number 'a' is denoted by $|a|$. The vertical bars used in the representation of the absolute value differ from how brackets are used.

For example, $|-4| = 4$, whereas $(-4) = -4$

Example 3.3-a **Simplifying Arithmetic Expressions Involving Absolute Values**

Simplify the following expressions:

(i) $-\left|\frac{-4}{3}\right|$ (ii) $-|8(-2)|$

Solution

(i) $-\left|\frac{-4}{3}\right|$ Simplifying the absolute value portion,

$= -\left(\frac{4}{3}\right)$ Simplifying the bracket portion,

$= \frac{-4}{3}$

Therefore, $-\left|\frac{-4}{3}\right| = \frac{-4}{3}$.

(ii) $-|8(-2)|$ Simplifying within the absolute value portion,

$= -|-16|$ Simplifying the absolute value portion,

$= -(16)$ Simplifying the bracket portion,

$= -16$

Therefore, $-|8(-2)| = -16$.

Example 3.3-b **Subtracting Arithmetic Expressions Involving Absolute Values**

Simplify the following expressions:

(i) $10 - |8 - 15|$ (ii) $-5 + |-10 + 8|$

Solution

(i) $10 - \|8 - 15\|$	Simplifying within the absolute value portion,	(ii) $-5 + \|-10 + 8\|$	Simplifying within the absolute value portion,
$= 10 - \|-7\|$	Simplifying the absolute value portion,	$= -5 + \|-2\|$	Simplifying the absolute value portion,
$= 10 - (7)$	Simplifying the bracket portion,	$= -5 + 2$	Adding,
$= 10 - 7$	Subtracting,	$= -3$	
$= 3$		Therefore, $-5 + \|-10 + 8\| = -3$.	

Therefore, $10 - |8 - 15| = 3$.

Addition and Subtraction of Signed Numbers

- When adding two positive numbers, the answer is always positive (+).
  For example,

  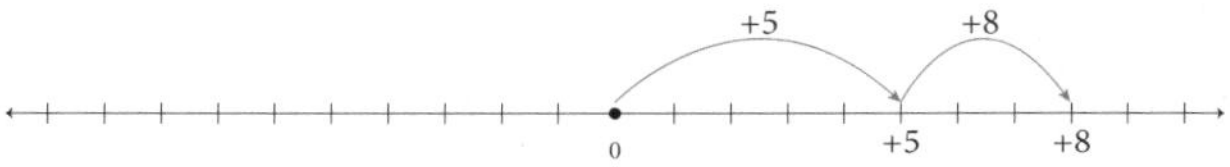

  Adding + 5 and + 3:
  $(+5) + (+3) = 5 + 3 = \mathbf{8}$
  This is the same as **+ 8.**

- When adding two negative numbers, the answer is always negative (–).
  For example,

  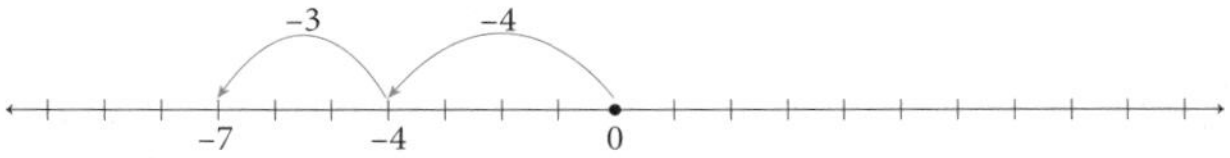

  Adding –4 and –3:
  $(-4) + (-3) = -4 - 3 = \mathbf{-7}$

- When adding numbers that have different signs, subtract the smaller number from the larger number and the answer will have the sign of the larger, dominant number.
  For example,

  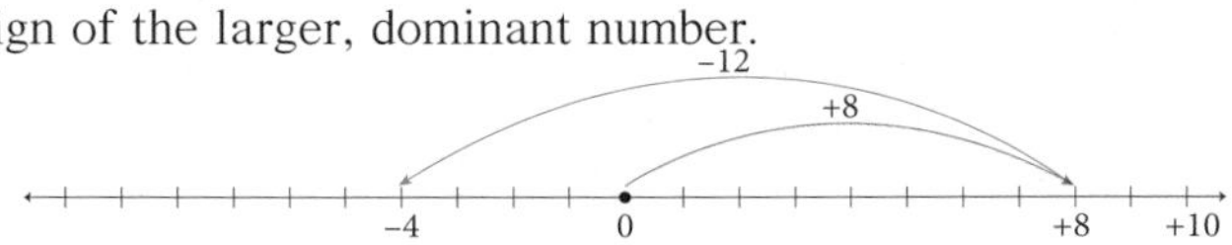

  (i) Adding +8 and –12 (or –12 and +8):
  $+8 + (-12) = 8 - 12 = \mathbf{-4}$

  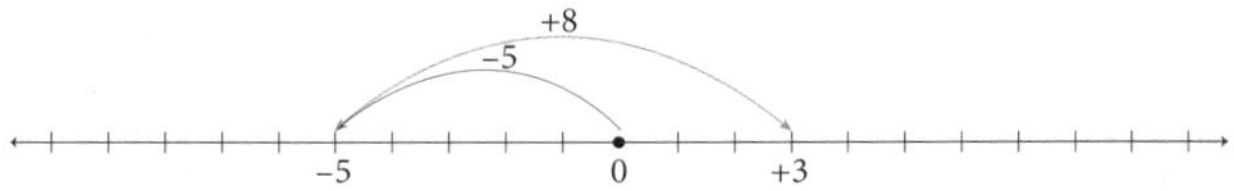

  (ii) Adding –5 and +8 (or +8 and –5):
  $-5 + (+8) = -5 + 8 = +3 = \mathbf{3}$

- When subtracting negative numbers, first change all the subtraction problems to addition problems, then follow the rule for the addition of signed numbers.

  For example,

  (i) Subtracting 12 from 18:
  $18 - 12 = 18 + (-12) = 6$

  (ii) Subtracting –12 from 18:
  $18 - (-12) = 18 + 12 = 30$

  (iii) Subtracting 12 from –18:
  $-18 - 12 = -18 + (-12) = -30$

  (iv) Subtracting –12 from –18:
  $-18 - (-12) = -18 + 12 = -6$

Multiplication and Division of Signed Numbers

When signed numbers are multiplied or divided, the result will be a number with either a '+' or a '–' sign.

The following are rules to be followed when multiplying or dividing **two signed numbers:**

(a) Multiplying two signed numbers:

Multiplying two signed numbers:

(+) (+) = (+)

(–) (–) = (+)

(+) (–) = (–)

(–) (+) = (–)

- The product of two numbers with the **same sign** is **positive**.

  For example,

  (i) $(+5)(+4) = +20$

  (ii) $(-5)(-4) = +20$

- The product of two numbers with **different signs** is **negative**.

  For example,

  (i) $(+5)(-4) = -20$

  (ii) $(-5)(+4) = -20$

(b) Dividing two signed numbers:

Dividing two signed numbers:

$\frac{(+)}{(+)} = (+)$

$\frac{(-)}{(-)} = (+)$

$\frac{(-)}{(+)} = (-)$

$\frac{(+)}{(-)} = (-)$

- The quotient of two numbers with the **same sign** is **positive**.

  For example,

  (i) $\frac{+12}{+8} = +\frac{3}{2}$

  (ii) $\frac{-12}{-8} = +\frac{3}{2}$

- The quotient of two numbers with **different signs** is **negative**.

  For example,

  (i) $\frac{-12}{+8} = -\frac{3}{2}$

  (ii) $\frac{+12}{-8} = -\frac{3}{2}$

Note: When multiplying or dividing more than 2 signed numbers, group them into pairs and determine the sign using the rules for multiplication and division of signed numbers.

For example,

(i) $\underbrace{(-3)(-2)}\ \underbrace{(+4)(-1)}(-5)$

$= \underbrace{(6)(-4)}(-5)$

$= (-24)(-5)$

$= 120$

(ii) $\frac{\overbrace{(-15)(+8)}(-50)}{\underbrace{(-25)(14)}}$

$= \frac{\overbrace{-(15 \times 8)(-50)}}{-(25 \times 14)}$

$= \frac{+15 \times 8 \times 50}{-25 \times 14} = -\frac{15 \times \overset{4}{\cancel{8}} \times \overset{2}{\cancel{50}}}{\underset{1}{\cancel{25}} \times \underset{7}{\cancel{14}}}$

$= -\frac{15 \times 4 \times 2}{14}$

$= -\frac{120}{7}$

Exponents with Negative Bases

Table 3.3-a

Exponents with Negative Bases

When an exponent has a negative base there are four possible scenarios:

Negative Base with Exponents	Example	Sign of Answer
Positive and Even	$(-2)^6 = \underbrace{(-2)(-2)}\underbrace{(-2)(-2)}\underbrace{(-2)(-2)} = 64$	+
Positive and Odd	$(-2)^5 = \underbrace{(-2)(-2)}\underbrace{(-2)(-2)}(-2) = -32$	–
Negative and Even	$(-2)^{-6} = \frac{1}{(-2)^6} = \frac{1}{\underbrace{(-2)(-2)}\underbrace{(-2)(-2)}\underbrace{(-2)(-2)}} = \frac{1}{64} = 0.015625$	+
Negative and Odd	$(-2)^{-5} = \frac{1}{(-2)^5} = \frac{1}{\underbrace{(-2)(-2)}\underbrace{(-2)(-2)}(-2)} = \frac{1}{-32} = -0.03125$	–

From the above scenarios you will note:

- A negative number (base) with an even exponent results in a positive answer (because pairs of even negatives become positive).
- A negative number (base) with an odd exponent results in a negative answer (because after pairs of even negatives, one negative will be left over).

A negative base of an exponent expressed within a bracket, as in $(-a)^n$, results in a different answer compared to a negative base expressed without a bracket, as in $-a^n$.

In $(-a)^n$, the exponent applies to both the negative sign and a.

In $-a^n$, the exponent applies only to a and the negative sign remains in the answer.

For example,

(i) In $(-5)^4$, (-5) is multiplied 4 times; i.e., $(-5)^4 = (-5)(-5)(-5)(-5) = 625$

(ii) In $(-5)^3$, (-5) is multiplied 3 times; i.e., $(-5)^3 = (-5)(-5)(-5) = -125$

(iii) In -5^4, only 5 is multiplied 4 times and the negative remains; i.e., $-5^4 = -[5 \times 5 \times 5 \times 5] = -625$

(iv) In -5^3, only 5 is multiplied 3 times and the negative remains; i.e., $-5^3 = -[5 \times 5 \times 5] = -125$

Arithmetic Operations of Exponential Expressions with Signed Numbers

Example 3.3-c

Solving Expressions using the Product Rule

Solve the following expressions:

(i) $(-5)^4 \times (-5)^{-1}$

(ii) $(-2)^5 \times (-2)^2 \times (-2)^0 \times 2$

Solution

(i) $(-5)^4 \times (-5)^{-1}$

$= (-5)^{(4-1)}$

$= (-5)^3$

$= -125$

(ii) $(-2)^5 \times (-2)^2 \times (-2)^0 \times 2$

$= (-2)^{(5+2+0)} \times 2$

$= (-2)^7 \times 2$

$= -128 \times 2$

$= -256$

Example 3.3-d

Solving Expressions using the Quotient Rule

Solve the following expressions:

(i) $(-3)^7 \div (-3)^2$ (ii) $(-5)^3 \div (-5)^0$

Solution

(i) $(-3)^7 \div (-3)^2$
$= (-3)^{(7-2)}$
$= (-3)^5$
$= -243$

(ii) $(-5)^3 \div (-5)^0$
$= (-5)^{(3-0)}$
$= (-5)^3$
$= -125$

Example 3.3-e

Solving Expressions using the Power of a Product Rule

Solve the following expressions:

(i) $(-5 \times 2)^3$ (ii) $(-3 \times 2)^{-2}$

Solution

(i) $(-5 \times 2)^3$
$= (-5)^3 \times 2^3$
$= -125 \times 8$
$= -1{,}000$

or

$(-5 \times 2)^3$
$= (-10)^3$
$= -1{,}000$

(ii) $(-3 \times 2)^{-2}$
$= -3^{-2} \times 2^{-2}$
$= \dfrac{1}{(-3)^2} \times \dfrac{1}{2^2}$
$= \dfrac{1}{9} \times \dfrac{1}{4}$
$= \dfrac{1}{36}$

or

$(-3 \times 2)^{-2}$
$= (-6)^{-2}$
$= \dfrac{1}{(-6)^2}$
$= \dfrac{1}{36}$

Example 3.3-f

Solving Expressions using the Power of a Quotient Rule

Solve the following expressions:

(i) $(-2 \div 3)^{-2}$ (ii) $(-2)^{-3}$

Solution

(i) $(-2 \div 3)^{-2}$
$= \left(\dfrac{-2}{3}\right)^{-2}$
$= \left(\dfrac{3}{-2}\right)^{2}$
$= \dfrac{3^2}{(-2)^2}$
$= \dfrac{9}{4}$

(ii) $(-2)^{-3}$
$= \dfrac{1}{(-2)^3}$
$= \dfrac{1}{-8}$
$= -\dfrac{1}{8}$

Example 3.3-g

Evaluating Exponents with Powers

Solve the following expressions:

(i) $(-2^3)^3$ (ii) $(-3^3)^2$

Solution

(i) $(-2^3)^3$
$= (-2)^{3 \times 3}$
$= (-2)^9$
$= -512$

(ii) $(-3^3)^2$
$= (-3)^{3 \times 2}$
$= (-3)^6$
$= 729$

Principal Roots

Roots of Positive Numbers

When the index of the root is even, any positive number will have two solutions, with one being the negative of the other. The positive solution is known as its principal root.

For example, $\sqrt{9}$ has two roots: +3 and −3, because $(3) \times (3) = 9$, and $(-3) \times (-3) = 9$

This is usually written as ± 3 and read as "plus or minus 3". The positive root is called the principal root.

Similary, $\sqrt[4]{16}$ has two roots: +2 and −2. Because $(2) \times (2) \times (2) \times (2) = 16$ and $(-2) \times (-2) \times (-2) \times (-2) = 16$. i.e., the roots are ±2 and the principal root is 2.

When the index of the root is odd, there is only one solution and it is positive. This positive solution is known as its principal root.

For example,

$\sqrt[3]{27} = 3$ because $(3) \times (3) \times (3) = 27$

Similary, $\sqrt[5]{32} = 2$, because $(2) \times (2) \times (2) \times (2) \times (2) = 32$

Roots of Negative Numbers

When the index of the root is even, there is no real solution to any negative number.

For example,

$\sqrt[2]{-4}$ has no real roots.

$\sqrt[4]{-81}$ has no real roots.

When the index of the root is odd, there is a solution to any negative number. The negative real solution is the principal root.

For example,

$\sqrt[5]{-32} = -2$ because $(-2)(-2)(-2)(-2)(-2) = -32$

$\sqrt[3]{-27} = -3$ because $(-3)(-3)(-3) = -27$

For negative numbers, when the index of the root is odd, the negative real root is the principal root.

Table 3.3-b Types of Real Numbers

Type	Description	Examples
Natural Numbers	Counting numbers (numbers starting from 1).	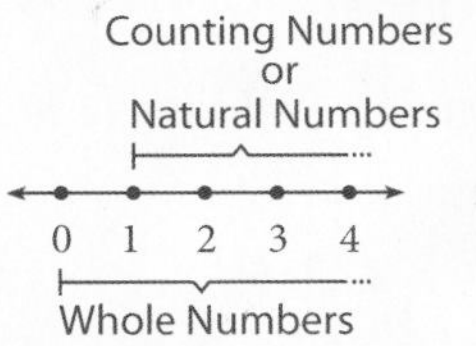
Whole Numbers	Natural numbers, including zero.	
Integers	Natural numbers (positive integers), their negatives (negative integers), and zero.	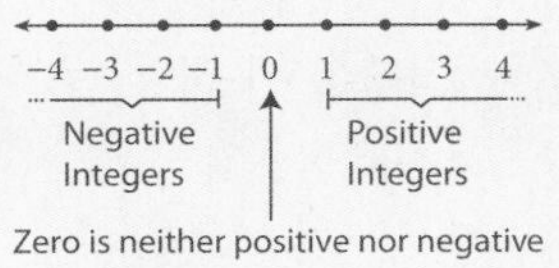
Rational Numbers	Numbers that can be expressed as one integer divided by another non-zero integer; i.e., numbers that can be written as a quotient of integers with non-zero divisors.	$-\frac{5}{2}$, 0.75, $\frac{3}{2}$
Irrational Numbers	Numbers that cannot be expressed as a rational number.	$\sqrt{2}$, π, 2.718281......

Natural numbers are positive integers. Zero is neither positive nor negative.

Rational numbers can be expressed as $\frac{a}{b}$, where a and b are integers and $b \neq 0$.

Irrational numbers cannot be expressed as $\frac{a}{b}$, where a and b are integers and $b \neq 0$.

Terminating decimals and repeating decimals are also rational numbers because they can be expressed as a quotient of integers.

Terminating decimals are decimals that end.

For example, 0.375 which can be expressed as $\frac{3}{8}$.

Repeating decimals are decimals that do not end but show a repeating pattern.

For example, 0.185185... is usually written as $0.\overline{185}$ and can be expressed as $\frac{5}{27}$.

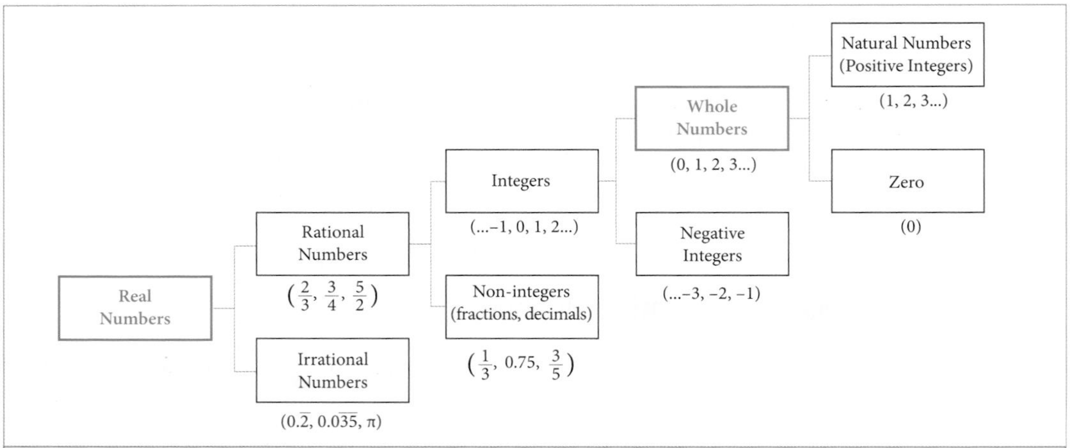

Exhibit 3.3 Real Number System With Examples

3.3 | Exercises

Answers to odd-numbered problems are available at the end of the textbook.

For Problems 1 to 6, place the correct sign '<' or '>' in the space between the given pairs of numbers.

1. a. $-5 \square 0$ b. $-2 \square +6$
2. a. $0 \square -3$ b. $-5 \square +3$
3. a. $+8 \square -3$ b. $+1 \square -2$
4. a. $-5 \square +4$ b. $+3 \square -7$
5. a. $-6 \square -8$ b. $-5 \square -2$
6. a. $-7 \square -9$ b. $-8 \square -4$

For Problems 7 to 10, arrange the numbers in order from smallest to largest.

7. a. 5, −6, 8, −8, −5, 2 b. −8, 4, −6, 3, −9, 7
8. a. −2, −3, 5, 2, −1, 4 b. 12, −13, 15, 2, −8, −3
9. a. 9, −5, −8, 3, 7, 10 b. 12, −13, 15, 2, −8, −3
10. a. −3, 6, 1, −7, −1, 7 b. −12, 0, 12, −16, 15, −5

Evaluate Problems 11 to 20.

11. a. $|-16|$ b. $-|3|$
12. a. $|-8|$ b. $-|12|$
13. a. $-|-5|$ b. $-[-|-9|]$
14. a. $-|-7|$ b. $-[-|-3|]$
15. a. $|-4| - |-7|$ b. $-|-8| + |-3|$
16. a. $-|-15| - |-3|$ b. $|-5| + |-4|$
17. a. $|-10| \times |-5|$ b. $|-15| \div |-3|$
18. a. $|-10| \times |-2|$ b. $|-12| \div |-4|$
19. a. $-|6| \times |-3|$ b. $-|-20| \div |-5|$
20. a. $|-8| \times |4|$ b. $-|-24| \div |-6|$

Evaluate Problems 21 to 38.

21. a. $-8 + (-5 - 7)$ b. $2 - (-3) + 1$
22. a. $-9 + (-3 - 8)$ b. $5 - (-7) + 8$
23. a. $-3 - (-7) + 8$ b. $(-4 + 9) - (-3 - 6)$
24. a. $-7 - (-9) - 1$ b. $(-5 + 3) + (-4 - 9)$
25. a. $4 + (-3) - [5 + (-11)]$ b. $-6 + (-4) - [-(15 - 8)]$
26. a. $5 + (-4) - [7 + (-9)]$ b. $-8 + (-15) - [-(6 - 7)]$
27. a. $2(-3)(-5)$ b. $-4(-3)(-2)$
28. a. $6(-2)(-4)$ b. $-5(-3)(-2)$
29. a. $-64 \div (-8)$ b. $45 \div (-5)$
30. a. $-48 \div (-6)$ b. $36 \div (-4)$
31. a. $-5 + (-2)(-5) - (6 - 3)$ b. $7(2 - 3) - 4(-7 + 1)$
32. a. $-8(5 - 6) - 3(-6 + 2)$ b. $-7 + (-3)(-4) - (-8 - 3)$

33. a. $(5+7)^2-5^2-7^2$ b. $2^2-2^4-20\times 3$
34. a. $(9-12)^2-9^2-12^2$ b. $7\times 8-3^2-2^3$
35. a. $(20\times 4-8^2)^2+9$ b. $(3\times 9-3^2)+12$
36. a. $-12\div 4-3\times 2^4$ b. $-5\times 3^3\div 9+5^2$
37. a. $-11^2-4\times 54\div(5-2)^3-3$ b. $-31-[(15\div 3)\times 32]\div 2^2(23\div 13)$
38. a. $[(1+12)(1-5)]^2\div(5-3\times 2^2-4)$ b. $3(7^2+2\times 15\div 3)-(1-3\times 4)^2$

Express Problems 39 to 46 as a single exponent and then evaluate.

39. a. $(-6)^5\times(-6)^3$ b. $8^{-6}\times 8^9$
40. a. $(-2)^5\times(-2)^6$ b. $4^{-7}\times 4^8$
41. a. $(-4)^5\div(-4)^3$ b. $-5^4\div(-5)^2$
42. a. $(-2)^7\div(-2)^4$ b. $-4^6\div(-4)^4$
43. a. $-\left(\frac{1}{2}\right)^2\div\left(\frac{1}{2}\right)^3$ b. $\left(-\frac{3}{5}\right)^3\div\left(-\frac{3}{5}\right)^1$
44. a. $-\left(\frac{1}{4}\right)^4\div\left(\frac{1}{4}\right)^2$ b. $\left(-\frac{5}{8}\right)^2\div\left(-\frac{5}{8}\right)^0$
45. a. $(-2^3)^2\div(-2)^5$ b. $-(3^2)\div(-3)^6$
46. a. $(-3^2)^3\div(-3)^7$ b. $-(2^2)^2\div(-2)^3$

Evaluate Problems 47 to 50.

47. a. $(-2)^2+(-3)^3$ b. $(-3)^2-(-2)^3$
48. a. $(-4)^2+(-5)^3$ b. $(-5)^2-(-4)^2$
49. a. $(-2)^3-(-3)^2-1^5$ b. $(-7)^1+(5)^0-(-3)^2$
50. a. $(-3)^0+(-4)^1-(-2)^3$ b. $(-3)^2-(-2)^3-2^2$

3.4 | Significant Digits and Scientific Notation

Significant Digits

Significant Digits are critical when reporting data as they provide information on how well the data is measured or reported.

The **accuracy of a number** is determined by the number of significant digits in the number. The **precision of a number** is based on the place value of the rightmost significant digit.

For example,

- 4,700 is accurate to 2 significant digits and precise to the nearest hundred.
- 12.25 is accurate to 4 significant digits and precise to the nearest hundredths.

Note: The number of significant digits in a number is calculated by following the rules given in Table 3.4-a.

Determining the Number of Significant Digits in a Number

Table 3.4-a **Determining the number of significant digits**

The general rules for determining the number of significant digits are as follows:

	General Rule	Example	
1.	All non-zero digits are significant.	$\underline{2}\,\underline{7}\,0$	2 significant digits
		$\underline{3}\,\underline{1}\,.\,\underline{4}$	3 significant digits
2.	All zeros between two significant digits are significant.	$\underline{3}\,\underline{0}\,\underline{0}\,\underline{5}$	4 significant digits
		$\underline{1}\,\underline{0}\,\underline{5}\,.\,\underline{0}\,\underline{3}$	5 significant digits
3.	Leading zeros are not significant.	$0\,.\,0\,\underline{5}$	1 significant digit
		$0\,.\,0\,0\,\underline{3}\,\underline{2}\,\underline{5}$	3 significant digits
4.	Trailing zeros to the right of the decimal point are significant.	$\underline{2}\,\underline{5}\,\underline{0}\,.\,\underline{0}$	4 significant digits
		$0\,.\,0\,0\,\underline{3}\,\underline{8}\,\underline{0}$	3 significant digits

Trailing zeros in a whole number with the decimal point at the end are significant.

For example, the number 250. has 3 significant digits as there is a decimal point at the end of the number.

Example 3.4-a

Identifying Significant Digits

Identify the number of significant digits of the following numbers:

(i) 89,000	(ii) 108.750	(iii) 706.00	(iv) 30.9
(v) 0.075	(vi) 0.00875	(vii) 0.750	(viii) 0.04070

Solution

(i) 89, 000 — the three zeros: Not significant. Number of significant digits = 2 (Rule 1)

(ii) 108.750 — last 0: Significant. All digits are significant. Number of significant digits = 6 (Rules 1 and 4)

(iii) 706.00 — 0, 0, 0: Significant. All digits are significant. Number of significant digits = 5 (Rules 1, 2, and 4)

(iv) 30.9 — 0: Significant. All digits are significant. Number of significant digits = 3 (Rules 1 and 2)

(v) 0.075 — 0, 0: Not significant. Number of significant digits = 2 (Rules 1 and 3)

(vi) 0.00875 — 0, 0, 0: Not significant. Number of significant digits = 3 (Rules 1 and 3)

(vii) 0.750 — last 0: Significant; first 0: Not significant. Number of significant digits = 3 (Rules 1, 3, and 4)

(viii) 0.04070 — 0, 0: Not significant; 0, 0 (after 4 and after 7): Significant. Number of significant digits = 4 (Rules 1, 2, 3, and 4)

Note:

- *4,500 has 2 significant digits (Rule 1).*
- *4,500.0 has 5 significant digits (Rules 1, 2, and 4).*
- *4,500.00 has 6 significant digits (Rules 1, 2, and 4).*

Rounding Numbers to Required Significant Digits

It is often necessary to round numbers to keep the result of calculations to the required number of significant digits.

The general methods for rounding numbers to required significant digits are as follows:

Table 3.4-b

Rules for Rounding Numbers to Significant Digits

Start at the left of the number and count from left to right until the required number of significant digits and identify (by underlining) the last significant digit.

	If the digit immediately to the right of the identified digit is:	Rounding Whole Numbers to required significant digits (The examples given are for rounding a given number to 3 significant digits)	Rounding Decimal Numbers to required significant digits (The examples given are for rounding a given number to 3 significant digits)
1.	Less than 5	Leave the identified digit unchanged and replace all digits to the right of it with zeros.	Leave the identified digit unchanged and drop all digits to the right of it.
	Example: (Rounding to 3 significant digits)	27<u>8</u>,312 = 278,000 (3 < 5)	3.0<u>7</u>23 = 3.07 (2 < 5)

2.	Greater than or equal to 5, but followed by at least one non-zero digit	Add 1 to the identified digit and replace all digits to the right of it with zeros.	Add 1 to the identified digit and drop all digits to the right of it.
	Example: (Rounding to 3 significant digits)	i. 30<u>8</u>,765 = 309,000 (7 >5) ii. 29<u>6</u>,572 = 297,000 (5 = 5, 72 >0)	i. 21.<u>4</u>76 = 21.5 (7 >5) ii. 13. <u>3</u>502 = 13.4 (5 = 5, 02 >0)
3. a.	Equal to 5, but followed by all zero digits or no other digits	If the identified digit is an **even digit**, leave the identified digit unchanged and replace all digits to the right of it with zeros. *Note: Zero is an even digit.*	a. If the identified digit is an even digit, leave the identified digit unchanged and drop all digits to the right of it. *Note: Zero is an even digit.*
	Example: (Rounding to 3 significant digits)	i. 40<u>8</u>,500 = 408,000 (8 even; 5 = 5; 00 = 0) ii. 7,4<u>6</u>5 = 7460 (6 even; 5 = 5)	i. 7.0<u>4</u>50 = 7.04 (4 even; 5 = 5; 0 = 0) ii. 24.<u>8</u>5 = 24.8 (8 even; 5 = 5)
3. b.		If the identified digit is an **odd digit**, add 1 to the identified digit to make it even and replace all digits to the right of it with zeros.	b. If the identified digit is an odd digit, add 1 to the identified digit to make it even and drop all digits to the right of it.
	Example: (Rounding to 3 significant digits)	i. 38<u>3</u>,500 = 384,000 (3 odd; 5 = 5; 00 = 0) ii. 74<u>1</u>5 = 742 (1 odd; 5 = 5)	i. 43.<u>7</u>500 = 43.8 (5 = 5; 00 = 0) ii. 9.3<u>9</u>5 = 9.40 (5 = 5)

Example 3.4-b

Rounding Whole Numbers to Indicated Significant Digits

Round the following numbers to the indicated significant digits:

(i) 62,578 to 3 significant digits (ii) 124,390 to 2 significant digits

(iii) 704,534 to 3 significant digits (iv) 8,047,500 to 4 significant digits

(v) 340,650 to 4 significant digits (vi) 500,067 to 4 significant digits

Solution

(i) Rounding 62,578 to 3 significant digits

62,<u>5</u>78 = 62,600 (7 >5)

(ii) Rounding 124,390 to 2 significant digits

1<u>2</u>4,390 = 120,000 (4 <5)

Solution *continued*

(iii) Rounding 704,534 to 3 significant digits

$$70\underline{4},534 = 705,000 \quad (\uparrow =5)$$

(iv) Rounding 8,047,500 to 4 significant digits

$$8,04\underline{7},500 = 8,048,000 \quad (\uparrow =5)$$

(v) Rounding 340,650 to 4 significant digits

$$340,\underline{6}50 = 340,600 \quad (\uparrow =5)$$

(vi) Rounding 500,067 to 4 significant digits

$$500,\underline{0}67 = 500,100 \quad (\uparrow >5)$$

Example 3.4-c

Rounding Decimal Numbers to Indicated Significant Digits

Round the following numbers to the indicated significant digits:

(i) 0.8090 to 2 significant digits (ii) 1.0621 to 3 significant digits (iii) 0.0635 to 2 significant digits

(iv) 0.08250 to 2 significant digits (v) 0.043517 to 2 significant digits (iv) 4,527.25 to 3 significant digits

Solution

(i) Rounding 0.8090 to 2 significant digits

$$0.8\underline{0}90 = 0.81 \quad (\uparrow >5)$$

(ii) Rounding 1.0621 to 3 significant digits

$$1.0\underline{6}21 = 1.06 \quad (\uparrow <5)$$

(iii) Rounding 0.0635 to 2 significant digits

$$0.06\underline{3}5 = 0.064 \quad (\uparrow =5)$$

(iv) Rounding 0.08250 to 2 significant digits

$$0.08\underline{2}50 = 0.082 \quad (\uparrow =5)$$

(v) Rounding 0.043517 to 2 significant digits

$$0.04\underline{3}517 = 0.044 \quad (\uparrow =5)$$

(vi) Rounding 4,257.25 to 3 significant digits

$$4,2\underline{5}7.25 = 4,260 \quad (\uparrow >5)$$

Rounding Rules for Addition and Subtraction of Decimal Numbers

When adding or subtracting decimal numbers, the final answer should have the same number of decimal places as the number with the least number of decimal places. The rules for rounding to a given precision are the same as the rules for rounding decimal numbers. For a review of these rules, refer back to Chapter 2.

Example 3.4-d

Rounding to a Number with the Least Number of Decimal Places

(i) Add 565.346 and 6.35 (ii) Subtract 3.9 from 34.45

Solution

(i)
$$\begin{array}{r} \overset{1}{5}65.346 \\ +\ \ \ 6.35 \\ \hline 571.696 \end{array}$$

565.346 ← 3 decimal places
6.35 ← 2 decimal places

565.346 has 3 decimal places and 6.35 has 2 decimal places. The least number of decimal places is 2.

Therefore, rounding the answer 571.696 to 2 decimal places is 571.70.

(ii)
$$\begin{array}{r} 34.45 \\ -\ \ 3.9 \\ \hline 30.55 \end{array}$$

34.45 ← 2 decimal places
3.9 ← 1 decimal place

34.45 has 2 decimal places and 3.9 has 1 decimal place. The least number of decimal places is 1.

Therefore, rounding the answer 30.55 to 1 decimal place is 30.6.

Rounding Rules for Multiplication and Division of Decimal Numbers

When multiplying or dividing decimal numbers, the final answer should have the same number of significant digits as the number with the least number of significant digits in any of the numbers being multiplied or divided. Here, we must use the rules for rounding with significant digits introduced earlier in Table 3.4-b.

Example 3.4-e

Rounding to a Number with the Least Number of Significant Digits

(i) Multiply 10.46 and 1.2 (ii) Divide 370.25 by 10.5

Solution

(i)
$$\begin{array}{r} 10.46 \\ \times\ \ \ 1.2 \\ \hline 2092 \\ 10460 \\ \hline 12.552 \end{array}$$

10.46 ← 4 significant digits
1.2 ← 2 significant digits

10.46 has 4 significant digits and 1.2 has 2 significant digits. The least number of significant digits is 2.

Therefore, rounding the answer 12.552 to 2 significant digits is 13.

(ii)
$$\frac{370.25}{10.5} = 35.26190...$$

370.25 ← 5 significant digits
10.5 ← 3 significant digits

370.25 has 5 significant digits and 10.5 has 3 significant digits. The least number of significant digits is 3.

Therefore, rounding the answer 35.26190... to 3 significant digits is 35.3.

Special Situation in Rounding to Indicated Significant Digits

Consider the multiplication: 3,125 × 144

3,125 has 4 significant digits and 144 has 3 significant digits. Therefore, the answer should be rounded to 3 significant digits. However, when we multiply these numbers, the answer is 450,000 which only has 2 significant digits.

To indicate that the answer has 3 significant digits, place the symbol '~' above the first zero that is to be included as a significant digit to have a total of 3 significant digits; i.e., place the symbol '~' above the 3rd digit (zero), to indicate it as a significant digit.

450,000 — 2 significant digits

45$\tilde{0}$,000 — Now it has 3 significant digits

Similarly, consider the multiplication: 3,906.25 × 115.2

3,906.25 has 6 significant digits and 115.2 has 4 significant digits. Therefore, the answer should be rounded to 4 significant digits. However, when we multiply these numbers, the answer is 450,000 which only has 2 significant digits.

To indicate that the answer has 4 significant digits, place the symbol '~' above the second zero that is to be included as a significant digit to have a total of 4 significant digits; i.e., place the symbol '~' above the 4th digit (second zero), to indicate it as a significant digit.

We may also use scientific notation (which you will learn later in this section), to indicate the number of significant digits.

$$45\tilde{0},000 = \underbrace{4.50}_{\text{3 significant digits}} \times 10^5$$

$$450,\tilde{0}00 = \underbrace{4.500}_{\text{4 significant digits}} \times 10^5$$

Example 3.4-f **Rounding Numbers to Indicated Significant Digits**

Round the number 50,040.365 first to 6, then to 5, 4, and 3 significant digits.

Solution

$$50,040.365 = \underbrace{50,040.4}_{\text{6 significant digits}} = 5.00404 \times 10^4$$

$$50,040.365 = \underbrace{50,040.}_{} \text{ or } \underbrace{50,04\tilde{0}}_{} = 5.0040 \times 10^4$$

5 significant digits

$$50,040.365 = \underbrace{50,040}_{\text{4 significant digits}} = 5.004 \times 10^4$$

$$50,040.365 = \underbrace{50,\tilde{0}00}_{\text{3 significant digits}} = 5.00 \times 10^4$$

Scientific Notation

Scientific notation is a method of expressing numbers using decimal numbers with one non-zero digit to the left of the decimal point multiplied by the power of 10; i.e., scientific notation is based on the base number 10.

For example, 52,500 in scientific notation is written as 5.25×10^4.

$$52,500 = \underbrace{5.25}_{\text{Coefficient}} \times 10^4$$

Exponent (or power) → 4; Base → 10

Note:

- *The base is always 10.*
- *The coefficient should always be greater than or equal to 1, and less than 10.*

Converting Numbers from Standard Notation to Scientific Notation

Any number raised to the power of 0 is 1.

Therefore, $10^0 = 1$.

	Converting Numbers from Standard Notation to Scientific Notation	Example
1.	For numbers 1 up to 10, the , exponent will be 0. For example, to convert 9.5 to scientific notation, multiply 9.5 with the factor 10^0. Then power $10^0 = 1$.	9.5 9.5 × 100

2.	For numbers 10 and above, the exponent will be positive.	
	For example, to convert 525.6 to scientific notation, follow these steps:	525.6
	Count the number of digits in the number from the left up to the end of the decimal point and subtract one. This will be the exponent (or power).	3 digits – 1 Exponent = 2
	Move the decimal point to place it after the first digit from the left. This will be the coefficient.	525.6 Coefficient = 5.256
	Write the number in scientific notation as: Coefficient × 10^{Exponent}	5.256×10^2
3.	For numbers less than 1, the exponent will be negative.	
	For example, to convert 0.00752 to scientific notation, follow these steps:	0.00752
	Move the decimal point to place it after the first non-zero digit in the number. This will be the coefficient.	Coefficient = 7.52
	Count the number of places the decimal point is moved to the right. This will be the exponent (power) in negative.	0.00752 3 decimal places to the right Exponent = –3
	Write the number in scientific notation as: Coefficient × 10^{Exponent}	7.52×10^{-3}

Example 3.4-g

Converting Numbers from Standard Notation to Scientific Notation

Convert the following to scientific notation:

(i) 6,526 (ii) 135.275 (iii) 0.000058 (iv) 7.2

Solution

(i) $6526 = 6.526 \times 10^3$

(ii) $135.275 = 1.35275 \times 10^2$

(iii) $0.000058 = 5.8 \times 10^{-5}$

(iv) $7.2 = 7.2 \times 10^0$

Converting Numbers from Scientific Notation to Standard Notation

	Converting Numbers from Scientific Notation to Standard Notation	Example
1.	When the exponent of base 10 is 0:	
	To convert to standard notation, simply drop the factor 10^0.	8.75×10^0 = 8.75
2.	When the exponent of base 10 is a postive number: The answer will be a large number. To convert to standard notation, move the decimal point to the right by the same number of places of the exponent.	3.45×10^4 Exponent of base 10 = 4 = 3.45 ⟵ 4 places to the right = 34,500
3.	When the exponent of base 10 is a negative number: The answer will be a smaller number. To convert to standard notation, move the decimal point to the left by the same number of places of the exponent.	2.45×10^{-3} Exponent of base 10 = –3 = 2.45 ⟵ 3 places to the left = 0.00245

Example 3.4-h Coverting Numbers from Scientific Notation to Standard Notation

Convert the following numbers from scientific notation to standard notation.

(i) 2.07×10^{3} (ii) 5.18×10^{-4} (iii) 9×10^{0} (iv) 7.29×10^{0}

Solution

(i) 2.07×10^{3} Moving the decimal point 3 places to the right,

$= 2.07$

$= 2{,}070$

(ii) 5.18×10^{-4} Moving the decimal point 4 places to the left,

$= 5.18$

$= 0.000518$

(iii) 9×10^{0} Dropping the factor 10^{0},

$= 9$

(iv) 7.29×10^{0} Dropping the factor 10^{0},

$= 7.29$

Addition and Subtraction of Numbers in Scientific Notation

We have learned that numbers with exponents can be added or subtracted when they have the same base and same exponents (power).

Numbers in scientific notation have the same base 10. However, they may or may not have the same exponent.

1. To add or subtract numbers in scientific notation whose exponents are the same, factor out the exponent and add or subtract the numbers within the brackets.

For example,

(i) $4 \times \mathbf{10^{5}} + 3 \times \mathbf{10^{5}}$ Taking out 10^{5} as common factor,

$= (4 + 3) \times \mathbf{10^{5}}$ Adding numbers within brackets,

$= 7 \times \mathbf{10^{5}}$

(ii) $9 \times \mathbf{10^{6}} - 5 \times \mathbf{10^{6}}$ Taking 10^{6} as common factor,

$= (9 - 5) \times \mathbf{10^{6}}$ Subtracting numbers within the brackets,

$= 4 \times \mathbf{10^{6}}$

2. To add or subtract numbers in scientific notation whose exponents are the not the same, they must be converted to have the same exponent. It is easier to convert the smaller exponent to make it equal to the larger exponent.

Follow these steps to add (or subtract) numbers in scientific notation (with different exponents):

	Steps	Example
1.	Determine the number by which the smaller exponent needs to be increased to make it equal to the larger exponent.	$9.8 \times 10^{5} + 6.2 \times 10^{4}$ Larger exponent = 5 Smaller exponent = 4 $5 - 4 = 1$

2.	Increase the smaller exponent by this number and move the decimal point of the coefficient of the number to the left by the same number of places.	$9.8 \times 10^5 + 6.2 \times 10^{(4+1)}$ $= 9.8 \times 10^5 + 0.62 \times 10^5$ (This answer is not in scientific notation.)
3.	Add (or subtract) the new coefficient and factor out the common exponent in power of 10.	$(9.8 + 0.62) \times 10^5$ $= 10.42 \times 10^5$
4.	If the answer is not in scientific notation (i.e., if the coefficient is not between 1 and 10), then convert it to scientific notation. To convert to scientific notation, move the decimal point to the left until the coefficient is between 1 and 10. For each place the decimal point is moved, raise the exponent by 1.	$10.42 \times 10^{(5+1)}$ $= 1.042 \times 10^6$

Example 3.4-i **Adding Numbers in Scientific Notation**

Add the following:

(i) $5.1 \times 10^{-2} + 6.3 \times 10^{-2}$ (ii) $8.47 \times 10^{-3} + 5.28 \times 10^{-1}$ (iii) $7.41 \times 10^2 + 2.6 \times 10^{-3}$

Solution

(i) $5.1 \times 10^{-2} + 6.3 \times 10^{-2}$ — Exponents are equal. Taking common factor,

$= (5.1 + 6.3) \times 10^{-2}$ — Adding numbers within brackets,

$= 11.4 \times 10^{-2}$ — Converting to scientific notation,

$= 11.14 \times 10^{(-2+1)}$ — Increasing the exponent by 1 and moving the decimal point 1 place to the left,

$= 1.114 \times 10^{-1}$ — Answer in scientific notation.

(ii) $8.47 \times 10^{-3} + 5.28 \times 10^{-1}$ — Exponents are not equal.
Larger exponent – smaller exponent = –1 – (–3) = –1 + 3 = 2

$= 8.74 \times 10^{(-3+2)} + 5.28 \times 10^{-1}$ — Increasing the smaller exponent by 2 and moving the decimal point to the left by 2 places,

$= 0.0874 \times 10^{-1} + 5.28 \times 10^{-1}$ — Taking common factor 10^{-1},

$= (0.0874 + 5.28) \times 10^{-1}$ — Adding numbers within brackets,

$= 5.27041 \times 10^{-1}$ — Answer in scientific notation.

(iii) $7.41 \times 10^2 + 2.6 \times 10^{-3}$ — Exponents are not equal.
Larger exponent – smaller exponent = 2 – (–3) = 2 + 3 = 5,

$= 7.41 \times 10^2 + 2.6 \times 10^{(-3+5)}$ — Increasing the smaller exponent by 5 and moving the decimal point to the left by 5 places,

$= 7.41 \times 10^2 + 0.000026 \times 10^2$ — Taking common factor 10^2,

$= (7.41 + 0.000026) \times 10^2$ — Adding numbers within bracket,

$= 7.410026 \times 10^2$ — Answer in scientific notation.

Example 3.4-j Subtracting Numbers in Scientific Notation

Subtract the following:

(i) $7.24 \times 10^{-4} - 2.5 \times 10^{-4}$ (ii) $5.28 \times 10^{-2} - 9.59 \times 10^{-5}$ (iii) $4.78 \times 10^{3} - 6.5 \times 10^{-2}$

Solution

(i) $7.24 \times 10^{-4} - 2.5 \times 10^{-4}$ — Exponents are equal. Taking common factor 10^{-4},

$= (7.24 - 2.5) \times 10^{-4}$ — Subtracting numbers within brackets,

$= 4.74 \times 10^{-4}$ — Answer in scientific notation.

(ii) $5.28 \times 10^{-2} - 9.59 \times 10^{-5}$ — Exponents are not equal.
Larger exponent – smaller exponent = $-2 - (-5) = -2 + 5 = 3$,

$= 5.28 \times 10^{-2} - 9.59 \times 10^{(-5+3)}$ — Increasing the smaller exponent by 3 and moving the decimal point to the left by 3 places,

$= 5.28 \times 10^{-2} - 0.00959 \times 10^{-2}$ — Taking common factor 10^{-2},

$= (5.28 - 0.00959) \times 10^{-2}$ — Subtracting numbers within brackets,

$= 5.27041 \times 10^{-2}$ — Answer in scientific notation,

(iii) $4.78 \times 10^{3} - 6.5 \times 10^{-2}$ — Exponents are not equal.
Larger exponent – smaller exponent = $3 - (-2) = 3 + 2 = 5$,

$= 4.78 \times 10^{3} - 6.5 \times 10^{(-2+5)}$ — Increasing the smaller exponent by 5 and moving the decimal point of it to the left by 5 places,

$= 4.78 \times 10^{3} - 0.000065 \times 10^{3}$ — Taking common factor 10^{3},

$= (4.78 - 0.000065) \times 10^{3}$ — Subtracting numbers within bracket,

$= 4.779935 \times 10^{3}$ — Answer in scientific notation.

Example 3.4-k Combined Addition and Subtraction of Numbers in Scientific Notation

Evaluate:

$2.5 \times 10^{5} + 8.2 \times 10^{4} - 4.7 \times 10^{3}$

Solution

$2.5 \times 10^{5} + 8.2 \times 10^{4} - 4.7 \times 10^{3}$

$= 2.5 \times 10^{5} + 8.2 \times 10^{(4+1)} - 4.7 \times 10^{(3+2)}$ — Largest exponent = 5. Converting all exponents to 5 by moving the decimal places to the left and increasing the exponents,

$= 2.5 \times 10^{5} + 0.82 \times 10^{5} - 0.047 \times 10^{5}$ — Factoring out 10^{5},

$= (2.5 + 0.82 - 0.047) \times 10^{5}$ — Performing arithmetic operations within brackets,

$= 3.273 \times 10^{5}$ — Answer in scientific notation.

Multiplication of Numbers in Scientific Notation

Multiplying a number by another number with exponents of the same base is equivalent to multiplying their coefficients and adding their exponents.

Numbers in scientific notation have the same base 10.

Therefore, to multiply numbers in scientific notation, multiply their coefficients and add their exponents (power of 10). If the answer is not in scientific notation (i.e., coefficient is not between 1 and 10), convert it to scientific notation.

For example,

$(6.02 \times 10^{3}) \times (4 \times 10^{5})$	Multiplying the coefficients and adding the exponents,
$= (6.02 \times 4) \times 10^{(3+5)}$	Performing arithmetic operation within brackets,
$= 24.08 \times 10^{8}$	Answer is not in scientific notation.
$= 24.08 \times 10^{(8+1)}$	Converting to scientific notation,
$= 2.408 \times 10^{9}$	Answer in scientific notation.

Note: If a decimal number gets smaller by moving the decimal point to the left, then the exponent gets larger, by the number of decimal places moved.

Example 3.4-l **Multiplying Numbers in Scientific Notation**

Multiply the following:

(i) $(5.4 \times 10^{-3}) \times (2.2 \times 10^{-5})$ (ii) $(4.75 \times 10^{6}) \times (1.5 \times 10^{-2})$ (iii) $(7.5 \times 10^{-6}) \times (5.0 \times 10^{4})$

Solution

(i) $(5.4 \times 10^{-3}) \times (2.2 \times 10^{-5})$	Multiplying the coefficients and adding the exponents,
$= (5.4 \times 2.2) \times 10^{[-3+(-5)]}$	Performing arithmetic operation within brackets,
$= 11.88 \times 10^{-8}$	Answer is not in scientific notation.
$= 11.88 \times 10^{(-8+1)}$	Converting to scientific notation,
$= 1.188 \times 10^{-7}$	Answer in scientific notation.
(ii) $(4.75 \times 10^{6}) \times (1.5 \times 10^{-2})$	Multiplying the coefficients and adding the exponents,
$= (4.75 \times 1.5) \times 10^{[6+(-2)]}$	Performing arithmetic operation within brackets,
$= 7.125 \times 10^{4}$	Answer in scientific notation.
(iii) $(7.5 \times 10^{-6}) \times (5.0 \times 10^{4})$	Multiplying the coefficients and adding the exponents,
$= (7.5 \times 5.0) \times 10^{(-6+4)}$	Performing arithmetic operation within brackets,
$= 37.5 \times 10^{-2}$	Answer is not in scientific notation.
$= 37.5 \times 10^{(-2+1)}$	Converting to scientific notation,
$= 3.75 \times 10^{-1}$	Answer in scientific notation.

Division of Numbers in Scientific Notation

Dividing a number by another number with exponents of the same base is equivalent to dividing their coefficients and subtracting their exponents.

Numbers in scientific notation have the same base 10.

Therefore, to divide two numbers in scientific notation, divide their coefficients and subtract their exponents (power of 10). If the answer is not in scientific notation (i.e., coefficient is not between 1 and 10), convert it to scientific notation.

For example,

$2.48 \times 10^6 \div 8.0 \times 10^2$	Dividing the coefficients and subtracting the exponents,
$= \frac{2.48}{8.0} \times 10^{(6-2)}$	Performing arithmetic operations,
$= 0.31 \times 10^4$	Answer is not in scientific notation.
$= 0.31 \times 10^{(4-1)}$	Converting to scientific notation,
$= 3.1 \times 10^3$	Answer in scientific notation.

Note: If a decimal number gets larger by moving the decimal point to the right, then the exponent gets smaller by the number of decimal places moved.

Example 3.4-m **Dividing Numbers in Scientific Notation**

Divide the following:

(i) $(4.68 \times 10^{-3}) \div (6.5 \times 10^{-5})$ (ii) $(3.5 \times 10^{8}) \div (4.0 \times 10^{-4})$ (iii) $(9.2 \times 10^{-3}) \div (1.15 \times 10^{2})$

Solution

(i) $(4.68 \times 10^{-3}) \div (6.5 \times 10^{-5})$	Dividing the coefficients and subtracting the exponents,
$= \frac{4.68}{6.5} \times 10^{[-3-(-5)]}$	Performing arithmetic operations,
$= 0.72 \times 10^2$	Answer is not in scientific notation.
$= 0.72 \times 10^{(2-1)}$	Converting to scientific notation,
$= 7.2 \times 10^1$	Answer in scientific notation.
(ii) $(3.5 \times 10^{8}) \div (4.0 \times 10^{-4})$	Dividing the coefficients and subtracting the exponents,
$= \frac{3.5}{4.0} \times 10^{[8-(-4)]}$	Performing arithmetic operations,
$= 0.875 \times 10^{12}$	Answer is not in scientific notation.
$= 0.875 \times 10^{(12-1)}$	Converting to scientific notation,
$= 8.75 \times 10^{11}$	Answer is scientific notation.
(iii) $(9.2 \times 10^{-3}) \div (1.15 \times 10^{2})$	Dividing the coefficients and subtracting the exponents,
$= \frac{9.2}{1.15} \times 10^{(-3-2)}$	Performing arithmetic operations,
$= 8 \times 10^{-5}$	Answer in scientific notation.

Example 3.4-n **Combined Multiplication and Division of Numbers in Scientific Notation**

Evaluate:

$$\frac{(7.4 \times 10^6) \times (3.75 \times 10^5)}{2.5 \times 10^4}$$

Solution

$$\frac{(7.4 \times 10^6) \times (3.75 \times 10^5)}{2.5 \times 10^4}$$

Multiplying the coefficients within the numerator and dividing it by the coefficient in the denominator. Then adding the exponents within the numerator and subtracting the exponent of the denominator,

$$= \left(\frac{7.4 \times 3.75}{2.5}\right) \times 10^{(6 + 5 - 4)}$$

Performing arithmetic operations within brackets,

$$= 11.1 \times 10^7$$

Answer is not in scientific notation.

$$= 11.1 \times 10^{(7 + 1)}$$

Converting to scientific notation,

$$= 1.11 \times 10^8$$

Answer in scientific notation.

3.4 | Exercises

Answers to odd-numbered problems are available at the end of the textbook.

For Problems 1 to 10, determine the number of significant digits in each of the numbers.

1. a. 700 b. 9,070
2. a. 40,600 b. 10,200
3. a. 5.70 b. 30.40
4. a. 9.00 b. 20.80
5. a. 6.250 b. 70.0164
6. a. 4.530 b. 20.325
7. a. 0.4700 b. 24.805
8. a. 0.2010 b. 15.407
9. a. 0.008 b. 0.0224
10. a. 0.000004 b. 0.0825

For Problems 11 to 20 round the numbers to (i) 3 significant digits and (ii) 2 significant digits.

11. a. 5,065 b. 1,982
12. a. 5,460 b. 1,978
13. a. 589.025 b. 57.3892
14. a. 821.782 b. 40.9055
15. a. 48.4848 b. 25.859
16. a. 99.0999 b. 91.555
17. a. 0.7850 b. 6.07344
18. a. 0.8090 b. 9.0085
19. a. 0.98901 b. 6.6666
20. a. 0.5555 b. 7.7777

For Problems 21 to 26, perform the indicated arithmetic operations and round the answer to the same number of decimal places as the number with the least number of decimal places.

21. a. 142.135 + 9.12 b. 324.761 + 28.4
22. a. 215.241 + 6.37 b. 532.863 + 59.9
23. a. 287.657 – 6.42 b. 466.945 – 54.8
24. a. 354.657 – 7.89 b. 465.976 – 99.7
25. a. 30.6 + 4.703 – 9.009 b. 44.9 – 1.906 – 0.61
26. a. 50.7 + 9.856 – 21.05 b. 27.02 – 9.005 – 0.081

For Problems 27 to 32, perform the indicated arithmetic operations and round the answer to the same number of significant digits as the number with the least number of significant digits.

27. a. 67.86×9.8 b. 152.92×45.5
28. a. 59.43×8.2 b. 253.15×38.4
29. a. $99.33 \div 9.9$ b. $225.25 \div 25.5$
30. a. $46.66 \div 0.6$ b. $315.15 \div 15.15$
31. a. $54.75 \times 1.21 \times 4{,}500$ b. $1.90 \times 380 \div 0.95$
32. a. $25.5 \times 1.8 \times 3{,}600$ b. $5.07 \times 4{,}500 \div 13.5$

For Problems 33 to 42, write the numbers in scientific notation.

33. a. 235 b. 42,300
34. a. 745 b. 15,700
35. a. 12.75 b. 78.91
36. a. 18.25 b. 90.54
37. a. 0.58 b. 0.048
38. a. 0.74 b. 0.089
39. a. 0.0038 b. 0.0002
40. a. 0.0096 b. 0.0007
41. a. 0.06×10^{8} b. 0.0025×10^{-9}
42. a. 0.03×10^{5} b. 0.0046×10^{-10}

For Problems 43 to 52, write the numbers in standard notation.

43. a. 4.6×10^{4} b. 2.9×10^{0}
44. a. 3.7×10^{3} b. 4.75×10^{1}
45. a. 3.09×10^{6} b. 4.654×10^{4}
46. a. 7.54×10^{4} b. 8.015×10^{5}
47. a. 8.9×10^{-1} b. 2.16×10^{-4}
48. a. 6.8×10^{-2} b. 4.65×10^{-3}
49. a. 3.15×10^{-3} b. 6.15×10^{-5}
50. a. 1.29×10^{-4} b. 9.17×10^{-3}
51. a. 0.0056×10^{3} b. 406.5×10^{-6}
52. a. 0.0076×10^{4} b. 675.7×10^{-5}

For Problems 53 to 62, perform the arithmetic operations and write the answers in scientific notation. Do not round the anwser.

53. $(8.5 \times 10^{5}) + (3.84 \times 10^{4})$
54. $(6.35 \times 10^{6}) + (5.07 \times 10^{7})$
55. $(9.82 \times 10^{-3}) + (1.58 \times 10^{-4})$
56. $(7.92 \times 10^{-5}) + (9.72 \times 10^{-3})$
57. $(3.1 \times 10^{9}) - (2.6 \times 10^{8})$
58. $(8.2 \times 10^{7}) - (4.7 \times 10^{6})$
59. $(7.54 \times 10^{-2}) - (3.25 \times 10^{-3})$
60. $(2.58 \times 10^{-2}) - (1.99 \times 10^{-1})$
61. $(2.5 \times 10^{4}) + (8.9 \times 10^{2}) - (1.5 \times 10^{3})$
62. $(6.7 \times 10^{3}) + (7.4 \times 10^{2}) - (8.6 \times 10^{1})$

For Problems 63 to 72, perform the arithmetic operations and write the answer in scientific notation. Do not round the answers.

63. $(2.0 \times 10^{5}) \times (8.6 \times 10^{8})$
64. $(4.75 \times 10^{4}) \times (2.0 \times 10^{6})$
65. $(7.5 \times 10^{-12}) \times (4.2 \times 10^{5})$
66. $(8.25 \times 10^{3}) \times (4 \times 10^{-6})$
67. $(4.8 \times 10^{5}) \div (1.5 \times 10^{8})$
68. $(9.25 \times 10^{10}) \div (5.0 \times 10^{4})$
69. $(3.84 \times 10^{-2}) \div (7.68 \times 10^{-4})$
70. $(6.48 \times 10^{-4}) \div (9.72 \times 10^{-6})$
71. $(9.8 \times 10^{-4}) \times (5 \times 10^{-3}) \div (3.5 \times 10^{-9})$
72. $(5.4 \times 10^{-5}) \times (8 \times 10^{-6}) \div (7.2 \times 10^{-14})$

3 | Review Exercises

Answers to odd-numbered problems are available at the end of the textbook.

1. Find the difference between 2^{5} and 5^{2}.
2. Find the difference between 3^{4} and 4^{3}.
3. Express 243 as a power of 3 and then evaluate $243^{\frac{3}{5}}$.
4. Express 512 as a power of 2 and then evaluate $512^{\frac{4}{9}}$.

Express Problems 5 and 6 as a power of the indicated base value.

5. a. $(2^{6})^{\frac{1}{3}}$ as a power of 2

   b. $(5^{15})^{\frac{1}{5}}$ as a power of 5

6. a. $\left(\frac{3^9}{3^3}\right)^{\frac{1}{3}}$ as a power of 3

   b. $\left(\frac{2^{12}}{2^4}\right)^{\frac{1}{4}}$ as a power of 2

7. Express as a single exponent using laws of exponents, and then evaluate:

   a. $(3^2)^{\frac{1}{2}} \times (3^3)^{\frac{2}{3}}$ b. $(6^2)^{\frac{1}{3}} \times (6^3)^{\frac{1}{9}}$

8. Express as a single exponent using laws of exponents, and then evaluate:

a. $(2^2)^{\frac{1}{4}} \times (2^5)^{\frac{3}{10}}$ b. $(5^3)^{\frac{2}{3}} \times (5^2)^{\frac{1}{2}}$

For Problems 9 to 16, simplify using laws of exponents and then evaluate.

9. a. $\dfrac{2^3 \times 3^4 \times 2^2}{3 \times 2^5}$ b. $\dfrac{(5^2)^3 \times 5^4}{5^7}$

10. a. $\dfrac{5^2 \times 7^3 \times 5^4}{7 \times 5^6}$ b. $\dfrac{(2^5)^4 \times 2^2}{2^{17}}$

11. a. $(-5)^2 \times (4)^2$ b. $-10^4 \times 10^3$

12. a. $(-2)^2 \times (3)^2$ b. $-2^4 \times 2^2$

13. a. $(125)^{-\frac{1}{3}}$ b. $(49)^{-\frac{1}{2}}$ c. $\sqrt{\dfrac{64}{81}}$

14. a. $(16)^{-\frac{1}{4}}$ b. $(27)^{-\frac{1}{3}}$ c. $\sqrt{\dfrac{25}{36}}$

15. a. $\sqrt{7^4}$ b. $\sqrt{\dfrac{25}{36}}$ c. $\sqrt[3]{\dfrac{216}{125}}$

16. a. $\sqrt{5^6}$ b. $\sqrt{\dfrac{64}{81}}$ c. $\sqrt[3]{\dfrac{64}{27}}$

Evaluate Problems 17 to 32 and express the answers rounded to two decimal places wherever applicable.

17. a. $\dfrac{16 + 4(-3)}{10 - 4 + 1} + \dfrac{(16 + 4) - 3}{10 - (4 + 1)}$

b. $14 - 3\,[(6 - 9)(-4) + 12] \div (-2)$

18. a. $\dfrac{2(-6) + 4}{24 - (7 + 3)} + \dfrac{2(-6 + 4)}{24 - 7 + 3}$

b. $5(-4) - 3[(-9 + 6) + (-3) - 4]$

19. a. $[(1 + 12)(1 - 5)]^2 \div [(5 + 3) \times 2^2 - (-2)^2]$

b. $2^2[(9 - 7) \div 2 + 9 - 4]$

20. a. $8 \div 4 + (4 - 6^2) \div (13 - 5) \times (-2)^6$

b. $6 \div [4 \times (2 - 8) \div (3^2 + 3)] \div 4$

21. a. $64 \div (-2)^4 + 4(-3^2) \div 2 - 5$

b. $(-6)^2 - 9^2 \div 3^3 - (-3)(-2)$

22. a. $8 \div (-2)^3(-9) + 6(-5)^3 \div (-5)^2$

b. $(-8)^2 - 4^3 \div 2^2 - (-6)(-2)$

23. a. $6{,}000\left(1 + \dfrac{0.06}{12}\right)^{36}$

b. $2{,}000(1 + 0.004)^{-24}$

24. a. $4{,}000\left(1 + \dfrac{0.075}{12}\right)^{60}$

b. $5{,}000(1 + 0.003)^{-48}$

25. $\dfrac{3{,}000\,[(1.06)^{25} - 1]}{0.06}$

26. $\dfrac{1{,}400\,[(1.03)^{30} - 1]}{0.03}$

27. $\dfrac{950\,[1 - (1.03)^{-15}]}{0.03}$

28. $\dfrac{1{,}200\,[1 - (1.04)^{-20}]}{0.04}$

29. a. $-15 - (-15)$

b. $-14 - (-7)$

30. a. $13 - (-11) + 0$

b. $22 - (-4) - 6$

31. a. $8 + |2 - 7|$

b. $-|-23| - |10 - 15|$

32. a. $15 - |3 - 9|$

b. $-|-42| - |35 - 18|$

33. Determine the number of significant digits in each of the following numbers:

a. 7,101.1 b. 54.001 c. 0.0072

34. Determine the number of significant digits in each of the following numbers:

a. 54,020 b. 0.2055 c. 0.09081

35. Write the numbers in standard form.

a. 8.9×10^2 b. 5.6×10^{-2} c. 9.64×10^{-4}

36. Write the numbers in standard form.

a. 5.1×10^3 b. 6.8×10^{-4} c. 4.75×10^{-4}

For Problems 37 to 44, perform the arithmetic operations and write the answers in scientific notation. Do not round the answer.

37. a. $4.65 \times 10^{14} + 9.95 \times 10^{12}$

b. $7.02 \times 10^{-2} + 6.95 \times 10^{-3}$

38. a. $7.28 \times 10^6 + 4.35 \times 10^5$

b. $1.64 \times 10^{-12} + 5.5 \times 10^{-10}$

39. a. $4.01 \times 10^6 - 3.56 \times 10^4$

b. $3.56 \times 10^{-3} - 8.01 \times 10^{-4}$

40. a. $1.25 \times 10^7 - 9.75 \times 10^5$

b. $2.85 \times 10^{-1} - 7.45 \times 10^{-3}$

41. a. $(6.0 \times 10^4) \times (4.0 \times 10^7)$

b. $(7.5 \times 10^{-6}) \times (6.0 \times 10^{-5})$

42. a. $(7.75 \times 10^6) \times (2.0 \times 10^8)$

b. $(9.45 \times 10^{-5}) \times (3.0 \times 10^{-7})$

43. a. $(2.0 \times 10^5) \div (4.0 \times 10^8)$

b. $(1.45 \times 10^{-9}) \div (5.8 \times 10^{-3})$

44. a. $(1.75 \times 10^4) \div (3.50 \times 10^{-6})$

b. $(1.61 \times 10^{-7}) \div (4.83 \times 10^{-2})$

3 | Self-Test Exercises

Answers to all problems are available at the end of the textbook.

For the following problems, simplify and express the answers rounded to two decimal places wherever applicable.

1. Express the following as a power of the indicated bases:
   a. 625 as a power of 5.
   b. 729 as a power of 3.
   c. 128 as a power of 2.

2. Express the following as a power of the indicated bases:
   a. $(9)^{\frac{3}{2}}$ as a power of 3
   b. $(16)^{\frac{3}{4}}$ as a power of 2

3. Express the following as a power of the indicated bases:
   a. $3^4 \times 3^{(4+2)}$ as a power of 3
   b. $10^4 \times 10^{(3+2)}$ as a power of 10

4. Simplify using laws of exponents and then evaluate:
   a. $\frac{2^3 \times (3^2)^3 \times 3^4}{2^3 \times (2^3)^2 \times 3^5}$ b. $\frac{2^4 \times (3^2)^4 \times 2^2}{2^5 \times (3^3)^2 \times 2^0}$

Evaluate Problems 5 to 19.

5. a. $(2^2 \times 3 \times 5^0)^{-1}$ b. $(3^2 \times 2^{-2} \times 5)^0$

6. a. $\left(\frac{3}{2}\right)^2 + \frac{3}{8}$
   b. $\frac{3}{2} \div \frac{15}{8} \times \sqrt{16}$
   c. $4 \times \frac{8}{5} \div \frac{4}{3} + \sqrt{4} - 1$

7. a. $\frac{2}{5} \times \sqrt{100} + 2^4 \div \frac{5}{3}$
   b. $\frac{3}{4} + \left(\frac{3}{2}\right)^3$
   c. $\sqrt{36} \times \frac{4}{3} \div \frac{8}{6} - 7 + 2$

8. a. $\left(\frac{2}{3} + \frac{4}{3}\right)^5$ b. $\left(\frac{5^{-\frac{1}{3}}}{2^{-2}}\right)^3$

9. a. $\left(\frac{9^{\frac{2}{5}}}{9^{-\frac{3}{5}}}\right) \times 3^2$ b. $\left(\frac{8^{-\frac{5}{9}}}{9^{-\frac{7}{9}}}\right) \times 2^3$

10. a. $-5^3(-25)^3$ b. $-100^2 \times (-10)^4$

11. a. $3^{-2} \times 3^3$ b. $12^{-8} \times 12^9$

12. a. $(-3)^3 - (-1)^3$
    b. $(-2)^5 \times (4-5)^3 - (-10)$
    c. $1{,}250 \times (1 + 0.02 \times \frac{136}{365})^{-1}$

13. a. $(-5)^3 - (-4)^3$
    b. $(-4)^5 \div (-2)^6$
    c. $5{,}600 \times (1 + 0.04 \times \frac{219}{365})^{-1}$

14. a. $200(1.08)^7$
    b. $450(1.03)^{-2}$

15. a. $2{,}000\left[1 + \frac{0.075}{12}\right]^{-60}$
    b. $4{,}500\left[1 + \frac{0.048}{4}\right]^{-15}$

16. $\frac{3{,}600\,[(1.06)^5 - 1]}{0.06}$

17. $\frac{4{,}400\left[1 - (1.03)^{-20}\right]}{0.03}$

18. a. $-9 + |(-4) + (-2)|$
    a. $|8 - (-5) - (-3)|$
    b. $|12 - 8 \times 2| - |-4|$

19. a. $\frac{16^{\frac{1}{2}} \times 6}{81^{\frac{1}{2}}}$ b. $\frac{9^{\frac{1}{2}} \times 81^{\frac{1}{2}}}{13^2 - 5^2}$

20. Write the numbers in scientific notation:
    a. 10.09 b. 0.005 c. 60,200

21. Write the numbers in standard form:
    a. 2.7×10^3 b. 4.15×10^{-3} c. 3.0405×10^{-2}

For Problems 22 to 24, perform the arithmetic operations and express the answers in scientific notation. Do not round the answers.

22. a. $4.01 \times 10^4 + 9.99 \times 10^3$
    b. $2.004 \times 10^{-6} + 8.95 \times 10^{-5}$

23. a. $3.04 \times 10^6 - 2.512 \times 10^5$
    b. $4.06 \times 10^{-8} - 9.94 \times 10^{-7}$

24. a. $(6.50 \times 10^7) \times (8.0 \times 10^{-9})$
    b. $(1.225 \times 10^{14}) \div (8.75 \times 10^{-6})$

4 RATIOS AND PROPORTIONS

One of the ways in which we use mathematics in our daily lives is through the comparison of numbers and quantities of two or more items. Data expressed in numbers becomes more meaningful and easier to evaluate when relevant comparisons are made. We use ratios to find the unit price in determining the best price for an item, when different quantities of the same item are offered at different prices. Also, we use proportions to calculate unknown quantities that would otherwise be difficult to estimate. For example, if you wanted to calculate the amount of gas needed to travel 375 km, knowing that the fuel efficiency of your car is 9.8 litres per 100 km, then you would have to set up a proportion equation to determine the amount of gas needed. In this chapter, you will learn the concept and be able to solve problems relating to ratios, proportions, and pro-rations.

LEARNING OBJECTIVES

- Identify ratios and rates to compare quantities.
- Set up ratios and use them to solve problems involving allocation and sharing of quantities.
- Solve problems by finding unknown quantities using proportions as equivalent sets of ratios.
- Allocate quantities on a proportionate basis using pro-ration as an application of proportions.

CHAPTER OUTLINE

4.1 | Ratios

Introduction

Ratio is a comparison or relationship between two or more quantities.

A **ratio** is a comparison or relationship between two or more quantities with the same unit. Therefore, ratios are not expressed with units.

For example, if Andy (A) invested \$5,000 and Barry (B) invested \$4,000 in a business. The comparison of A's investment to B's investment in the same order is called the ratio of their investments.

Expressing a Ratio of Two Quantities

When comparing two quantities, there are different ways to express the ratio. In the example above, the ratio of A's investment to B's may be expressed in any of the following forms:

5,000 to 4,000 (separate the quantities using the word 'to')

5,000 : 4,000 (using a colon and read as '5,000 is to 4,000')

$\frac{5,000}{4,000}$ (as a fraction and read as '5,000 over 4,000')

In the above example, if the decimal equivalent of the fraction is used, then it must be stated as: "A's invesment is 1.25 times B's investment".

Note: When representing a ratio as a fraction, if the denominator is 1, the denominator (1) must still be written.

For example, if the ratio of two quantities is $\frac{3}{1}$ then it is incorrect to say that the ratio is 3. It should be stated as $\frac{3}{1}$ or 3 : 1.

Expressing a Ratio of More than Two Quantities

When comparing more than two quantities, we use a colon to represent a ratio.

For example, if A's investment is \$5,000, B's investment is \$4,000, and C's investment is \$1,000 in a business, then the ratio of their investments is expressed as:

$$A : B : C = 5,000 : 4,000 : 1,000$$

Terms of a Ratio

The quantities in a ratio are called the terms of the ratio.

For example, the terms of the ratio 5 : 7 : 19 are 5, 7, and 19.

Equivalent Ratios

When all the terms of the ratio are multiplied by the same number or divided by the same number, the result will be an equivalent ratio.

For example, when the terms of the ratio 12 : 15 are multiplied by 2, we obtain an equivalent ratio of 24 : 30.

$$12 : 15$$

$$12 \times \mathbf{2} : 15 \times \mathbf{2}$$

$$24 : 30$$

When the terms of the ratio 12 : 15 are divided by the common factor 3, we obtain the equivalent ratio of 4 : 5.

$$12 : 15$$

$$12 \div \mathbf{3} : 15 \div \mathbf{3}$$

$$4 : 5$$

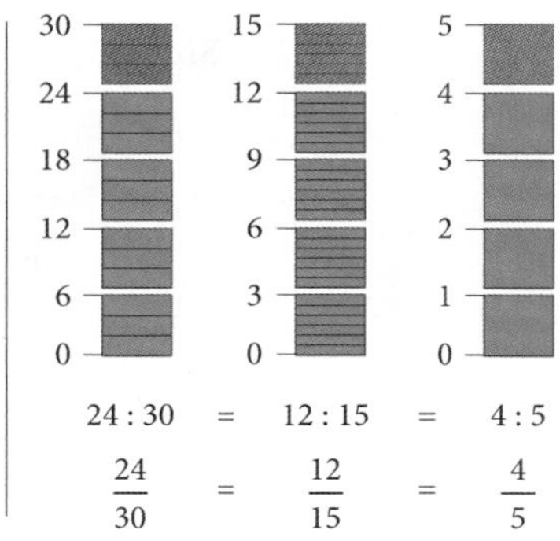

Therefore, the ratios 12 : 15, 24 : 30, and 4 : 5 are called **equivalent ratios**.

Example 4.1-a

Determining Equivalent Ratios

Determine whether the given pairs of ratios are equivalent.

(i) 18 : 12 and 12 : 8

(ii) 20 : 24 and 15 : 20

Solution

(i)

18 : 12	12 : 8
= 18 ÷ 6 : 12 ÷ 6	= 12 ÷ 4 : 8 ÷ 4
= 3 : 2	= 3 : 2

Therefore, the given pairs of ratios are equivalent.

(ii)

20 : 24	15 : 20
= 20 ÷ 4 : 24 ÷ 4	= 15 ÷ 5 : 20 ÷ 5
= 5 : 6	= 3 : 4

Therefore, the given pairs of ratios are not equivalent.

Reducing a Ratio to its Simplest or Lowest Terms

When two ratios are equal, they result in the same answer when reduced to their lowest terms.

Comparisons are easier when ratios are reduced to their lowest terms. When all the terms of a ratio are integers, the ratio can be reduced to its lowest terms by dividing all the terms by their common factors.

For example, if 'A' earns $3,000, 'B' earns $4,500, and 'C' earns $6,000, then the equivalent ratio of their earnings reduced to the lowest terms is calculated as follows:

$A : B : C$

3,000 : 4,500 : 6,000	Dividing each term by the common factor 100,
= 30 : 45 : 60	Dividing each term by the common factor 15,
= 2 : 3 : 4	Now, the ratio is in its lowest terms.

A ratio is in its simplest form when the terms do not have a common factor other than one.

By reducing the ratio to lowest terms, we can say that the earnings of A, B, and C are in the ratio of 2 : 3 : 4.

Comparing Quantities of Items That Have the Same Kind of Measure but Different Units

When writing ratios to compare quantities of items that have the same kind of measure, the units have to be the same.

For example, the ratio of 45 minutes to 2 hours is not 45 : 2. We are comparing 'time' in both these cases; therefore, the units used have to be the same.

45 minutes : 2 hours	Converting 2 hours to minutes using 1 hour = 60 minutes,
= 45 minutes : 120 minutes	Dividing by the common factor 15,
= 3 : 8	

Similarly, we determine the ratio of 2.5 kilometres to 3,000 metres as follows:

2.5 km : 3,000 m	Converting km to m, 2.5 km = 2,500 m,
= 2,500 m : 3,000 m	Dividing by the common factor 100,
= 25 : 30	Dividing by the common factor 5,
= 5 : 6	

Example 4.1-b

Comparing Quantities

Express each of the following ratios in its simplest form:

(i) 1.2 L to 800 mL

(ii) 16 weeks to 2 years

Solution

(i) 1.2 L to 800 mL

1.2 L : 800 mL	Converting 1.2 L to mL, 1.2 L = 1,200 mL,
= 1,200 mL : 800 mL	Dividing both terms by the common factor 400,
= 3 : 2	

Therefore, the ratio of 1.2 L to 800 mL is 3 : 2.

(ii) 16 weeks to 2 years

16 weeks : 2 years	Converting 2 years to weeks, 2 years = 104 weeks,
= 16 weeks : 104 weeks	Dividing both terms by the common factor 8,
= 2 : 13	

Therefore, the ratio of 16 weeks to 2 years is 2 : 13.

Reducing Ratios When One or More of the Terms of the Ratio Are Fractions

To reduce the ratio, first convert all the terms to integers by multiplying all the terms by their lowest common denominator, and then reduce to their lowest terms.

For example,

$\frac{15}{9} : \frac{7}{3} : 3$	Multiplying each term by the lowest common denominator 9,
15 : 21 : 27	Dividing each term by the common factor 3,
5 : 7 : 9	

Reducing Ratios When One or More of the Terms of the Ratio Are Decimal Numbers

he ratio remains the same hen all the terms are ultiplied or divided by the ame number.

To reduce the ratio, first convert all the terms to integers by moving the decimal of all the terms to the right by the same number of places, and then reduce to their lowest terms.

For example,

2.25 : 3.5 : 5	Moving the decimal point of each term by 2 places to the right,
225 : 350 : 500	Dividing each term by the common factor 25,
9 : 14 : 20	

Reducing Ratios When the Terms of the Ratio Are a Combination of Fractions and Decimals

To reduce the ratio, first convert all the fractional terms to decimals or decimal terms to fractions, then convert all the terms to integers. Finally, reduce to their lowest terms.

For example,

$5.8 : \frac{9}{2} : 4$	Multiplying each term by the common denominator 2,
11.6 : 9 : 8	Moving the decimal point of each term by 1 place to the right,
116 : 90 : 80	Dividing each term by the common factor 2,
58 : 45 : 40	

Reducing Ratios to an Equivalent Ratio Where the Smallest Term is 1

To make the comparison of quantities easier, we can also reduce a ratio to its equivalent ratio where the smallest term is equal to 1, by dividing all the terms by the smallest value.

For example, if the investment amounts of 3 partners 'A', 'B', and 'C' are \$35,000, \$78,750, and \$59,500, respectively, then the equivalent ratio of their investments, where the smallest term is 1, is calculated as follows:

A : B : C	
35,000 : 78,750 : 59,500	Dividing each term by the smallest term, 35,000,
1 : 2.25 : 1.7	Now, the ratio is reduced to its equivalent ratio with the smallest term equal to 1.

By reducing it so that the smallest term is equal to 1, we can state: (i) *B*'s investment is 2.25 times *A*'s investment and (ii) *C*'s investment is 1.7 times *A*'s investment.

Example 4.1-c

Reducing Ratios to Lowest Terms

Express the following ratios as equivalent ratios in their lowest whole numbers and then reduce them to ratios where the smallest term is 1:

(i) $2\frac{7}{9} : 3\frac{1}{3} : 5$ (ii) $2.5 : 1.75 : 0.625$ (iii) $1.25 : \frac{5}{6} : 2$

Solution

(i)

$2\frac{7}{9} : 3\frac{1}{3} : 5$	Converting the terms with mixed numbers to improper fractions,
$\frac{25}{9} : \frac{10}{3} : 5$	Multiplying each term by the lowest common denominator 9,
25 : 30 : 45	Dividing each term by the common factor 5,
5 : 6 : 9	Dividing each term by the smallest term 5,
1 : 1.2 : 1.8	

Therefore, $2\frac{7}{9} : 3\frac{1}{3} : 5$ reduced to its lowest terms is 5 : 6 : 9 and the equivalent ratio where the smallest term is 1 is 1 : 1.2 : 1.8.

(ii) 2.5 : 1.75 : 0.625

2.5 : 1.75 : 0.625	Moving the decimal point of each term by 3 places to the right,
2,500 : 1,750 : 625	Dividing each term by the common factor 125,
20 : 14 : 5	Dividing each term by the smallest term 5,
4 : 2.8 : 1	

Therefore, 2.5 : 1.75 : 0.625 reduced to its lowest terms is 20 : 14 : 5 and the equivalent ratio where the smallest term is 1 is 4 : 2.8 : 1.

(iii)

$1.25 : \frac{5}{6} : 2$	Multiply each term by 6,
7.5 : 5 : 12	Moving the decimal point of each term by 1 place to the right,
75 : 50 : 120	Dividing each term by the common factor 5,
15 : 10 : 24	Dividing each term by the smallest term 10,
1.5 : 1 : 2.4	

Therefore, $1.25 : \frac{5}{6} : 2$ reduced to lowest terms is 15 : 10 : 24 and the equivalent ratio where the smallest term is 1 is 1.5 : 1 : 2.4.

Order of a Ratio

The order of presenting terms in a ratio is important. For example, if A saves \$800, B saves \$1,500, and C saves \$1,200, then the ratio of the savings of A, B, and C is:

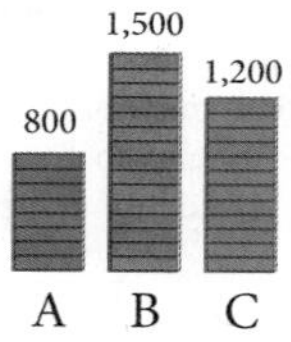

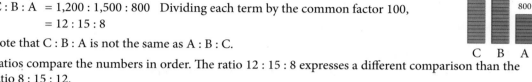

$$A : B : C = 800 : 1{,}500 : 1{,}200$$ Dividing each term by the common factor 100,

$$= 8 : 15 : 12$$

In the previous example, the ratio of the savings of C, B, and A is:

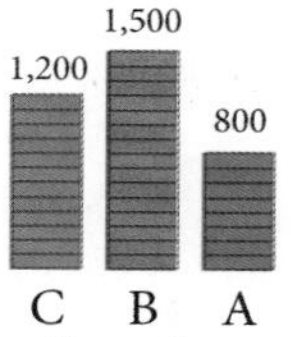

$$C : B : A = 1{,}200 : 1{,}500 : 800$$ Dividing each term by the common factor 100,

$$= 12 : 15 : 8$$

Note that C : B : A is not the same as A : B : C.

Ratios compare the numbers in order. The ratio 12 : 15 : 8 expresses a different comparison than the ratio 8 : 15 : 12.

Comparing Quantities

When using ratios to compare quantities of items that have different units of measure, the units of measurement of each quantity must be included in the ratio.

For example, when baking a cake, Maggie uses 4 kilograms of flour, 2 litres of water, and 6 eggs. Therefore, the ratio of flour to water to eggs is,

	flour (kg)	:	water (L)	:	eggs (numbers)	
=	4	:	2	:	6	Dividing each term by the common factor 2,
=	2	:	1	:	3	i.e., 2 kg flour : 1 litre water : 3 eggs

Rate, Unit Rate, and Unit Price

Rate

A rate is a special ratio that is used to compare two quantities or amounts that have different units of measure. The quantities of measurements being compared are called the terms of the ratio.

For example, if a car travels 100 km using 9 L of gas, then the rate is 100 km : 9 L.

The 1st term of the ratio is measured in kilometres and the 2nd term is measured in litres.

The word 'per' indicates that it is a rate and it is usually denoted by a slash "/".

Therefore, 100 km : 9 L is usually written as 100 km per 9 L or 100 km/9 L.

Rates are used in our day-to-day activities such as travelling, working, shopping, etc. For example: travelled 90 km in 1.5 hours, worked 75 hours in 2 weeks, paid \$4.80 for 3 L of milk, etc.

Example 4.1-d **Calculating Rate as a Ratio of Different Units of Measurements**

A laser printer printed 88 pages in 6 minutes. Express the rate in simplified form.

Solution

The unit of the first term is in number of pages and the unit of the second term is in minutes.

Therefore, the rate of printing = 88 pages : 6 minutes (or 88 pages / 6 minutes).

Then, in simplified form = 44 pages : 3 minutes (or 44 pages / 3 minutes).

Therefore, the printing rate is 44 pages / 3 minutes.

Unit Rate

If the denominator of a **ratio** is 1, the 1 must be written in the denominator.
If the denominator of a **rate** is 1, we usually do not write the 1 in the denominator.

Unit rate represents the number of units of the first quantity (or measurements) that corresponds to one unit of the second quantity. That is, unit rate is a rate in which the rate is expressed as a quantity which has a denominator of 1.

Rate can be converted to unit rate simply by dividing the first term by the second term.

For example,

A rate of 90 km in 1.5 hours, converted to unit rate:

= 90 km/1.5 hours

= 60 km/1 hour

= 60 km/hour

Simlarly,

A rate of 75 hours in 2 weeks, converted to unit rate:

= 75 hours/2 weeks

= 37.5 hours/1 week

= 37.5 hours/week

Example 4.1-e **Calculating Unit Rate**

A car travelled 300 kilometres in 5 hours. Calculate its speed.

Solution

Distance (km) : Time (hr)

= 300 : 5 Dividing each term by 5 to reduce the second unit to 1,

= 60 : 1

Therefore, the speed of the car is 60 km per hour or 60km/hr.

Example 4.1-f **Calculating Hourly Rate of Pay**

Peter worked 9 hours and earned $247.50. Calculate his hourly rate of pay.

Solution

Earnings ($) : Working Period (hrs)

= 247.50 : 9 Dividing each term by 9 to reduce the second unit to 1,

= 27.50 : 1

Therefore, his hourly rate of pay is $27.50 per hour or $27.50/hr.

Example 4.1-g **Using Unit Rates to Solve a World Problem**

A car travels 90 km in 1.5 hours. At this rate, how many kilometres will it travel in 5 hours?

Solution

This can be solved by first finding the unit rate.

90 km in 1.5 hours

Therefore, the number of km per hour $= \frac{90 \text{ km}}{1.5 \text{ hours}}$

$= 60$ km/hour

That is, the distance travelled in 1 hour = 60 km.

Therefore, the distance travelled in 5 hours = 60 × 5 = 300 km.

Example 4.1-h

Comparing Unit Rates

Car A requires 8.9 litres of gas to travel 100 km. Car B requires 45 litres of gas to travel 475 km. Which car has the better fuel economy?

Solution

Car A : 100 km requires 8.9 litres of gas.

$$\text{Therefore, the number of km per litre} = \frac{100 \text{ km}}{8.9 \text{ litres}}$$

$$= 11.24 \text{ km/litre of gas}$$

Car B : 475km requires 45 litres of gas.

$$\text{Therefore, the number of km per litre} = \frac{475 \text{ km}}{45 \text{ litres}}$$

$$= 10.56 \text{ km/litre of gas}$$

Therefore, Car A has the better fuel economy.

Unit Price

Unit price is the unit rate when it is expressed in unit currency, dollars, cents, etc. Unit price indicates the cost of an item for one unit of that item. The price is always the numerator and the unit is the denominator. That is, price is expressed per quantity of 1.

Price of gas is $1.36 per litre ($1.36/litre), price of grapes is $2 per kg ($2/kg), price of juice is $0.75 per can, etc., are examples of unit price.

If the total price of a given quantity of an item is known, to find its unit price divide the total price of the item by its quantity.

The unit price is used in comparing and making decisions in purchasing items when various options are available. We save money when we compare the unit price of the same item in different sized containers or different packages to determine the cheaper price per unit for our purchases.

Example 4.1-i

Calculating the Unit Price of an Item

If 3 litres of milk cost $4.80, then what is the unit price of milk?

Solution

Divide the total price of the given quantity of milk by its quantity to find the unit price of milk.

That is, $4.80 should be divided by 3 litres,

$$\frac{\$4.80}{3 \text{ litres}} = \$1.60 \text{ per litre}$$

Therefore the unit price of milk is $1.60 per litre ($1.60/litre).

Example 4.1-j

Comparing Unit Prices

5 kg of almonds cost $43.50 and 4 kg of almonds cost $34.20. Which is cheaper to buy based on its unit price?

Solution

5 kg of almonds cost $43.50.

$$\text{Therefore, unit price} = \frac{\$43.50}{5 \text{ kg}}$$

$$= \$8.70 \text{ per kg}$$

4 kg of almonds cost $34.20

$$\text{Therefore, unit price} = \frac{\$34.20}{4 \text{ kg}}$$

$$= \$8.55 \text{ per kg}$$

Therefore, based on unit price, buying 4 kg of almonds for $34.20 is cheaper than buying 5 kg of almonds for $43.50.

Note: Unit rate and unit price problems can also be solved using the method of proportions as demonstrated in the next section.

Sharing Quantities

Sharing quantities refers to the allocation or distribution of a quantity into two or more portions (or units) based on a given ratio.

For example, to allocate last year's \$1,000 profit among A, B, and C in the ratio of 2 : 3 : 5, first add the terms of the ratio (i.e., 2, 3, and 5), which results in a total of 10 units. These 10 units represent the total profit of \$1,000, where A's share constitutes 2 units, B's 3 units, and C's 5 units, as shown in the diagram below.

Each person's share can then be calculated, as follows:

$$A\text{'s share} = \frac{2}{10} \times 1{,}000 = \$200.00$$

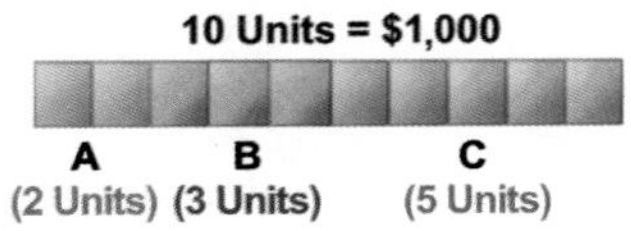

$$B\text{'s share} = \frac{3}{10} \times 1{,}000 = \$300.00$$

$$C\text{'s share} = \frac{5}{10} \times 1{,}000 = \$500.00$$

The total of the amount shared individually will be equal to the original amount shared.

The ratio of the amount shared individually, when reduced, will be equal to the original ratio.

- The total of *A*, *B*, and *C*'s shares will be equal to the profit amount of \$1,000.

That is, the shares of $A + B + C = 200 + 300 + 500 = 1{,}000$.

- If we reduce the ratio of the amounts shared by *A*, *B*, and *C* to its lowest terms, the result would be the original ratio. That is, 200 : 300 : 500 reduced to the lowest terms would be 2 : 3: 5.

If this year, the ratio of *A*'s share : *B*'s share : *C*'s share is changed to 5 : 3 : 2 (instead of last year's 2 : 3 : 5), and the profit amount of \$1,000 remained the same, then their individual shares will change.

Their shares are recalculated as shown below:

$$A\text{'s share} = \frac{5}{10} \times 1{,}000 = \$500.00$$

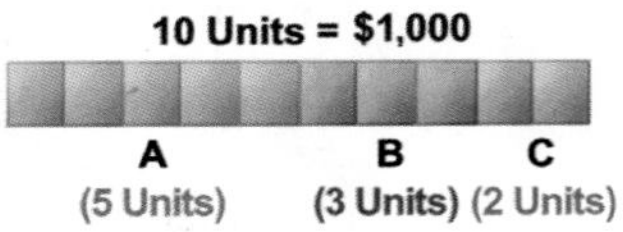

$$B\text{'s share} = \frac{3}{10} \times 1{,}000 = \$300.00$$

$$C\text{'s share} = \frac{2}{10} \times 1{,}000 = \$200.00$$

Note:

- *The total of A, B, and C's shares this year will be equal to the profit amount of \$1,000. That is, the shares of A + B + C = 500 + 300 + 200 = \$1,000*
- *If we reduce the ratio of the amounts shared by A, B, and C to its lowest terms, the result would be the original ratio. That is, 500 : 300 : 200 reduced to the lowest terms is 5 : 3 : 2.*

Example 4.1-k **Sharing Quantities Using Ratios**

A, *B*, and *C* start a business and invest \$3,500, \$2,100, and \$2,800, respectively. After a few months *C* decides to sell his share of the business to *A* and *B*. How much would *A* and *B* have to pay for *C*'s shares if *A* and *B* want to maintain their initial investment ratio?

Solution

Investments of *A*, *B*, and *C* are in the ratio of 3,500 : 2,100 : 2,800, which can be reduced to 5 : 3 : 4.

If *A* and *B* want to maintain their initial investment ratio of 5 : 3, then *C*'s share (of \$2,800) has to be paid for by *A* and *B* in the same ratio, 5 : 3.

By adding the ratio of *A* and *B*, we know that *C*'s share is to be divided into a total of 8 units, as illustrated:

$$A \text{ would have to pay } C: \frac{5}{8} \times 2{,}800.00 = \$1{,}750.00$$

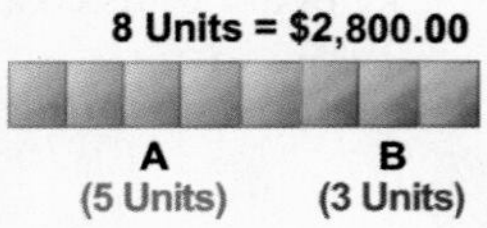

$$B \text{ would have to pay } C: \frac{3}{8} \times 2{,}800.00 = \$1{,}050.00$$

Therefore, A would have to pay \$1,750 and B would have to pay \$1,050 in order to maintain their initial investment ratio.

Example 4.1-l **Application Using Equivalent Ratios**

Andrew, Barry, and Cathy invested their savings in a bank. The investments ratio of Andrew to Barry is 2 : 3 and that of Barry to Cathy is 4 : 5. What is the investment ratio of Andrew: Barry: Cathy?

Solution

$A : B = 2 : \mathbf{3}$ and $B : C = \mathbf{4} : 5$

Find the equivalent ratio for $A : B$ and $B : C$ so that the number of units in B is the same in both cases.

This can be done by finding the equivalent ratio of $A : B$ by multiplying by 4 and that of $B : C$ by multiplying by 3.

$A : B = 2 : 3$ Multiplying each term by 4,

$= 8 : 12$

$B : C = 4 : 5$ Multiplying each term by 3,

$= 12 : 15$

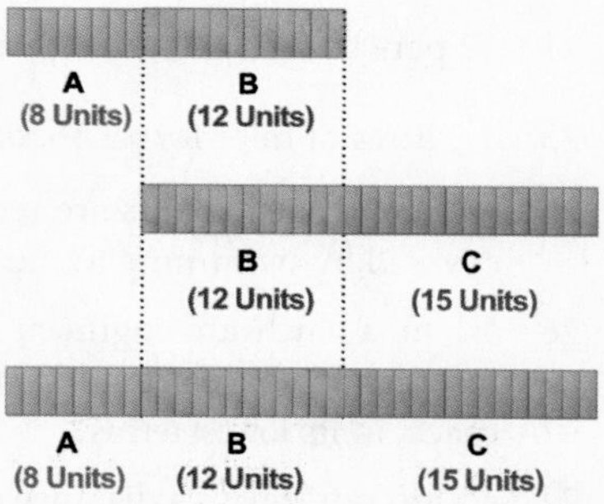

Therefore, the investment ratio of Andrew : Barry : Cathy is 8 : 12 : 15.

4.1 | Exercises

Answers to odd-numbered problems are available at the end of the textbook.

1. Find the ratio of the following:

   a. 9 months to 2 years b. 750 g to 3 kg c. 30 minutes to 1 hour and 15 minutes

2. Find the ratio of the following:

   a. 3 weeks to 126 days b. 120 g to 2 kg c. 55 minutes to 2 hours and 45 minutes

For Problems 3 to 6, express the ratios as (i) equivalent ratios in their lowest whole number and (ii) an equivalent ratio where the smallest term is 1.

3. a. 18 : 48 : 30 b. 175 : 50 : 125 c. 0.45 : 1 : 2

4. a. 27 : 45 : 72 b. 180 : 60 : 150 c. 2.4 : 0.75

5. a. $\frac{2}{3} : \frac{1}{5}$ b. $12 : \frac{5}{3} : 3$ c. $1.7 : 8.5 : \frac{34}{3}$

6. a. $\frac{3}{4} : \frac{2}{5}$ b. $65 : 91 : \frac{13}{2}$ c. $12 : 1.5 : \frac{3}{2}$

7. Which of the following ratios are equal?

   a. 4 : 6 and 6 : 10 b. 8 : 10 and 28 : 35 c. 6 : 8 and 27 : 32 d. 16 : 22 and 64 : 88

8. Which of the following ratios are equal?

   a. 16 : 20 and 24 : 30 b. 10 : 12 and 35 : 42 c. 12 : 14 and 30 : 42 d. 12 : 26 and 30 : 65

9. Which of the following is not an equivalent ratio of 6 : 9 : 12?

   a. 4 : 6 : 8 b. 2 : 3 : 4 c. 1 : 3 : 2 d. 8 : 12 : 16

10. Which of the following is not an equivalent ratio of 16 : 24 : 12?

    a. 20 : 30 : 15 b. 8 : 12 : 6 c. 28 : 42 : 21 d. 24 : 36 : 18

For Problems 11 to 18, find the unit rate.

11. 525 km in 7 hours = ? km/hr

12. 680 km in 8 hours = ? km/hr

13. 154 km to 14 litres = ? km/L

14. 228 km to 19 litres = ? km/L

15. 450 words typed in 6 minutes = ? words/minute

16. 496 words typed in 8 minutes = ? words/minute

17. 261 pages in 9 minutes = ? pages/minute

18. 192 pages in 8 minutes = ? pages/minute

For Problems 19 to 24, identify the option that is less expensive based on unit rate.

19. 2 kg of flour for $3.30, or 5 kg of flour for $8.40.

20. 3 kg of sugar for $3.90, or 5 kg of sugar for $6.25.

21. 12 pencils for $4.44, or 8 pencils for $2.88.

22. 6 litres of paint for $45.60, or 5 litres of paint for $37.25.

23. 1.2 litres of juice for $2.16, or 0.8 litres of juice for $1.40.

24. 2.2 kg of jam for $11.00, or 1.5 kg of jam for $7.20.

25. In a race, participants are required to swim 3,850 metres and bike 7 kilometres. Calculate the ratio of the distance covered by swimming to the distance covered by biking, in its lowest terms.

26. Adam, a hardware engineer, wants to install a microchip that is 38.2 mm in length into his laptop. The length of the installation space provided in his laptop is 4.8 cm. Calculate the ratio of the length of the microchip to the installation space, in its lowest terms.

27. An aircraft travels a distance of 3,105 km in 5 hours and 45 minutes. Calculate the ratio of the distance traveled to the time taken, reduced to a rate of kilometres per hour.

28. Speed is defined as the ratio of the distance travelled to the time taken. If Mary, who lives in Toronto, took 6 hours and 15 minutes to reach her parent's home in Montreal, which is 575 km away, calculate the speed at which she was travelling.

29. If *A* earns $196 for working 8 hours and *B* earns $98 for working 5 hours, whose average hourly rate is higher?

30. If Amanda travelled 325 km in 4 hours and 15 minutes and Ashton travelled 290 km in 3 hours and 30 minutes, whose average speed was greater?

31. Kate earned $210 for 7.5 hours of work and Susan earned $249.75 for 9 hours of work.
    a. Calculate their hourly rate.
    b. Whose hourly rate was higher and by how much?

32. Jack's monthly pay is $4,200. Steve's weekly pay is $975.
    a. Calculate their annual salary. (1 year = 12 months = 52 weeks)
    b. Whose annual salary is more and by how much?

33. Emily was planning to make an authentic Indian dish for her guests. She planned to use 36 eggs, 6 litres of water, 3 tablespoons of chilli powder, and 12 tomatoes.
    a. What is the ratio of the ingredients in her recipe?
    b. If she decides to reduce the quantity of chilli powder to $1\frac{1}{2}$ tablespoons, calculate the new ratio of the ingredients in her recipe.

34. In Murphy's battery manufacturing company, 600 kg of lead, 45 kg of carbon, 30 litres of battery acid, and 120 kg of rubber are used per day to make batteries.
    a. What is the ratio of the raw materials used per day to make batteries?
    b. If they alter the quantity of carbon used in the batteries and utilize 30 kg of carbon per day, calculate the new ratio of raw materials used per day.

35. A TV cable bill of $90 is shared between two house-mates, Mike and Sarah, in the ratio of $2 : 2\frac{1}{2}$. How much did each person pay?

36. Alexander and Alyssa invested a total of $10,000 in a web-design business. If the ratio of their investments is 3 : 5, what were their investments?

37. Amy and two of her friends received the first prize for a marketing case competition. They received an amount of $7,500; however, they decided to share the prize in the ratio of the amount of time each of them spent on the marketing case. If Amy spent 5 hours, Gary spent 8 hours, and Andrew spent 2 hours, what would be each person's share of the prize?

38. Three friends, Andy, Berry, and Cassandra, A, B, and C, jointly insured a commercial property in the ratio of $10 : 9 : 6$, respectively. How will an annual premium of $8,000 be distributed among the three of them?

• 39. Three friends, Alex, Brooks, and Charlie, have decided to invest $4,000, $6,000, and $2,000, respectively, to start a software development business. If Charlie decided to leave the business, how much would Alex and Brooks have to pay for Charlie's share if they want to maintain their initial investment ratio?

• 40. Chuck decided to build a yacht with his two friends Rob and Bob and they invested $9,000, $11,000, and $6,500, respectively. After the yacht was built, Bob decided to sell his share of the investment to Chuck and Rob. How much would each of them have to pay if they want to maintain the same ratio of their investments in the yacht?

• 41. Abey and Baxter invested equal amounts of money in a business. A year later, Abey withdrew $7,500 making the ratio of their investments $5 : 9$. How much money did each of them invest in the beginning?

• 42. Jessica and Russel invested equal amounts to start a business. Two months later, Jessica invested an additional $3,000 in the business, making the ratio of their investments $11 : 5$. How much money did each of them invest in the beginning?

• 43. If $A : B = 4 : 3$ and $B : C = 6 : 5$, find $A : B : C$.

• 44. If $X : Y = 5 : 2$ and $Y : Z = 7 : 6$, find $X : Y : Z$.

4.2 | Proportions

Proportions

When two sets of ratios are equal, we say that they are proportionate to each other. In the proportion equation, the ratio on the left side of the equation is equal to the ratio on the right side of the equation.

Consider an example where $A : B$ is $50 : 100$ and $C : D$ is $30 : 60$.

Reducing the ratio to its lowest terms, we obtain the ratio of $A : B$ as $1 : 2$ and the ratio of $C : D$ as $1 : 2$.

Since these ratios are equal, they are equally proportionate to each other and their proportion equation is:

$$\mathbf{A : B = C : D}$$

The proportion equation can also be formed by representing the ratios as fractions.

Equating the fraction obtained by dividing the 1st term by the 2nd term on the left side, to the one obtained by dividing the 1st term by the 2nd term on the right side we get:

$$\frac{\mathbf{A}}{\mathbf{B}} = \frac{\mathbf{C}}{\mathbf{D}}$$

This proportion equation can be simplified by multiplying both sides of the equation by the product of both denominators, which is $B \times D$.

$$\frac{A}{B} = \frac{C}{D} \quad \text{Multiplying both sides by } (B \times D),$$

$$\frac{A}{B}(B \times D) = \frac{C}{D}(B \times D) \quad \text{Simplifying,}$$

$$AD = BC$$

If two sets of fractions are equal, then the product obtained by cross-multiplying the fractions will be equal.

The same result can be obtained by equating the product of the numerator of the 1st ratio and the denominator of the 2nd ratio with the product of the denominator of the 1st ratio and the numerator of the 2nd ratio. This is referred to as cross-multiplication and is shown below:

$$\frac{A}{B} \times \frac{C}{D} \quad \text{Cross-multiplying,}$$

$$AD = BC$$

If 3 terms of the proportion equation are known, the 4th term can be calculated.

Therefore, $A : B = C : D$ is equivalent to $\frac{A}{B} = \frac{C}{D}$.

Proportion Equation With Sets of Ratios Having More Than Two Terms

If $A : B : C = D : E : F$,

Then this ratio can be expressed as $\frac{A}{B} = \frac{D}{E}$, $\frac{B}{C} = \frac{E}{F}$, and $\frac{A}{C} = \frac{D}{F}$.

Cross multiplying leads to $AE = BD$, $BF = CE$, and $AF = CD$

The given ratio can also be expressed as, $\frac{A}{D} = \frac{B}{E} = \frac{C}{F}$. Cross-multiplying leads to the same result.

If $A : B : C = D : E : F$

then,

$\frac{A}{B} = \frac{D}{E}$, $\frac{B}{C} = \frac{E}{F}$, $\frac{A}{C} = \frac{D}{F}$

or,

$\frac{A}{D} = \frac{B}{E} = \frac{C}{F}$

The equivalent ratio, $A : B : C = D : E : F$ can be illustrated in a table as shown:

1st Term	2nd Term	3rd Term
A	B	C
D	E	F

and expressed as, $A : D = B : E = C : F$

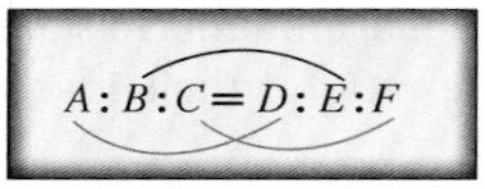

i.e., in fractional form, $\frac{A}{D} = \frac{B}{E} = \frac{C}{F}$

Cross-multiplying, leads to the same result, as shown above $AE = BD$, $BF = CE$, and $AF = CD$.

Example 4.2-a **Solving for the Unknown Quantity in Proportions**

Find the missing term in the following proportions:

(i) $4 : 5 = 8 : x$ (ii) $6 : x = 10 : 25$ (iii) $x : 1.9 = 2.6 : 9.88$ (iv) $3 : 3\frac{3}{4} = x : 5\frac{1}{4}$

Solution

(i) $4 : 5 = 8 : x$

Using fractional notation, $\frac{4}{5} = \frac{8}{x}$ or $\frac{4}{8} = \frac{5}{x}$

Cross-multiplying, $4x = 40$

Simplifying, $x = \frac{40}{4}$

Therefore, $x = 10$

1st Term	2nd Term
4	5
8	x

(ii) $6 : x = 10 : 25$

Using fractional notation, $\frac{6}{x} = \frac{10}{25}$ or $\frac{6}{10} = \frac{x}{25}$

Cross-multiplying, $150 = 10x$

Simplifying, $x = \frac{150}{10}$

Therefore, $x = 15$

1st Term	2nd Term
6	x
10	25

(iii) $x : 1.9 = 2.6 : 9.88$

Using fractional notation, $\frac{x}{1.9} = \frac{2.6}{9.88}$ or $\frac{1.9}{9.88} = \frac{x}{2.6}$

Cross-multiplying, $9.88x = 4.94$

Simplifying, $x = \frac{4.94}{9.88}$

Therefore, $x = 0.5$

1st Term	2nd Term
x	1.9
2.6	9.88

Solution *continued*

(iv) $3 : 3\frac{3}{4} = x : 5\frac{1}{4}$

Rewriting as an improper fraction, $3 : \frac{15}{4} = x : \frac{21}{4}$

Multiplying both sides by 4, $12 : 15 = 4x : 21$

Using fractional notation, $\frac{12}{15} = \frac{4x}{21}$ or $\frac{15}{21} = \frac{12}{4x}$

Cross-multiplying, $60x = 252$

Simplifying, $x = \frac{252}{60}$

Therefore, $x = 4.2$

1st Term	2nd Term
12	15
$4x$	21

Example 4.2-b

Solving Word Problems Using Proportions

Ben can walk a distance of 9 km in 2 hours. Calculate:

(i) The distance (in km) that Ben can walk in $3\frac{1}{2}$ hours.

(ii) How long (in hours) will it take him to walk 15 km?

Solution

(i) Calculating the distance in (km):

km : hr = km : hr

$9 : 2 = x : 3\frac{1}{2}$

Rewriting as an improper fraction, $9 : 2 = x : \frac{7}{2}$

Multiplying both sides by 2, $18 : 4 = 2x : 7$

Using fractional notation, $\frac{18}{4} = \frac{2x}{7}$ or $\frac{18}{2x} = \frac{4}{7}$

Cross-multiplying, $8x = 126$

Simplifying, $x = \frac{126}{8}$

$x = 15.75$

1st Term	2nd Term
18	4
$2x$	7

Therefore, Ben can walk a distance of 15.75 km in $3\frac{1}{2}$ hours.

(ii) Calculating the time that it will take him to walk 15km:

km : hr = km : hr

$9 : 2 = 15 : x$

Using fractional notation, $\frac{9}{2} = \frac{15}{x}$ or $\frac{2}{x} = \frac{9}{15}$

Cross multiplying, $9x = 30$

Simplifying, $x = \frac{30}{9}$

$x = 3.333333... = 3.33$

1st Term	2nd Term
9	2
15	x

Therefore, Ben can walk 15 km in 3.33 hours.

Example 4.2-c Sharing Using Proportions

Andrew (A), Brandon (B), and Chris (C) decide to form a partnership to start a snow removal business together. A invests \$31,500, B invests \$42,000, and C invests \$73,500. They agree to share the profits in the same ratio as their investments.

(i) What is the ratio of their investments?

(ii) In the first year of running the business, A's profit was \$27,000. What were B's and C's profits?

(iii) In the second year, their total profit was \$70,000. How much would each of them receive from this total profit?

Solution

(i) Ratio of their investments:

$A : B : C$	
31,500 : 42,000 : 73,500	Dividing each term by the common factor of 100,
315 : 420 : 735	Dividing each term by the common factor of 5,
63 : 84 : 147	Dividing each term by the common factor of 7,
9 : 12 : 21	Dividing each term by the common factor of 3,
3 : 4 : 7	

Therefore, the ratio of their investments is 3 : 4 : 7.

(ii) A's profit was \$27,000. B's and C's profits are calculated using one of the two methods, as follows:

Method 1:

$$\text{Ratio of Investment} = \text{Ratio of Profit}$$

$$A : B : C = A : B : C$$

Substituting terms,

$$3 : 4 : 7 = 27{,}000 : x : y$$

Using fractional notation,

$$\frac{3}{4} = \frac{27{,}000}{x} \quad \text{and} \quad \frac{3}{7} = \frac{27{,}000}{y}$$

Cross-multiplying, $3x = 108{,}000$ $\quad$ $3y = 189{,}000$

Simplifying, $x = \$36{,}000.00$ $\quad$ $y = \$63{,}000.00$

Therefore, B's profit is \$36,000.00. $\quad$ C's profit is \$63,000.00.

Method 2:

$$\text{Ratio of Investment} = \text{Ratio of Profit}$$

$$A : B : C = A : B : C$$

Substituting terms,

$$3 : 4 : 7 = 27{,}000 : x : y$$

Using fractional notation,

$$\frac{3}{27{,}000} = \frac{4}{x} = \frac{7}{y}$$

1st Term	2nd Term	3rd Term
3	4	7
27,000	x	y

Hence,

$$\frac{3}{27{,}000} = \frac{4}{x} \quad \text{and} \quad \frac{3}{27{,}000} = \frac{7}{y}$$

Cross-multiplying, $3x = 108{,}000$ $\quad$ $3y = 189{,}000$

Simplifying, $x = \$36{,}000.00$ $\quad$ $y = \$63{,}000.00$

Therefore, B's profit is \$36,000.00. $\quad$ C's profit is \$63,000.00.

Solution
continued

(iii) In the second year, their total profit was $70,000. The profit that each of them would receive is calculated by using one of the methods, as follows:

Method 1:

Since A, B, and C agreed to share profits in the same ratio as their investments, the ratio of their individual investments to their individual profit should be equal to the ratio of the total investment to the total profit.

By adding the ratio of their investments (3 + 4 + 7), we know that the total profit of $70,000 should be distributed over 14 units. Therefore,

$$\text{Ratio of Investment} = \text{Ratio of Profit}$$
$$A : B : C : \text{Total} = A : B : C : \text{Total}$$

Substituting terms,
$$3 : 4 : 7 : 14 = A : B : C : 70{,}000$$

Using fractional notation,
$$\frac{3}{14} = \frac{A}{70{,}000} \qquad \frac{4}{14} = \frac{B}{70{,}000} \qquad \frac{7}{14} = \frac{C}{70{,}000}$$

Cross-multiplying,
$$14A = 210{,}000 \qquad 14B = 280{,}000 \qquad 14C = 490{,}000$$
$$A = \$15{,}000.00 \qquad B = \$20{,}000.00 \qquad C = \$35{,}000.00$$

Method 2:
$$\text{Ratio of Investment} = \text{Ratio of Profit}$$
$$A : B : C : \text{Total} = A : B : C : \text{Total}$$

Substituting terms,
$$3 : 4 : 7 : 14 = A : B : C : 70{,}000$$

1st Term	2nd Term	3rd Term	4th Term
3	4	7	14
A	B	C	70,000

Using fractional notation,
$$\frac{3}{A} = \frac{4}{B} = \frac{7}{C} = \frac{14}{70{,}000}$$

Hence,
$$\frac{3}{A} = \frac{14}{70{,}000} \qquad \frac{4}{B} = \frac{14}{70{,}000} \qquad \frac{7}{C} = \frac{14}{70{,}000}$$

Cross-multiplying,
$$14A = 3 \times 70{,}000 \qquad 14B = 4 \times 70{,}000 \qquad 14C = 7 \times 70{,}000$$
$$A = \frac{3 \times 70{,}000}{14} \qquad B = \frac{4 \times 70{,}000}{14} \qquad C = \frac{7 \times 70{,}000}{14}$$

Simplifying,
$$A = \$15{,}000.00 \qquad B = \$20{,}000.00 \qquad C = 35{,}000.00$$

Method 3: Sharing Using Ratios:

A's share $= \frac{3}{14} \times 70{,}000.00 = \$15{,}000.00$

B's share $= \frac{4}{14} \times 70{,}000.00 = \$20{,}000.00$

C's share $= \frac{7}{14} \times 70{,}000.00 = \$35{,}000.00$

Therefore, A, B, and C will receive profits of $15,000.00, $20,000.00, and $35,000.00, respectively.

Pro-rations

Pro-ration is defined as sharing or allocating the quantities, usually the amounts, on a proportionate basis.

Consider an example where Sarah paid $690 for a math course but decided to withdraw from the course after attending half the course. As she attended only half the course, the college decided to refund half of her tuition fee, ($\frac{\$690}{2} = \$345$). As the college calculated the refund amount proportionate to the time she attended the course, we say that the college refunded her tuition fee on a **pro-rata basis.**

A few examples where pro-rated calculations are used are:

- When a propery is sold, the property tax paid in advance will be refunded on a pro-rata basis.
- When an insurance is cancelled before the end of the period for which the premiums were paid, the amount refunded is calculated on a pro-rata basis.
- Employees' overtime pay, part-time pay, and vacation time are calculated on a pro-rata basis.

Example 4.2-d Calculating the Pro-rated Amount of a Payment

Find the pro-rated insurance premium for seven months if the annual premium paid for car insurance is $2,250.

Solution

Ratio of the premiums paid:

Premium ($) : Time (months) = Premium ($) : Time (months)

Substituting terms, 2,250 : 12 = x : 7

Using fractional notation, $\frac{2{,}250}{12} = \frac{x}{7}$, or $\frac{2{,}250}{x} = \frac{12}{7}$

1st Term	2nd Term
2,250	12
x	7

Cross-multiplying, $12x = 15{,}750$

Solving, $x = \frac{15{,}750}{12}$

$x = \$1{,}312.50$

Therefore, the pro-rated premium for seven months is $1,312.50.

Example 4.2-e Calculating the Pro-rated Amount of a Refund

Johnson paid $350 for a 2-year weekly subscription of a health journal. After receiving 18 issues of the journal in his second year, he decided to cancel his subscription. What should be the amount of his refund? Assume 1 year = 52 weeks.

Solution

Paid for 104 issues (2 × 52) and received 70 issues (52+18); therefore, he should be refunded for 34 issues (104 – 70).

Issues (#) : Cost ($) = Issues (#) : Cost ($)

Substituting terms, 104 : 350 = 34 : x

Using fractional notation, $\frac{104}{350} = \frac{34}{x}$, or $\frac{104}{34} = \frac{350}{x}$

1st Term	2nd Term
104	350
34	x

Cross-multiplying, $104x = 34 \times 350$

Simpifying, $x = \frac{34 \times 350}{104}$

$= 114.423076...$

$= \$114.42$

Therefore, his refund should be $114.42.

4.2 | Exercises

Answers to odd-numbered problems are available at the end of the textbook.

1. Determine which of the following pairs of ratios are in proportion:

   a. 6 : 9 and 14 : 21 b. 5 : 15 and 2 : 8 c. 18 : 24 and 12 : 16 d. 12 : 60 and 6 : 24

2. Determine which of the following pairs of ratios are in proportion:

   a. 9 : 12 and 4 : 3 b. 10 : 30 and 8 : 24 c. 14 : 20 and 28 : 42 d. 15 : 12 and 24 : 30

For Problems 3 to 6, solve the proportions for the unknown value.

3.	a.	$x : 4 = 27 : 36$	b.	$24 : x = 6 : 9$	c.	$5 : 9 = x : 3$	d.	$1 : 2 = 5 : x$
4.	a.	$x : 8 = 6 : 24$	b.	$3 : x = 18 : 42$	c.	$15 : 5 = x : 15$	d.	$28 : 35 = 4 : x$
5.	a.	$x : 18\frac{1}{4} = 8 : 11\frac{3}{4}$	b.	$7\frac{1}{5} : x = 5\frac{4}{3} : 3\frac{2}{5}$	c.	$1 : 4\frac{1}{2} = x : 2\frac{3}{4}$	d.	$1\frac{1}{2} : 2\frac{1}{4} = 1\frac{3}{4} : x$
6.	a.	$x : 3.65 = 5.5 : 18.25$	b.	$2.2 : x = 13.2 : 2.5$	c.	$4.25 : 1.87 = x : 2.2$	d.	$2.4 : 1.5 = 7.2 : x$

7. A truck requires 96 litres of gas to cover 800 km. How many litres of gas will it require to cover 1,500 km?
8. Based on Alvin's past experience, it would take his team 5 months to complete two projects. How long would his team take to complete 8 similar projects?
9. Eric paid property tax of $3,600 for his land that measures 330 square metres. Using the same tax rate, what would his neighbour's property tax be if the size of the house is 210 square metres and is taxed at the same rate?
10. The city of Brampton charges $1,750 in taxes per year for a 2,000 square metre farm. How much would Maple Farms have to pay in taxes if they had a 12,275 square metre farm in the same area?
11. On a map, 4 cm represents 5.0 km. If the distance between Town *A* and Town *B* on the map is 9.3 cm, how many kilometres apart are these towns?
12. On a house plan, 1.25 cm represents 3 metres. If the actual length of a room is 5.4 metres, how will this length be represented in the plan in cm?
13. Steve invested his savings in a GIC, mutual funds, and a fixed deposit in the ratio of 5 : 4 : 3, respectively. If he invested $10,900 in mutual funds, calculate his investments in the GIC and the fixed deposit.
14. The ratio of the distance from Ann's house to Mark, Jeff, and Justin's houses is 3 : 5.25 : 2, respectively. If the distance from Ann's house to Mark's is 9.50 km, calculate the distance from Ann's house to Justin's and Ann's house to Jeff's.
15. A, B, and C, started a business with investments in the ratio of 5 : 4 : 3, respectively. A invested $25,000, and all three of them agreed to share profits in the ratio of their investments.
    a. Calculate C's investment.
    b. If A's profit was $30,000 in the first year, calculate B and C's profits.
    c. How much would each of them receive if, in the second year, the total profit was $135,000?
16. A, B, and C formed a partnership and invested in the ratio of 7 : 9 : 5, respectively. They agreed to share the profit in the ratio of their investments. A invested $350,000.
    a. Calculate B and C's investments in the partnership.
    b. If the partnership made a profit of $126,000 in the first year, calculate each partner's share of the profit.
    c. In the second year, if A made $38,500 in profit from the partnership, how much did B and C make?
17. A, B, and C invested $35,000, $42,000, and $28,000, respectively, to start an e-learning business. They realized that they required an additional $45,000 for operating the business. How much did each of them have to individually invest to maintain their original investment ratio?
18. Three wealthy business partners decided to invest $150,000, $375,000, and $225,000, respectively, to purchase an industrial plot on the outskirts of the city. They required an additional $90,000 to build an industrial shed on the land. How much did each of them have to individually invest to maintain their original investment ratio?
19. Chris, Diane, and David invested a total of $520,000 in the ratio of 3 : 4 : 6, respectively to start a business. Two months later, each of them invested an additional $25,000 into the business. Calculate their new investment ratio after the additional investments.
20. Michael and his two sisters purchased an office for $720,000. Their individual investments in the office were in the ratio of 5 : 4 : 3, respectively. After the purchase, they decided to renovate the building and purchase furniture, so each of them invested an additional $60,000. Calculate their new investment ratio after the additional investments.
21. A student pays $620 for a course that has 25 classes. Find the pro-rated refund she would receive if she only attends 5 classes before withdrawing from the course.
22. Megan joined a driving school that charges $375 for 12 classes. After attending 7 classes, she decided that she did not like the training and wanted to cancel the remaining classes. Calculate the pro-rated refund she should receive.
23. Frank bought a brand new car on August 01, 2014 and obtained pre-paid insurance of $1,058 for the period of August 01, 2014 to July 31, 2015. After 2 months of using the car, he sold it and cancelled his insurance. Calculate the pro-rated refund he should receive from the insurance company.

24. The owner of a new gaming business decided to insure his servers and computers. His insurance company charged him a premium of $2,000 per quarter, starting January 01. If the insurance started on February 01, how much pro-rated insurance premium did he have to pay for the rest of the first quarter? (Hint: Quarter of a year is 3 months).

25. If the annual salary of an employee is $45,000, calculate his bi-weekly salary using pro-ration. Assume that there are 52 weeks in a year and 26 bi-weekly payments.

26. Ashley received a job offer at a company that would pay her $2,800, bi-weekly. What would her annual salary be, assuming that she would receive 26 payments in a year?

27. Charles set up a new charity fund to support children in need. For every $10 collected by the charity, the Government donated an additional grant of $5 to the charity. At the end of 3 months, if his charity fund had a total of $135,000, including the Government grant, calculate the amount the charity received from the Government.

28. The tax on education materials sold in Ontario is such that for every $1.00 worth of materials sold, the buyer would have to pay an additional $0.05 in taxes. If $25,000.00 worth of textbooks were sold at a bookstore before taxes, calculate the total amount of tax to be paid by the purchasers.

• 29. A first semester class in a college has 6 more girls than boys and the ratio of the number of girls to boys in the class is 8 : 5.

    a. How many students are there in the class?

    b. If 4 girls and 3 boys joined the class, find the new ratio of girls to boys in the class.

• 30. The advisory board of a public sector company has 10 more men than women and the ratio of the number of men to women is 8 : 3.

    a. How many people are there on the board?

    b. If 4 men and 4 women joined the board, calculate the new ratio of men to women.

• 31. To estimate the number of tigers in a forest, a team of researchers tagged 84 tigers and released them into the forest. Six months later, 30 tigers were spotted, out of which 7 had tags. How many tigers were estimated to be in the forest?

• 32. Researchers were conducting a study to estimate the number of frogs in a pond. They put a bright yellow band on the legs of 60 frogs and released them into the pond. A few days later, 15 frogs were spotted, out of which 5 had bands. How many frogs were estimated to be in the pond?

4 | Review Exercises

Answers to odd-numbered problems are available at the end of the textbook.

1. What is the ratio of a Canadian quarter (25¢) to a Canadian $5 bill, reduced to its lowest terms?

2. What is the ratio of 12 minutes to 2 hours, reduced to its lowest terms?

3. Solve the following proportions for the unknown value:

    a. $x : 9 = 26 : 39$

    b. $16 : 24 = 12 : x$

    c. $x : 0.45 = 0.16 : 1.20$

4. Solve the following proportions for the unknown value:

    a. $x : 15 = 24 : 36$

    b. $8 : 14 = x : 35$

    c. $12.5 : 70 = x : 1.4$

5. Which of the following ratios are equal:

    a. 6 : 8 and 18 : 24

    b. 30 : 25 and 36 : 48

    c. 10 : 35 and 14 : 49

    d. 24 : 30 and 12 : 18

6. Which of the following ratios are equal:

    a. 16 : 20 and 18 : 30

    b. 4 : 10 and 10 : 24

    c. 35 : 50 and 21 : 36

    d. 20 : 16 and 30 : 24

7. If Christina, a graphic designer, receives an annual salary of $55,000, calculate her weekly salary using pro-rations. Assume that there are 52 weeks in a year.

8. As the CFO of a technology company, every year, Tyler would receive 26 bi-weekly payments of $6,000 each. Calculate his monthly salary.

9. The sales tax on an item costing $350.00 is $45.50. What will be the sales tax on an item costing $1,250.00?

10. Peter works 5.5 hours per day and his salary per day is $112.75. At this rate, how much will he receive if he works 7.5 hours per day?

11. Which is the better buy based on the unit price: 360 grams for $2.99 or 480 grams for $3.75?

12. Which is the better buy based on the unit price: 125 grams for $4.75 or 175 grams for $5.95?
13. A 450 gram loaf of bread costs $3.15 and has 15 slices.
    a. Find the cost per 100 grams of bread.
    b. Find the cost per slice of bread.
14. 250 grams of sliced cheese costs $4.50 and has 6 slices.
    a. Find the cost per 100 grams of cheese.
    b. Find the cost per slice of cheese.
15. Ali can run 12 km in 20 minutes.
    a. Calculate his speed in km/hour.
    b. At this speed, how far can he run in 1.5 hours?
16. A car can travel 486 km using 45 litres of gas.
    a. Calculate the fuel efficency of the car in km/litre.
    b. At this rate, how many litres of gas is required for a trip of 810 km?
17. Calculate the unit price for each of the following offers and identify which offer is the best, based on the unit price:
    a. 3 kg of oranges for $7.99
    b. 4 kg of oranges for $9.99
    c. 5 kg of oranges for $11.99
18. Calculate the unit price for each of the following offers and identify which offer is the best, based on the unit price:
    a. 5 kg of rice for $4.99
    b. 8 kg of rice for $7.99
    c. 10 kg of rice for $9.49
19. Jeffrey and Gina were classmates who graduated together from college. Jeffrey found a job as a banker that pays him $189 for 9 hours and Gina found a job as a freelance artist that pays her $174 for 8 hours of work. Who is being paid a higher hourly rate and by how much?
20. Gregory purchased a racing motorbike and Chris purchased a cruising motorbike. Jeffery travelled 765 km from Toronto to New York City in 8 hours and 20 minutes. Chris travelled 165 km from Toronto to Buffalo in 2 hours and 10 minutes. Based on this information, whose average speed was greater and by how much (in km/hr)?
21. If the ratio of sugar to flour in a pie is 3 : 5 and that of flour to eggs is 3 : 1, calculate the ratio of sugar : flour : eggs in the pie.
22. If the ratio of sales people to marketing people in an organization is 5 : 4 and the ratio of marketing people to finance people is 5 : 2, what is the ratio of sales people : marketing people : finance people in the organization?
23. Alexander, an investment banker, invests all his yearly earnings in stocks of high-tech, mining, and real-estate in the ratio of 4 : 5 : 3, respectively. Calculate his investment in mining stocks if his investment in high-tech stocks was $10,900.
24. The ratio of the driving distance from London to Hamilton, Mississauga, and Toronto is 3 : 4 : 5, respectively. If the distance from London to Hamilton is 125 km, calculate the distance from London to Mississauga and from London to Toronto.
25. Three college classmates, Khan, Thomas, and Lee decided to start a small business and invested $1,000, $2,500, and $3,500, respectively. If Lee decided to leave the business, how much would Khan and Thomas have to pay for Lee's shares if they wanted to maintain their initial investment ratio?
26. Calvin decided to build a shopping complex with his two brothers, Kevin and Alex. They invested $200,000, $350,000, and $450,000, respectively. After the complex was built, Kevin decided to sell his share of the investment to Calvin and Alex. How much would each of them have to pay if they wanted to maintain the same ratio of their investments in the complex?
27. A, B, and C invested a total of $900 in the ratio of 3 : 4 : 5, respectively, to purchase a billiards table for their club house. After the table was delivered, each invested an additional $200 to purchase balls and cue sticks. Calculate their new investment ratio after their additional investments.
28. Samuel, his wife, and his mother jointly purchased an estate for $1,350,000. Their individual investments in the estate were in the ratio of 5 : 3 : 1, respectively. Each of them decided to invest an additional $250,000 to develop the estate into a small family resort. Calculate their new investment ratio after the additional investments.
29. Anton, Cheryl, and Ellen invested $4,000, $7,500, and $6,000, respectively, to start a video production studio. The company did very well in the first year and they wanted to invest an additional $5,250 in total to expand their business. How much would each of them have to individually invest to maintain their original investment ratio?
30. Russel, an investment banker, invested $8,000, $12,000, and $4,000 in stocks of three different companies. The market showed potential to grow so he decided to invest an additional $1,500 in total in stocks of the same companies. How did he invest this amount into stocks of the three companies to maintain the original investment ratio?

4 | Self-Test Exercises

Answers to all problems are available at the end of the textbook.

1. Which is cheaper: a 240 gram box of cereal for $3.69, or a 360 gram box of cereal for $4.89.
2. Which is cheaper: a 600 gram of spread for $3.72, or a 400 gram of spread for $2.80.
3. A 500 km trip by car took 6 hours and 45 minutes. Calculate the speed of the car in km/hr.
4. The average speed of a car is 75 km/hour. At this speed, how many hours will it take to travel 700 km?
5. Solve for the unknown quantity:
   a. $35 : 7 = 60 : x$
   b. $45 : x = 70 : 63$
6. Solve for the unknown quantity:
   a. $25 : 9 = x : 2.7$
   b. $x : 8 = 2\frac{1}{4} : 2\frac{1}{2}$
7. The scale on a map is 3 cm = 50 km. Calculate the actual distance between the two cities that are 12.75 cm apart on a map.
8. The property tax on a property assessed at $430,000.00 is $4,235.50. Calculate the property tax on a similar property assessed at $612,750.00.
9. An investment of $1,500 earned $820 in interest in one year. What amount should be invested at this rate to earn $1,459 in interest?
10. A car travelled 250 km. If the fuel efficency of the car is 9 litres per 100 km, calculate the amount of gas used for the trip.
11. Which offer is the best based on the unit price?
    a. 75 grams of chocolate for $1.49
    b. 100 grams of chocolate for $1.99
    c. 125 grams of chocolate for $2.25
12. Andrew's earnings to Bill's was in the ratio of 3 : 5 and Bill's to Cathy's was in the ratio of 4 : 6. What was the ratio of the earnings of Andrew : Bill : Cathy?
13. For every $25 that a not-for-profit foundation transferred to a relief fund, the Government donated $10 towards the same cause. After 2 months of fundraising, the foundation had a total of $9,450, including the Government's contribution. Calculate the amount donated by the Government.
14. Georgia paid a yearly subscription amount of $250 to receive a business magazine monthly. After receiving two issues, she cancelled her subscription. Calculate the pro-rated refund she should receive from the magazine company.
15. A, B, and C invested $9,000, $15,000, and $12,000 respectively, to start a small business. An additional $6,000 is required for operating the business. How much must each of them invest to mantain their original investment ratio?
16. Nabil and Mohammad invested a total of $100,000 in the ratio of 3 : 5, respectively. After one year, both of them withdrew $10,000 from the invesment. Calculate the ratio of their investments after the withdrawal.
17. Profits are distributed to the three partners, Alice, Bill, and Carol, based on their investments of $60,000, $40,000 and $96,000, respectively. If the profit last year was $58,800, calculate their share of the profits.

5 PERCENTS AND PERCENT CHANGES

Percents and percent changes make comparisons easy and are used often in our daily lives in making business decisions. Due to their simplicity, percents are a widely accepted measure for expressing fractions or decimal numbers. Some examples of the use of percents include interest rate charged by banks on loans, discounts offered at stores, sales tax charged on items purchased, commissions received by sales representatives, etc.

LEARNING OBJECTIVES

- Convert percents to equivalent fractions and decimal numbers.
- Solve percent problems using different methods.
- Calculate bases, rates, or portions of quantities, expressed in percents.
- Identify the terminology used in percent change.
- Use percents to measure percent increase and decrease.

CHAPTER OUTLINE

5.1 Percents

5.2 Percent Changes

5.1 | Percents

Introduction

ercent is the number f parts per hundred, % = $\frac{C}{100}$ = 0.1C

In Chapter 2, you learned that fractions and decimal numbers are used to represent portions (parts) of a whole number or quantity. In this chapter, you will learn about **percent** as another form of representing portions of a whole quantity.

Percent (per cent or per hundred, in the literal meaning) is used to express a quantity out of 100 units and is represented by the symbol '%'.

For example, 5% means 5 **per** hundred, 5 out of 100, $\frac{5}{100}$, 5 hundredths, or 0.05.

- 100% means 100 out of 100 (i.e, the whole quantity)
- 75% means 75 out of 100 (i.e., $\frac{75}{100} = \frac{3}{4}$ or 0.75)
- 50% means 50 out of 100 (i.e., $\frac{50}{100} = \frac{1}{2}$ or 0.50)
- 25% means 25 out of 100 (i.e., $\frac{25}{100} = \frac{1}{4}$ or 0.25)

Note: 200% means 2 times (or double or twice) the whole quantity (although technically correct, it is not meaningful to say 200 out of 100). Similarily, 350% means $3\frac{1}{2}$ times the whole quantity.

Relationship Among Percents, Fractions, and Decimal Numbers

Fractions and decimal numbers can be converted to percents and vice-versa. For example, 3 out of 4 equal parts of a quantity can be represented as a fraction, decimal number, or in percent form, as follows:

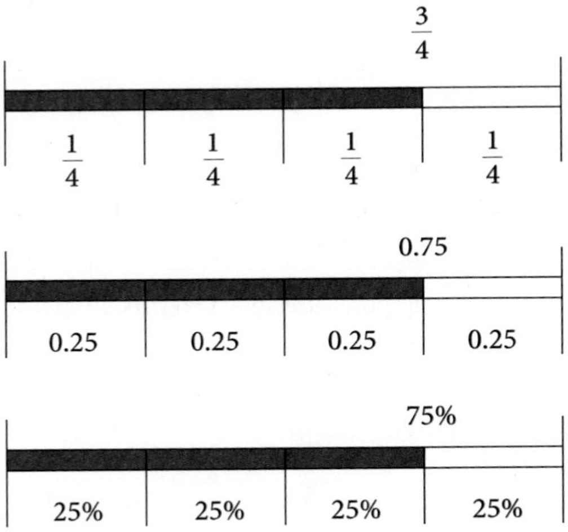

As a fraction, it is $\frac{3}{4}$.

As a decimal, it is 0.75.

As a percent, it is 75%.

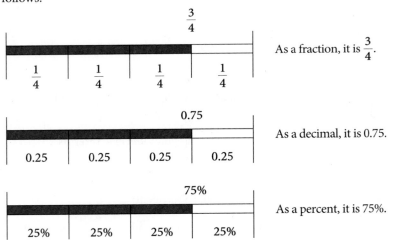

In day-to-day business, percents are commonly used to represent interest rates, sales, discounts, commissions, comparison of changes in quantity, etc. However, in actual calculations, fractions (ratios) or decimal equivalents are used. Therefore, it is necessary to know the methods for converting from one form to the other.

Converting Percents to Fractions

- **If the percent is a whole number,** remove the percent sign, divide by 100 (or multiply by $\frac{1}{100}$), and reduce to its lowest terms.

For example, to convert 60% to a fraction in its lowest terms:

$60\% = \frac{60}{100}$ — Reduce this fraction to the lowest terms.

$= \frac{3}{5}$

Therefore, $60\% = \frac{3}{5}$.

- **If the percent includes a decimal number**, remove the percent sign, divide by 100, change it to its fractional equivalent by eliminating the decimal in the numerator, and reduce to its lowest terms.

For example, to convert 42.5% to a fraction:

$42.5\% = \frac{42.5}{100}$ — Eliminate the decimal in the numerator by multiplying both the numerator and the denominator by 10.

$= \frac{425}{1,000}$ — Reduce this fraction to the lowest terms.

$= \frac{17}{40}$

Therefore, $42.5\% = \frac{17}{40}$.

- **If the percent is a fraction or a mixed number** (combination of a whole number and a fraction), either convert it to its decimal equivalent or convert it to an improper fraction and follow the steps below.

For example, to convert $6\frac{1}{2}\%$ to a fraction:

Method 1: By converting it to its decimal equivalent:

$6\frac{1}{2}\% = \frac{6\frac{1}{2}}{100}$ — Rewrite the numerator in decimal form.

$= \frac{6.5}{100}$ — Eliminate the decimal by multiplying both the numerator and denominator by 10.

$= \frac{65}{1,000}$ — Reduce the fraction to its lowest terms.

$= \frac{13}{200}$

Method 2: By converting it to its fractional equivalent:

$6\frac{1}{2}\% = \frac{6\frac{1}{2}}{100} = 6\frac{1}{2} \div 100$ — Convert the mixed number to an improper fraction.

$= \frac{13}{2} \div 100$

$= \frac{13}{2} \times \frac{1}{100}$ — Simplify.

$= \frac{13}{200}$

Therefore, $6\frac{1}{2}\% = \frac{13}{200}$.

Example 5.1-a

Converting Percents to Fractions

Convert each percent to its equivalent fraction or mixed number and simplify to lowest term.

(i) 45% (ii) $8\frac{1}{3}\%$ (iii) 6.25% (iv) 175% (v) $\frac{1}{5}\%$

Solution

(i) $45\% = \frac{45}{100} = \frac{9}{20}$

(ii) $8\frac{1}{3}\% = 8\frac{1}{3} \div 100 = \frac{25}{3} \times \frac{1}{100} = \frac{25}{300} = \frac{1}{12}$

(iii) $6.25\% = \frac{6.25}{100} = \frac{6.25}{100} \times \frac{100}{100} = \frac{625}{10{,}000} = \frac{1}{16}$

(iv) $175\% = \frac{175}{100} = \frac{7}{4} = 1\frac{3}{4}$

(v) $\frac{1}{5}\% = \frac{1}{5} \div 100 = \frac{1}{5} \times \frac{1}{100} = \frac{1}{500}$

Converting Fractions or Mixed Numbers to Percents

To convert a fraction or a mixed number to a percent, first convert the fraction or the mixed number to a decimal number. Then, convert the decimal number to a percent by moving the decimal point by 2 places to the right and inserting the % sign. This is the same as multiplying the decimals by 100 and inserting the % sign.

For example,

- To convert $\frac{3}{8}$ to a percent:

  $\frac{3}{8} = 0.375$ — Convert the fraction to its decimal equivalent.

  $= 0.375\%$ — Convert the decimal to a percent, by moving the decimal point 2 places to the right and placing the % sign.

  $= 37.50\%$ — This is the same as 0.375 × 100% = 37.50%.

  Therefore, $\frac{3}{8} = 37.50\%$.

- To convert $5\frac{1}{2}$ to a percent: — Convert the mixed number to its decimal equivalent.

  $5\frac{1}{2} = 5.50$ — Convert the decimal to a percent by moving the decimal point 2 places to the right and placing the % sign.

  $= 5.50\%$

  $= 550\%$ — This is the same as 5.50 × 100% = 550%.

  Therefore, $5\frac{1}{2} = 550.00\%$.

Example 5.1-b

Converting Fractions or Mixed Numbers to Percents

Convert each of the following fractions to a decimal and then to its equivalent percent.

(i) $\frac{3}{25}$ (ii) $5\frac{1}{4}$ (iii) $\frac{18}{5}$ (iv) $\frac{1}{200}$

Solution

(i) $\frac{3}{25} = 0.12$

$= 0.12\% = 12\%$

(ii) $5\frac{1}{4} = 5.25$

$= 5.25\% = 525\%$

(iii) $\frac{18}{5} = 3.60$

$= 3.60\% = 360\%$

(iv) $\frac{1}{200} = 0.005$

$= 0.005\% = 0.5\%$

Example 5.1-c **Solving Application Problems Using Percents**

Peter and Angela study Business Mathematics, but at different colleges. Peter managed to score 46 out of 60 on his final exam, while Angela scored 63 out of 75 on her exam. Who scored better?

Solution

By observation, it is not possible to answer the question because Peter's score is expressed on a base of 60, while Angela's score is on a base of 75. To compare their scores, we need to convert them to their percent equivalents, as shown below:

Peter's score: $\frac{46}{60} = 0.766666... = 76.67\%$

Angela's score: $\frac{63}{75} = 0.84 = 84.00\%$

Therefore, Angela scored better than Peter on the exam.

Converting Percents to Decimal Numbers

- **If the percent is a whole number or a decimal number,** remove the '%' sign and move the decimal point 2 places to the left. This is the same as dividing the number by 100 and dropping the '%' sign.

For example,

- To convert 45% to a decimal number,

  $45\% = 45.0$ — Remove the % sign and move the decimal point 2 places

  $= 0.45$ — to the left. This is the same as $\frac{45}{100} = 0.45$.

  Therefore, 45% = 0.45.

- To convert 0.38% to a decimal number,

  $0.38\% = 0.38$ — Remove the % sign and move the decimal point 2 places

  $= 0.0038$ — to the left. This is the same as $= \frac{0.38}{100} = 0.0038$.

  Therefore, 0.38% = 0.0038.

- **If the percent is a fraction or a mixed number** (combination of a whole number with a fraction), change it to its decimal equivalent and follow the same steps as shown above.

- For example, to convert $2\frac{1}{2}\%$ to a decimal number,

  $2\frac{1}{2}\% = 2.5\%$ — Convert the fractional portion to a decimal number.

  $= 2.5\%$ — Remove the % sign and move the decimal point 2 places

  $= 0.025$ — to the left. This is the same as $\frac{2.5}{100} = 0.025$.

  Therefore, $2\frac{1}{2}\% = 0.025$.

Example 5.1-d **Converting Percents to Decimal Numbers**

Convert each percent to its equivalent decimal number.

(i) 85% (ii) $5\frac{1}{4}\%$ (iii) 20.75% (iv) 225% (v) $\frac{2}{3}\%$

Solution

(i) $85\% = 85.0\% = 85.0 = 0.85$

(ii) $5\frac{1}{4}\% = 5.25\% = 5.25 = 0.0525$

(iii) $20.75\% = 20.75 = 0.2075$

(iv) $225\% = 225.0\% = 2.250 = 2.25$

(v) $\frac{2}{3}\% = 0.666666...\% = 0.666666... = 0.006666... = 0.00\overline{6}$

Converting Decimal Numbers to Percents

To convert a decimal number or a whole number to a percent, move the decimal point 2 places to the right and insert the '%' sign. This is the same as multiplying the number by 100 and inserting the '%' sign.

For example,

- To convert 0.35 to a percent,

  0.35 = 0.35 — Move the decimal point 2 places to the right and insert the % sign,

  = 35% — This is the same as 0.35 × 100% = 35%.

  Therefore, 0.35 = 35%.

- To convert 5 to a percent,

  5 = 5.00 — Move the decimal point 2 places to the right and insert the % sign,

  = 500% — This is the same as 5 × 100% = 500%.

  Therefore, 5 = 500%.

Example 5.1-e

Converting Decimal Numbers to Percents

Convert each of the following decimal numbers to its equivalent percent.

(i) 5.25 (ii) 0.45 (iii) 0.03 (iv) 0.002

Solution

(i) 5.25 = 5.25% = 525%

(ii) 0.45 = 0.45% = 45%

(iii) 0.03 = 0.03% = 3%

(iv) 0.002 = 0.002% = 0.2%

Example 5.1-f

Solving Application Problems Using Percents

Alexander earns 3 times the amount that Emma earns. What percent is Alexander's earnings compared to Emma's earnings?

Solution

Here, '3 times' when converted to a percent = 3 × (100%) = 300%.

Therefore, Alexander's earnings are 300% of Emma's.

Note: This also means that Alexander earns 200% more than Emma.

Example 5.1-g

Comparing Fractions and Percents

Out of 54 students in class A, 43 students passed the final exam. In class B, 78% of the students passed the final exam. Which class had a better pass rate?

Solution

Class A: Fraction of students passed = $\frac{43}{54}$

Percent of students passed = $\frac{43}{54} \times 100\%$

= 79.629629...%

= 79.63%

Class B: Percent of students passed = 78.00%

Therefore, class A had a better pass rate.

Solving Percent Problems

Many methods may be used to solve percent problems. Described below are three common methods:

Method 1: Formula Method

Every percent problem will contain three variables: *B*, *P*, and *R*.

Base (*B*): Whole quantity or value (100%). It usually follows the word 'of', or 'percent of'.

Portion (*P*): Portion of the whole quantity or value (portion of the base).

R% converted to a ratio (or decimal) is $\frac{R}{100}$ (or $0.01R$).

Rate (*R*): Relationship between base and portion, expressed as percent. It usually carries the percent sign (%) or the word '**percent**'. Every percent statement can be expressed as: ***P* is *R*% of *B*.** The value of ***R*** is used as a decimal or fractional equivalent in calculations.

Based on the above explanation, it is easy to identify the variables **'*B*'** and **'*R*'**. Once identified, the third variable will be **'*P*'**.

The relationship between these variables can be expressed as follows:

$$\textbf{\textit{Portion}} = \textbf{\textit{Rate}} \times \textbf{\textit{Base}}$$

As a formula, this is,

Formula 5.1

Portion

$$P = R \times B$$

Rearranging, we obtain $R = \frac{P}{B}$ and $B = \frac{P}{R}$.

Therefore, if any two of these quantities are known, then the third quantity can be calculated.

P, R, B Triangle

Here is a triangle that can be used to help in rearranging the formula $P = R \times B$ to solve for R *or* B.

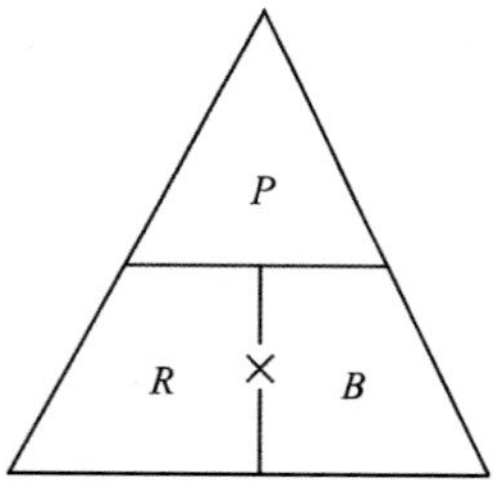

Variables beside each other at the bottom are multiplied ($R \times B$, as shown).

Variable P is divided by the variables at the bottom: $R \times B$.

Cover the variable that needs to be solved to see the new formula.

For example, if you want to solve for '*R*', the formula can be determined by covering '*R*' and reading the remaining variables in the above triangle to get, $R = \frac{P}{B}$.

Method 2: Algebraic Method

Solving problems using algebraic methods involve forming an equation for an unknown '*x*' and then solving for '*x*'. In this method, we assume that the unknown is '*x*', and form equation(s) for the given problem (or statement) using key words to represent certain arithmetic operations.

The following are key words and phrases that are commonly used to indicate various arithmetic operations.

Operation symbols	Key words
Addition (+)	Add, sum, plus, and, more than, increased by, appreciate, rise
Subtraction (−)	Subtract, difference, minus, less than, decreased by, depreciate, fall
Multiplication (× or () or ·)	Multiply, product, times, of
Division (÷ or /)	Divide, ratio, per, divided by, quotient
Equal (=)	Is, was, gives, given by
Unknown value	What, how much, (usually denoted by some letter, such as '*x*')

For example, use these key words to form the algebraic equation of the following:

- What percent of 200 is 60

  $x\% \times 200 = 60$

  $x\% \times 200 = 60$

- \$52 is 13% of what amount

  $\$52 = 13\% \times x$

  $\$52 = 13\%x$

- 40% of what amount is \$280

  $40\% \times x = \$280$

  $40\%x = 280$

- How much is 2% of 75

  $x = 2\% \times 75$

  $x = 2\% \times 75.$

Method 3: Ratio-Proportion Method

The whole amount or quantity is represented by 100% and is known as the **base (*B*)**. The **portion (*P*)** is a part of the base and it forms a **percent (*R*%)** of the base. Thus, in the ratio-proportion method, we first identify the base and portion in the problem, then using the proportion equation we solve for the unknown.

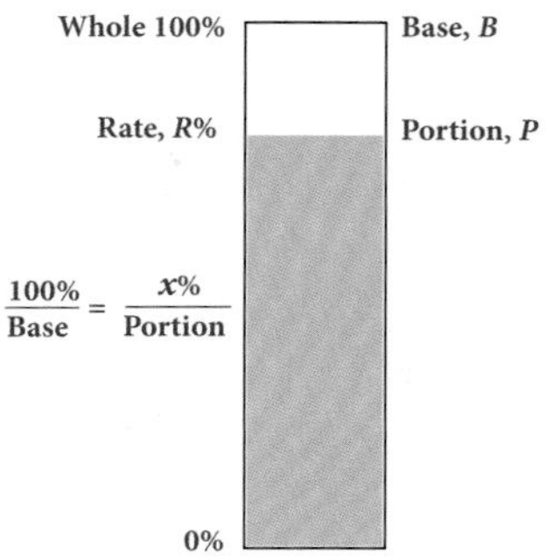

Portion : Base = Rate % : 100%

$$P : B = R\% : 100\%$$

$$\frac{P}{B} = \frac{R\%}{100\%}$$

$$\frac{P}{B} = \frac{R}{100}$$

Example 5.1-h

Calculating the Portion of a Whole Quantity

What is 75% of \$250? (Or, 75% of \$250 is how much?)

Solution

Method 1: Using the Formula Method

$R\% = 75\%$ (value with % sign); i.e., $R = 0.75$

$B = \$250.00$ (value that follows the word 'of')

$P = R \times B$

$P = 0.75 \times 250.00$

$= \$187.50$

Therefore, 75% of \$250.00 is \$187.50.

Method 2: Using the Algebraic Method

What is 75% of \$250?

$x = 75\% \times 250.00$

i.e. $x = 75\% \times 250.00$ — Expressing the percent as a fraction,

$x = \left(\frac{75}{100}\right) \times 250.00$ — Simplifying,

$= 0.75 \times 250.00$

$= \$187.50$

Therefore, 75% of \$250.00 is \$187.50.

Solution *continued*

Method 3: Using the Ratio-Proportion Method

Here, the whole amount of \$250 is the base and is represented by 100%. 75% is a portion of the base, as illustrated:

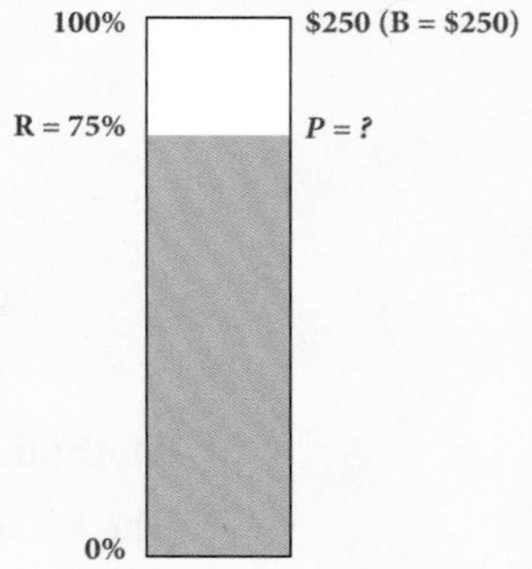

Portion : Base = Rate : 100%

$$P : B = R\% : 100\%$$

$$P : 250 = 75\% : 100\%$$

$$\frac{P}{250.00} = \frac{75\%}{100\%}$$

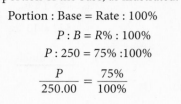

$$\frac{P}{250.00} = \frac{75}{100}$$ Cross-multiplying,

$$100P = 250.00 \times 75$$ Solving for P,

$$P = \frac{250.00 \times 75}{100}$$ Simplifying,

$$= \$187.50$$

Therefore, 75% of \$250.00 is \$187.50.

Note: The following examples use the Formula Method; however, you can solve them using any of the three methods described above.

Example 5.1-i **Calculating the Portion When Rate is More Than 100%**

What is 150% of 200?

Solution

$R\% = 150\%$ (value with % sign)

$= 1.50$

$B = 200$ (value that follows the word 'of')

$P = ?$ (other value)

Using $P = R \times B$ Substituting values for 'R' and 'B', and simplifying,

$= 1.50 \times 200 = 300$

Therefore, 150% of 200 is 300.

Example 5.1-j **Calculating the Rate When Portion and Base are Known**

What percent of \$775 is \$1,250? (Or, \$1,250 is what percent of \$775?)

Solution

$B = \$775.00$ (value that follows the word 'of')

$P = \$1,250.00$ (the other value)

$R = ?$ (value for the word percent)

Using Formula, $P = R \times B$ Rearranging,

$$R = \frac{P}{B}$$ Substituting values for 'P' and 'B',

$$R = \frac{1,250.00}{775.00}$$ Simplifying,

$$R\% = \frac{1,250.00}{775.00} \times 100\% = 161.290322...\% = 161.29\%$$

Therefore, 161.29% of \$775.00 is \$1,250.00.

Example 5.1-k

Calculating the Base When Portion and Rate are Known

50% of what number is 200?

Solution

$R\% = 50\%$ (value with % sign) = 0.50

$P = 200$ (the other value)

$B = ?$ (value that follows the word 'of')

Using Formula, $P = R \times B$ — Rearranging,

$$B = \frac{P}{R}$$ Substituting values for '*P*' and '*R*',

$$B = \frac{200}{0.5}$$ Simplifying,

$$= 400$$

Therefore, 50% of 400 is 200.

Example 5.1-l

Application Problem Based on Repeating Decimals

Sandra owns $25\frac{1}{3}\%$ of a web development company. If the company is valued at $180,000 what is the value of Sandra's ownership in the company?

Solution

Do not round values calculated in intermediary steps. Store these values in your calculator and recall them for subsequent calculations.

Identify the Base, Portion, and Rate.

$B = \$180{,}000.00$ (whole value)

$R\% = 25\frac{1}{3}\%$ (the value with % sign)

$= 25.333333...\%$

$= 0.253333...$

$P = R \times B$

$= 0.253333... \times 180{,}000.00$

$= \$45{,}600.00$

Alternatively, this can be solved by converting the mixed number to an improper fraction:

$R\% = 25\frac{1}{3}\%$ — Converting the mixed number to an improper fraction,

$= \frac{76}{3}\%$ — Expressing the percent as a fraction,

$= \frac{76}{3} \times \frac{1}{100}$ — Substituting in the formula $P = R \times B$,

$P = R \times B$

$= \frac{76}{3} \times \frac{1}{100} \times 180{,}000.00$ — Simplifying,

$= \$45{,}600.00$

Therefore, the value of Sandra's ownership in the company is $45,600.00.

5.1 | Exercises

Answers to odd numbered problems are available at the end of the textbook.

For the following problems, express the answers rounded to two decimal places, wherever applicable. Calculate the missing values in Problems 1 to 18.

		Percents	Decimals	Fractions (or mixed numbers) in lowest terms
1.	a.	75%		
	b.		0.30	
	c.			$\frac{1}{4}$
3.	a.	5%		
	b.		0.20	
	c.			$\frac{3}{5}$
5.	a.	150%		
	b.		0.175	
	c.			$\frac{12}{25}$
7.	a.	12.5%		
	b.		0.05	
	c.			$4\frac{1}{2}$
9.	a.	0.6%		
	b.		0.005	
	c.			$4\frac{3}{5}$
11.	a.	0.05%		
	b.		0.0025	
	c.			$1\frac{1}{8}$
13.	a.	$\frac{3}{5}\%$		
	b.		1.08	
	c.			$\frac{3}{80}$
15.	a.	$1\frac{1}{4}\%$		
	b.		2.025	
	c.			$\frac{1}{400}$
17.	a.	$6\frac{1}{2}\%$		
	b.		2.5	
	c.			$\frac{4}{25}$

		Percents	Decimals	Fractions (or mixed numbers) in lowest terms
2.	a.	50%		
	b.		0.70	
	c.			$\frac{1}{5}$
4.	a.	2%		
	b.		0.8	
	c.			$\frac{3}{8}$
6.	a.	225%		
	b.		0.225	
	c.			$\frac{7}{20}$
8.	a.	7.5%		
	b.		0.03	
	c.			$3\frac{3}{4}$
10.	a.	0.8%		
	b.		0.003	
	c.			$1\frac{3}{15}$
12.	a.	0.08%		
	b.		0.075	
	c.			$2\frac{3}{8}$
14.	a.	$\frac{3}{8}\%$		
	b.		2.04	
	c.			$\frac{22}{75}$
16.	a.	$2\frac{3}{4}\%$		
	b.		1.075	
	c.			$\frac{1}{250}$
18.	a.	$10\frac{3}{5}\%$		
	b.		7.5	
	c.			$\frac{13}{50}$

Calculate the following:

19. a. 20% of 350   b. 12.5% of 800

20. a. 45% of 180   b. 2.5% of 960

21. a. 0.25% of 75   b. $\frac{1}{4}$% of 200 km

22. a. 0.755% of 120   b. $\frac{1}{8}$% of 450 km

23. a. 130% of 40   b. $5\frac{1}{2}$% of $1,000

24. a. 285% of 110   b. $12\frac{3}{4}$% of $1,260

Calculate the following:

25. What is 2.5% of 80?
26. What is 40% of 160?
27. $8\frac{1}{4}$% of $200 is how much?
28. $25\frac{3}{4}$% of $2,680 is how much?
29. How much is $\frac{1}{4}$% of $108?
30. How much is $\frac{3}{4}$% of 350 kg?
31. What number is 125% of 6?
32. What number is 250% of 12?

Calculate the following:

33. 12 is what percent of 30?
34. 18 is what percent of 40?
35. What percent of 4 is 16?
36. What percent of 9 is 45?
37. What percent of 220 is 100?
38. What percent of 22.10 is 110.50?
39. 280 metres is what percent of a kilometre?
40. 180 gram is what percent of 3 kilogram?

Calculate the following:

41. 400 is 50% of what number?
42. 225 is 25% of what number?
43. 15% of what amount is $27.90?
44. 30% of what amount is 708?
45. 120% of what amount is 156?
46. 215% of what amount is 258?
47. $16.50 is 0.75% of what amount?
48. $16.40 is 0.5% of what amount?
49. How much tax was charged on a table that costs $250, if the tax rate is 13%?
50. The monthly gross salary of an employee is $6,250. 26% of the salary was deducted for taxes. How much money was deducted for taxes?
51. 5% of commission on sales was $1,250. What was the sales amount?
52. 3% interest on a loan was $210. What was the loan amount?
53. In a survey of 450 people, 117 responded 'yes'. What percent of the people surveyed responded 'no'?
54. 144 out of 600 students took Business Mathematics. What percent of students did not take the course?
55. A company that makes games, sets sales targets at $280,000 per year for each of its sales people. If Amanda, an excellent salesperson, achieved 250% of her target this year, calculate her sales for the year.
56. If the population of Canada was estimated to be 35,749,600 on January 2015, and the population of Ontario was estimated to be $37\frac{2}{3}$% of Canada's population, calculate the population of Ontario, rounded up to the nearest whole number.

• 57. When there was a boom in the real estate market, Lucy sold her property for $410,440, which was 130% of the amount she originally paid. Calculate the amount she originally paid for the property.

• 58. Ronald, an investment banker sold his shares for $18,568.50 when there was a boom in the stock market. Calculate the amount he paid for the shares if the selling price was 180.65% of the original amount he paid for the shares.

• 59. Evan, a business development representative of a leading pharmaceutical firm, took his client out for a dinner that cost $180.75 before taxes. If the tax was $23.50, calculate the tax rate.

• 60. A leading information technology company donated $87,790 out of its 2014 fiscal revenue of $17,558,643 towards socially responsible causes. What percent of the revenue did the company contribute toward these causes?

• 61. Neel Plastics Manufacturing Corporation targets to obtain $120,000 of funding from their investors, to purchase new machinery. If they were only able to obtain 25.5% of their total target, calculate the amount of money that is yet to be received.

• 62. Pamela and Martha run a business that made a profit of $12,750. As Pamela invested a higher amount in the business, she received 57.5% of the profits and Martha received the remaining. Calculate Martha's share of the profit, in dollars.

5.2 | Percent Changes

Introduction

The percent by which a quantity increases or decreases from its initial (original) value is called **percent change (%*C*)**; i.e., the amount of change (increase or decrease) is calculated as a percent change (%*C*) of its initial value.

$$\text{Amount of Change} = \%C \times \text{Initial Value}$$

The amount of change is the difference between the Final Value (V_f) and the Initial Value (V_i); i.e., the amount can also be calculated by subtracting the Initial Value from the Final Value.

$$\text{Amount of Change} = \text{Final Value} - \text{Initial Value}$$

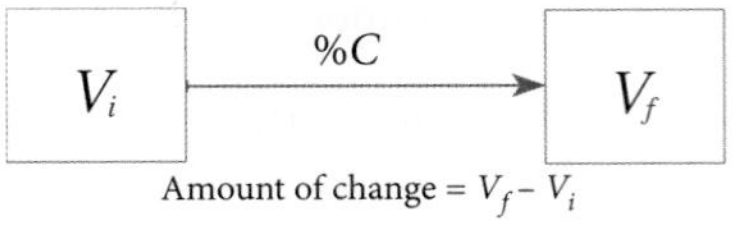

Therefore, $\%C \times \text{Initial Value} = \text{Final Value} - \text{Initial Value}$

To find a percent increase or decrease, find the amount of increase or decrease and then determine its percent value compared to the initial value.

$$\%C = \frac{(\text{Final Value} - \text{Initial Value})}{\text{Initial Value}}$$

Percent Change ⟶ $\%C = \dfrac{(V_f - V_i)}{V_i}$ ⟵ Amount of Change (numerator); ⟵ Initial Value (denominator)

Percent change is calculated as a ratio of the amount of change to the initial value. This ratio is converted to its percent equivalent by multiplying it by 100 and inserting a '%' sign, as shown below.

Formula 5.2-a

Percent Change

$$\%C = \frac{(V_f - V_i)}{V_i} \times 100\%$$

$$\text{Final Value} = \text{Initial Value} + \text{Amount of Change}$$

$V_f = V_i + \%C \times V_i$ Factoring by the common factor V_i,

$V_f = V_i(1 + \%C)$

Formula 5.2-b

Final Value

$$V_f = V_i(1 + \%C)$$

Using Formula 5.2-b, the formula to calculate the initial value (V_i) is derived as follows,

$V_f = V_i(1 + \%C)$ Rearranging,

$V_i(1 + \%C) = V_f$ Solving for V_i,

$$V_i = \frac{V_f}{1 + \%C}$$

Formula 5.2-c

Initial Value

$$V_i = \frac{V_f}{1 + \%C}$$

- If the final value is greater than the initial value, then the percent change is a percent increase, which is a positive value (%*C*).
- If the final value is smaller than the initial value, then the percent change is a percent decrease, which is a negative value (–%*C*).
- Percent change is measured either as a percent increase (profit, rise, appreciation, etc.) or as a percent decrease (loss, fall, depreciation, etc.), compared to the initial value.

Example 5.2-a

Calculating the Amount of Increase and Final Value

The price of an item that originally sold at $150 is increased by 20%. Calculate the dollar amount of the increase and the price after the increase.

Solution

V_i = $150 → $\%C = 20\%$ (increase) → V_f = ?

n there is an increase from
nitial value, the %C will be
ive and the final value will
eater than the initial value.

ful Check:
%C is positive, then the
value must be greater
the initial value.

Method 1:

$$\textit{Amount of Change} = \%C \times \textit{Initial Value}$$
$$= 20\% \times 150.00$$
$$= 0.2 \times 150.00$$
$$= \$30.00 \text{ (increase)}$$

$$\textit{Final Value} = \textit{Inital Value} + \textit{Amount of Change}$$
$$= 150.00 + 30.00$$
$$= \$180.00$$

Method 2:

Using Formula 5.2-b,

$$V_f = V_i\,(1 + \%C) \quad \text{Substituting values,}$$
$$= 150.00\,(1 + 20\%) \quad \text{Converting \% to decimal,}$$
$$= 150.00\,(1 + 0.20) \quad \text{Solving,}$$
$$= 150.00\,(1.2)$$
$$= \$180.00$$

$$\textit{Amount of Change} = \textit{Final Value} - \textit{Initial Value}$$
$$= 180.00 - 150.00$$
$$= \$30.00$$

Therefore, the amount of increase is $30.00 and the price after the increase is $180.00.

Example 5.2-b

Calculating the Amount of Decrease and Final Value

An item normally sells for $400 and is discounted (reduced in price) by 15% during a sale. Calculate the dollar amount of discount and the price after the discount.

Solution

V_i = $400 → $\%C = 15\%$ (decrease) → V_f = ?

n there is a decrease from
nitial value, %C will be
tive and the final value will
ss than the initial value.

ful check:
%C is negative, then the
value must be smaller
the inital value.

Method 1:

$$\textit{Amount of Change} = \%C \times \textit{Initial Value}$$
$$= -\,15\% \times 400.00$$
$$= -\,0.15 \times 400.00$$
$$= -\,\$60.00 \text{ (decrease)}$$

$$\textit{Final Value} = \textit{Initial Value} - \textit{Amount of Change}$$
$$= 400.00 - 60.00$$
$$= \$340.00$$

Method 2:

Using Formula 5.2-b,

$$V_f = V_i\,(1 + \%C) \quad \text{Substituting values,}$$
$$= 400.00\,(1 - 15\%) \quad \text{Converting \% to decimal,}$$
$$= 400.00\,(1 - 0.15) \quad \text{Solving,}$$
$$= 400.00\,(0.85)$$
$$= \$340.00$$

$$\textit{Amount of Change} = \textit{Final Value} - \textit{Initial Value}$$
$$= 340.00 - 400.00$$
$$= -\,\$60.00 \text{ (decrease)}$$

Therefore, the amount of discount is $60.00 and the price after the discount is $340.00.

Example 5.2-c

Calculating Percent Increase

A store had sales of \$50,000 in July and \$80,000 in August. Calculate the percent change in sales from July to August.

Solution

Final Value, V_f = \$80,000.00

Initial Value, V_i = \$50,000.00

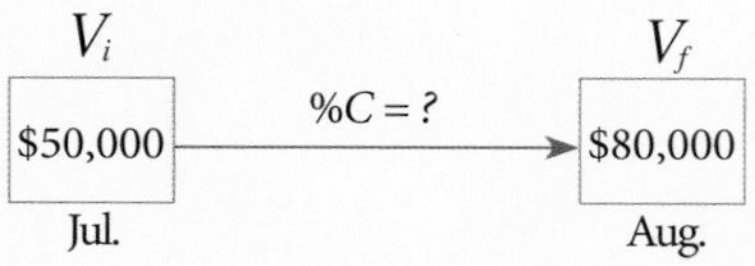

Using Formula 5.2-a, $\%C = \frac{(V_f - V_i)}{V_i} \times 100\%$ — Substituting values,

$= \frac{80{,}000.00 - 50{,}000.00}{50{,}000.00} \times 100\%$ — Solving,

$= \frac{30{,}000.00}{50{,}000.00} \times 100\%$

= 60.00% (increase)

Therefore, the percent change in sales from July to August is an increase of 60.00%.

Example 5.2-d

Calculating Percent Decrease

A store's total expenses were \$2,400 in September and \$1,800 in October. Calculate the percent change in expenses from September to October.

Solution

Final Value, V_f = \$1,800.00

Initial Value, V_i = \$2,400.00

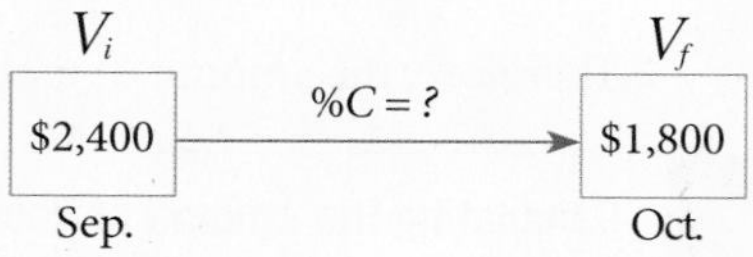

Using Formula 5.2-a, $\%C = \frac{(V_f - V_i)}{V_i} \times 100\%$ — Substituting values,

$= \frac{1{,}800.00 - 2{,}400.00}{2{,}400.00} \times 100\%$ — Solving,

$= \frac{-6{,}000.00}{2{,}400.00} \times 100\%$

= −25.00% (which is a decrease)

Therefore, the percent change in expenses from September to October is a decrease of 25.00%.

Example 5.2-e

Calculating Initial Value When the Percent Change is Positive

The value of a stock increased by 35% since it was purchased. If the stock is now selling at \$81, what was its value when it was purchased?

Solution

%C = 35% (increase)

V_f = \$81.00

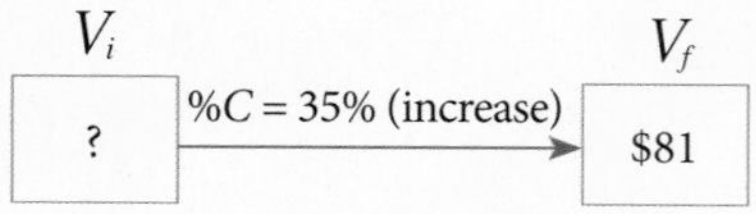

Using Formula 5.2-c, $V_i = \frac{V_f}{1 + \%C}$ — Substituting values,

$= \frac{81.00}{1 + 35\%}$ — Converting % to decimal,

$= \frac{81.00}{1 + 0.35}$ — Solving,

$= \frac{81.00}{1.35}$

= \$60.00

Therefore, the the value of the stock when it was purchased was \$60.00.

Example 5.2-f

Calculating Initial Value When the Percent Change is Negative

After a discount of 25%, an item was sold for $450. Calculate the price of the item before the discount.

Solution

$\%C = -25\%$ (discount)

$V_f = \$450.00$

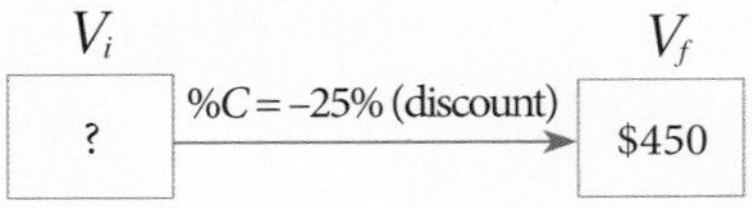

Using Formula 5.2-c, $V_i = \dfrac{V_f}{1 + \%C}$ — Substituting values,

$= \dfrac{450.00}{1 - 25\%}$ — Converting % to decimal,

$= \dfrac{450.00}{1 - 0.25}$ — Solving,

$= \dfrac{450.00}{0.75}$

$= \$600.00$

Therefore, the price of the item before the discount was $600.00.

Example 5.2-g

Understanding Relative Percent Change Applications

Company A's profit increased from $165,000 to $170,000 last year. Company B's profit increased from $122,000 to $126,000 in the same year. Which company showed a better relative change in profit?

Solution

At first instinct, you may think you need to only calculate the difference in profits and compare them to arrive at the answer. That is, Company A's profit for the year increased by 170,000 – 165,000 = $5,000. Company B's profit for the year increased by 126,000 – 122,000 = $4,000. Therefore, you might say that Company A has grown more than Company B. However, this comparison is **incorrect** because you need to determine the company which had a better **relative** change in profit.

To compare the relative change in profits, you have to calculate the 'percent change' in profits of companies A and B last year.

> financial applications, it is ore important to calculate ercent changes and sociated values instead of lying on a mere difference etween two values.

Using Formula 5.2-a, $\%C = \dfrac{(V_f - V_i)}{V_i} \times 100\%$

Company A's Percent Change in Profit:

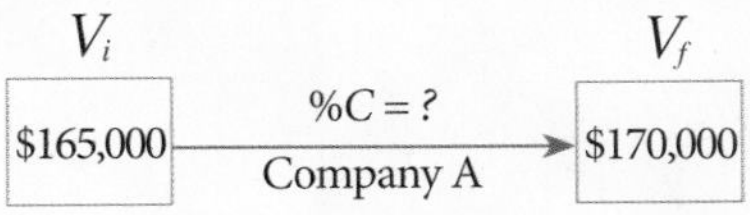

$\%C_A = \dfrac{170{,}000.00 - 165{,}000.00}{165{,}000.00} \times 100\%$

$= \dfrac{5{,}000.00}{165{,}000.00} \times 100\%$

$= 3.030303...\% = 3.03\%$

Company B's Percent Change in Profit:

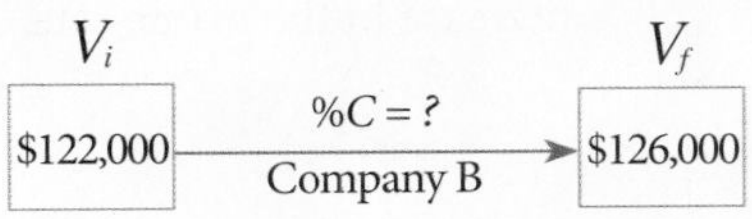

$\%C_B = \dfrac{126{,}000.00 - 122{,}000.00}{122{,}000.00} \times 100\%$

$= \dfrac{4{,}000.00}{122{,}000.00} \times 100\%$

$= 3.278688...\% = 3.28\%$

Therefore, even though Company B had a smaller increase in profit than Company A during the year, Company B had a better relative growth (3.28%) compared to Company A (3.03%).

Note: There are many methods used in calculating percent changes. Described in the following example are three common methods used to solve a percent change problem.

Example 5.2-h Calculating Final Value When Percent Change is Positive, Using Different Methods

If a $20 hourly rate of pay is increased by 10%, find the new hourly rate.

Solution

$\%C = +10\% = +0.1,\ V_i = \$20,\ V_f = ?$

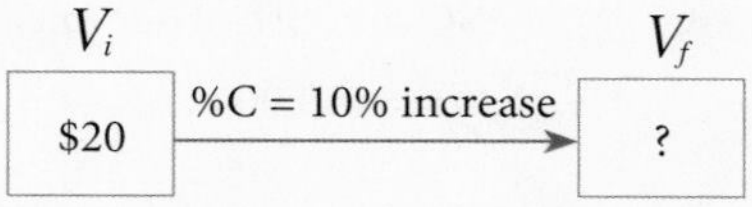

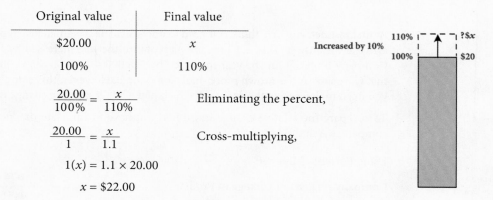

Method 1: Using Algebraic Method

Initial Value + Amount of Increase = Final Value

$V_i + \%C \times V_i = V_f$ Substituting values,

$20.00 + 0.1\ (20.00) = V_f$ Solving,

$20.00 + 2.00 = V_f$

$V_f = \$22.00$

Method 2: Using Formula Method

Using Formula 5.2-b,

$V_f = V_i\ (1 + \%C)$ Substituting values,

$V_f = 20.00\ (1 + 10\%)$ Solving,

$= 20.00\ (1 + 0.10)$

$= 20.00\ (1.10)$

$= \$22.00$

Therefore, the new hourly rate is $22.00.

Method 3: Using Ratio-Proportion Method

In this method, we compare the original value and final value using ratios and proportions to find the unknown value.

The original value of $20 represents 100%. This is increased by 10% to a final value of 110%, as illustrated:

Original value	Final value
$20.00	x
100%	110%

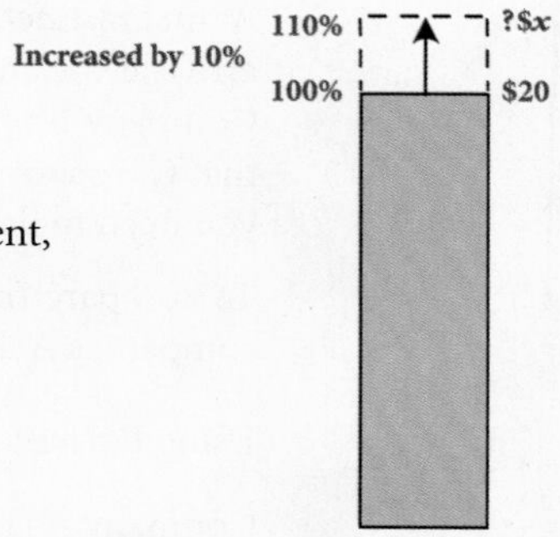

$\frac{20.00}{100\%} = \frac{x}{110\%}$ Eliminating the percent,

$\frac{20.00}{1} = \frac{x}{1.1}$ Cross-multiplying,

$1(x) = 1.1 \times 20.00$

$x = \$22.00$

Therefore, the new hourly rate is $22.00.

Example 5.2-i Calculating Percent Change When Initial and Final Values are Given as a Percent

If the Bank of Canada increased its prime lending rate from 2.25% to 3.35%, calculate the percent increase in the prime rate.

Solution

$V_i = 2.25\%,$

$V_f = 3.35\%,$

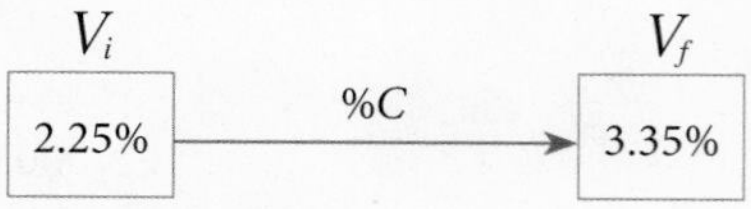

Solution
continued

Using Formula 5.2-a, $\%C = \frac{(V_f - V_i)}{V_i} \times 100\%$ Substituting the values,

$= \frac{3.35\% - 2.25\%}{2.25\%} \times 100\%$ Simplifying,

$= \frac{1.10\%}{2.25\%} \times 100\%$

$= \frac{1.10}{2.25} \times 100\%$

$= 0.488888... \times 100\% = 48.89\%$

Therefore, the percent increase in prime rate is 48.89%.

Percent increase cannot be reversed by the same percent decrease.

100.00 increased by 0% = $110.00.

owever, $110.00 decreased y 10% ≠ $100.00

For example,

$100.00 increased by 10% results in $110.00.

V_i: $100 → %C = 10% (Increase) → V_f: **$110**

$V_f = 100.00 + 10\% \text{ of } 100.00 = 100.00 + 10.00 = \$110.00$

However, $110.00 decreased by 10% results in $99.00.

V_f: **$99** ← %C = –10% (Decrease) ← V_i: $110

$V_f = 110.00 - 10\% \text{ of } 110.00 = 110.00 - \$11.00 = \$99.00$

100.00 decreased y 10% = $90.00.

owever, $90.00 increased y 10% ≠ $100.00

Similarly, percent decrease cannot be reversed by the same percent increase.

For example,

$100.00 decreased by 10% results in $90.00.

V_i: $100 → %C = –10% (Decrease) → V_f: **$90**

$V_f = 100.00 - 10\% \text{ of } 100.00 = 100.00 - 10.00 = \$90.00$

However, $90.00 increased by 10% results in $99.00.

V_f: $99 ← %C = 10% (Increase) ← V_i: **$90**

$V_f = 90.00 + 10\% \text{ of } 90.00 = 90.00 + 9.00 = \$99.00$

To reverse a percent increase or percent decrease, the proper method should be used, as shown below.

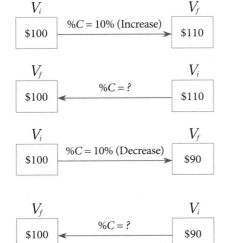

V_i: $100 → %C = 10% (Increase) → V_f: $110

V_f: $100 ← %C = ? ← V_i: $110

Using Formula 5.2-a,

$\%C = \frac{(V_f - V_i)}{V_i} \times 100\%$

$= \frac{100.00 - 110.00}{110.00} \times 100\%$

$= -9.090909... = -9.09\%$(Decrease)

V_i: $100 → %C = 10% (Decrease) → V_f: $90

V_f: $100 ← %C = ? ← V_i: $90

Using Formula 5.2-a,

$\%C = \frac{(V_f - V_i)}{V_i} \times 100\%$

$= \frac{100.00 - 90.00}{90.00} \times 100\%$

$= \frac{10.00}{90.00} \times 100\%$

$= 11.111111... = 11.11\%$ (Increase)

Example 5.2-j

Calculating Percent Change When the Statement is Reversed

If Ali earns 25% more than Brian, then Brian earns what percent less than Ali?

Solution

Method 1: Using the Algebraic Method

Let Ali's earnings be A and Brian's earnings be B.

$A = B + 25\%$ of B (or $A = 125\%$ of B)

$A = 1.25B$ Expressing B as a fraction of A,

$$B = \frac{1}{1.25}A$$

$$B = 0.80A$$

That is, Brian earns 80% of Ali's earnings, which is the same as stating that Brian earns 20% less than Ali.

Therefore, if Ali earns 25% more than Brian, then Brian earns 20% less than Ali.

Method 2: Using the Formula Method, Assuming a Value for B

Let Brian's earnings, = \$1,000.00

Then Ali's earnings, = \$1,000.00 + 25% of \$1,000.00

= 1,000.00 + 250.00

= \$1,250.00

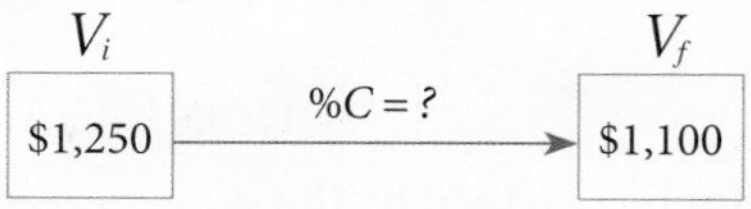

Using Formula 5.2-a, $\%C = \frac{(V_f - V_i)}{V_i} \times 100\%$ Substituting values,

$\%C = \frac{1{,}000.00 - 1{,}250.00}{1{,}250.00} \times 100\%$ Solving,

$= \frac{-250.00}{1{,}250.00} \times 100\%$

$= -20.00\%$ (Less)

Therefore, if Ali earns 25% more than Brian, then Brian earns 20.00% less than Ali.

Example 5.2-k

Calculating Percent Change When the Value of a Currency Increases (Appreciates) or Decreases (Depreciates) Against Another Currency

If the US dollar appreciated by 10% relative to the Canadian dollar, by what percent has the Canadian dollar depreciated relative to the US dollar?

Solution

Method 1: Assuming US\$ 1 = C\$ x

Assume US\$1 = C\$$x$

If the US dollar appreciated by 10%, then,

US\$1 = C\$1.10x

US\$$\frac{1}{1.10}$ = C\$$x$Dividing both sides by 1.10,

US\$0.909090... = C\$$x$

C\$$x$ = US\$0.909090...

Therefore, if the US\$ appreciated by 10% relative to C\$, than the value of C\$$x$ is depreciated from US\$1 to US\$ 0.909090...

Solution
continued

Method 2: Using the Formula Method

V_i		V_f
US$1	$\%C = ?$ →	0.090909...

Using Formula 5.2-a, $\%C = \frac{(V_f - V_i)}{V_i} \times 100\%$ Substituting the values,

$$\%C = \frac{\text{US\$0.909090...} - \text{US\$1}}{\text{US\$1}}$$ Solving,

$$= -0.090909... = -9.09\%$$

Therefore, if the US dollar appreciated by 10% relative to the Canadian dollar, then the Canadian dollar depreciated by 9.09% relative to the US dollar.

Percent Change When the Initial Value (V_i) is Negative

In the algebraic equation $V_i + \textit{Amount of Increase} = V_f$,

where, $\textit{Amount of Increase} = \%C \times V_i$

When V_i is increased by an amount, regardless of the value or sign for V_i, add the amount of increase to determine V_f; i.e., the amount added to V_i should be positive.

$$V_i + \textit{Amount of Increase} = V_f$$

When V_i is decreased by an amount, regardless of the value or sign for V_i, subtract the amount of decrease to determine V_f; i.e., the amount that is subtracted from V_i should be positive.

$$V_i - \text{Amount of Decrease} = V_f$$

Therefore, the amount that is added or subtracted should always be a positive quantity. The sign in the formula will determine if this amount is an increase or a decrease.

When the original quantity (V_i) is negative, use the absolute sign for V_i to calculate the amount of increase or decrease. This ensures that the amount of increase or decrease will be a positive answer.

Therefore, when V_i is negative,

$$\textit{Amount of Increase or Decrease} = \%C \times \textit{Absolute value of } V_i$$

$$= \%C\,|V_i|$$

he absolute value of a umber 'a', written as |a|, vill always be a positive umber (regardless f the sign for 'a').

or example, |–5| = 5 nd |5| = 5.

If the final value is greater than the initial value,

Initial Value + Amount of Increase = Final Value

$$V_i + \%C\,|V_i| = V_f$$

$$\%C = \frac{(V_f - V_i)}{|V_i|}$$

Therefore, the value of %C will be positive.

If the final value is smaller than the initial value,

Initial Value – Amount of Decrease = Final Value

$$V_i - \%C\,|V_i| = V_f$$

$$\%C = -\frac{(V_f - V_i)}{|V_i|}$$

Therefore, the value of %C will be negative.

Example 5.2-l

Percent Change When Initial Value (V_i) is a Negative Value

The average temperature in Toronto last winter was –4°C. If the average temperature this winter increased by 1.15°C, calculate the percent change in this year's winter temperature from last year's winter.

Solution

Method 1:

Since V_i is negative,

Amount of Increase $= \%C\,|V_i|$

$1.15 = \%C\,|-4|$ Eliminating absolute sign,

$1.15 = \%C\,(4)$ Solving,

$$\%C = \frac{1.15}{4} \times 100\%$$

$= 28.75\%$ (increase)

Therefore, this year's winter temperature increased by 28.85% from last year's winter.

Method 2:

$V_i = -4°C$

Amount of increase $= 1.15°C$

$V_f - V_i = 1.15$

$V_f = V_i + 1.15$

$= -4 + 1.15$

$= -2.85$

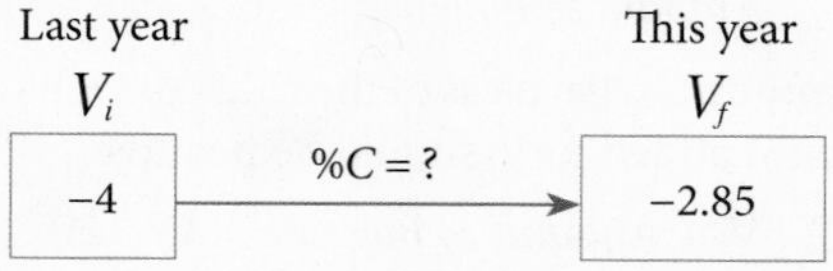

Since V_i is negative,

$$\%C = \frac{(V_f - V_i)}{|V_i|} \times 100\%$$ Substituting values, ($V_f - V_i = 1.15$ and $V_i = -4$)

$$\%C = \frac{1.15}{|-4|} \times 100\%$$ Eliminating absolute sign,

$$= \frac{1.15}{4} \times 100\%$$ Solving,

$= 28.75\%$ (Increase)

Therefore, this year's winter temperature increased by 28.85% from last year's winter.

Example 5.2-m

Percent Change Comparing Unit Quantities

A jeweler made and sold 500 g of silver chains for \$90.00. If he reduced the weight of the silver in the chain to 450 g and reduced the price to \$85.50, by what percent did the unit rate change?

Solution

Unit price of the 500 g silver chain: $\frac{90.00}{500} = \$0.18$ per gram of silver

Unit price of the 450 g silver chain: $\frac{85.50}{450} = \$0.19$ per gram of silver

There is an increase in the unit price of the chain.

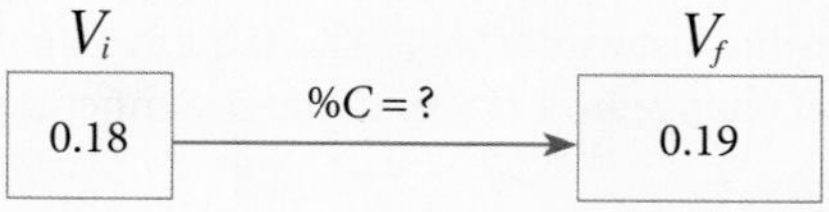

$$\%C = \frac{(V_f - V_i)}{V_i}$$ Substituting values,

$$\%C = \frac{0.19 - 0.18}{0.18} \times 100\%$$ Solving,

$= 0.055555... \times 100\% = 5.56\%$ increase

Therefore, the unit rate increased by 5.56%.

5.2 | Exercises

Answers to odd-numbered problems are available at the end of the textbook.

For the following problems, express the answers rounded to two decimal places, wherever applicable.

Calculate the missing values in Problems 1 to 4.

1.

	Initial Value	Percent Increase	Final Value
a.	$270	45%	?
b.	$4,500	137.5%	?
c.	?	25%	$600
d.	?	262.5%	$2,250
e.	$150	?	$225
f.	$3,400	?	$9,200

2.

	Initial Value	Percent Increase	Final Value
a.	$250	35%	?
b.	$3,500	112.5%	?
c.	?	40%	$800
d.	?	187.5%	$6,950
e.	$170	?	$204
f.	$7,500	?	$24,500

3.

	Initial Value	Percent Decrease	Final Value
a.	$145	45%	?
b.	$1,275	112.5%	?
c.	?	25%	$412.5
d.	?	23.75%	$3,400
e.	$740	?	$400
f.	$5,200	?	$1,600

4.

	Initial Value	Percent Decrease	Final Value
a.	$525	35%	?
b.	$6,800	137.5%	?
c.	?	40%	$525
d.	?	18.75%	$4,800
e.	$222	?	$120
f.	$8,125	?	$2,500

5. If Harley's salary of $2,000 per month is increased by 5.5%, what is his new salary?
6. Revenues of Python Graphics Corporation rose by 280% from last year. If their revenue last year was $860,760, calculate their revenue this year.
7. After a discount of $12\frac{1}{2}$%, a publishing company purchased an offset printing press for $245,000. Calculate the original price of the machine.
8. A clothing retail outlet purchased clothes in bulk from a wholesaler for $86,394. This was after a discount of $10\frac{3}{4}$% on the purchase. Calculate the original price of the clothes.
9. If calculators that sell in stores for $30 each are being offered online for $24 each, calculate the percent discount offered online.
10. If Lilo's student loan of $12,000 will increase to $12,860 by the end of the year, calculate the percent increase of her loan.
11. Dawson purchased a pair of shoes on Boxing Day that was discounted by 10% from the original price of $50. Calculate the amount he paid for the pair of shoes.
12. Jamie went to the mall during the holiday season to purchase a wall painting for his mother. He liked a painting that was selling for $199.99 and which had a seasonal discount of 18% on its selling price. How much would this painting cost Jamie after the discount?
13. A sales tax of 13% increased the cost of a meal at a restaurant to $34.50. What was the cost of the meal before taxes?
14. After paying income taxes of 45%, Carla's take-home annual income was $45,000. Calculate her income before deducting income taxes.
15. The average daytime summer temperature in Calgary increased by 3.0°C this year. If the average daytime summer temperature last year was 29°C, calculate the percent change in the average daytime summer temperature this year.
16. The average yearly snowfall in Vancouver increased by 3 cm this year. If the average yearly snowfall last year was 47.5 cm, calculate the percent change in average yearly snowfall this year.
17. The value of a car depreciated by 18.5% from the purchase price of $36,450 a year ago. What is its current price?
18. A company laid off 12% of its 675 employees. How many are currently employed?
19. The average price for an airline ticket to Vancouver from Toronto currently is $812. This is an increase of 12.5% from last year's average price. What was the average price last year?

20. The current price for the monthly Metro Pass is $141.50. This is 7.4% more than last year's price. What was last year's price?
21. During a sale, a TV regularly priced at $999 was sold for $779. What was the discount percent?
22. Sales at the store dropped from $83,570 to $69,500 over a two-year period. What was the percent decrease in sales during this period?
23. A shirt regularly priced at $37.50 was sold at a discount of 17.5%. Calculate the discounted price of the shirt.
24. A town's population increased by 13.5% from 27,000 people. What is the current population?
25. James' current annual salary is $63,536. This is an increase of 4.5% from last year's salary. What was his salary last year?
26. The current enrollment at a college is 22,575, and represents an increase of 7.5% from last year. What was the enrollment last year?
27. If the current fixed mortgage rate of 5.4% rises to 6.6%, calculate the percent increase in the mortgage rate.
28. If the prime rate of 3.5% increases to 4.2%, calculate the percent increase in the prime rate.
29. If Roger scored 20% more than Judie, by what percent is Judie's score less than Roger's?
30. If Harry earns 15% more than Beary per hour, by what percent is Beary's earning less than Harry's?
31. If the Canadian dollar appreciated by 5% relative to the British pound, by what percent has the British pound depreciated relative to the Canadian dollar?
32. If the Australian dollar appreciated by 15% relative to the British pound, by what percent has the British pound depreciated relative to the Australian dollar?
33. The average winter temperature in Toronto increased by 2.0°C this year. If the average winter temperature last year was –15°C, calculate the percent change in average winter temperature this year.
34. The average winter temperature in Montreal increased by 1.15°C this year. If the average winter temperature last year was –10°C, calculate the percent change in the average winter temperature this year.
35. Gabrielle's portfolio of shares comprised of investments of $8,600 and $12,400 in the telecommunication and information technology industries, respectively. If the market price of her telecommunication shares dropped by 65% and that of information technology grew by 25%, by what percent did the total value of her investments change?
36. Kemi had her money invested in two types of mutual funds: $2,800 in low-risk funds and $700 in high-risk funds. If the value of her high-risk funds grew by 30% and that of the low-risk funds dropped by 10%, by what percent did the total value of her investments change?
37. Sandra posted an advertisement on an auction site to sell her phone for 50% more than what she had paid for it. Since it did not sell within a month, she decreased the advertised price by 50% after which the phone sold immediately. By what percent, more or less than the purchase price, did she sell the phone?
38. If the temperature rose by 12% from the average temperature, then fell by 12%, by what percent did the final temperature increase or decrease from the average temperature?
39. Last month, a 750g box of cereal was sold at a grocery store for $3.00. However, this month, the cereal manufacturer has launched the same cereal in a 600g box, which is being sold at $2.50. By what percent did the unit rate change?
40. A 450 g pack of butter was sold for $3.50. If the manufacturer reduced the size of the pack to 250 g and sold it at a reduced price of $2.00, by what percent did the unit price change?

- 41. The price of a telecommunications share dropped by $2.50 at the end of the first year and dropped by a further $3.45 at the end of the second year. If the price of the share at the end of the second year was $12.55, calculate the percent change in the price of the share at the end of each year from its price at the beginning of each year. What was the percent drop in the price over the two-year period?
- 42. Amtex Computers Inc. sells refurbished laptops online. They were selling a particular model at $400 at the beginning of the year and reduced the price by $80 at the end of the first year. At the end of the second year, they increased the price by $64. Calculate the percent change in the price of this model at the end of each year from its price at the beginning of each year. Calculate the percent discount offered in the second year from the original price of $400.
- 43. The labour cost for manufacturing a $30,000 car increased by 5%. If the cost of labour was 30% of the total cost for manufacturing the car, by what amount did the cost of the car increase?
- 44. The material cost for manufacturing a $2,000 TV decreased by 10%. If the cost of material was 40% of the total cost for manufacturing the TV, by what amount did the cost of the TV decrease?

- 45. Tudor and Rani, two sales representatives in a company, were earning $2,815 per month and $2,875 per month, respectively. After a yearly appraisal, if Tudor's salary increased by 14% and Rani's increased by 11%, who had the higher salary?
- 46. Reggie's annual salary increased from $42,000.00 to $46,830.00 this year and his colleague Gerald's annual salary increased from $39,500.00 to $44,437.50. Who received a higher rate of increase this year?

5 | Review Exercises

Answers to odd-numbered problems are available at the end of the textbook.

For the following problems, express the answers rounded to two decimal places, wherever applicable.

Calculate the missing values in Problems 1 and 2:

1.

	Percent	Decimal	Fraction in Lowest Terms
a.	80%	?	?
b.	?	0.25	?
c.	?	?	$\frac{3}{2}$
d.	$6\frac{1}{2}\%$	?	?
e.	?	0.048	?
f.	?	?	$\frac{2}{25}$

2.

	Percent	Decimal	Fraction in Lowest Terms
a.	2%	?	?
b.	?	0.245	?
c.	?	?	$\frac{5}{12}$
d.	$12\frac{2}{5}\%$	?	?
e.	?	1.075	?
f.	?	?	$\frac{3}{80}$

3. Answer the following:
   a. 125% of what number is 45?
   b. What percent of $180 is $36?
   c. How much is $\frac{3}{8}$% of $60?
4. Answer the following:
   a. 225% of what number is 180?
   b. What percent of $750 is $300?
   c. How much is $\frac{2}{5}$% of $30?
5. Paul sold a property for $575,000, which was 125% of the purchase price. Calculate the purchase price.
6. Peter sold his shares for $14,437.50. Calculate the amount he paid for the shares if his selling price was 275% of the amount he paid for the shares.
7. Lian scored 45 out of 60 on a math test. What was his percent grade on the test?
8. There were 48 questions in a test. Ann answered 40 questions correctly. What percent of the questions did she answer correctly?
9. The total expenditure for the construction of a highway was $1,280,000. If this is 111% of the budgeted amount, calculate the amount budgeted to build the highway.
10. If Henry's business expenditures were $14,480.00 in March and $14,806.50 in April, which were 112% and 122% of his budgeted expenditures for March and April, respectively, calculate his total budgeted expenditures for the two months.
11. Assume that out of the 300,000 people who immigrated to Canada in 2014, 12.25% were from China, 9.75% were from the Philippines, and the rest were from other countries.
   a. Calculate the number of people who immigrated to Canada from China.
   b. If the combined number of immigrants from China and the Philippines constituted 0.195% of the population of Canada, calculate the population of Canada in 2014. (Round the answer up to the nearest whole number.)
12. A dinner at a restaurant cost you $27.80 and you tipped the waiter 15% of the cost.
   a. What was the value of the tip?
   b. If the tip that you gave the waiter was 2% of all the money he made from tips that night, calculate the amount that the waiter earned from tips that night.
13. a. What is 180 increased by 70%?
   b. $90 decreased by 90% is how much?
   c. How much is $4,500 increased by 150%?
   d. What amount increased by 25.75% is 855.10 kg?
14. a. What is 2,680 increased by 85%?
   b. $880.45 decreased by 85% is how much?
   c. How much is $1,850.50 increased by 300%?
   d. What amount increased by $90\frac{1}{2}\%$ is 110.49 kg?
15. a. What amount decreased by 10% is $477?
   b. What amount increased by 180% is 20.65?
   c. $1,200 decreased by what percent is $300?
   d. 750 kg is what percent less than 1,000 kg?

16. a. What amount increased by 28% is 231.75?
    b. What amount increased by 600% is 24.92?
    c. $800 increased by what percent is $1,800?
    d. 102 km is what percent more than 85 km?

17. The sales tax of 13% increased the cost of a dinner at a restaurant to $55.37. What was the cost of dinner before taxes?

18. After paying income taxes of 32%, Sally's annual pay was $35,600. Calculate Sally's income before deducting income taxes.

19. If toner cartridges that sell in stores for $45 each are being offered online for $36 each, calculate the percent discount offered online.

20. A college tuition fee of $4,500 increases to $4,900. Calculate the percent increase of the fee.

21. The average summer temperature in Toronto increased by 3.5°C this year. If the average daytime temperature last year was 28°C, calculate the percent change in the average summer temperature this year.

22. The average winter snowfall in Montreal increased by 2.5 cm this year. If the average winter snowfall last year was 50 cm, calculate the percent change in average winter snowfall this year.

23. The selling price of an apartment was $335,000. This is 34% more than the purchase price. Calculate the original purchase price.

24. The selling price of a home was $663,000. This is 23.5% more than the purchase price. Calculate the original purchase price.

25. A car dealer reduced the price of a car by 8.75%. The current price of the car is $38,000. What was the price of the car before the reduction?

26. A property developer reduced the price of a house by 6.25%. The current price of the house is $703,125. What was the price of the house before the reduction?

27. A marketing department's expenses rose by 30% from last year. If its expenses this year are $234,260, calculate its expenses last year.

28. A manufacturing company paid $56,400 (after a discount) for a heavy-duty packing machine from Japan. If it received a discount of 21%, calculate the original price of the machine.

29. On a mathematics quiz, Chelsea scored 15% more than Zane. By what percent is Zane's score less than Chelsea's?

30. If Sabrina's annual salary is 10% more than Christina's, by what percent is Christina's annual earnings less than Sabrina's?

• 31. Holistic Energy Ltd. spends $1,200, $1,400, $800, and $1,700 on average on replacing printer cartridges for their black & white inkjet printers, colour inkjet printers, black & white laser printers, and colour laser printers, respectively, every month.
    a. What percent of the total expenditures on printer cartridges do they spend on colour laser printers every month?
    b. If they decide to reduce the expenses on both colour inkjet printers and colour laser printers by 50%, what percent of the total expenditures would they spend on black & white laser printers?

• 32. A manufacturing company has 280 production people, 21 quality inspectors, 15 sales people, 6 marketing people, and 15 people in other departments such as HR, Finance, etc.
    a. What percent of the total employees is quality inspectors?
    b. If 15% of the production people quit their jobs, what percent of the total remaining employees is quality inspectors?

• 33. Katelyn's financial manager invested her savings in a portfolio of shares that comprised of investments of $2,000, $1,800, and $3,100 in the infrastructure, hi-tech, and garment industries, respectively. Towards the end of 2011, if the value of her shares in the infrastructure industry rose by 20% while the rest remained the same, calculate the percent change in the value of her total investments.

• 34. Preston's website company invests their annual savings in different mutual funds. In 2010, they invested $12,500 in high-growth funds, $5,000 in medium-growth funds, and $2,000 in low-growth funds. If the value of their low-growth funds dropped by 10% this year while the rest stayed the same, by what percent did the total value of their investments change?

5 | Self-Test Exercises

Answers to all problems are available at the end of the textbook.

For the following problems, express the answers rounded to two decimal places, wherever applicable.

1. Calculate the missing values:

	Percent	Decimal	Fraction in Lowest Terms
a.	$10\frac{3}{5}\%$	?	?
b.	?	2.25	?
c.	?	?	$\frac{1}{400}$
d.	$\frac{1}{2}\%$	?	?
e.	?	0.002	?
f.	?	?	$\frac{97}{365}$

2. a. What percent of $30 is $3.75?

   b. 22.5% of $1,500 is how much?

   c. 75 is 15% of what number?

3. Colton's store expenses for the month of July and August were $33,480 and $36,580, which were 110% and 90% of the budgeted expenditures for the months of July and August, respectively. Calculate the total budgeted expenses for the two months.

4. Sandra earns an annual salary of $60,000, and every month she spends $1,400 on rent, $600 on car expenses, $200 on loan repayment, $800 on miscellaneous expenses, and saves $2,000.

   a. What percent of her annual salary is her annual expenses?

   b. If she invests 25% of the $2,000 savings in a mutual fund every month, what percent of the annual salary is invested in the fund over the year.

Calculate the missing values in Problems 5 and 6.

5.

	Initial Value	Percent Increase	Final Value
a.	$80	?	$125
b.	$725	13%	?
c.	?	0.5%	$4.75

6.

	Initial Value	Percent Decrease	Final Value
a.	$60	?	$45
b.	$113	20%	?
c.	?	4%	$297.60

7. What amount when reduced by 13% results in $696?

8. What amount when increased by 5% results in $1,365?

9. Calculate the percent decrease if an initial value of 20 is decreased to 17.

10. What is the amount of decrease if the initial value was 75 and the percent decrease is 28%?

11. What is the percent increase if the original value was 20 and the final value is 37?

12. Calculate the original price for a pair of shoes if Ruby paid $140 for it after receiving a discount of 7%.

13. A car dealer is offering a 12% discount on a car that was priced at $31,800. Calculate the price of the car after the discount.

14. If a discount of $51 is equivalent to a 60% decrease from the initial value, calculate the initial value.

• 15. In 2014, a stock lost 60% of its value. In 2015, the stock's value increased by 80%. Calculate the percent change in the stock's value over the two-year period.

• 16. The overall increase in the price of a house from 2013 to 2015 was 4%. If the price increased by 5% from 2013 to 2014 and its value in 2014 was $472,500, calculate the value of the house in 2015.

• 17. The price of a share dropped by 3% from 2013 to 2014, and was worth $4.25 in 2014. If the overall share price fell by 5% between 2013 and 2015, calculate its price in 2015.

• 18. The price of a share that was purchased for $20 increased by 30% during the first year and decreased by 30% during the second year.

   a. Calculate the value of the share at the end of the two years.

   b. Calculate the percent change in the share price over the two-year period.

• 19. The value of a share dropped by $1.25 at the end of the first year, and a further $2.50 at the end of the second year. If the price of the share at the end of the second year was $12.55, calculate the percent change in the price of the share:

   a. For each of the two years.

   b. Over the two-year period.

• 20. The value of a currency appreciated by 20% last month and then depreciated by 20% this month. By what percent did the currency appreciate or depreciate over the two-month period?

6 APPLICATIONS OF RATIOS AND PERCENTS

Have you ever wondered how businesses decide the selling price of a product, how your money grows when it is in a savings account of a bank; how to calculate your hourly wage when you know your annual salary; why you lose money when you covert it to another currency; or how the stock market performs? As you will learn in this chapter, by using your knowledge of percents, ratios, and proportions, you will be able to solve basic business questions like these.

LEARNING OBJECTIVES

- Calculate the amount and rate of markup.
- Calculate the amount and rate of markdown.
- Calculate the amount and rate of simple interest, principal, time period, and maturity value of investments and loans.
- Calculate gross pay based on annual salary, sales commissions, and hourly rate.
- Convert currencies between countries using exchange rates.
- Determine index numbers and their applications.

CHAPTER OUTLINE

6.1 | Markup and Markdown

Markup

Markup is the amount that a business adds to the cost of a product to arrive at the selling price of that product.

Cost + Markup = Selling Price

Therefore, ***Markup = Selling Price – Cost***

The amount of markup includes: 1. the business overhead expenses, such as rent, utilities, insurance, advertising, etc., that are necessary to operate the business, and 2. the desired operating profit of the business.

Markup is usually expressed as a percent of cost, known as the rate of markup.

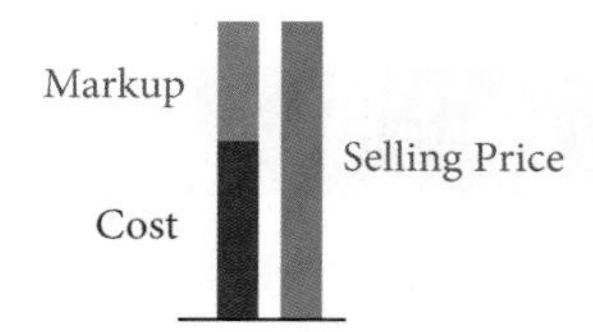

Exhibit 6.1-a Relationship among Markup, Cost, and Selling Price

$$\textbf{\textit{Markup}} = \textbf{\textit{Rate of Markup}} \times \textbf{\textit{Cost}}$$

Therefore, $\textbf{\textit{Rate of Markup}} = \left(\dfrac{\textbf{\textit{Markup}}}{\textbf{\textit{Cost}}}\right) \times \textbf{100\%}$

Example 6.1-a **Calculating Selling Price and Rate of Markup**

A store purchases printers for $800 each. If the markup on each printer is $600, calculate:

(i) The selling price

(ii) The rate of markup

Solution

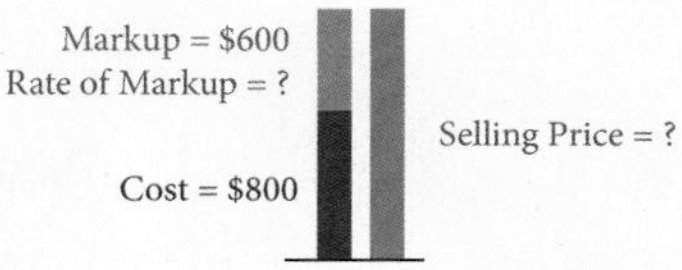

(i) $\textit{Selling Price} = \textit{Cost} + \textit{Markup}$

$$= 800.00 + 600.00$$

$$= \$1{,}400.00$$

Therefore, the selling price of each printer is $1,400.00.

(ii) $\textit{Rate of Markup} = \left(\dfrac{\textit{Markup}}{\textit{Cost}}\right) \times 100\%$

$$= \left(\frac{600.00}{800.00}\right) \times 100\%$$

$$= 75.00\%$$

Therefore, the rate of markup is 75.00%.

Example 6.1-b **Calculating Cost and Rate of Markup**

A retailer sells a handbag for $87.75. If the markup on each handbag is $22.75, calculate:

(i) The cost of each handbag

(ii) The rate of markup on each handbag

Solution

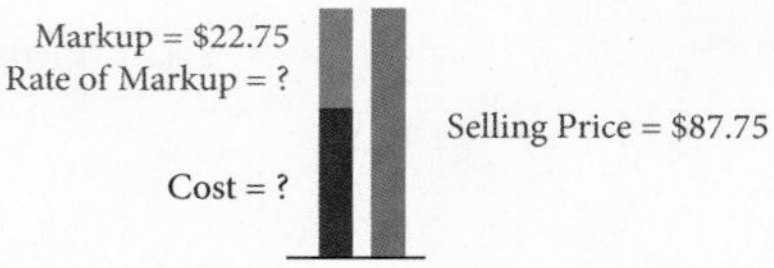

(i) $\textit{Cost} + \textit{Markup} = \textit{Selling Price}$

$$\textit{Cost} = \textit{Selling Price} - \textit{Markup}$$

$$= 87.75 - 22.75$$

$$= \$65.00$$

Therefore, the cost of each handbag is $65.00.

Solution *continued*

(ii) $$\text{Rate of Markup} = \left(\frac{\text{Markup}}{\text{Cost}}\right) \times 100\%$$

$$= \left(\frac{22.75}{65.00}\right) \times 100\%$$

$$= 35.00\%$$

Therefore, the rate of markup is 35.00%.

Example 6.1-c Calculating Markup and Rate of Markup

A wholesaler purchases cell phones for \$65.60 each and sells them for \$82.00 each. Calculate:

(i) The amount of markup on each cell phone

(ii) The rate of markup

Solution

(i) $$\text{Markup} = \text{Selling Price} - \text{Cost}$$

$$= 82.00 - 65.60$$

$$= \$16.40$$

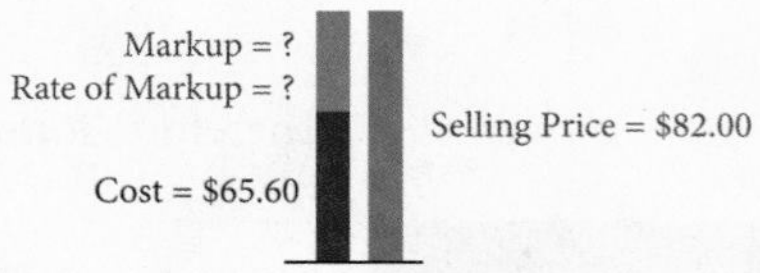

Therefore, the amount of markup on each cell phone is \$16.40.

(ii) $$\text{Rate of Markup} = \left(\frac{\text{Markup}}{\text{Cost}}\right) \times 100\%$$

$$= \left(\frac{16.40}{65.60}\right) \times 100\%$$

$$= 25.00\%$$

Therefore, the rate of markup on each cell phone is 25.00%.

Example 6.1-d Calculating Markup and Selling Price

A wholesaler purchases a product for \$2,000. If he has a markup of 40% on the cost of the product, calculate:

(i) The amount of markup

(ii) The selling price of the product

Solution

(i) $$\text{Markup} = \text{Rate of Markup} \times \text{Cost}$$

$$= 0.40 \times 2{,}000.00$$

$$= \$800.00$$

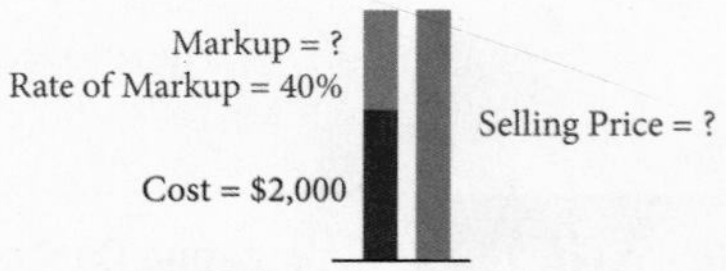

Therefore, the amount of markup is \$800.00.

(ii) $$\text{Selling Price} = \text{Cost} + \text{Markup}$$

$$= 2{,}000.00 + 800.00$$

$$= \$2{,}800.00$$

Therefore, the selling price is \$2,800.00.

Example 6.1-e

Calculating Cost and Selling Price

A car dealership sells used cars with a 20% markup on cost. The amount of markup on a used car sold was $2,950. Calculate:

(i) The cost of the car to the dealer

(ii) The selling price

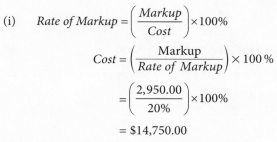

Solution

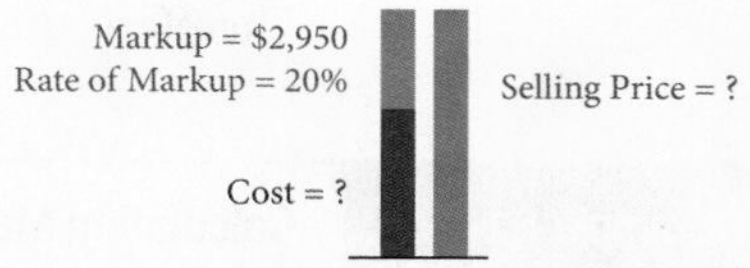

(i) $$\textit{Rate of Markup} = \left(\frac{\textit{Markup}}{\textit{Cost}}\right) \times 100\%$$

$$\textit{Cost} = \left(\frac{\text{Markup}}{\textit{Rate of Markup}}\right) \times 100\,\%$$

$$= \left(\frac{2{,}950.00}{20\%}\right) \times 100\%$$

$$= \$14{,}750.00$$

Therefore, the cost of the car is $14,750.00.

(ii) $$\textit{Selling Price} = \textit{Cost} + \textit{Markup}$$

$$= 14{,}750.00 + 2{,}950.00$$

$$= \$17{,}700.00$$

Therefore, the selling price is $17,700.00.

Markdown

he Selling Price of an item efers to the regular (or ormal) selling price; i.e., he price before Markdown.

Markdown is the amount by which the selling price of a product is reduced in determining the sale price.

Selling Price – Markdown = Sale Price

Therefore, ***Markdown = Selling Price – Sale Price***

In business, the selling price of an item is often reduced for various reasons, such as competition, clearance of seasonal items, etc.

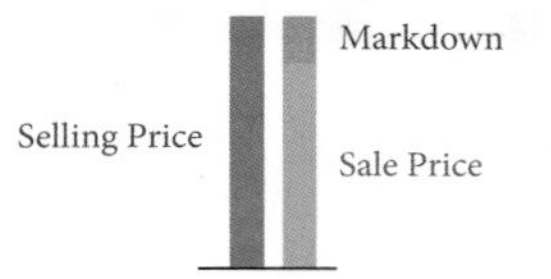

Exhibit 6.1-b Relationship among Selling Price, Markdown, and Sale Price

he Sale Price of an item efers to the reduced (or iscounted) selling price. i.e., he price after Markdown.

Markdown is usually expressed as a percent of the selling price, known as the rate of markdown.

Markdown = Rate of Markdown × Selling Price

Therefore, $$\textbf{\textit{Rate of Markdown}} = \left(\frac{\textbf{\textit{Markdown}}}{\textbf{\textit{Selling Price}}}\right) \times \mathbf{100\%}$$

Example 6.1-f

Calculating Sale Price (Reduced Selling Price) and Rate of Markdown

Calculate the sale price and rate of markdown of an item that regularly sells for $680, but is now being marked down by $204.

Solution

$$\textit{Selling Price} - \textit{Markdown} = \textit{Sale Price}$$

$$\textit{Sale Price} = \textit{Selling Price} - \textit{Markdown}$$

$$= 680.00 - 204.00$$

$$= \$476.00$$

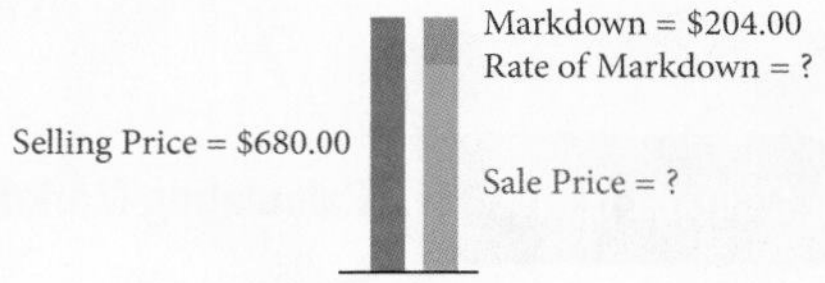

Therefore, the sale price of the item is $476.00.

Solution
continued

$$\text{Rate of Markdown} = \left(\frac{\text{Markdown}}{\text{Selling Price}}\right) \times 100\%$$

$$= \left(\frac{204.00}{680.00}\right) \times 100\%$$

$$= 30.00\%$$

Therefore, the rate of markdown is 30.00%.

Example 6.1-g

Calculating Markdown and Sale Price (Reduced Selling Price)

An item was marked down by 20% from the regular selling price of $1,250. Calculate:

(i) The amount of markdown

(ii) The sale price

Solution

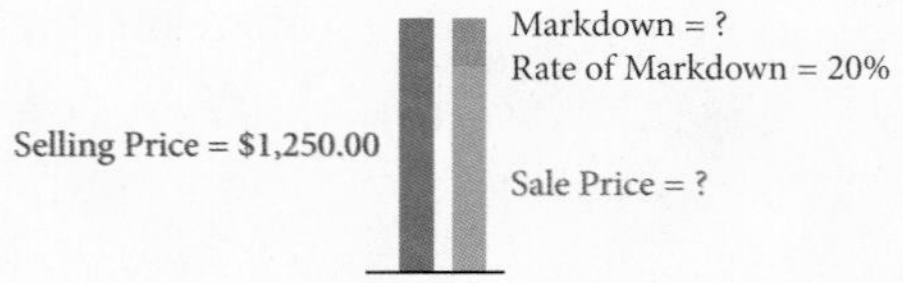

(i) $\text{Markdown} = \text{Rate of Markdown} \times \text{Selling Price}$

$$= 0.20 \times 1{,}250.00$$

$$= \$250.00$$

Therefore, the amount of markdown was $250.00.

(ii) $\text{Sale Price} = \text{Selling Price} - \text{Markdown}$

$$= 1{,}250.00 - 250.00$$

$$= \$1{,}000.00$$

Therefore, the sale price was $1,000.00.

Example 6.1-h

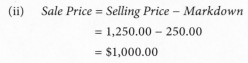

Calculating the Selling Price and Rate of Markdown

After a markdown of $276.50, an item was sold for $513.50. Calculate:

(i) The regular selling price

(ii) The rate of markdown

Solution

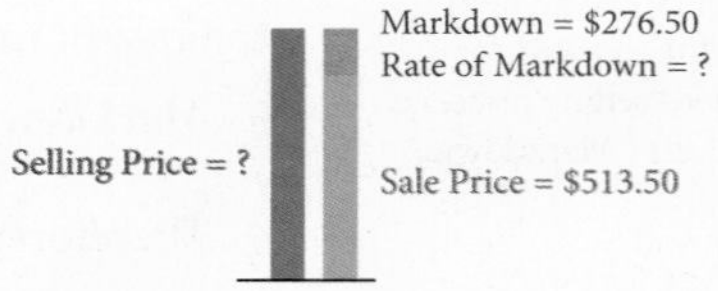

(i) $\text{Selling Price} = \text{Sale Price} + \text{Markdown}$

$$= 513.50 + 276.50$$

$$= \$790.00$$

Therefore, the regular selling price was $790.00.

(ii) $\text{Rate of Markdown} = \left(\frac{\text{Markdown}}{\text{Selling Price}}\right) \times 100\%$

$$= \left(\frac{276.50}{790.00}\right) \times 100\%$$

$$= 0.35 \times 100\% = 35.00\%$$

Therefore, the rate of markdown was 35.00%.

Example 6.1-i

Calculating Markdown and Rate of Markdown

During a sale, a shirt that was regularly priced at $49.00, sold for $41.65. Calculate:

(i) The amount of markdown

(ii) Rate of markdown

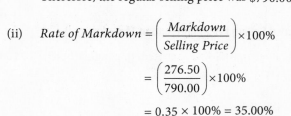

Solution

(i) $\textit{Sale Price} = \textit{Selling Price} - \textit{Markdown}$

$$\textit{Markdown} = \textit{Selling Price} - \textit{Sale Price}$$
$$= 49.00 - 41.65$$
$$= \$7.35$$

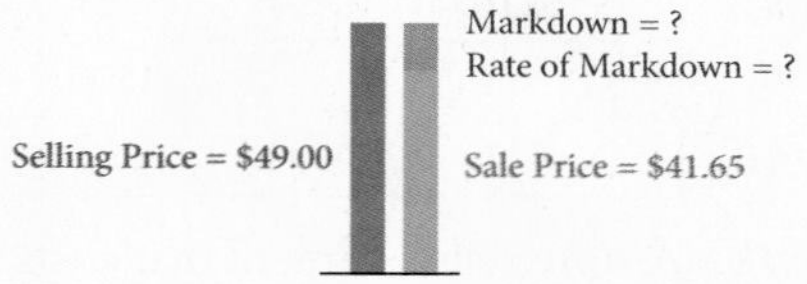

Therefore, the markdown was $7.35.

(ii) $$\textit{Rate of Markdown} = \left(\frac{\textit{Markdown}}{\textit{Selling Price}}\right) \times 100\%$$

$$= \left(\frac{7.35}{49.00}\right) \times 100\%$$
$$= 0.15 \times 100\%$$
$$= 15.00\%$$

Therefore, the rate of markdown was 15.00%.

Example 6.1-j **Calculating Selling Price and Sale Price (Reduced Selling Price)**

During a sale, an item was marked down by $150 after a markdown of 20%. Calculate,

(i) The regular selling price

(ii) The sale price

Solution

(i) $\textit{Markdown} = \textit{Rate of Markdown} \times \textit{Selling Price}$

$$\textit{Selling Price} = \frac{\textit{Markdown}}{\textit{Rate of Markdown}}$$
$$= \frac{150.00}{0.20}$$
$$= \$750.00$$

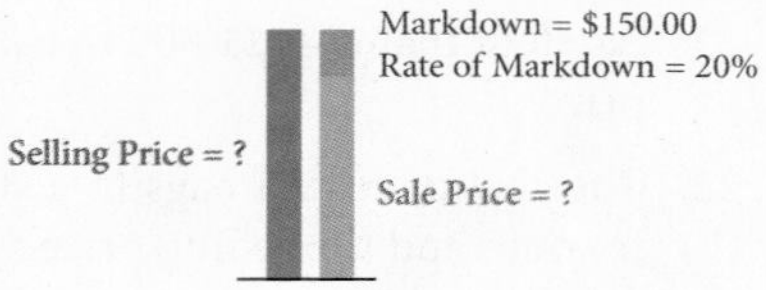

Therefore, the regular selling price was $750.00.

(ii) $\textit{Sale Price} = \textit{Selling Price} - \textit{Markdown}$

$$= 750.00 - 150.00$$
$$= \$600.00$$

Therefore, the sale price was $600.00.

6.1 | Exercises

Answers to odd-numbered problems are available at the end of the textbook.

For the following problems, express the answers rounded to two decimal places, wherever applicable.

Calculate the missing values in Problems 1 to 10:

	Cost ($)	Markup ($)	Selling Price ($)	Rate of Markup (%)
1.	$99.00	$24.75	?	?
2.	$37.50	$15.00	?	?
3.	?	$52.50	$490.00	?
4.	?	$67.50	$517.50	?
5.	$52.00	?	$97.50	?
6.	$50.40	?	$63.00	?
7.	$252.00	?	?	35.00%

	Cost ($)	Markup ($)	Selling Price ($)	Rate of Markup (%)
8.	$210.00	?	?	90.00%
9.	?	$175.00	?	12.50%
10.	?	$62.90	?	40.00%

11. A store sells a camera that costs $270 for $430. Find the amount of markup and the rate of markup.
12. A bicycle costs a store $64.50. If the store sells the bicycle for $93.15, calculate the amount of markup and the rate of markup.
13. A furniture shop purchased a certain mattress for $625, and marked it up by $325. Calculate the selling price and the rate of markup.
14. A store purchases monitors for $86.25 each. The store's markup is $31.50. Calculate the selling price and the rate of markup.
15. A computer store used a markup rate of 40%. Find the amount of markup and the selling price of a computer software DVD that the store bought for $38.75.
16. I purchased a laptop for $187.50 for the purpose of reselling it later. If my rate of markup is 90% of the cost, what is the amount of markup and the selling price?
17. The selling price of an item is $540. If the markup is $108, calculate the cost and rate of markup of the item.
18. A DVD player is sold for $124 after a markup of $27. Calculate the cost and rate of markup of the DVD player.
19. A bookstore uses a 40% markup on calculators and the amount of markup of a particular calculator was $24. Calculate the bookstore's purchase price of the calculator and its selling price.
20. If a $96 markup of an item represents an 80% rate of markup on cost, calculate the cost and the selling price of that item.
21. An item that cost $1,800 to a store is marked up by 35% of the cost. Calculate the amount of markup and the selling price.
22. The cost of school bags to a store is $19 each. The store marked it up by 20% of the cost. Calculate the amount of markup and the selling price.
23. A bookstore sells a finance math textbook for $142.80. The cost of the book to the store is $105.00. Calculate the amount of markup and the rate of markup on cost.
24. The cost of an item to a store is $80 and its retail selling price is $130. Calculate the amount of markup and the rate of markup on cost.
25. The amount of markup of an item is $7.50 and the rate of markup on cost is 15%. Calculate the cost and the selling price of the item.
26. A store sells each refrigerator at a markup of $224.70. If the rate of markup on cost is 30%, calculate the cost and the selling price of each refrigerator.

Calculate the missing values in Problems 27 to 36:

	Selling Price ($)	Markdown ($)	Sale Price ($)	Rate of Markdown (%)
27.	$94.75	$74.50	?	?
28.	$90.40	$22.60	?	?
29.	$136.00	?	?	22.50%
30.	$72.90	?	?	40.00%
31.	?	$34.00	$46.00	?
32.	?	$36.75	$173.25	?
33.	$25.00	?	$17.50	?
34.	$58.50	?	$29.25	?
35.	?	$31.71	?	25.00%
36.	?	$150.00	?	37.50%

37. During a sale, a sofa that regularly sells for $250 is marked down by $75. Calculate the sale price and the rate of markdown.
38. A scanner that regularly sells for $99 was sold after a markdown of $29. Calculate the sale price and the rate of markdown.
39. A treadmill with a regular selling price of $190 is on sale for 15% off the original price. Calculate the amount of markdown and the sale price.
40. The regular selling price of a rocking chair is $139. During a sale, it was sold after a markdown of 25%. Find the amount of markdown and the sale price.
41. A store offers an $18 discount on a bookcase and it was sold for $30. Calculate the regular selling price of the bookcase and the rate of discount offered.
42. Calculate the regular selling price and the rate of markdown of an item sold for $27.30 after a markdown of $18.20 during a sale.
43. A fax machine that regularly sells for $127.50 is marked down to $86.70 during a special sale. Find the percent markdown and the amount of markdown during the sale.
44. A camcorder regularly selling for $299.00 was marked down to sell for $233.22. Find the percent markdown and the amount of markdown.
45. During a sale, a furniture store marked down all the items by 35%. The amount of markdown on a bed was $166.25. Find the regular selling price and the sale price.
46. A winter jacket was sold after a markdown of $16.25. If this represents a markdown rate of 13%, find the regular selling price and the sale price of the winter jacket.

- 47. A TV that regularly sells for $699.00 was sold for $615.12. Calculate the amount of markdown and the rate of markdown.
- 48. During a sale, Mythili bought a piano for $4,532.50. If the regular selling price was $4,900.00, calculate the amount of markdown and the rate of markdown.
- 49. Girija bought a dress for $22 after a markdown of 12%. Calculate the regular selling price and the amount of markdown.
- 50. Aran bought a video game for $31.96 after a markdown of 15%. Calculate the regular selling price and the amount of markdown.
- 51. A toaster that regularly sells for $37.50 was sold after a markdown of $3.75. Calculate the sale price and the rate of markdown.
- 52. A football was sold after a markdown of $19.25. If the original price was $55.00, calculate the sale price and the rate of markdown.
- 53. During a sale, a humidifier was sold for $279.65 after a markdown of 15%. Calculate the regular selling price and the amount of markdown.
- 54. After a markdown of 12.5%, a bicycle was sold for $112. Calculate the regular selling price and the amount of markdown.

6.2 | Simple Interest

Calculations Involving Simple Interest

Interest is a fee that borrowers pay to lenders for using their money temporarily for a period of time. For example, when we invest money, the financial institution uses our money and therefore, pays us interest for the time period it has been invested. Similarly, when we borrow money from a financial institution, we pay interest to them for the time period borrowed.

In simple interest calculations, **Interest (*I*)** is calculated as a **percent (%)** of the initial amount of money invested or borrowed, known as the **Principal (*P*)**. Therefore,

$$\textit{Interest} = \textit{Principal} \times \textit{Interest Percent}$$

$$\textit{Interest} = \textit{Principal} \times \textit{Interest Rate} \times \textit{Time}$$

$$I = P \times r \times t$$

This can be rearranged to solve for the variables **P**, **r**, and **t** as follows:

$$P = \frac{I}{r \times t} \qquad r = \frac{I}{P \times t} \qquad t = \frac{I}{P \times r}$$

P, r, t triangle

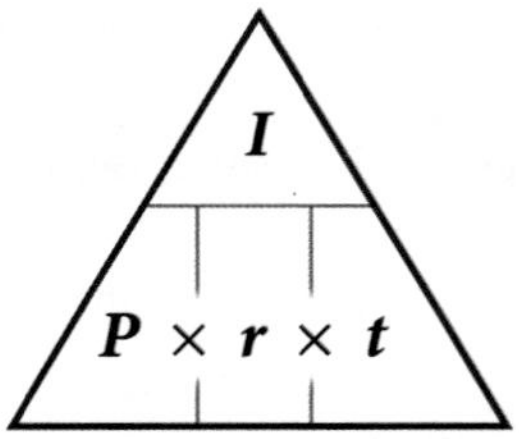

Here is a triangle that can be used to help in rearranging the formula $I = Prt$ to find the variable P, r, or t.

Variables beside each other at the bottom are multiplied, ($P \times r \times t$, as shown).

Variables at the bottom are divided by the variable on top, I.

Cover the variable that you want to solve to see the new formula.

For example, if you want to solve for '*P*', the formula can be found by covering '*P*' and reading the remaining variables in the above triangle to obtain, $P = \frac{I}{rt}$

Interest rate is usually expressed as percent per annum (r% p.a.) or percent per month (r% p.m.), and time (t) is expressed in days, months, or years.

In calculations, '*r*' is used as the decimal or fractional equivalent of the percent rate.

If '***r***' is expressed as per annum (***r***% p.a.), then '***t***' should be in years.

If '***r***' is expressed as per month (***r***% p.m.), then '***t***' should be in months.

In this section, we will use annual interest rates (r% p.a.) and time periods (t) expressed in years (or converted to years) when calculating the amount of interest.

For example,

Usually, the unit of '*t*' is converted to match the unit of '*r*' using 1 year = 12 months or 1 year = 365 days.

(i) $t = 4 \text{ months} = \frac{4}{12}$ year

(ii) $t = 1 \text{ year and } 3 \text{ months} = 15 \text{ months} = \frac{15}{12}$ years

(iii) $t = 125 \text{ days} = \frac{125}{365}$ year

As time goes by, the value of money increases by the amount of interest earned for that period. Therefore, when money is returned after a period of time, interest is added to the principal and the accumulated value is known as the **Maturity Value (*S*)**.

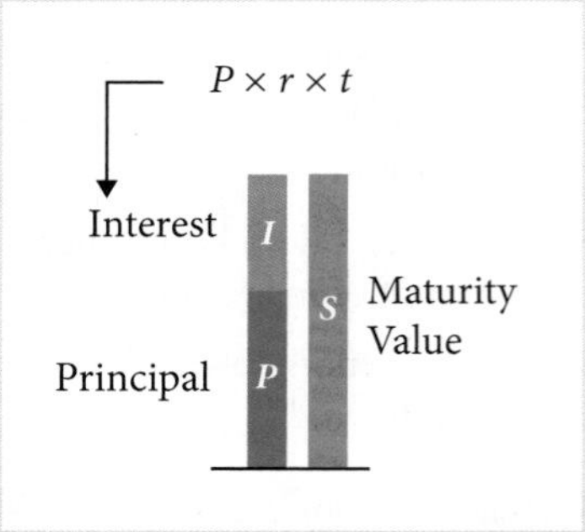

Maturity Value = Principal + Interest

$$S = P + I$$

This can be rearranged to solve for the variables I and P, as follows:

$$I = S - P$$

$$P = S - I$$

Example 6.2-a **Calculating the Amount of Interest**

Calculate the amount of interest earned from an investment of $2,250 for 6 months at an interest rate of 4.2% p.a.

Solution

$r = 4.2\% \text{ p.a.} = 0.042 \text{ p.a.}$

$t = 6 \text{ months} = \frac{6}{12}$ year

Solution *continued*

$P = \$2250.00$

$$I = P \times r \times t$$
$$= 2{,}250.00 \times 0.042 \times \frac{6}{12} = \$47.25$$

Therefore, the amount of interest earned is $47.25.

Example 6.2-b

Calculating Principal

Calculate the amount of money that should be invested now at an annual interest rate of 6% for 3 years to earn an interest of $675.

Solution

$r = 6\%$ p.a. $= 0.06$ p.a.

$t = 3$ years

$I = \$675.00$

$$P = \frac{I}{r \times t}$$
$$= \frac{675.00}{(0.06 \times 3)} = \$3{,}750.00$$

Therefore, $3,750.00 should be invested now.

Example 6.2-c

Calculating the Amount of Interest and Maturity Value

Tony invested $7,500 for 2 years at an annual interest rate of 4.8%. Calculate:

(i) The amount of interest earned from this investment

(ii) The maturity value at the end of 2 years

Solution

$r = 4.8\%$ p.a. $= 0.048$ p.a.

$t = 2$ years

$P = \$7{,}500.00$

(i) $I = P \times r \times t$

$= 7{,}500.00 \times 0.048 \times 2 = \$720.00$

Therefore, the amount of interest earned in 2 years is $720.00.

(ii) $S = P + I$

$= 7{,}500.00 + 720.00 = \$8{,}220.00$

Therefore, the maturity value at the end of 2 years is $8,220.00.

Example 6.2-d

Calculating the Amount of Interest and Interest Rate

An investment of $4,500.00 results in a maturity value of $4,938.75 after 18 months. Calculate:

(i) The amount of interest earned (ii) The annual interest rate

Solution

$P = \$4{,}500.00$

$S = \$4{,}938.75$

$t = 18 \text{ months} = \frac{18}{12} \text{ years}$

(i) $I = S - P$

$= 4{,}938.75 - 4{,}500.00 = \$438.75$

Therefore, the amount of interest earned in 18 months is $438.75.

Solution
continued

(ii) $r = \dfrac{I}{P \times t}$

$$= \frac{438.75}{\left(4{,}500.00 \times \dfrac{18}{12}\right)} = 0.065 \times 100\% = 6.50\% \text{ p.a.}$$

Therefore, the annual interest rate is 6.50%.

6.2 | Exercises

Answers to odd-numbered problems are available at the end of the textbook.

For the following problems, express the answers rounded to two decimal places, wherever applicable.

Calculate the Interest (I) and the Maturity Value (S) for Problems 1 to 6.

	Principal (**P**)	Rate (**r**)	Time (**t**)	Interest (**I**)	Maturity Value (**S**)
1.	$900	5% p.a.	3 years	?	?
2.	$6,250	4% p.a.	2 years	?	?
3.	$1,480	4.5% p.a.	18 months	?	?
4.	$2,500	3.5% p.a.	15 months	?	?
5.	$5,840	6% p.a.	75 days	?	?
6.	$7,300	3% p.a.	250 days	?	?

7. Calculate the amount of interest earned on a $2,600 investment made for 2 years at 3.5% p.a.
8. Calculate the amount of interest charged on a $1,250 loan borrowed for 4 years at 4.25% p.a.
9. How much interest is owed on a $1,500 loan borrowed for 1 year 9 months at 4.8% p.a.?
10. How much interest is earned from an investment of $2,400 made for 2 years 3 months at 3.6% p.a.?
11. Khan borrowed $1,460 at 5% p.a. for 200 days. Calculate the amount of interest due on the loan and the maturity value of the loan.
12. Ann invested $4,380 for 100 days in an account that pays 3% p.a. Calculate the amount of interest earned and the maturity value of the investment.
13. An amount of $3,600 is borrowed at a simple interest rate of 6% p.a. for 2 years and 7 months. Calculate the amount of interest and the maturity value of the loan.
14. Saul borrowed $1,750 for 9 months at a simple interest rate of 5% p.a.. Calculate the amount of interest and the maturity value of the loan.

Calculate the missing values in Problems 15 to 24.

	Principal (**P**)	Rate (**r**)	Time (**t**)	Interest (**I**)	Maturity Value (**S**)
15.	$750	?	3 years	?	$930
16.	$1,300	?	2 years	?	$1,404
17.	$5,000	4.5% p.a.	?	$500	?
18.	$8,000	3.5% p.a.	?	$1,120	?
19.	?	?	9 months	$60	$2,600
20.	?	?	15 months	$120	$1,720
21.	$1,600	4% p.a.	?	?	$1,792
22.	$950	3% p.a.	?	?	$1,000
23.	?	6% p.a.	120 days	$36	?
24.	?	5% p.a.	180 days	$63	?

25. At what annual interest rate will a $6,000 investment result in a maturity value of $6,600 in 2 years?
26. At what annual interest rate will a $1,250 investment result in a maturity value of $1,625 in 5 years?
27. In how many years will $3,000 invested at 3% p.a. result in a maturity value of $3,360?
28. How many years will it take for a deposit of $5,000 earning interest at 6% p.a. to reach $6,500?
29. What amount invested at 4% p.a. for 4 years will result in an interest amount of $400?
30. The amount of interest charged on a loan for 3 years at 6% p.a. is $810. Calculate the amount of the loan.
31. A loan of $4,800 was paid off at the end of 5 months with a payment of $4,940. Calculate the annual interest rate charged on the loan.
32. John deposited $3,600 in a savings account. The balance in this account after 9 months was $3,681. Calculate the annual interest rate earned from this investment.

- 33. The maturity value of an investment is $4,460, which included a 5.5% p.a. simple interest for 1 year and 4 months. Calculate the amount invested and the amount of interest earned from this investment.
- 34. Shaunti paid off a loan by making a payment of $5,058, which included simple interest at 6% p.a.. If she obtained the loan 8 months ago, calculate the amount borrowed and the the amount of interest paid on this loan.
- 35. An amount of $3,200 is borrowed for 180 days. At the end of the term, $3,420 is paid to settle the loan. Calculate the annual simple interest rate charged on the loan.
- 36. Jane borrowed $900 and paid $960 after 145 days to settle the loan. Calculate the annual simple interest rate charged on the loan.
- 37. How many days will it take for an investment of $6,000 to accumulate to $6,700 at 5% p.a. simple interest?
- 38. If the maturity value of a loan of $2,000 at 4.2% p.a. simple interest was $2,250, determine the term of the loan in nearest days.
- 39. If the simple interest charged on a $2,500 loan for a period of 1 year and 8 months was $180, what was the annual simple interest rate charged on this loan?
- 40. If the maturity value of an investment of $10,000.00 for 1 year and 2 months is $10,437.50, calculate the the annual simple interest rate.

6.3 | Payroll

Payroll

Employees of an organization receive payment from their employers for their services. In this section, we will calculate (or use) the gross pay given to employees based on an annual salary, hourly rate of pay, or commission.

Annual Salary

Annual salary employees are usually supervisory, managerial, or professional employees who work on an annual basis and are not paid an hourly rate. If you are employed by an organization paying you an annual salary, this is the amount that you will be paid for your service over a period of one year.

Pay Period

Pay period refers to the frequency of payments (how often payments are being made). The most common pay periods are:

One monthly payment is not equal to four weekly payments.

- Monthly (once a month): 12 payments throughout the year.
(1 year = 12 months)
- Semi-monthly (twice a month): 24 payments throughout the year.
(Twice a month: 2 × 12 = 24 semi-monthly pay periods)

A semi-monthly payment is not equal to a bi-weekly payment.

- Weekly (once a week): 52 payments throughout the year
(1 year = 52 weeks)
- Bi-weekly (every two weeks): 26 payments throughout the year.
(Once in two weeks, $\frac{52}{2}$ = 26 bi-weekly pay periods)

Note: In the examples and exercises in this section, we will be using 52 weekly pay periods or 26 bi-weekly pay periods. However, it is possible to have 53 weekly pay periods or 27 bi-weekly pay periods depending on the year and the payment days.

$$\textbf{\textit{Pay for a pay period}} = \frac{\textbf{\textit{Annual salary}}}{\textbf{\textit{Number of pay periods}}}$$

Therefore,

$$\textbf{\textit{Annual salary}} = \textbf{\textit{Pay for a pay period}} \times \textbf{\textit{Number of pay periods}}$$

Example 6.3-a **Calculating Payment for a Pay Period, Given the Annual Salary**

Ann works for a publishing company and receives an annual salary of $62,400. Calculate her gross pay for a pay period, if paid:

(i) monthly (ii) semi-monthly (iii) weekly (iv) bi-weekly

Solution

$$\textit{Pay for a pay period} = \frac{\textit{Annual salary}}{\textit{Number of pay periods}}$$

(i) $\textit{Monthly pay} = \frac{\textit{Annual salary}}{\textit{12 pay periods}} = \frac{62,400.00}{12} = \$5,200.00$

Therefore, if paid monthly, her pay would be $5,200.00.

(ii) $\textit{Semi-monthly pay} = \frac{\textit{Annual salary}}{\textit{24 pay periods}} = \frac{62,400.00}{24} = \$2,600.00$

Therefore, if paid semi-monthly, her pay would be $2,600.00.

(iii) $\textit{Weekly pay} = \frac{\textit{Annual salary}}{\textit{52 pay periods}} = \frac{62,400.00}{52} = \$1,200.00$

Therefore, if paid weekly, her pay would be $1,200.00.

(iv) $\textit{Bi-weekly pay} = \frac{\textit{Annual salary}}{\textit{26 pay periods}} = \frac{62,400.00}{26} = \$2,400.00$

Therefore, if paid bi-weekly, her pay would be $2,400.00.

Example 6.3-b **Calculating Annual Salary, the Equivalent Monthly Pay, and Semi-Monthly Pay, Given the Weekly Pay**

Sam is paid $1,500 weekly. Calculate:

(i) Annual salary (ii) Equivalent monthly pay (iii) Equivalent semi-monthly pay

Solution

(i) $\textit{Annual salary} = \textit{Pay for a pay period} \times \textit{Number of pay periods}$

$= 1,500.00 \times 52$

$= \$78,000.00$

Therefore, the annual salary is $78,000.00.

$$\textit{Pay for a pay period} = \frac{\textit{Annual salary}}{\textit{Number of pay periods}}$$

(ii) $\textit{Monthly pay} = \frac{78,000.00}{12}$

$= \$6,500.00$

Therefore, the equivalent monthly pay is $6,500.00.

Solution *continued*

(iii) $$\text{Semi-monthly pay} = \frac{78{,}000.00}{24} = \$3{,}250.00$$

Therefore, the equivalent semi-monthly pay is $3,250.00.

Example 6.3-c **Calculating Semi-Monthly Pay Given the Bi-Weekly Pay**

James' bi-weekly pay is $2,700. Calculate his equivalent semi-monthly pay.

Solution

Since James is paid bi-weekly, he will receive 26 payments throughout the year.

$$\begin{aligned} \textit{Annual salary} &= \textit{Pay for a period} \times \textit{Number of pay periods} \\ &= 2{,}700.00 \times 26 \\ &= \$70{,}200.00 \end{aligned}$$

$$\begin{aligned} \textit{Semi-monthly pay} &= \frac{\textit{Annual salary}}{\textit{Number of pay periods}} \\ &= \frac{70{,}200.00}{24} \\ &= \$2{,}925.00 \end{aligned}$$

Therefore, the equivalent semi-monthly pay is $2,925.00.

Example 6.3-d **Calculating the Weekly Pay Given the Semi-Monthly Pay**

Lisa's semi-monthly pay is $1,892.80. Calculate her equivalent weekly pay.

Solution

Since Lisa is paid semi-monthly, she will receive 24 payments throughout the year.

$$\begin{aligned} \textit{Annual salary} &= \textit{Pay for a period} \times \textit{Number of pay periods} \\ &= 1{,}892.80 \times 24 \\ &= \$45{,}427.20 \end{aligned}$$

$$\begin{aligned} \textit{Weekly pay} &= \frac{\textit{Annual salary}}{\textit{Number of pay periods}} \\ &= \frac{45{,}427.20}{52} \\ &= \$873.60 \end{aligned}$$

Therefore, the equivalent weekly pay is $873.60.

Hourly Rate of Pay

Hourly rate of pay employees usually have a variable and unpredictable workload. They receive payment based on an hourly rate of pay for the number of hours worked during the pay period.

Depending on the type of profession/job, the number of working hours per week (workweek) may vary. The most common workweeks are: 40 hours, 37.5 hours, 35 hours, and 32.5 hours.

By knowing the hourly rate of pay and the number of hours one has worked during a pay period, you can calculate the total gross pay for that pay period.

$$\textit{Pay for a pay period} = \textit{Hourly Rate} \times \textit{Number of Hours Worked}$$

$$\textit{Weekly Pay} = \textit{Hourly Rate} \times \textit{Workweek}$$

$$\textit{Hourly rate} = \frac{\textit{Weekly pay}}{\textit{Workweek}}$$

Example 6.3-e **Calculating Bi-Weekly Pay, Given the Hourly Rate and the Workweek**

Aran is paid bi-weekly. His workweek is 35 hours and his hourly rate is \$29.50. Calculate his:

(i) Bi-weekly pay (ii) Equivalent semi-monthly pay

Solution

(i) Bi-weekly pay:

Number of working hours for 2 weeks = 2 × 35 = 70 hours

Total Pay = *Hourly Rate* × *Number of Hours Worked*

= 29.50 × 70

= \$2,065.00

Therefore, his bi-weekly pay is \$2,065.00.

(ii) Equivalent semi-monthly pay:

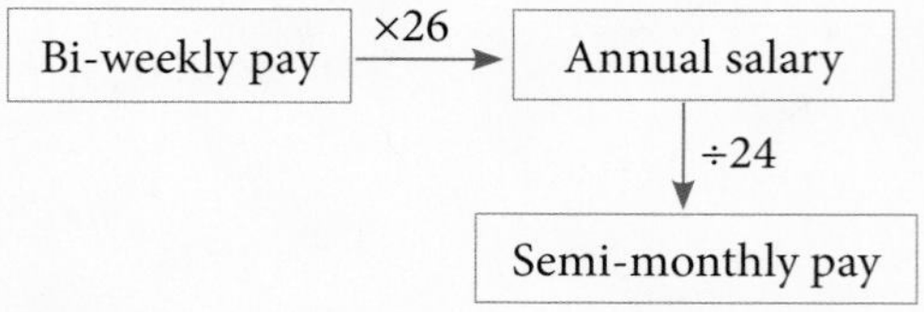

From (i), *Bi-weekly pay* = 2,065.00

Therefore, *Annual salary* = 2,065.00 × 26

= \$53,690.00

$$\textit{Equivalent semi-monthly pay} = \frac{53{,}690.00}{24}$$

= 2,237.083333... = \$2,237.08

Therefore, the equivalent semi-monthly pay is \$2,237.08.

Example 6.3-f **Calculating Weekly Pay and Hourly Rate, Given the Annual Pay and the Workweek**

Mythili is being paid \$39,000 per annum. Her workweek is 40 hours. Calculate her:

(i) Weekly pay (ii) Hourly rate of pay

Solution

(i) Weekly pay:

$$\textit{Weekly pay} = \frac{\textit{Annual salary}}{\textit{Number of pay periods}}$$

$$= \frac{39{,}000.00}{52}$$

= \$750.00

Therefore, her weekly pay is \$750.00.

(ii) Hourly rate of pay:

$$\textit{Hourly rate} = \frac{\textit{Weekly pay}}{\textit{Workweek}}$$

$$= \frac{750.00}{40}$$

= \$18.75

Therefore, her hourly rate is \$18.75.

Example 6.3-g **Calculating Workweek and Annual Salary, Given the Bi-Weekly Pay and the Hourly Rate**

Albert is paid \$1,687.50 bi-weekly. His hourly rate of pay is \$22.50. Calculate his:

(i) Regular workweek (ii) Equivalent annual salary

Solution

(i) Regular workweek:

$$\textit{Total pay} = \textit{Hourly rate} \times \textit{Number of hours worked}$$

$$1{,}687.50 = 22.50 \times \textit{Number of hours worked bi-weekly}$$

$$\textit{Number of hours worked bi-weekly} = \frac{1{,}687.50}{22.50}$$

$$= 75 \text{ hours}$$

$$\textit{Number of hours worked per week} = \frac{75}{2}$$

$$= 37.5 \text{ hours}$$

Therefore, his regular workweek is 37.5 hours.

(ii) Equivalent annual salary:

$$\textit{Annual salary} = \textit{Pay for a pay period} \times \textit{Number of pay periods}$$

$$= 1{,}687.50 \times 26$$

$$= \$43{,}875.00$$

Therefore, his annual salary is $43,875.00.

Overtime Rate of Pay

If you work more than the specified number of hours per week (workweek), you will be eligible for overtime payment for the additional hours worked. This extra payment is calculated using an overtime rate. The overtime rate of pay is usually more than one and one-half (1.5) times the regular rate of pay. This factor (1.5 times or 2 times) that employers use to calculate the overtime rate is called the **overtime factor**.

Overtime Rate = Overtime factor × Hourly rate

Overtime Pay = Overtime rate × Number of hours worked overtime

Example 6.3-h

Calculating Regular Rate of Pay and Overtime Rate of Pay, Given Annual Salary, Workweek, and Overtime Factor

Cindy earns $46,800 per year. Her workweek is 40 hours and her overtime factor is 1.5. Calculate her:

(i) Regular rate of pay

(ii) Overtime rate of pay

Solution

(i) Regular rate of pay:

$$\textit{Pay for a pay period} = \frac{\textit{Annual salary}}{\textit{Number of pay periods}}$$

$$\textit{Weekly pay} = \frac{46{,}800.00}{52}$$

$$= \$900.00$$

$$\textit{Hourly rate} = \frac{\textit{Weekly pay}}{\textit{Workweek}}$$

$$= \frac{900.00}{40}$$

$$= \$22.50 \text{ per hour}$$

Therefore, her regular rate of pay is $22.50 per hour.

Solution *continued*

(ii) Overtime rate of pay:

$$Overtime\ rate = Overtime\ factor \times Hourly\ rate$$
$$= 1.5 \times 22.50$$
$$= \$33.75$$

Therefore, her overtime rate of pay is $33.75 per hour.

Example 6.3-i **Calculating Pay for a Pay Period Including Overtime Pay**

Fred earns $58,500 annually and is paid bi-weekly. His regular workweek is 37.5 hours. Overtime is paid at 1.5 times the regular rate. Calculate his pay for the last pay period in which he worked 85 hours.

Solution

$$Pay\ for\ a\ pay\ period = \frac{Annual\ salary}{Number\ of\ pay\ periods}$$

$$Bi\text{-}weekly\ pay = \frac{58{,}500.00}{26} = \$2{,}250.00$$

$$Weekly\ pay = \frac{Bi\text{-}weekly\ pay}{2} = \frac{2{,}250.00}{2} = \$1{,}125.00$$

$$Hourly\ rate = \frac{Weekly\ pay}{Workweek} = \frac{1{,}125.00}{37.50} = \$30.00\ \text{per hour}$$

$$Overtime\ factor = 1.5$$

$$Overtime\ rate = Overtime\ factor \times Hourly\ rate$$
$$= 1.5 \times 30.00$$
$$= \$45.00\ \text{per hour}$$

$$Overtime\ hours\ during\ a\ two\text{-}week\ pay\ period = 85 - 37.5 \times 2$$
$$= 85 - 75$$
$$= 10\ \text{hours}$$

$$Overtime\ Pay = Overtime\ rate \times Number\ of\ hours\ worked\ overtime$$
$$= 45.00 \times 10$$
$$= \$450.00$$

$$Pay\ for\ last\ pay\ period = Bi\text{-}weekly\ pay + Overtime\ pay$$
$$= 2{,}250.00 + 450.00$$
$$= \$2{,}700.00$$

Therefore, Fred's pay for the last pay period is $2,700.00.

Commissions

Sales commissions are usually given to sales people to encourage them to sell more, because the more they sell, the more they will earn. If the employment is based on commission, then the gross pay for a given pay period is calculated based on a percent of sales, known as the commission rate.

In this section we will use only a straight (single) commission rate in calculating the gross pay for a pay period.

$$\boldsymbol{Commission = Commission\ rate \times Amount\ of\ sales}$$

Example 6.3-j **Calculating Salary Based on a Straight (Single) Commission Rate**

David's salary is 5% of the sales that he makes for the month. If he makes $50,000 in sales in one month, what is his salary for that month?

Solution

$$\begin{aligned} \textit{Commission} &= \textit{Commission rate} \times \textit{Amount of sales} \\ &= 0.05 \times 50{,}000.00 \\ &= \$2{,}500.00 \end{aligned}$$

Therefore, David's salary for the month is $2,500.00.

Example 6.3-k **Calculating the Amount of Sales, Given the Amount and the Rate of Commission**

Mercy is paid 4.5% sales commission. She earned $2,025 in commission last month. Calculate her sales for last month.

Solution

$$\textit{Commission} = \textit{Commission rate} \times \textit{Amount of sales}$$

$$\begin{aligned} \textit{Amount of sales} &= \frac{\textit{Commission}}{\textit{Commission rate}} \\ &= \frac{2{,}025.00}{0.045} \\ &= \$45{,}000.00 \end{aligned}$$

Therefore, Mercy's sales for last month were $45,000.00.

Example 6.3-l **Calculating the Rate of Commission, Given the Amount of Commission and the Amount of Sales**

Carol earned a commission of $11,375 from the sale of a house sold for $650,000. Calculate the rate of commission she charged for the sale of the house.

Solution

$$\textit{Commission} = \textit{Commission rate} \times \textit{Amount of sales}$$

$$\textit{Commission rate} = \frac{\textit{Commission}}{\textit{Amount of sales}}$$

$$\begin{aligned} \textit{Commission rate} &= \frac{11{,}375.00}{650{,}000.00} \\ &= 0.0175 \\ &= 1.75\% \end{aligned}$$

Therefore, she charged a rate of commission of 1.75%.

6.3 | Exercises

Answers to odd-numbered problems are available at the end of the textbook.

For the following problems, express the answers rounded to two decimal places, wherever applicable.

Calculate the missing values in Problems 1 to 10:

	Annual Salary($)	Monthly Pay ($)	Semi-Monthly Pay ($)	Bi-Weekly Pay ($)	Weekly Pay ($)
1.	$48,750.00	?	?	?	?
2.	$32,760.00	?	?	?	?
3.	?	$3,380.00	?	?	?
4.	?	$4,550.00	?	?	?
5.	?	?	$1,787.50	?	?
6.	?	?	$2,047.50	?	?
7.	?	?	?	$1,350.00	?
8.	?	?	?	$1,540.50	?
9.	?	?	?	?	$673.50
10.	?	?	?	?	$864.00

11. Scott is paid an annual salary of $36,400. Calculate his bi-weekly pay and the equivalent monthly pay.
12. Judy receives an annual salary of $45,000. Calculate her weekly pay and the equivalent monthly pay.
13. Floyd's bi-weekly pay is $1,912.50. Calculate his annual salary and the equivalent monthly pay.
14. Barb receives a weekly pay of $936. Calculate her annual salary and the equivalent monthly pay.
15. Joyce receives a monthly pay of $4,143.75. Calculate her annual salary and the equivalent weekly pay.
16. Chris receives a monthly pay of $2,625. Calculate his annual salary and the equivalent bi-weekly pay.
17. Lionel receives a bi-weekly pay of $1,980 from his employer. If the emlopyer changed the pay period to semi-monthly instead of bi-weekly, calculate the semi-monthly payment he would receive.
18. An employee receives a weekly pay of $720. Calculate the equivalent semi-monthly pay this employee would receive.
19. Calculate the bi-weekly pay and the equivalent semi-monthly pay of an employee receiving an annual salary of $68,640.
20. Calculate the semi-monthly pay and equivalent bi-weekly pay of an employee receiving an annual salary of $42,900.

Calculate the missing values in Problems 21 to 28:

	Annual Salary($)	Weekly Pay ($)	Workweek (Hrs/Week)	Hourly Rate ($/hr)	Overtime Factor	Overtime Rate ($/hr)
21.	$57,200.00	?	40.0	?	1.50	?
22.	$47,775.00	?	47.5	?	2.00	?
23.	?	$747.50	32.5	?	?	$34.50
24.	?	$938.00	35.0	?	?	$40.20
25.	?	$513.50	?	$15.75	1.50	?
26.	?	$890.00	?	$22.25	2.00	?
27.	?	?	37.5	$17.20	2.25	?
28.	?	?	32.5	$24.00	1.75	?

29. Susan's annual salary of $68,000 is based on a 35-hour workweek and she is paid weekly. Calculate the following: (a) her weekly pay, (b) her overtime rate of pay at 1.5 times the regular rate of pay, and (c) her gross pay for a week in which she worked 6 hours overtime.
30. James receives an annual salary of $46,800. His workweek is 37.5 hours. Calculate the following: (a) his weekly pay, (b) his overtime rate of pay at 2 times the regular rate of pay, and (c) his gross pay for a week in which he worked 9 hours overtime.
31. Terry receives a weekly pay of $1,267.50. He has a 32.5-hour workweek. Calculate his hourly rate of pay and his annual salary.
32. Ron's weekly pay of $918.75 is based on a 37.5-hour workweek. Calculate his hourly rate of pay and his annual salary.
33. Alex earns an hourly rate of pay of $23.70 for a 35-hour workweek. Calculate his weekly pay and his annual salary.
34. Tom earns $25 per hour and his workweek is 40 hours. Calculate his weekly pay and his annual salary.

Calculate the missing values in Problems 35 to 40:

	Sales ($)	Commission Rate (%)	Commission ($)
35.	$45,500	4.5%	?
36.	$21,375	7.5%	?
37.	?	5.0%	$2,925
38.	?	7.0%	$1,775
39.	$46,500	?	$1,395
40.	$35,000	?	$1,925

41. Tracy is paid a fixed commission of 5.5% on her sales in a month. How much will she be paid in a month in which her sales are $47,500?
42. Nancy is paid a fixed commission of 3.75% on all sales during the month. Sales for last month were $38,550. What were her gross earnings for last month?

- 43. Dianne is paid a commission of 4.5% on all sales in a month. Determine her sales for the month in which she earned $2,317.50 in commission.
- 44. Joana receives a commission of 6.5% on all sales during that period. Last week she earned $1,935.05. What were her sales for last week?
- 45. Bill is paid on a fixed commission rate basis and his gross pay in September was $2,730 on sales totalling $42,000. Calculate his rate of commission.
- 46. Jennifer is paid on a fixed commission rate based on her sales. Calculate the rate of commission if she earned $3,696 in a month when her sales were $67,200.

6.4 | Currency Conversion

Currency Conversion

:xchange rates are used o convert currencies •etween countries.

The exchange rate, also called the foreign exchange rate or forex rate, is used for converting currencies between countries. The exchange rate allows you to calculate the amount of a currency required to purchase one unit of another currency.

For example, to convert Canadian currency to US currency, it is important to know how many Canadian dollars are equivalent to one US dollar, or vice versa.

The value of a currency may fluctuate constantly during the day and the exchange rate may vary accordingly. For example, on March 31, 2015, US$1 was equal to C$1.2684 and C$1 was equal to US$ 0.7883 at 20:00 hours EST. Thus, the exchange rate on that date and time was US$1 = C$1.2684 and C$1 = US$0.7883.

Currency Cross-Rate Table

Currency exchange rates are generally displayed in a table called the Currency Cross-Rate Table for quick reference. Below, is a currency cross-rate table from March 31, 2015.

Table 6.4-a **Currency Cross-Rate Table as of March 31, 2015**

			One Unit of				
Currency		Symbol	C$	US$	€	£	A$
Canadian dollar	Equivalent to	C$	-	1.2684	1.3638	1.8822	0.9666
US dollar		US$	0.7883	-	1.0749	1.4837	0.7621
Euro		€	0.7333	0.9302	-	1.3801	0.7089
British pound		£	0.5312	0.6740	0.7246	-	0.5137
Australian dollar		A$	1.0343	1.3123	1.4107	1.9468	-

The vertical columns of the table represent one unit of the currency to be converted and the horizontal rows represent its equivalent value in another currency.

For example, US$1 = A$1.3123 and £1 = US$1.4837.

Based on the exchange rates provided in Table 6.4-a, the exchange rates of foreign currency per Canadian dollars (C$) and vice versa are provided in Table 6.4-b for easy reference.

Table 6.4-b

Exchange Rates of Foreign Currency per C$ and C$ per Unit of Foreign Currency

Currency	Symbol	Unit per C$	C$ per unit
US dollar	US$	0.7883	1.2684
Euro	€	0.7333	1.3638
British pound	£	0.5312	1.8822
Australian dollar	A$	1.0343	0.9666

For calculations involving conversion from one currency to another, we will either use the cross-rate table or the exchange rates provided in the question. We will be using the method of proportions to solve examples that follow.

Example 6.4-a

Converting Currency from C$ to US$

Based on the exchange rates provided in Table 6.4-a (Currency Cross-Rate Table), how many US dollars will you receive when you convert C$400?

Solution

From the cross-rate table,

US$1 = C$1.2684

US$: C$ = US$: C$

1: 1.2684 = x : 400.00

US$	C$
1	1.2684
x	400.00

In fractional form, $\frac{1}{x} = \frac{1.2684}{400.00}$ or $\frac{1}{1.2684} = \frac{x}{400.00}$

Cross-multiplying and solving for x,

$$1.2684x = 400.00$$

$$x = \frac{400.00}{1.2684}$$

$$= 315.357931... = \text{US\$}315.36$$

Therefore, you will receive US$315.36 when you convert C$400.00.

Example 6.4-b

Converting Currency from C$ to US$ and from US$ to C$

If US$1 = C$1.2684, calculate:

(i) The amount you will receive if you convert US$1,000 to Canadian dollars.

(ii) The amount you will receive if you convert C$1,000 to US dollars.

Solution

(i) US$: C$ = US$: C$

1 : 1.2684 = 1,000.00 : x

US$	C$
1	1.2684
1,000.00	x

In fractional form, $\frac{1}{1{,}000.00} = \frac{1.2684}{x}$ or $\frac{1}{1.2684} = \frac{1{,}000.00}{x}$

Cross-multiplying and solving for x,

$$x = 1{,}000.00 \times 1.2684$$

$$= \text{C\$}1{,}268.40$$

Therefore, you will receive C$1,268.40 when you convert US$1,000.00.

(ii) US$: C$ = US$: C$

1 : 1.2684 = x : 1,000.00

Solution *continued*

US$	C$
1	1.2684
x	1,000.00

In fractional form, $\frac{1}{x} = \frac{1.2684}{1,000.00}$ or $\frac{1}{1.2684} = \frac{x}{1,000.00}$

Cross-multiplying and solving for x,

$$1.2684x = 1,000.00$$

$$x = \frac{1,000.00}{1.2684}$$

$$= 788.394828... = \text{US}\$788.39$$

Therefore, you will receive US$788.39 when you convert C$1,000.00.

Example 6.4-c **Converting from One Currency to Another Currency, Given Exchange Rates**

Samantha is travelling from Canada to London for vacation. If £1 = C$1.8822, how much will she receive if she converts C$1,000 to British pounds?

Solution

£ : C$ = £ : C$

1 : 1.8822 = x : 1,000.00

£	C$
1	1.8822
x	1,000.00

In fractional form, $\frac{1}{x} = \frac{1.8822}{1,000.00}$ or $\frac{1}{1.8822} = \frac{x}{1,000.00}$

Cross-multiplying and solving for x,

$$1.8822x = 1,000.00$$

$$x = \frac{1,000.00}{1.8822}$$

$$= 531.293167... = £531.29$$

Therefore, she will receive £531.29 when she converts C$1,000.00.

Example 6.4-d **Series of Currency Conversions**

If US$1 = C$1.2684 and C$1 = A$1.0343, calculate the amount of US dollars you will receive with A$100.

Solution

First, find out how many Canadian dollars you will receive with A$100.

C$: A$ = C$: A$

1 : 1.0343 = x : 100.00

C$	A$
1	1.0343
x	100.00

In fractional form, $\frac{1}{x} = \frac{1.0343}{100.00}$ or $\frac{1}{1.0343} = \frac{x}{100.00}$

Cross-multiplying and solving for x,

$$1.0343x = 100.00$$

$$x = \frac{100.00}{1.0343}$$

$$= \text{C}\$96.683747...$$

Now, determine how many US dollars you will receive with C$96.683747...

US$: C$ = US$: C$

1 : 1.2684 = x : 96.683747...

Solution
continued

US$	C$
1	1.2684
x	96.683747...

In fractional form, $\frac{1}{x} = \frac{1.2684}{96.683747...}$ or $\frac{1}{1.2684} = \frac{x}{96.683747...}$

Cross-multiplying and solving for x,

$$1.2684x = 96.683747...$$

$$x = \frac{96.683747...}{1.2684}$$

$$= 76.224966... = \text{US\$}76.22$$

Therefore, you will receive US$76.22 when you convert A$100.00.

Buying and Selling Currencies

If you would like to convert currencies, you should go to a bank or another financial institution that is authorized to buy and sell currencies. These financial institutions usually have different exchange rates for buying and selling currencies, which is their stated buying rate and selling rate. They use the actual currency exchange rates and their rate of commission to create their own buying and selling rates for each currency. Commission is charged for their services on these transactions.

- Buying rate (buy rate) is the rate at which the financial institution buys a particular foreign currency from the customers.
- Selling rate (sell rate) is the rate at which the financial institution sells a particular foreign currency to the customers.

Example 6.4-e

Currency Conversion Including Commission in Buying or Selling Currencies

Sarah plans to travel to the US from Canada and approaches a local bank to purchase US$1,000. Assume US$1 = C$1.2684 and that the bank charges a commission of 0.75% to sell or buy US dollars. Calculate:

(i) The amount in Canadian dollars that Sarah would have to pay for US$1,000.

(ii) If Sarah changes her plan and wishes to convert US$1,000 back to Canadian dollars, how much will she receive from the same bank, assuming the same exchange rate and the same commission rate?

Solution

When calculating the buying or selling rate, it does not matter if you calculate the commission first and then convert the value, or vice-versa. You will always obtain the same answer.

(i) US$: C$ = US$: C$

1 : 1.2684 = 1,000.00 : x

US$	C$
1	1.2684
1,000.00	x

In fractional form, $\frac{1}{1{,}000.00} = \frac{1.2684}{x}$ or $\frac{1}{1.2684} = \frac{1{,}000.00}{x}$

Cross-multiplying and solving for x,

$$x = 1.2684 \times 1{,}000.00$$

$$= 1{,}268.40$$

Amount in C$ before the bank's commission = C$1,268.40.

Bank's commission:

$0.0075 \times 1{,}268.40 = \text{C\$}9.513$ — Adding the bank's 0.75% commission,

Total = 1,268.40 + 9.513

= 1,277.913 = C$1,277.91 — Amount that Sarah will pay the bank.

When you buy currencies, you will pay the converted amount and the financial institution's commission.

Or

$1{,}268.40\ (1 + 0.0075) = 1{,}277.913 = \text{C\$}1{,}277.91$

Therefore, Sarah would have to pay C$1,277.91 for US$1,000.00.

Solution *continued*

(ii) US\$1,000 = C\$1,268.40 — As calculated in (i).

0.0075 × 1,268.40 = C\$ 9.513 — Subtracting the bank's 0.75% commission,

Total = 1,268.40 – 9.513

Total = 1,258.887 = C\$1,258.89 — Amount the bank will pay Sarah.

When you sell currencies, you will receive the converted currency less the financial institution's commission.

Or

C\$1,268.40 (1 – 0.0075) = 1,258.887 = C\$1,258.89

Therefore, Sarah will receive C\$1,258.89 from the bank.

Example 6.4-f

Calculating Bank's Rate of Commision to Buy and Sell Foreign Currency

When the exchange rate is US\$1 = C\$1.2684, a bank has the following buy rate and sell rate for US dollars:

Buy rate: US\$1 = C\$1.2589

Sell rate: US\$ = C\$1.2843

Calculate the following:

(i) Bank's rate of commision to buy US\$

(ii) Bank's rate of commision to sell US\$

Solution

(i) Assume you want to sell US\$1,000 to the bank. (i.e., the bank is buying from you: use buy rate).

Using bank's buy rate, you will receive: 1,000.00 × 1.2589 = C\$1,258.90.

Using exchange rate US\$1.00 = C\$1.2684,

US\$	C\$
1	1.2684
1,000.00	x

$$\frac{1}{1{,}000.00} = \frac{1.2684}{x}$$

$$x = \text{C\$}1{,}268.40$$

Therefore, the bank's commision = C\$(1,268.40 – 1,258.90)

= C\$9.50

$$\text{Bank's rate of commision to buy} = \frac{\textit{Amount of commision}}{\textit{Amount based on exchange rate}} \times 100\%$$

$$= \frac{\text{C\$}9.50}{\text{C\$}1{,}268.40} \times 100\%$$

= 0.748975...%

= 0.75%

Therefore, the bank's rate of commision to buy US\$ is 0.75%.

(ii) Assume you want to buy US\$1000 from the bank (i.e., the bank is selling to you: use sell rate)

Using bank's sell rate, you will pay: 1,000.00 × 1.2843 = C\$1,284.30

Using exchange rate US\$ = C\$1.2684,

US\$	C\$
1	1.2684
1,000.00	x

$$\frac{1}{1{,}000.00} = \frac{1.2684}{x}$$

$$x = \text{C\$}1{,}268.40$$

Solution
continued

Therefore, bank's commision = C$(1,284.30 – 1,268.40)

= C$15.90

$$\text{Bank's rate of commision to sell} = \frac{\textit{Amount of commision}}{\textit{Amount based on exchange rate}}$$

$$= \frac{C\$15.90}{C\$1{,}268.40} \times 100\%$$

= 1.253547...%

= 1.25%

Therefore, the bank's rate of commison to sell US$ is 1.25%.

6.4 | Exercises

Answers to odd-numbered problems are available at the end of the textbook.

Based on the following exchange rates, answer Problems 1 to 4:

£1 = A$1.9468, US$1 = C$1.2684, €1 = US$1.0749, C$1 = £0.5312

1. Convert A$200 to British pounds (£).
2. Convert C$3,000 to US dollars (US$).
3. Convert US$5,000 to Euros (€).
4. Convert £10 to Canadian dollars (C$).

Based on the following exchange rates, answer Problems 5 to 8:

€1 = C$1.3638, A$1 = US$0.7621, US$1 = £0.6740, C$1 = A$1.0343

5. Convert C$2,500 to Euros (€).
6. Convert US$2,850 to Australian dollars (A$).
7. Convert £18 to US dollars (US$).
8. Convert A$300 to Canadian dollars (C$).
9. A bank in Ottawa charges 2.5% commission to buy and sell currencies. Assume the exchange rate is US$1 = C$1.2684.
   a. How many Canadian dollars will you have to pay to purchase US$1,500?
   b. How much commission in Canadian dollars (C$) will you pay the bank for the above transaction?
10. A bank in Montreal charges 2.25% commission to buy and sell currencies. Assume the exchange rate is US$1 = C$1.2684.
    a. How many Canadian dollars will you receive from the bank if you sell US$1,375?
    b. How much commission will you pay the bank for this transaction?
11. Mark converted US$4,500 into Canadian dollars at a bank that charged him a commission of 0.25%. How much did he receive from the bank? Assume that the exchange rate was C$1 = US$0.7883.
12. Carmin converted £2,000 into Canadian dollars. If the commission the bank was charging was 0.90%, calculate how many Canadian dollars she received. Assume that the exchange rate was C$1 = £0.5312.
13. If C$1 = A$1.0343 and A$1 = US$0.7621, how many Canadian dollars will you receive with US$1,000?
14. If C$1 = £0.5312 and £1 = US$1.4837, how many Canadian dollars will you receive with US$1,000?
15. • David planned to travel to Australia from Canada and purchased A$5,000. A week later, he decided to cancel his trip and wanted to convert his Australian dollars back into Canadian dollars at the same bank. How much money did he lose or gain? Assume that the bank charged a commission of 0.5% to buy and sell currencies, and that the exchange rate was C$1 = A$1.0343.
16. • Lisa purchased US$10,000 from a bank in America, which charged her a commission of 0.80%, and sold the US dollars to a bank in Canada, which charged her 0.80% commission. How much money did she lose or gain? Assume that the exchange rate was C$1 = US$0.7883.

- 17. Dell left Canada for the UK with C$8,000. When he reached the UK, he converted all his cash into British pounds. The conversion rate was £1 = C$1.8822. After spending £1,000 in the UK, he returned to Canada. Calculate the number of Canadian dollars he received when he converted the remaining British pounds into Canadian dollars at an exchange rate of C$1 = £1.9000.
- 18. Jason travelled from Toronto to Australia, where he converted C$3,000 to Australian dollars at an exchange rate of C$1 = A$1.0343. He spent A$2,000 in Australia before returning to Toronto. How many Canadian dollars did he receive when he converted the remaining Australian dollars into Canadian dollars at an exchange rate of C$1 = A$1.0200?
- 19. A bank in London, Ontario has a selling rate of £1 = C$1.8963. If the exchange rate is £1 = C$1.8775, calculate the rate of commission that the bank charges.
- 20. A bank in London, Ontario has a buying rate of A$1 = C$0.9618. If the exchange rate is A$1 = C$0.9714, calculate the rate of commission that the bank charges.

6.5 | Index Numbers

Index Numbers

The Index Number is used to express the relative value of an item compared to a base value.

The price of many items constantly fluctuates at different points in time. You may have noticed that the cost of transportation, entertainment, education, housing, etc., have constantly been on the rise. Index Numbers are used to quantify such economic changes over time.

An **index number** is a comparison of the value of an item on a selected date to the value of the same item on a designated date, known as the base date. That is, if the index number is lower than the base value, the value of that item has gone down since the base date; if the index number is higher than the base value, the value of that item has gone up since the base date.

For example, the index number of 120.5 for an item on a selected date indicates that the value of that item is 20.5% above the base period price of 100 for the same item.

The index number is calculated as follows:

$$\textit{Index number} = \frac{\textit{Value on selected date}}{\textit{Value on base date}} \times \textit{Base value}$$

Example 6.5-a **Calculating the Index Number for Gasoline in 2015 Using 2002 as the Base Year**

If the price of gasoline in 2002 was $0.75 per litre, and in 2015, the price had risen to $1.15 per litre, calculate the index number for gas using 2002 as the base year with a base value of 100.

Solution

Year	Index	Price ($)
2002	100	0.75
2015	x	1.15

In fractional form, $\frac{100}{x} = \frac{0.75}{1.15}$

Cross-multiplying and solving,

$$0.75x = 100 \times 1.15$$

$$x = \frac{1.15}{0.75} \times 100$$

$$= 153.333333...$$

$$= 153.33$$

or

$$\textit{Index number} = \frac{\textit{Value on selected date}}{\textit{Value on base date}} \times \textit{Base value}$$

$$= \frac{1.15}{0.75} \times 100$$

$$= 153.333333...$$

$$=153.33$$

Therefore, the index number for gas in 2015 is 153.33.

Solution *continued*

Note: 2002 is referred to as the base date i.e., the value 100 is the index for the base date). Since the index number for 2015 is greater than 100, the value of the item has increased.

ie., percent change = 153.33 – 100 = 53.33%.

Therefore, the price of gas in 2015 has increased by 53.33% from its price in 2002.

Example 6.5-b

Calculating the Index Number for Basic Phone Services in 2015 Using 2002 as the Base Year

If the price of basic phone services in 2002 was $39 per month, and it decreased to $20 per month in 2015, calculate the index for the price of basic phone services in 2015 using 2002 as the base year with base value of 100.

Solution

Year	Index	Price ($)
2002	100	39.00
2015	x	20.00

In fractional form, $\frac{100}{x} = \frac{39.00}{20.00}$

Cross-multiplying and solving,

$$39.00x = 100 \times 20.00$$

$$x = \frac{20.00 \times 100}{39.00}$$

$$= 51.282051...$$

$$= 51.28$$

or

$$\textit{Index number} = \frac{\textit{Value on selected date}}{\textit{Value on base date}} \times \textit{Base value}$$

$$= \frac{20.00}{39.00} \times 100$$

$$= 51.282051...$$

$$= 51.28$$

Therefore, the index number for basic phone services in 2015 is 51.28.

Note: 2002 is referred to as the base date (i.e., the value 100 is the index for the base date). Since the index number, 51.28, is less than the base index of 100, the price of basic phone services in 2015 has decreased.

ie., percent change = 51.28 – 100 = – 48.72%

Therefore, the price of basic phone service has decreased by 48.72% from its price in 2002.

Consumer Price Index (CPI)

The Consumer Price Index (CPI) is an indicator of changes in consumer prices experienced by Canadians.

The Consumer Price Index (CPI) is a good example of how useful index numbers can be in day-to-day life. CPI is an indicator of changes in consumer prices. In Canada, Statistics Canada obtains this number by calculating the cost of about 600 consumer goods and services under eight major categories (food, shelter, recreation, health, transport, clothes, housing, and alcohol and tobacco products) purchased by consumers and comparing this cost over time.

CPI is calculated by comparing the cost of a fixed basket of items at a particular period to the cost at base period. The CPI value is usually rounded to one decimal place.

CPI is calculated as follows:

$$CPI = \frac{\textit{Value on selected date}}{\textit{Value on base date}} \times 100$$

Example 6.5-c

Calculating CPI in 2014 Using 2005 as the Base Year

The basket of goods and services included in the CPI cost $16,500 in 2005. The same basket cost $20,650 in 2014.

(i) Calculate the CPI in 2014 using 2005 as the base year with a base value of 100.

(ii) Calculate the percent change in the cost from 2005 to 2014.

Solution

(i)

Year	Index	Price ($)
2005	100	16,500.00
2014	x	20,650.00

In fractional form, $\frac{100}{x} = \frac{16,500.00}{20,650.00}$

Cross-multiplying and solving,

$$16,500.00x = 100 \times 20,650.00.00$$

$$x = \frac{20,650.00 \times 100}{16,500.00}$$

$$= 125.151515...$$

$$= 125.2$$

or

$$Index\ number = \frac{Value\ on\ selected\ date}{Value\ on\ base\ date} \times 100$$

$$CPI_{2014} = \frac{20,650.00}{16,500.00} \times 100$$

$$= 125.151515...$$

$$= 125.2$$

Therefore, the CPI in 2014 is 125.2.

(ii) Percent change in cost:

Using $\%C = \frac{V_f - V_i}{V_i} \times 100\%$

$$= \frac{20,650.00 - 16,500.00}{16,500.00} \times 100\%$$

$$= 25.151515...$$

$$= 25.15\%$$

Therefore, the percent change in cost from 2005 to 2014 was 25.15% (= 25.2%).

Example 6.5-d

Calculating the Value of an Item after a Time Period Based on Given Index

An item was worth $1,750 in year 2005. How much was it worth in 2014 if the index for year 2005 was 107.0 and that for year 2014 was 125.0?

Solution

Year	Index	Price ($)
2005	107.0	1,750.00
2014	125.0	x

In fractional form, $\frac{107.0}{125.0} = \frac{1,750.00}{x}$

or

$$Index\ number = \frac{Value\ on\ selected\ date}{Value\ on\ base\ date} \times Base\ value$$

$$107.0 = \frac{1,750.00}{Value\ on\ base\ date} \times Base\ value \quad (1)$$

$$125.0 = \frac{x}{Value\ on\ base\ date} \times Base\ value \quad (2)$$

(1) divided by (2):

$$\frac{107.0}{125.0} = \frac{1,750.00}{x}$$

Cross-multiplying and solving,

$$107.0x = 125.0 \times 1,750.00$$

$$x = \frac{125.0 \times 1,750.00}{107.0}$$

$$= 2,044.392523...$$

$$= \$2,044.39$$

Therefore, the item was worth $2,044.39 in 2014.

CPI for Canada is calculated and issued by Statistics Canada on a monthly basis and is released during the 3rd week of the following month (around the 20th).

For example, CPI for Feb. 2015 was released on Mar. 20 2015. (CPI for Feb. 2015 = 125.4).

When there are considerable changes in consumer spending patterns, the base period for CPI is adjusted periodically by Statistics Canada. In 2004, the base period was changed from 1992 to 2002, which is the current base period used in CPI calculations (CPI for 2002 = 100). The annual CPI from 2002 to 2014 is provided in Table 6.5.

Table 6.5 **CPI from the Years 2002 to 2014**

Year	2002	2003	2004	2005	2006	2007	2008	2009	2010	2011	2012	2013	2014
CPI	100.0	102.8	104.7	107.0	109.1	111.5	114.4	114.4	116.5	119.9	121.7	122.8	125.2

Purchasing Power of a Dollar and Inflation

The Purchasing Power of Money is the number of goods/services that can be purchased with a unit of currency.

CPI is used to measure the purchasing power of a dollar and inflation. Wages of workers, private and public pension programs, personal income tax deductions, social and welfare payments, spousal and child support payments, etc., are adjusted periodically based on the changes in CPI. Purchasing power of a dollar is calculated as follows:

$$Purchasing\ power\ of\ a\ dollar = \frac{\$1}{CPI} \times 100$$

Inflation is a rise on the general level of prices of goods and services in an economy over time.

Inflation is the rate at which price of goods and services increases.

When prices increase, CPI increases and the purchasing power of money decreases. Inflation rate is the rate of change in CPI over a period of time, and is calculated as follows:

$$Inflation\ rate\ (from\ Year\ A\ to\ Year\ B) = \frac{CPI_{Year\ B} - CPI_{Year\ A}}{CPI_{Year\ A}} \times 100\%$$

\$100 today does not buy the same amount of goods and services as before. Similarly, \$100 to be received in the future is worth less than \$100 received today. Unless our income rises to match the price increase (inflation), we will not be able to maintain the same standard of living as before. Therefore, inflation is crucial in financial planning.

Real income is the income after adjusting for inflation and is calculated as follows:

$$Real\ income = \frac{Money\ income}{CPI} \times 100$$

Example 6.5-e **Calculating Purchasing Power of a Dollar Given CPI**

If the CPI was 121.7 for 2012 and 125.2 for 2014, determine the purchasing power of a dollar for the two years. Compare with the base year 2002.

Solution

$$Purchasing\ power\ in\ 2012 = \frac{\$1}{121.7} \times 100 = 0.821692...$$
$$= 82.17\%$$

$$Purchasing\ power\ in\ 2014 = \frac{\$1}{125.2} \times 100 = 0.798722...$$
$$= 79.87\%$$

Therefore, the dollar in 2012 could purchase 82.17% of what could be purchased in 2002, and the dollar in 2014 could purchase 79.87% of what could be purchased in 2002.

Example 6.5-f

Calculating Inflation Rate Given CPI

If the CPI was 122.8 in 2013 and 125.2 at the end of 2014, what would be the inflation rate from 2013 to 2014?

Solution

$$Inflation\ rate\ (from\ 2013\ to\ 2014) = \frac{CPI_{2014} - CPI_{2013}}{CPI} \times 100\%$$

$$= \frac{125.2 - 122.8}{122.8} \times 100\%$$

$$= 1.954397...\%$$

$$= 1.95\%$$

Therefore, the inflation rate from 2013 to 2014 would be 1.95%.

Example 6.5-g

Purchasing Power of a Dollar and Inflation

Peter's income was $26,000 in 2002 (base year), $38,000 in 2010, and $40,000 in 2014. The CPI was 116.5 in 2010 and 125.2 in 2014. Determine Peter's real income in 2010 and 2014.

Solution

$$Real\ income = \frac{Money\ income}{CPI} \times 100$$

$$Real\ Income\ in\ 2010 = \frac{38{,}000.00}{116.5} \times 100$$

$$= 32{,}618.02575... = \$32{,}618.03$$

$$Real\ Income\ in\ 2014 = \frac{40{,}000.00}{125.2} \times 100$$

$$= 31{,}948.88179... = \$31{,}948.88$$

Therefore, Peter's real income in 2010 was $32,618.03 and his real income in 2014 was $31,948.88.

Stock Index

S&P/TSX is an index of stock prices of the largest companies on the Toronto Stock Exchange.

Stock index is an application of index numbers and is used to measure the performance of stock markets. For example, the Standard and Poor's Toronto Stock Exchange Composite Index reflects the share prices of all the companies trading on the Toronto Stock Exchange. Here, the "basket" composed of ordinary goods and services that all consumers use on an average is replaced by a portfolio composed of the shares of the big companies that are listed on the Toronto Stock Exchange. This index is an indicator of the health of the Toronto Stock Exchange. If S&P/TSX goes up, it means that the overall value of the shares in the Exchange is going up; it is important to note that individually, some companies may be performing better than others, but collectively, the companies are performing well. The base value used for the S&P/TSX is 1,000, set in 1975. S&P/TSX is calculated as follows:

$$\boldsymbol{S\&P/TSX\ Composite\ Index = \frac{Value\ of\ portfolio\ on\ selected\ date}{Value\ of\ portfolio\ on\ base\ date} \times 1{,}000}$$

In March 2014, the S&P/TSX index reached 14,000, which means that the value of the portfolio in 2014 was 14 times its value in 1975.

Example 6.5-h

Calculating S&P/TSX

If the S&P/TSX portfolio cost $200,000 in 2009, and the same portfolio cost $2,865,000 in 2014, calculate the S&P/TSX Composite Index in 2014.

Solution

$$S\&P/TSX\ Composite\ Index = \frac{Value\ of\ portfolio\ on\ selected\ date}{Value\ of\ portfolio\ on\ base\ date} \times 1{,}000$$

$$= \frac{2{,}865{,}000.00}{200{,}000.00} \times 1{,}000$$

$$= 14{,}325$$

Therefore, in 2014, the S&P/TSX Composite Index was 14,325.

6.5 | Exercises

Answers to odd-numbered problems are available at the end of the textbook.

1. Determine the index for 2012 and 2014 for the value of a car using 2008 as the base year.

Year	2008	2012	2014
Value of Car	$34,000	$38,000	$40,000

2. Determine the index for 2010 and 2014 for the price of a tire using 2007 as the base year.

Year	2007	2010	2014
Price of a Tire	$45	$60	$90

3. Determine the index for 2014 for the price of a monthly metro pass for adults and students using 2002 as the base year.

Year	Adult Metro Pass Adult	Student Metro Pass
2002	$98.75	$83.25
2014	$133.75	$108.00

4. Determine the index for 2014 for the cost of an adult and child movie ticket using 2006 as the base year.

Year	Adult Movie Ticket Adult	Child Movie Ticket
2006	$9.00	$6.00
2014	$14.50	$11.00

Use the index given below to answer Problems 5 to 8.

Year	1	2	3	4	5	6	7
Index	100.0	105.0	107.5	111.0	110.0	118.5	120.0

5. If an item was worth $2,500 in year 3, how much was it worth in year 5 and year 7?
6. If an item was worth $4,000 in year 2, how much was it worth in year 4 and year 6?
7. If an item was worth $2,000 in year 5, how much was it worth in year 2 and year 3?
8. If an item was worth $5,000 in year 6, how much was it worth in year 3 and year 4?

Use the CPI from year 2002 to 2014 provided in Table 6.5 to answer Problems 9 to 16.

9. What real income in 2014 would be equivalent to an income of $60,000 in 2006?
10. What real income in 2014 would be equivalent to an income of $50,000 in 2007?
11. Calculate the inflation rate for the period 2010 to 2014.
12. Calculate the inflation rate for the period 2011 to 2014.
13. The college tuition fee for the year 2008 was $3,200. What would the tuition fee be for the year 2014 if the tuition fee increased with the inflation rate during this period?
14. Tony earned $58,000 in 2004. How much would he have earned in 2014 if his earnings grew with the inflation rate during this period?
15. Calculate the purchasing power of a dollar for 2013 and 2014 relative to the base year 2002.
16. Calculate the purchasing power of a dollar for 2011 and 2012 relative to the base year 2002.

Use the following data to answer Problems 17 to 20:

End of the Year	2010	2011	2012	2013	2014
S&P/TSX Index	11,538	11,907	12,169	13,419	14,753

17. If you had invested $25,000 at the end of 2011, what would have been its value at the end of 2014?
18. If you had invested $75,000 at the end of 2010, what would have been its value at the end of 2014?
19. What amount invested at the end of 2012 would have resulted in a value of $50,000 at the end of 2014?
20. What amount invested at the end of 2011 would have resulted in a value of $150,000 at the end of 2014?

6 | Review Exercises

Answers to odd-numbered problems are available at the end of the textbook.

1. A store purchases laptops for $425 each and sells each for $650. Calculate the amount of markup and the rate of markup.
2. A distributor buys computers for $775 each and sells each for $950. Calculate the amount of markup and the rate of markup.
3. Calculate the amount of markup and the selling price of an item that has a cost of $1,250 and a rate of markup of 60%.
4. A furniture store buys dining tables for $375 each and sells them after a markup of 40%. Calculate the amount of markup on the selling price of each dining table.
5. A sports jacket that cost a store $150 was sold after a markup of $75. Calculate the rate of markup and the selling price.
6. Calculate the rate of markup and the selling price of a bottle of wine if the cost is $12.50 and the markup is $2.50.
7. During a sale, a humidifier that sells for $125 is marked down by $25. Calculate the sale price and the rate of markdown.
8. All winter tires in a store are marked down by $35 during a clearance sale. Calculate the sale price and the rate of markdown on a winter tire that was originally priced for $140.
9. The regular selling price of an item is $399. During a sale, it was marked down by 15%. Calculate the amount of markdown and the sale price.
10. A toaster that sells for $39.50 is marked down by 25%. Calculate the amount of markdown and the sale price.
11. • After a discount of $12.50, an item was sold for $37.50. Calculate the regular selling price of the item and the rate of markdown.
12. • After a markdown of $73.50, an item was sold for $416.50. Calculate the regular selling price of the item and the rate of markdown.
13. Calculate the amount of interest earned from an investment of $7,500 for 8 months at 4.5% p.a.
14. Steve borrowed $4,250 for 15 months at 3.2% p.a. How much interest would he have to pay on the loan?
15. What amount must be invested now to earn $375 in interest in 3 years at 4% p.a.?
16. An investment at 3% p.a. earned interest of $225 over a period of 2 years. Find the amount invested.
17. At what annual interest rate will an investment of $2,400 earn interest of $660 in 5 years?
18. The interest on a loan of $3,600 for 3 years is $486. Calculate the annual interest rate charged on the loan.
19. Ram's bi-weekly pay is $1,750. Calculate his annual salary and the equivalent monthly pay.
20. Sam's monthly pay is $4,680. Calculate his annual salary and the equivalent bi-weekly pay.
21. Rodney's weekly pay is $787.50 and his workweek is 35 hours. If his overtime factor is 2, calculate his hourly rate of pay and the overtime rate of pay.
22. John's bi-weekly pay is $1,820 and his regular workweek is 40 hours. If his overtime factor is 1.5, calculate his hourly rate of pay and the overtime rate of pay.
23. A secretary is paid $14.50 per hour and her workweek is 37.5 hours. Calculate her annual salary and her semi-monthly pay.
24. A bank teller is paid $17.25 per hour and her workweek is 35 hours. Calculate her annual salary and her semi-monthly pay.
25. • Chris is receiving a semi-monthly pay of $2,246.40. Calculate his annual salary and the equivalent bi-weekly pay.
26. • Lisa is receiving a bi-weekly pay of $2,121.60. Calculate her annual salary and the equivalent semi-monthly pay.
27. • Amy receives a commission rate of 6% on all sales in a month. Last month, she earned $2,160. Calculate her sales during last month.
28. • Roger, a real estate agent, receives a 2% commission on the sales of houses. He earned a commission of $8,500 from the sale of a house. Find the selling price of the house.

Use the following exchange rates to answer Problems 29 to 34:

£1 = A$1.9468, C$1 = £0.5312, €1 = C$1.3638, A$1 = US$0.7621

29. Convert A$1,500 to British pounds (£).
30. Convert £2,500 to Canadian dollars (C$).
31. Convert C$1,250 to Euros (€).
32. Convert US$2,000 to Australian dollars (A$).
33. Charles converted US$3,000 into Canadian dollars at a bank that charged him a commission rate of 0.75%. How much did he receive from the bank? Use C$1 = US$0.7883
34. Dylan converted £2,000 into US dollars. If the bank was charging a commission rate of 0.50%, calculate the amount he received from the bank. Use US$1 = £0.6740.

Use the CPI given in Table 6.5 to answer Problems 35 to 40.

35. If an item was worth $25,000 in 2010, how much was it worth in 2013?
36. If an item was worth $7,500 in 2009, how much was it worth in 2014?
37. What real income in 2014 would be equivalent to an income of $5,000 in 2010?
38. What real income in 2013 would be equivalent to an income of $4,000 in 2011?
39. Calculate the purchasing power of a dollar in 2010 relative to the base year 2002.
40. Calculate the purchasing power of a dollar in 2009 relative to the base year 2002.

6 | Self-Test Exercises

Answers to all problems are available at the end of the textbook.

1. A store that sells fruits, purchases oranges for $19.75 a box and sells them after a markup of 44%. Calculate the amount of markup and the selling price of each box of oranges.
2. A car dealer bought a car for $27,500 and sold it after a markup of $3,575. Calculate the rate of markup on cost and the selling price.
3. A hardware store purchases electric drills at $49.50 each and sells each for $94.05. Calculate the amount of markup and the rate of markup.
4. After a markup of $22, an item was sold for $77. Calculate the rate of markup and the cost of the item.
5. During a sale, a snow blower that regularly sells for $749.00 is sold for $561.75. Calculate the amount of markdown and the rate of markdown.
6. After a markdown of $45, an item was sold for $315. Calculate the regular selling price of the item and the rate of markdown.
7. During a clearance sale, all monitors are marked down by 20%. Calculate the sale price and the amount of markdown of a monitor that was originally priced for $96.
8. At what annual interest rate will $650 earn interest of $62.40 in 2 years?
9. Find the principal which will earn interest of $202.50 at 3.6% p.a. in 15 months.
10. How much interest would you have to pay on a loan of $2,190 for 180 days at 4.2% p.a.?
11. Ruben's weekly pay is $810. Calculate his annual salary and the equivalent monthly pay.

• 12. Kathy's annual salary is $34,944 based on a 35-hour workweek.
   a. What would be her bi-weekly pay?
   b. What is her hourly rate of pay?

• 13. An emloyee was receiving a bi-weekly pay of $2,340. If the employer changed the pay period to semi-monthly, instead of bi-weekly, calculate the employee's semi-monthly pay.

• 14. Warren is paid a commission on all his sales. He is paid monthly. Last month his pay was $2,400 and his sales were $32,000. Calculate the commission rate.

15. A bank charges 1.25% commission for each transaction. How many Canadian dollars would you have to pay to purchase A$1,500? Assume the exchange rate is C$1 = A$1.0343.
16. Anil wants to convert US$2,250 to Canadian dollars. If the exchange rate is C$1= US$0.7883 and the bank's commission rate is 0.75%, how many Canadian dollars will he receive?
17. A bank has a buying rate of £1 = 1.8912. If the exchange rate is £1 = C$ 1.8822, calculate the rate of commision that the bank charges to buy British pounds.

Use the CPI given in Table 6.5 to answer Problems 18 to 20.

18. If an item was worth $32,500 in 2011, how much was it worth in 2014?
19. What real income in 2014 would be equivalent to an income of $80,000 in 2010?
20. What amount in 2012 had the same purchasing power as $10,000 in 2014?

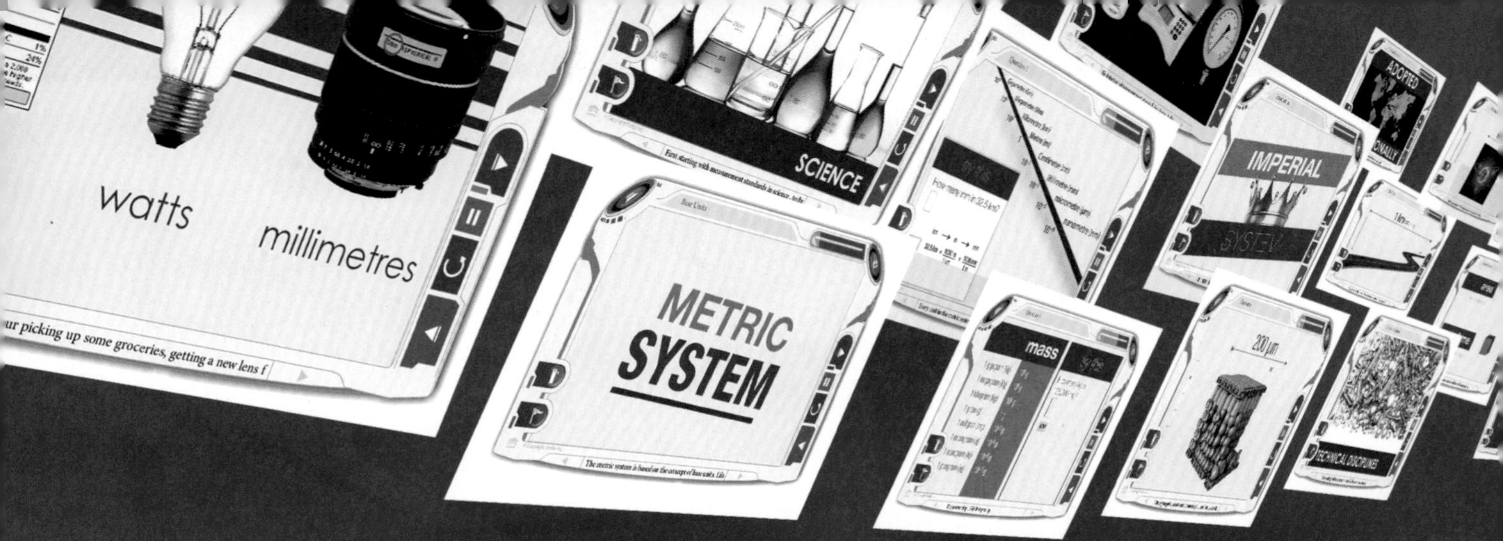

7 UNITS OF MEASUREMENT

The primary ways to describe an object are by its length (how long is it?), mass (how heavy is it?), or capacity (how much space/volume does it occupy?). Each of these measurements can be expressed in different units. It is important that these units are well defined so that measurements made in different units may be converted to a common unit and compared. In this chapter, you will learn about the two major systems of measurements: the metric system that is used in most parts of the world, and the US Customary system that is mainly used in the USA. You will also learn about the different units of measurements for length, mass, and capacity used within each system, and the conversions of these units between the two systems in order to understand and interpret information such as how 90 km compares to 60 miles, 70 kg compares to 145 pounds, 55 litres compares to 20 gallons, etc. In addition, conversions among units of temperature will be discussed.

LEARNING OBJECTIVES

- Read, write, and interpret symbols and prefixes used in the metric and US Customary system of units.
- Convert within metric units of length, mass, and capacity.
- Convert within US Customary units of length, mass, and capacity.
- Convert between metric and US Customary units of length, mass, and capacity.
- Convert units of temperature between the Celsius scale, Fahrenheit scale, and Kelvin scale.

CHAPTER OUTLINE

7.1 | Metric System of Measurement

Introduction

The units of measurement in the metric system are derived from scientific principles. The **British units** of measurement, the subsequent **US Customary units** of measurement and the **Imperial units** of measurement are based on different initial standards, stemming from nature and everyday activities.

Length, weight, capacity (volume), temperature, etc. are measured using several different units of measurement. The two measurement systems generally in use are the **Metric system** and the **US Customary system.**

The metric system is widely used in science, medicine, technology, and engineering. Most of world trade utilizes the metric system of measurement. However, the USA and three other countries (Liberia, Yemen, and Myanmar) have not fully adapted to the metric system.

The metric system for measurement is simple to use and can be more easily understood than the US Customary system because in the metric system, all the units are related to one another by powers of ten.

Converting within Metric Units of Measurement

The metric system uses metre (m), gram (g), and litre (L) as the base units for the measurements of length, mass, and capacity, respectively. The Celsius (°C) scale is used for temperature.

In this section, you will learn how to convert the commonly used units for length, mass, and capacity within the following metric units:

- **Length:** kilometre (km), metre (m), centimetre (cm), and millimetre (mm)
- **Mass:** kilogram (kg), gram (g), and milligram (mg)
- **Capacity:** litre (L) and millilitre (mL)

The conversion factors that relate to the different units in the metric system, including the prefixes used, are shown in Table 7.1.

Table 7.1 **Conversion Factors**

Prefix	Symbol	Factor	Factor in Word	Factor in Powers of 10
kilo-	k	1,000	Thousand	10^3
hecto-	h	100	Hundred	10^2
deca-	da	10	Ten	10^1
	Base Unit	**1**		
deci-	d	$\frac{1}{10} = 0.1$	One-tenth	10^{-1}
centi-	c	$\frac{1}{100} = 0.01$	One-hundredth	10^{-2}
milli-	m	$\frac{1}{1{,}000} = 0.001$	One-thousandth	10^{-3}

ne prefix and symbol for nits from kilo- to milli- e written in lower case.

ne **Base Unit** is etre (for length), am (for mass), and re (for capacity).

ne prefixes hecto-, deca-, d deci-units are usually ot used as units of easurement for length, ass, and capacity. The efix centi- is used only the measurement of ngth, as in centimetre.

Converting units within the metric system involves moving the decimal point to the right or to the left, by the appropriate number of places (which is the same as multiplying or dividing by the required powers of 10).

The conversion within the units of measurement can also be shown in a horizontal line diagram, in order from the largest to the smallest.

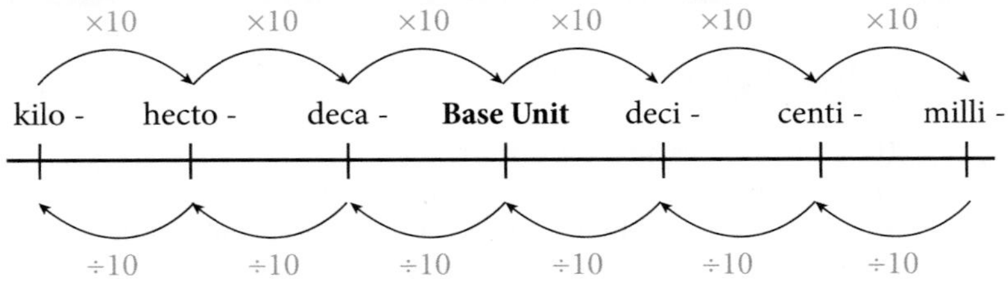

The conversion from a larger unit to a smaller unit represents moving the decimal point to the right or multiplying by powers of 10 as required.

For example, to convert 10.5 kilometres (km) to metres (m), move the decimal point 3 places to the right or multiply by 10^3 (or 1,000).

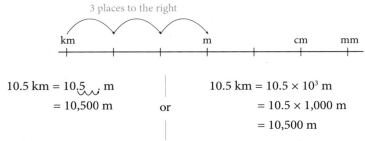

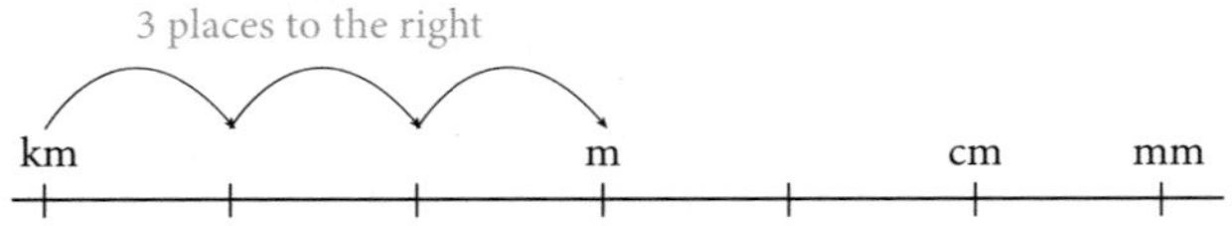

$$10.5 \text{ km} = 10.5\_\_\_ \text{ m} = 10{,}500 \text{ m}$$

or

$$10.5 \text{ km} = 10.5 \times 10^3 \text{ m} = 10.5 \times 1{,}000 \text{ m} = 10{,}500 \text{ m}$$

The conversion from a smaller unit to a larger unit represents moving the decimal point to the left or dividing by powers of 10 as required.

For example, to convert 425 centimetres (cm) to metres (m), move the decimal point 2 places to the left or divide by 10^2 (or 100).

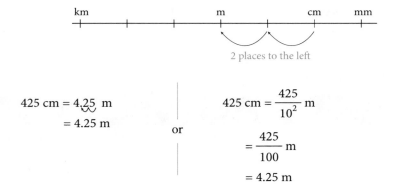

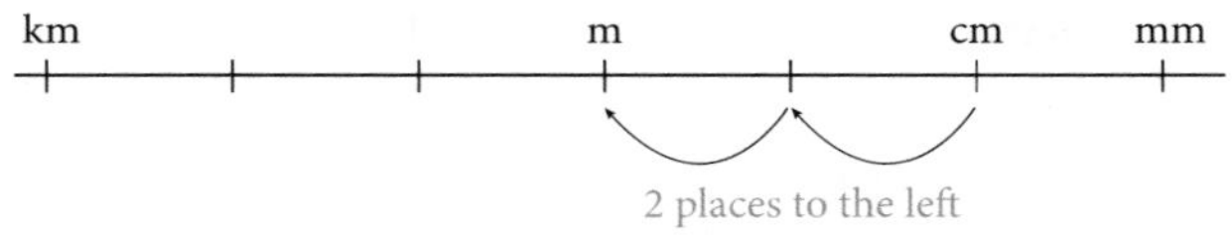

$$425 \text{ cm} = 4.25 \text{ m} = 4.25 \text{ m}$$

or

$$425 \text{ cm} = \frac{425}{10^2} \text{ m} = \frac{425}{100} \text{ m} = 4.25 \text{ m}$$

Length

Converting from larger units to smaller units	Converting from smaller units to larger units
$1 \text{ km} = (1 \times 1{,}000) \text{ m} = 1{,}000 \text{ m}$	$1 \text{ m} = \left(\frac{1}{1{,}000}\right) \text{km} = 0.001 \text{ km}$
$1 \text{ m} = (1 \times 100) \text{ cm} = 100 \text{ cm}$	$1 \text{ cm} = \left(\frac{1}{100}\right) \text{m} = 0.01 \text{ m}$
$1 \text{ cm} = (1 \times 10) \text{ mm} = 10 \text{ mm}$	$1 \text{ mm} = \left(\frac{1}{10}\right) \text{cm} = 0.1 \text{ cm}$

Mass

metric ton or metric nne (t) = 1,000 kg

Converting from larger units to smaller units	Converting from smaller units to larger units
$1 \text{ kg} = (1 \times 1{,}000) \text{ g} = 1{,}000 \text{ g}$	$1 \text{ g} = \left(\frac{1}{1{,}000}\right) \text{kg} = 0.001 \text{ kg}$
$1 \text{ g} = (1 \times 1{,}000) \text{ mg} = 1{,}000 \text{ mg}$	$1 \text{ mg} = \left(\frac{1}{1{,}000}\right) \text{g} = 0.001 \text{ g}$

Capacity

e capitalized 'L' is sed to represent litre in der to avoid confusion ith the number 1.

cubic metre or metre be (m³) = 1,000 L

Converting from larger units to smaller units	Converting from smaller units to larger units
$1 \text{ L} = (1 \times 1{,}000) \text{ mL} = 1{,}000 \text{ mL}$	$1 \text{ mL} = \left(\frac{1}{1{,}000}\right) \text{L} = 0.001 \text{ L}$

Example 7.1-a

Converting Measurements

Convert the following measurements:

(i) 7.5 cm to millimetres (ii) 1,120 cm to metres

(iii) 2.56 kg to grams (iv) 21,750 mL to litres

Solution

(i) 7.5 cm to millimetres:

$7.5 \text{ cm} = 7.5 \times 10 \text{ mm} = 75 \text{ mm}$

(same as 7.5 = 75 mm)

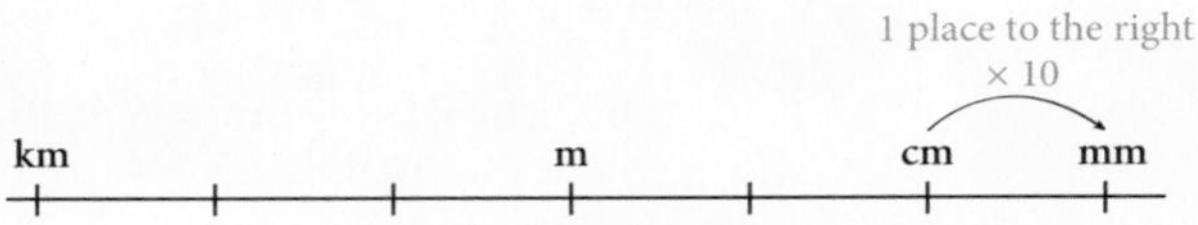

(ii) 1,120 cm to metres:

$$1{,}120 \text{ cm} = \frac{1{,}120}{100} \text{ m} = 11.2 \text{ m}$$

(same as 1,120 = 11.2 m)

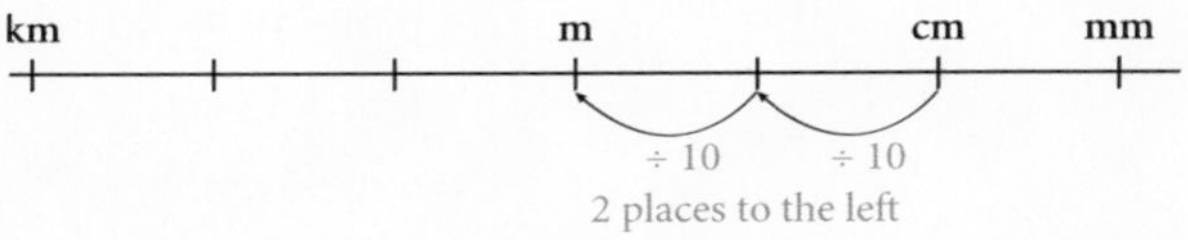

(iii) 2.56 kg to grams:

$2.56 \text{ kg} = 2.56 \times 1{,}000 \text{ g} = 2{,}560 \text{ g}$

(same as 256 = 2,560 g)

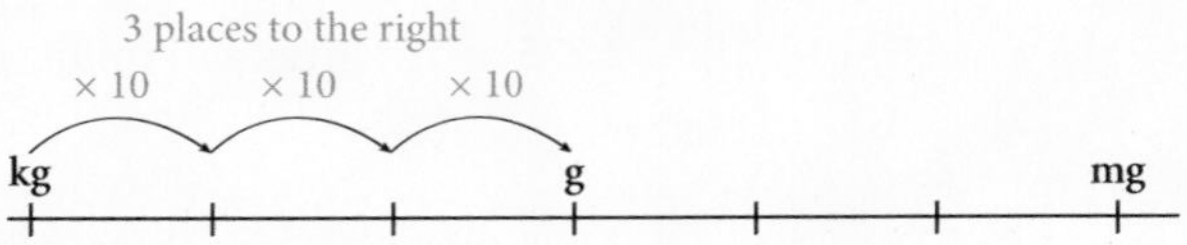

(iv) 21,750 mL to litres:

$$21{,}750 \text{ mL} = \frac{21{,}750}{1{,}000} \text{ L} = 21.75 \text{ L}$$

(same as 21,750 = 21.75 L)

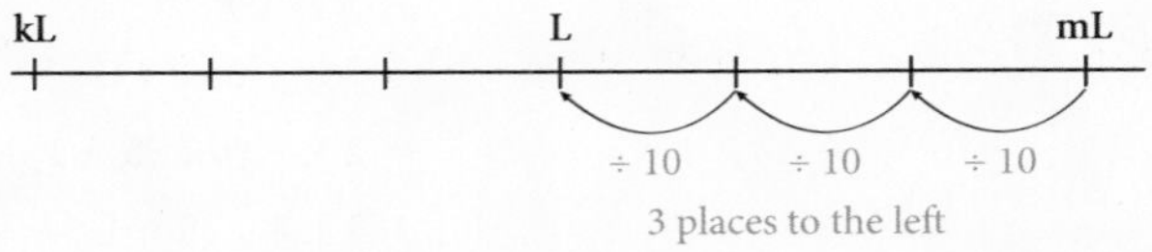

Example 7.1-b

Converting Measurements in Multiple Units

Convert the following measurements:

(i) 12 m 25 cm to centimetres (ii) 2 kg 456 g to grams (iii) 3 L 75 mL to millilitres

Solution

(i) 12 m 25 cm to centimetres:

$$\begin{aligned} 12 \text{ m } 25 \text{ cm} &= 12 \text{ m} + 25 \text{ cm} \\ &= (12 \times 100) \text{ cm} + 25 \text{ cm} \\ &= 1{,}200 \text{ cm} + 25 \text{ cm} \\ &= 1{,}225 \text{ cm} \end{aligned}$$

Therefore, 12 m 25 cm is equal to 1,225 cm.

Solution *continued*

(ii) 2 kg 456 g to grams:

$$2 \text{ kg } 456 \text{ g} = 2 \text{ kg} + 456 \text{ g}$$
$$= (2 \times 1{,}000) \text{ g} + 456 \text{ g}$$
$$= 2{,}000 \text{ g} + 456 \text{ g}$$
$$= 2{,}456 \text{ g}$$

Therefore, 2 kg 456 g is equal to 2,456 g.

(iii) 3 L 75 mL to millilitres:

$$3 \text{ L } 75 \text{ mL} = 3 \text{ L} + 75 \text{ mL}$$
$$= (3 \times 1{,}000) \text{ mL} + 75 \text{ mL}$$
$$= 3{,}000 \text{ mL} + 75 \text{ mL}$$
$$= 3{,}075 \text{ mL}$$

Therefore, 3 L 75 mL is equal to 3,075 mL.

Example 7.1-c **Converting Measurements and Expressing in Multiple Units**

Convert the following measurements:

(i) 695 cm to metres and centimetres

(ii) 2,275 mL to litres and millilitres

Solution

(i) 695 cm to metres and centimetres:

Method 1:

$$695 \text{ cm} = \left(\frac{695}{100}\right) \text{m} = 6.95 \text{ m}$$
$$= 6 \text{ m} + 0.95 \text{ m}$$
$$= 6 \text{ m} + (0.95 \times 100) \text{ cm}$$
$$= 6 \text{ m} + 95 \text{ cm}$$
$$= 6 \text{ m } 95 \text{ cm}$$

Method 2:

$$695 \text{ cm} = 600 \text{ cm} + 95 \text{ cm}$$
$$= \left(\frac{600}{100}\right) \text{m} + 95 \text{ cm}$$
$$= 6 \text{ m } 95 \text{ cm}$$

Therefore, 695 cm is equal to 6 m 95 cm.

(ii) 2,275 mL to litres and millilitres:

Method 1:

$$2{,}275 \text{ mL} = \left(\frac{2{,}275}{1{,}000}\right) \text{L} = 2.275 \text{ L}$$
$$= 2 \text{ L} + 0.275 \text{ L}$$
$$= 2 \text{ L} + (0.275 \times 1{,}000) \text{ mL}$$
$$= 2 \text{ L} + 275 \text{ mL}$$
$$= 2 \text{ L } 275 \text{ mL}$$

Method 2:

$$2{,}275 \text{ mL} = 2{,}000 \text{ mL} + 275 \text{ mL}$$
$$= \left(\frac{2{,}000}{1{,}000}\right) \text{L} + 275 \text{ mL}$$
$$= 2 \text{ L } 275 \text{ mL}$$

Therefore, 2,275 mL is equal to 2 L 275 mL.

Example 7.1-d **Converting Measurements Involving Two Steps**

Convert the following measurements:

(i) 5 km 20 m to centimetres

(ii) 3,125,000 mg to kilograms and grams

Solution

(i) 5 km 20 m to centimetres:

Method 1:

Step 1: Convert 5 km 20 m to metres,

$$\begin{aligned} 5 \text{ km } 20 \text{ m} &= 5 \text{ km} + 20 \text{ m} \\ &= (5 \times 1{,}000) \text{ m} + 20 \text{ m} \\ &= 5{,}000 \text{ m} + 20 \text{ m} \\ &= 5{,}020 \text{ m} \end{aligned}$$

Step 2: Convert 5,020 m to centimetres,

$$\begin{aligned} 5{,}020 \text{ m} &= (5{,}020 \times 100) \text{ cm} \\ &= 502{,}000 \text{ cm} \end{aligned}$$

Method 2:

$$\begin{aligned} 5 \text{ km } 20 \text{ m} &= 5 \text{ km} + 20 \text{ m} \\ &= (5 \times 10^5) \text{ cm} + (20 \times 10^2) \text{ cm} \\ &= 500{,}000 \text{ cm} + 2{,}000 \text{ cm} \\ &= 502{,}000 \text{ cm} \end{aligned}$$

Therefore, 5 km 20 m is equal to 502,000 cm.

(ii) 3,125,000 mg to kilograms and grams:

Method 1:

Step 1: Convert 3,125,000 mg to grams

$$\begin{aligned} 3{,}125{,}000 \text{ mg} &= \left(\frac{3{,}125{,}000}{1{,}000}\right) \text{g} \\ &= 3{,}125 \text{ g} \end{aligned}$$

Step 2: Convert 3,125 g to kilograms and grams

$$\begin{aligned} 3{,}125 \text{ g} &= \left(\frac{3{,}125}{1{,}000}\right) \text{kg} \\ &= 3.125 \text{ kg} \\ &= 3 \text{ kg} + 0.125 \text{ kg} \\ &= 3 \text{ kg} + (0.125 \times 1{,}000) \text{ g} \\ &= 3 \text{ kg} + 125 \text{ g} \\ &= 3 \text{ kg } 125 \text{ g} \end{aligned}$$

Method 2:

$$\begin{aligned} 3{,}125{,}000 \text{ mg} &= \left(\frac{3{,}125{,}000}{10^6}\right) \text{kg} \\ &= 3.125 \text{ kg} \\ &= 3 \text{ kg} + 0.125 \text{ kg} \\ &= 3 \text{ kg} + (0.125 \times 10^3) \text{ g} \\ &= 3 \text{ kg} + 125 \text{ g} \\ &= 3 \text{ kg } 125 \text{ g} \end{aligned}$$

Therefore, 3,125,000 mg is equal to 3 kg 125 g.

Example 7.1-e **Word Problems Involving Conversion of Measurements**

Megan bought 1.5 kg of flour and used 925 g of it. Calculate the quantity of flour remaining, in grams.

Solution

Since the answer needs to be expressed in grams, convert all measurements into grams.

$$\begin{aligned} 1.5 \text{ kg} &= (1.5 \times 1{,}000) \text{ g} \quad [\text{using } 1 \text{ kg} = 1{,}000 \text{ g}] \\ &= 1{,}500 \text{ g} \end{aligned}$$

As she used 925 g of flour, this needs to be subtracted from the total.

$$\begin{aligned} \text{Remaining flour} &= (1{,}500 - 925) \text{ g} \\ &= 575 \text{ g} \end{aligned}$$

Therefore, the quantity of flour remaining is 575 g.

7.1 | Exercises

Answers to odd-numbered problems are available at the end of the textbook.

Calculate the missing values in Problems 1 to 8.

1.

	metres (m)	centimetres (cm)	millimetres (mm)
a.	2.40	?	?
b.	?	860	?
c.	?	?	34,420

2.

	metres (m)	centimetres (cm)	millimetres (mm)
a.	1.20	?	?
b.	?	975	?
c.	?	?	23,170

3.

	metres (m)	centimetres (cm)	millimetres (mm)
a.	0.25	?	?
b.	?	58	?
c.	?	?	8,470

4.

	metres (m)	centimetres (cm)	millimetres (mm)
a.	0.67	?	?
b.	?	95	?
c.	?	?	5,200

5.

	kilometres (km)	metres (m)	centimetres (cm)
a.	1.62	?	?
b.	?	2,390	?
c.	?	?	2,320

6.

	kilometres (km)	metres (m)	centimetres (cm)
a.	1.25	?	?
b.	?	1,454	?
c.	?	?	1,190

7.

	kilometres (km)	metres (m)	centimetres (cm)
a.	0.65	?	?
b.	?	154	?
c.	?	?	1,770

8.

	kilometres (km)	metres (m)	centimetres (cm)
a.	0.17	?	?
b.	?	230	?
c.	?	?	9,400

For Problems 9 to 12, convert the measurements to the units indicated.

9. a. 23 m 21 cm = ___ cm b. 16 cm 7 mm = ___ mm c. 5 km 252 m = ___ m
10. a. 7 m 49 cm = ___ cm b. 45 cm 8 mm = ___ mm c. 2 km 725 m = ___ m
11. a. 335 cm = ___ m ___ cm b. 603 mm = ___ cm ___ mm c. 1,487 m = ___ km ___ m
12. a. 793 cm = ___ m ___ cm b. 379 mm = ___ cm ___ mm c. 6,745 m = ___ km ___ m
13. Arrange the following measurements in order from smallest to largest:
    0.15 km, 150,800 mm, 155 m, 15,200 cm
14. Arrange the following measurements in order from largest to smallest:
    19,750 cm, 1.97 km, 1,950 m, 195,700 mm
15. The distance between my house and the office is 1.7 km. I walked 925 m. How many more metres would I have to walk to reach the office?
16. In a 2.5 km race, there is a checkpoint at 875 m from the finish line. Calculate the distance, in metres, that I would have to run to reach the checkpoint.
17. Ali is 1.75 m tall. Eric is 30 mm taller than Ali. Calculate Eric's height, in centimetres.
18. Five-year-old Aran is 1.2 m tall. His sister, Girija, is 40 mm taller than him. Calculate Girija's height, in centimetres.

Calculate the missing values in Problems 19 to 26.

19.

	kilograms (kg)	grams (g)
a.	2.62	?
b.	?	6,750

20.

	kilograms (kg)	grams (g)
a.	3.79	?
b.	?	8,620

21.

	kilograms (kg)	grams (g)
a.	0.84	?
b.	?	580

22.

	kilograms (kg)	grams (g)
a.	0.32	?
b.	?	930

23.

	kilograms (kg)	grams (g)	milligrams (mg)
a.	1.65	?	?
b.	?	4,950	?
c.	?	?	6,440

24.

	kilograms (kg)	grams (g)	milligrams (mg)
a.	2.45	?	?
b.	?	8,700	?
c.	?	?	3,890

25.

	kilograms (kg)	grams (g)	milligrams (mg)
a.	0.76	?	?
b.	?	35,760	?
c.	?	?	50,300

26.

	kilograms (kg)	grams (g)	milligrams (mg)
a.	0.45	?	?
b.	?	25,090	?
c.	?	?	20,080

For Problems 27 to 30, convert the measurements to the units indicated.

27. a. 18 kg 79 g = ___ g   b. 2 kg 116 mg = ___ mg   c. 3 t 74 kg = ___ kg

28. a. 7 kg 89 g = ___ g   b. 14 kg 547 mg = ___ mg   c. 15 t 90 kg = ___ kg

29. a. 5,903 g = ___ kg ___ g   b. 2,884 mg = ___ g ___ mg   c. 9,704 kg = ___ t ___ kg

30. a. 5,014 g = ___ kg ___ g   b. 6,629 mg = ___ g ___ mg   c. 3,075 kg = ___ t ___ kg

31. Arrange the following measurements in order from smallest to largest:
    0.075 t, 123,200 g, 850,250 mg, 125 kg
32. Arrange the following measurements in order from largest to smallest:
    0.025 t, 50,750 mg, 125,700 g, 27 kg
33. If one tablespoon of salt weighs 5.5 g, how many tablespoons of salt are there in a box containing 1.1 kg of salt?
34. If a bowl can hold 40 g of cereal, how many bowls of cereal will you obtain from a box that has 1.35 kg of cereal?
35. Linda is baking a cake. She bought 0.75 kg of sugar and used 575 g of it. Calculate the quantity of sugar left, in grams.
36. Ben bought 1.3 kg of meat and cooked 650 g of it for dinner. Calculate the quantity of meat left, in grams.
37. 450 g of butter cost $3.25. At this price, how much will it cost to buy 2.25 kg of butter?
38. 250 g of cheese cost $2.75. At this price, how much will it cost to buy 2 kg of cheese?

Calculate the missing values in Problems 39 to 42.

39.

	litre (L)	millilitre (mL)
a.	3.25	?
b.	?	5,060

40.

	litre (L)	millilitre (mL)
a.	1.75	?
b.	?	1,975

41.

	litre (L)	millilitre (mL)
a.	0.045	?
b.	?	220

42.

	litre (L)	millilitre (mL)
a.	0.015	?
b.	?	5,730

For Problems 43 to 46, convert the measurements to the units indicated.

43. a. 5 L 85 mL = ___ L b. 2 L 5 mL = ___ L
44. a. 9 L 25 mL = ___ L b. 1 L 205 mL = ___ L
45. a. 2,708 mL = ___ L ___ mL b. 12,080 mL = ___ L ___ mL
46. a. 6,503 mL = ___ L ___ mL b. 32,096 mL = ___ L ___ mL
47. A bottle can hold 900 mL of orange juice. Calculate the total volume of orange juice in five bottles. Express the answer in litres.
48. Andy drinks 250 mL of milk every day. Calculate the quantity of milk he will require for 7 days. Express the answer in litres.
49. A milk carton contains 1.75 L of milk. If three glasses with a volume of 320, mL, each are filled with milk from the packet, how much milk will be left in the carton? Express the answer in millilitres.
50. A bottle can hold 1.5 L of wine. If four glasses with a volume of 280 mL, each, are filled with wine from the bottle, how much wine will be left in the bottle? Express the answer in millilitres.

7.2 | US Customary System of Measurement

In the United States, units in the **US Customary system** are primarily used for the purposes of measurements. **Imperial units** of measurement were historically used in the British Commonwealth countries.

While the Imperial and US Customary systems are very similar, they are not identical. There are a number of differences between them.

For example,

- The imperial ton is 2,240 pounds, whereas the US ton is 2,000 pounds. (1 U.S. ton = 0.893 Imperial ton)
- The imperial gallon is the volume of 10 pounds of water, whereas the US gallon is the volume of 81/3 pounds of water. (1 U.S. gallon = 0.833 Imperial gallons)

The US Customary system uses the yard (yd), the pound (lb), and the gallon (gal) as the base units for the measurements of length, mass, and capacity, respectively. The Fahrenheit (°F) scale is used for temperature.

In the United States, many items are measured using US Customary units. For example, road distance is measured in miles, butter is measured in pounds, and gasoline is measured in gallons.

The **base unit** is yard (for length), pound (for mass), and gallon (for capacity).

In this section, you will learn how to convert within the commonly used units for length, mass, and capacity within the following US Customary units:

- **Length:** mile (mi), yard (yd), foot (ft), and inch (in)
- **Mass:** ton (ton), pound (lb), and ounce (oz)
- **Capacity:** gallon (gal), quart (qt), pint (pt), cups (c), and fluid ounce (fl oz)

Converting within US Customary Units of Measurements

Length

- 1 mile is 1,760 yd or 5,280 feet — 1 mi = 1,760 yd = 5,280 ft
- 1 yard is 3 feet — 1 yd = 3 ft
- 1 foot is 12 inches — 1 ft = 12 in

Mass

- 1 ton is 2,000 pounds 1 ton = 2,000 lb
- 1 pound is 16 ounces 1 lb = 16 oz

The US Customary unit for ton is called 'short ton' and is represented by the word 'ton'. This is to distinguish it from the metric ton that has the symbol 't', where t = 1,000 kg.

Capacity

- 1 gallon is 4 quarts 1 gal = 4 qt
- 1 quart is 2 pints 1 qt = 2 pt
- 1 pint is 2 cups 1 pt = 2 c
- 1 cup is 8 fluid ounces 1 c = 8 fl oz

There are a number of methods or ways for converting measurements from one unit to the other. In Section 7.1, in converting units within the metric system, we multiplied or divided by powers of 10 because factors that relate to the different units in the metric system are in the order of 10, 100, 1,000, $\frac{1}{10}, \frac{1}{100}, \frac{1}{1,000}$, etc.

Converting units within the US Customary system can be done using various methods. Sometimes, conversions can be performed easily by using direct multiplication or division, using the conversion factors as shown in the diagram below.

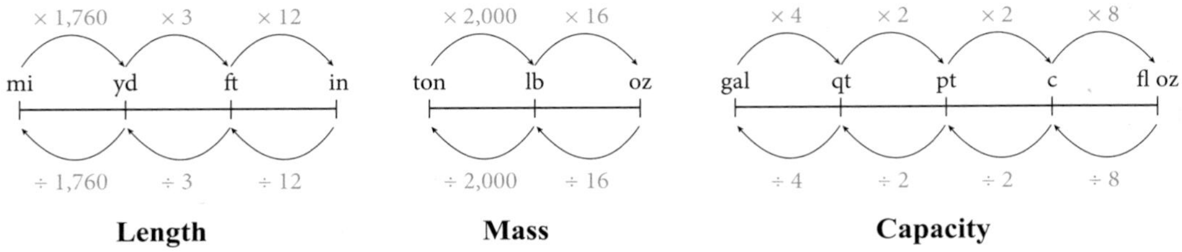

For example, since 1 yd = 3 ft and 1 ft = 12 in, in order to convert 5 yards to inches, multiply by first converting yards to feet and then feet to inches.

i.e., 5 yd = 5 × 3 ft = 15 ft
= 15 ft
= 15 × 12 in
= 180 in

Example 7.2-a **Converting a Measurement with Multiple Units to One with a Single Unit, Using Direct Multiplication**

Convert the following measurements:

(i) 2 ft 10 in to inches (ii) 5 lb 9 oz to ounces (iii) 2 gal 3 qt to quarts

Solution

(i) 2 ft 10 in to inches:

2 ft 10 in = 2 ft + 10 in
= (2 × 12) in + 10 in [using 1 ft = 12 in, 2 feet = 2 × 12 inches]
= 24 in + 10 in
= 34 in

Therefore, 2 ft 10 in is equal to 34 in.

Solution *continued*

(ii) 5 lb 9 oz to ounces:

$$\begin{aligned} 5 \text{ lb } 9 \text{ oz} &= 5 \text{ lb} + 9 \text{ oz} \\ &= (5 \times 16) \text{ oz} + 9 \text{ oz} \qquad [\text{using } 1 \text{ lb} = 16 \text{ oz}, 5 \text{ lb} = 5 \times 16 \text{ oz}] \\ &= 80 \text{ oz} + 9 \text{ oz} \\ &= 89 \text{ oz} \end{aligned}$$

Therefore, 5 lb 9 oz is equal to 89 oz.

(iii) 2 gal 3 qt to quarts:

$$\begin{aligned} 2 \text{ gal } 3 \text{ qt} &= 2 \text{ gal} + 3 \text{ qt} \\ &= (2 \times 4) \text{ qt} + 3 \text{ qt} \qquad [\text{using } 1 \text{ gal} = 4 \text{ qt}, 2 \text{ gal} = 2 \times 4 \text{ qt}] \\ &= 8 \text{ qt} + 3 \text{ qt} \\ &= 11 \text{ qt} \end{aligned}$$

Therefore, 2 gal 3 qt is equal to 11 qt.

Example 7.2-b **Converting a Measurement with a Single Unit to one with Multiple Units, Using Direct Division**

Convert the following measurements:

(i) 6,730 ft to miles and feet (ii) 73 oz to pounds and ounces (iii) 95 qt to gallons and quarts

Solution

Divide the given, smaller, unit by the known conversion factor using the method of long division. The quotient will be the larger unit and the remainder will be the smaller unit.

(i) 6,730 ft to miles and feet:

$$6{,}730 \text{ ft} = \left(\frac{6{,}730}{5{,}280}\right) \text{mi} \qquad [\text{using } 1 \text{ mile} = 5{,}280 \text{ ft}]$$

$$\begin{array}{r} 1 \\ 5{,}280\overline{)\,6{,}730} \\ \underline{5{,}280} \\ 1{,}450 \end{array}$$

$= 1 \text{ mi } 1{,}450 \text{ ft}$

Therefore, 6,730 ft is equal to 1 mi 1,450 ft.

(ii) 73 oz to pounds and ounces:

$$73 \text{ oz} = \left(\frac{73}{16}\right) \text{lb} \qquad [\text{using } 1 \text{ lb} = 16 \text{ oz}]$$

$$\begin{array}{r} 4 \\ 16\overline{)\,73} \\ \underline{64} \\ 9 \end{array}$$

$= 4 \text{ lb } 9 \text{ oz}$

Therefore, 73 oz is equal to 4 lb 9 oz.

(iii) 95 qt to gallons and quarts:

$$95 \text{ qt} = \left(\frac{95}{4}\right) \text{gal} \qquad [\text{using } 1 \text{ gal} = 4 \text{ qt}]$$

$$\begin{array}{r} 23 \\ 4\overline{)\,95} \\ \underline{8} \\ 15 \\ \underline{12} \\ 3 \end{array}$$

$= 23 \text{ gal } 3 \text{ qt}$

Therefore, 95 qt is equal to 23 gal 3 qt.

There are times when we need to apply a method to convert between units. In this section, you will learn about two commonly used methods used to perform conversions of units within the US Customary system:

(i) the conversion factor (ratio) method , also known as dimensional analysis, and

(ii) the proportion method.

Conversion Factor (Ratio) Method

Changing a measurement from one unit to another can be achieved using the conversion factor (ratio) method, which is also known as dimensional analysis.

For a known relationship between the two units, we can find two conversion factors to use in converting units.

For example, consider the relationship 1 foot = 12 inches.

Dividing both sides by 12 inches,

$$\frac{1\text{ foot}}{12\text{ inches}} = \frac{\cancel{12\text{ inches}}}{\cancel{12\text{ inches}}} = 1$$

Similarly, dividing both sides by 1 foot,

$$\frac{\cancel{1\text{ foot}}}{\cancel{1\text{ foot}}} = \frac{12\text{ inches}}{1\text{ foot}}$$

$$= \frac{12\text{ inches}}{1\text{ foot}}$$

Therefore, the relationship between two units can be written as two conversion factors or ratios, as in $\frac{1\text{ foot}}{12\text{ inches}}$ or $\frac{12\text{ inches}}{1\text{ foot}}$, both equaling 1.

Since the conversion factor is equal to 1, this can be used to multiply the given measurement to convert it from one unit to another.

Example 7.2-c

Finding Conversion Factors for a Given Relationship

Find the two conversion factors for the known relationship, 1 yard = 3 feet.

Solution

1 yard = 3 feet

Dividing both sides by 3 feet: $\frac{1\text{ yard}}{3\text{ feet}} = \frac{3\cancel{\text{ feet}}}{3\cancel{\text{ feet}}} = 1$

Similarly, dividing both sides by 1 yard: $\frac{1\cancel{\text{ yard}}}{1\cancel{\text{ yard}}} = \frac{3\text{ feet}}{1\text{ yard}} = 1$

Therefore, the two conversion factors are $\frac{1\text{ yard}}{3\text{ feet}}$ and $\frac{3\text{ feet}}{1\text{ yard}}$.

Example 7.2-d

Using a Conversion Factor to Convert Units of Measurements

Convert 90 in. to feet. Use 1 foot = 12 inches.

Solution

90 in. to feet:

Step 1: Write the two conversion factors: $\frac{1\text{ foot}}{12\text{ inches}}$ and $\frac{12\text{ inches}}{1\text{ foot}}$

Step 2: Write the measurement to be converted: 90 inches

Step 3: Identify the correct conversion factor that will cancel the unit to be converted (in this case, the conversion factor that has the unit 'inches' in its denominator): $\frac{1\text{ foot}}{12\text{ inches}}$

Step 4: Multiply the measurement to be converted by this conversion factor:

$90\text{ inches} \times \frac{1\text{ foot}}{12\text{ inches}}$

Solution *continued*

Step 5: Cross-cancel the units that appear in both the numerator and denominator and simplify the fraction to get the answer:

$$90 \text{ inches} = 90 \cancel{\text{inches}} \times \frac{1 \text{ foot}}{12 \cancel{\text{inches}}}$$

$$= \left(\frac{90}{12}\right) \text{feet}$$

$$= 7.5 \text{ feet}$$

Therefore, 90 inches is equal to 7.5 feet.

Since the conversion factor has a value equal to 1, this conversion factor method can be expanded to perform conversions in a single step.

For example, knowing that 1 foot = 12 inches and 1 yard = 3 feet, the conversion factor can be expanded as follows:

$$\frac{1 \text{ foot}}{12 \text{ inches}} \times \frac{1 \text{ yard}}{3 \text{ feet}}$$

When simplified,

$$\frac{1 \cancel{\text{foot}}}{12 \text{ inches}} \times \frac{1 \text{ yard}}{3 \cancel{\text{feet}}} = \frac{1 \text{ yard}}{36 \text{ inches}}$$

Therefore, this results in a new conversion factor of $\frac{1 \text{ yard}}{36 \text{ inches}}$; i.e., 1 yard = 36 inches.

Example 7.2-e

Using the Expanded Conversion Factor Method to Convert the Units of Measurements

Convert the following measurements:

(i) 5.9 yd to inches

(ii) 4.5 gal to cups

Solution

(i) 5.9 yd to inches:

Multiply with the conversion factor $\left(\frac{3 \text{ feet}}{1 \text{ yard}}\right)$ and $\left(\frac{12 \text{ inches}}{1 \text{ feet}}\right)$ to cross-cancel the units 'yards' and 'feet'.

$$5.9 \text{ yards} = 5.9 \cancel{\text{yards}} \times \left(\frac{3 \cancel{\text{feet}}}{1 \cancel{\text{yard}}}\right) \times \left(\frac{12 \text{ inches}}{1 \cancel{\text{feet}}}\right)$$

$$= 5.9 \times 3 \times 12 \text{ in.}$$

$$= 212.4 \text{ in.}$$

Therefore, 5.9 yd is equal to 212.4 in.

(ii) 4.5 gal to cups:

Multiply with the conversion factor $\left(\frac{4 \text{ quarts}}{1 \text{ gallon}}\right)$, $\left(\frac{2 \text{ pints}}{1 \text{ quart}}\right)$, and $\left(\frac{2 \text{ cups}}{1 \text{ pint}}\right)$ to cross-cancel the units 'gal', 'qt', and 'pt'.

$$4.5 \text{ gallons} = 4.5 \cancel{\text{gallons}} \times \left(\frac{4 \cancel{\text{quarts}}}{1 \cancel{\text{gallon}}}\right) \times \left(\frac{2 \cancel{\text{pints}}}{1 \cancel{\text{quart}}}\right) \times \left(\frac{2 \text{ cups}}{1 \cancel{\text{pint}}}\right)$$

$$= 4.5 \times 4 \times 2 \times 2 \text{ cups}$$

$$= 72 \text{ cups}$$

Therefore, 4.5 gal is equal to 72 c.

Proportion Method

When forming the proportion equation, the order in which the units of the terms in the ratio are written should be consistent on either side of the equation;

i.e., km : m = km : m

This is similar to the method learned in Chapter 4 (Ratios and Proportions).

In this method, we equate two sets of ratios, where one of the ratios is formed from a given or known relationship. The second ratio is formed from the question asked, using the value for the unit to be converted and the unit required. These two ratios are equated to form the proportion equation and the unknown unit is solved for by using cross-multiplication and simplification.

Example 7.2-f **Using the Proportion Method to Convert Units of Measurements**

Convert the following measurements:

(i) 8.5 miles to feet (ii) 25 pints to gallons

Solution

(i) 8.5 miles to feet:

$$\text{mi} : \text{ft} = \text{mi} : \text{ft}$$

$$8.5 : x = 1 : 5{,}280 \qquad \text{[Using 1 mile = 5,280 feet]}$$

In fractional form, $\frac{8.5}{x} = \frac{1}{5{,}280}$

Cross-multiplying, $x = 8.5 \times 5{,}280 = 44{,}880$ ft.

Therefore, 8.5 mi is 44,880 ft.

(ii) 25 pints to gallons:

First, converting from pints to quarts,

$$\text{qt} : \text{pt} = \text{qt} : \text{pt}$$

$$x : 25 = 1 : 2 \qquad \text{[Using 1 qt = 2 pt]}$$

In fractional form, $\frac{x}{25} = \frac{1}{2}$

Cross-multiplying, $2x = 25$

$$x = \frac{25}{2} = 12.5$$

i.e., 25 pt = 12.5 qt

Converting from quarts to gallons,

$$\text{gal} : \text{qt} = \text{gal} : \text{qt}$$

$$x : 12.5 = 1 : 4 \qquad \text{[Using 1 gal = 4 qt]}$$

In fractional form, $\frac{x}{12.5} = \frac{1}{4}$

Cross-multiplying, $4x = 12.5$

$$x = \frac{12.5}{4} = 3.125$$

i.e., 25 pt = 12.5 qt = 3.125 gal

Therefore, 25 pt is equal to 3.125 gal.

Note: The Conversion Factor method is preferable over the Proportion method when two or more steps are involved in the conversion.

For example, converting 25 pt to gallons in Example 7.2-f can be performed using the Conversion Factor method, as follows:

Convert 25 pt to gallons,

1st conversion factor of 1 qt = 2 pt
2nd conversion factor of 1 gal = 4 qt

$$25 \text{ pt} = 25 \text{ pt} \times \left(\frac{1 \text{ qt}}{2 \text{ pt}}\right) \times \left(\frac{1 \text{ gal}}{4 \text{ qt}}\right)$$

$$= \left(\frac{25}{2 \times 4}\right) \text{gal} = 3.125 \text{ gal}$$

Therefore, 25 pt is equal to 3.125 gal.

Example 7.2-g **Converting Measurements in a Word Problem**

A wire of length 10.5 yd is cut into 7 equal pieces. Calculate the length of each piece, in feet.

Solution

Since the answer needs to be measured in feet, convert all measurements into feet before doing any calculations.

$10.5 \text{ yd} : x = 1 \text{ yd} : 3 \text{ ft}$

$x = 10.5 \text{ x } 3$

$x = 31.5 \text{ ft}$

If the rod is cut into seven equal pieces, then the total length needs to be divided by seven.

$$\frac{31.5 \text{ ft}}{7} = 4.5 \text{ ft}$$

Therefore, the length of each piece is 4.5 ft.

Note: It is also correct to divide the rod into seven pieces, before converting that length from yards to feet.

7.2 | Exercises

Answers to odd-numbered problems are available at the end of the textbook.

Calculate the missing values in Problems 1 to 8.

1.

	yard (yd)	feet (ft)	inch (in.)
a.	42	?	?
b.	?	48	?
c.	?	?	648

2.

	yard (yd)	feet (ft)	inch (in.)
a.	84	?	?
b.	?	72	?
c.	?	?	540

3.

	yard (yd)	feet (ft)	inch (in.)
a.	46.5	?	?
b.	?	22.5	?
c.	?	?	2,880

4.

	yard (yd)	feet (ft)	inch (in.)
a.	67.5	?	?
b.	?	37.5	?
c.	?	?	3,960

5.

	miles (mi)	yard (yd)	feet (ft)
a.	3	?	?
b.	?	6,160	?
c.	?	?	10,560

6.

	miles (mi)	yard (yd)	feet (ft)
a.	2	?	?
b.	?	9,680	?
c.	?	?	18,480

7.

	miles (mi)	yard (yd)	feet (ft)
a.	2.25	?	?
b.	?	2,200	?
c.	?	?	6,192

8.

	miles (mi)	yard (yd)	feet (ft)
a.	42.5	?	?
b.	?	3,080	?
c.	?	?	25,080

In Problems 9 to 12, convert the measurements to the units indicated.

9. a. 12 yd 1.5 ft = ___ ft b. 11 ft 10 in. = ___ in. c. 1 mi 121 yd = ___ yd

10. a. 15 yd 7.5 ft = ___ ft b. 12 ft 11 in. = ___ in. c. 2 mi 45 yd = ___ yd

11. a. 78 ft = ___ yd ___ ft b. 570 in. = ___ ft ___ in. c. 5,705 yd = ___ mi ___ yd

12. a. 56 ft = ___ yd ___ ft b. 420 in. = ___ ft ___ in. c. 7,350 yd = ___ mi ___ yd

13. A sheet of paper is 7 ft long. A piece that is 5 ft 9 in. long is cut from it. Calculate the length of the paper left, in inches.
14. An iron rod is 7 ft in length. One piece of 5 ft 3 in. is cut from it. Calculate the length of the remaing portion of the rod, in inches.
15. A rope of length 13.5 yd is cut into 9 equal pieces. Calculate the length of each piece, in feet.
16. A wooden fence of length 32 yd is made up of 12 equal panels. Calculate the length of each panel, in feet.
17. The length of a river is 39,600 ft. Calculate the length of the river, in miles.
18. The height of a mountain is 81,840 ft. Calculate the height of the mountain, in miles.

Calculate the missing values in Problems 19 to 26.

19.

	pound (lb)	ounce (oz)
a.	?	288
b.	8	?

20.

	pound (lb)	ounce (oz)
a.	?	384
b.	12	?

21.

	pound (lb)	ounce (oz)
a.	?	232
b.	25.25	?

22.

	pound (lb)	ounce (oz)
a.	?	296
b.	19.75	?

23.

	ton (ton)	pound (lb)
a.	35	?
b.	?	14,500

24.

	ton (ton)	pound (lb)
a.	37	?
b.	?	23,500

25.

	ton (ton)	pound (lb)
a.	12.75	?
b.	?	65,000

26.

	ton (ton)	pound (lb)
a.	17.25	?
b.	?	47,000

In Problems 27 to 30, convert the measurements to the units indicated.

27. a. 11 lb 10 oz = ___ oz b. 2 ton 1,250 lb = ___ lb

28. a. 9 lb 3 oz = ___ oz b. 5 ton 1,175 lb = ___ lb

29. a. 55,825 lb = ___ ton ___ lb b. 150 oz = ___ lb ___ oz

30. a. 79,125 lb = ___ ton ___ lb b. 200 oz = ___ lb ___ oz

31. Arrange the following measurements in order from largest to smallest:
    34,400 oz, 1.2 ton, 2,250 lb
32. Arrange the following measurements in order from smallest to largest:
    0.95 ton, 1,920 lb, 29,760 oz
33. A cake weighing 2 lb 8 oz is cut into 8 equal portions. Calculate the weight of each piece, in ounces.
34. The weight of 12 cans of softdrink is 5 lb 4 oz. Calculate the weight of each can of soft drink, in ounces.

35. A wholesaler bought 1.25 tons of cashews. He wanted to sell them in packages of 2.5 pounds, each. Calculate the number of packages that can be made.

36. A bookstore received a shipment of 1,600 mathematics textbooks. The total weight of the shipment is 2.2 tons. Calculate the weight of each book, in pounds.

Calculate the missing values in Problems 37 to 44.

37.

	quart (qt)	pint (pt)	cup (c)
a.	22	?	?
b.	?	38	?
c.	?	?	68

38.

	quart (qt)	pint (pt)	cup (c)
a.	28	?	?
b.	?	26	?
c.	?	?	74

39.

	quart (qt)	pint (pt)	cup (c)
a.	32.5	?	?
b.	?	45	?
c.	?	?	94

40.

	quart (qt)	pint (pt)	cup (c)
a.	47.5	?	?
b.	?	51	?
c.	?	?	102

41.

	gallon (gal)	quart (qt)	pint (pt)
a.	12	?	?
b.	?	18	?
c.	?	?	56

42.

	gallon (gal)	quart (qt)	pint (pt)
a.	15	?	?
b.	?	24	?
c.	?	?	64

43.

	gallon (gal)	quart (qt)	pint (pt)
a.	7.5	?	?
b.	?	14	?
c.	?	?	50

44.

	gallon (gal)	quart (qt)	pint (pt)
a.	9.5	?	?
b.	?	22	?
c.	?	?	30

In Problems 45 to 48, convert the measurements to the units indicated.

45. a. 9 qt 1 pt = ___ pt   b. 15 pt 3 c = ___ c   c. 12 gal 1 qt = ___ qt

46. a. 14 qt 1 pt = ___ pt   b. 27 pt 1 c = ___ c   c. 17 gal 1 qt = ___ qt

47. a. 19 pt = ___ qt ___ pt   b. 39 c = ___ pt ___ c   c. 2 mi 45 yd = ___ yd

48. a. 23 pt = ___ qt ___ pt   b. 55 c = ___ pt ___ c   c. 75 qt = ___ gal ___ qt

49. Arrange the following measurements in order from smallest to largest:

    29 c, 6 qt, 14 pt, 2 gal

50. Arrange the following measurements in order from largest to smallest:

    45 c, 23 pt, 10 qt, 3 gal

51. Mythili drinks 2 c of milk every day. How many gallons of milk will she require for a month of 30 days?

52. If a family uses an average of 8 c of milk everyday, how many gallons of milk will be required for a week?

53. A juice container had 12 pt of juice. If 15 c of juice was used from the container, how many cups of juice is left in the container?

54. A water bottle contained 8 qt of spring water. If 25 c of water was used from the bottle, how many cups of water are left in the bottle?

7.3 | Conversion Between Metric and US Customary Units

Converting units between the metric and US Customary systems is achieved by using conversion tables. Conversion tables for the conversion of commonly used metric and US Customary units of measurement are provided below:

Length

- **Metric units:** kilometre (km), metre (m), centimetre (cm), and millimetre (mm)
- **US Customary units:** mile (mi), yard (yd), foot (ft), and inch (in.)

Conversion Table

US Customary Units	Metric Units
1 mi	1.609 km
1 yd	0.9144 m
1 ft	30.48 cm
1 in.	2.54 cm

Example 7.3-a

Converting Metric Units of Length to US Customary Units

Convert the following measurements:

(i) 250 km to miles (ii) 45 m to feet

Solution

(i) 250 km to miles:

Use $\left(\frac{1\text{ mi}}{1.609\text{ km}}\right)$ as the conversion factor to cross-cancel the unit 'km'.

$$\begin{aligned}250\text{ km} &= 250\cancel{\text{ km}} \times \left(\frac{1\text{ mi}}{1.609\cancel{\text{ km}}}\right)\\ &= 250 \times \frac{1}{1.609}\text{ mi}\\ &= 155.376009...\text{ mi}\\ &= 155.38\text{ mi}\end{aligned}$$

Therefore, 250 km is equal to 155.38 mi.

(ii) 45 m to feet:

Use $\left(\frac{100\text{ cm}}{1\text{ m}}\right)$ as the first conversion factor to cross-cancel the unit 'm' and $\left(\frac{1\text{ ft}}{30.48\text{ cm}}\right)$ as the second conversion factor to cross-cancel the unit 'cm'.

$$\begin{aligned}45\text{ m} &= 45\cancel{\text{ m}} \times \left(\frac{100\cancel{\text{ cm}}}{1\cancel{\text{ m}}}\right) \times \left(\frac{1\text{ ft}}{30.48\cancel{\text{ cm}}}\right)\\ &= 45 \times \frac{100}{30.48}\text{ ft}\\ &= 147.637795...\text{ ft}\\ &= 147.64\text{ ft}\end{aligned}$$

Therefore, 45 m is equal to147.64 ft.

Example 7.3-b

Converting US Customary Units of Length to Metric Units

Convert the following measurements:

(i) 8.75 yd to centimetres (ii) 2.5 mi to metres

Solution

(i) 8.75 yd to centimetres:

Use $\left(\frac{0.9144 \text{ m}}{1 \text{ yd}}\right)$ as the first conversion factor to cross-cancel the unit 'yd' and $\left(\frac{100 \text{ cm}}{1 \text{ m}}\right)$ as the second conversion factor to cross-cancel the unit 'm'.

$$8.75 \text{ yd} = 8.75 \cancel{\text{yd}} \times \left(\frac{0.9144 \cancel{\text{m}}}{1 \cancel{\text{yd}}}\right) \times \left(\frac{100 \text{ cm}}{1 \cancel{\text{m}}}\right)$$

$$= 8.75 \times 0.9144 \times 100 \text{ cm}$$

$$= 800.1 \text{ cm}$$

Therefore, 8.75 yd is equal to 800.1 cm.

(ii) 2.5 mi to metres:

Use $\left(\frac{1.609 \text{ km}}{1 \text{ mi}}\right)$ as the first conversion factor to cross-cancel the unit 'mi' and $\left(\frac{1{,}000 \text{ m}}{1 \text{ km}}\right)$ as the second conversion factor to cross-cancel the unit 'km'.

$$2.5 \text{ mi} = 2.5 \cancel{\text{mi}} \times \left(\frac{1.609 \cancel{\text{km}}}{1 \cancel{\text{mi}}}\right) \times \left(\frac{1{,}000 \text{ m}}{1 \cancel{\text{km}}}\right)$$

$$= 2.5 \times 1.609 \times 1{,}000 \text{ m}$$

$$= 4{,}022.5 \text{ m}$$

Therefore, 2.5 mi is equal to 4,022.5 m.

Mass

- **Metric units:** kilogram (kg), gram (g), and milligram (mg)
- **US Customary units:** ton (ton), pound (lb), and ounce (oz)

Conversion Table

US Customary Units	Metric Units
1 ton	907.2 kg
1 lb	0.454 kg
1 oz	28.35 g

Example 7.3-c

Converting Metric Units of Mass to US Customary Units

Convert the following measurements:

(i) 2.5 kg to pounds (ii) 400 g to ounces

Solution

(i) 2.5 kg to pounds:

Use $\left(\frac{1 \text{ lb}}{0.454 \text{ kg}}\right)$ as the conversion factor to cross-cancel the unit 'kg'.

Solution *continued*

$$2.5\text{ kg} = 2.5\,\cancel{\text{kg}} \times \left(\frac{1\text{ lb}}{0.454\,\cancel{\text{kg}}}\right)$$

$$= 2.5 \times \frac{1}{0.454}\text{ lb}$$

$$= 5.506607\ldots\text{ lb}$$

$$= 5.51\text{ lb}$$

Therefore, 2.5 kg is equal to 5.51 lb.

(ii) 400 g to ounces:

Use $\left(\frac{1\text{ oz}}{28.35\text{ g}}\right)$ as the conversion factor to cross cancel the unit 'g'.

$$400\text{ g} = 400\,\cancel{\text{g}} \times \left(\frac{1\text{ oz}}{28.35\,\cancel{\text{g}}}\right)$$

$$= 400 \times \frac{1}{28.35}\text{ oz}$$

$$= 14.109347\ldots\text{ oz}$$

$$= 14.11\text{ oz}$$

Therefore, 400 g is equal to 14.11 oz.

Example 7.3-d

Converting US Customary Units of Mass to Metric Units

Convert the following measurements:

(i) 1.75 lb to grams (ii) 225 oz to kilograms

Solution

(i) 1.75 lb to grams:

Use $\frac{0.454\text{ kg}}{1\text{ lb}}$ as the first conversion factor to cross-cancel the unit 'lb' and $\left(\frac{1{,}000\text{ g}}{1\text{ kg}}\right)$ as the second conversion factor to cross-cancel the unit 'kg'.

$$1.75\text{ lb} = 1.75\,\cancel{\text{lb}} \times \frac{0.454\,\cancel{\text{kg}}}{1\,\cancel{\text{lb}}} \times \left(\frac{1{,}000\text{ g}}{1\,\cancel{\text{kg}}}\right)$$

$$= 1.75 \times 0.454 \times 1{,}000\text{ grams}$$

$$= 794.5\text{ grams}$$

Therefore, 1.75 lb is equal to 794.5 g.

(ii) 225 oz to kilograms:

Use $\left(\frac{28.35\text{ g}}{1\text{ oz}}\right)$ as the first conversion factor to cross-cancel the unit 'oz' and $\left(\frac{1\text{ kg}}{1{,}000\text{ g}}\right)$ as the second conversion factor to cross-cancel the unit 'g'.

$$225\text{ oz} = 225\,\cancel{\text{oz}} \times \left(\frac{28.35\,\cancel{\text{g}}}{1\,\cancel{\text{oz}}}\right) \times \left(\frac{1\text{ kg}}{1{,}000\,\cancel{\text{g}}}\right)$$

$$= 225 \times \frac{28.35}{1{,}000}\text{ kg}$$

$$= 6.37875\text{ kg}$$

$$= 6.38\text{ kg}$$

Therefore, 225 oz is equal to 6.38 kg.

Capacity

- **Metric units:** litre (L) and millilitre (mL)
- **US Customary units:** gallon (gal), quart (qt), pint (pt), cups (c), and fluid ounce (fl oz)

Conversion Table

US Customary Units	Metric Units
1 gal	3.785 L
1 qt	0.946 L
1 pt	473.2 mL
1 c	236.6 mL
1 fl oz	29.57 mL

Example 7.3-e **Converting Metric Units of Capacity to US Customary Units**

Convert the following measurements:

(i) 60 L to gallons (ii) 425 mL to fluid ounces

Solution

(i) 60 L to gallons:

Use $\left(\frac{1 \text{ gal}}{3.785 \text{ L}}\right)$ as the conversion factor to cross-cancel the unit 'L'.

$$60 \text{ L} = 60 \cancel{\text{L}} \times \left(\frac{1 \text{ gal}}{3.785 \cancel{\text{L}}}\right)$$

$$= 60 \times \frac{1}{3.785} \text{ gal}$$

$$= 15.852047... \text{ gal}$$

$$= 15.85 \text{ gal}$$

Therefore, 60 L is equal to 15.85 gal.

(ii) 425 mL to fluid ounces:

Use $\left(\frac{1 \text{ fl oz}}{29.57 \text{ mL}}\right)$ as the conversion factor to cross-cancel the unit 'mL'.

$$425 \text{ mL} = 425 \cancel{\text{mL}} \times \left(\frac{1 \text{ fl oz}}{29.57 \cancel{\text{mL}}}\right)$$

$$= 425 \times \frac{1}{29.57} \text{ fl oz}$$

$$= 14.372675... \text{ fl oz}$$

$$= 14.37 \text{ fl oz}$$

Therefore, 425 mL is equal to14.37 fl oz.

Example 7.3-f **Converting US Customary Units of Capacity to Metric Units**

Convert the following measurements:

(i) 2.5 gal to litres (ii) 30 fl oz to litres

Solution

(i) 2.5 gal to litres:

Use $\left(\frac{3.785\text{ L}}{1\text{ gal}}\right)$ as the conversion factor to cross-cancel the unit 'gal'.

$$\begin{aligned}2.5\text{ gal} &= 2.5\,\cancel{\text{gal}} \times \left(\frac{3.785\text{ L}}{1\,\cancel{\text{gal}}}\right)\\ &= 2.5 \times 3.785\text{ L}\\ &= 9.4625\text{ L}\\ &= 9.46\text{ L}\end{aligned}$$

Therefore, 2.5 gal is equal to 9.46 L.

Useful Comparisons

- 1 kg is a little more than 2 pounds.
- 1 L is a little more than a quart.
- 1 km is a little more than half a mile.
- 1 m is a little more than a yard.
- 1 cm is a little less than half an inch.

(ii) 30 fl oz to litres:

Use $\left(\frac{29.57\text{ mL}}{1\text{ fl oz}}\right)$ as the first conversion factor to cross-cancel the unit 'fl oz' and $\left(\frac{1\text{ L}}{1{,}000\text{ mL}}\right)$ as the second conversion factor to cross-cancel the unit 'mL'.

$$\begin{aligned}30\text{ fl oz} &= 30\,\cancel{\text{fl oz}} \times \left(\frac{29.57\,\cancel{\text{mL}}}{1\,\cancel{\text{fl oz}}}\right) \times \left(\frac{1\text{ L}}{1{,}000\,\cancel{\text{mL}}}\right)\\ &= 30 \times \frac{29.57}{1{,}000}\text{ L}\\ &= 0.8871\text{ L}\\ &= 0.89\text{ L}\end{aligned}$$

Therefore, 30 fl oz is equal to 0.89 L.

Conversion of Temperature Scales

Celsius and Fahrenheit Scale

There are two main temperature scales in use:

(1) °C, the Celsius scale

(2) °F, the Fahrenheit scale

The Celsius scale (°C) is part of the metric system, used in most countries. The Fahrenheit scale (°F) is primarily used in the USA.

The Celsius scale (°C) derives from the basis that pure water, at sea level pressure, freezes at 0°C and boils at 100°C. The Fahrenheit scale (°F) derives from the basis that pure water, at sea level pressure, freezes at 32°F and boils at 212°F.

Therefore, the difference between the freezing and boiling points of water is 100° in the Celsius scale (100°C – 0°C) and 180° in the Fahrenheit scale (212°F – 32°F).

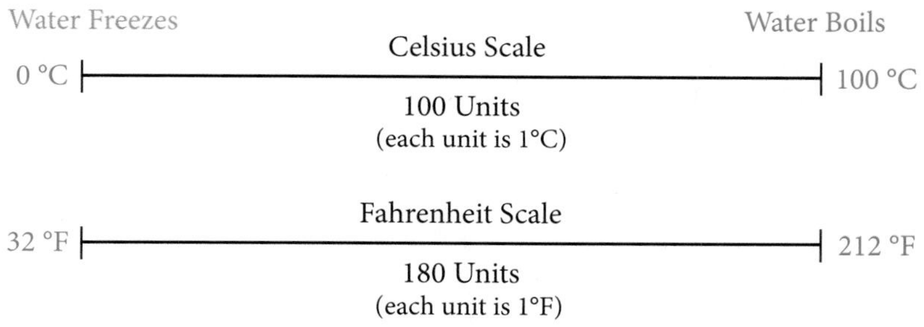

100 units in the Celsius scale, starting from 0°C, is equivalent to 180 units in the Fahrenheit scale, starting from 32°F.

Therefore, to convert from °C to °F, multiply °C by a factor of 1.80 $\left(=\frac{180}{100}\right)$ and add 32°.

$$°F = 1.80(°C) + 32°$$

Similarly, to convert from °F to °C, subtract 32°F and divide by 1.80.

$$°C = \frac{(°F - 32)}{1.80}$$

On a hot day, a temperature of 38°C is about 100°F and a room temperature of 73°F is about 23°C.

Conversion Table

°C to °F	$°F = 1.80(°C) + 32$
°F to °C	$°C = \frac{(°F - 32)}{1.80}$

Example 7.3-g Converting Between the Celsius (° C) Scale and Fahrenheit (° F) Scale

Convert the following:

(i) 25°C to Fahrenheit (ii) 90°F to Celsius

Solution

(i) 25°C to Fahrenheit:

$$°F = 1.80(°C) + 32$$
$$= 1.80(25) + 32$$
$$= 77°F$$

Therefore, 25°C is equal to 77°F.

(ii) 90°F to Celsius:

$$°C = \frac{(°F - 32)}{1.80}$$
$$= \frac{(90 - 32)}{1.80}$$
$$= \frac{58}{1.80} = 32.222222...°C = 32.22°C$$

Therefore, 90°F is equal to 32.22°C.

Example 7.3-h **Comparing Temperatures Measured Using Different Scales**

Which is the higher temperature: 80°C or 175°F?

Solution

Convert 80°C to °F and compare with 175°F.

$$°F = 1.80(°C) + 32$$
$$= 1.80(80) + 32$$
$$= 176°F$$

i.e., 80°C = 176°F > 175°F

i.e., 80°C > 175°F

or

Convert 175°F to °C and compare with 80°C.

$$°C = \frac{(°F - 32)}{1.80} = \frac{(175 - 32)}{1.80}$$
$$= 79.44°C$$

i.e., 175°F = 79.44°C < 80°C

Therefore, 80°C is a higher temperature than 175°F.

Kelvin Scale

Another unit of measure for temperature is the Kelvin. This temperature scale is an extension of the Celsius scale (°C). It is symbolized using K (not °K), and is used frequently in physics and chemistry. Kelvin does not have negative numbers; i.e., it begins at absolute zero, at which there is complete absence of heat energy.

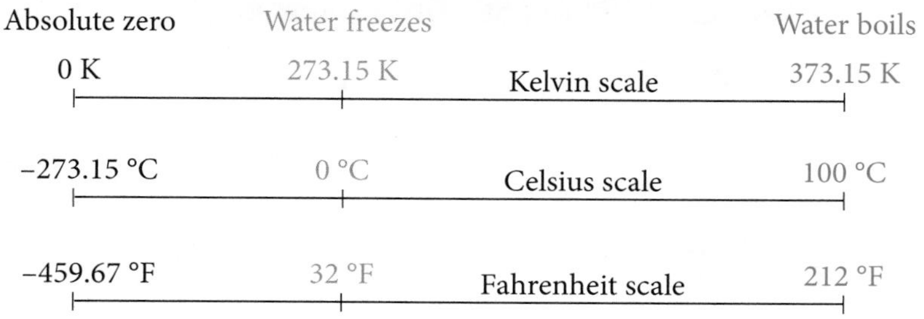

To convert between Celsius (°C) and Kelvin (K) measurements and to convert between Fahrenheit (°F) and Kelvin (K), use the conversion tables below.

Conversion Table

°C to K	$K = °C + 273.15$	°F to K	$K = \dfrac{(°F - 32)}{1.8} + 273.15$
K to °C	$°C = K - 273.15$	K to °F	$°F = 1.8(K - 273.15) + 32$

Example 7.3-i **Converting Between the Celsius (°C) Scale and the Kelvin (K) Scale**

Convert the following:

(i) 25°C to Kelvin (ii) 300 K to Celsius (iii) 75°F to Kelvin (K) (iv) 350 K to Fahrenheit (°F)

Solution

(i) 25°C to Kelvin:

$$K = °C + 273.15$$
$$= 25 + 273.15$$
$$= 298.15 \text{ K}$$

Therefore, 25°C is equal to 298.15 K.

(ii) 300 K to Celsius:

$$°C = K - 273.15$$
$$= 300 - 273.15$$
$$= 26.85 \text{ °C}$$

Therefore, 300 K is equal to 26.85 °C.

(iii) 75°F to Kelvin (K):

$$K = \frac{(°F - 32)}{1.80} + 273.15$$
$$= \frac{(75 - 32)}{1.80} + 273.15$$
$$= \frac{43}{1.80} + 273.15$$
$$= 23.888888... + 273.15$$
$$= 297.038888... = 297.04 \text{ K}$$

Therefore, 75°F is equal to 297.04 K.

(iv) 350 K to Fahrenheit (°F):

$$°F = 1.8(K - 273.15) + 32$$
$$= 1.8(350 - 273.15) + 32$$
$$= 1.8(76.85) + 32$$
$$= 138.33 + 32$$
$$= 170.33 \text{ °F}$$

Therefore, 350 K is equal to 170.33 °F.

Comparison Among Temperature Scales

The following table provides a comparison among the temperature scales.

Temperature Scales			Description
Fahrenheit	Celsius	Kelvin	
212 °F	100 °C	373.15 K	Boiling point of water at sea level
73.4 °F	23 °C	296.15 K	Average room temperature
32 °F	0 °C	273.15 K	Freezing point of water at sea level
– 81.4 °F	– 63 °C	210.15 K	Lowest recorded temperature in Canada: Snag, Yukon in 1947
– 128.6 °F	– 89.2 °C	183.95 K	Lowest recorded temperature on Earth: Vostok, Antarctica in 1983

7.3 | Exercises

Answers to odd-numbered problems are available at the end of the textbook.

For the following problems, express the answers rounded to two decimal places, wherever applicable.

Calculate the missing values in Problems 1 to 12.

1.

	Metric Units	US Customary Units
a.	250 km	? mi
b.	? km	120 mi

2.

	Metric Units	US Customary Units
a.	175 km	? mi
b.	? km	80 mi

3.

	Metric Units	US Customary Units
a.	17.5 m	? yd
b.	? m	22 yd

4.

	Metric Units	US Customary Units
a.	11 m	? yd
b.	? m	12.5 yd

5.

	Metric Units	US Customary Units
a.	250 m	? ft
b.	? m	75 ft

6.

	Metric Units	US Customary Units
a.	12 m	? ft
b.	? m	45.5 ft

7.

	Metric Units	US Customary Units
a.	100 cm	? in.
b.	? cm	3.5 in.

8.

	Metric Units	US Customary Units
a.	80 cm	? in.
b.	? cm	7.5 in.

9.

	Metric Units	US Customary Units
a.	250 km	? mi
b.	? km	120 mi

10.

	Metric Units	US Customary Units
a.	175 km	? mi
b.	? km	80 mi

11.

	Metric Units	US Customary Units
a.	17.5 m	? yd
b.	? m	22 yd

12.

	Metric Units	US Customary Units
a.	11 m	? yd
b.	? m	12.5 yd

13. Arrange the following measurements in order from largest to smallest:

    82.5 ft, 900 in., 4,250 cm, 28 yd, 24 m

14. Arrange the following measurements in order from smallest to largest:

    1,280 cm, 44 ft, 15 yd, 450 in., 12 m

15. June bought 5.5 metres of fabric and used 10 feet of it to make a curtain. Calculate the remaining quantity of fabric, in metres.

16. A swimming pool is 12.5 metres wide. It is divided into 5 lanes of equal width. Calculate the width of each lane, in feet.

17. The distance from Toronto to Niagara Falls is 320 km. After driving 100 miles from Toronto, calculate the distance left to reach Niagara Falls, in kilometres.

18. The distance from Niagara Falls to New York is 410 miles. After driving 550 kilometres from Niagara Falls, what is the distance to be travelled, in kilometres, to reach New York?

Calculate the missing values in Problems 19 to 26.

19.

	Metric Units	US Customary Units
a.	3,500 kg	? tons
b.	? kg	2.5 tons

20.

	Metric Units	US Customary Units
a.	4,250 kg	? tons
b.	? kg	4 tons

21.

	Metric Units	US Customary Units
a.	15.5 kg	? lb
b.	? kg	45 lb

22.

	Metric Units	US Customary Units
a.	70 kg	? lb
b.	? kg	135.5 lb

23.

	Metric Units	US Customary Units
a.	1,200 g	? lb
b.	? g	6.5 lb

24.

	Metric Units	US Customary Units
a.	750 g	? lb
b.	? g	4.5 lb

25.

	Metric Units	US Customary Units
a.	200 g	? oz
b.	? g	4 oz

26.

	Metric Units	US Customary Units
a.	175 g	? oz
b.	? g	2.5 oz

27. Arrange the following measurements in order from largest to smallest :

    2.5 kg, 2,450 g, 5.7 lb, 80 oz

28. Arrange the following measurements in order from smallest to largest:

    4.5 kg, 4,560 g, 9.5 lb, 155 oz

29. Carol bought 2 pounds of butter and used 750 grams of it to make a cake. Calculate the quantity of butter remaining, in grams.

30. A recipe requires 600 grams of butter. I bought 1.5 pounds of butter and used 600 grams of it. Calculate the quantity of butter remaining, in grams.

31. William weighs 80 kg. His brother weighs 25 pounds less than him. Calculate his brother's weight, in kg.

32. A travel bag weighs 2.25 kg. The total weight of the travel bag with its contents is 50 pounds. Calculate the weight of the contents in the bag, in kg.

Calculate the missing values in Problems 33 to 42.

33.

	Metric Units	US Customary Units
a.	50 L	? gal
b.	? L	10.5 gal

34.

	Metric Units	US Customary Units
a.	25.5 L	? gal
b.	? L	30 gal

35.

	Metric Units	US Customary Units
a.	15 L	? qt
b.	? L	14 qt

36.

	Metric Units	US Customary Units
a.	22 L	? qt
b.	? L	12 qt

37.

	Metric Units	US Customary Units
a.	7.5 L	? pt
b.	? L	14 pt

38.

	Metric Units	US Customary Units
a.	6 L	? pt
b.	? L	10.5 pt

39.

	Metric Units	US Customary Units
a.	4.5 L	? c
b.	? L	14 c

40.

	Metric Units	US Customary Units
a.	5 L	? c
b.	? L	18 c

41.

	Metric Units	US Customary Units
a.	8 mL	? fl. oz
b.	? mL	20.5 fl. oz

42.

	Metric Units	US Customary Units
a.	3.5 mL	? fl. oz
b.	? mL	15 fl. oz

43. Arrange the following measurements in order from largest to smallest:
3.5 L, 4.8 qt, 10.5 pt, 1 gal

44. Arrange the following measurements in order from smallest to largest:
7.5 L, 8.5 qt, 15 pt, 1.7 gal

45. The capacity of a fuel tank of a car is 54 litres. The tank is 1/3 empty. Calculate the capacity of the fuel in the tank, in gallons.

46. The fuel tank of a van can hold 18 gallons. It is 2/3 empty. Calculate the capacity of the fuel in the tank, in litres.

47. A container had 3.5 litres of milk. Ten cups of milk were used from this container. Calculate the quantity of milk, in litres, that remains in the container.

48. A bottle contained 1.2 litres of juice. Someone drinks 3 cups of juice from this bottle. Calculate the quantity remaining, in litres.

In Problems 49 to 72, convert the temperatures. Round the answers to the nearest one decimal place, wherever applicable.

49. 21 °C = ___°F
50. 10 °C = ___ °F
51. 98.6 °F = ___°C
52. 85 °F = ___ °C
53. 140 °C = ___°F
54. 180 °C = ___°F
55. 112 °F = ___°C
56. 400 °F = ___ °C
57. −15 °F = ___°C
58. −40 °F = ___ °C
59. 280 K = ___°C
60. 260 K = ___°C
61. 19 °C = _____ K
62. −10 °C = _____ K
63. 80 °F = _____ K
64. 100 °F = _____K
65. 300 K = _____ °C
66. 250 K = _____ °C
67. 200 K = _____ °F
68. 350 K = _____ °F
69. −20 °C = _____ K
70. 35 °C = _____ K
71. −80 °F = _____ K
72. −40 °F = _____ K

7 | Review Exercises

Answers to odd-numbered problems are available at the end of the textbook.

For the following problems, express your answers rounded to two decimal places, wherever applicable.

1. a. 7 m 5 cm = ___ cm
   b. 15 km 50 m =___ m
   c. 75 mm =___ cm __ mm
   d. 905 cm =___ m ___ cm

2. a. 37 m 2 cm = ___ cm
   b. 6 km 59 m = ___ m
   c. 1,026 mm = ___ cm __ mm
   d. 405 cm = ___ m ___ cm

3. a. 39 yd 1 ft = ___ ft
   b. 4 ft 7 in. = ___ in.
   c. 115 in. = ___ ft___ in.
   d. 5,290 yd = ___ mi___ yd

4. a. 43 yd 2 ft = ___ ft
   b. 15 ft 1 in. = ___ in.
   c. 102 in. = ___ ft___ in.
   d. 3,085 yd = ___ mi___ yd

5. a. 10 kg 32 g = ___ g
   b. 45 g 52 mg = ___ mg
   c. 3.62 kg = ___ kg___ g
   d. 42,007 mg = ___ g ___ mg

6. a. 3 kg 753 g = ___ g
   b. 7 g 87 mg = ___ mg
   c. 2.783 kg = ___ kg___ g
   d. 29,005 mg = ___ g ___ mg

7. a. 6 lb 7 oz = ___ oz
   b. 29,005 mg = ___ g ___ mg
   c. 32,000 lb = ___ ton ___ lb
   d. 120 oz = ___ lb ___ oz

8. a. 26 lb 2 oz = ___ oz
   b. 1 ton 249 lb = ___ lb
   c. 23,000 lb = ___ ton ___ lb
   d. 245 oz = ___ lb ___ oz

9. a. 6 L 49 mL = ___ mL
   b. 9,006 mL = ___ L ___ mL
   c. 9 gal 2 qt = ___ qt
   d. 75 pt = ___ qt ___ pt

10. a. 86 L 630 mL = ___ mL
    b. 2,092 mL = ___ L ___ mL
    c. 15 gal 3 qt = ___ qt
    d. 32 pt = ___ qt ___ pt

11. a. 410°F = ___ °C
    b. 80°C = ___ °F
    c. 125°F = ___ °C
    d. 30°C = ___ °F

12. a. 82°F = ___ °C
    b. 25°C = ___ °F
    c. 300°F = ___ °C
    d. 5°C = ___ °F

13. a. 240 K = _____ °C
    b. 21°C = ______ K
    c. 42°F = ___ K
    d. 300 K = ___ °F

14. a. 212 K = _____ °C
    b. 27 °C = ______ K
    c. 75°F = ___ K
    d. 200 K = ___ °F

Perform the conversions in Problems 15 to 20.

15. a. 65 km to miles
    b. 9 m to feet
    c. 2.5 yd to centimetres
    d. 3.2 mi to metres

16. a. 89 km to miles
    b. 4 m to feet
    c. 6.5 yd to centimetres
    d. 0.5 mi to metres

17. a. 5 kg to pounds
    b. 1,250 g to ounces
    c. 0.25 lb to grams
    d. 320 oz to kilograms

18. a. 4.4 kg to pounds
    b. 750 g to ounces
    c. 1.25 lb to grams
    d. 150 oz to kilograms

19. a. 35 L to gallons
    b. 26 mL to fluid ounces
    c. 17 gal to litres
    d. 42 fl oz to litres

20. a. 115 L to gallons
    b. 12 mL to fluid ounces
    c. 45 gal to litres
    d. 75 fl oz to litres

21. Arrange the following measurements in order from largest to smallest:

    7.5 km, 9,200 yd, 5.25 mi

22. Arrange the following measurements in order from smallest to largest:

    3.75 mi, 7,000 yd, 6 km

23. Arrange the following measurements in order from largest to smallest:

    7 lb, 3 kg, 115 oz

24. Arrange the following measurements in order from smallest to largest:

    4.5 kg, 9 lb, 150 oz

25. Arrange the following measurements in order from largest to smallest:

    70 L, 18 gal, 75 qt

26. Arrange the following measurements in order from smallest to largest:

    11 gal, 40 L, 45 qt

27. Paul travelled 23 km by car to the train station in Toronto. From there, he travelled another 125 mi to Cleveland, USA, by train. Calculate the total distance travelled, in (a) kilometres and (b) miles.

28. The total distance a marathon runner needs to run to complete the race is 26 miles and 385 yards. If after completing 32 km 200 m of the distance the runner pauses for a short break, how much further would he have to run to complete the race, in (a) miles and (b) kilometres?

29. Diana went on a diet and lost 26 pounds. Her weight at the end of the dieting period was 79 kg. What was her original weight, in (a) pounds and (b) kilograms?

30. The maximum weight an elevator can carry is 340 kg. Three people with an average weight of 65 kg and 2 people with an average weight of 155 pounds are waiting to get into the elevator. Determine if the elevator will be able to carry all 5 of them at the same time.

31. Tracy rented a car with a full tank and used up 8.5 gallons of fuel. If the total capacity of the fuel tank is 42.5 L and she needs to return the car with a full tank, how much fuel would she need to purchase, in (a) gallons and (b) litres?

32. Jerry brought in a 31 gal barrel of fruit punch for an anniversary party. If at the end of the party, 32 L of fruit punch remained in the barrel, calculate the quantity of fruit punch consumed, in (a) gallons and (b) litres.

33. Anita is making chocolate chip cookies, and the recipe states to bake the cookies for 20 minutes at 350°F. What temperature should she set her oven at, in °C? Provide the answer rounded to the nearest degree.

34. On January 6th, the temperature in Toronto, Ontario was −12°C. The same day, the temperature in Orlando, Florida was 85°F. What was the difference in temperature between the two cities that day, in (a) °C and (b) °F? Provide the answers rounded to one decimal place.

7 | Self-Test Exercises

Answers to all problems are available at the end of the textbook.

For the following problems, round your answers to two decimal places, wherever applicable.

1. a. 27 cm 3 mm = ___ cm
   b. 12 m 50 cm = ___ m
   c. 8,105 m = ___ km ___ m
   d. 1,065 mm = ___ cm ___ mm

2. a. 15 yd 2 ft = ___ ft
   b. 5 ft 2 in. = ___ in
   c. 430 in. = ___ ft ___ in
   d. 5,700 yd = ___ mi ___ yd

3. a. 53 kg 107 g = ___ g
   b. 6 g 223 mg = ___ mg
   c. 5,519 mg = ___ g ___ mg
   d. 84,176 g = ___ kg ___ g

4. a. 7 lb 15 oz = ___ oz
   b. 4 ton 30 lb = ___ lb
   c. 40,000 lb = ___ ton ___ lb
   d. 149 oz = ___ lb ___ oz

5. a. 5 L 7 mL = ___ mL
   b. 9,060 mL = ___ L ___ mL
   c. 26 gal 1 qt = ___ qt
   d. 83 pt = ___ qt ___ pt

6. a. 15 °F = ___ °C
   b. −10 °C = ___ °F
   c. 350 K = ___ °C
   d. 22 °F = ___ K

Perform the conversions in Problems 7 to 9.

7. a. 250 km to miles
   b. 45 m to feet
   c. 8.75 yd to centimetres
   d. 2.5 mi to metres

8. a. 2.5 kg to pounds
   b. 400 g to ounces
   c. 1.75 lb to grams
   d. 225 oz to kilograms

9. a. 60 L to gallons
   b. 425 mL to fluid ounces
   c. 2.5 gal to litres
   d. 30 fl oz to litres

10. Arrange the following measurements in order from largest to smallest:

    65 m, 215 ft, 2,500 in.

11. Arrange the following measurements in order from smallest to largest:

    2.5 lb, 1,200 g, 45 oz

12. Arrange the following measurements in order from largest to smallest:

    84 L, 22 gal, 175 pt

13. Helicopter A is flying at an altitude of 8,250 ft above ground and Helicopter B is at 2,208 m above ground. What is the difference in altitude between the two helicopters, in (a) feet and (b) metres?

14. A baby weighed 7.3 pounds at birth and another baby weighed 2.8 kg. Calculate the difference in weight of the two babies, in (a) ounces and (b) grams.

15. A carton contains 0.75 gal of milk. After pouring 5 glasses of milk, each holding 250 mL, calculate the amount of milk left in the carton, in (a) gallons and (b) millilitres.

16. Roger is conducting a chemistry experiment, where the solution needs to be heated at exactly 100°C. His lab partner sets the burner at 176°F, but Roger does not think that this is right. In C°, what should be the change in temperature setting at the burner?

8 BASIC ALGEBRA

Algebra is a branch of mathematics that introduces the concept of using variables to represent numbers. These variables, together with numbers, use rules of operations to express statements and equations. Algebra provides a framework from which formulas are derived to solve general problems and will help develop logical-thinking and problem-solving skills in a systematic and analytical way. The study of algebra is required in any occupational field, including business.

LEARNING OBJECTIVES

- Identify exponents and evaluate exponents using rules of exponents.
- Perform basic arithmetic operations on algebraic expressions.
- Setup basic linear equations with one variable.
- Solve linear equations with one variable using various arithmetic operations.
- Create, rearrange, and use equations to solve for unknown variables.

CHAPTER OUTLINE

8.1 Algebraic Expressions

8.2 Simple Algebraic Equations and Word Problems

8.3 Exponents

8.4 Logarithms

8.5 Rearranging Equations and Formulas

8.1 | Algebraic Expressions

Introduction

Algebraic expressions consist of one or more terms, with a combination of variables, numbers, and operation signs. In order to solve most problems in mathematics, the use of equations and formulas is necessary. These equations and formulas are formed using algebraic expressions.

lgebra is a branch of athematics that is used analyze and solve ay-to-day business and nance problems. It deals ith different relations and perations by using letters nd symbols to represent umbers, values, etc.

In arithmetic, we use only numbers in expressions. For example,

$$25 + 15, \quad 75 - 22, \quad 8 \times 9, \quad \frac{9}{5}$$

In algebra, we use both numbers and variables (letters and symbols that represent various numbers) in expressions. For example,

$$2x + 5, \quad 30 - 5y, \quad 6(2a + 5), \quad \frac{b+3}{2}$$

Also, in algebra, we use variables, numbers, and operation signs to translate word problems into equations.

For example, "The sum of two numbers is 100", can be represented by the equation:

$x + y = 100$

If $x = 40$, then $y = 60$.

If $x = 10$, then $y = 90$.

Note: In algebraic expressions involving multiplication, the number and the variable(s) can also be written together without the operation sign for multiplication.

For example, 5a means $5 \times a$, or $5(a)$, or $5 \cdot a$. Similarly, xy means $x \times y$, or $x(y)$, or $x \cdot y$.

The following key words will help in translating word problems into algebraic expressions and forming equations.

Arithmetic Operations and their Meanings

Keyword	Meaning
Addition (+)	add, sum, total, and, plus, more than, increased by, appreciate, rise
Subtraction (−)	subtract, difference, minus, less than, decreased by, depreciate, fall
Multiplication (×), (·)	multiply, product, times, of
Division (÷)	divide, ratio, divided by, quotient, per
Equal (=)	is, was, gives, given by

For example,

In words	In algebraic expression
• Ten more than a number	$x + 10$
• A number more than ten	$10 + x$
• A number less than twenty	$20 - x$
• Twenty less than a number	$x - 20$
• Product of five and a number	$5x$
• Divide 20 by a number	$\frac{20}{x}$
• Divide a number by 20	$\frac{x}{20}$

•	Half of a number	$\frac{1}{2}x = \frac{x}{2}$
•	Twice a number	$2x$
•	Ten more than the product of two numbers	$xy + 10$
•	'x' less than 'y' *or* 'y' less 'x'	$y - x$
•	'y' less than 'x' *or* 'x' less 'y'	$x - y$
•	Seventy decreased by 3 times a number	$70 - 3x$
•	'm' subtracted from 'n'	$n - m$

Terminology used in Algebraic Expressions

Terminology	Description	Examples
Variable	Letters that represent one or more numbers.	x, y, a, b are variables. In the expression $2m + 5n - 6$, m and n are variables.
Term	A number, variable, or a combination of numbers and variables which are multiplied or divided together.	$5, x, 5x^2y, 2xy, \frac{4}{a}, \frac{b}{3}$ have 1 term. The expression $5x + y$ has 2 terms. The expression $\frac{x}{4} - y^2 + \frac{x}{y} - \frac{1}{x}$ has 4 terms.
Expression	A mathematical phrase made up of a combination of terms and operations.	Expressions with one variable: $(2x + 5)$, $(9x - 3)$. Expressions with two variables: $(5x - 7y + 5)$, $(xy + 3x + 7)$
Coefficient	The product of all numerical factors in front of the variables of a term.	Coefficient of x^2 is 1, coefficient of $-3\,(2y^3)$ is -6. In the expression $5x^2 - 2y + 3$, the coefficient of the 1st term, is 5, and the coefficient of the 2nd term, is -2.
Constant	A term that only has a number with no variables.	In the expression $2x + 3y + 5$, the 3rd term, +5, is a constant. In the expression $5x^2 - 8$, the 2nd term, -8, is a constant.
Like terms	Terms that have the same variables and exponents. They differ only in their numerical coefficient. Constant terms are like terms.	$5x$, $9x$ are like terms. $30a^2, -4a^2, 9a^2$ are like terms. $5, -9$ are like terms.
Unlike terms	Terms that have different variables or the same variables with different exponents.	$12y, 3y^2$ are unlike terms. $x^2, x, 1$ are unlike terms.
Factors	Refer to each of the combinations of variables and/or numbers multiplied together in a term.	5 and x are factors of the term $5x$. 3, x, and y are factors of the term $3xy$.
Monomial	An algebraic expression that only has one term.	$8, 7x, 4y, 2xy$ are monomials.

Polynomial	Algebraic expression that has two or more terms.	$(8x^2 - 5x + 3)$ is a polynomial with 3 terms where, the 1st term is $8x^2$, the 2nd term is $-5x$, and the 3rd term is 3. Coefficient of the 1st term is 8, coefficient of the 2nd term is -5. The 3rd term is a constant.
Binomial	Polynomial with 2 terms.	$(4x - 3y)$, $(x - 5)$, $(4xy + 7x)$ are binomials.
Trinomial	Polynomial with 3 terms.	$(2x + 3y + 5)$, $(xy + x - 2)$, $(2x + xy + 3z)$ are trinomials.

Evaluating Algebraic Expressions

In an algebraic expression, the process of replacing all the variables and simplifying the expression is referred to as evaluating the algebraic expression. The simplified answer is the value of the expression.

Example 8.1-a **Evaluating Algebraic Expressions**

Evaluate the following expressions:

(i) $2x + y$, where $x = 10$ and $y = 5$

(ii) $\dfrac{3xy + 3x}{2y + 5}$, where $x = 3$ and $y = 2$

Solution

(i) $2x + y$ — Substituting $x = 10$ and $y = 5$,

$= 2(10) + 5$ — [$2x$ means $2(x)$]

$= 20 + 5 = 25$

(ii) $\dfrac{3xy + 3x}{2y + 5}$ — Substituting $x = 3$ and $y = 2$,

$= \dfrac{3(3)(2) + 3(3)}{2(2) + 5}$

$= \dfrac{18 + 9}{4 + 5} = \dfrac{27}{9} = 3$

Example 8.1-b **Evaluating Algebraic Expressions with Exponents**

Evaluate the following expressions:

(i) $\dfrac{(5x)^2 \times 4y}{50}$, where $x = 2$ and $y = 3$

(ii) $2(x^2 + 3x) - 5y$, where $x = 4$ and $y = -3$

Solution

(i) $\dfrac{(5x)^2 \times 4y}{50}$ — Substituting $x = 2$ and $y = 3$,

$= \dfrac{[5(2)]^2 \times 4(3)}{50}$

$= \dfrac{10^2 \times 12}{50} = \dfrac{100 \times 12}{50} = 24$

(ii) $2(x^2 + 3x) - 5y$ — Substituting $x = 4$ and $y = -3$,

$= 2[(4)^2 + 3(4)] - 5(-3)$

$= 2(16+12) + 15 = 56 + 15 = 71$

Basic Arithmetic Operations with Algebraic Expressions

All arithmetic operations can be applied to algebraic expressions by following the applicable rules (BEDMAS, exponents, signed numbers, etc.)

Addition and Subtraction of Monomials

Addition and subtraction of monomials can be performed by combining the like terms following the rules of signed numbers. If a coefficient of a term is not written, it is 1.

Example 8.1-c **Adding and Subtracting Monomials**

(i) Add $6x$ and $3x$

(ii) Add $4x^2y$ and x^2y

(iii) Subtract $5x^3$ from $7x^3$

(iv) Subtract $8x$ from the sum of $7x$ and $4x$

Solution

(i) $6x + 3x$ — Adding like terms,
$= 9x$

(ii) $4x^2y + x^2y$ — Adding like terms,
$= 5x^2y$

(iii) $7x^3 - 5x^3$ — Subtracting like terms,
$= 2x^3$

(iv) $(7x + 4x) - (8x)$ — Removing brackets,
$= 7x + 4x - 8x$ — Adding and subtracting like terms,
$= 3x$

Addition and Subtraction of Polynomials

Addition of Polynomials Indicated With a Plus '+' Sign Outside the Brackets

Brackets can be removed without changing any of the signs of the terms within the brackets.

Subtraction of Polynomials Indicated With a Negative '–' Sign Outside the Brackets

Brackets can be removed by distributing the negative sign to terms within the brackets.

When adding or subtracting algebraic expressions, first collect the like terms and group them, then add or subtract the coefficients of the like terms.

Example 8.1-d **Adding and Subtracting Algebraic Expressions**

(i) Add $(3x + 7)$ and $(5x + 3)$

(ii) Add $(4y^2 - 8y - 9)$ and $(2y^2 + 6y - 2)$

(iii) Subtract $(x^2 + 5x - 7)$ from $(2x^2 - 2x + 3)$

(iv) Subtract $(5y^2 + 8y - 6)$ from $(-2y^2 - 7y + 5)$

Solution

(i) $(3x + 7) + (5x + 3)$ — Removing brackets,
$= 3x + 7 + 5x + 3$ — Grouping like terms,
$= \underbrace{3x + 5x}\,\underbrace{+ 7 + 3}$ — Adding like terms,
$= 8x + 10$

(ii) $(4y^2 - 8y - 9) + (2y^2 + 6y - 2)$ — Removing brackets,
$= 4y^2 - 8y - 9 + 2y^2 + 6y - 2$ — Grouping like terms,
$= \underbrace{4y^2 + 2y^2}\,\underbrace{- 8y + 6y}\,\underbrace{- 9 - 2}$ — Adding and subtracting like terms,
$= 6y^2 - 2y - 11$

(iii) $(2x^2 - 2x + 3) - (x^2 + 5x - 7)$ — Removing brackets,
$= 2x^2 - 2x + 3 - x^2 - 5x + 7$ — Grouping like terms,
$= \underbrace{2x^2 - x^2}\,\underbrace{- 2x - 5x}\,\underbrace{+ 3 + 7}$ — Adding and subtracting like terms,
$= x^2 - 7x + 10$

Solution *continued*

(iv) $(-2y^2 - 7y + 5) - (5y^2 + 8y - 6)$ Removing brackets by distributing the negative sign to terms within the bracket,

$= -2y^2 - 7y + 5 - 5y^2 - 8y + 6$ Grouping like terms,

$= \underbrace{-2y^2 - 5y^2}\ \underbrace{- 7y - 8y}\ \underbrace{+ 5 + 6}$ Adding and subtracting like terms,

$= -7y^2 - 15y + 11$

Multiplication

Multiplying a Monomial by a Monomial

When multiplying a monomial by a monomial, multiply the coefficients and multiply all variables. If there are any similar variables, use the exponent notation.

Example 8.1-e **Multiplying Monomials by Monomials**

(i) Multiply $6x^2y$ and $5xy$

(ii) Multiply $(3a^3)$, $(-4ab)$, and $(2b^2)$

Solution

(i) $(6x^2y)\,(5xy)$ Grouping coefficients and variables,

$= (6)(5)(x^2)(x)(y)(y)$ Multiplying,

$= 30x^3y^2$

(ii) $(3a^3)\,(-4ab)\,(2b^2)$ Grouping coefficients and variables,

$= (3)(-4)(2)(a^3)(a)(b)(b^2)$ Multiplying,

$= -24a^4b^3$

Multiplying a Polynomial by a Monomial

When multiplying a polynomial by a monomial, multiply **each term** of the polynomial by the monomial. This is also known as the distributive property of multiplication.

$$a(b + c) = ab + ac$$

Then, group the like terms and simplify using addition and subtraction.

Example 8.1-f **Multiplying Polynomials by Monomials**

(i) Multiply $2x^3$ and $(3x^2 + 2x - 5)$

(ii) Expand and simplify $8x\,(x+3) + 4x\,(x - 4)$

Solution

(i) $2x^3\,(3x^2 + 2x - 5)$ Expanding,

$= 6x^5 + 4x^4 - 10x^3$

(ii) $8x\,(x+3) + 4x\,(x - 4)$ Expanding,

$= 8x^2 + 24x + 4x^2 - 16x$ Grouping like terms,

$= \underbrace{8x^2 + 4x^2} + \underbrace{24x - 16x}$ Adding and subtracting like terms,

$= 12x^2 + 8x$

Multiplying a Binomial by a Binomial

When multiplying two binomials, each term of the first binomial is multiplied by each term of the second binomial. This is the same as adding the product of the **F**irst terms, **O**utside terms, **I**nside terms, and **L**ast terms of each binomial, which can be remembered by acronym "**FOIL**".

$$(a+b)(c+d) = a\cdot c + a\cdot d + b\cdot c + b\cdot d$$

(F, O, I, L)

The same result is obtained by using the distributive property to expand.

$$(a+b)(c+d) = a(c+d) + b(c+d)$$
$$= a\cdot c + a\cdot d + b\cdot c + b\cdot d$$

Then, group the like terms and simplify using addition and subtraction.

Example 8.1-g **Multiplying Two Binomials**

(i) Multiply $(x+5)$ and $(x+6)$

(ii) Multiply $(2x+3)$ and $(3x-4)$

Solution

(i) $(x+5)(x+6)$

$(x+5)(x+6)$ (F, O, I, L)

$= x^2 + 6x + 5x + 30$

$= x^2 + 11x + 30$

or

$x(x+6) + 5(x+6)$

$= x^2 + 6x + 5x + 30$

$= x^2 + 11x + 30$

(ii) $(2x+3)(3x-4)$

$(2x+3)(3x-4)$ (F, O, I, L)

$= 6x^2 - 8x + 9x - 12$

$= 6x^2 + x - 12$

or

$2x(3x-4) + 3(3x-4)$

$= 6x^2 - 8x + 9x - 12$

$= 6x^2 + x - 12$

Special Products of Binomials

- Squaring a binomial, i.e., multiplying a binomial by itself.

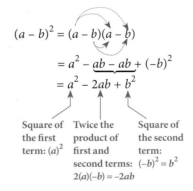

$(a+b)^2 = a^2 + 2ab + b^2$

$(a-b)^2 = a^2 - 2ab + b^2$

$$(a+b)^2 = (a+b)(a+b)$$
$$= a^2 + ab + ab + b^2$$
$$= a^2 + 2ab + b^2$$

Square of the first term: $(a)^2$; Twice the product of first and second terms: $2(a)(b) = 2ab$; Square of the second terms: $(b)^2$

$$(a-b)^2 = (a-b)(a-b)$$
$$= a^2 - ab - ab + (-b)^2$$
$$= a^2 - 2ab + b^2$$

Square of the first term: $(a)^2$; Twice the product of first and second terms: $2(a)(-b) = -2ab$; Square of the second term: $(-b)^2 = b^2$

- Product of two binomials having the same two terms but with opposite signs separating the terms, i.e., product of the sum and difference of two terms.

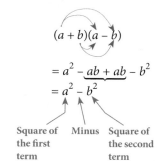

$(a + b)(a - b) = a^2 - b^2$

$$(a + b)(a - b)$$
$$= a^2 - ab + ab - b^2$$
$$= a^2 - b^2$$

Square of the first term | Minus | Square of the second term

Example 8.1-h **Squaring a Binomial**

Multiply the following expressions using the special product of binomials.

(i) $(2x + y)(2x + y)$ (ii) $(3x + 4)(3x + 4)$

(iii) $(3x - 2y)(3x - 2y)$ (iv) $(5x - 6)(5x - 6)$

Solution

(i) $(2x + y)(2x + y)$

$= (2x + y)^2$ Using $(a + b)^2 = a^2 + 2ab + b^2$,

$= (2x)^2 + 2(2x)(y) + (y)^2$

$= 4x^2 + 4xy + y^2$

Therefore, $(2x + y)(2x + y) = 4x^2 + 4xy + y^2$.

(ii) $(3x + 4)(3x + 4)$

$= (3x + 4)^2$ Using $(a + b)^2 = a^2 + 2ab + b^2$,

$= (3x)^2 + 2(3x)(4) + (4)^2$

$= 9x^2 + 24x + 16$

Therefore, $(3x + 4)(3x + 4) = 9x^2 + 24x + 16$.

(iii) $(3x - 2y)(3x - 2y)$

$= (3x - 2y)^2$ Using $(a - b)^2 = a^2 - 2ab + b^2$,

$= (3x)^2 - 2(3x)(2y) + (2y)^2$

$= 9x^2 - 12xy + 4y^2$

Therefore, $(3x - 2y)(3x - 2y) = 9x^2 - 12xy + 4y^2$.

(iv) $(5x - 6)(5x - 6)$

$= (5x - 6)^2$ Using $(a - b)^2 = a^2 - 2ab + b^2$,

$= (5x)^2 - 2(5x)(6) + (6)^2$

$= 25x^2 - 60x + 36$

Therefore, $(5x - 6)(5x - 6) = 25x^2 - 60x + 36$.

Example 8.1-i **Multiplying the Sum and Difference of Two Terms**

Multiply the following expressions using the special product of binomials.

(i) $(3x + y)(3x - y)$

(ii) $(2x + 5)(2x - 5)$

Solution

(i) $(3x + y)(3x - y)$ Using $(a + b)(a - b) = a^2 - b^2$,

$(3x)^2 - (y)^2$

$9x^2 - y^2$

Therefore, $(3x + y)(3x - y) = 9x^2 - y^2$.

(ii) $(2x + 5)(2x - 5)$ Using $(a + b)(a - b) = a^2 - b^2$,

$(2x)^2 - (5)^2$

$4x^2 - 25$

Therefore, $(2x + 5)(2x - 5) = 4x^2 - 25$.

Multiplying a Polynomial by a Polynomial

When multiplying a polynomial by a polynomial, each term of the first polynomial must be multiplied by each term of the second polynomial. Then, using the distributive property, expand, group the like terms, and simplify using addition and subtraction.

Example 8.1-j **Multiplying Polynomials by Polynomials**

(i) Multiply $(x^2 + 7)$ and $(2x^2 + 5x + 2)$

(ii) Multiply $(x - 4)$ and $(2x^2 - x - 3)$

(iii) Expand and simplify $(x + 5)(2x - 6) + (3x - 4)(x - 5)$

(iv) Expand and simplify $(x - 3)(3x - 1) - (2x - 3)(x + 4)$

Solution

(i) $(x^2 + 7)(2x^2 + 5x + 2)$

$= x^2(2x^2 + 5x + 2) + 7(2x^2 + 5x + 2)$ Expanding,

$= 2x^4 + 5x^3 + \underbrace{2x^2 + 14x^2} + 35x + 14$ Adding like terms,

$= 2x^4 + 5x^3 + 16x^2 + 35x + 14$

(ii) $(x - 4)(2x^2 - x - 3)$

$= x(2x^2 - x - 3) - 4(2x^2 - x - 3)$ Expanding,

$= 2x^3 - x^2 - 3x - 8x^2 + 4x + 12$ Grouping like terms,

$= 2x^3 \underbrace{- x^2 - 8x^2} \underbrace{- 3x + 4x} + 12$ Adding and subtracting like terms,

$= 2x^3 - 9x^2 + x + 12$

(iii) $(x + 5)(2x - 6) + (3x - 4)(x - 5)$

$= [x(2x - 6) + 5(2x - 6)] + [3x(x - 5) - 4(x - 5)]$ Expanding,

$= (2x^2 - 6x + 10x - 30) + (3x^2 - 15x - 4x + 20)$ Removing brackets,

$= 2x^2 - 6x + 10x - 30 + 3x^2 - 15x - 4x + 20$ Grouping like terms,

$= \underbrace{2x^2 + 3x^2} \underbrace{- 6x + 10x - 15x - 4x} \underbrace{- 30 + 20}$ Adding and subtracting like terms,

$= 5x^2 - 15x - 10$

Solution
continued

(iv) $(x-3)(3x-1)-(2x-3)(x+4)$

$= [x(3x-1)-3(3x-1)]-[2x(x+4)-3(x+4)]$ Expanding by removing brackets,

$= (3x^2-x-9x+3)-(2x^2+8x-3x-12)$ Removing brackets,

$= 3x^2-x-9x+3-2x^2-8x+3x+12$ Grouping like terms,

$= \underbrace{3x^2-2x^2}-\underbrace{x-9x-8x+3x}+\underbrace{3+12}$ Adding and subtracting like terms,

$= x^2-15x+15$

Division

Dividing a Monomial by a Monomial

When dividing a monomial by a monomial, group the coefficients and each of the variables separately and simplify them. If there are similar variables, use the exponent notation.

Example 8.1-k **Dividing Monomials by Monomials**

(i) Divide $8x^2y$ by $6x$

(ii) Divide $-9x^2$ by $3x^3$

Solution

(i) $\frac{8x^2y}{6x}=\frac{8}{6}\cdot\frac{x^2}{x}\cdot y=\frac{4}{3}xy$

(ii) $\frac{-9x^2}{3x^3}=\frac{-9}{3}\cdot\frac{x^2}{x^3}=\frac{-3}{1}\cdot\frac{1}{x}=\frac{-3}{x}$

Dividing a Polynomial by a Monomial

When dividing a polynomial by a monomial, divide **each term** of the polynomial by the monomial. The process is similar to dividing a monomial by a monomial.

Example 8.1-l **Dividing Polynomials by Monomials**

(i) Divide $(9x^3+12x^2)$ by $6x$

(ii) Divide $(4x^4+2x^3-7x)$ by $4x^4$

Solution

(i) $\frac{9x^3+12x^2}{6x}=\frac{9x^3}{6x}+\frac{12x^2}{6x}=\frac{3x^2}{2}+2x$

(ii) $\frac{4x^4+2x^3-7x}{4x^4}=\frac{4x^4}{4x^4}+\frac{2x^3}{4x^4}-\frac{7x}{4x^4}=1+\frac{1}{2x}-\frac{7}{4x^3}$

Factoring Algebraic Expressions with Common Factors

Factoring algebraic expressions involves finding the highest common factor for both the coefficients and variables in all the terms. Once the factor is found, the expression will become a product of a monomial and a polynomial or a combination of both.

Example 8.1-m **Factoring Algebraic Expressions**

Factor the following:

(i) $12x+18y$

(ii) $8y^2+20y$

(iii) $9xy^3+6xy^4-9x^3y^5$

(iv) $14(2x+y)-7x(2x+y)$

Solution

(i) $12x + 18y$

$12x = 2 \cdot 2 \cdot 3 \cdot x$

$18y = 2 \cdot 3 \cdot 3 \cdot y$

HCF is $2 \cdot 3 = 6$.

Divide the original expression by the HCF of 6 to determine the second factor.

$$\frac{12x + 18y}{6} = \frac{12x}{6} + \frac{18y}{6} = 2x + 3y$$

i.e., the second factor is $(2x + 3y)$.

Therefore, $12x + 18y = 6(2x + 3y)$.

(ii) $8y^2 + 20y$

$8y^2 = 2 \cdot 2 \cdot 2 \cdot y \cdot y$

$20y = 2 \cdot 2 \cdot 5 \cdot y$

HCF is $2 \cdot 2 \cdot y = 4y$.

Divide the original expression by the HCF of $4y$ to determine the second factor.

$$\frac{8y^2 + 20y}{4y} = \frac{8y^2}{4y} + \frac{20y}{4y} = 2y + 5$$

i.e., the second factor is $(2y + 5)$.

Therefore, $8y^2 + 20y = 4y(2y + 5)$.

(iii) $9xy^3 + 6xy^4 - 9x^3y^5$

The HCF is $3xy^3$.

Divide the original expression by the HCF of $3xy^3$ to determine the second factor.

$$\frac{9xy^3 + 6xy^4 - 9x^3y^5}{3xy^3} = \frac{9xy^3}{3xy^3} + \frac{6xy^4}{3xy^3} - \frac{9x^3y^5}{3xy^3} = 3 + 2y - 3x^2y^2$$

i.e., the second factor is $(3 + 2y - 3x^2y^2)$.

Therefore, $9xy^3 + 6xy^4 - 9x^3y^5 = 3xy^3(3 + 2y - 3x^2y^2)$.

(iv) $14(2x + y) - 7x(2x + y)$

Using the factor of each term, HCF is $7(2x + y)$.

Divide the original expression by the HCF of $7(2x + y)$ to determine the second factor.

$$\frac{14(2x + y) - 7x(2x + y)}{7(2x + y)} = \frac{14(2x + y)}{7(2x + y)} - \frac{7x(2x + y)}{7(2x + y)} = 2 - x$$

i.e., the second factor is $(2 - x)$.

Therefore, $14(2x + y) - 7x(2x + y) = 7(2x + y)(2 - x)$.

8.1 | Exercises

Answers to odd-numbered problems are available at the end of the textbook.

Write the algebraic expression for the following:

1. a. Three less than twice a number.
   b. Two times a number divided by five.
   c. Twenty-five increased by three times a number.
2. a. A number less than four times a number.
   b. Fifteen divided by three times a number.
   c. Twenty increased by twice a number.

3. Identify the indicated terms in the following expressions and state their coefficients:
   a. 2nd term and 3rd term in $3x^2 + 7xy - 4y + 7$
   b. 3rd term and 4th term in $x^2 - 5x - y + 3$
   c. 1st term and 3rd term in $9xy + 7x - 6y + 2$
4. Identify the indicated terms in the following expressions and state their coefficients:
   a. 1st term and 4th term in $-x^2 + 9xy + y + 7$
   b. 2nd term and 3rd term in $7xy - 4y + 7$
   c. 1st term and 3rd term in $10x^2 + 5xy - 6x + 7y$
5. Identify the constant term and the coefficients of the terms in each of the following expressions:
   a. $5x^2 - 3xy + 5$ b. $-2y^2 + 3x + 1$ c. $-2xy^2 - 2x^2y + 7$
6. Identify the constant term and the coefficients of the terms in each of the following expressions:
   a. $-2y^2 + 3y - 4$ b. $y^5 - 2y^7 - 2$ c. $2x^3 - 3x^2 + 1$

For Problems 7 to 10, identify like terms, group them, and simplify.

7. a. $12A + 4B - 7A - B$ b. $6x + 8y - 5x - 3y + 7$
8. a. $6B + 8A - A - 2B$ b. $14 - 3x + 10y + 4y$
9. a. $-2x + 5y - 12x + 8x + 7y$ b. $6xy^2 - 2x^2y - 4x^2 + 2xy^2 + 3x^2y + 2x^2 + 4$
10. a. $3x + 6x - 20x + 8y + 8y + 5x$ b. $3x^2y - 12xy^2 - 6x^2y - 5xy - 2xy - 4xy^2$

For Problems 11 to 14, simplify and evaluate the expressions.

11. a. $6y + 4y - 7y$, where $y = 10$ b. $2z - z + 7z$, where $z = 7$
12. a. $3x + 5x - 8x$, where $x = 4$ b. $3A - A + 6A$, where $A = 10$
13. a. $(6x)(3x) - (5x)(4x)$, where $x = 3$ b. $(2x)(0.5x + 4x)(5x + x)$, where $x = 5$
14. a. $(10x \times 4.5x) - (11x \times 4x)$, where $x = 50$ b. $(4x)(12x + 0.25x)(0.5x + x)$, where $x = 3$

For Problems 15 to 18, identify like terms, group them, simplify, and evaluate.

15. $3a + 6b - 16c - a + 8b + 4c + 2$, where $a = 3, b = 2, c = 1$
16. $3x - 60y - 17z - 2x + 62y + 4z + 1$, where $x = 5, y = 8, z = 2$
17. $x^2 - x + 2x^2 - x$, where $x = 5$
18. $-a^2 - 3a + 3a^2 + 4a$, where $a = 15$

Evalute the following expressions, given $x = 2$ and $y = 3$:

19. a. $\dfrac{19x - 5y}{9}$ b. $x^2 + 6x + 8$
20. a. $\dfrac{7x - 5y}{3}$ b. $-x^2 + 10x + 7$
21. a. $\dfrac{(3x)^2(5y)}{6y}$ b. $-2x^2 + 3x + 8y$
22. a. $\dfrac{(2x)^2(2y)}{5y}$ b. $4x^2 + 10x - 4y$

Simplify the following expressions:

23. a. $13x^2 + 8x - 2x^2 + 9x$ b. $-18y - 5y^2 + 19y - 2y^2$
24. a. $7x + 12x^2 - 4x + 5x^2$ b. $-14y - 2y^2 + 7y + 7y^2$
25. a. $6x - 3x + 2y^2 + y^2$ b. $4xy^2 - x^2y^2 - 3xy^2 + 2x^2y^2$
26. a. $9x^2 - 6x^2 + 7y - 6y$ b. $3x^2y^2 - 2xy^2 - 8x^2y^2 + xy^2$
27. a. $\dfrac{3x + 5x}{5x}$ b. $\dfrac{12y - 3y}{4y + 2y}$
28. a. $\dfrac{8x}{x + 5x}$ b. $\dfrac{20y - 5y}{-4y + 7y}$

29. a. $\frac{(16y)(8x)}{(4x)(8y)}$ b. $\frac{(6x)(-18y)}{(3x)(-24y)}$

30. a. $\frac{(20y)(4x)}{(2x)(5y)}$ b. $\frac{(7x)(18y)}{(14x)(-27y)}$

31. $3[5-3(4-x)]-2-5[3(5x-4)+8]-9x$

32. $5-\frac{1}{4}\{x-8[3-5(2x-3)+3x]-3\}$

33. $6[4(8-y)-5(3+3y)]-21-7[3(7+4y)-4]+198y$

34. $\frac{1}{5}\{y-15[2-3(3y-2)-7y]-4\}$

35. $y-\{4x-[y-(2y-9)-x]+2\}$

36. $2y+\{-6y-z[3x+(-4x+3)]+5\}$

37. $(x-1)-\{[x-(x-3)]-x\}$

38. $9x-\{3y+[4x-(y-6x)]-(x+7y)\}$

39. $5\{-2y+3[4x-2(3+x)]\}$

40. $4\{-7y+8[5x-3(4x+6)]\}$

41. $2y+\{8[3(2y-5)-(8y+9)+6]\}$

42. $7x-\{5[4(3x-8)-(9x+10)]+14\}$

Expand and simplify the following expressions:

43. $(2y-1)(y-4)-(3y+2)(3y-1)$

44. $(y+4)(y-3)+(y-2)(y-3)$

45. $(2x+3)(2x-1)-4(x^2-7)$

46. $4(2x-1)(x+3)-3(x-2)(3x-4)$

47. $3(x-2)(4-3x)+4(2x-1)(3-x)$

48. $2(3x+2)(1-3x)+3(2x-1)(4-x)$

49. $4(3x^2+4)-2(x+3)(x+5)$

50. $3(5x^2-1)-(2x-4)(3x+5)$

51. $3(2-3x)(2+x)-(1-x)(x-3)$

52. $(x-2)(3x+2)-(3x+2)(x-5)$

Simplify the following expressions:

53. $\frac{-x^2y-xy^2}{xy}$

54. $\frac{x^2y-3xy^2}{xy}$

55. $\frac{x^2y-3xy^2+4x^2y+xy}{xy}$

56. $\frac{3x^3y^3+6x^2y-3xy^2+3xy}{3xy}$

57. $\frac{6xy^2}{7}\cdot\frac{21x^2}{y}\cdot\frac{1}{36xy^2}$

58. $\frac{12x^2y^3}{5}\cdot\frac{15x^2}{4xy}\cdot\frac{1}{30x^3y}$

59. $\frac{(3x+9)}{14}\cdot\frac{(7x+21)}{x+3}$

60. $\frac{16}{(3x^2y+4x)}\cdot\frac{(6x^2y+8x)}{12}$

61. $\frac{(x^2-5x)}{(2x+10)}\cdot\frac{(3x+15)}{4x}$

62. $\frac{(3xy+4y)}{8y}\cdot\frac{12y^2}{(3x+4)}$

63. $\frac{(15xy-15y)}{(4x-12)}\cdot\frac{(3x-9)}{(4x-12)}$

64. $\frac{(x^2+xy)}{(7x-14)}\cdot\frac{(14x-28)}{(x+y)}$

Expand the following expressions by using special products of binomials:

65. a. $(x+5)^2$ b. $(2x+3y)^2$

66. a. $(x+7)^2$ b. $(3x+4y)^2$

67. a. $(3-x)^2$ b. $(3x-2y)^2$

68. a. $(7-x)^2$ b. $(2x-3y)^2$

69. a. $(1-3x)^2$ b. $(3-2x)^2$

70. a. $(6x-1)^2$ b. $(2y-1)^2$

71. a. $(x+5)(x-5)$ b. $(1+7x)(1-7x)$

72. a. $(12x-1)(12x+1)$ b. $(2a+4b)(2a-4b)$

Expand and simplify the following expressions:

73. $(x+3)^2+(x-2)^2$

74. $(x+5)^2+(x-4)^2$

75. $(4+x)^2-(x-3)(x+3)$

76. $(3+x)^2+(x+5)(x-5)$

77. $(3x-2)^2+(2x-3)(2x+3)$

78. $(2x+5)(2x-5)+(1-4x)^2$

79. $(2x-4)^2-(y+3)^2$

80. $(5x-6)^2-(x+5)^2$

Factor the following expressions:

81. $6x^2y - 3xy - 9y$
82. $10ab - 8bc$
83. $15y^2 - 12y - 3$
84. $8a^3 - 4a^2$
85. $6ab - 8bc + 7ac + 3cb$
86. $10x^2 - 6x - 4x^2$
87. $6xy - 9yz$
88. $12a^2b - 16ab - 24b$
89. $10x^3 - 4x^2$
90. $33x^2 - 3x - 11x^2$
91. $60y^2 - 40y - 180y^2$
92. $4xy - 12yz + 3xz + 15zy$
93. $5x(y + 2) + 3(y + 2)$
94. $7x(m - 4) + 3(m - 4)$
95. $4y(x - 5) - x^2 + 5x$
96. $3y(x - 1) + 2x^2 - 2x$
97. $xy - 2y + 5x - 10$
98. $4x - xy - 20y + 5y^2$
99. $x^2 + x - xy - y$
100. $2x^2 + 3y + 2x + 3xy$
101. $x^2 - 4y + 4x - xy$
102. $5x^2y - 10x^2 + y^2 - 2y$

8.2 | Simple Algebraic Equations and Word Problems

Introduction

An algebraic equation is a mathematical sentence expressing equality between two algebraic expressions (or an algebraic expression and a number).

When two expressions are joined by an equal (=) sign, it indicates that the expression to the left of the equal sign is equal to the expression to the right of the equal sign.

All equations have an equal (=) sign that separates the equation into two equal parts the left side (LS) and right side (RS).

For example, when two algebraic expressions, $5x + 7$ and $x + 19$, are equal, the two expressions are joined by an equal (=) sign and the equation is written as:

$$\underbrace{5x + 7}_{} = \underbrace{x + 19}_{}$$

'Left side' (LS) = 'Right side' (RS)

The **solution** to the equation is determined by performing arithmetical operations in finding the value of the variable that makes the left side (LS) equal to the right side (RS).

The value of the variable that makes both sides (LS and RS) equal is the solution to the equation.

In algebra, there are a variety of equations. In this section you will learn one type of equation, known as a **linear equation with one variable**.

Examples of a linear equation with one variable are:

$2x = 8$ $\qquad$ $3x + 5 = 14$ $\qquad$ $5x + 7 = x + 19$

An equation is either true or false depending on the value of the variable.

For example, the equation $2x = 8$ is true only if $x = 4$; i.e., LS = 2(4) = 8 (RS).

If $x = 3$ $\qquad$ LS = $2(3) \neq 8$ (RS)

Equations may be classified into the following three types:

1. **Conditional** - these equations are only true when the variable has a specific value.
2. **Identity** - these equations are true for any value for the variable.

   For example, $2x + 10 = 2(x + 5)$ is an identity, true for any value of x.
3. **Contradiction** - these equations are not true for any value of the variable.

   For example, $x + 5 = x + 4$; is a contradiction, not true for any value of x.

Equivalent Equations

Equations with the same solutions are called **equivalent equations**.

For example, $2x + 5 = 9$ and $2x = 4$ are equivalent equations because the solution $x = 2$ satisfies each equation.

Similarly, $3x - 4 = 5$, $2x = x + 3$, and $x + 1 = 4$ are equvialent equations because the solution $x = 3$ satisfies each equation.

Properties of Equality

Performing the same operation on both sides of an equation will result in an equivalent equation.

If $a = b$, then,

$b = a$	Symmetric Property	Interchanging LS and RS.
$a + \mathbf{c} = b + \mathbf{c}$	Addition Property	Adding the same quantity on both sides.
$a - \mathbf{c} = b - \mathbf{c}$	Subtraction Property	Subtracting the same quantity on both sides.
$a \cdot \mathbf{c} = b \cdot \mathbf{c}$	Multiplication Property	Multiplying by the same quantity on both sides.
$\frac{a}{\mathbf{c}} = \frac{b}{\mathbf{c}}$	Division Property, $c \neq 0$	Dividing by the same quantity on both sides.

The above properties are used to solve equations.

Equations with Fractional Coefficients

If an equation contains fractional coefficients, then the fractional coefficients can be changed to whole numbers by multiplying each term by the lowest common denominator (LCD) of all the fractions.

For example,

$$\frac{2}{3}x = \frac{5}{2} + 4$$

Since the LCD of the denominators 3 and 2 is 6, multiply each term by 6,

$$6\left(\frac{2}{3}x\right) = 6\left(\frac{5}{2}\right) + 6(4)$$

Simplifying,

$$4x = 15 + 24$$

Now, the equation is with whole number coefficients.

$$4x = 39$$

Equations with Decimal Coefficients

If an equation contains decimal coefficients, then the decimal coefficients can be changed to whole numbers by multiplying each term by the lowest decimal place value.

For example,

$$\underline{1.25}x = \underline{0.2} + 4$$

Since the lowest place value is hundredths, multiply each term by 100,

$$100(1.25x) = 100(0.2) + 100(4)$$

Simplifying,

$$125x = 20 + 400$$

Now, the equation is with whole number coefficients.

$$125x = 420$$

Steps to Solve Algebraic Equations with One Variable

Step 1: If the equation contains fractions and/or decimals coefficients, it is possible to work with them as they are. Alternatively, the equation may be written in whole numbers, as explained above, to make calculations and rearrangements easier.

Step 2: Expand and clear brackets in the equation, if present, by following the order of arithmetic operations (BEDMAS).

Step 3: Use the addition and subtraction property to collect and group all **variable** terms on the **left side** of the equation and all **constants** on the right side of the equation.

Step 4: Use the division and multiplication property to ensure that the coefficient of the variable is +1.

Step 5: After completing Step 4, there should be a single variable on the left side and one or more numbers on the right side. Compute the right side of the equation to find the solution.

Step 6: Verify the answer by substituting into the original problem.

Step 7: State the answer.

Example 8.2-a Solving Equations Using the Addition and Subtraction Properties

Solve the following equations and verify the solutions:

(i) $x - 11 = 4$

(ii) $8 + x = 20$

Solution

(i) $x - 11 = 4$ Adding **11** to both sides,

$x - 11 + \mathbf{11} = 4 + \mathbf{11}$

$x = \mathbf{15}$

Verify by substituting $x = 15$:

$LS = x - 11$	$RS = 4$
$= \mathbf{15} - 11$	
$= 4$	

LS = RS

Therefore, the solution is $x = 15$.

(ii) $8 + x = 20$ Subtracting **8** from both sides,

$8 - \mathbf{8} + x = 20 - \mathbf{8}$

$x = \mathbf{12}$

Verify by substituting $x = 12$:

$LS = 8 + x$	$RS = 20$
$= 8 + \mathbf{12}$	
$= 20$	

LS = RS

Therefore, the solution is $x = 12$.

Example 8.2-b Solving Equations Using the Multiplication and Division Properties

Solve the following equations and verify the solutions:

(i) $5x = 20$

(ii) $\frac{3}{8}x = 12$

Solution

(i) $5x = 20$ Dividing both sides by 5, and simplifying,

$\frac{5x}{\mathbf{5}} = \frac{20}{\mathbf{5}}$

$x = 4$

Verify by substituting $x = 4$:

$LS = 5x$	$RS = 20$
$= 5(4)$	
$= 20$	

LS = RS

Therefore, the solution is $x = 4$.

(ii) $\frac{3}{8}x = 12$ Multiplying both sides by $\mathbf{\frac{8}{3}}$ (the reciprocal of $\frac{3}{8}$),

$\mathbf{\frac{8}{3}} \cdot \frac{3}{8}x = \mathbf{\frac{8}{3}} \cdot 12$

$x = 4 \times 8$

$x = 32$

or

$\frac{3}{8}x = 12$ Multiplying both sides by 8,

$\mathbf{8} \cdot \frac{3}{8}x = \mathbf{8} \cdot 12$

$3x = 96$ Dividing both sides by 3, and simplifying,

$\frac{3x}{\mathbf{3}} = \frac{96}{\mathbf{3}}$

$x = 32$

Verify by substituting $x = 32$:

$LS = \frac{3}{8}x$	$RS = 12$
$= \frac{3}{8} \times 32$	
$= 12$	

LS = RS

Therefore, the solution is $x = 32$.

Example 8.2-c **Solving Equations with Variables on Both Sides**

Solve the following equations and verify the solutions:

(i) $3x - 8 = 12 - 2x$ (ii) $15 + 6x - 4 = 3x + 31 - x$

Solution

(i) $3x - 8 = 12 - 2x$ Adding $2x$ to both sides,

$3x + \mathbf{2x} - 8 = 12 - 2x + \mathbf{2x}$

$5x - 8 = 12$ Adding 8 to both sides,

$5x - 8 + \mathbf{8} = 12 + \mathbf{8}$

$5x = 20$ Dividing both sides by 5 and simplifying,

$\frac{5x}{\mathbf{5}} = \frac{20}{\mathbf{5}}$

$x = 4$

Verify by substituting $x = 4$:

LS = $3x - 8$	RS = $12 - 2x$
$= 3(4) - 8$	$= 12 - 2(4)$
$= 12 - 8$	$= 12 - 8$
$= 4$	$= 4$

LS = RS

Therefore, the solution is $x = 4$.

(ii) $\mathbf{15} + 6x \mathbf{- 4} = \mathbf{3x} + 31 \mathbf{- x}$ Combining like terms (LS $15 - 4 = 11$, and RS $3x - x = 2x$),

$11 + 6x = 2x + 31$ Subtracting $2x$ from both sides,

$11 + 6x - \mathbf{2x} = 2x - \mathbf{2x} + 31$

$11 + 4x = 31$ Subtracting 11 from both sides and simplifying,

$11 - \mathbf{11} + 4x = 31 - \mathbf{11}$

$4x = 20$ Dividing both sides by 4 and simplifying,

$\frac{4x}{\mathbf{4}} = \frac{20}{\mathbf{4}}$

$x = 5$

Verify by substituting $x = 5$:

LS = $15 + 6x - 4$	RS = $3x + 31 - x$
$= 15 + 6(5) - 4$	$= 3(5) + 31 - 5$
$= 15 + 30 - 4$	$= 15 + 31 - 5$
$= 41$	$= 41$

LS = RS

Therefore, the solution is $x = 5$.

Example 8.2-d Solving Equations with Fractions

Solve the following equation and verify the solution:

$\frac{x}{3} - \frac{1}{12} = \frac{1}{6} + \frac{x}{4}$

Solution

$$\frac{x}{3} - \frac{1}{12} = \frac{1}{6} + \frac{x}{4}$$

LCD of 3, 4, 6, and 12 is 12. Multiplying each term by 12,

$$\mathbf{12} \cdot \frac{x}{3} - \mathbf{12} \cdot \frac{1}{12} = \mathbf{12} \cdot \frac{1}{6} + \mathbf{12} \cdot \frac{x}{4}$$

$$4x - 1 = 2 + 3x$$

Subtracting $3x$ from both sides,

$$4x - \mathbf{3x} - 1 = 2 + 3x - \mathbf{3x}$$

$$x - 1 = 2$$

Adding 1 to both sides,

$$x - 1 + \mathbf{1} = 2 + \mathbf{1}$$

$$x = 3$$

Verify by substituting $x = 3$:

$\text{LS} = \frac{x}{3} - \frac{1}{12}$	$\text{RS} = \frac{1}{6} + \frac{x}{4}$
$= \frac{3}{3} - \frac{1}{12}$	$= \frac{1}{6} + \frac{3}{4}$
$= \frac{12}{12} - \frac{1}{12}$	$= \frac{2}{12} + \frac{9}{12}$
$= \frac{11}{12}$	$= \frac{11}{12}$

LS = RS

Therefore, the solution is $x = 3$.

Example 8.2-e Solving Equations with Decimals

Solve the following equation and verify the solution:

$0.15x + 1.2 = 0.4x - 0.8$

Solution

$$0.15x + 1.2 = 0.4x - 0.8$$

Lowest decimal place value is hundredths.

$$\mathbf{100}(0.15x) + \mathbf{100}(1.2) = \mathbf{100}(0.4x) - \mathbf{100}(0.8)$$

Multiplying all the terms by 100,

$$15x + 120 = 40x - 80$$

Using symmetric property,

$$40x - 80 = 15x + 120$$

Subtracting $15x$ from both sides,

$$40x - \mathbf{15x} - 80 = 15x - \mathbf{15x} + 120$$

$$25x - 80 = 120$$

Adding 80 to both sides,

$$25x - 80 + \mathbf{80} = 120 + \mathbf{80}$$

$$25x = 200$$

Dividing both sides by 25 and simplifying,

$$\frac{25x}{\mathbf{25}} = \frac{200}{\mathbf{25}}$$

$$x = 8$$

Verify by substituting $x = 8$:

$\text{LS} = 0.15x + 1.2$	$\text{RS} = 0.4x - 0.8$
$= 0.15(8) + 1.2$	$= 0.4(8) - 0.8$
$= 1.2 + 1.2$	$= 3.2 - 0.8$
$= 2.4$	$= 2.4$

LS = RS

Therefore, the solution is $x = 8$.

Example 8.2-f **Solving Equations Using All the Properties**

Solve the following equations by using all the properties of equations:

(i) $8x + 7 - 3x = -6x - 15 + x$

(ii) $2(3x - 7) = 28 - 3(x + 1)$

(iii) $\frac{1}{4}(x + \frac{2}{3}) = \frac{3}{2}(x - 1)$

(iv) $0.45(2x + 3) - 2.55 = 0.6(3x - 5)$

Solution

(i) $8x + 7 - 3x = -6x - 15 + x$ Grouping like terms on both sides,

$8x - 3x + 7 = -6x + x - 15$

$5x + 7 = -5x - 15$ Adding $5x$ to both sides,

$5x + \mathbf{5x} + 7 = -5x + \mathbf{5x} - 15$

$10x + 7 = -15$ Subtracting 7 from both sides,

$10x + 7 - \mathbf{7} = -15 - \mathbf{7}$

$10x = -22$ Dividing both sides by 10 and simplifying,

$\frac{10x}{\mathbf{10}} = -\frac{22}{\mathbf{10}}$

$x = -2.2$

(ii) $2(3x - 7) = 28 - 3(x + 1)$ Expanding both sides,

$6x - 14 = 28 - 3x - 3$ Adding $3x$ to both sides and simplifying,

$6x + \mathbf{3x} - 14 = 28 - 3x + \mathbf{3x} - 3$

$9x - 14 = 25$ Adding 14 to both sides and simplifying,

$9x - 14 + \mathbf{14} = 25 + \mathbf{14}$

$9x = 25 + 14$

$9x = 39$ Dividing both sides by 9 and simplifying,

$\frac{9x}{\mathbf{9}} = \frac{39}{\mathbf{9}}$

$x = 4\frac{1}{3} = 4.333333...$

(iii) $\frac{1}{4}(x + \frac{2}{3}) = \frac{3}{2}(x - 1)$ Expanding to clear the brackets and simplifying,

$\frac{1}{4}x + \frac{1}{6} = \frac{3}{2}x - \frac{3}{2}$ LCD of 2, 4, and 6 is 12.

Multiplying each term by 12 and simplifying,

$\mathbf{12} \cdot \frac{1}{4}x + \mathbf{12} \cdot \frac{1}{6} = \mathbf{12} \cdot \frac{3}{2}x - \mathbf{12} \cdot \frac{3}{2}$

$3x + 2 = 18x - 18$ Using symmetric property,

$18x - 18 = 3x + 2$

$18x - 3x - 18 = 3x - 3x + 2$ Subtracting $3x$ from both sides,

$15x - 18 = 2$ Adding 18 to both sides,

$15x - \mathbf{18} + 18 = 2 + \mathbf{18}$

$15x = 20$ Dividing both sides by 15 and simplifying,

$\frac{15x}{\mathbf{15}} = \frac{20}{\mathbf{15}}$

$x = \frac{4}{3}$

Solution *continued*

(iv) $0.45(2x + 3) - 2.55 = 0.6(3x - 5)$ — Expanding to clear brackets and simplifying,

$0.90x + 1.35 - 2.55 = 1.8x - 3.0$ — Lowest decimal place values is hunredths. Multiplying all the terms by 100,

$\mathbf{100} \cdot 0.90x + \mathbf{100} \cdot 1.35 - \mathbf{100} \cdot 2.55 = \mathbf{100} \cdot 1.8x - \mathbf{100} \cdot 3.0$

$90x + \underbrace{135 - 255} = 180x - 300$ — Collecting like terms,

$90x - 120 = 180x - 300$ — Using symmetric property,

$180x - 300 = 90x - 120$ — Subtracting $90x$ from both sides,

$180x \mathbf{- 90x} - 300 = 90x \mathbf{- 90x} - 120$

$90x - 300 = -120$ — Adding 300 to both sides,

$90x - 300 \mathbf{+ 300} = -120 \mathbf{+ 300}$

$90x = 180$ — Dividing both sides by 90 and simplifying,

$\frac{90x}{\mathbf{90}} = \frac{180}{\mathbf{90}}$

$x = 2$

Steps to Solve Word Problems

Step 1: Read the entire problem and understand the situation.

Step 2: Identify the given information and the question to be answered.

Step 3: Look for key words. Some words indicate certain mathematical operations.

Step 4: Choose a variable to represent the unknown(s).

Step 5: State what that variable represents, including the unit of measure.

Step 6: Where necessary, draw a simple sketch to identify the information. This helps with envisioning the question more clearly.

Step 7: Create an equation (or set of equations) to describe the relationship between the variables and the constants in the question.

Step 8: Group like terms, isolate the variable, and solve for the unknown.

Example 8.2-g **Solving a Word Problem Using Algebraic Equations**

If Harry will be 65 years old in 5 years, how old is he today?

Solution

Let Harry's age today be x years.

Therefore, in 5 years, Harry's age will be:

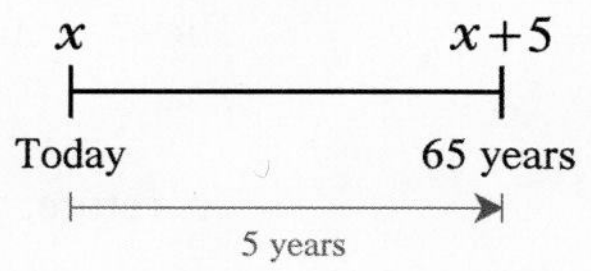

$x + 5 = 65$

Solving for x, $x = 65 - 5$

$= 60$

Therefore, Harry is 60 years old today.

Example 8.2-h

Solving a Word Problem Using Algebraic Equations

The perimeter of a rectangular garden is 50 metres. The length is 5 metres more than the width. Find the dimensions of the garden. (Hint: perimeter = 2 times the length + 2 times the width).

Solution

Let the width be w metres.

Therefore, the length is: $length = (w + 5)$ metres

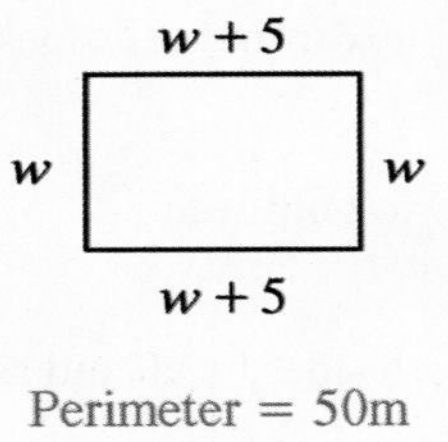

$$Perimeter = 2(length) + 2(width)$$
$$50 = 2(w + 5) + 2w$$
$$50 = 2w + 10 + 2w$$
$$2w + 10 + 2w = 50$$
$$4w + 10 = 50$$
$$4w = 50 - 10$$
$$4w = 40$$
$$w = 10$$

Therefore, the width of the garden is 10 metres, and the length = 10 + 5 = 15 metres.

Example 8.2-i

Solving a Word Problem Using Algebraic Equations

A TV costs \$190 more than a DVD player. The total cost of the TV and the DVD player is \$688. Calculate the cost of the TV and the cost of the DVD player.

Solution

Let the cost of the DVD player be $\$x$.

Therefore, the cost of the TV is $\$(x + 190.00)$.

The total cost is \$688.00.

$$x + (x + 190.00) = 688.00$$
$$x + x + 190.00 = 688.00$$
$$2x + 190.00 = 688.00$$
$$2x = 688.00 - 190.00$$
$$2x = 498.00$$
$$x = \frac{498.00}{2}$$
$$x = \$249.00$$

The cost of the TV = $x + 190.00$

$$= 249.00 + 190.00 = \$439.00$$

Therefore, the cost of the DVD player is \$249.00 and the cost of the TV is \$439.00.

Example 8.2-j

Solving a Word Problem Using Algebraic Equations

The perimeter of a triangle is the sum of the length of all 3 sides. A triangle with sides x cm, $(2x + 10)$ cm, and $(2x - 20)$ cm has a perimeter of 100 cm. Calculate the length of each side of the triangle.

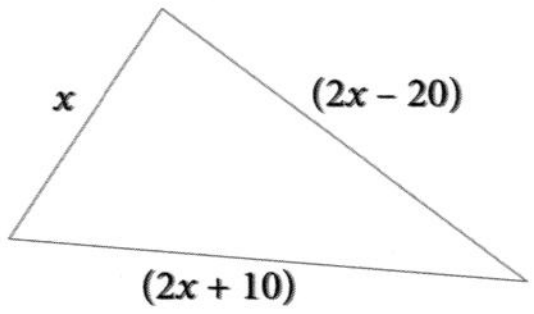

Solution

The sum of 3 sides of the triangle = perimeter of the triangle.

$$x + (2x + 10) + (2x - 20) = 100$$

$$x + 2x + 10 + 2x - 20 = 100$$

$$5x - 10 = 100$$

$$5x = 100 + 10$$

$$5x = 110$$

$$x = \frac{110}{5} = 22 \text{ cm}$$

Therefore, the lengths of the sides of the triangle are: $x = 22$ cm, $(2x + 10) = 2(22) + 10 = 54$ cm, and $(2x - 20) = 2(22) - 20 = 24$ cm.

8.2 | Exercises

Answers to odd-numbered problems are available at the end of the textbook.

Write and solve the algebraic equations for the following:

1. The sum of a number and six is ten.
2. A number decreased by fifteen is five.
3. Six times a number is seventy-two.
4. The product of a number and four is twenty-eight.
5. A number divided by five is four.
6. A number divided by three is three.
7. Two-thirds a number is twelve.
8. Two-fifths a number is six.

Solve the following algebraic equations using properties of equations, and round the answer to 2 decimal places, wherever applicable:

9. $x - 20 = 10$
10. $x - 25 = 17$
11. $22 = 40 - x$
12. $54 = 23 - x$
13. $21 + x = 4$
14. $50 + x = 45$
15. $16 + x = 22$
16. $12 + x = 38$
17. $11x + 4 = 17$
18. $7x - 16 = 22$
19. $x - \frac{4}{5} = \frac{3}{5}$
20. $x - \frac{1}{6} = \frac{5}{6}$
21. $\frac{10}{15} = x - \frac{4}{3}$
22. $\frac{x}{7} + 15 = 24$
23. $x + \frac{2}{5} = \frac{1}{4}$
24. $2x - \frac{2}{3} = \frac{5}{6}$
25. $5x = 20$
26. $4x = 24$
27. $\frac{2x}{3} + 1 = \frac{5x}{8} + 2$
28. $\frac{x}{2} - \frac{1}{6} = \frac{1}{3} + \frac{3x}{5}$
29. $\frac{7x}{8} - 4 = \frac{x}{4} + 6$
30. $\frac{8x}{3} - 5 = \frac{x}{3} + 2$
31. $10y - 0.09y = 17$
32. $x + 0.13 = 70$
33. $0.3x - 3.2 = 0.4 - 0.6x$
34. $4 + 0.2x = 0.7x - 0.5$
35. $0.4x - 1.38 = 0.3x - 1.2$
36. $1.2x - 0.7 = 2.7 - 0.5x$
37. $0.43x + 0.25 = 0.29x - 0.03$
38. $0.6x - 1.2 = 0.9 - 1.5x$

39. $8x + 7 - 3x = -6x - 15 + x$

40. $x - 2 - 4x = -3x - 8 + 5x$

41. $2(3x - 7) = 28 - 3(x + 1)$

42. $4(2x - 5) = 32 - 4(x - 2)$

43. $(4 + 6)(2 + 4x) = 45 - 2.5(x + 3)$

44. $(5 + 0.5x)(1 + 3) = -1.2(2x + 4) + 25$

45. $15 + 5(x - 10) = 3(x - 1)$

46. $2(x - 3) + 3(x - 5) = 4$

47. $4(y + 7) - 2(y - 4) = 3(y - 2)$

48. $8(2y + 4) - 6(3y + 7) = 3y$

49. $\frac{x-7}{2} + \frac{x+2}{3} = 41$

50. $\frac{7}{12}(2x + 1) + \frac{3}{4}(x + 1) = 3$

51. $\frac{5}{y+4} = \frac{3}{y-2}$

52. $\frac{3}{x+1} = \frac{2}{x-3}$

53. $\frac{7}{5x-3} = \frac{5}{4x}$

54. $\frac{5}{y+2} = \frac{3}{y}$

Solve the following word problems using algebraic equations:

55. If three times a number plus twenty is seven times that number, what is the number?
56. Fifteen less than three times a number is twice that number. What is the number?
57. A 25-metre long wire is cut into two pieces. One piece is 7 metres longer than the other. Find the length of each piece.
58. A 9-metre long pipe is cut into two pieces. One piece is twice the length of the other piece. Find the length of each piece.
59. \$500 is shared between Andy and Becky. Andy's share is \$150 less than Becky's share. Calculate the amount of each of their shares.
60. \$200 is shared between Bill and Ann. Ann's share is \$50 more than Bill's share. Calculate the amount of each of their shares.
61. Movie tickets that were sold to each child was \$3 cheaper than those sold to each adult. If a family of 2 adults and 2 children paid \$34 to watch a movie at the cinema, what was the price of each adult ticket and each child ticket?
62. Giri had twice the number of quarters (25 cents) in his bag than dimes (10 cents). If he had a total of 54 coins, how many of them were quarters? What was the total dollar value of these coins?
63. A square garden, with sides of length x, is widened by 4 metres and lengthened by 3 metres. Write the equation for the area (A) of the expanded garden. If each side was originally 10 metres in length, find the new area. (Hint: Area of a Rectangle = Length × Width)
64. A square garden, with sides of length x, has had its width reduced by 4 metres and its length reduced by 2 metres. Write the equation for the Area (A) of the smaller garden. If each side was originally 20 metres in length, find the new area.
65. Aran bought a shirt and a pair of pants for \$34.75. The pair of pants cost \$9.75 more than the shirt. Calculate the cost of the shirt.
66. Mythili bought a schoolbag and a toy for \$30.45. The school bag cost \$5.45 more than the toy. Calculate the cost of the school bag.
67. Sam is paid \$720 a week. He worked 9 hours of overtime last week and received \$954. Calculate his overtime pay per hour.
68. Lisa is paid \$840 a week. Her overtime rate is \$28 per hour. Last week she received \$1,036. How many hours of overtime did she work last week?
69. The sum of the three angles of any triangle is 180°. If $3x$, $7x$, and $8x$, are the measures of the three angles of a triangle, calculate the measure of each angle of the triangle.
70. The sum of the three angles of any triangle is 180°. If $3x$, $4x$, and $5x$ are the measures of the three angles of a triangle, calculate the measure of each angle of the triangle.
71. The perimeter of a triangle is the sum of the lengths of the three sides of the triangle. The perimeter of a triangle with sides x cm, $(x + 10)$ cm, and $2x$ cm is 70 cm. Calculate the length of each side of the triangle.
72. The perimeter of a triangle is the sum of the lengths of the three sides of the triangle. The perimeter of a triangle with sides $x + 10$, $2x + 10$, and $3x$ is 110 cm. Calculate the length of each side of the triangle.

8.3 | Exponents

Introduction

The concept of exponents was covered in Chapter 3, Section 3.1, where whole-numbered exponents were used to express repeated multiplication or division of the same numbers.

hen all the factors e equal, the product the factor is a wer of that factor.

$$\underbrace{(a)\,(a)\,(a)\,(a)\ldots \times a}_{\text{'n' factors of 'a'}} = a^n \qquad \frac{1}{\underbrace{(a)\,(a)\,(a)\,(a)\,(a)\ldots \times a}_{\text{'n' factors of 'a'}}} = \frac{1}{a^n} = a^{-n}$$

For example,

$$\underbrace{(2)(2)(2)(2)(2)}_{\text{5 factors of 2}} = 2^5 \qquad \frac{1}{\underbrace{(8)\,(8)\,(8)}_{\text{3 factors of 8}}} = \frac{1}{8^3} = 8^{-3}$$

(In 2^5 and 8^{-3}: exponent, base.)

The above exponential principle is applied to express repeated multiplication of a variable or an algebraic term.

In algebra, when 'n' is a positive integer, the general form for writing exponential expressions using variables is represented by:

$$\underbrace{(x)(x)(x)\ldots\,(x)}_{\text{'n' factors of 'x'}} = x^n \qquad \frac{1}{\underbrace{(x)(x)(x)\ldots\,(x)}_{\text{'n' factors of 'x'}}} = \frac{1}{x^n} = x^{-n}$$

Some useful applications of the above with examples are provided below:

	Exponential Form	Expanded Form	Example
(i)	ax^n	$a(x)(x)(x)\ldots\,(x)$	$2x^5 = 2(x)(x)(x)(x)(x)$
(ii)	$(ax)^n$	$(ax)(ax)(ax)\ldots\,(ax)$	$(2x)^5 = (2x)(2x)(2x)(2x)(2x) = 32x^5$
(iii)	$-ax^n$	$-1\cdot a(x)(x)(x)\ldots\,(x)$	$-2x^5 = -1\cdot 2(x)(x)(x)(x)(x)$
(iv)	$(-ax)^n$	$(-ax)(-ax)(-ax)\ldots\,(-ax)$	$(-2x)^5 = (-2x)(-2x)(-2x)(-2x)(-2x) = -32\cdot x^5$ $(-2x)^4 = (-2x)(-2x)(-2x)(-2x) = 16x^4$
(v)	$-x^n$	$-1\cdot(x)(x)(x)\ldots\,(x)$	$-x^5 = -1\cdot(x)(x)(x)(x)(x)$
(vi)	$(-x)^n$	$(-x)(-x)(-x)\ldots\,(-x)$	$(-x)^5 = (-x)(-x)(-x)(-x)(-x) = -x^5$ $(-x)^4 = (-x)(-x)(-x)(-x) = x^4$
(vii)	ax^{-n}	$a\cdot\frac{1}{(x)(x)(x)\ldots\,(x)}$	$2x^{-5} = 2\cdot\frac{1}{(x)(x)(x)(x)(x)} = \frac{2}{x^5}$
(viii)	$(ax)^{-n}$	$\frac{1}{(ax)(ax)(ax)\ldots\,(ax)}$	$(2x)^{-5} = \frac{1}{(2x)(2x)(2x)(2x)(2x)} = \frac{1}{32x^5}$

Note: The examples above assume that x is a positive number.

Rules of Exponents and Evaluation of Exponents

'Rules of exponents' are also referred to as 'laws of exponents' or 'properties of exponents'. The following are the basic rules of exponents.

$(x^m)(x^n) = x^{m+n}$

$\frac{x^m}{x^n} = x^{m-n}$

$(x^m)^n = x^{mn}$

$(xy)^m = x^m y^m$

$\left(\frac{x}{y}\right)^m = \frac{x^m}{y^m}$

$\left(\frac{x}{y}\right)^{-m} = \left(\frac{y}{x}\right)^m$

$x^{-1} = \frac{1}{x}$

$x^0 = 1$

$x^1 = x$

Table 8.3 **Rules of Exponents**

	Rule	Description	Example
1.	Product Rule	To multiply powers of the same base, write the base and add the exponents. $x^m \cdot x^n = x^{(m+n)}$	$x^4 \cdot x^3 = x^{(4+3)} = x^7$
2.	Quotient Rule	To divide powers of the same base, write the base and subtract the exponent. $\frac{x^m}{x^n} = x^{(m-n)}$	$\frac{x^5}{x^2} = x^{(5-2)} = x^3$
3.	Power of a Power Rule	To raise a power to another power, write the base and multiply the exponents. $(x^m)^n = x^{mn}$	$(x^4)^2 = x^{(4 \cdot 2)} = x^8$
4.	Power of a Product Rule	To simplify power of a product, raise each factor to the same exponent. $(xy)^m = x^m \cdot y^m$	$(x \cdot y)^5 = x^5 \cdot y^5$
5.	Power of a Quotient Rule	To simplify power of a quotient, raise each factor in the numerator and the denominator to the same exponent. $\left(\frac{x}{y}\right)^m = \frac{x^m}{y^m}$	$\left(\frac{x}{y}\right)^4 = \frac{x^4}{y^4}$
6.	Negative Exponent Rule	To simplify negative exponents, write the reciprocal of the base and use a positive exponent. $\left(\frac{x}{y}\right)^{-m} = \left(\frac{y}{x}\right)^m$, $x^{-m} = \frac{1}{x^m}$, $\frac{1}{x^{-m}} = x^m$	$\left(\frac{x}{y}\right)^{-3} = \left(\frac{y}{x}\right)^3$, $x^{-5} = \frac{1}{x^5}$, $\frac{1}{x^{-4}} = x^4$, $x^{-1} = \frac{1}{x}$, $\frac{1}{x^{-1}} = x$
7.	Zero as Exponent Rule	Any base (except 0) raised to the power zero is equal to 1. $x^0 = 1$	$5^0 = 1, (xy)^0 = 1, \left(\frac{x}{y}\right)^0 = 1$
8.	One as Exponent Rule	No change to the base. $x^1 = x$	$7^1 = 7, (xy)^1 = xy, \left(\frac{x}{y}\right)^1 = \frac{x}{y}$

Note: There are no rules for addition or subtraction of exponents. These operations have to be done separately.

For example, $2^3 + 2^5 = (2 \times 2 \times 2) + (2 \times 2 \times 2 \times 2 \times 2)$

$= 8 + 32 = 40$

Example 8.3-a **Multiplying Expressions Using Product Rule**

Simplify each of the following expressions:

(i) $3x^2 \cdot 4x^5$ (ii) $-2x \cdot 4x^3 \cdot 2x^4$

(iii) $2x^2 \cdot y^4 \cdot 3x^2 \cdot y^2$ (iv) $x^n \cdot x^{2n} \cdot x^{(n-1)}$

Solution

(i) $3x^2 \cdot 4x^5$ Regrouping the factors,

$= 3 \cdot 4 \cdot x^2 \cdot x^5$ Applying Product Rule and simplifying,

$= 12 \cdot x^{(2+5)}$

$= 12x^7$

(ii) $-2x \cdot 4x^3 \cdot 2x^4$ Regrouping the factors,

$= -2 \cdot 4 \cdot 2 \cdot x \cdot x^3 \cdot x^4$ Applying Product Rule and simplifying,

$= -16x^{(1+3+4)}$

$= -16x^8$

(iii) $2x^2 \cdot y^4 \cdot 3x^2 \cdot y^2$ Regrouping the factors with same bases,

$= 2 \cdot 3 \cdot x^2 \cdot x^2 \cdot y^4 \cdot y^2$ Applying Product Rule and simplifying,

$= 6x^{(2+2)} \cdot y^{(4+2)}$

$= 6x^4y^6$

(iv) $x^n \cdot x^{2n} \cdot x^{(n-1)}$ Applying Product Rule,

$= x^{[n+2n+(n-1)]}$

$= x^{4n-1}$

Example 8.3-b **Multiplying and Dividing Expressions Using Product Rule and Quotient Rule**

Simplify each of the following expressions:

(i) $\dfrac{6x^5}{8x^2}$ (ii) $\dfrac{-15x^4 \cdot 8x^2}{10x^3}$

(iii) $\dfrac{-25x^2 \cdot 3y^3}{-5xy^2}$ (iv) $\dfrac{2x^n \cdot 3x^{2n}}{4x^{n-1}}$

Solution

(i) $\dfrac{6x^5}{8x^2}$ Regrouping factors,

$= \dfrac{6}{8} \cdot \dfrac{x^5}{x^2}$ Applying Quotient Rule and simplifying,

$= \dfrac{3}{4} \cdot x^{(5-2)}$

$= \dfrac{3}{4} \cdot x^3$

(ii) $\dfrac{-15x^4 \cdot 8x^2}{10x^3}$ Regrouping factors,

$= \dfrac{-15 \cdot 8}{10} \cdot \dfrac{x^4 \cdot x^2}{x^3}$ Applying Product Rule and Quotient Rule and simplifying,

$= -12x^{(4+2-3)}$

$= -12x^3$

Solution
continued

(iii) $\dfrac{-25x^2 \cdot 3y^3}{-5xy^2}$ — Regrouping factors,

$= \dfrac{-25 \cdot 3}{-5} \cdot \dfrac{x^2 \cdot y^3}{x \cdot y^2}$ — Applying Product Rule and Quotient Rule and simplifying,

$= 15x^{(2-1)} \cdot y^{(3-2)}$

$= 15xy$

(iv) $\dfrac{2x^n \cdot 3x^{2n}}{4x^{n-1}}$ — Regrouping factors,

$= \dfrac{2 \cdot 3}{4} \cdot \dfrac{x^n \cdot x^{2n}}{x^{n-1}}$ — Applying Product Rule and Quotient Rule and simplifying,

$= \dfrac{3}{2} \cdot x^{[n+2n-(n-1)]}$

$= \dfrac{3}{2} \cdot x^{(3n-n+1)}$

$= \dfrac{3}{2}x^{(2n+1)}$

Example 8.3-c **Simplifying Expressions Using Power of a Power Rule**

Simplify each of the following expressions:

(i) $(2x^2)^4$ (ii) $(2x^3 \cdot 3y^2)^3$

(iii) $(-3x^3)^2$ (iv) $(-2x^2 \cdot y^4)^3$

Solution

(i) $(2x^2)^4$ — Regrouping and raising each factor to the power of 4,

$= 2^4 \cdot (x^2)^4$ — Applying Power of a Power Rule and simplifying,

$= 16 \cdot x^{(2 \cdot 4)}$

$= 16x^8$

(ii) $(2x^3 \cdot 3y^2)^3$ — Regrouping and raising each factor to the power of 3,

$= (2 \cdot 3 \cdot x^3 \cdot y^2)^3$ — Applying Power of a power Rule and simplifying,

$= 6^3 \cdot (x^3)^3 \cdot (y^2)^3$

$= 216x^9y^6$

(iii) $(-3x^3)^2$ — Regrouping and raising each factor to the power of 2,

$= (-3)^2 \cdot (x^3)^2$ — Applying Power of a Power Rule and simplifying,

$= 9x^6$

(iv) $(-2x^2 \cdot y^4)^3$ — Regrouping and raising each factor to the power of 3,

$= (-2)^3 \cdot (x^2)^3 \cdot (y^4)^3$ — Applying Power of a Power Rule and simplifying,

$= -8 \cdot x^6 \cdot y^{12}$

$= -8x^6y^{12}$

Example 8.3-d **Simplifying Expressions using the Power of a Quotient Rule**

Simplify each of the following expressions:

(i) $\left(\dfrac{x^5 \cdot y^2}{x^2}\right)^4$ (ii) $\left(\dfrac{x^3 \cdot y^4}{x^5y}\right)^2$

Solution

(i) $\left(\frac{x^5 \cdot y^2}{x^2}\right)^4$ Regrouping factors with same the base,

$= \left(\frac{x^5}{x^2} \cdot y^2\right)^4$ Simplifying using Power of a Quotient Rule,

$= (x^{(5-2)} \cdot y^2)^4$

$= (x^3 \cdot y^2)^4$ Simplifying using Power of a Power Rule,

$= (x^3)^4 \cdot (y^2)^4$

$= x^{(3 \cdot 4)} \cdot y^{(2 \cdot 4)}$

$= x^{12}y^8$

(ii) $\left(\frac{x^3 \cdot y^4}{x^5 y}\right)^2$ Regrouping factors with the same base,

$= \left(\frac{x^3}{x^5} \cdot \frac{y^4}{y}\right)^2$ Simplifying using Quotient Rule,

$= \left(x^{(3-5)} \cdot y^{(4-1)}\right)^2$

$= (x^{-2} \cdot y^3)^2$ Simplifying using Power of a Power Rule,

$= x^{-2 \cdot 2} \cdot y^{3 \cdot 2}$

$= x^{-4}y^6$

Example 8.3-e **Simplifying Expressions using the Negative Exponent Rule**

Rewrite the following expressions:

(i) $(x^{-5})^2$ (ii) $x^{-4} \cdot y^{-2}$ (iii) $\frac{5x^{-4} \cdot y^{-3}}{x^2 y}$

Solution

(i) $(x^{-5})^2$

$= x^{-10}$

$= \frac{1}{x^{10}}$

(ii) $x^{-4} \cdot y^{-2}$

$= \frac{1}{x^4} \cdot \frac{1}{y^2}$

$= \frac{1}{x^4 y^2}$

(iii) $\frac{5x^{-4} \cdot y^{-3}}{x^2 y}$

$= \frac{5x^{-4}}{x^2} \cdot \frac{y^{-3}}{y}$

$= 5x^{(-4-2)} \cdot y^{(-3-1)}$

$= 5x^{-6} \cdot y^{-4}$

$= 5 \cdot \frac{1}{x^6} \cdot \frac{1}{y^4}$

$= \frac{5}{x^6 y^4}$

Fractional Exponents

When the exponent, 'n', of a variable is a fraction, we call it a fractional exponent. The fractional exponent, $\frac{1}{n}$, replaces the radical sign, $\sqrt{\ }$.

For example,

The square root of $x = \sqrt{x} = x^{\frac{1}{2}}$.

The cube root of $x = \sqrt[3]{x} = x^{\frac{1}{3}}$.

Similarly, the nth root of $x = \sqrt[n]{x} = x^{\frac{1}{n}}$.

$x^{\frac{1}{n}} = \sqrt[n]{x}$

$x^{-\frac{1}{n}} = \frac{1}{x^{\frac{1}{n}}} = \frac{1}{\sqrt[n]{x}}$

$x^{\frac{m}{n}} = \left(x^{\frac{1}{n}}\right)^m = \left(\sqrt[n]{x}\right)^m$

$x^{-\frac{m}{n}} = \frac{1}{x^{\frac{m}{n}}} = \frac{1}{\left(\sqrt[n]{x}\right)^m}$

$= \frac{1}{\sqrt[n]{x^m}}$

Fractional exponents obey all the rules of exponents.

(i) $x^{\frac{1}{n}} = \sqrt[n]{x}$

For example, if $x = 16$ and $n = 4$, then, $16^{\frac{1}{4}} = \sqrt[4]{16} = 2$

(ii) $x^{-\frac{1}{n}} = \frac{1}{x^{\frac{1}{n}}} = \frac{1}{\sqrt[n]{x}}$

For example, if $x = 27$, and $n = 3$, then $(27)^{-\frac{1}{3}} = \frac{1}{(27)^{\frac{1}{3}}} = \frac{1}{\sqrt[3]{27}} = \frac{1}{3}$

(iii) $x^{\frac{m}{n}} = \left(x^{\frac{1}{n}}\right)^m = [\sqrt[n]{x}\,]^m$ (This refers to finding the nth root of x, then raising the result to the power of m.)

For example, if $x = 16$, $m = 3$, and $n = 4$, then, $16^{\frac{3}{4}} = \left(16^{\frac{1}{4}}\right)^3 = [\sqrt[4]{16}\,]^3 = [2]^3 = 8$

or

$x^{\frac{m}{n}} = (x^m)^{\frac{1}{n}} = \sqrt[n]{x^m}$ (This refers to raising 'x' to the power of 'm', then finding the nth root of the result.)

For example, if $x = 16$, $m = 3$, and $n = 4$, then, $16^{\frac{3}{4}} = (16^3)^{\frac{1}{4}} = \sqrt[4]{16^3} = \sqrt[4]{4{,}096} = 8$

Note: The first method is easier because finding the nth root first results in a smaller number, which is then easier solved when raised to the power of 'm'.

(iv) $x^{-\frac{m}{n}} = \frac{1}{x^{\frac{m}{n}}} = \frac{1}{(\sqrt[n]{x})^m}$

For example, if $x = 27$, $m = 4$, and $n = 3$,

then, $24^{-\frac{4}{3}} = \frac{1}{24^{\frac{4}{3}}} = \frac{1}{(\sqrt[3]{27})^4} = \frac{1}{(3)^4} = \frac{1}{81}$

Example 8.3-f Simplifying Algebraic Expressions Using the Fractional Exponent Rule

Simplify each of the following expressions:

(i) $\left(\frac{\sqrt[4]{x^8}}{\sqrt[2]{x^3}}\right)^2$ (ii) $\left(\frac{\sqrt[3]{x^{12}}}{\sqrt[4]{x^8}}\right)^{\frac{1}{2}}$

Solution

(i) $\left(\frac{\sqrt[4]{x^8}}{\sqrt[2]{x^3}}\right)^2$ Rewriting using Fractional Exponent Rule,

$= \left(\frac{x^{\frac{8}{4}}}{x^{\frac{3}{2}}}\right)^2$ Simplifying the exponents within the bracket,

$= \frac{(x^2)^2}{\left(x^{\frac{3}{2}}\right)^2}$ Applying the Power of a Power Rule and simplifying,

$= \frac{x^{(2\cdot 2)}}{x^{\left(\frac{3}{2}\cdot 2\right)}}$

$= \frac{x^4}{x^3}$ Applying the Quotient Rule and simplifying,

$= x^{(4-3)}$

$= x$

Solution
continued

(ii) $\left(\dfrac{\sqrt[3]{x^{12}}}{\sqrt[4]{x^{8}}}\right)^{\frac{1}{2}}$ Rewriting using Fractional Exponent Rule,

$= \left(\dfrac{x^{\frac{12}{3}}}{x^{\frac{8}{4}}}\right)^{\frac{1}{2}}$ Simplifying the exponents within the bracket,

$= \dfrac{(x^{4})^{\frac{1}{2}}}{(x^{2})^{\frac{1}{2}}}$ Applying the Power of a Power Rule, and simplifying,

$= \dfrac{x^{(4 \cdot \frac{1}{2})}}{x^{(2 \cdot \frac{1}{2})}}$

$= \dfrac{x^{2}}{x}$ Applying the Quotient Rule,

$= x^{(2-1)} = x$

8.3 | Exercises

Answers to odd-numbered problems are available at the end of the textbook.

Simplify the following and express the answer with a positive exponent:

1. $x^3 \cdot x^7$
2. $x^5 \cdot x^4$
3. $4x^4 \cdot 2x$
4. $3x^3 \cdot 5x^2$
5. $(-5x^6)(-3x^2)$
6. $(-4x^3)(-2x)$
7. $(-2x^3)(3x^5)$
8. $(4x^6)(-3x^3)$
9. $x^2 \cdot x^5 \cdot x^7$
10. $x^6 \cdot x^4 \cdot x$
11. $2x^3 \cdot 3x^2 \cdot 4x$
12. $3x^5 \cdot 4x^4 \cdot 5x$
13. $x^7 \div x^4$
14. $x^5 \div x^2$
15. $6x^6 \div 2x^2$
16. $8x^5 \div 4x^2$
17. $x^8 \cdot x^2 \div x^7$
18. $x^3 \cdot x^7 \div x^6$
19. $(x^2)^4 \cdot (x^3)^5$
20. $(3x^3)^2 \cdot (2x)^3$
21. $(4x^0)^4$
22. $(3x^0)^3$
23. $\left(\dfrac{2x^4}{5y^2}\right)^3$
24. $\left(\dfrac{3x^3}{2y^4}\right)^4$
25. $\left(\dfrac{2x^3}{5y^2}\right)^2$
26. $\left(\dfrac{3x^4}{5y^3}\right)^4$
27. $\dfrac{x^2 y^2}{(xy)^2}$
28. $\dfrac{x^5 y^6}{(x^2 y^3)^2}$
29. $(2x^2)^{-4}$
30. $(3x^3)^{-2}$
31. $(x^{-5} \cdot 2y^{-1})^{-1}$
32. $(2x^{-3} \cdot y^{-2})^{-1}$
33. $(3x^{-3} \cdot y^3)^{-2}$
34. $(4x^4 \cdot y^{-3})^{-3}$
35. $(2x^2 \cdot y^{-4})^3$
36. $(2x^{-3} \cdot y^2)^4$
37. $\left(\dfrac{x}{y}\right)^{-2}\left(\dfrac{x}{y}\right)^3$
38. $\left(\dfrac{x}{y}\right)^{-3}\left(\dfrac{x}{y}\right)^5$
39. $\left(\dfrac{x}{y}\right)^2\left(\dfrac{x}{y}\right)^3\left(\dfrac{x}{y}\right)^{-4}$
40. $\left(\dfrac{x}{y}\right)^4\left(\dfrac{x}{y}\right)^3\left(\dfrac{x}{y}\right)^{-5}$
41. $(x^3)^2 (x^2)^3 (x^3)^{-1}$
42. $(x^5)^{-1} (x^3)^2 (x^2)^{-3}$
43. $-2x^2 (-2x)^2$
44. $3x^3 (-3x)^3$
45. $\left(\dfrac{4x\ 5y}{16xy^4}\right)^2$
46. $\left(\dfrac{5x^3 y^2}{12x y^3}\right)^3$
47. $\dfrac{(-x^2 y)^3}{-x^2 y^3}$
48. $\dfrac{(-x y)^3}{-x y^2}$
49. $\dfrac{(-2x^2 y^3)^3}{(x y)^2}$
50. $\dfrac{(-3x^3 y^2)^2}{(x y)^3}$
51. $\dfrac{(3x y)^2}{3y^6}$
52. $\dfrac{(2x y)^3}{4y^6}$
53. $\dfrac{(3x^2 y^3)^2}{9xy}$
54. $\dfrac{(5x^4 y)^3}{25xy}$
55. $\dfrac{(-4x^5 y^2)^2}{16x^2 y^2}$
56. $\dfrac{(-2x^2 y^2)^4}{8x^3 y^3}$

57. $\sqrt[5]{x}$ 58. $\dfrac{1}{\sqrt[3]{x}}$ 59. $\dfrac{1}{\sqrt{x^3}}$ 60. $\sqrt[4]{x^2}$

61. $\sqrt[6]{x^5}$ 62. $\dfrac{1}{\sqrt[4]{x^3}}$ 63. $\dfrac{1}{\sqrt[3]{x^4}}$ 64. $\sqrt[5]{x^3}$

65. $\left(\sqrt[4]{x^3}\right)^8$ 66. $\left(\sqrt[3]{x^5}\right)^{10}$ 67. $(2x)^{-\frac{1}{3}}$ 68. $(3x)^{-\frac{1}{4}}$

69. $\sqrt[4]{x^6 x^{10}}$ 70. $\sqrt[6]{x^8 x^4}$ 71. $\sqrt[3]{x^9 y^{12}}$ 72. $\sqrt[4]{x^{12} y^8}$

73. $\sqrt[3]{x^9 x^6}$ 74. $\sqrt[2]{x^{10} x^{-6}}$ 75. $(27x^6)^{\frac{1}{3}}$ 76. $(81x^8)^{\frac{1}{4}}$

77. $\left(\dfrac{x^9}{x^3}\right)^{\frac{1}{3}}$ 78. $\left(\dfrac{x^{19}}{x^4}\right)^{\frac{1}{4}}$ 79. $\dfrac{(-x)^3(-x)^4}{x^5}$ 80. $\dfrac{(-x)^6(-x)^4}{x^9}$

8.4 | Logarithms

Concept of Logarithm and its Relation to Exponents

In the previous section, power of a variable (or term or number) was introduced using exponents and bases.

Power, $a^x = \underbrace{a \cdot a \cdot a \cdot \ldots a}_{x \text{ factor of } a}$

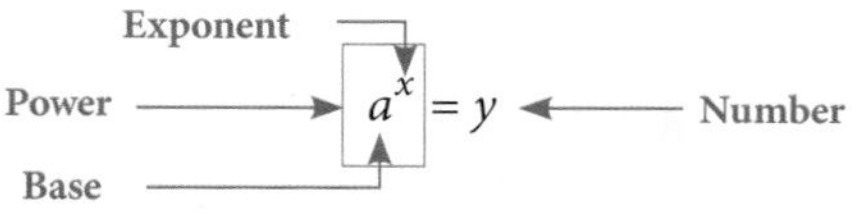

In exponential form	Base	Exponent
$a^x = y$	a	x
$10^3 = 1,000$	10	3
$5^2 = 25$	5	2

Read as: base 'a' raised to the 'x' is 'y' or 'a' to the power of 'x' is 'y'.

In this section you will learn how to determine the exponent, x, to which the base, a, must be raised to obtain y; i.e., to determine the exponent of the base, a, to produce y.

Logarithm is defined as the exponent, x, to which a base, a, must be raised to obtain y.

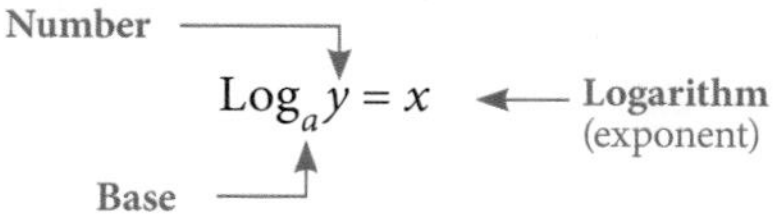

In logarithmic form	Base	Exponent	In exponential form
$\log_a y = x$	a	x	$a^x = y$
$\log_{10} 1,000 = 3$	10	3	$10^3 = 1,000$
$\log_5 25 = 2$	5	2	$5^2 = 25$

Read as: logarithm of 'y' to the base 'a' is 'x' or log 'y' to the base 'a' is 'x'.

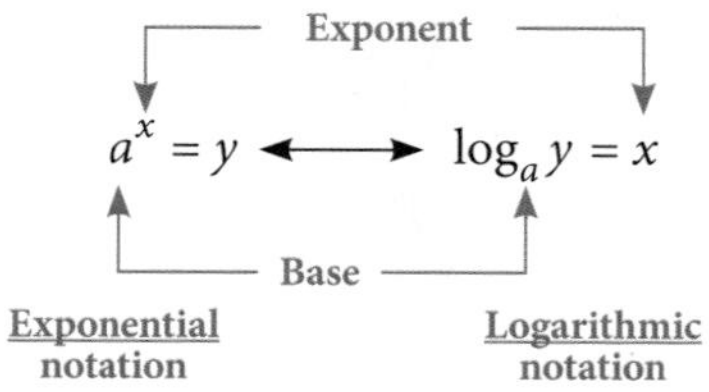

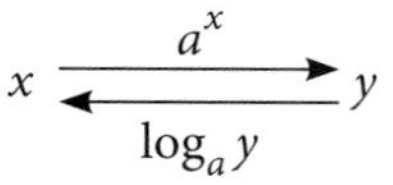

Exponents and logarithms are inverse functions.

For example,

- $10^3 = 1{,}000 \longleftrightarrow \text{log10 } 1{,}000 = 3$

$$3 \underset{\log_{10} 1{,}000}{\overset{10^3}{\rightleftarrows}} 1{,}000$$

- $5^2 = 25 \longleftrightarrow \log_5 25 = 2$

$$2 \underset{\log_5 25}{\overset{5^2}{\rightleftarrows}} 25$$

As seen above, a logarithm is the exponent to which the base is raised to get a number.

Any positive number can be used as the base for logarithms.

For example, 100 is the same as 10^2. Here, the base is 10 and the exponent is 2. Therefore, the logarithm of 100 to the base 10 is 2.

$$\underbrace{10^2 = 100}_{\textbf{Exponential form}} \quad \text{is the same as} \quad \underbrace{\log_{10} 100 = 2}_{\textbf{Logarithmic form}}$$

Similarly, 125 is the same as 5^3. Here, the base is 5 and the exponent is 3; therefore, the logarithm of 125 to the base 5 is 3.

$$\underbrace{5^3 = 125}_{\textbf{Exponential form}} \quad \text{is the same as} \quad \underbrace{\log_5 125 = 3}_{\textbf{Logarithmic form}}$$

Example 8.4-a

Converting Exponential Form to Logarithmic Form

Convert the following to logarithmic form:

(i) $6^2 = 36$ (ii) $2^6 = 64$ (iii) $7^3 = 343$

(iv) $2^{-5} = \frac{1}{32}$ (v) $a^b = c$

Solution

Using $a^x = y \longleftrightarrow \log_a y = x$,

(i) $6^2 = 36$

$\log_6 36 = 2$

(ii) $2^6 = 64$

$\log_2 64 = 6$

(iii) $7^3 = 343$

$\log_7 343 = 3$

(iv) $2^{-5} = \frac{1}{32}$

$\log_2 \frac{1}{32} = -5$

(v) $a^b = c$

$\log_a c = b$

Example 8.4-b

Converting Logarithmic Form to Exponential Form

Convert the following to exponential form:

(i) $\log_3 81 = 4$ (ii) $\log_2 128 = 7$ (iii) $\log_3 2{,}187 = 7$

(iv) $\log_2 \left(\frac{1}{16}\right) = -4$ (v) $\log_a b = c$

Solution

Using $\log_a y = x \longleftrightarrow a^x = y$,

(i) $\log_3 81 = 4$

$3^4 = 81$

(ii) $\log_2 128 = 7$

$2^7 = 128$

(iii) $\log_3 2{,}187 = 7$

$3^7 = 2{,}187$

(iv) $\log_2 \left(\frac{1}{16}\right) = -4$

$2^{-4} = \frac{1}{16}$

(v) $\log_a b = c$

$a^c = b$

Common Logarithms (log)

Common logarithms are always to the base 10. If no base is shown in the common logarithmic expression, it is assumed to be of base 10 and is referred to by the symbol 'log'.

Common Logarithmic Form	Exponential Form
$\log_{10}1{,}000 = \log 1{,}000 = 3$	$10^3 = 1{,}000$
$\log_{10}100 = \log 100 = 2$	$10^2 = 100$
$\log_{10}10 = \log 10 = 1$	$10^1 = 10$
$\log_{10}1 = \log 1 = 0$	$10^0 = 1$
$\log_{10}y = \log y = x$	$10^x = y$

Example 8.4-c

Finding Common Logarithm of Numbers

Calculate the following, rounding to 4 decimal places.

(i) log 10,000 (ii) log 40 (iii) log 6.5 (iv) log 0.25

Solution

Using **log** button on the calculator,

(i) $\log 10{,}000 = 4$

(ii) $\log 40 = 1.602059... = 1.6021$

(iii) $\log 6.5 = 0.812913... = 0.8129$

(iv) $\log 0.25 = -0.602059... = -0.6021$

Natural Logarithms (ln)

Natural logarithms are always to the base 'e' where the constant $e = 2.718282...$

'e' is a special number in mathematics (similar to π, which is equal to 3.141592...) and is found by $\left(1 + \frac{1}{n}\right)^n$, where '$n$' is a large number.

Assume $n = 100{,}000$; therefore, $e = \left(1 + \frac{1}{100{,}000}\right)^{100{,}000} = 2.718282...$

In business and financial calculators, the natural logarithm key, **'ln'**, is the only logarithmic key available. The common logarithm key, **log**, is not available. Natural logarithm is referred to by the symbol '**ln**' (pronounced "lawn"), which has the base 'e'.

If the base of a logarithmic expression is 'e', then it is simply expressed by the symbol '**ln**'.

We know $x^0 = 1$
Thus, $10^0 = 1$
and $e^0 = 1$
Therefore,
$\log_{10}1 = 0 \rightarrow \log 1 = 0$
$\ln_e 1 = 0 \rightarrow \ln 1 = 0$

Natural Logarithmic Form	Exponential Form
$\log_e 1 = \ln 1 = 0$	$e^0 = 1$
$\log_e e = \ln e = 1$	$e^1 = 2.718282...$
$\log_e 10 = \ln 10 = 2.302585...$	$e^{2.302585} = 10$
$\log_e 1.005 = \ln 1.005 = 0.00498754...$	$e^{0.00498754} = 1.005$

The rules of logarithms are used to evaluate the exponent 'n' in business and finance mathematics formulas.

Example 8.4-d

Finding Natural Logarithm of Numbers

Calculate the following, rounding to 4 decimal places.

(i) ln 1,000 (ii) ln 50 (iii) ln 1.05 (iv) ln 0.50

Solution

Using the LN button on the calculator,

(i) $\ln 1{,}000 = 6.907755... = 6.9078$ (ii) $\ln 50 = 3.912023... = 3.9120$ (iii) $\ln 1.05 = 0.048790... = 0.0488$ (iv) $\ln 0.50 = -0.693147... = -0.6931$

Rules of Logarithms

Table 8.4 **Rules of Logarithms**

	Rule	Description	Rule in Common Logarithmic Form
1.	Product Rule	Logarithm of a product equals the sum of the logarithms of the factors.	$\log_a (AB) = \log_a A + \log_a B$
2.	Quotient Rule	Logarithm of a quotient equals the difference between the logarithms of the numerator (dividend) and the logarithm of the denominator (divisor).	$\log_a \left(\frac{A}{B}\right) = \log_a A - \log_a B$
3.	Power Rule	Logarithm of a number raised to a power equals the product of the power and the logarithm of the number.	$\log_a (A)^n = n \log_a \cdot A$
4.	Logarithm of 1 Rule	Logarithm of 1 is zero.	$\log_a 1 = 0$
5.	Logarithm of the Base Rule	Logarithm of the base is one.	$\log_a a = 1$
6.	Logarithm of a Base Raised to a Power Rule	Logarithm of the base raised to a power is equal to the power.	$\log_a (a)^n = n$
7.	Logarithm of Roots (radicals) Rule	Convert the roots (radicals) to exponents and then apply the Power Rule.	$\log_a (\sqrt[n]{A}) = \log_a (A)^{\frac{1}{n}} = \frac{1}{n} \cdot \log_a A$

Note:

$(M+N) \neq \log_a M + \log_a N$

$(M-N) \neq \log_a M - \log_a N$

$_a M)(\log_a N) \neq \log_a M + \log_a N$

$\frac{M}{N} \neq \log_a M - \log_a N$

1. *Rules of logarithms can be used to combine two or more logarithmic expressions into a single logarithmic expression.*
2. *Common logarithms (log) and natural logarithms (ln) follow the same rules.*
3. *To change the base of a logarithm, use the following formula:*

$$\log_a b = \frac{\log_c b}{\log_c a}, \quad \text{(i.e., changing from base 'a' to base 'c'.)}$$

Example: $\log_e A = \frac{\log_{10} A}{\log_{10} e}$ (i.e., $\ln A = \frac{\log A}{\log e}$)

$\log_{10} A = \frac{\log_e A}{\log_e 10}$ (i.e., $\log A = \frac{\ln A}{\ln 10}$).

Example 8.4-e

Evaluating Logarithms Using Rules of Logarithms

Evaluate the following common logarithms.

(i) $\log(100 \times 100)$ (ii) $\log\left(\frac{75}{50}\right)$ (iii) $\log 125^5$ (iv) $\log 10^9$

Solution

(i) $\log(100 \times 100)$ Using Product Rule,

$= \log 100 + \log 100$

$= 2 + 2$

$= 4$

or

$\log(100 \times 100)$ Using exponents,

$= \log(100)^2$ Using Power Rule,

$= 2 \cdot \log(100)$

$= 2 \cdot (2)$

$= 4$

(ii) $\log\left(\frac{75}{50}\right)$ Using Quotient Rule,

$= \log 75 - \log 50$

$= 1.875061... - 1.698970...$

$= 0.176091... = 0.1761$

(iii) $\log(125)^5$ Using Power Rule,

$= 5 \cdot \log(125)$

$= 5 \cdot (2.09690...)$

$= 10.484550... = 10.4846$

(iv) $\log(10)^9$ Using Power Rule,

$= 9 \cdot \log(10)$

$= 9 \cdot (1)$

$= 9$

Example 8.4-f

Evaluating Logarithms Using Rules of Logarithms

Evaluate the following using natural logarithms.

(i) $\ln(275 \times 75)$ (ii) $\ln\left(\frac{4,750}{3,275}\right)$ (iii) $\ln(4.25)^6$ (iv) $\ln(e)^4$

Solution

(i) $\ln(275 \times 75)$ Using Product Rule,

$= \ln 275 + \ln 75$

$= 5.616771... + 4.317488...$

$= 9.934259... = 9.9343$

(ii) $\ln\left(\frac{4,750}{3,275}\right)$ Using Quotient Rule,

$= \ln 4,750 - \ln 3,275$

$= 8.465899... - 8.094073...$

$= 0.371826... = 0.3718$

(iii) $\ln(4.25)^6$ Using Power Rule,

$= 6 \cdot \ln(4.25)$

$= 6 \cdot (1.446918...)$

$= 8.681513... = 8.6815$

(iv) $\ln(e)^4$ Using Power Rule,

$= 4 \cdot \ln(e)$

$= 4 \cdot (1) = 4$

or

$\ln(e)^4$ Using Logarithm of the Base Rule,

$= \log_e(e)^4$

$= 4$

Example 8.4-g **Writing Single Logarithms**

Write each of the following as a single logarithm and evaluate.

(i) $2 \log 3 + \log 5$ (ii) $3 \log 4 - \log 8$ (iii) $5 \log 2 + \log 4 - \log 8$ (iv) $\log \sqrt[3]{216}$

Solution

(i) $2 \log 3 + \log 5$

$= \log 3^2 + \log 5$

$= \log (3^2 \times 5)$

$= \log 45$

$= 1.653212... = 1.6532$

(ii) $3 \log 4 - \log 8$

$= \log (4)^3 - \log 8$

$= \log \left(\frac{4^3}{8}\right)$

$= \log 8$

$= 0.903089... = 0.9031$

(iii) $5 \log 2 + \log 4 - \log 8$

$= \log 2^5 + \log 4 - \log 8$

$= \log 32 + \log 4 - \log 8$

$= \log (32 \times \frac{4}{8})$

$= \log 16$

$= 1.204119... = 1.2041$

(iv) $\log \sqrt[3]{216}$

$= \log (216)^{\frac{1}{3}}$

$= \frac{1}{3} \log 216$

$= \frac{1}{3} (2.334453...)$

$= 0.778151... = 0.7782$

Example 8.4-h **Solving Equations**

Solve for 'n' in the following equations:

(i) $1{,}024 = 2^n$

(ii) $3{,}749 = 1{,}217(1.005)^n$

Solution

Using natural logarithms:

(i) $1{,}024 = 2^n$ Taking ln on both sides,

$\ln 1{,}024 = \ln 2^n$ Using Power Rule,

$\ln 1{,}024 = n \ln 2$ Isolating n,

$n = \frac{\ln 1{,}024}{\ln 2}$

$= \frac{6.931471...}{0.693147...}$

$= 10$

or

Using common logarithms:

$1{,}024 = 2^n$ Taking log on both sides,

$\log 1{,}024 = \log 2^n$ Using Power Rule,

$\log 1{,}024 = n \cdot \log 2$ Isolating n,

$n = \frac{\log 1{,}024}{\log 2}$

$= \frac{3.010299...}{0.301029...}$

$= 10$

(ii) $3{,}749 = 1{,}217(1.005)^n$ Dividing both sides by 1,217,

$\frac{3{,}749}{1{,}217} = (1.005)^n$ Taking ln on both sides,

$\ln\left(\frac{3{,}749}{1{,}217}\right) = \ln (1.005)^n$ Using Power Rule,

$\ln\left(\frac{3{,}749}{1{,}217}\right) = n \ln 1.005$ Isolating n,

$n = \frac{\ln\left(\frac{3{,}749}{1{,}217}\right)}{\ln 1.005}$

$= \frac{1.125100\ldots}{0.004987\ldots}$

$= 225.582147... = 225.5821$

or

$3{,}749 = 1{,}217(1.005)^n$ Dividing both sides by 1,217,

$\frac{3{,}749}{1{,}217} = (1.005)^n$ Taking log on both sides,

$\log\left(\frac{3{,}749}{1{,}217}\right) = n \cdot \log (1.005)$ Isolating n,

$n = \frac{\log\left(\frac{3{,}749}{1{,}217}\right)}{\log 1.005}$

$= \frac{0.488624...}{0.002166...}$

$= 225.582147... = 225.5821$

8.4 | Exercises

Answers to odd-numbered problems are available at the end of the textbook.

Express the following in logarithmic form:

1. a. $10^5 = 100{,}000$ b. $4^5 = 1{,}024$
2. a. $10^4 = 10{,}000$ b. $4^4 = 256$
3. a. $2^6 = 64$ b. $6^5 = 7{,}776$
4. a. $2^3 = 8$ b. $6^4 = 1{,}296$
5. a. $3^2 = 9$ b. $9^4 = 6{,}561$
6. a. $3^3 = 27$ b. $8^2 = 64$

Express the following in exponential form:

7. a. $\log_{10}100 = 2$ b. $\log_4 64 = 3$
8. a. $\log_{10}1{,}000 = 3$ b. $\log_4 4{,}096 = 6$
9. a. $\log_2 32 = 5$ b. $\log_5 625 = 4$
10. a. $\log_2 4 = 2$ b. $\log_5 125 = 3$
11. a. $\log_3 729 = 6$ b. $\log_6 216 = 3$
12. a. $\log_3 243 = 5$ b. $\log_6 1{,}296 = 4$

Calculate the following (rounding to 4 decimal places):

13. a. $\log 225$ b. $\log 1.54$
14. a. $\log 27$ b. $\log 2.5$
15. a. $\log 35$ b. $\log 0.25$
16. a. $\log 155$ b. $\log 0.75$
17. a. $\ln 10.05$ b. $\ln 1.005$
18. a. $\ln 0.675$ b. $\ln 750$
19. a. $\ln 0.165$ b. $\ln 1.02$
20. a. $\ln 12.51$ b. $\ln 72$

Solve for 'n' (rounding to 2 decimal places):

21. $250 = (30)^n$
22. $320 = (15)^n$
23. $(1.05)^n = 1.31$
24. $2.5 = (1.05)^n$
25. $7{,}500 = (45)^n + 500$
26. $8{,}000 = (35)^n + 1{,}500$
27. $10{,}000 = 2{,}000(1.2)^n$
28. $15{,}000 = 5{,}000\,(1.04)^n$

Express the following as a sum or difference of two or more natural logarithms:

29. $\ln\left(\frac{3}{7}\right)$
30. $\ln\left(\frac{40}{13}\right)$
31. $\ln(4 \times 9)$
32. $\ln(7 \times 8)$
33. $\ln\left(\frac{AB}{C}\right)$
34. $\ln\left(\frac{x}{ab}\right)$
35. $\ln\left(\frac{X}{YZ}\right)$
36. $\ln\left(\frac{xy}{c}\right)$
37. $\ln\left(\frac{3x}{2yz}\right)$
38. $\ln\left(\frac{5x}{2ab}\right)$
39. $\ln\left(\frac{xy}{\sqrt{z}}\right)$
40. $\ln\left(\frac{x}{\sqrt{yz}}\right)$

If $\log_a x = M$ and $\log_a y = N$, express the value of each of the following in terms of M and N.

41. $\log_a\left(\frac{x}{y}\right)$
42. $\log_a\left(\frac{y}{x}\right)$
43. $\log_a(xy^2)$
44. $\log_a(x^2y)$
45. $\log_a\left(\frac{x^2}{y}\right)$
46. $\log_a\left(\frac{x}{y^2}\right)$
47. $\log_a(xy)^{-\frac{1}{2}}$
48. $\log_a(yx)^{-\frac{1}{2}}$
49. $\log_a(\sqrt[5]{x^4})$
50. $\log_a\left(\frac{1}{\sqrt[3]{x^2y^2}}\right)$
51. $\log_a\left(\frac{1}{\sqrt[3]{xy}}\right)$
52. $\log_a\left(\frac{1}{\sqrt{xy^3}}\right)$

Express the following as a single natural logarithm:

53. $\ln 8 + \ln 5$
54. $\ln 25 + \ln 4$
55. $\ln 15 - \ln 3$
56. $\ln 60 - \ln 15$
57. $2\ln 5 + 3\ln 3$
58. $2\ln 8 + 3\ln 3$
59. $5\ln 2 - 2\ln 3$
60. $4\ln 5 - 3\ln 2$
61. $2\ln 5$
62. $5\ln 2$
63. $3\ln 6$
64. $6\ln 3$
65. $2\ln\left(\frac{x}{y}\right)$
66. $5\ln\left(\frac{a}{b}\right)$
67. $4\ln(a \times b)$
68. $3\ln(xy)$
69. $3\ln a + 2\ln b - 5\ln c$
70. $4\ln x - 2\ln y + 3\ln z$
71. $3\ln 2 + 4\ln 3 - 2\ln 4$
72. $2\ln 3 + 3\ln 2 - 4\ln 2$

Express the following in the form $K\log_{10} M$, simplify, and then evaluate to 2 decimal places, wherever applicable.

73. $\log_{10}\sqrt{1{,}000}$
74. $\log_{10}\sqrt[4]{10{,}000}$
75. $\log_{10}\sqrt{36}$
76. $\log_{10}\sqrt{625}$
77. $\log_{10}\sqrt[4]{81}$
78. $\log_{10}\sqrt[3]{216}$
79. $\log_{10}\sqrt[3]{9^2}$
80. $\log_{10}\sqrt[5]{32^3}$

Solve for 'n' (rounding to 2 decimal places):

81. $n = \ln\left(\frac{4,285}{4,000}\right)$

82. $n = \ln\left(\frac{6,750}{3,200}\right)$

83. $n = \ln\left(\frac{3,645}{2,175}\right)$

84. $n = \ln\left(\frac{75,000}{2,200}\right)$

85. $n = \frac{\ln\left(\frac{7,200}{4,725}\right)}{\ln(1.01)}$

86. $n = \frac{\ln\left(\frac{5,120}{2,250}\right)}{\ln(1.005)}$

87. $n = \frac{\ln(2.5)}{\ln(1.03)}$

88. $n = \frac{\ln(3)}{\ln(1.02)}$

8.5 | Rearranging Equations and Formulas

Introduction

Equations are mathematical statements formed by placing an equal (=) sign between two expressions to indicate that the expression on the left side is equal to the expression on the right side of the equal sign.

For example, $5x + 3 = y - x$

Formulas are similar to equations. In formulas, the relationship among many variables is written as a rule for performing calculations. Formulas are written so that a single variable, known as the subject of the formula, is on the left side of the equation, and everything else is on the right side.

For example, $I = Prt$

Isolating Variables

To isolate a particular variable in an equation or a formula, rearrange the terms and simplify, so that the required variable is on the left side of the equation and all the other variables and numbers are on the right side of the equation. Rearrangement can be performed by using the rules that you have learned in the previous sections of this chapter and the following guidelines:

- Add or subtract the same quantity to or from both sides.
- Multiply or divide both sides by the same quantity.
- Take powers or roots on both sides.
- Expand the brackets and collect the like terms.
- Remove the fractions by multiplying both sides by the denominator or LCM.

For example, consider the formula for simple interest: $I = Prt$.

To solve for any of the variables, 'I', 'P', 'r', or 't' in this simple interest formula, we can rearrange the variables as shown below:

$I = Prt$ is the same as $Prt = I$

Solving for 'P':

$$\frac{Prt}{rt} = \frac{I}{rt}$$ Dividing both sides by 'rt',

$$P = \frac{I}{rt}$$

Solving for 'r':

$$\frac{Prt}{Pt} = \frac{I}{Pt}$$ Dividing both sides by 'Pt',

$$r = \frac{I}{Pt}$$

Solving for 't':

$$\frac{Prt}{Pr} = \frac{I}{Pr}$$ Dividing both sides by 'Pr',

$$t = \frac{I}{Pr}$$

Example 8.5-a

Rearranging to Isolate Variables

Rearrange and isolate the variables indicated in the brackets:

(i) $S = C + M$ (M)

(ii) $C + E + P = S$ (P)

(iii) $P = RB$ (R)

(iv) $y = mx + b$ (m)

(v) $S = P(1 + rt)$ (P)

Solution

(i) $S = C + M$ (M)

$M + C = S$ Subtracting 'C' from both sides,

$M + C - C = S - C$

$M = S - C$

(ii) $C + E + P = S$ (P) Subtracting 'C' and 'E' from both sides,

$C + E + P - C - E = S - C - E$

$P = S - C - E$

(iii) $P = RB$ (R)

$RB = P$ Dividing both sides by 'B',

$$\frac{RB}{B} = \frac{P}{B}$$

$$R = \frac{P}{B}$$

(iv) $y = mx + b$ (m)

$mx + b = y$ Subtracting 'b' from both sides,

$mx + b - b = y - b$

$mx = y - b$ Dividing both sides by 'x',

$$\frac{mx}{x} = \frac{y - b}{x}$$

$$m = \frac{y - b}{x}$$

(v) $S = P(1 + rt)$ (P)

$P(1 + rt) = S$ Dividing both sides by '(1 + rt)',

$$\frac{P(1 + rt)}{(1 + rt)} = \frac{S}{(1 + rt)}$$

$$P = \frac{S}{(1 + rt)}$$

Example 8.5-b

Solving for Variables Using the Rearranged Simple Interest Formula

In the simple interest formula $I = Prt$, find:

(i) 'I', when $P = \$1,000$, $r = 5\%\ (= 0.05)$, $t = 3$ years

(ii) 'P', when $I = \$150$, $r = 3\%\ (= 0.03)$, $t = 1$ year

(iii) 'r', when $I = \$500$, $P = \$8,000$, $t = 2$ years

(iv) 't', when $I = \$40$, $P = \$800$, $r = 5\%\ (= 0.05)$

(v) 'P' when $I = \$3,180$, $r = 3\%$, $(= 0.03)$, $t = 2$ years

Round the answers to 2 decimal places, wherever applicable.

Solution

(i) Substituting the values for 'P', 'r', and 't' in the formula:

$$I = Prt$$

$$I = 1{,}000.00 \times 0.05 \times 3 = \$150.00$$

(ii) Substituting the values for 'I', 'r', and, 't' in the rearranged formula:

$$P = \frac{I}{rt}$$

$$P = \frac{150.00}{(0.03 \times 1)} = \$5{,}000.00$$

(iii) Substituting the values for 'I', 'P', and 't' in the rearranged formula:

$$r = \frac{I}{Pt}$$

$$r = \frac{500.00}{8{,}000.00 \times 2} = 0.03125 = 3.125\% = 3.13\%$$

(iv) Substituting the values for 'I', 'P', and 'r' in the rearranged formula:

$$t = \frac{I}{Pr}$$

$$t = \frac{40.00}{800.00 \times 0.05} = 1 \text{ year}$$

(v) Substituting the values for 'I', 'r', and 't' in the rearranged formula:

$$P = \frac{I}{1 + rt}$$

$$P = \frac{3{,}180.00}{(1 + 0.03 \times 2)}$$

$$= \frac{3{,}180.00}{1 + 0.06}$$

$$= \frac{3{,}180.00}{1.06} = \$3{,}000.00$$

Example 8.5-c

Rearranging to Isolate Variables Involving Brackets and Fractions

Rearrange to isolate the variables indicated in the brackets.

(i) $S = P(1 + rt)$ (t)

(ii) $y = \dfrac{x + a}{x - a}$ (x)

Solution

(i) $S = P(1 + rt)$ (t)

$P(1 + rt) = S$	Expanding the bracket,
$P + P \cdot rt = S$	Subtracting 'P' from both sides,
$P \cdot r \cdot t = S - P$	Dividing both sides by '$P \cdot r$',
$t = \dfrac{S - P}{P \cdot r}$	

(ii) $y = \dfrac{x + a}{x - a}$ (x)

$y = \dfrac{x + a}{x - a}$	Multiplying both sides by '$(x - a)$',
$(x - a)y = x + a$	Expanding the brackets,
$xy - ay = x + a$	Adding 'ay' to both sides,
$xy = x + a + ay$	Subtracting 'x' from both sides,

Solution *continued*

$xy - x = a + ay$	Factoring 'x' on the left side and 'a' on the right side,
$x(y - 1) = a(1 + y)$	Dividing both sides by '$(y - 1)$',
$x = \dfrac{a(1 + y)}{(y - 1)}$	
$x = \dfrac{a(y + 1)}{y - 1}$	

Example 8.5-d **Rearranging to Isolate Variables Involving Powers and Roots**

Rearrange to isolate the variables indicated in the brackets.

(i) $F = \dfrac{mV^2}{r}$ (V)

(ii) $y = \sqrt{x - a}$ (x)

Solution

(i) $F = \dfrac{mV^2}{r}$ (V)

$\dfrac{mV^2}{r} = F$	Multiplying both sides by 'r',
$mV^2 = \mathrm{F} \cdot \mathrm{r}$	Dividing both sides by 'm',
$V^2 = \dfrac{F \cdot r}{m}$	Taking square root on both sides,
$V = \sqrt{\dfrac{F \cdot r}{m}}$	

(ii) $y = \sqrt{x - a}$ (x)

$\sqrt{x - a} = y$	Taking square on both sides,
$x - a = y^2$	Adding 'a' to both sides,
$x = a + y^2$	

Example 8.5-e **Rearranging to Isolate Variables Involving Factors**

Rearrange to isolate the variables indicated in the brackets.

(i) $a(x - y) = b(x + y)$ (x)

(ii) $y = (x + y)(x - y)$ (x)

Solution

(i) $a(x - y) = b(x + y)$ (x)

$a(x - y) = b(x + y)$	Expanding both sides,
$ax - ay = bx + by$	Subtracting 'bx' from both sides,
$ax - ay - bx = by$	Adding 'ay' to both sides,
$ax - bx = by + ay$	Factoring 'x' on left side and 'y' on right side,
$x(a - b) = y(b + a)$	Dividing both sides by '$(a - b)$',
$x = \dfrac{y(b + a)}{a - b}$	
$x = \dfrac{y(a + b)}{(a - b)}$	

Solution *continued*

(ii) $y = (x + y)(x - y)$ (x)

$(x + y)(x - y) = y$ Expanding left side,

$x^2 - y^2 = y$ Adding 'y^2' to both sides,

$x^2 = y + y^2$ Taking square roots on both sides,

$x = \sqrt{y + y^2}$ Taking 'y' as a factor within the square root,

$x = \sqrt{y(1 + y)}$

Example 8.5-f **Rearranging Formula and Evaluating to Find the Value of a Subject**

The formula for the area 'A' of a rectangle of length 'l' and width 'w' is $A = l \cdot w$

(i) Rearrange the formula to find 'w' as the subject.

(ii) Calculate the width (w) of a rectangle if $A = 200\ \text{cm}^2$ and $l = 25$ cm.

Solution

$A = l \cdot w$

(i) $l \cdot w = A$ Dividing both sides by 'l',

$w = \dfrac{A}{l}$

(ii) Substituting the value for 'A' and 'l' in the rearranged formula,

$w = \dfrac{200}{25} = 8$ cm

Example 8.5-g **Rearranging Formula and Evaluating to Find the Value of a Subject**

The formula for the area 'A' of a circle is $A = \pi r^2$, where r is the radius of the circle.

(i) Rearrange the formula to find 'r' as the subject.

(ii) Find the radius of a circle with an area of $400\ \text{cm}^2$. Use $\pi = 3.14$.
(Round the answer to two decimal places.)

Solution

$A = \pi r^2$

(i) $\pi r^2 = A$ Dividing both sides by π,

$r^2 = \dfrac{A}{\pi}$ Taking square root on both sides,

$r = \sqrt{\dfrac{A}{\pi}}$

(ii) Substituting the values for 'A' and π in the rearranged formula,

$r = \sqrt{\dfrac{400}{3.14}}$

$= 11.286652... = 11.29$ cm

8.5 | Exercises

Answers to odd-numbered problems are available at the end of the textbook.

Rearrange to isolate the variables indicated in the brackets:

1. $4x + 5 = y$ (x)
2. $x + 6y = 15$ (y)
3. $3x - y = 7$ (x)
4. $2y - x = 5$ (y)
5. $S = C + M$ (C)
6. $L - N = d \cdot L$ (d)
7. $N = L(1 - d)$ (L)
8. $C = 2\pi r$ (r)

9. $C + E + P = S$ (E)

10. $S - P - E = C$ (P)

11. $5x - 6 = 2x + y$ (x)

12. $3 - 5x = x + y$ (x)

13. $b = \frac{ac}{1 + a}$ (a)

14. $b = \frac{ac}{1 - a}$ (c)

15. $c = \frac{a - c}{b}$ (b)

16. $c = \frac{a + c}{b}$ (a)

17. $b = \frac{c + ac}{a - 2}$ (a)

18. $b = \frac{c - ac}{a + 2}$ (c)

19. $c = \frac{ab - b}{4 + a}$ (b)

20. $c = \frac{ab + b}{4 - a}$ (a)

21. $6(a - x) = y$ (x)

22. $4(x + a) = y$ (x)

23. $3(a + x) = x$ (x)

24. $5(y + a) = y$ (y)

25. $V^2 = u^2 + 2as$ (u)

26. $V^2 = u^2 + 2as$ (s)

27. $x^2 + y^2 = r^2$ (y)

28. $S = ut + at^2$ (u)

29. $5(x + 2) = 3(x - 7)$ (x)

30. $4(9 - 5) = 5(y + 4)$ (y)

31. $x - y = xy$ (x)

32. $x - xy = y$ (y)

33. $y = \frac{x + 5}{x - 5}$ (x)

34. $x = \frac{y + 2}{y - 2}$ (y)

35. $y = \sqrt{2x + 5}$ (x)

36. $y = \sqrt{7 - 3x}$ (x)

37. $y = 8 - \sqrt{x}$ (x)

38. $y = \sqrt{x} + 4$ (x)

39. $r = \sqrt{\frac{A}{4\pi}}$ (A)

40. $C = \sqrt{a^2 + b^2}$ (a)

41. $\frac{x}{y} + 5 = x$ (y)

42. $7 - \frac{x}{y} = x$ (y)

43. $A = \frac{(a + b)h}{2}$ (a)

44. $A = \frac{(a + b)h}{2}$ (h)

45. $y = (x - 4)(x + 4)$ (x)

46. $y = (3 - x)(3 + x)$ (x)

47. The formula for the area, 'A', of a square is $A = S^2$, where S is the length of the side.
    a. Rearrange the formula to find 'S' as the subject.
    b. Find the length of a square with an area of 441 cm^2.

48. The formula for the area, 'A', of a triangle is $A = \frac{b \cdot h}{2}$, where 'b' is the base and 'h' is the height.
    a. Rearrange the formula to find 'h' as the subject.
    b. Find the height of a triangle with an area of 198 cm^2 and a base length 18 cm.

49. The formula for the surface area, 'A', of a sphere is $A = 4\pi r^2$, where r is the radius of the sphere.
    a. Rearrange the formula to find r as the subject.
    b. Find the radius of a sphere with an area of 800 cm^2. (Use $\pi = 3.14$ and round the answer to 2 decimal places.)

50. The formula for the volume 'V' of a cone is given by the formula $V = \frac{1}{3}\pi r^2 h$, where r is the radius of the base and h is the perpendicular height.
    a. Rearrange the formula to find r as the subject.
    b. Find the base radius of a cone with a volume of 900 cm^3 and a perpendicular height of 10 cm. (Use $\pi = 3.14$ and round the answer to 2 decimal places.)

8 | Review Exercises

Answers to odd-numbered problems are available at the end of the textbook.

Simplify the following expressions then evaluate for the given value of the variables in the brackets:

1. a. $-4x^2 + 3x - 5 + 7x^2 - 2x + 3$ $(x = 2)$
   b. $4x^2 - 5 + 7x - 2x^2 - x - 3,$ $(x = -1)$
2. a. $3x^2 - x + 2 + x^2 - 5x - 2,$ $(x = 3)$
   b. $-5y^2 - 7y + 3 + y^2 - 5y + 2$ $(y = -2)$
3. a. $-y^2 + 4xy + x^2 - 6y^2 - xy - 11x^2$ $(x = 1, y = 2)$
   b. $(x - 4)(x + 2) + 3(x + 2),$ $(x = 3)$
4. a. $-4x^2 + 6xy - 6y^2 + 6x^2 - 2xy + 3y^2$ $(x = 2, y = 1)$
   b. $(y - 2)(y - 3) + 2(y - 2)$ $(y = 4)$
5. a. $(2x - 3)^2 - (x + 3)^2$ $(x = 4)$
   b. $(5 + x)^2 + (4 - x)(4 + x)$ $(x = 5)$
6. a. $(2x + 1)^2 - (x - 2)^2$ $(x = 1)$
   b. $(3 - x)^2 + (x - 3)(x + 3)$ $(x = 2)$

Factor the following expressions then evaluate for the given value of the variables in the brackets:

7. a. $6x^2 - 4x$ $(x = 1)$
   b. $3y^3 - 12y^2$ $(y = -2)$
8. a. $8y^2 - 64y$ $(y = 2)$
   b. $16x^2 - 4x^3$ $(x = -1)$
9. a. $7xy + 14x^2$ $(x = 3, y = 2)$
   b. $9x^3 - 6x^2 + 3x$ $(x = 1)$
10. a. $15y^2 + 10xy$ $(x = -1, y = 2)$
    b. $16x^3 + 8x^2 - 4x$ $(x = 2)$

Write the algebraic equation for the following:

11. a. Twelve increased by three times a number.
    b. The difference between a number and five.
12. a. Eight decreased by twice a number.
    b. Six less than the total of a number and ten.
13. a. The product of three more than a number and the number.
    b. Sum of ten times a number and fifteen.
14. a. Sum of fifteen and half of a number.
    b. Product of two times a number and seven.

Write the algebraic equation for the following and solve:

15. a. Seventeen more than five times a number is forty-two.
    b. A number divided by fifteen is forty-five.
16. a. The product of five and a number is seventy-five.
    b. Three more than two times a number is nine.
17. a. The difference between a number and ten is ten.
    b. The product of four times a number and three is thirty-six.
18. a. The sum of two times a number and eight is one hundred.
    b. A number divided by three is seven.

Solve for the unknown variable, x, using the principles of equations:

19. a. $5x - 5 = 10$ b. $\frac{x}{3} + 4 = 10$
20. a. $3x - 5 = -17$ b. $\frac{x}{4} - 2 = 1$
21. a. $12 - 3x = 3 - 4x$ b. $4(x + 4) = 24$
22. a. $4x - 2 = 13 - 6x$ b. $3(2x - 5) = 3$

Simplify the following and express the answer with a positive exponent:

23. a. $(-x)^2 \cdot (x)^{-4}$ b. $(-x)^3 \cdot (x)^4$
24. a. $(-x)^3 \cdot (x)^{-6}$ b. $x^3 \cdot (-x)^4$
25. a. $\frac{x^8}{x^4}$ b. $\frac{x^{-6}}{x^{-4}}$
26. a. $\frac{x^7}{x^5}$ b. $\frac{x^{-2}}{x^{-3}}$
27. a. $\left(\frac{x}{y}\right)^{-\frac{1}{2}}$ b. $\sqrt[3]{6}$
28. a. $\left(\frac{1}{x}\right)^{-\frac{2}{3}}$ b. $\sqrt[5]{x^{10}}$
29. a. $\frac{x^9}{x^5 \cdot x^2}$ b. $\frac{x^{-4}}{x^5 \cdot x^{-9}}$
30. a. $\frac{x^4 \cdot x^2}{x^3}$ b. $\frac{x^{-5}}{x^4 \cdot x^{-3}}$
31. a. $(x^4)(3x^3)$ b. $\frac{x^6}{x^2}$
32. a. $(x^3)(2x^5)$ b. $\frac{x^9}{x^6}$
33. a. $\left(\frac{x^2}{y}\right)^3\left(\frac{x}{2y^2}\right)^2$ b. $\frac{2x^{-5}y^6}{x^3y^{-4}}$
34. a. $\left(\frac{2x^2}{y}\right)^2\left(\frac{3x}{y^2}\right)^3$ b. $\frac{12x^{-5}y^2}{6x\,6y^{-8}}$
35. a. $\left(\frac{4x^3}{2y^2}\right)^3$ b. $(8x^6)^{\frac{1}{3}}$
36. a. $\left(\frac{3x^2}{4y^3}\right)^2$ b. $\left(\frac{x^0}{y^3}\right)^3$

37. a. $\left(\frac{x^7}{x^0}\right)^2$ b. $\left(\frac{3x^{-2}y^7}{6x^3y^{-5}}\right)^2$

38. a. $(4x^2)^{\frac{1}{2}}$ b. $\left(\frac{6x^{-3}y^4}{2xy^{-2}}\right)^{-3}$

Solve for 'n' and express the answer to 2 decimal places:

39. a. $2,060 = 1,225(1.02)^n$ b. $5,215 = (1.005)^n + 600$

40. a. $6,075 = 4,150(1.03)^n$ b. $4,815 = (1.04)^n + 900$

41. a. $2,187 = 3^n$ b. $1,000 = 7^n - 1,401$

42. a. $15,625 = 5^n$ b. $6,000 = 3^n - 561$

43. a. $n = \frac{\ln\left(\frac{2,775}{1,200}\right)}{\ln(1.03)}$ b. $n = \frac{\ln(3)}{\ln(1.02)}$

44. a. $n = \frac{\ln\left(\frac{4,950}{1,250}\right)}{\ln(1.005)}$ b. $n = \frac{\ln(1,200)}{\ln(5)}$

45. a. $n = \frac{\log(500)}{\log(2)}$ b. $n = \frac{\log(2)}{\log(1.05)}$

46. a. $n = \frac{\log\left(\frac{4,235}{1,615}\right)}{\log(1.048)}$ b. $n = \frac{\log(320)}{\log(4)}$

47. The formula for the circumference of a circle is $C = 2\pi r$. Rearrange to isolate the variable 'r'.
    a. Find 'r' to 2 decimal places when $C = 75$ cm.
    b. Find the area 'A' of the above circle to the nearest cm^2, using the formula $A = \pi r^2$.

48. The formula for the volume of a cylinder is $V = \pi r^2 h$.
    a. Isolate the variable 'r'.
    b. Find 'r' when $V = 300$ cm^3 and $h = 15$ cm. Round to 2 decimal places.

49. The formula for the volume of a cone is $V = \frac{1}{3}\pi r^2 h$.
    a. Isolate the variable 'h'.
    b. Find 'h', when $r = 11$ cm and $V = 4,560$ cm^3. Round the answer to 2 decimal places.

50. The formula for the volume of a cone is $V = \frac{1}{3}\pi r^2 h$.
    a. Isolate the variable 'r'.
    b. Find 'r', when $V = 2,280$ cm^3 and $h = 15$ cm. Round the answer to 2 decimal places.

8 | Self-Test Exercises

Answers to all problems are available at the end of the textbook.

Simplify the following expressions, then evaluate for the given value of the variables in the brackets:

1. a. $2x^2 + 5x + 1 - 4 - 3x - x^2$ $(x = 2)$
   b. $-3x^2 + 2x + 2x^2 - 8x + 10$ $(x = -3)$
2. a. $9x^2 - 4xy + y^2 - 6y^2 - 3xy + 10x^2$ $(x = 1, y = 2)$
   b. $5(2x - 3y) - 2(3x - 2y) + 7$ $(x = 2 \text{ and } y = 1)$
3. $(x + 3)^2 - (x + 2)(x - 2)$ $(x = 3)$
4. $(2x + 5)^2 - (3x - 1)^2$ $(x = 1)$

Factor the following expressions then evaluate for the given value of the variables in the brackets:

5. a. $18y^2 - 12y$ $(y = -2)$
   b. $15y^3 + 12y^2 + 3y$ $(y = 1)$
6. a. $14xy - 21x^2$ $(x = 2, y = -1)$
   b. $8xy^2 - 6x^2y$ $(x = 1, y = -1)$

Write the in algebraic expressions for the following:

7. a. Twenty-five less than three times a number.
   b. A number increased by eighteen.
8. a. The difference between twice a number and six.
   b. A number divided by three.

Write the following as algebraic equations and solve:

9. a. Nine less than twice a number is twenty-one.
   b. Twenty-two is five times a number less than three.
10. a. Four times eight is sixteen times a number.
    b. Thirty is a product of six and a number.

Solve for the unknown variable 'x', using the principles of equations:

11. a. $24 - 5x = 4$ b. $\frac{x}{3} - 2 = 4$

12. a. $8 + 2x = 4 - 5x$ b. $3(3x - 3) = 33$

Simplify the following and express the answer with a positive exponent:

13. a. $(-x)^3(-x)^4$ b. $(x^0 y^4)^5 (-y)^{-2}$

14. a. $\frac{(-x)^5}{(-x)^2}$ b. $\frac{(-x)^{-5}(-x)^{-3}}{(-x)^{-4}}$

15. a. $(x^{-6})^{\frac{1}{3}}$ b. $\frac{x^{-3} \cdot x^{-4}}{x^2}$

16. a. $\sqrt[3]{x^6}$ b. $\frac{(x^{-5} \cdot x^2)^{-3}}{(x^{-2})^4}$

Simplify the following and express the answer with a positive exponent:

17. a. $(3x^3)^2$

    b. $(4x^2y^3)^2$

18. a. $(16x^0y^4)^{\frac{1}{2}}$

    b. $(-2x^{-2}y^{-4})^{-1}(2x^{-2})^2$

19. a. $\left(\frac{x^6}{x^2}\right)^{-\frac{1}{2}}$

    b. $(x^{-3}y)^2$

20. a. $\frac{x^{-7}x^{-3}}{x^{-10}}$

    b. $(x^4y^4)(-2x^{-3}y)(2x^2)^{-2}$

Solve for 'n' and express the answer to 2 decimal places:

21. a. $n = \frac{\ln\left(\frac{2,200}{1,200}\right)}{\ln(1.04)}$

    b. $n = \frac{\ln(1,475)}{\ln(10)}$

22. a. $n = \frac{\log(5,000)}{\log(3)}$

    b. $n = \frac{(\log 1,250)}{\log(1.5)}$

23. a. $460 = 240(1.05)^n$

    b. $750 = (1.05)^n + 600$

24. Given the formula $C = \frac{5}{9}(F - 32)$:

    a. Isolate 'F'.

    b. Find the value of 'F' when C = 30°C. Round to 2 decimal places.

25. Given the formula $A = 2\pi r(r + h)$:

    a. Isolate 'h'.

    b. Find the value of 'h' when A = 1,200 cm^2 and r = 10 cm. Round to 2 decimal places.

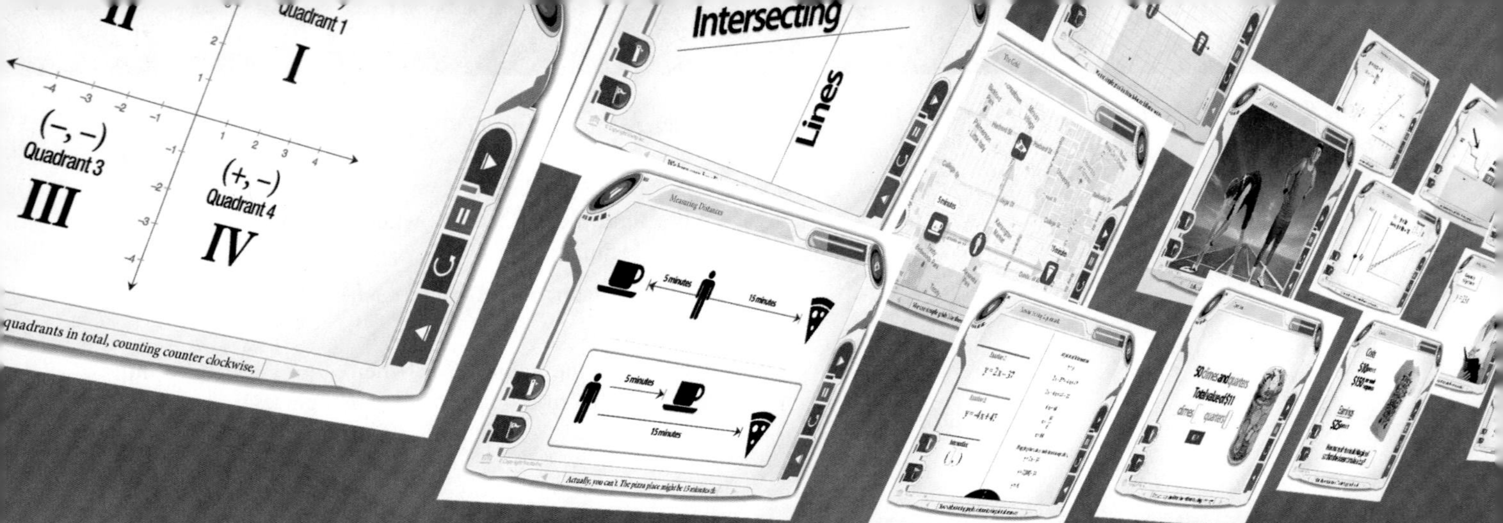

9 GRAPHS AND SYSTEMS OF LINEAR EQUATIONS

A linear graph is an illustrative way to express an equation with two variables. A linear equation describes a relationship in which the value of one of the variables depends on the value of the other variable. Therefore, the solutions are a set of ordered pairs replacing the respective variables in the equation. Many word problems can be solved easily by translating them to systems of equations with two or more variables. A 'system' of equations is a set of equations considered together. 'Linear' equations produce straight lines when graphed. The simplest linear system is one with two equations and two variables. A system of linear equations can be solved by several methods. In this chapter, you will learn how to graph linear equations and understand how graphs represent the solution to these equations. You will also learn how to solve systems of linear equations by plotting the equations on the same graph or by using algebraic approaches, such as the substitution and elimination methods.

LEARNING OBJECTIVES

- Identify the basic terminology of rectangular coordinate systems.
- Express linear equations in standard form and slope-intercept form.
- Determine the slope and y-intercept of a line from its equation.
- Construct a table of values for a linear equation.
- Graph a linear equation using the table of values, slope-intercept, and x- and y- intercepts.
- Determine the equation of a line from a graph.
- Determine the equation of parallel and perpendicular lines.
- Classify systems of linear equations.
- Solve linear systems graphically.
- Solve linear systems using the substitution or elimination method.
- Write and solve systems of equations to word problems.

CHAPTER OUTLINE

9.1 | Rectangular Coordinate System

Introduction

Graphs provide information in a visual form and they are drawn on a rectangular coordinate system known as the Cartesian coordinate system (invented by René Descartes). Understanding the rectangular coordinate system is important in order to be able to read and draw graphs.

This system uses a horizontal and a vertical number line, each known as an axis. These two perpendicular axes cross at the point (O), known as the origin.

The horizontal number line (moving to the left or the right) is known as the X-axis and the vertical number line (moving up or down) is known as the Y-axis, as illustrated in Exhibit 9.1-a.

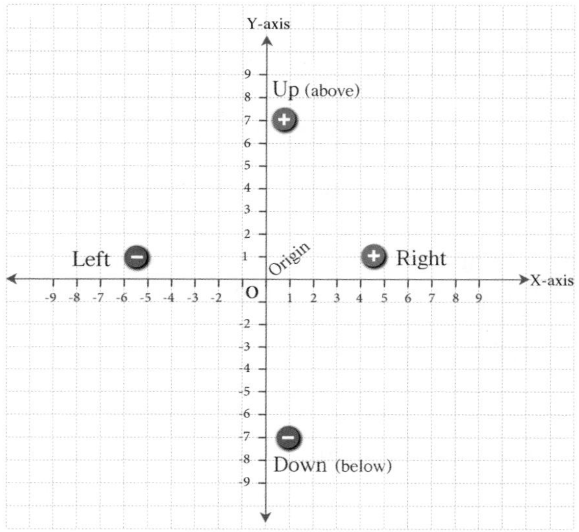

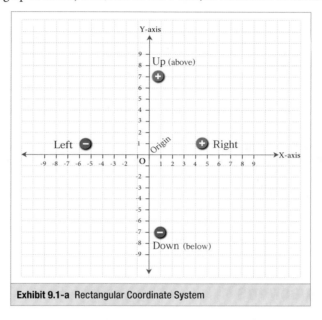

Exhibit 9.1-a Rectangular Coordinate System

Sign Convention

The numbers to the **right** of the origin along the X-axis are **positive** (+) and those to the left are **negative** (–). The numbers **above** the origin along the Y-axis are **positive** (+) and those below are **negative** (–).

The purpose of the rectangular coordinate system and the sign convention is to locate a point relative to the X- and Y-axes and in reference to the origin 'O'.

ach ordered pair, (x, y), epresents only one point n the graph. The x and values of the ordered air determine the cation of that point.

Ordered pairs are used to locate a point in the coordinate system. Numbers in an ordered pairs are known as **coordinates**. The ordered pair (x, y) describes a point in the plane by its x- and y-coordinates. Ordered pairs are usually written within brackets, with the value for x always written first, followed by y, and separated by a comma. The origin is identified by the coordinates (0, 0) since both its x and y values are 0.

As illustrated in Exhibit 9.1-b, the coordinate of a point P, written as the ordered pair (2, 3), refers to the point P which is 2 units to the right and 3 units above, in reference to the origin.

Note: The first value in the bracket is the x-coordinate (horizontal distance from the Y-axis) and the second value in the bracket is the y-coordinate (vertical distance from the X-axis) of the point; i.e., the x-coordinate of point P is 2 units and the y-coordinate of point P is 3 units, as illustrated in Exhibit 9.1-b.

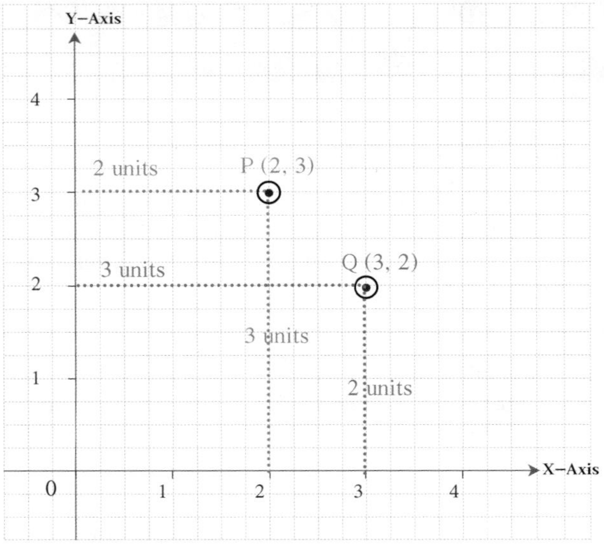

Exhibit 9.1-b Ordered Pairs

It is known as **rectangular coordinate system** because the *x*- and *y*-coordinates form a rectangle with the X- and Y- axes.

It is important to identify the coordinate numbers in their order. They are known as ordered pairs because the order in which they appear determines their position on the graph. Changing their order will result in a different point.

For example,

Pay close attention to the order in which coordinate pairs are written.

(2, 3) and (3, 2) are different points.

(2, 3) refers to a point 'P', which is 2 units to the right of the origin and 3 units above the origin.

(3, 2) refers to a point 'Q', which is 3 units to the right of the origin and 2 units above the origin.

Quadrants

The X- and Y- axes divide the coordinate plane into 4 regions, known as the **quadrants**. Quadrants are numbered counter-clockwise from one (I) to four (IV), as illustrated in Exhibit 9.1-c.

That is, the upper right quadrant is Quadrant I, the upper left quadrant is Quadrant II, the lower left quadrant is Quadrant III, and the lower right quadrant is Quadrant IV. Table 9.1 shows the sign convention of the coordinates, the respective examples are plotted on the graph in Exhibit 9.1-d.

Table 9.1 **Sign Convention of Coordinates in Different Quadrants, Axes, and Origin**

Quadrant, Axis, Origin	Sign of x-coordinate	Sign of y-coordinate	Example (plotted in Exhibit 9.1-d)
Quadrant I	Positive (+)	Positive (+)	A (3, 2)
Quadrant II	Negative (−)	Positive (+)	B (−3, 4)
Quadrant III	Negative (−)	Negative (−)	C (−5, −2)
Quadrant IV	Positive (+)	Negative (−)	D (5, −3)
X–Axis	Positive (+) or Negative (−)	Zero (0)	E (4,0), F (−2,0)
Y–Axis	Zero (0)	Positive (+) or Negative (−)	G (0,3), H (0,−4)
Origin	Zero (0)	Zero (0)	0 (0,0)

Points with one or more zeros (0) as coordinates are on axes and not in quadrants.

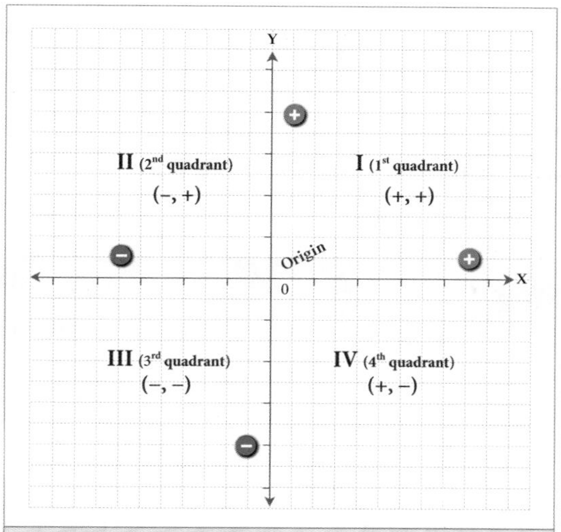

Exhibit 9.1-c The Quadrants

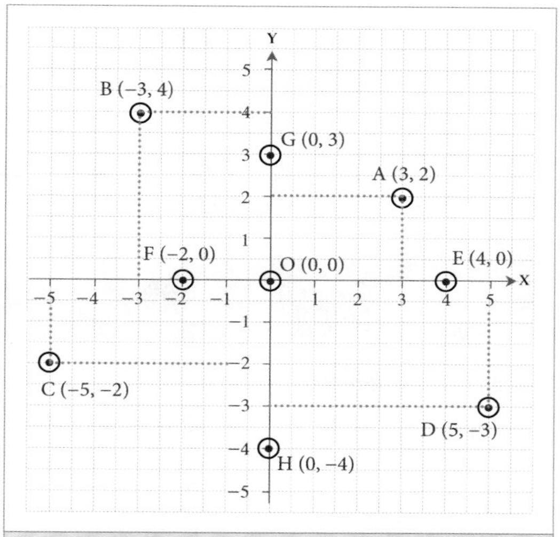

Exhibit 9.1-d Coordinates in Different Quadrants

Example 9.1-a Identifying *x*- and *y*-Coordinates

Find the *x*- and *y*-coordinates of the points A, B, C, D, E, F, G and H, labelled in the graph.

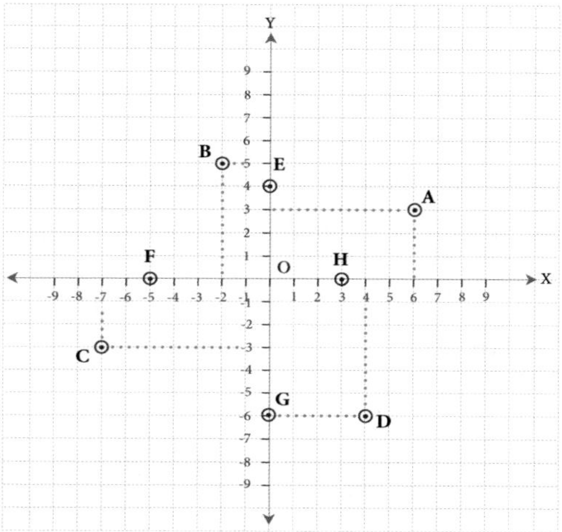

Solution

A: (6, 3)	B: (−2, 5)	C: (−7, −3)	D: (4, −6)
E: (0, 4)	F: (−5, 0)	G: (0, −6)	H: (3, 0)

Example 9.1-b Identifying the Quadrant or the Axis

Identify the quadrant or the axis in which the following points are located:

(i) A (−15, 20)	(ii) B (20, 5)	(iii) C (9, 0)	(iv) D (0, 20)
(v) E (12, −18)	(vi) F (0, −6)	(vii) G (−30, −15)	(viii) H (−1, 0)

Solution

(i) A (−15, 20) ⟶ (−, +) = 2nd Quadrant

(ii) B (20, 5) ⟶ (+, +) = 1st Quadrant

(iii) C (9, 0) ⟶ (+, 0) = X-Axis (Right)

(iv) D (0, 20) ⟶ (0, +) = Y-Axis (Up)

Solution
continued

(v)	E (12, −18)	⟶	(+, −)	= 4th Quadrant
(vi)	F (0, −6)	⟶	(0, −)	= Y-Axis (Down)
(vii)	G (−30, −15)	⟶	(−, −)	= 3rd Quadrant
(viii)	H (−1, 0)	⟶	(−, 0)	= X-Axis (Left)

9.1 | Exercises

Answers to odd-numbered problems are available at the end of the textbook.

Plot the following points on a graph:

1. a. A (−3, 5) b. B (5, −3) c. C (0, −4)
2. a. A (−6, 0) b. B (4, −2) c. C (0, −7)
3. a. D (6, 0) b. E (−2, 4) c. F (5, 2)
4. a. D (8, 0) b. E (−3, −5) c. F (5, 5)

In which quadrant or axis do the following points lie?

5. a. A (−1, 2) b. B (5, −1) c. C (3, 5)
6. a. A (1, 6) b. B (4, −3) c. C (−7, 3)
7. a. D (−4, 0) b. E (−2, −7) c. F (0, 5)
8. a. D (6, 0) b. E (−1, −13) c. F (0,−7)

Plot the following pairs of points on a graph and calculate the length of each horizontal line joining the pair of points:

9. a. (3, 4) and (5, 4) b. (−7, 1) and (2, 1)
10. a. (2, −6) and (7, −6) b. (−5, −4) and (0, −4)
11. a. (−5, 3) and (0, 3) b. (−2, −2) and (6, −2)
12. a. (−6, 8) and (−1, 8) b. (7, −5) and (2, −5)

Plot the following pairs of points on a graph and calculate the length of each vertical line joining the pair of points:

13. a. (3, 6) and (3, 1) b. (5, 2) and (5, −5)
14. a. (−3, −5) and (−3, −9) b. (−3, 0) and (−3, 6)
15. a. (5, 6) and (5, 2) b. (7, 2) and (7, −4)
16. a. (−3, 5) and (−3, −4) b. (−3, 5) and (−3, 0)
17. Three vertices of a square, ABCD, have points *A* (−3, 3), B (1, 3), and C (1, −1). Find the coordinates of the 4th vertex, D.
18. Three vertices of a square, EFGH, have points *E* (−1, −2), *F* (6, −2), and *G* (6, 5). Find the coordinates of the 4th vertex, *H*.
19. Three vertices of a rectangle, PQRS, have points *P* (−3, 4), *Q* (6, 4), and *R* (6, −1). Find the coordinates of the 4th vertex, *S*.
20. Three vertices of a rectangle, TUVW, have points *T* (−4, 7), *U* (5, 7), and *V* (5, 4). Find the coordinates of the 4th vertex, *W*.
21. A vertical line has a length of 7 units and the coordinates at one end of the line is (1, 5). Find the possible coordinates at the other end of the line.
22. A vertical line has a length of 5 units and the coordinates at one end of the line is (−3, 1). Find the possible coordinates at the other end of the line.
23. A horizontal line has a length of 6 units and the coordinates at one end of the line is (−1, 3). Find the possible coordinates at the other end of the line.
24. A horizontal line has a length of 8 units and the coordinates at one end of the line is (−1, −2). Find the possible coordinates at the other end of the line.

9.2 | Graphing Linear Equations

Introduction

A linear equation is an algebraic equation with one or two variables (each with an exponent of one), which produces a straight line when plotted on a graph.

Examples of linear equations with one variable are:

$3x - 5 = 0,$ $\quad x - 3 = 0,$ $\quad 5y + 7 = 0,$ $\quad y + 2 = 0$

Examples of linear equations with two variables are:

$2x - 3y + 3 = 0,$ $\quad y = 2x + 3,$ $\quad 4y = 3x,$ $\quad x + y = 0$

Linear equations with two variables are generally represented by the variables x and y and expressed either in the standard form of $Ax + By = C$ (A, B, and C are integers) or in the slope-intercept form of $y = mx + b$ (m and b are integers or fractions).

The process of finding the value of the variables for which the equation(s) are true is known as solving the equations. Linear equations with two variables have an infinite pairs of values as solutions; therefore, it is convenient to represent these solutions by drawing a graph.

Linear Equations in Standard Form

For an equation in standard form, the value of A is usually positive.

The 'standard' form for a linear equation with two variables, x and y, is written as $Ax + By = C$, where A, B, and C are integers, A is positive, and A, B, and C, have no common factors other than 1.

For example, consider the following simple linear equation with two variables: $2x - y = -3$

This equation is in the standard form of $Ax + By = C$, where $A = 2$, $B = -1$, and $C = -3$.

- If a given equation has fractions, then multiply each term by the lowest common denominator (LCD) and rearrange to the standard form.
- If a given equation has decimals, then multiply each term by a multiple of 10 to eliminate the decimals and rearrange to the standard form.
- If a given equation has no fractions or decimals, then rearrange to the standard form.

Example 9.2-a **Writing Linear Equations in Standard Form**

Write the following linear equations in standard form:

(i) $\frac{2}{3}x + \frac{1}{2}y - 3 = 0$ $\qquad$ (ii) $0.3x = 1.25y + 2$ $\qquad$ (iii) $5 - 2x - 3y = 0$

Solution

(i) $\frac{2}{3}x + \frac{1}{2}y - 3 = 0$ $\qquad$ Multiplying each term by the LCD of 6 and simplifying,

$4x + 3y - 18 = 0$ $\qquad$ Rearranging,

$4x + 3y = 18$

Therefore, the equation $\frac{2}{3}x + \frac{1}{2}y - 3 = 0$, in standard form, is $4x + 3y = 18$.

(ii) $0.3x = 1.25y + 2$ $\qquad$ Multiplying each term by 100,

$30x = 125y + 200$ $\qquad$ Dividing each term by 5 and simplifying,

$6x = 25y + 40$ $\qquad$ Rearranging,

$6x - 25y = 40$

Therefore, the equation $0.3x = 1.25y + 2$, in standard form, is $6x - 25y = 40$.

Solution *continued*

(iii) $5 - 2x - 3y = 0$ Rearranging,

$-2x - 3y = -5$ Multiplying each term by -1,

$2x + 3y = 5$

Therefore, the equation $5 - 2x - 3y = 0$, in standard form, is $2x + 3y = 5$.

Linear Equations in Slope-Intercept Form

The 'slope-intercept' form for a linear equation with two variables, x and y, is written in the form of $\boldsymbol{y = mx + b}$, where $\boldsymbol{m}$ and $\boldsymbol{b}$ are either integers or fractions. '$\boldsymbol{m}$' represents the slope and '$\boldsymbol{b}$' represents the y-intercept.

For example, consider a simple linear equation such as $y = 2x + 3$. This equation is in the slope-intercept form of $y = mx + b$, where the slope, $m = 2$, and the y-intercept, $b = 3$.

Example 9.2-b

Writing Linear Equations in Slope-Intercept Form

Write the following linear equations in slope-intercept form and identify the slope of the y-intercept.

(i) $4x + 3y = 18$ (ii) $6x = 25y + 40$

Solution

(i) $4x + 3y = 18$ Rearranging the term with y on the left,

$3y = -4x + 18$ Dividing each term by 3 and simplifying,

$y = -\frac{4}{3}x + 6$ This is in the form, $y = mx + b$

Therefore, the slope $m = -\frac{4}{3}$ and the y-intercept is 6.

(ii) $6x = 25y + 40$ Rearranging the term with y on the left,

$-25y = -6x + 40$ Multiplying each term by -1,

$25y = 6x - 40$ Dividing each term by 25 and simplifying,

$y = \frac{6}{25}x - \frac{8}{5}$ This is in the form, $y = mx + b$.

Therefore, the slope $m = \frac{6}{25}$ and the y-intercept is $-\frac{8}{5}$.

It is not possible to solve equations that are either in standard form or in slope-intercept form because they have two variables, x and y. If an equation has two variables, then it is possible to solve for a set of values by replacing one variable (either x or y) with any number and then solving for the value of the other variable.

For example, consider the equation: $y = 2x + 3$

Choosing $x = 1$ and substituting $x = 1$ in the equation $y = 2x + 3$,

$$y = 2(1) + 3 = 5$$

Therefore, $x = 1$ and $y = 5$ is one of the solutions of the equation; i.e., (1, 5) is a pair of solution that satisfies the equation.

Choosing $x = 2$ and substituting for $x = 2$ in the equation $y = 2x + 3$,

$$y = 2(2) + 3 = 7$$

Therefore, $x = 2$ and $y = 7$ is another solution to the equation; i.e., (2, 7) is another pair of solution that satisfies the equation.

Similarly, we can obtain any number of points that satisfy the equation by choosing different values for x, and computing the corresponding value for y.

Graphing a linear equation means representing the solution of the equation on a graph. The graph of the linear equation will be a line. Conversely, any point on the line is a solution to the linear equation.

Graphing Linear Equations Using a Table of Values

Follow these steps to graph a linear equation using a table of values:

Step 1: Create a table of values by choosing a value for the variable x.

Step 2: Compute the corresponding value for the variable y.

Step 3: Form the ordered pair (x, y).

Step 4: Repeat Steps 1 to 3 two more times to create at least 3 ordered pairs.

Step 5: Plot the ordered pairs (points) on the coordinate system, choosing a scale.

Step 6: Join the points in a straight line.

Step 7: Label the graph with the equation of the line.

)rawing a linear graph equires only two points. Iowever, at least 3 points vill ensure that the formed ne truly represents the iven linear equation.

For example, consider a linear equation, $y = 2x + 3$. We will use 4 ordered pairs that are on this line by choosing values for x and finding the corresponding values for y, then drawing the graph.

- Choosing $x = 3$,

$$y = 2x + 3$$
$$= 2(3) + 3$$
$$= 6 + 3 = 9$$

(3, 9) is a point on the line.

- Choosing $x = 2$,

$$y = 2x + 3$$
$$= 2(2) + 3$$
$$= 4 + 3 = 7$$

(2, 7) is a point on the line.

- Choosing $x = 1$,

$$y = 2x + 3$$
$$= 2(1) + 3$$
$$= 2 + 3 = 5$$

(1, 5) is a point on the line.

- Choosing $x = 0$,

$$y = 2x + 3$$
$$= 2(0) + 3$$
$$= 0 + 3 = 3$$

(0, 3) is a point on the line.

$y = 2x + 3$		
x	y	(x, y)
3	9	(3, 9)
2	7	(2, 7)
1	5	(1, 5)
0	3	(0, 3)

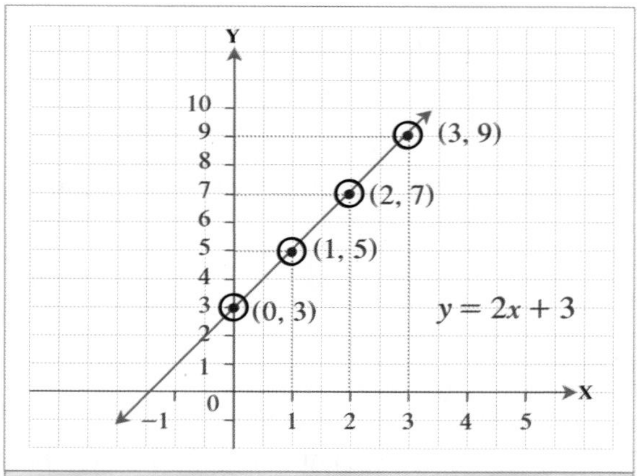

Exhibit 9.2-a Graphing a Linear Equation Using a Table of Values

Since all the points fall on a line when joined, it verifies that the plotted line represents the equation.

Graphing Linear Equations Using the *x*-intercept and the *y*-intercept

***x*-intercept** is the point at which the line crosses the X-axis and where the y-coordinate is zero.

***y*-intercept** is the point at which the line crosses the Y-axis and where the x-coordinate is zero.

If the intercepts are not at the origin (0, 0), we may use the x-intercept and y-intercept as two points to draw a linear graph and use a 3rd point to test the drawn line.

If the intercepts are at the origin (0, 0), then compute another ordered pair to use as the 2nd point to draw the line from this point to the origin. Also, use a 3rd point to test the drawn line.

For example, consider a linear equation, $y = 3x + 9$, where we will find the x-intercept, y-intercept, another ordered pair, and draw the graph.

At the x-intercept the y-coordinate is zero.

Finding the x-intercept:

Substituting $y = 0$ in the given equation and solving for x,

$0 = 3x + 9$, thus, $x = -3$.

Therefore, $(-3, 0)$ is the x-intercept.

At the y-intercept the x-coordinate is zero.

Finding the y-intercept:

Substituting $x = 0$ in the given equation and solving for y,

$y = 3(0) + 9$, thus, $y = 9$.

Therefore, $(0, 9)$ is the y-intercept.

Finding another ordered pair as a 3rd point on this line:

This is to use as a test point to verify the plotted line joining the x-intercept and y-intercept.

Choosing $x = -1$, substituting this in the given equation, and solving for y,

$y = 3(-1) + 9 = 6$

Therefore, $(-1, 6)$ is a point on the line $y = 3x + 9$.

- Plot the ordered pairs on the coordinate system choosing a scale.
- Draw a line to join the x-intercept and y-intercept.

$y = 3x + 9$			
x	y	(x, y)	
-3	0	(-3, 0)	x-intercept
0	9	(0, 9)	y-intercept
-1	6	(-1, 6)	Test point

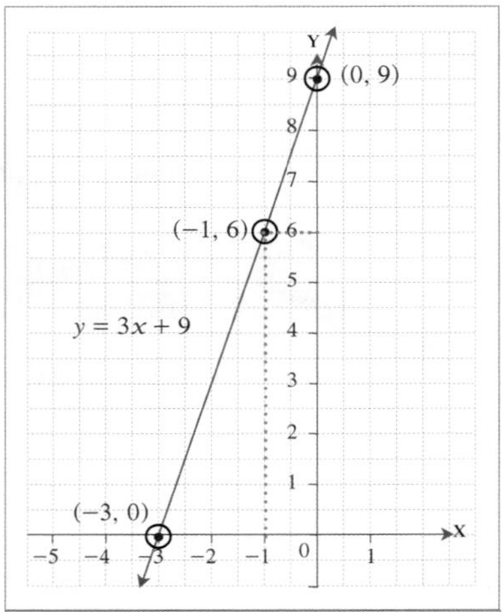

Exhibit 9.2-b Graphing a Linear Equation Using the x-intercept and the y-intercept

Since the point $(-1, 6)$ falls on the line when plotted on the graph, it verifies that the plotted line represents the equation.

Graphing Linear Equations Using the Slope and the y-intercept

A linear equation in the form of $y = mx + b$ is known as the equation in slope-intercept form, where 'm' is the slope and 'b' is the y-intercept.

If the equation is in the standard form, $Ax + By = C$, it can be rearranged to represent the slope-intercept form, as follows:

$$Ax + By = C$$

$$By = -Ax + C$$

$$y = -\frac{A}{B}x + \frac{C}{B}$$

This is in the form $y = mx + b$.

Where the slope, $m = -\frac{A}{B}$, and the y-intercept, $b = \frac{C}{B}$.

The Slope and y-intercept of a Line

The slope (m) is the steepness of the line relative to the X-axis. It is the ratio of the change in value of y (known as 'rise') to the corresponding change in value of x (known as 'run').

If $P(x_1, y_1)$ and $Q(x_2, y_2)$ are two different points on a line, then the slope of the line between the points PQ is:

$$m = \frac{\textit{Change in y value}}{\textit{Change in x value}} = \frac{\Delta y}{\Delta x} = \frac{\textit{Rise}}{\textit{Run}} = \frac{y_2 - y_1}{x_2 - x_1}$$

This is illustrated in Exhibit 9.2-c and Exhibit 9.2-d:

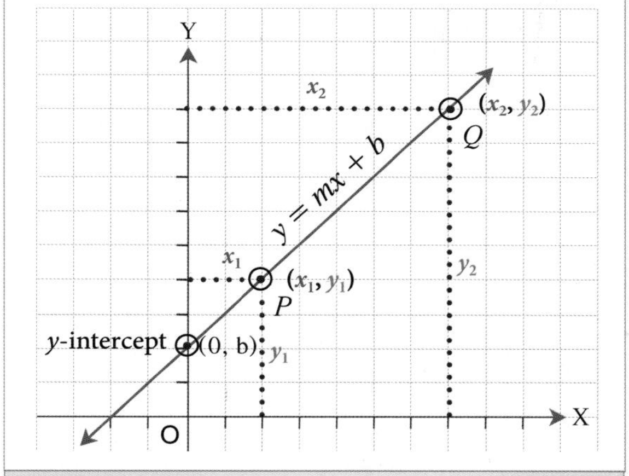

Exhibit 9.2-c Coordinates of Points P and Q

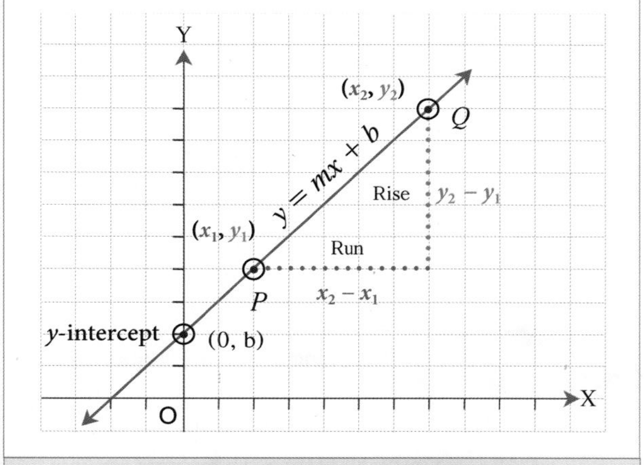

Exhibit 9.2-d Rise and Run Between Points P and Q

Example 9.2-c

Finding the Slope and y-intercept of a Linear Equation and Graphing the Equation

Find the slope and y-intercept of the linear equation, $-2x + 3y - 12 = 0$, and graph the equation.

Solution

$-2x + 3y - 12 = 0$	Rearranging the term with y on the left,
$3y = 2x + 12$	Dividing each term by 3 and simplifying,
$y = \frac{2}{3}x + 4$	This is in the form $y = mx + b$,

Therefore, the slope m is $\frac{2}{3}$, and the y-intercept, b is 4.

Therefore, (0, 4) is a point on the line and the slope,

$$m = \frac{\textit{Change in y value}}{\textit{Change in x value}} = \frac{\text{Rise}}{\text{Run}} = \frac{2}{3}$$

Solution *continued*

Representing this on a graph:

(i) First, plot the y-intercept (0, 4).

(ii) From this point, move 3 units to the right and then move 2 units up to locate the new point (3, 6). This is the same as moving 2 units up, then 3 units to the right to locate the new point (3, 6).

(iii) Similarly, from the point (3, 6) move 3 units to the right and 2 units up to locate another point (6, 8).

(iv) Draw the line through these points to graph the equation.

Or,

(i) From the y-intercept (0, 4), move 3 units to the left and then move 2 units down to locate the point (−3, 2).

(ii) Similarly, by using the same order for both the Rise and the Run, another point is (−6, 0).

(iii) Draw the line through these points to graph the equation.

Note: All the points will lie on the same line.

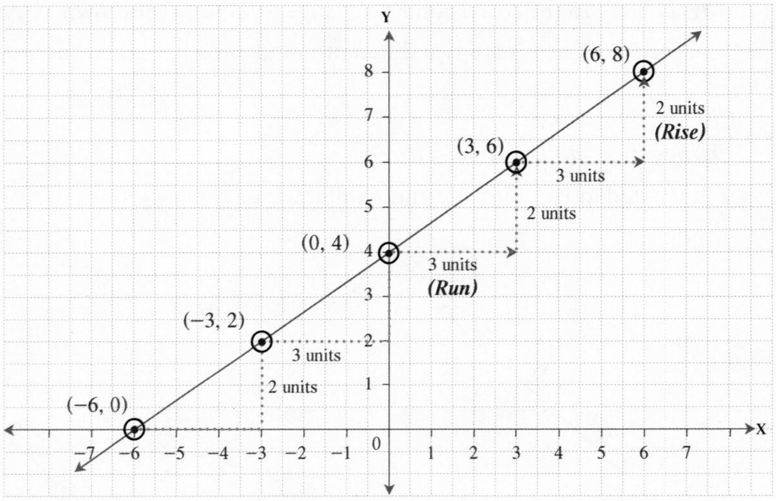

Example 9.2-d

Graphing a Linear Equation in the Slope-Intercept Form

Graph the equation $y = -\frac{3}{4}x - 2$.

Solution

The equation is in the form $y = mx + b$.

Therefore, $xm = -\frac{3}{4}$, the y-intercept, $b = -2$, which gives the point (0, −2), and the slope,

$$m = \frac{\textit{Change in y value}}{\textit{Change in x value}} = \frac{\textit{Rise}}{\textit{Run}} = \frac{-3}{4}, \textit{ or } = \frac{3}{-4}$$

First plot the point (0, −2). Then, using the slope, $m = \frac{-3}{4}$, from the point (0, −2), move 4 units to the right and 3 units down to locate the new point, (4, −5).

Alternatively, first plot the point (0, −2). Then, using the slope, $m = \frac{3}{-4}$, from the point (0, −2), move 4 units to the left and 3 units up to get another point on the line, (−4, 1).

Solution
continued

Draw a line through these points to graph the equation.

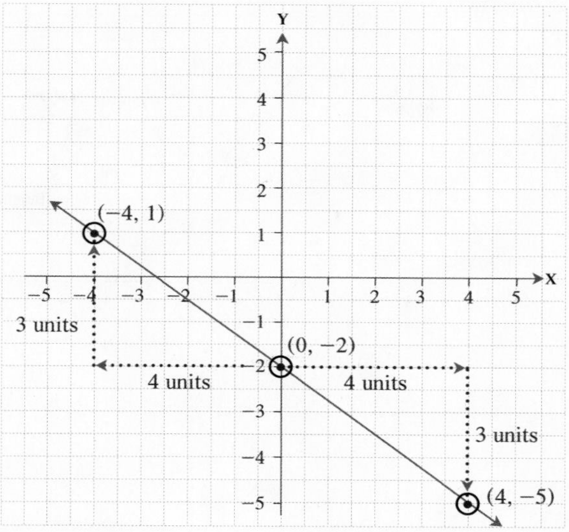

Slope, Direction, and Steepness of a Line

The slope, m, of a line is a number that describes the direction of the line and the steepness of the slope.

The **direction** of the line either slopes upwards to the right, downwards to the right, is horizontal or vertical.

If the slope of the line is positive, then the line rises to the right.

(i) If the sign of the coefficient of 'm' is positive, then the line slopes upwards to the right (i.e., the line rises from left to right), as illustrated in Exhibit 9.2-e.

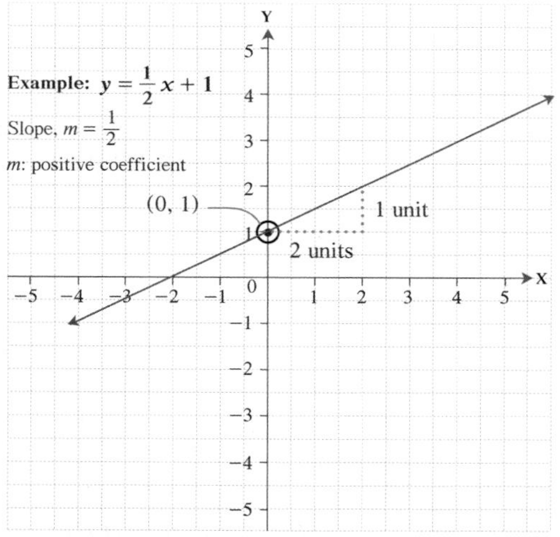

Exhibit 9.2-e The Graph of a Line When 'm' is Positive

If the slope of a line is negative, then the line falls to the right.

(ii) If the sign of the coefficient of 'm' is negative, then the line slopes downwards to the right (i.e., the line falls from left to right), as illustrated in Exhibit 9.2-f.

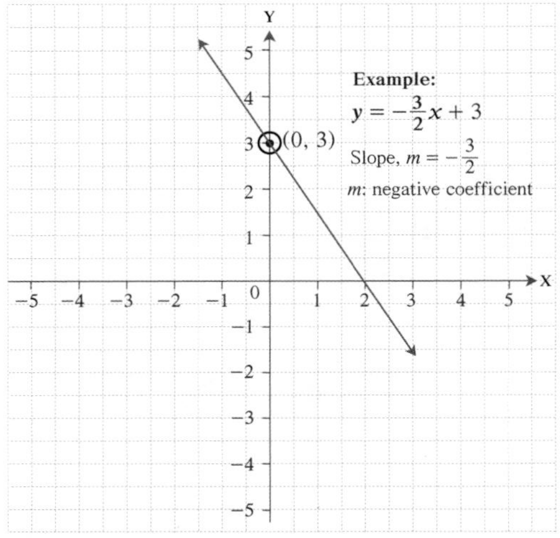

Exhibit 9.2-f The Graph of a Line When 'm' is Negative

If the slope of a line is zero, then the line is horizontal.

(iii) If the coefficient of 'm' is zero, then the line is horizontal (parallel to the X-axis). A slope of zero indicates that when the x-coordinate increases or decreases, the y-coordinate does not change (Rise = 0).

The equation of a horizontal line will be in the form $y = b$, and the y-intercept of the line is $(0, b)$.

For example, in the equation, $y = 3$, $(y = 0x + 3)$, the slope is zero and the value of the y-coordinate is 3 for all values of x.

Therefore, the line is horizontal and passes through (0, 3), as illustrated in Exhibit 9.2-g.

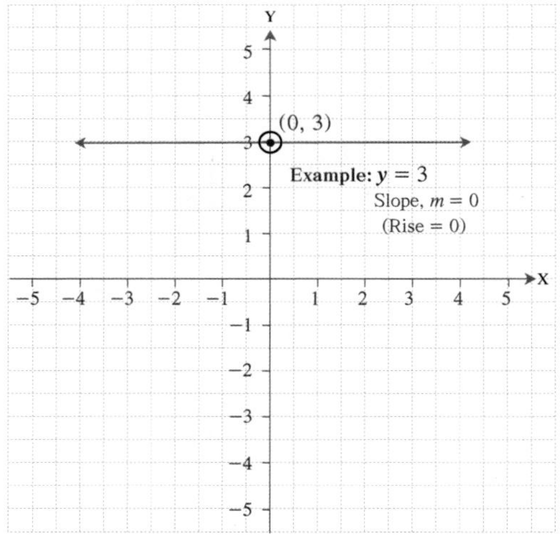

Exhibit 9.2-g The Graph of a Line when 'm' is Zero

If the slope of a line is undefined, then the line is vertical.

(iv) If the coefficient 'm' is undefined, then the line is vertical (parallel to the Y-axis). An undefined slope indicates that when the y-coordinate increases or decreases, the x-coordinate does not change (Run = 0).

The equation of a vertical line will be in the form $x = a$, and the x-intercept of the line is $(a, 0)$.

For example, in the equation, $x = 2$, the value of the x-coordinate is 2 for all values of y.

Therefore, the line is vertical and passes through (2, 0), as illustrated in Exhibit 9.2-h.

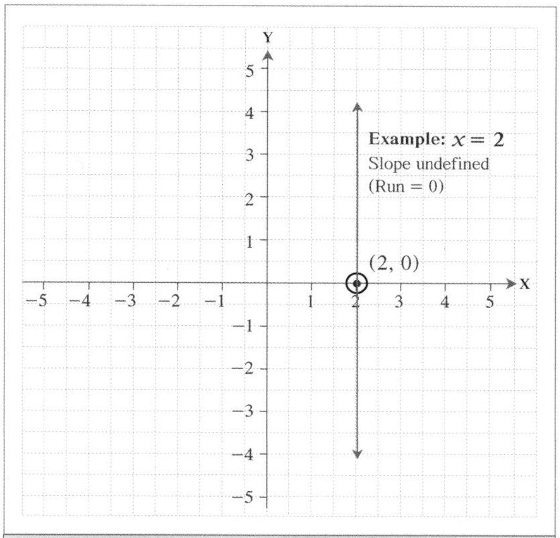

Exhibit 9.2-h The Graph of a Line When 'm' is Undefined

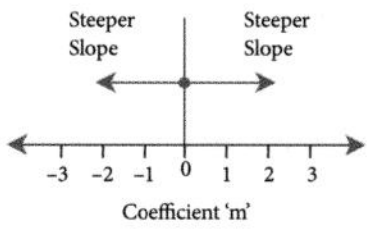

(v) The **steepness** of the line is also measured by the coefficient of the slope 'm' of the line. The farther the coefficient 'm' is away from zero, the steeper is the slope. The closer the coefficient 'm' is to zero, the flatter is the slope.

A higher value for a positive slope indicates a steeper rise.

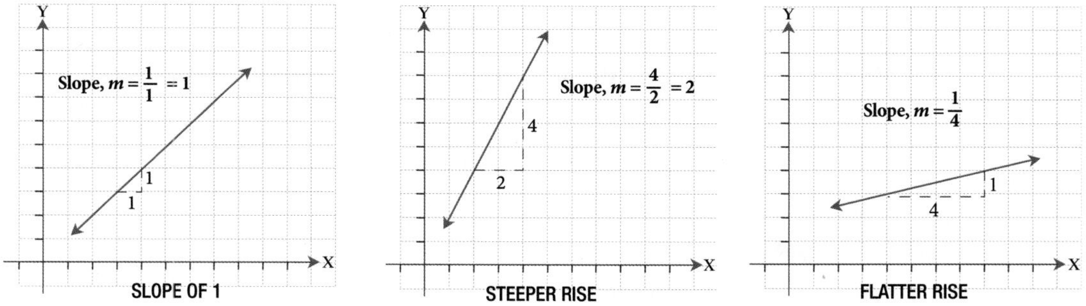

Positive slopes

A smaller value for a negative slope indicates a steeper fall.

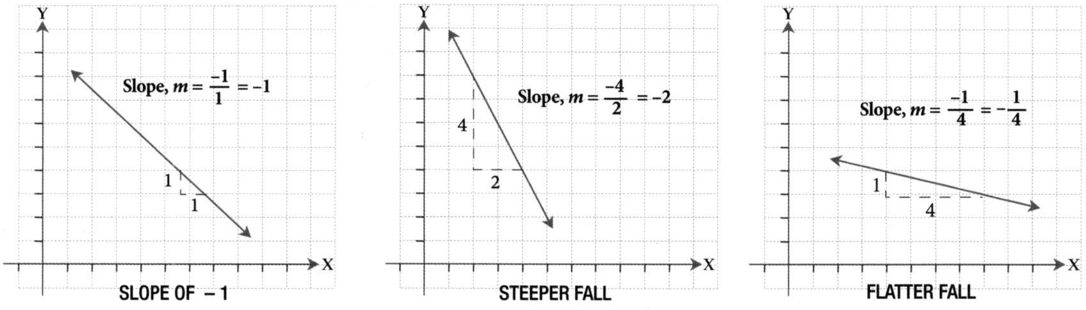

Negative slopes

Line Passing Through the Origin

An equation with a y-intercept (or x-intercept) equal to 0 will have the graph passing through the origin.

Lines passing through the origin have the point (0, 0) is on the line. That is, the coordinate of the y-intercept is (0, 0). The equation of a line passing through the origin will be in the form $y = mx$.

For example, in the equation, $\mathbf{y = 2x}$, the slope, $m = 2$, and y-intercept = 0.

Similarly, in the equation $\mathbf{y = -x}$, the slope $m = -1$, and y-intercept = 0.

Therefore, the lines pass through the origin (0, 0), as illustrated in Exhibit 9.2-i.

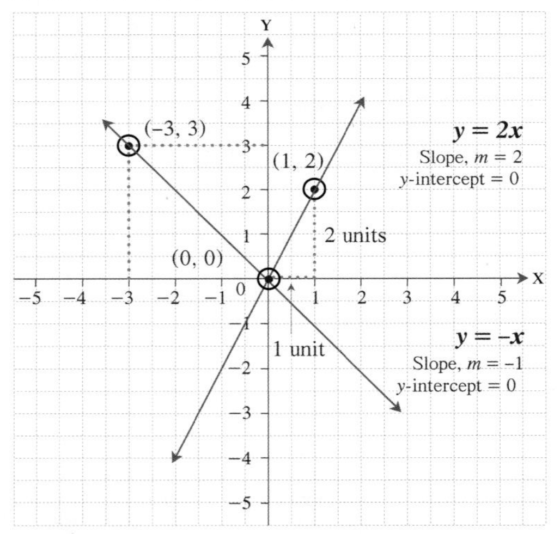

Exhibit 9.2-i Graph of a Line Passing Through the Origin

Example 9.2-e **Finding the Equation of a Line Given the Slope and One Point**

Find the equation of a line having a slope of −2 and passing through (3, 5).

Solution

$m = -2$, point = (3, 5)

Substituting for m in the slope-intercept equation, $y = mx + b$, we obtain,

$y = -2x + b$

Substituting the coordinates of the given point (3, 5) in the above equation to solve for b,

$5 = -2(3) + b,$

$b = 5 + 6 = 11$

Therefore, the equation of the line is $y = -2x + 11$.

Example 9.2-f **Finding the Slope and the Equation of a Line Given Two Points**

Find the equation of a line that passes through points (3, 2) and (4, 5).

Solution

Step 1: Calculate the slope.

$$m = \frac{\textit{Change in y value}}{\textit{Change in x value}} = \frac{y_2 - y_1}{x_2 - x_1} = \frac{5-2}{4-3} = \frac{3}{1}$$

Step 2: Replace m with the calculated slope.

Substituting for m in the slope-intercept equation, $y = mx + b$, we obtain, $y = 3x + b$.

Solution *continued*

Step 3: Substitute one ordered pair into the equation to solve for b.

Substituting the coordinate (3, 2) into the above equation to solve for b,

$2 = 3(3) + b,$

$b = -7$

Step 4: Write the equation in the slope-intercept form, $y = mx + b$, by substituting for the values of m and b, as calculated.

Therefore, the equation of the line is $y = 3x - 7$.

Example 9.2-g

Finding the Equation of a Line Given a Graph

Find the equation of the line that is plotted in the graph shown:

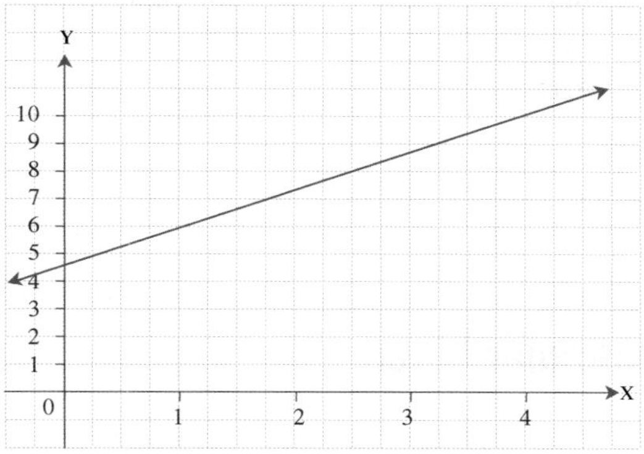

Solution

Start by choosing any two points (with integer coordinates) on the line: e.g., (1, 6) and (4, 10).

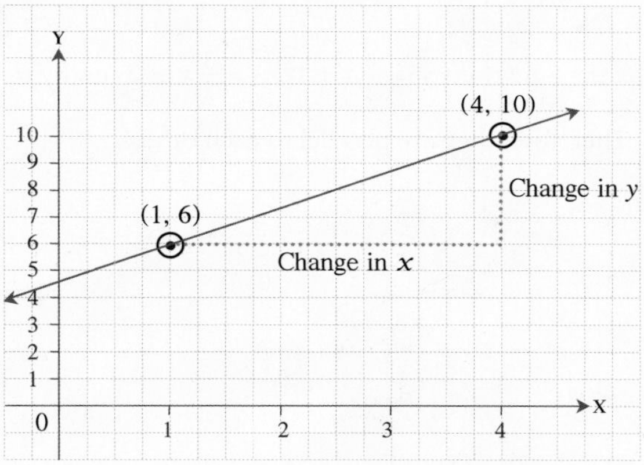

The slope of the line is, $m = \dfrac{y_2 - y_1}{x_2 - x_1} = \dfrac{10 - 6}{4 - 1} = \dfrac{4}{3}.$

Let the equation of the line be $y = mx + b$ Substituting $m = \dfrac{4}{3}$,

Therefore, $y = \dfrac{4}{3}x + b$

Solution *continued*

Substituting the coordinates of one of the points (1, 6) into the above equation, and solving for b,

$$y = \frac{4}{3}(x) + b$$

$$6 = \frac{4}{3}(1) + b$$

Solving for b,

$$b = 6 - \frac{4}{3}(1) = \frac{18 - 4}{3}$$

$$= \frac{14}{3}$$

Therefore, the equation of the line in slope-intercept form is: $y = \frac{4}{3}x + \frac{14}{3}$.

$y = \frac{4}{3}x + \frac{14}{3}$ Multiplying each term by 3, and simplifying,

$3y = 4x + 14$ Rearranging,

$4x - 3y = -14$

Therefore, the equation of the line in standard form, is $4x - 3y = -14$.

Parallel and Perpendicular Lines

Parallel Lines

Lines having the same slope are parallel to each other. All vertical lines are parallel to each other and all horizontal lines are parallel to each other.

For example,

(i) Lines represented by the equations $y = \frac{3}{2}x + 6$, $y = \frac{3}{2}x + 3$, and $y = \frac{3}{2}x - 6$ have the same slope (equal to $\frac{3}{2}$). Therefore, they are parallel to each other.

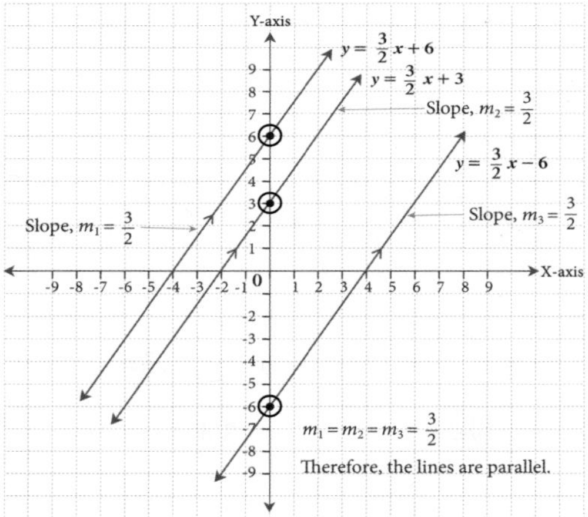

(ii) Lines represented by the equations $x = -4$, $x = 2$, and $x = 5$ are vertical lines and have undefined slopes. Therefore, they are parallel to each other. Vertical lines are parallel to the Y-axis.

ll points on a vertical
ıe will have the same
coordinate and the
ope is undefined.

ıe equation of a vertical
ıe is in the form $x = a$,
here a represents the
coordinate of all the
oints on the line.

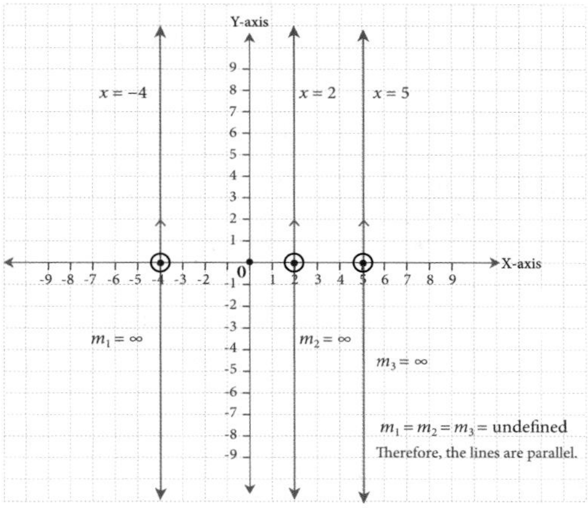

(iii) Lines represented by the equations $y = 4$, $y = 2$, and $y = -2$ are horizontal lines and have slopes equalling zero. Therefore, they are parallel to each other. Horizontal lines are parallel to the X-axis.

ll points on a horizontal
ıe will have the same
coordinate and
e slope is zero.

ıe equation of a horizontal
ıe is in the form $y = b$,
here b represents the
coordinate of all the
oints of the line.

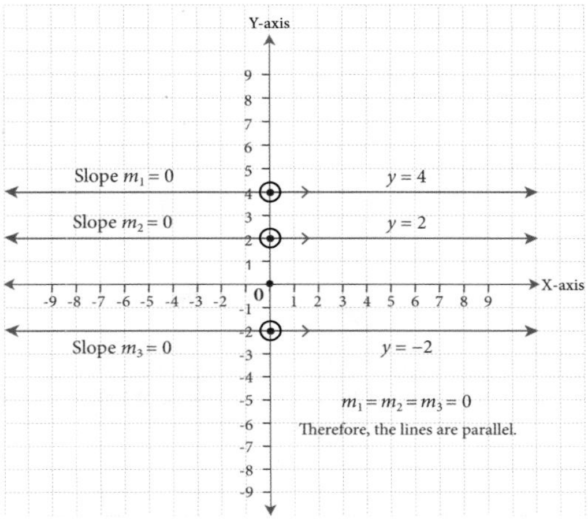

Example 9.2-h

Writing the Equation of a Line Parallel to a Given Line and Passing Through a Given Point

Write the equation of a line parallel to $3x + y = 5$ and that passes through the point P (2, 4).

Solution

$3x + y = 5$ Rearranging to slope-intercept form,

$y = -3x + 5$ Therefore, the slope, $m = -3$.

Lines that are parallel have the same slope.

The slope of the line parallel to this will have the same slope, $m = -3$.

Let the equation of the line parallel to $3x + y = 5$ be $y = mx + b$. It passes through (2, 4) and has a slope, $m = -3$.

$y = mx + b$ Substituting the coordinates (2, 4) and slope $m = -3$,

$4 = -3(2) + b$ Solving for b,

$4 = -6 + b$

$b = 10$

Therefore, the equation of the line that is parallel to $3x + y = 5$ and that passes through the point P(2, 4) is $y = -3x + 10$.

Perpendicular Lines

If the product of the slopes of two lines is −1, then the two lines are perpendicular to each other. This is the same as stating that if the slope of one line is the **negative reciprocal** of the other, then the two lines are perpendicular to each other.

For example, lines represented by $y = 2x + 4$ and $y = -\frac{1}{2}x + 1$ are perpendicular to each other because their slopes are negative reciprocals of each other.

Two lines are perpendicular if the product of their slopes is −1.

$$m_1 = 2,\ m_2 = -\frac{1}{2}$$

$$m_1 \cdot m_2 = 2\left(-\frac{1}{2}\right)$$

$$= -1$$

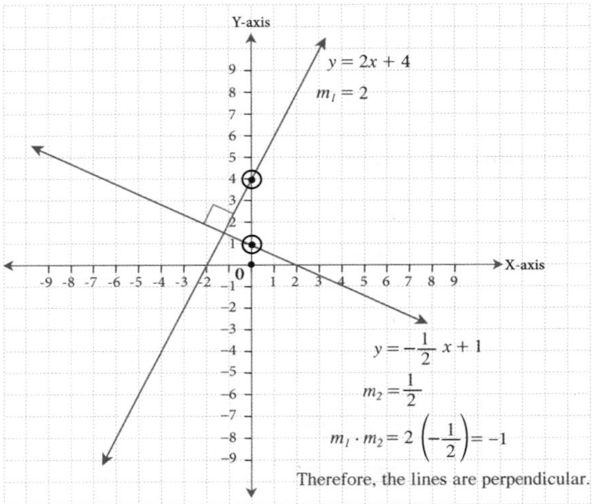

Also, all vertical lines (slope = undefined) and horizontal lines (slope = zero) are perpendicular to each other. For example, lines represented by $y = 2$ and $x = 4$ are perpendicular to each other.

Two lines are also perpendicular if one is vertical (parallel to Y-axis), and the other is horizontal (parallel to X-axis).

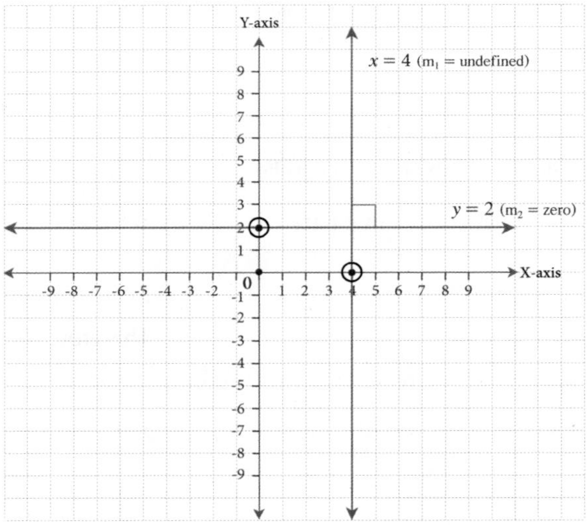

Example 9.2-i **Writing the Equation of a Line Perpendicular to a Given Line and Passing Through a Given Point**

Write the equation of the line perpendicular to $x + 3y = 9$ and that passes through the point $(-4, 2)$.

Solution

$x + 3y = 9$ Rearranging to slope-intercept form,

$3y = -x + 9$

$y = \frac{-1}{3}x + 3$ Therefore, the slope, $m = -\frac{1}{3}$.

Solution *continued*

Lines that are perpendicular have slopes that are a negative reciprocal to each other.

The slope of the line perpendicular to this will be the negative reciprocal, which is 3.

Let the equation of the line perpendicular to $x + 3y = 9$ be $y = mx + b$. It passes through the point $(-4, 2)$ and has a slope, $m = 3$.

$y = mx + b$ — Substituting the coordinates $(-4, 2)$ and slope $m = 3$,

$2 = 3(-4) + b$ — Solving for b,

$2 = -12 + b$

$b = 14$

Therefore, the equation of the line that is perpendicular to $x + 3y = 9$ and that passes through the point $(-4, 2)$, is $y = 3x + 14$.

9.2 | Exercises

Answers to odd-numbered problems are available at the end of the textbook.

1. For the equation $2x + 3y = 18$, find the missing values in the following ordered pairs:

   a. (3, ?) b. (−6, ?) c. (0, ?)
   d. (?, 0) e. (?,−4) f. (?, 2)

2. For the equation $x + 5y = 20$, find the missing values in the following ordered pairs:

   a. (0, ?) b. (−15, ?) c. (5, ?)
   d. (?, 6) e. (?,−3) f. (?, 0)

3. For the equation $y = -\frac{2}{3}x + 1$, find the missing values in the following ordered pairs.

   a. (6, ?) b. (−3, ?) c. (0, ?)
   d. (?, 0) e. (?,−3) f. (?, 5)

4. For the equation $y = -\frac{3}{2}x + 1$, find the missing values in the following ordered pairs.

   a. (2, ?) b. (−3, ?) c. (0, ?)
   d. (?, 0) e. (?,−3) f. (?, 9)

Write the following equations in slope-intercept form:

5. $4y + 6x = -3$
6. $9y + 2x = 18$
7. $3y - 2x = 15$
8. $5y - 2x = -20$
9. $\frac{x}{2} + \frac{y}{3} = 1$
10. $\frac{x}{4} + \frac{y}{5} = 2$

Write the following equations in standard form:

11. $y = \frac{5}{2}x + 1$
12. $y = \frac{2}{5}x - 1$
13. $y = -\frac{3}{4}x - 3$
14. $y = -\frac{4}{3}x + 4$
15. $y = \frac{1}{2}x + \frac{3}{2}$
16. $y = \frac{3}{2}x - \frac{1}{4}$

Graph the following equations using a table of values:

17. $y = x + 3$
18. $y = 3x + 2$
19. $y = -5x + 1$
20. $y = -2x + 3$
21. $2x + y + 1 = 0$
22. $4x + y + 2 = 0$
23. $2x - y - 3 = 0$
24. $x - y - 1 = 0$

Find the x-intercept and y-intercept for the following equations:

25. $3x + y = -2$
26. $5x + y = -3$
27. $x + y - 3 = 4$
28. $x + y - 4 = 7$
29. $y = 2x + 4$
30. $y = 4x + 1$
31. Point 'A' is in the 3rd quadrant and Point 'B' is in the 1st quadrant. Find the sign of the slope of the line AB.
32. Point 'C' is in the 4th quadrant and Point 'D' is in the 2nd quadrant. Find the sign of the slope of the line CD.

Find the slopes and y-intercepts of the following equations and graph the equations:

33. $2x - 3y - 18 = 0$
34. $5x - 2y + 10 = 0$
35. $-4x + 7y - 21 = 0$
36. $-7x + 8y - 32 = 0$

Find the equations of the lines that pass through the following points:

37. (1, 2) and (5, 2)
38. (5, 0) and (4, 5)
39. (−3, −5) and (3, 1)
40. (−4, −7) and (5, 2)

Find the equations of the lines that have:

41. Slope = 1 and passing through (2, 6).
42. Slope = −5 and passing through (3, −2).
43. Slope = 2 and passing through the origin.
44. Slope = 4 and passing through the origin.
45. x-intercept = 4 and y-intercept = −5.
46. x-intercept = −3 and y-intercept = 3.

Find the slopes of the lines passing through:

47. (2, 1) and (6, 1)
48. (−6, 4) and (2, 4)
49. (−5, 4) and (3, −1)
50. (5, 6) and (5, −4)
51. The slope of a line is 3. The line passes through A (4, y) and B (6, 8). Find y.
52. The slope of a line is 2. The line passes through A (x, 8) and B (2, 4). Find x.
53. Points A (2, 3), B (6, 5), and C (10, y) are on a line. Find y.
54. Points D (3, 2), E (6, 5), and F (x, 1) are on a line. Find x.

Find the equation of the line (in standard form) for each of the graphs shown below:

55.

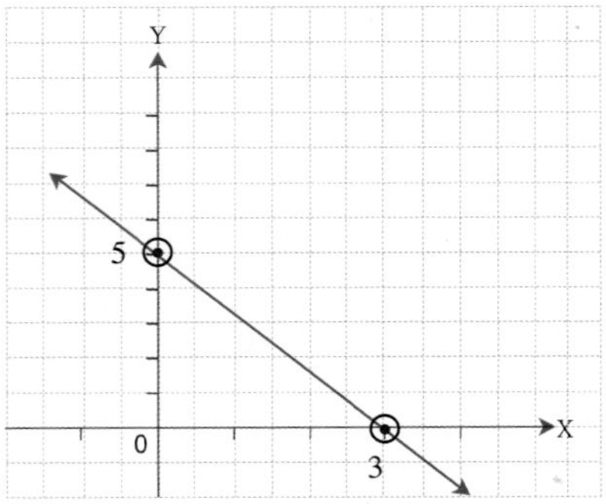

56.

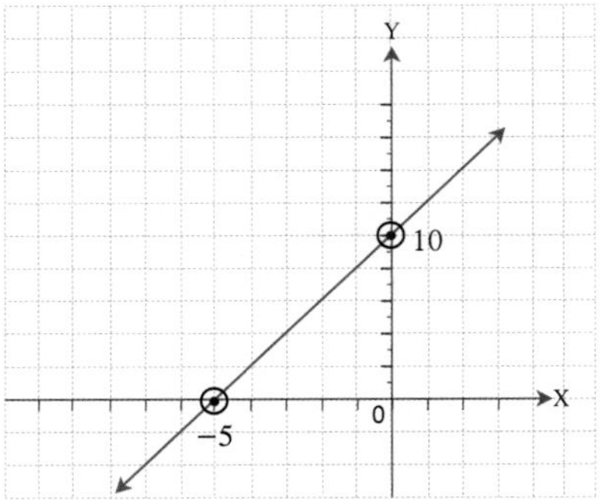

57.

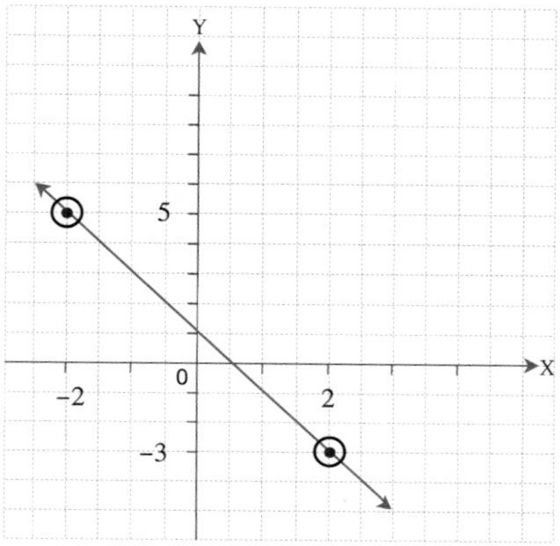

58.

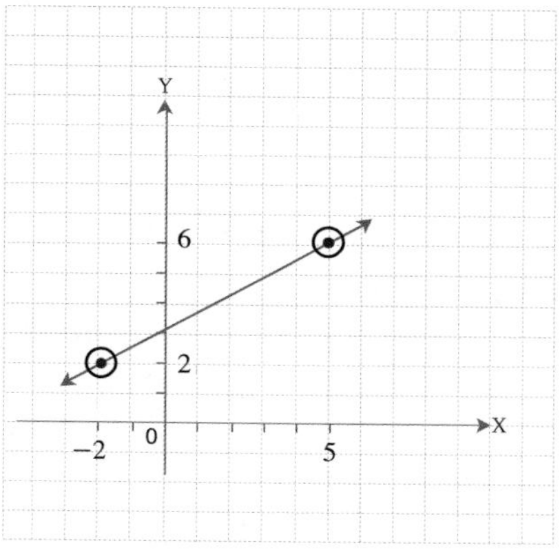

Determine the equations for the following lines:

59. A line parallel to $3y - 2x = 6$ and passing through the point P(2, −3).
60. A line parallel to $y = 3x - 1$ and passing through the point P(−2, −4).
61. A line parallel to $3x - 9y = -2$ and passing through the y-intercept of the line $5x - y = 20$.
62. A line parallel to $3x + y = -2$ and passing through the x-intercept of the line $2x + 3y - 4 = 0$.
63. A line perpendicular to $x + y = 3$ and passing through the point P(−2, 5).
64. A line perpendicular to $4x + y + 1 = 0$ and passing through the point P(3, 4).
65. A line perpendicular to $2x - y = 5$ and passing through the x-intercept of the line $3x + 2y - 6 = 0$.
66. A line perpendicular to $3x + y + 9 = 0$ and passing through the y-intercept of the line $2x + 3y - 10 = 0$.

9.3 | Solving Systems of Linear Equations with Two Variables, Graphically

Introduction

In the previous section, you learned that a linear equation with two variables produces a straight line when plotted on a graph. If the graph of an equation is linear, then all the points (**ordered pairs**) on the line are the solution to that linear equation.

For example, $2x + y = 4$ is a linear equation with two variables, x and y. The graph of this equation is a line and all the points (ordered pairs) on this line are solutions to this equation as shown in the diagram below.

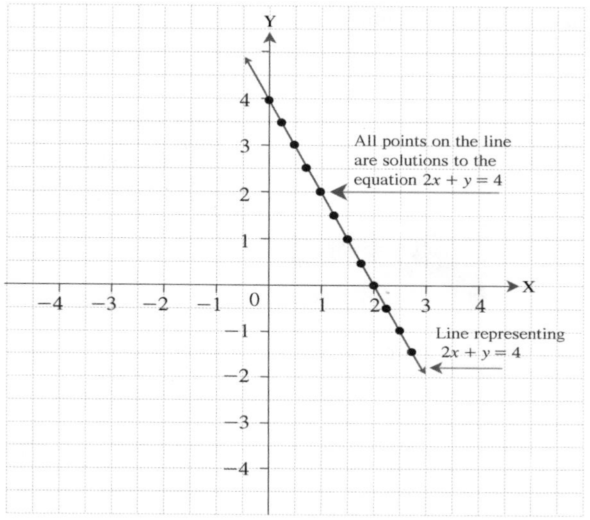

Exhibit 9.3-a Graph of $2x + y = 4$

System of Equations

Two or more equations analyzed together are known as a system of equations. In this section, we will be analyzing two linear equations with two variables.

The solution to a system of two equations with two variables is an ordered pair of numbers (coordinates) that satisfy both equations.

If we graph a system of two linear equations, and if they intersect, then the point at which the two lines intersect will be the solution to both lines.

For example, $2x + y = 4$ and $x - 2y = -3$ form a system of two linear equations. The graphs of these equations intersect at (1, 2), as shown in the following diagram. This point, (1, 2), is the solution to the system of two linear equations.

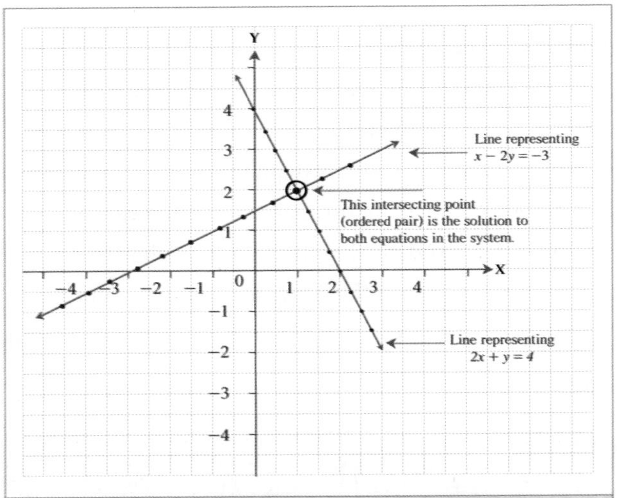

Exhibit 9.3-b Graph of $2x + y = 4$ and $x - 2y = -3$

Graphs of Two Linear Equations May Intersect at One Point, Not Intersect, or Coincide

- **If they intersect** (***lines are not parallel***), it indicates that there is only one solution.
- **If they do not intersect** (***lines are parallel and distinct***), it indicates that there is no solution.
- **If they coincide** (***lines are the same***), it indicates that there are an infinite number of solutions.

Consistent and Inconsistent Systems

A linear system of two equations that has **one or an infinite number of solutions** is known as a **consistent linear system.**

A linear system of two equations that has **no solution** is called an **inconsistent linear system.**

If the graphs of 2 linear equations intersect at one point or if the lines coincide (representing the same line) then they are "consistent" as a system. Otherwise, they are "inconsistent" as a system.

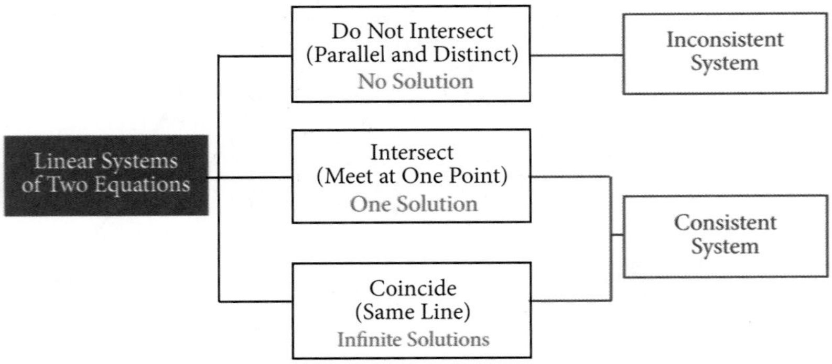

Dependent and Independent Equations

If a system of equations has an **infinite number of solutions** then the **equations are dependent.**

If a system of equations has **one or no solution,** then the **equations are independent.**

f the graphs of 2 linear
equations coincide
representing the same
ine), then they are
nown as a "dependent
ystem of equations",
otherwise they are known
as an "independent
ystem of equations".

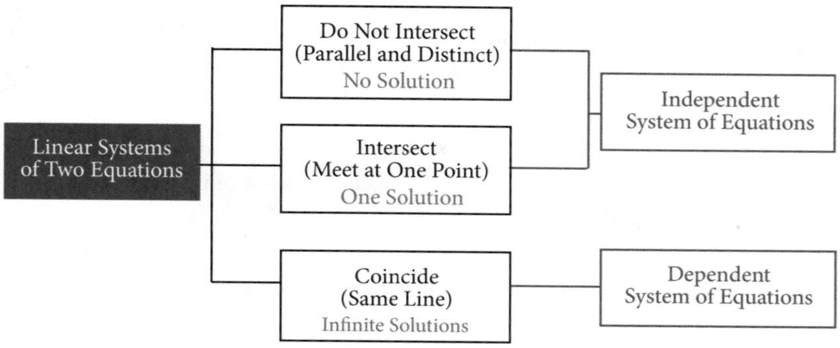

Intersecting Lines

Slopes of lines:	Different
y-intercepts:	May or may not be the same. *Will be different, unless the lines intersect on the Y-axis or at the origin.*
Number of solutions:	One
System:	Consistent
Equations:	Independent

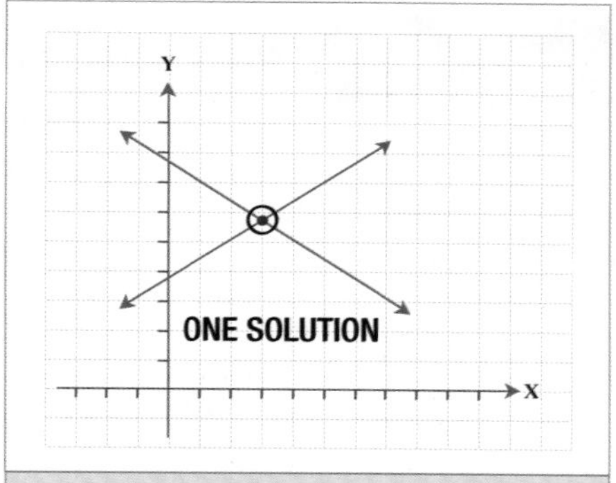

Exhibit 9.3-c Intersecting Lines

Parallel and Distinct Lines

Slopes of lines:	Same
y-intercepts:	Different
Number of solutions:	None
System:	Inconsistent
Equations:	Independent

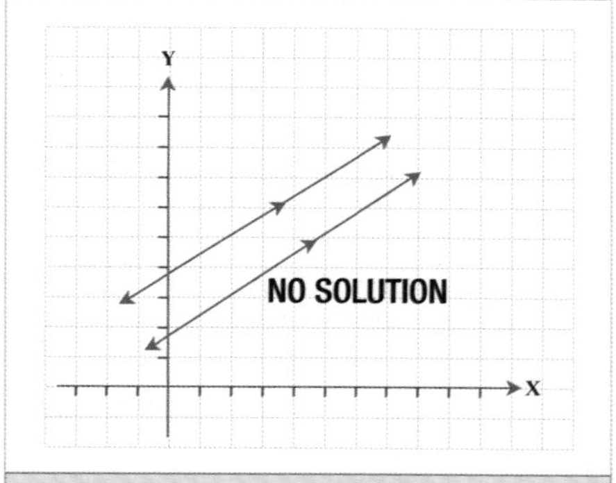

Exhibit 9.3-d Parallel and Distinct Lines

Coincident Lines

Slopes of lines:	Same
y-intercepts:	Same
Number of solutions:	Infinite
System:	Consistent
Equations:	Dependent

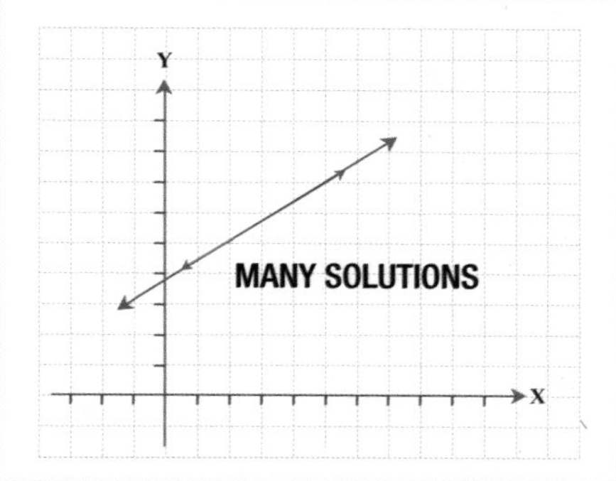

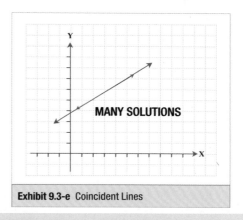

Exhibit 9.3-e Coincident Lines

Solving Linear Systems Graphically

The following steps will help to solve a system of two linear equations with two variables graphically:

Step 1: Rewrite both equations in the form of $y = mx + b$ (or $Ax + By = C$) and clear off any fractions or decimal numbers.

Step 2: Graph the first equation by either using the slope and y-intercept method (or using the x-intercept and y-intercept) or using a table of values. The graph will be a straight line.

Step 3: Graph the second equation on the same axes as in Step 2. This will be another straight line.

Step 4: If the two lines intersect at a point, then the point of intersection is the solution to the given system of equations, also known as an ordered pair (x, y).

Step 5: Check the solution obtained by substituting the values for the variables in each of the original equation. If the answer satisfies the equations, then it is the solution to the given system of equations.

Note: In Step 2, the order in which the equations are graphed or the method used to graph the equations does not matter.

Example 9.3-a **Solving and Classifying Systems of Linear Equations**

Solve the following system of equations by graphing, and classify the system as consistent or inconsistent and the equations as dependent or independent.

$x - y + 1 = 0$

$x + y - 3 = 0$

Solution

Step 1: $x - y + 1 = 0$ Writing the equation in $y = mx + b$ form,

$y = x + 1$ Equation 1

$x + y - 3 = 0$ Writing the equation in $y = mx + b$ form,

$y = -x + 3$ Equation 2

Step 2: Equation 1 : $y = x + 1$

$m = 1$ and $b = 1$

Therefore, the slope is $\frac{1}{1}$ and the y-intercept is (0, 1).

Step 3: Equation 2 : $y = -x + 3$

$m = -1$ and $b = 3$

Therefore, the slope is $\frac{-1}{1}$ and the y-intercept is (0, 3).

Graphing equations 1 and 2 using the slope and y-intercept form:

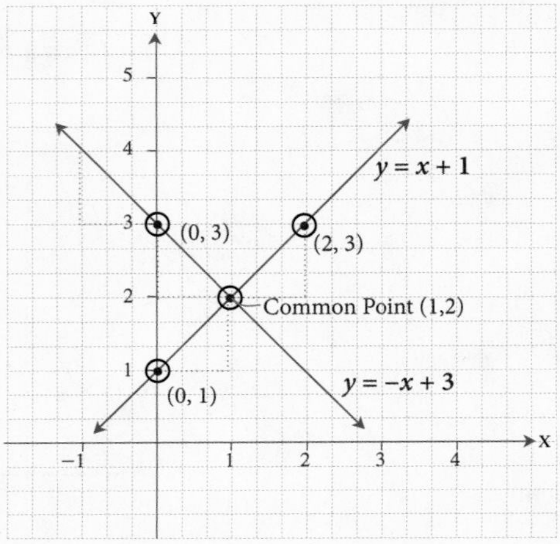

Step 4: The two lines intersect at the common point (1, 2).

Step 5: Check the solution (1, 2) in Equations (1) and (2).

Equation (1), $y = x + 1$

$LS = y = 2$

$RS = x + 1 = 1 + 1 = 2$

Therefore, $LS = RS$

Equation (2), $y = -x + 3$

$LS = y = 2$

$RS = -x + 3 = -1 + 3 = 2$

Therefore, $LS = RS$

Therefore, the solution is (1, 2). The system is consistent (has a solution) and the equations are independent (lines are not coincident).

Example 9.3-b

Classifying Systems of Linear Equations

Solve this system of equations by graphing, and classify the system as consistent or inconsistent and the equations as dependent or independent.

$3x + y - 3 = 0$

$3x + y + 2 = 0$

Solution

Step 1: $3x + y - 3 = 0$ Writing the equation in $y = mx + b$ form,

$y = -3x + 3$ Equation (1)

$3x + y + 2 = 0$ Writing the equation in $y = mx + b$ form,

$y = -3x - 2$ Equation (2)

Since the slopes are the same, the lines are parallel.

Step 2: Equation (1): $y = -3x + 3$

$m = -3$ and $b = 3$

Therefore, the slope is $\frac{-3}{1}$ and the y-intercept is (0, 3).

Step 3: Equation (2): $y = -3x - 2$

$m = -3$ and $b = -2$

Therefore, the slope is $\frac{-3}{1}$ and the y-intercept is (0, −2).

Graphing equations (1) and (2) using the slope and y-intercept form:

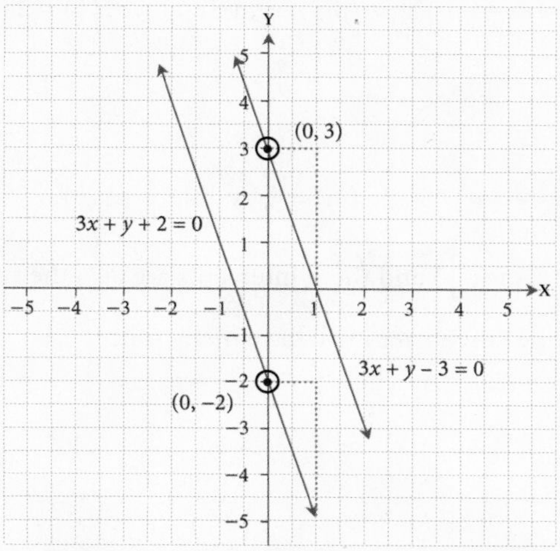

The lines have the same slopes but different y-intercepts. Therefore, the lines are parallel and distinct; i.e., they have no solutions.

The system is inconsistent (no solution) and the equations are independent (lines are not coincident).

Example 9.3-c

Analyzing System of Equations

Without graphing, determine whether each system has one solution, no solution, or many solutions.

(i) $4x + y = 9$, $2x + y = 5$ (ii) $2y + x = 4$, $2x + 4y = 16$ (iii) $2x - 3y + 6 = 0$, $6x - 9y = -18$

Solution

(i) Rewrite the equations in slope and y-intercept form ($y = mx + b$):

$4x + y = 9$

$y = -4x + 9 \longrightarrow$ Slope (m) = -4, y-intercept (b) = 9

$2x + y = 5$

$y = -2x + 5 \longrightarrow$ Slope (m) = -2, y-intercept (b) = 5

The slopes of the lines are different (-4 and -2).

Therefore, the lines are not parallel. They will intersect at one point. The system will have one solution.

(ii) Rewrite the equations in slope and y-intercept form ($y = mx + b$):

$2y + x = 4$

$2y = -x + 4$

$y = -\frac{1}{2}x + 2 \longrightarrow$ Slope (m) = $-\frac{1}{2}$, y-intercept (b) = 2

$2x + 4y = 16$

$4y = -2x + 16$

$y = -\frac{1}{2}x + 4 \longrightarrow$ Slope (m) = $-\frac{1}{2}$, y-intercept (b) = 4

The slopes of the lines are the same ($-\frac{1}{2}$) but the y-intercepts are different.

Therefore, the lines are parallel but distinct. The system will have no solutions.

(iii) Rewrite the equations in slope and y-intercept form ($y = mx + b$):

$2x - 3y + 6 = 0$

$3y = 2x - 6$

$y = \frac{2}{3}x + 2 \longrightarrow$ Slope (m) = $\frac{2}{3}$, y-intercept (b) = 2

$6x - 9y = -18$

$9y = 6x + 18$

$y = \frac{2}{3}x + 2 \longrightarrow$ Slope (m) = $\frac{2}{3}$, y-intercept (b) = 2

The slopes of the lines are the same ($\frac{2}{3}$) and the y-intercepts are also the same (2).

Therefore, the two lines coincide. The system will have many solutions.

9.3 | Exercises

Answers to odd-numbered problems are available at the end of the textbook.

For Problems 1 to 8, without graphing, using the slope property of parallel and perpendicular lines, identify whether each of the pairs of the following lines are parallel, perpendicular, or intersecting.

1. $y = x + 1$
   $4x + 4y = -1$
2. $6x - 5y = 10$
   $y = -\frac{6}{5}x - 12$
3. $x - 3y = -60$
   $y = \frac{1}{3}x - 4$
4. $3x - 2y = -12$
   $2x + 3y = -12$
5. $2x + 5y = -5$
   $y = \frac{5}{2}x - 4$
6. $7x + 4y = 16$
   $y = -\frac{4}{7}x + 3$
7. $3x + 2y = -24$
   $y = \frac{3}{2}x + 3$
8. $3x - 2y = -6$
   $y = \frac{3}{2}x - 16$

For Problems 9 to 16, without graphing, determine whether each system has one solution, no solution, or many solutions.

9. $3x + 4y = 4$
   $2x + y = 6$
10. $3x - 2y = 6$
    $x + 2y = 6$
11. $x - y = 1$
    $2x + y = 5$
12. $x + y = 7$
    $2x - y = 8$
13. $3y - 2x = 1$
    $12y - 8x = -4$
14. $2x - y - 4 = 0$
    $6x - 3y + 12 = 0$
15. $2x = 3y - 1$
    $8x = 12y + 4$
16. $x + 2y = 5$
    $x + 4y = 9$
17. Find the value of 'A' for which the lines $Ax - 2y - 5 = 0$ and $8x - 4y + 3 = 0$ are parallel.
18. Find the value of 'B' for which the lines $3x + 2y + 8 = 0$ and $6x - By - 3 = 0$ are parallel.
19. Find the value of 'A' for which the lines $x + 3y + 1 = 0$ and $Ay + 2x + 2 = 0$ are coincident.
20. Find the value of 'B' for which the lines $y = Bx + 3$ and $x - 2y + 6 = 0$ are coincident.

For Problems 21 to 40, solve the system of equations by graphing, then classify the system of equations as consistent or inconsistent and the equations as dependent or independent.

21. $y = 3x - 2$
    $y = -7x + 8$
22. $y = 3x + 9$
    $y = x - 4$
23. $y = -x + 2$
    $2y = -2x + 6$
24. $y = 2x + 6$
    $2y = -3x + 6$
25. $y = -4x + 7$
    $2y + 8x = 14$
26. $y = -2x + 3$
    $2y + 4x = 6$
27. $3x - y - 8 = 0$
    $6x - 2y - 1 = 0$
28. $y = 2x - 4$
    $3y = -2x + 4$
29. $y - x + 1 = 0$
    $y + 2x - 5 = 0$
30. $y = x - 2$
    $3y = -2x + 9$
31. $5x + y + 9 = 0$
    $x - 3y + 5 = 0$
32. $3x - 2y + 1 = 0$
    $y + 4x - 6 = 0$

33. $3x + 2y = -4$

$y + \frac{3}{2}x + 2 = 0$

34. $2x - y = 6$

$6x - 3y = 15$

35. $4x - 2y = 6$

$-2y + 4x - 8 = 0$

36. $2y - x - 6 = 0$

$y = \frac{1}{2}x + 3$

37. $x - y = 6$

$2x + y = 3$

38. $4x - 8y = 0$

$2x - 4y = -8$

39. $y + \frac{1}{2}x + 1 = 0$

$4y - x - 4 = 0$

40. $y = x + 5$

$x + 2y = 10$

9.4 | Solving Systems of Linear Equations with Two Variables, Algebraically

Introduction

Solving systems of linear equations using algebraic methods is the most accurate for the following reasons:

1. It eliminates graphing errors.
2. It provides the exact answer for systems of equations that have fractions or that have fractional answers.

There are two algebraic (non-graphical) methods for solving systems of linear equations. They are:

- **Substitution method**
- **Elimination method**

Substitution Method

The substitution method is preferable if either one of the equations in the system has a variable with a coefficient of 1 or −1. The substitution method is easier to use when one variable stands alone on one side of the equation.

In this method, the following steps are used to solve systems of two linear equations with two variables:

Step 1: Rewrite both equations in the form of $Ax + By = C$, where A, B, and C are integers.

Step 2: Choose the simplest equation from Step 1 and solve to find an expression for one variable in terms of the other variable.

Step 3: Substitute the expression for the variable from Step 2 into the other equation (the one not used in Step 2). This will result in an equation for one of the variables.

Step 4: Solve the equation in Step 3 for the one variable.

Step 5: Solve for the other variable using any one of the equations in Step 1 and by substituting with the value of the known variable.

The answer for the two variables found in Step 4 and Step 5 will be the solution to the given system of equations.

Step 6: Check if the solution obtained for the variables is true by substituting these values in each of the original equations. If the solution satisfies the equations, then it is the solution to the given systems of equations.

Note: In Step 2, if possible, it is best to select the equation in which the coefficient on any one of the variables is equal to one, since this will make the calculations in 'Steps 3 and 4' easier.

Example 9.4-a

Solving a System of Equations by Substituting for the Variable 'y'

Solve the system of equations given below:

$y - 3x + 2 = 0$

$3y + x - 14 = 0$

Solution

Step 1: Rewriting the equations in the form of $Ax + By = C$,

$$y - 3x + 2 = 0$$

$$y - 3x = -2 \qquad \text{Equation } (1)$$

$$3y + x - 14 = 0$$

$$3y + x = 14 \qquad \text{Equation } (2)$$

Step 2: The coefficient of y in Equation (1) is one.

$$y - 3x = -2 \qquad \text{Equation } (1)$$

$$y = 3x - 2$$

Step 3: Substituting $3x - 2$ for y in Equation (2),

$$3y + x = 14$$

$$3(3x - 2) + x = 14$$

Step 4: Solving for 'x',

$$9x - 6 + x = 14$$

$$9x + x = 14 + 6$$

$$10x = 20$$

$$x = 2$$

Step 5: Substituting for $x = 2$ in Equation (1),

$$y - 3x = -2$$

$$y - 3(2) = -2$$

$$y - 6 = -2$$

$$y = 6 - 2$$

$$y = 4$$

Therefore, the solution is (2, 4).

Step 6: Checking the solution in Equations (1) and (2),

Equation (1), $y - 3x = -2$

$$\text{LS} = y - 3x$$

$$\text{LS} = 4 - 3(2)$$

$$= -2$$

$$= \text{RS (True)}$$

Therefore, LS = RS.

Equation (2), $3y + x = 14$

$$\text{LS} = 3y + x$$

$$\text{LS} = 3(4) + 2$$

$$= 14$$

$$= \text{RS (True)}$$

Therefore, LS = RS.

Example 9.4-b

Solving a System of Equations by Substituting for the Variable 'x'

Solve the system of equations given below:

$x + 2y = 6$

$4x + 3y = 4$

Solution

Step 1: The equations are in the form of $Ax + By = C$,

$$x + 2y = 6 \quad \text{Equation } ①$$

$$4x + 3y = 4 \quad \text{Equation } ②$$

Step 2: The coefficient of x in Equation ① is one.

$$x + 2y = 6$$

$$x = 6 - 2y$$

Step 3: Substituting $6 - 2y$ for x in Equation ②,

$$4x + 3y = 4$$

Step 4: Solving for 'y',

$$4(6 - 2y) + 3y = 4$$

$$24 - 8y + 3y = 4$$

$$5y = 20$$

$$y = 4$$

Step 5: Substituting $y = 4$ in Equation ①,

$$x + 2y = 6$$

$$x + 2(4) = 6$$

$$x = -2$$

Therefore, the solution is $(-2, 4)$.

Step 6: Checking the solution in Equations ① and ②,

Equation ①, $x + 2y = 6$

$$LS = x + 2y$$

$$LS = -2 + 2(4)$$

$$= -2 + 8$$

$$= 6$$

$$= RS \text{ (True)}$$

Therefore, LS = RS.

Equation ②, $4x + 3y = 4$

$$LS = 4x + 3y$$

$$LS = 4(-2) + 3(4)$$

$$= -8 + 12$$

$$= 4$$

$$= RS \text{ (True)}$$

Therefore, LS = RS.

Elimination Method

The elimination method is preferable if none of the equations in the system has a variable with a coefficient of 1 or −1. The elimination method is easier to use when equations are in the form of $Ax + By = C$.

In this method, the following steps are used to solve systems of two linear equations with two variables:

Step 1: Rewrite both equations in the form of $Ax + By = C$, where, A, B, and C are integers.

Step 2: Multiply one or both equations by a suitable integer so that it will create the same (or opposite) coefficient for any one of the variables in both equations.

The purpose is to eliminate one of the variables by subtracting (or adding) these two equations.

Step 3: Subtract (or add) the two equations from Step 2 to obtain one equation with only one variable.

Step 4: Solve the equation in Step 3 to find the one variable.

Step 5: Solve for the other variable using either one of the equations in Step 1 and by substituting with the value of the known variable.

The answer for the two variables found in Step 4 and Step 5 will be the solution to the given system of equations.

Step 6: Check if the solution obtained for the variables is true by substituting these values in each of the original equations.

Note: In Step 2, it does not matter which of the variables you choose to create to be the same (or opposite) coefficient.

*In Step 3, you will **subtract** if both equations have the same coefficient for the variable to be eliminated. If the coefficients are opposite, then you will **add** to eliminate that variable.*

Example 9.4-c **Solving a System of Equations by Eliminating the Variable 'x'**

Solve the system of equations given below:

$3x + 2y = 12$

$6x - 3y = 3$

Solution

Step 1: The equations are in the form of $Ax + By = C$,

$3x + 2y = 12$ Equation (1)

$6x - 3y = 3$ Equation (2)

Step 2: Choosing the variable to be eliminated; in this case, 'x'.

The variable 'x' in Equations (1) and (2) has coefficients of 3 and 6, respectively.

Multiplying Equation (1) by 2,

$2(3x + 2y) = 2(12)$

$6x + 4y = 24$ Equation (3)

$6x - 3y = 3$ Equation (2)

Step 3: Subtracting Equation (2) from (3),

$(6x + 4y) - (6x - 3y) = 24 - 3$

Step 4: Solving for 'y',

$6x - 6x + 4y + 3y = 21$

$7y = 21,$

$y = \frac{21}{7} = 3$

Step 5: Substituting $y = 3$ in Equation (1) and solving for 'x',

$3x + 2y = 12$

$3x + 2(3) = 12$

$3x = 12 - 6 = 6$

$x = 2$

Therefore, the solution is (2, 3).

Step 6: Checking the solution in Equations (1) and (2),

Equation (1),

$3x + 2y = 12$

LS $= 3x + 2y$

LS $= 3(2) + 2(3)$

$= 6 + 6$

$= 12$

= RS (True)

Therefore, LS = RS.

Equation (2),

$6x - 3y = 3$

LS $= 6x - 3y$

LS $= 6(2) - 3(3)$

$= 12 - 9$

$= 3$

= RS (True)

Therefore, LS = RS.

Example 9.4-d **Solving a System of Equations by Eliminating the Variable 'y'**

Solve the system of equations given below:

$3x + 2y = 22$

$8x - 5y = 7$

Solution

Step 1: The equations are in the form of $Ax + By = C$,

$3x + 2y = 22$ Equation (1)

$8x - 5y = 7$ Equation (2)

Step 2: Choosing the variable to be eliminated; in this case, 'y',

The variable 'y' in Equations (1) and (2) has coefficients of 2 and −5, respectively.

Multiplying Equation (1) by 5, and multiplying Equation (2) by 2,

$5(3x+ 2y) = 5(22)$ $2(8x - 5y) = 2(7)$

$15x + 10y = 110$ $16x - 10y = 14$

$15x + 10y = 110$ Equation (3)

$16x - 10y = 14$ Equation (4)

Step 3: Adding Equations (3) and (4),

$(15x + 10y) + (16x - 10y) = 110 + 14$

Step 4: Solving for 'x',

$15x + 10y + 16x - 10y = 124$

$31x = 124$

$x = 4$

Step 5: Substituting $x = 4$ in Equation (1) and solving for 'y',

$3x + 2y = 22$

$3(4) + 2y = 22$

$12 + 2y = 22$

$2y = 22 - 12$

$2y = 10$

$y = 5$

Therefore, the solution is (4, 5).

Step 6: Checking the solution in Equations (1) and (2),

Equation (1),

$3x + 2y = 22$

$LS = 3x + 2y$

$LS = 3(4) + 2(5)$

$= 12 + 10$

$= 22$

$= RS$ (True)

Therefore, LS = RS.

Equation (2),

$8x - 5y = 7$

$LS = 8x - 5y$

$LS = 8(4) - 5(5)$

$= 32 - 25$

$= 7$

$= RS$ (True)

Therefore, LS = RS.

Solving Systems of Equations With Fractions

When one or more of the variables in a system of equations has fractional coefficients, clear the fraction by multiplying each equation by its lowest common denominator (**LCD**).

For example, consider the following system of equations:

$$\frac{2}{3}x + \frac{1}{2}y = 1$$

$$\frac{1}{3}x - \frac{3}{4}y = -2$$

To clear the fractions, multiply each equation by its **LCD** (lowest common denominator).

$\frac{2}{3}x + \frac{1}{2}y = 1$	The LCD is 6; therefore, multiplying each term by 6,
$4x + 3y = 6$	Equation ①
$\frac{1}{3}x - \frac{3}{4}y = -2$	The LCD is 12; therefore, multiplying each term by 12,
$4x - 9y = -24$	Equation ②

Therefore, the equations of the given system are equivalent to:

$$4x + 3y = 6$$

$$4x - 9y = -24$$

This system can then be solved by the Elimination method.

Solving Systems of Equations With Decimal Numbers

When one or more of the variables in a system of equations has decimal numbers as coefficients, clear the decimal numbers by multiplying each equation by 10 or by 100, etc., depending on the number of decimal places.

For example, consider the following system of equations:

$$0.05x + 0.15y = 2.4$$

$$2.5x + 0.5y = 2.2$$

To clear the decimal numbers, multiply the first equation by 100 (to eliminate 2 decimal places) and the second equation by 10 (to eliminate 1 decimal place).

$0.05x + 0.15y = 2.4$	Multiplying by 100,
$5x + 15y = 240$	Dividing by 5,
$x + 3y = 48$	Equation ①
$2.5x + 0.5y = 2.2$	Multiplying by 10,
$25x + 5y = 22$	Equation ②

Therefore, the equations of the given system are equivalent to:

$$x + 3y = 48$$

$$25x + 5y = 22$$

This system can then be solved by the Substitution or Elimination method.

Systems With No Solutions

If a false equation is obtained (such as $0 = 4$) when solving a system of two linear equations with two variables, then the system has no solutions. That is, the graph of the equation will be parallel and distinct. A system of equations with no solutions is inconsistent and independent.

Example 9.4-e

Solving a System With No Solutions

Solve the following system of equations by using the Elimination method:

$2x + 3y = 6$

$6x + 9y = 45$

Solution

Step 1: $2x + 3y = 6$ Equation (1)

$6x + 9y = 45$ Equation (2)

Step 2: Choosing the variable to be eliminated; in this case, 'x'.

The variable 'x' in Equations (1) and (2) has coefficients of 2 and 6, respectively.

Multiplying Equation (1) by 3,

$$3(2x+ 3y) = 3(6)$$

$$6x + 9y = 18 \quad \text{Equation (3)}$$

Step 3: Subtracting Equation (3) from (2),

$$(6x + 9y) - (6x + 9y) = 45 - 18$$

$$6x + 9y - 6x - 9y = 27$$

$$0 = 27 \quad \text{This cannot be true.}$$

Therefore, the system has no solution.

The system is inconsistent and independent. That is, the graph of the system will have parallel and distinct lines, as shown below.

Equation (1)

$2x + 3y = 6$

x-intercept: (3, 0)

y-intercept: (0, 2)

Equation (2)

$6x + 9y = 45$

x-intercept: (7.5, 0)

y-intercept: (0, 5)

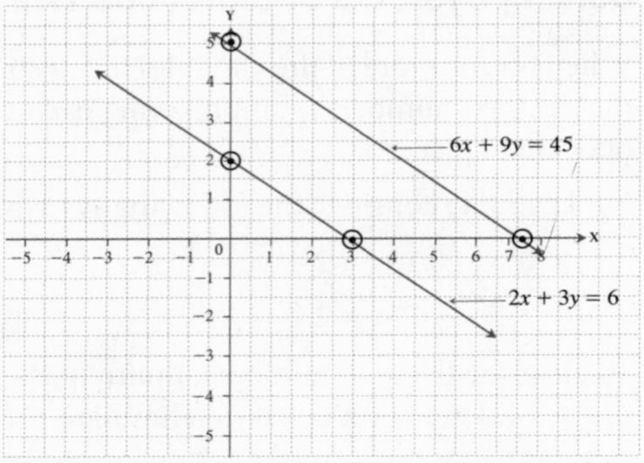

Systems With Many (Infinite) Solutions

If an identity of $0 = 0$ is obtained when solving a system of two linear equations with two variables, then the system has many (infinite) solutions. A system of equations with many solutions is consistent and dependent. That is, the graph of the equation will be the same.

Example 9.4-f

Solving a System With Many (Infinite) Solutions

Solve the following system of equations by using the Substitution method:

$2x + y - 7 = 0$

$3y = -6x + 21$

Solution

Step 1: $2x + y - 7 = 0$

$$2x + y = 7 \quad \text{Equation (1)}$$

$$3y = -6x + 21$$

$$6x + 3y = 21 \quad \text{Equation (2)}$$

Solution
continued

Step 2: The coefficient of y in Equation (1) is 1.

Rearranging, $2x + y = 7$

$$y = -2x + 7$$

Step 3: Substituting $y = -2x + 7$ into Equation (2),

$$6x + 3y = 21$$
$$6x + 3(-2x + 7) = 21$$
$$6x - 6x + 21 = 21$$
$$0 = 0$$

Therefore, the system will have many (infinite) solutions; i.e., the system will have coincident lines. The system is consistent and dependent.

Equation (1):

$2x + y = 7$

x-intercept: (3.5, 0)

y-intercept: (0, 7)

Equation (2):

$6x + 3y = 21$

x-intercept: (3.5, 0)

y-intercept: (0, 7)

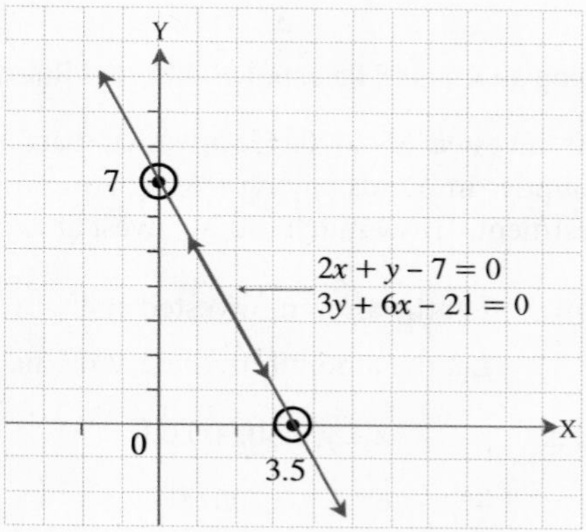

Writing a System of Linear Equations from Word Problems With Two Unknowns

In some problems, there may be two unknowns that need to be determined based on the given information. Although one of the unknowns can be expressed in terms of the other, it is best to write a system of equations in two variables and solve for the unknowns using one of the methods learned above.

The following steps will assist in writing the equations:

Step 1: Choose two different variables (x and y) to represent each of the unknown quantities and specify clearly what each variable represents and its unit of measure.

Step 2: Based on the given information, translate the word expressions into mathematical equations.

Step 3: Solve the equations for the unknown variables.

Step 4: Indicate the solutions to the word problem, including units.

Step 5: Check the solutions with the statement in the word problem.

Example 9.4-g **Finding Unknown Numbers**

The sum of two numbers is 46. The difference between the numbers is 8. Find the numbers.

Solution

Step 1: Let the larger number be x and the smaller number be y

Step 2: $x + y = 46$ Equation (1)

$x - y = 8$ Equation (2)

Step 3: Adding Equations (i) and (ii),

$$2x = 54$$
$$x = 27$$

Solution *continued*

Step 4: Substituting $x = 27$ into Equation (1),

$$x + y = 46$$
$$27 + y = 46$$
$$y = 46 - 27$$
$$= 19$$

Step 5: Therefore, the numbers are 27 and 19.

Step 6: Check:

$27 + 19 = 46$ (True)

$27 - 19 = 8$ (True)

Example 9.4-h **Finding an Amount Invested at Different Rates**

Steve invested $50,000. He invested part of it in a fixed deposit paying 4% per annum and the remainder in bonds paying 6% per annum. After one year, he received $2,700 as interest from both investments. How much did he invest at each rate?

Solution

Step 1: Let the amount invested at 4% be $$x$.

Let the amount invested at 6% be $$y$.

Step 2:

$x + y = 50{,}000.00$ Equation (1)

$4\%x + 6\%y = 2{,}700.00$

$0.04x + 0.06y = 2{,}700$ Multiplying by 100,

$4x + 6y = 270{,}000.00$ Dividing by 2,

$2x + 3y = 135{,}000.00$ Equation (2)

Step 3: From Equation (1), $x + y = 50{,}000.00$

$$x = 50{,}000.00 - y$$

Substituting, $x = 50{,}000 - y$ in Equation (2),

$$2x + 3y = 135{,}000.00$$
$$2(50{,}000 - y) + 3y = 135{,}000.00$$
$$-2y + 3y = 135{,}000.00 - 100{,}000.00$$
$$y = 35{,}000.00$$

Substituting this in Equation (1),

$$x + y = 50{,}000.00$$
$$x = 50{,}000.00 - y$$
$$= 50{,}000.00 - 35{,}000.00$$
$$x = 15{,}000.00$$

Step 4: Therefore the amount invested in the fixed deposit at 4% per annum is $15,000 and the amount deposited in bonds at 6% per annum is $35,000.

Step 5: Check:

Total interest $= 15{,}000.00 \times 4\% + 35{,}000.00 \times 6\%$

$= 600.00 + 2{,}100.00$

$= 2{,}700.00$ (True)

Example 9.4-i **Finding Number of Coins Consisting of Quarters and Dimes**

Aran collected 81 coins in quarters (25¢) and dimes (10¢). If all the coins are worth \$15.00, find the number of quarters and dimes collected.

Solution

Step 1: Let the number of quarters be x and the number of dimes be y

Step 2: $x + y = 81$ Equation (1)

Value of x quarters = \$$0.25x$

Value of y dimes = \$$0.10y$

$0.25x + 0.10y = 15.00$ Multiplying by 100,

$25x + 10y = 1500$ Dividing by 5,

$5x + 2y = 300$ Equation (2)

Step 3: Rearranging Equation (1), $x + y = 81$

$y = 81 - x$

Substituting $y = 81 - x$ in Equation (2),

$$5x + 2y = 300$$
$$5x + 2(81 - x) = 300$$
$$5x + 162 - 2x = 300$$
$$3x = 300 - 162$$
$$3x = 138$$
$$x = 46$$

Substituting $x = 46$ in Equation (1),

$$y = 81 - x$$
$$y = 81 - 46$$
$$= 35$$

Step 4: Therefore, the number of quarters is 46 and the number of dimes is 35.

Step 5: Check:

Total coins = 46 + 35 = 81 (True)

Total amount = 0.25 (46) + 0.10 (35)

= 11.50 + 3.50

= 15.00 (True)

9.4 | Exercises

Answers to odd-numbered problems are available at the end of the textbook.

Solve the following systems of equations by using the Substitution method:

1. $y - 3x + 8 = 0$
   $y - x + 4 = 0$
2. $4x - 7y + 6 = 0$
   $x - 3y + 2 = 0$
3. $3x - 2y = 8$
   $x + 3y = 15$
4. $6x - 9y + 2 = 0$
   $x - 2y - 5 = 0$
5. $x - 3y = 12$
   $5x + 2y = 9$
6. $3x + y = -8$
   $3x - 4y = -23$
7. $5x + 4y = 14$
   $x - 3y = -1$
8. $x - 9y = 6$
   $3x - 7y = 16$

9. $3x - 2y = 20$

$y + 4x = 23$

10. $9x - 2y = 12$

$5y + 3x = 21$

11. $7x - 5y + 3 = 0$

$-3x + y + 1 = 0$

12. $6x - 5y + 13 = 0$

$-3x + y - 8 = 0$

Solve the following systems of equations by using the Elimination method:

13. $3y + 2x = 24$

$2x - 2y = 14$

14. $7x - 3y = -5$

$5x - 9y = 7$

15. $5x + 3y = 19$

$3x - 5y = -9$

16. $5x - 3y = 2$

$3x - 5y = 7$

17. $5x - 2y + 1 = 0$

$2x - 3y - 4 = 0$

18. $4x + 5y = 11$

$2x + 3y = 5$

19. $5x - 7y = 19$

$2x + 3y = -4$

20. $9x + 8y = 10$

$3x + 2y = 4$

21. $2y + 3x = 14$

$9x - 4y = 2$

22. $3x - 5y = 4$

$5x + 3y = -16$

23. $3y + 7x = 15$

$3x + 5y + 1 = 0$

24. $9y + 4x - 1 = 0$

$4x + 5y + 3 = 0$

Solve the following systems of equations by either using the Substitution or the Elimination method:

25. $0.5x - 0.3y = -1.2$

$0.2x - 0.7y = 0.1$

26. $1.2x + 0.6y = 0$

$3.5x + 1.7y = 0.01$

27. $0.7x - 0.4y = 2.9$

$0.6x - 0.3y = 2.4$

28. $1.5x + y = 1$

$0.8x + 0.7y = 1.2$

29. $\frac{x}{5} + \frac{y}{6} = 3$

$\frac{x}{2} - \frac{y}{3} = 3$

30. $\frac{x}{6} - \frac{y}{3} = \frac{2}{3}$

$\frac{x}{4} - \frac{y}{12} = -\frac{3}{2}$

31. $\frac{x}{4} + \frac{y}{2} = 2\frac{1}{4}$

$\frac{2x}{3} + \frac{y}{6} = \frac{3}{2}$

32. $\frac{3x}{10} + \frac{y}{5} = \frac{1}{2}$

$\frac{x}{3} + \frac{y}{3} = \frac{1}{2}$

33. $4(x - 3) + 5(y + 1) = 12$

$(y + 7) - 3(x + 2) = 1$

34. $4(x + 3) - 3(y + 4) = 21$

$2(x + 4) + 5(y - 3) = 10$

35. $2(x - 2) - 3(y - 1) = 11$

$5(x + 1) + 2(y - 4) = 8$

36. $3(x + 1) - 6(y + 2) = 6$

$5(2x - 4) + 7(y + 1) = -17$

37. Two meals for adults and three meals for children cost \$48, whereas, three meals for adults and two meals for children cost \$52. How much does one adult meal cost?

38. Three DVDs and four movie tickets cost \$94, whereas, four DVDs and three movie tickets cost \$81. How much does one DVD cost?

39. The sum of a son's age and of his father's age, in years, is 92. The difference in their ages is 28. How old are the son and the father?

40. The sum of 2 numbers is 56; when the smaller number is subtracted from the larger number, the result is 22. What are the numbers?

41. Hanna charges \$20 for the first shirt that you purchase at her store. However, for every additional shirt, she charges \$15. Write an equation that shows the relationship between her total revenue (y) and the number of shirts sold (x). If you plot a graph of y vs. x, what are the y-intercept and the slope of the line that would represent the equation?

42. An online music store charges \$2 for the first song that you download. For every additional song that you download, you will be charged only \$1.50. Write an equation that shows the relationship between the total revenue (y) and the number of songs sold (x). If you plot a graph of y vs. x, what are the y-intercept and the slope of the line that would represent the equation?

43. Viktor invested \$25,000, part of it at 5% per annum and the remainder at 4% per annum. If the total interest after one year was \$1,150, how much did he invest at each rate?

44. Two investments were made by Adam, totalling \$22,500. Part of it was invested at 6% per annum and the remainder at 5% per annum. The total interest received after one year was \$1,295. Find the amount invested at each rate.

45. There are 130 coins consisting of quarters (25¢) and dimes (10¢). If the coins are worth \$27.70, how many quarters and dimes are there?

46. There are 175 coins consisting of dimes (10¢) and nickels (5¢). The coins are worth \$15.00. How many dimes and nickels are there?

47. The sum of two angles is 180°. One angle is 24° less than three times the other angle. Find the measure of the angles.

48. The sum of two angles is 90°. One angle is 15° more than twice the other angle. Find the measure of the angles.

49. A can of juice contains 15% sugar and another can contains 5% sugar. How many liters of each should be mixed together to get 10 liters of juice that has 10% sugar?

50. Solution A has 25% acid and solution B has 50% acid. How many liters of a solution A and B should be mixed to get 10 liters of 40% acid?

9 | Review Exercises

Answers to odd-numbered problems are available at the end of the textbook.

1. In which quadrant or axis do the following points lie?

   a. A (5, –1) b. B (–2, 3)
   c. C (3, 0) d. D (4, –2)
   e. E (2, 0) f. F (0, 4)

2. In which quadrant or axis do the following points lie?

   a. A (4, –1) b. B (–5, 0)
   c. C (–2, –7) d. D (0, –3)
   e. E (6, 6) f. F (5, 4)

3. Plot the following points and join them in the order of A, B, C, D. Identify the type of quadrilateral and find its area and perimeter.

   a. A (6, –3) b. B (6, –6)
   c. C (–2, –6) d. D (–2, –3)

4. Plot the following points and join them in the order of P, Q, R, S. Identify the type of quadrilateral and find its area and perimeter.

   a. P (–2, 4) b. Q (–8, 4)
   c. R (–8, –2) d. S (–2, –2)

Graph the following equations using a table of values with four points:

5. $4x - y = 2$
6. $2x + 3y = 12$
7. $x + y - 4 = 0$
8. $x + 2y - 4 = 0$
9. $y = \frac{1}{2}x + 2$
10. $y = -\frac{1}{3}x - 2$

Graph the following equations using the x-intercept, y-intercept, and another point:

11. $3x - 4y = 12$
12. $x - 2y = -1$
13. $x - 2y - 6 = 0$
14. $3x + y - 4 = 0$
15. $y = 4x$
16. $x = 2y$

Graph the following equations using the slope and y-intercept method:

17. $y = 4x + 6$
18. $y = 5x + 4$
19. $3x + 2y - 12 = 0$
20. $2x + 3y + 6 = 0$
21. $y = -\frac{3}{4}x - 1$
22. $y = -\frac{1}{3}x - 1$

Find the equation of the line that passes through the following points:

23. (3, 2) and (7, 5)
24. (4, 6) and (2, 4)
25. (5, –4) and (–1, 4)
26. (0, –7) and (–6, –1)
27. (1, –2) and (4, 7)
28. (3, –4) and (–1, 4)

29. Write the equation of a line parallel to $3x - 4y = 12$ and that passes through the point P(–2, 3).

30. Write the equation of a line parallel to $2x - 3y = 9$ and that passes though the point P(2, –3).

31. Write the equation of a line perpendicular to $2y = x + 4$ and that passes through the point P(–2, 5).

32. Write the equation of a line perpendicular to $3x + 4y + 6 = 0$ and that passes through the point P(4, –1).

Without graphing, determine whether each of the following systems of equations has one solution, no solution, or many solutions:

33. $3x - 2y + 13 = 0$
    $3x + y + 7 = 0$

34. $4x + 6y - 14 = 0$
    $2x + 3y - 7 = 0$

35. $x - 3y + 2 = 0$
    $3x - 9y + 11 = 0$

36. $15x + 3y = 10$
    $5x + y = -3$

37. $2x - 4y = 6$
    $x - 2y = 3$

38. $3x - y + 2 = 0$
    $9x - 3y + 6 = 0$

Solve the following systems of equations by using the Graphical method:

39. $y = -2x - 1$
    $y = 3x - 11$

40. $y = 2x + 3$
    $y = -2x - 1$

41. $2x - 3y - 6 = 0$
    $x + 2y - 10 = 0$

42. $3x + 4y - 5 = 0$
    $2x - y + 4 = 0$

43. $2y = x$
    $y = -x + 3$

44. $3y = 2x$
    $y = -3x + 11$

45. $x + 4y = 8$
    $2x + 5y = 13$

46. $x + y = 3$
    $2x - y = 12$

47. $x + 4y + 12 = 0$
    $9x - 2y - 32 = 0$

48. $x - y - 1 = 0$
    $2x + 3y - 12 = 0$

49. $3x + 2y = 5$
    $y = 2x - 1$

50. $4x + 3y = 12$
    $9 - 3x = y$

Solve the following systems of equations by using the Elimination method:

51. $8x + 7y = 23$
    $7x + 8y = 22$

52. $2x + y = 8$
    $3x + 2y = 7$

53. $9x - 2y = -32$
    $x + 4y = -12$

54. $5x - 2y + 3 = 0$
    $3x - 2y - 1 = 0$

55. $4x + 3y = 12$
    $18 - 6x = 2y$

56. $2x + y + 2 = 0$
    $6x = 2y$

Solve the following systems of equations by using either the Substitution method or the Elimination method:

57. $0.4x - 0.5y = -0.8$
    $0.3x - 0.2y = 0.1$

58. $0.2x - 0.3y = -0.6$
    $0.5x + 0.2y = 2.3$

59. $\frac{5x}{3} - \frac{5y}{2} = -5$
    $\frac{x}{3} - \frac{y}{4} = 2$

60. $\frac{x}{4} + \frac{y}{2} = 2$
    $\frac{x}{6} + \frac{2y}{3} = \frac{4}{3}$

61. $(2x + 1) - 2(y + 7) = -1$
    $4(x + 5) + 3(y - 1) = 28$

62. $2(3x + 2) + 5(2y + 7) = 13$
    $3(x + 1) - 4(y - 1) = -15$

63. Find the value of two numbers if their sum is 95 and the difference between the larger number and the smaller number is 35.

64. Find the value of two numbers if their sum is 84 and the difference between the larger number and the smaller number is 48.

65. 300 tickets were sold for a theatrical performance. The tickets cost \$28 for adults and \$15 for kids. If \$7,230 was collected, how many adults and how many children attended this play?

66. 640 tickets were sold for a soccer game between Toronto FC and Liverpool FC. The tickets cost \$35 for adults and \$20 for students. If \$16,250 was collected from sales, how many adults and students attended the game?

9 | Self-Test Exercises

Answers to all problems are available at the end of the textbook.

1. Write the following equations in the form $Ax + By = C$:

   a. $y = \frac{2}{3}x - \frac{4}{2}$ b. $6 - 2x + \frac{1}{4} = 0$

2. Three vertices of a rectangle ABCD have the points A (−3, 4), B (5, 4), and C (5, −1). Find the coordinates of the 4th vertex and the area of the rectangle.

3. Find the slope and y-intercept of the following lines:

   a. $2x - 3y + 6 = 0$ b. $3x + 4y - 5 = 0$

4. Find the equation of the line, in standard form, that passes through the points P (−4, 5) and Q (1, 1).

5. Graph the equation $2x - 3y = 9$ using a table of values with 4 points.

6. Use the slope of the lines to determine whether the pairs of lines are parallel:

   a. $3y = 6x - 9$ and $4x - 2y = -6$

   b. $3y + 4x = 0$ and $3x + 4y = 2$

7. Write the equation of a line, in standard form, that is parallel to $3x - 2y + 9 = 0$ and that passes through the point (−6, −3).

   (Hint: Parallel lines will have the same slope.)

8. Graph the equation $3y + 4x = 0$ using the x-intercept, y-intercept, and another point on the line.

9. Given the following slopes (m) and y-intercepts (b), write the equations in standard form:

   a. $m = -\frac{1}{2}, b = -4$ b. $m = \frac{2}{3}, b = -2$

10. Graph the line that contains the point (–3, 5) and that has a slope of $\frac{-3}{4}$.

11. Write the equation of a line parallel to $2x + 3y = 6$ and that passes through the point P(–6, –1).

12. Write the equation of the line perpendicular to $5x - y = 4$ and that passes through the point P(1, 2).

13. Write the equation of the line passing through the points P(–3, 5) and Q(5, –1).

14. Write the equation of the line that passes through the origin and that is perpendicular to the line passing through the points P(–3, 5) and Q(5, –1).

15. Write the equation of the line having an x-intercept equal to 5 and y-intercept equal to –3.

16. Write the equation of the line passing through the origin and that is parallel to $y = 5x - 1$.

Without graphing, determine whether each of the following systems of equations has one solution, no solution, or many solutions:

17. $4x + 3y - 16 = 0$ and $2x - y + 2 = 0$

18. $x - 3y + 11 = 0$ and $2x - 6y + 4 = 0$

19. $y = 4x + 8$ and $8x - 2y + 8 = 0$

Solve the following systems of equations by using the Graphical method:

20. $y = 3x + 6$
    $6x - 2y + 12 = 0$

21. $2x + 3y + 4 = 0$
    $3x - y + 7 = 0$

Solve the following systems of equations by using the Substitution method:

22. $2x + 4y + 6 = 0$
    $y - 3x + 9 = 0$

23. $3x + y = -8$
    $2x + 3y = 4$

Solve the following systems of equations by using the Elimination method:

24. $6x - 4y + 3 = 0$
    $4x - 6y - 3 = 0$

25. $3x + 5y - 19 = 0$
    $5x - 2y + 11 = 0$

26. Find the value of two numbers if their sum is 65 and the difference between the larger number and the smaller number is 5.

27. In a coin box, there are 3 times as many quarters (25¢) as dimes (10¢). If the total value of all these coins is $21.25, how many quarters are there?

28. The cost of admission to a concert was $75 for adults and $50 for students. If 400 tickets were sold and $28,125 was collected, how many adult tickets were sold?

29. Henry works in a computer store and earns $500 a month plus a commission of 10% on the sales he makes. The relationship between his earnings (y) in a month and the number of computers he sells (x) is given by the equation $y = 500 + 0.10x$.

    a. What would his commission be if his earnings are $14,000 in a month?

    b. What would his earnings be if his sales are $250,000 in a month?

30. The fixed costs (FC) of a factory for the month are $5,000 and the variable costs (VC) to manufacture each product are $5. The total costs ($TC$) for the month are the sum of the fixed costs and the variable costs per unit, multiplied by the number of products produced and sold (x).

    The relationship between TC, FC, VC, and x is expressed by the equation $TC = (VC)x + FC$.

    a. What would be the total cost if 90 products were sold this month?

    b. How many products were sold this month if the total cost is $11,375?

10 BASIC GEOMETRY

Geometry is a branch of Mathematics that is concerned with the properties, measurements, and relationships of 2-dimensional plane figures and 3-dimensional solid objects, as well as the study of their sizes, shapes, and positions. Geometry (translates to "Earth Measurement" from Greek) is linked to many other topics in Mathematics and is used daily. It is also applied everywhere by almost everyone in the fields of art, architecture, engineering, land surveys, astronomy, sculptures, space, nature, sports, machines, etc.

Geometry has many practical day-to-day uses in the workplace and at home. For example, you use Geometry to determine the quantity of paint needed to paint walls, the amount of carpet needed for your home, the length of fence needed for the garden, etc. In this chapter, you will learn the most basic form of geometry, called Euclidean Geometry, involving points, lines, angles, lengths, areas and volumes.

LEARNING OBJECTIVES

- **Recognize and use various notations to represent points, lines, line segments, rays, and angles.**
- **Classify angles and determine the angle relationships between parallel lines and transversals.**
- **Classify triangles, quadrilaterals, and polygons based on properties of their sides and angles.**
- **Apply properties of similar and congruent triangles in solving problems involving triangles.**
- **Compute the perimeter and area of plane figures, such as triangles, quadrilaterals, and circles.**
- **Compute the surface area and volume of common three-dimensional solid objects.**

CHAPTER OUTLINE

10.1 | Lines and Angles

Introduction

Geometry is a branch of Mathematics that deals with the study of relative positions, properties, and relations of geometric objects (such as points, lines, angles, surfaces, solids, and calculations involving lengths, angles, perimeters, areas, and volumes of such objects). Geometry can be traced as far back as the early historical era, to the ancient Egyptians and Babylonians. However, Geometry was revolutionized by the ancient Greeks, including Pythagoras, Plato, and most notably, Euclid, who invented **Euclidean Geometry**, which is the focus of this chapter.

Euclidean Geometry begins with the notion of a point. Recall from Chapter 9 that a **point** in the Cartesian plane represents a **location** in the plane, determined by its x-coordinate, representing its horizontal position with respect to the origin, and its y-coordinate, representing its vertical position with respect to the origin. It has no dimensions; that is, it has no length, width, or height.

We label a point in the Cartesian plane using a dot, a capital letter (most often P), and ordered coordinates in brackets. The point $P(3, 5)$ in the Cartesian plane is illustrated in Exhibit 10.1-a.

ften, when working with ıclidean Geometry, we e only concerned with the lative position of a point other points, and not ; specific position in the artesian plane. As such, we ten omit the coordinates ıd label the point using a ɔt and a capital letter (P).

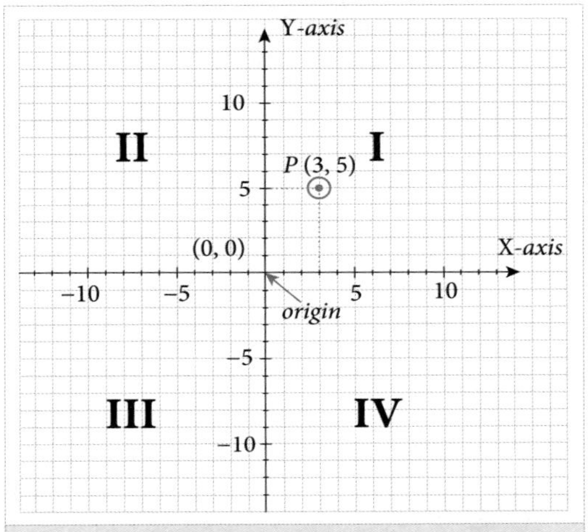

Exhibit 10.1-a Labelling a Point in the Cartesian Plane

Lines, Line Segments, and Rays

A line is an object that has only one dimension: length. A line is created by joining two points, includes all the points that fall directly between them, and extends indefinitely in opposite directions. Therefore, a line is straight, has no gaps, and extends indefinitely in both directions. It is denoted with the labels of the two points over-lined with a double-arrowhead. It has no end-points.

Line

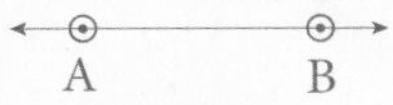

Line $\overleftrightarrow{AB}$ (or $\overleftrightarrow{BA}$)

A line segment is the portion of a line bound between two points. A line segment is created by joining two points and includes all the points that fall directly between them. It is denoted with the labels of the two points, over-lined with a straight line. It has two end-points.

Line Segment

Line Segment $\overline{AB}$ (or $\overline{BA}$)

A ray is the portion of a line bound in one direction by a point. A ray is created by joining two points, includes all the points that fall directly between them, and extends indefinitely in one direction only. It is denoted with the labels of the two points, over-lined with a single arrowhead. It has only one end-point.

Ray

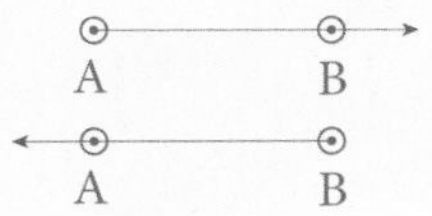

Ray $\overrightarrow{AB}$

Ray $\overrightarrow{BA}$

Note: When labeling a ray, the order of the letters matters. For example, ray $\overrightarrow{\mathbf{AB}}$ *originates at point A and extends indefinitely in the direction of point B, while ray* $\overrightarrow{\mathbf{BA}}$ *originates at point B and extends indefinitely in the direction of point A.*

Example 10.1-a **Identifying Lines, Line Segments, and Rays**

Identify and label the following geometric objects:

(i) (ii) (iii) (iv)

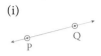

Solution

(i) Line $\overleftrightarrow{\mathbf{PQ}}$ or $\overleftrightarrow{\mathbf{QP}}$ (ii) Ray $\overrightarrow{\mathbf{NM}}$ (iii) Line segment $\overline{\mathbf{CD}}$ or $\overline{\mathbf{DC}}$ (iv) Ray $\overrightarrow{\mathbf{YX}}$

Angle Measures in Degrees

An angle is formed when two rays intersect at their endpoints. The point of intersection is called the **vertex** of the angle and the two rays are called the sides of the angle. The angle is identified by the symbol $\angle$, followed by the letters of the three points of the two rays, with the vertex in the middle.

For example, rays $\overrightarrow{BA}$ and $\overrightarrow{BC}$ form the angle $\angle$ ABC or $\angle$ CBA. When the context is clear, we may simply refer to this angle as $\angle$ B.

When labeling an angle, the vertex is always written in the middle.

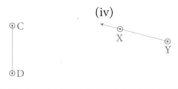

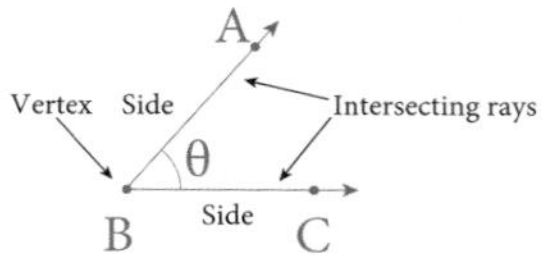

$\angle$ ABC (or $\angle$ CBA) = θ

Or simply $\angle$ B = θ

The size of the angle is measured in degrees (denoted with the symbol "°"), where one revolution of a circle is 360°. One degree is a $\frac{1}{360}$ slice of one revolution of a circle. Imagine a circle centered at point B, divided into 360 equal sectors through B. The degree measure of $\angle$ ABC is the number of sectors that can fit in the wedge formed between rays $\overrightarrow{BA}$ and $\overrightarrow{BC}$. Exhibit 10.1-b shows a circle divided into 36 sectors, where each sector represents 10°.

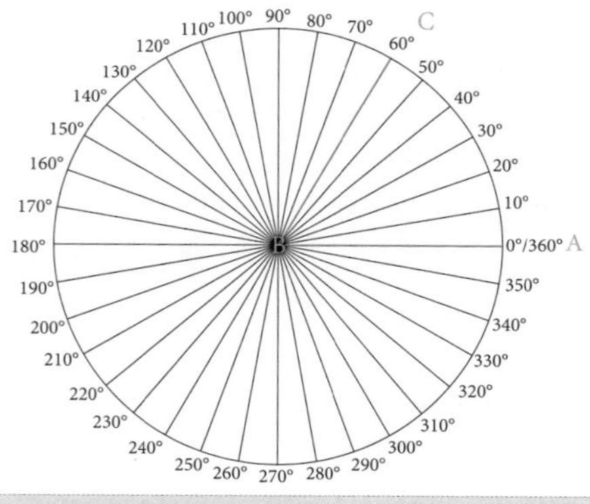

Exhibit 10.1-b Circle Divided into 36 Sectors, Where Each Sector Represents 10°

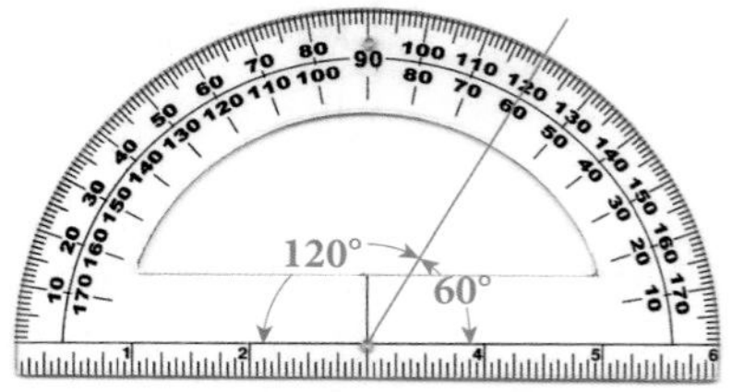

A protractor is used to measure and draw angles in degrees.

Two rays from the center of a circle extending in opposite directions create a line which divides the circle into two equal halves, thus, the angle between two opposite rays has an angle measure equal to $\frac{1}{2}$ a revolution or $\frac{360°}{2} = 180°$.

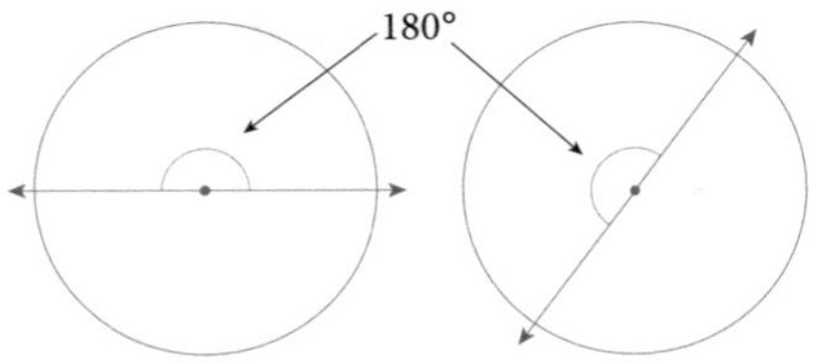

Two perpendicular lines through the center of a circle cut the circle into four equal quadrants, thus the angle between two perpendicular rays has an angle measure equal to $\frac{1}{4}$ a revolution or $\frac{360°}{4} = 90°$.

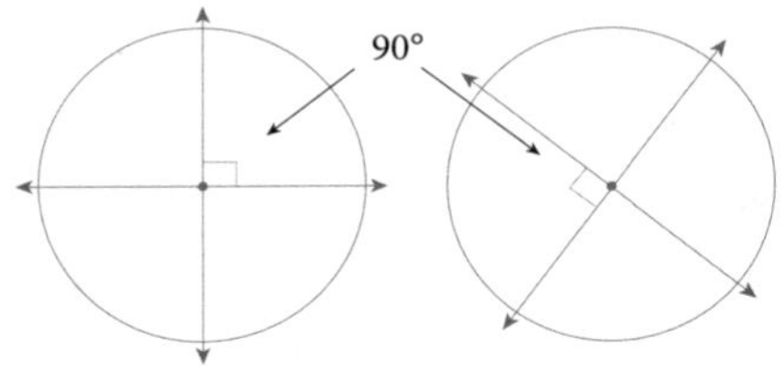

Classification of Angles

Angles are classified according to their size in degrees.

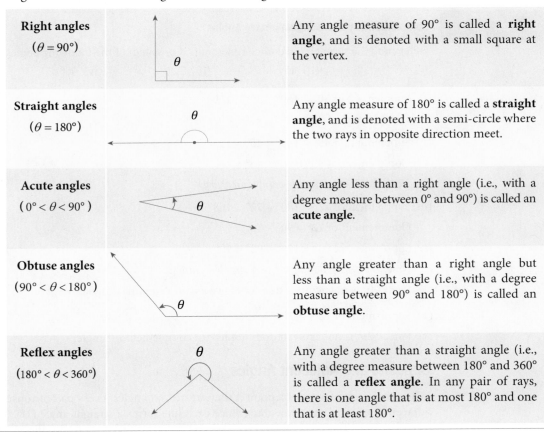

Right angles ($\theta = 90°$)	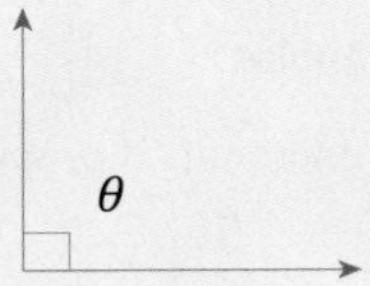	Any angle measure of 90° is called a **right angle**, and is denoted with a small square at the vertex.
Straight angles ($\theta = 180°$)	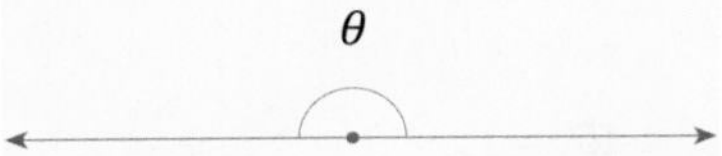	Any angle measure of 180° is called a **straight angle**, and is denoted with a semi-circle where the two rays in opposite direction meet.
Acute angles ($0° < \theta < 90°$)	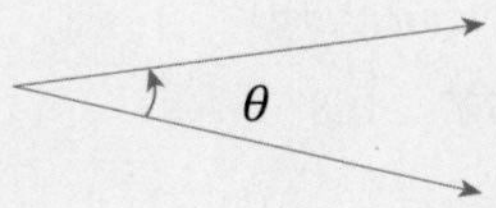	Any angle less than a right angle (i.e., with a degree measure between 0° and 90°) is called an **acute angle**.
Obtuse angles ($90° < \theta < 180°$)	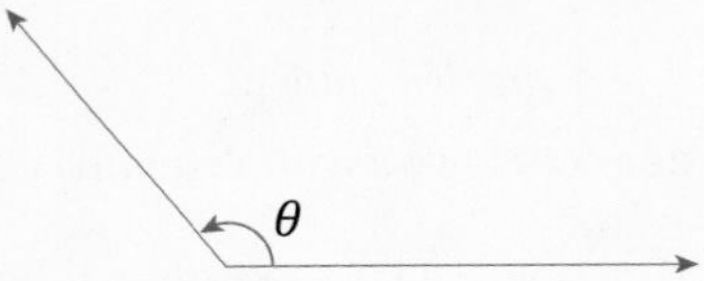	Any angle greater than a right angle but less than a straight angle (i.e., with a degree measure between 90° and 180°) is called an **obtuse angle**.
Reflex angles ($180° < \theta < 360°$)	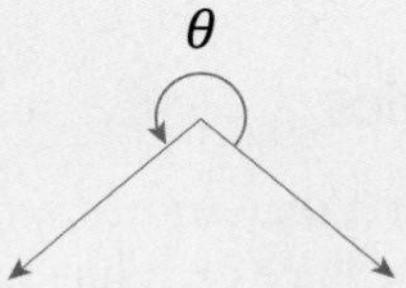	Any angle greater than a straight angle (i.e., with a degree measure between 180° and 360° is called a **reflex angle.** In any pair of rays, there is one angle that is at most 180° and one that is at least 180°.

Example 10.1-b **Classifying Angles**

Identify the following angles as acute, right, obtuse, straight, or reflex:

(i)

(ii)

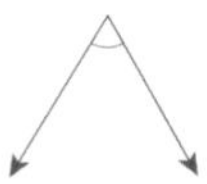

(iii)

(iv)

(v)

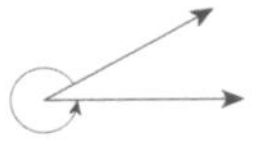

Solution

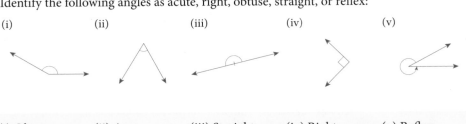

(i) Obtuse (ii) Acute (iii) Straight (iv) Right (v) Reflex

Supplementary and Complementary Angles

Angle pairs with measures that sum to a right angle (90°) or a straight angle (180°) are given special names:

Supplementary angles $(\theta + \varphi = 180°)$	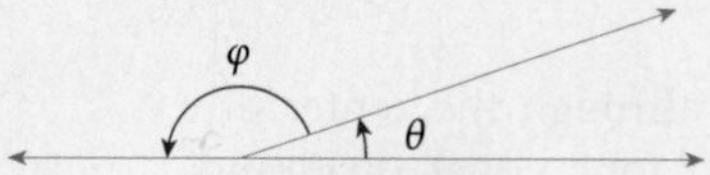	Two angles are called **supplementary angles** if their sum is 180°. Each angle is called a supplement of the other.
Complementary angles $(\theta + \varphi = 90°)$	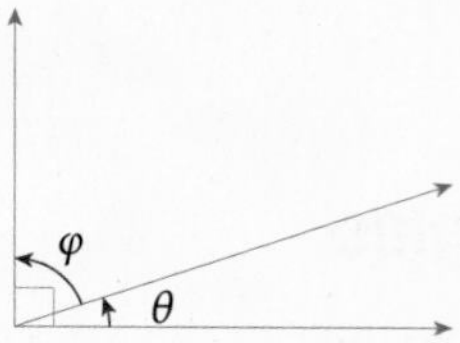	Two angles are called **complementary angles** if their sum is 90°. Each angle is called a complement of the other.

Since the sum of complementary angles is 90°, each angle must be acute (i.e., less than 90°). As a result, only acute angles have complements.

Example 10.1-c

Complementary and Supplementary Angles

Determine the supplement and complement (if possible) of the following angles:

(i) 30° (ii) 45° (iii) 72° (iv) 90° (v) 126°

Solution

(i) Supplement of 30° = 180° – 30° = 150°

Complement of 30° = 90° – 30° = 60°

(ii) Supplement of 45° = 180° – 45° = 135°

Complement of 45° = 90° – 45° = 45°

Note: A 45°-angle is self-complementary.

(iii) Supplement of 72° = 180° – 72° = 108°

Complement of 72° = 90° – 72° = 18°

(iv) Supplement of 90° = 180° – 90° = 90°

Note: A 90° (right)-angle is self-supplementary.

Since 90° is not acute, it does not have a complementary angle.

(v) Supplement of 126° = 180° – 126° = 54°

Since 126° is not acute, it does not have a complementary angle.

Opposite and Adjacent Angles

When two lines intersect at a point P, they create four angles. Every pair of consecutive angles, called **adjacent angles**, is supplementary, since each line forms a straight angle (180°) at point P and the other line cuts it into two angles, which have a sum of 180°. As a result, the angles opposite to each other, called **opposite angles**, are always equal (congruent).

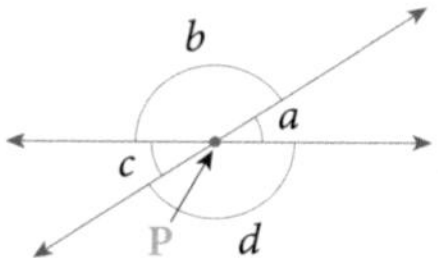

Adjacent angle		Opposite angle	
$\angle a + \angle b = 180°$	$\longrightarrow$	$\angle a = 180° - \angle b$	Therefore, $\angle a = \angle c$
$\angle b + \angle c = 180°$	$\longrightarrow$	$\angle c = 180° - \angle b$	
$\angle b + \angle c = 180°$	$\longrightarrow$	$\angle b = 180° - \angle c$	Therefore, $\angle b = \angle d$
$\angle c + \angle d = 180°$	$\longrightarrow$	$\angle d = 180° - \angle c$	

Note: When two lines intersect, the adjacent angles are supplementary (sum of 180°) and opposite angles are congruent (equal).

Example 10.1-d

Opposite and Adjacent Angles

Determine the measures of the three unknown angles in the following diagram:

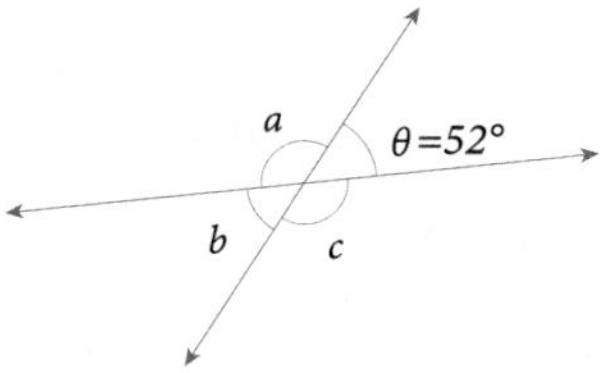

Solution

(i) Since angle a is adjacent to angle θ, it is supplementary to angle θ.
Therefore, $\angle a = 180° - 52° = 128°$.

(ii) Since angle b is opposite to angle θ, it is congruent to angle θ.
Therefore, $\angle b = 52°$.

(iii) Since angle c is adjacent to angle θ, it is supplementary to angle θ.
Therefore, $\angle c = 180° - 52° = 128°$.

Parallel Lines and Transversal Angles

Parallel lines are lines in a plane which do not meet (or intersect) even when extended. To demonstrate that the lines are parallel, small arrowheads are drawn.

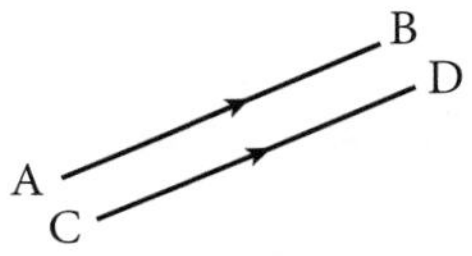

Also, the symbol "//" is used to indicate that the lines are parallel, e.g. $\overline{AB} // \overline{CD}$.

A transversal is a line that intersects two or more other lines. When a transversal intersects parallel lines, the angles it forms with each of the two parallel lines are congruent.

'arallel lines never intersect ven when extended. They re identified by arrowheads narked on the pair of lines.

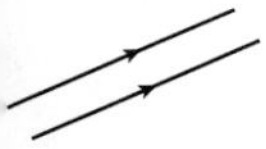

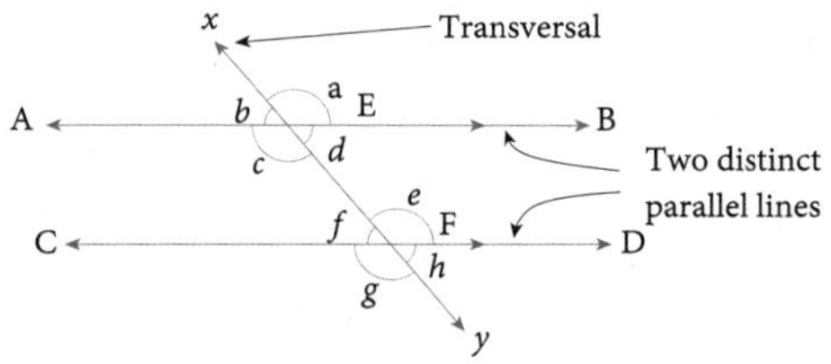

In the above diagram $\overline{AB} // \overline{CD}$, xy is a transversal, which intersects the parallel lines at 'E' and 'F'. The four angles, a, b, c, and d, around the point 'E' are congruent to the four angles, e, f, g, and h, around point 'F', respectively; i.e., $[\angle a = \angle e,\quad \angle b = \angle f,\quad \angle c = \angle g, \text{ and } \angle d = \angle h]$

This means that there are special relationships with special names between the angles formed by the transversal and each of the parallel lines, as classified below:

orresponding angles have pattern that looks like the tter F:

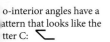

o-interior angles have a attern that looks like the tter C:

Corresponding angles (Ex.: $\angle d = \angle h$)	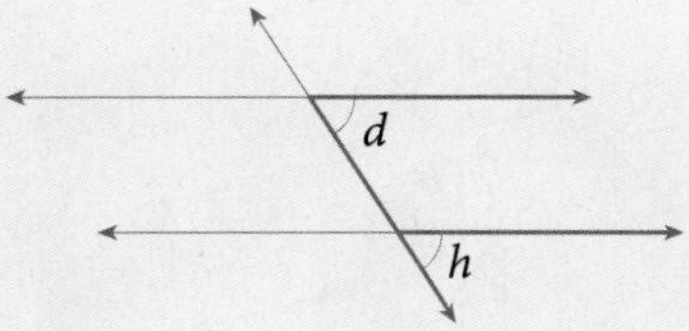	The angles formed on the same corner of the intersection between the transversal and each of the parallel lines are called **corresponding angles**, and they are *congruent*.
Co-interior angles (Ex.: $\angle d + \angle e = 180°$)	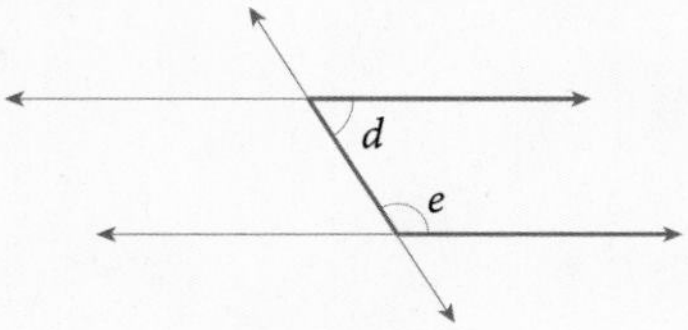	The angles formed on the same side of the transversal and on the interior of the parallel lines are called **co-interior angles**, and they are *supplementary*.

Alternate angles have a pattern that looks like the letter Z:

Opposite angles have a pattern that looks like the letter X: ✕

Alternate angles (Ex.: $\angle c = \angle e$)	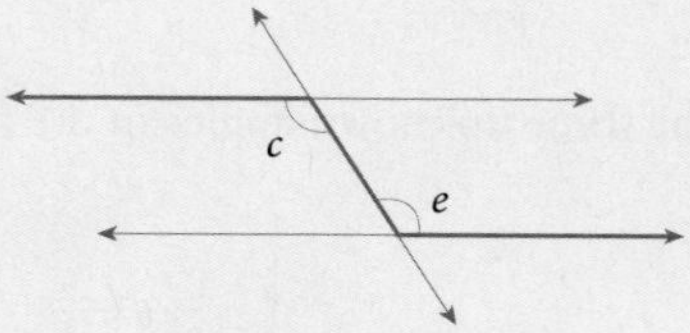	The angles formed on opposite sides of the transversal and on the interior of the parallel lines are called **alternate angles**, and they are *congruent.*
Opposite angles (Ex.: $\angle a = \angle c$ and $\angle e = \angle g$)	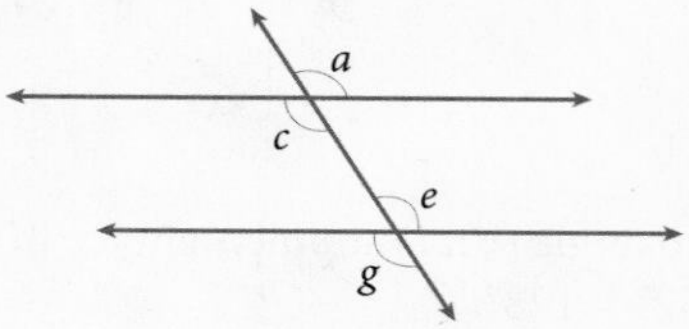	The angles formed by any intersecting lines that are opposite to the same vertex are called **opposite angles** and they are *congruent.*

For example, consider the angles formed by two distinct parallel lines (AB//CD) and a transversal *xy*.

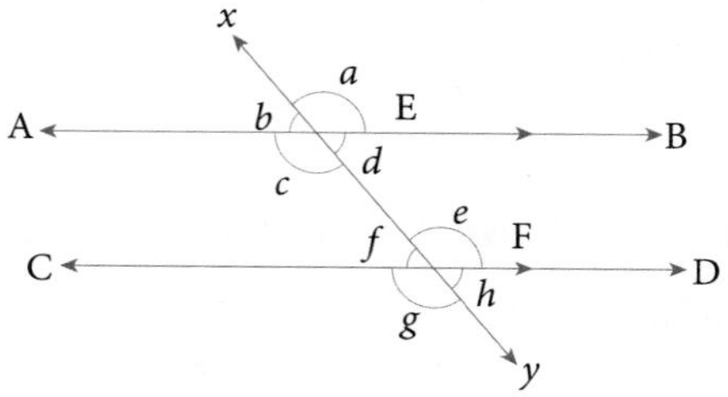

Corresponding angles are congruent	Co-interior angles are supplementary
$\angle a = \angle e$ $\angle b = \angle f$ $\angle c = \angle g$ $\angle d = \angle h$	$\angle d + \angle e = 180°$ $\angle c + \angle f = 180°$
Alternate angles are congruent	**Opposite angles are congruent**
$\angle d = \angle f$ $\angle c = \angle e$	$\angle a = \angle c$ $\angle b = \angle d$ $\angle e = \angle g$ $\angle f = \angle h$

Example 10.1-e **Identifying Relationships Between Angles**

State the relationship to angle θ of each of the five unknown angles, *a*, *b*, *c*, *d*, and *e*, identified in the following diagram, and also state whether the angle is congruent or supplementary to θ:

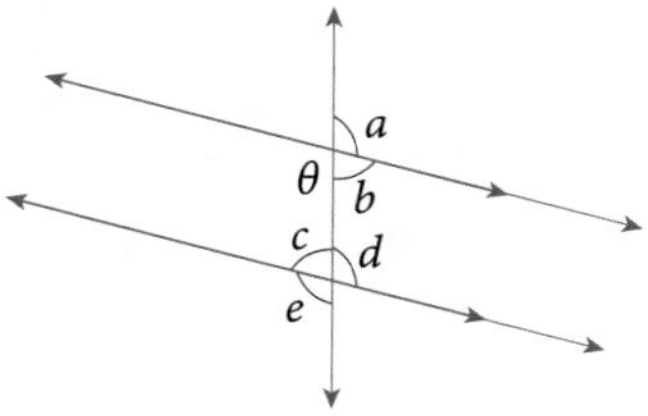

Solution

(i) Angle a is opposite to angle θ, hence it is congruent to θ.

(ii) Angle b is adjacent to angle θ, hence it is supplementary to θ.

(iii) Angle c is co-interior to angle θ, hence it is supplementary to θ.

(iv) Angle d is alternate to angle θ, hence it is congruent to θ.

(v) Angle e is corresponding to angle θ, hence it is congruent to θ.

Example 10.1-f **Calculating Measure of Transversal Angles**

Calculate the angle measure of the five unknown angles identified in Example 10.1-e, given that angle $\theta = 105°$.

Solution

(i) Since angle a is congruent to θ, $a = \theta = 105°$.

(ii) Since angle b is supplementary to θ, $b = 180 - \theta = 180 - 105 = 75°$.

(iii) Since angle c is supplementary to θ, $c = 180 - \theta = 180 - 105 = 75°$.

(iv) Since angle d is congruent to θ, $d = \theta = 105°$.

(v) Since angle e is congruent to θ, $e = \theta = 105°$.

Example 10.1-g **An Application of Transversal Angles – Intersections of Roads**

Alder Road, Birch Street, and Cedar Avenue are all straight roads that run in different directions – their intersections form a triangle. Alder Road intersects Birch Street at an angle of 72° and Cedar Avenue at an internal angle of 47°, both as measured from within the triangle. Using the angle relationship learned in this section, find the angle of intersection between Birch Street and Cedar Avenue.

Solution

Step 1: Draw a diagram representing the intersection of roads and mark the known angles. Name the triangle as XYZ and let θ be the angle of intersection between Birch Street and Cedar Avenue.

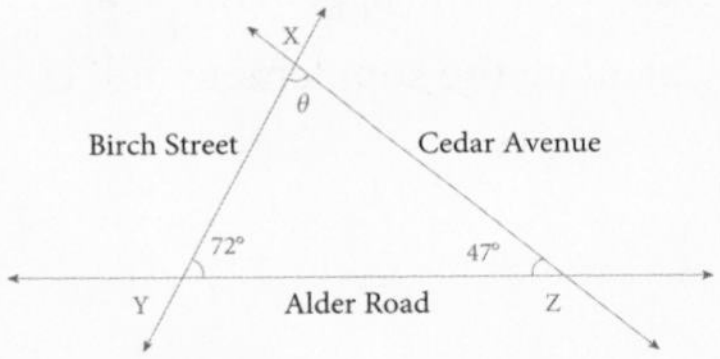

Step 2: To make use of the angle relationships that we learned in this section, draw an imaginary road, parallel to Alder Road, that runs through X, the intersection of Birch Street and Cedar Avenue.

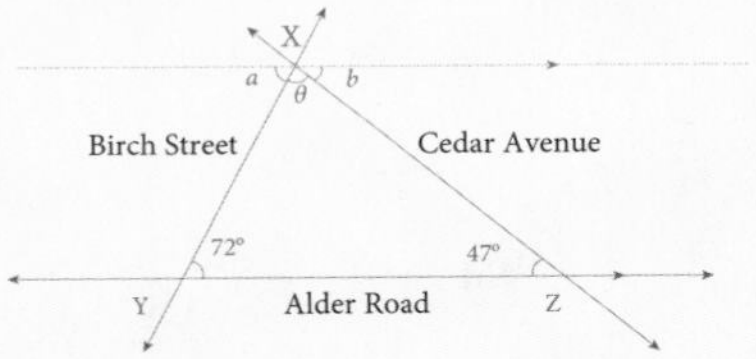

Step 3: Calculate the alternate transversal angles that are formed and use those to calculate the angle of intersection between Birch Street and Cedar Avenue.

$\angle a = 72°$ (Alternate Angle)

$\angle b = 47°$ (Alternate Angle)

Step 4: The three angles a, θ, and b at the vertex X of the triangle XYZ must be equal to 180° (angles in a straight line).

$$\angle a + \theta + \angle b = 180°$$

$$\theta = 180° - \angle a - \angle b$$

$$= 180° - 72° - 47°$$

$$\theta = 61°$$

Therefore, the angle of intersection between Birch Street and Cedar Avenue is 61°.

The above example demonstrates that the three internal angles of a triangle must add up to 180°. We will examine this further as we begin to analyze plane figures in the next section.

10.1 | Exercises

Answers to odd numbered problems are available at the end of the textbook.

1. Draw and label the following geometric objects:
   a. Line $\overleftrightarrow{EF}$ b. Line segment $\overline{GH}$ c. Ray $\overrightarrow{JK}$
2. Draw and label the following geometric objects:
   a. Line $\overleftrightarrow{ST}$ b. Line segment $\overline{UV}$ c. Ray $\overrightarrow{XW}$
3. Identify and name the following geometric objects:

a. 

b. 

c. 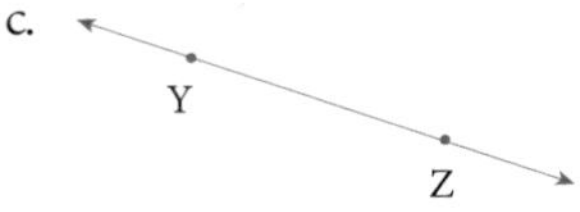

4. Identify and name the following geometric objects:

a. 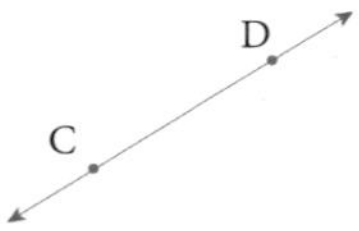

b. 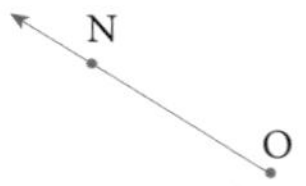

c. 

For the figures shown in problems 5 to 8, answer the following questions:

(i) Name the angle using the three-letter naming convention (e.g. $\angle$ ABC).
(ii) Classify the angle as acute, right, or obtuse.
(iii) Determine the approximate angle measure using a protractor.
(iv) Calculate the supplement and complement (if applicable) of the angle.

5. a. 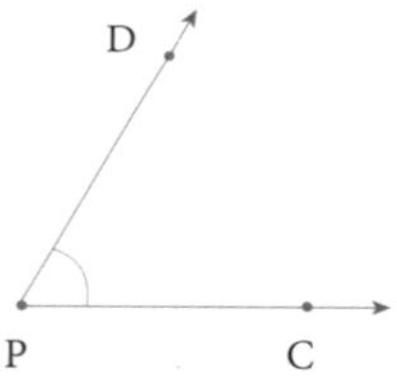

b. 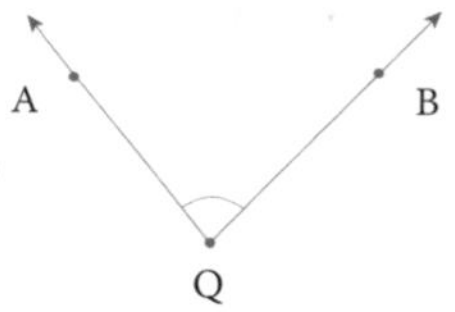

6. a. 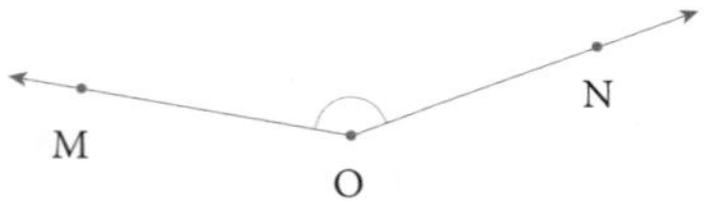

b. 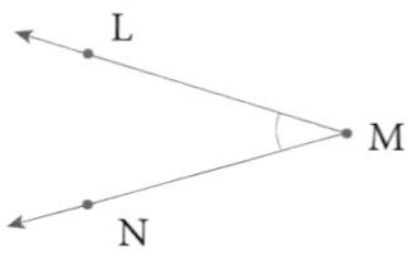

7. a. 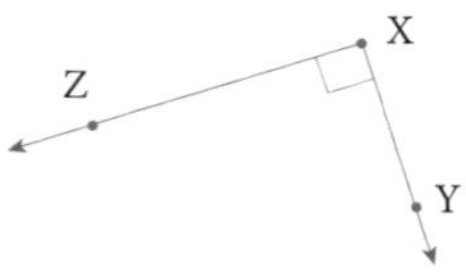

b. 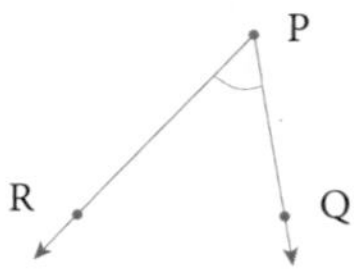

8. a. 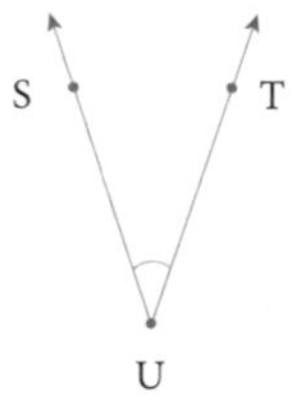

b. 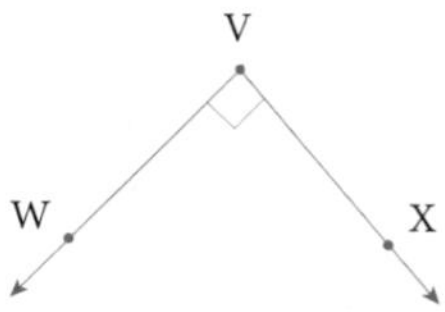

9. Determine the measure of the angle that is complementary to: a. 32.5° b. 18°
10. Determine the measure of the angle that is complementary to: a. 83.1° b. 5°
11. Determine the measure of the angle that is supplementary to: a. 123.4° b. 89°
12. Determine the measure of the angle that is supplementary to: a. 7.8° b. 92°

For the figures shown in Problems 13 to 16, determine the congruent pairs of angles:

13. a.

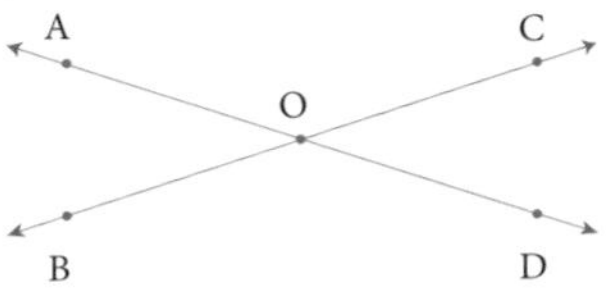

b.

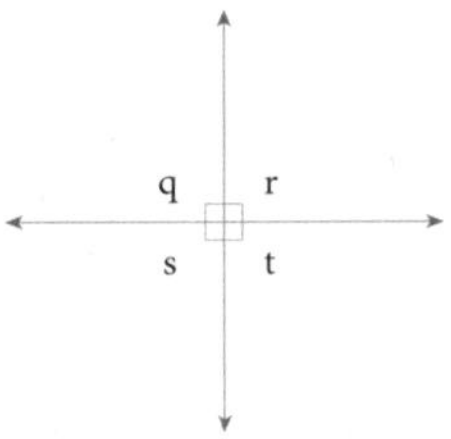

14. a.

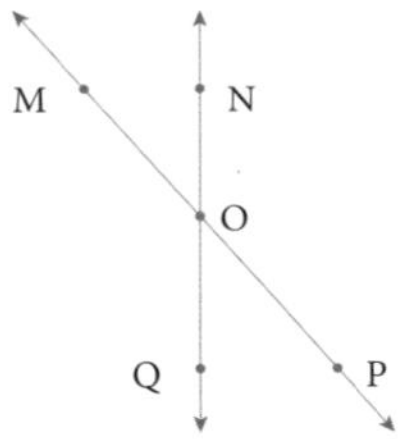

b.

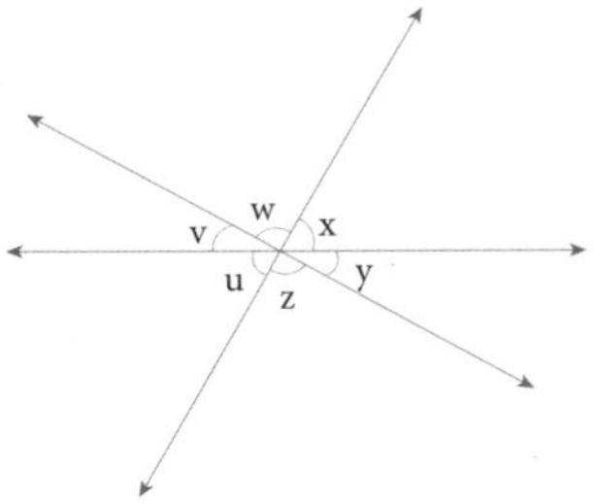

15.

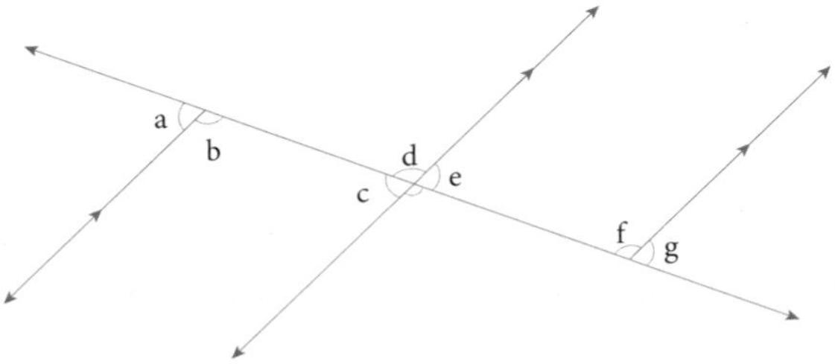

16.

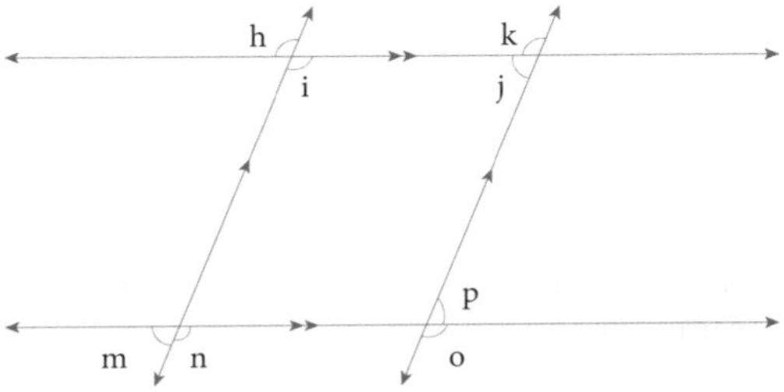

For the figures shown in problems 17 to 20, determine the value of the unknown angles.

17. a.

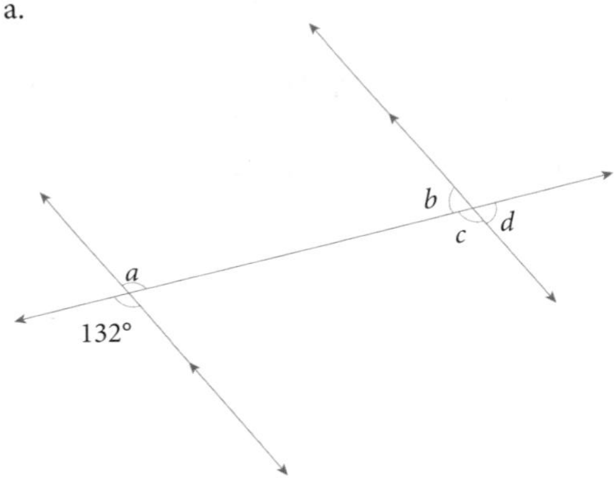

b.

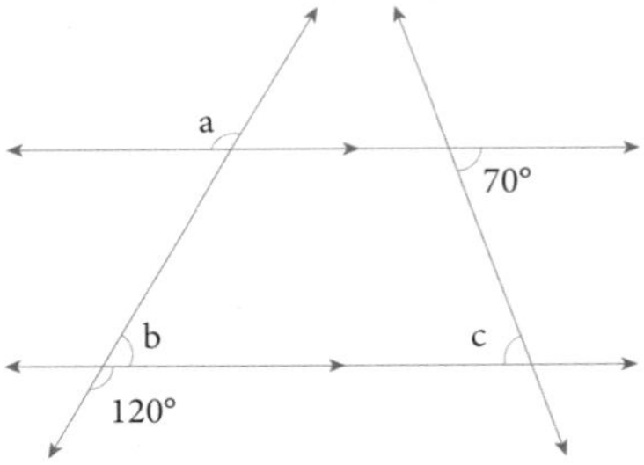

18. a.

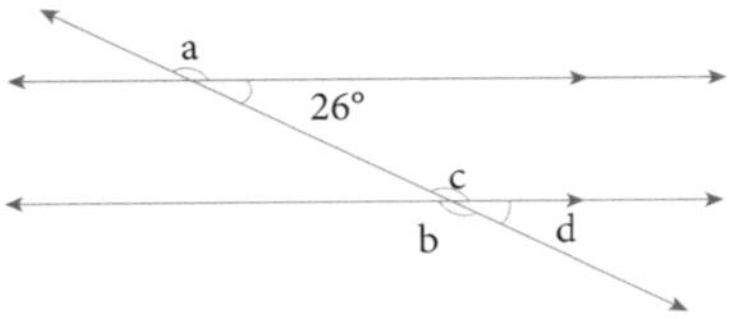

b.

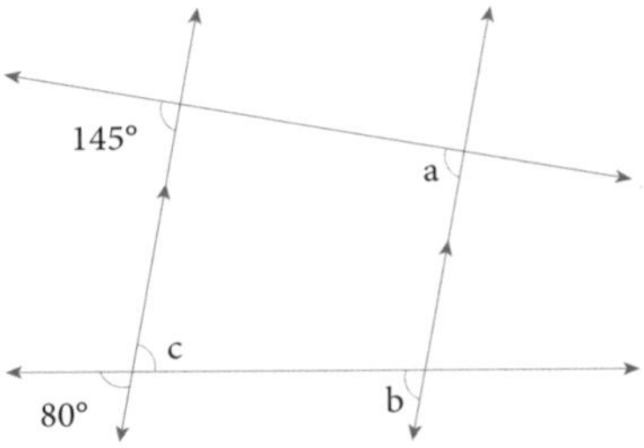

19. a.

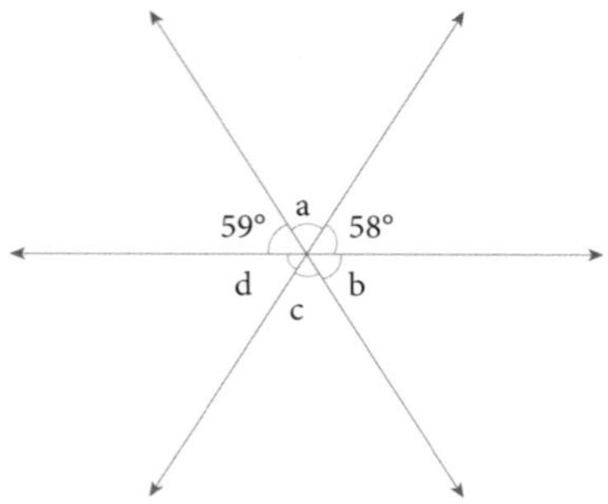

b.

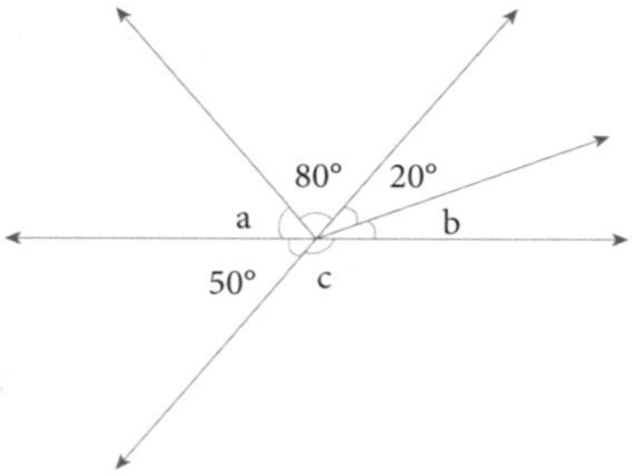

20. a.

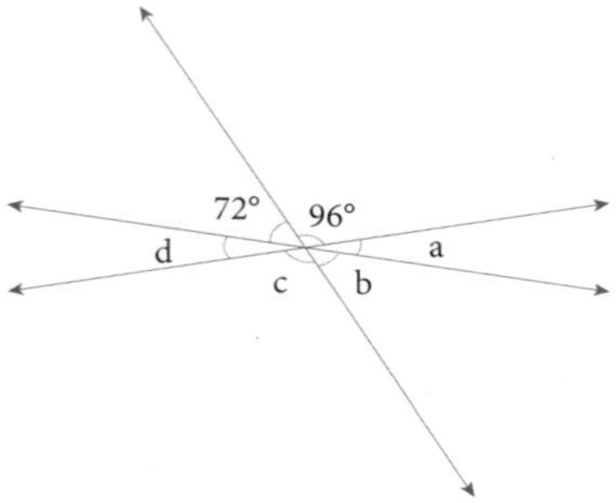

b.

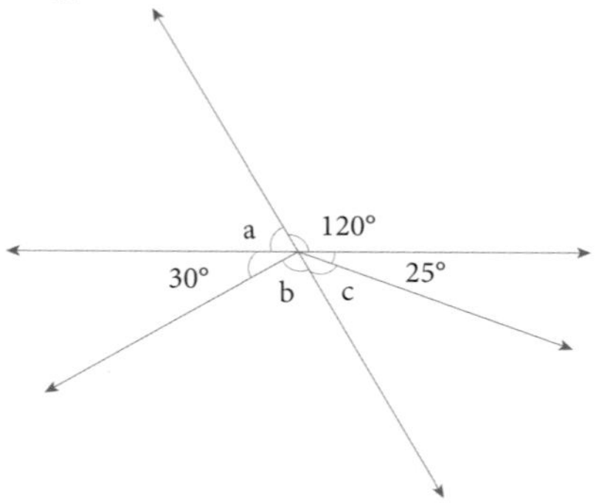

21. A small island is situated at the south of Lois Lake, separated from the mainland by two tributaries of Lois Lake: Crag Creek to the west and Slip Stream to the east. A straight highway called River Road connects the island to the mainland in either direction. The River Road bridge over Crag Creek forms an angle of 77° with the creek, and the bridge over Slip Stream forms an angle of 71° with the stream, both on the island's side. Assuming that both Crag Creek and Slip Stream are fairly straight, determine the angle that they form with each other when they branch off Lois Lake.

22. The southwest corner of the intersection of Main and Queen forms an angle of 104°. Further down Main Street, the southwest corner of the intersection of Main and King forms an angle of 63°. Determine the acute angle formed by the intersection of Queen and King, assuming that all three roads are perfectly straight.

For the figures shown in Problems 23 and 24, use transversal angles and the fact that the sum of the three internal angles of a triangle always equals 180°:

23. a. Calculate the value of θ.

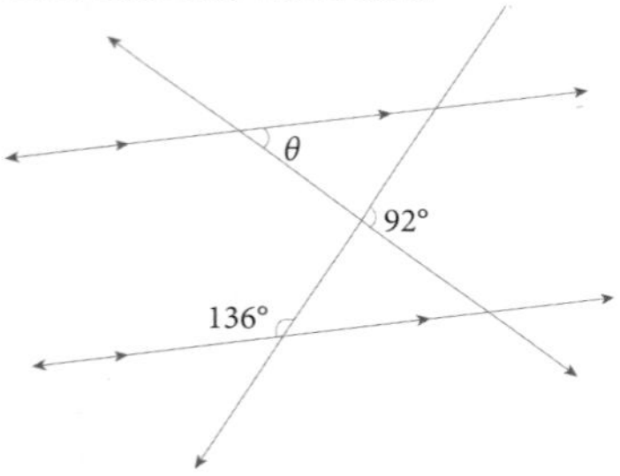

b. Calculate the value of a, b, and c.

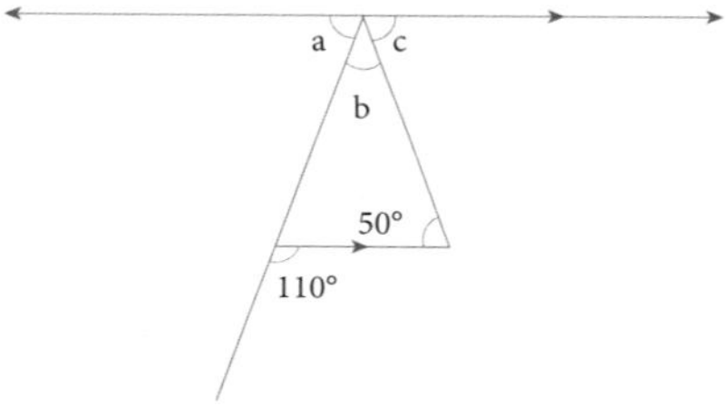

24. a. Calculate the value of θ.

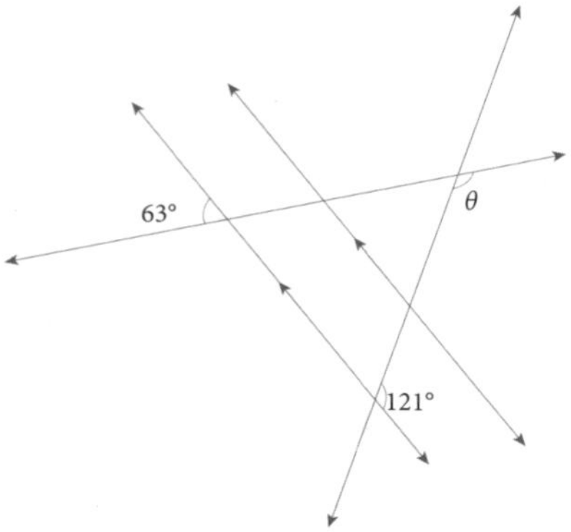

b. Calculate the value of a, b, and c.

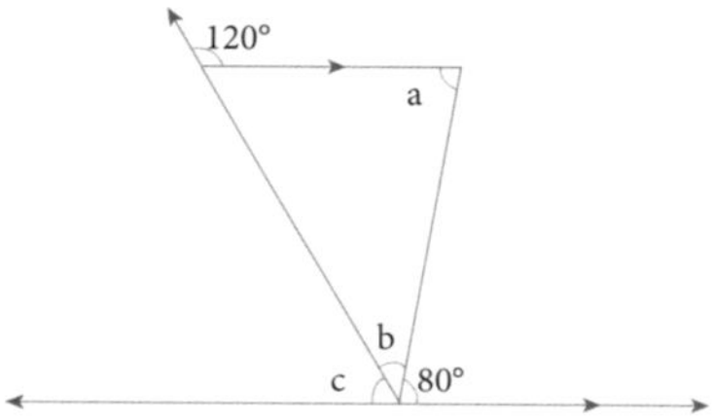

10.2 | Classification and Properties of Plane Figures

Introduction

The study of Geometry that deals with the objects or figures that are flat (2-dimensions) and that can be drawn in the Cartesian plane is known as **Plane Geometry**. In Plane Geometry, we study the properties and relations of plane figures such as triangles, quadrilaterals, polygons, and circles. A plane figure is continuous and closed, meaning that it can be drawn without lifting the pencil from the page and that the start-point is the same as the end-point of the object.

A few examples of plane figures are shown below:

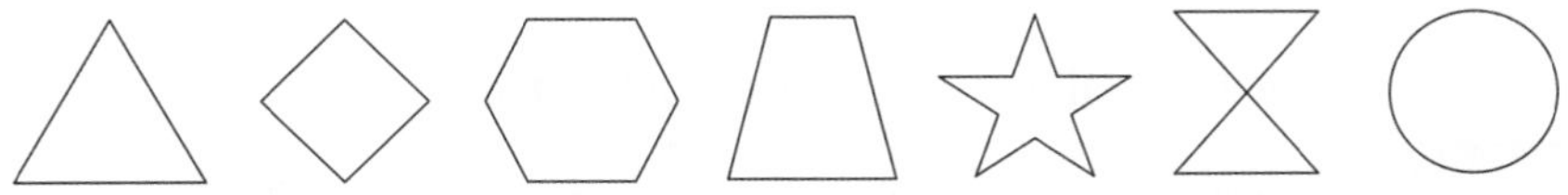

Exhibit 10.2-a Example of Plane Figures

Polygons

A polygon is a plane figure that is created by joining a finite number of line segments together at their vertices; i.e., a polygon is a plane figure that is bound by three or more straight edges, known as sides. The first 6 shapes in Exhibit 10.2-a are polygons. The circle (i.e., the 7th shape) in Exhibit 10.2-a is not a polygon, as it is not formed by joining a finite number of line segments together. However, the circle is a special shape and you will learn of its properties later in the chapter.

A **simple polygon** is a polygon which does not intersect itself. The first 5 shapes in Exhibit 10.2-a are simple polygons. A polygon that is not simple (i.e., it intersects itself) is called a **complex polygon**. The hourglass shape (i.e., the 6th shape) in Exhibit 10.2-a is an example of a complex polygon.

A **convex polygon** is a simple polygon whose internal angles are each all less than 180°. The first 4 shapes in Exhibit 10.2-a are convex polygons. Every simple polygon that is not convex is called a **concave polygon**. The star shape (i.e. the 5th shape) in Exhibit 10.2-a is an example of a concave polygon.

A **regular convex polygon** is a convex polygon whose sides are all the same length and whose internal angles have the same measure. The first 3 shapes in Exhibit 10.2-a are regular, convex polygons.

Polygons are named according to the number of sides that they have. The first eight, regular, convex polygons are shown below:

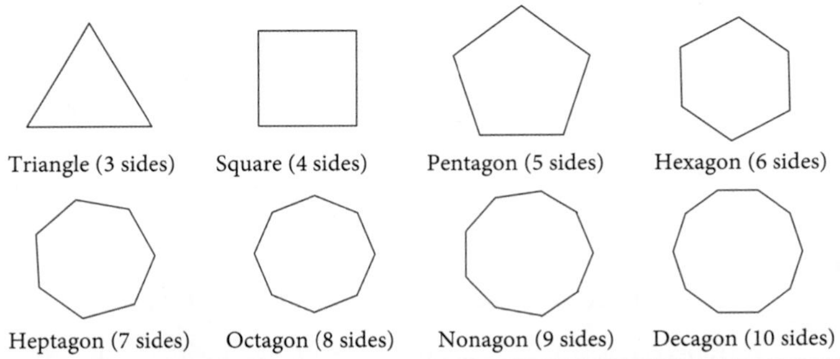

Exhibit 10.2-b Names of first eight regular convex polygons

An internal angle of a simple polygon is an angle at a vertex where two line segments meet, as measured from the inside of the simple polygon.

If lines are drawn from one vertex of an n-sided polygon to a vertex across from it, there will be $(n - 2)$ triangles that can be drawn within the polygon.

For example,

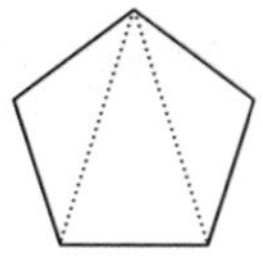

$n = 5$
(3 Triangles)

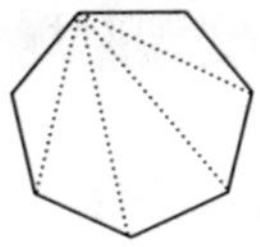

$n = 7$
(5 Triangles)

Therefore, the sum of the internal angles of any n-sided polygon $= (n - 2) \times 180°$. This is known as the **Internal Angles Theorem (IAT) – Part 1**.

Therefore, every internal angle in a regular n-sided convex polygon $= \dfrac{(n-2) \times 180°}{n}$. This is known as the **Internal Angles Theorem (IAT) – Part 2**.

Example 10.2-a

Internal Angles of Regular Convex Polygons

Using the Internal Angles Theorem (IAT) - Part 2, calculate the measure of each internal angle of the first eight regular convex polygons, listed in Exhibit 10.2-b.

Solution

Using $\theta = \dfrac{(n-2)\times 180°}{n}$

	Name of Polygon	Number of Sides (n)	Measure of Each Internal Angle
(i)	Triangle	3	$\theta = \dfrac{(3-2)\times 180°}{3} = \dfrac{180°}{3} = 60°$
(ii)	Square	4	$\theta = \dfrac{(4-2)\times 180°}{4} = \dfrac{360°}{4} = 90°$
(iii)	Pentagon	5	$\theta = \dfrac{(5-2)\times 180°}{5} = \dfrac{540°}{5} = 108°$
(iv)	Hexagon	6	$\theta = \dfrac{(6-2)\times 180°}{6} = \dfrac{720°}{6} = 120°$
(v)	Heptagon	7	$\theta = \dfrac{(7-2)\times 180°}{7} = \dfrac{900°}{7} \approx 128.6°$
(vi)	Octagon	8	$\theta = \dfrac{(8-2)\times 180°}{8} = \dfrac{1{,}080°}{8} = 135°$
(vii)	Nonagon	9	$\theta = \dfrac{(9-2)\times 180°}{9} = \dfrac{1{,}260°}{9} = 140°$
(viii)	Decagon	10	$\theta = \dfrac{(10-2)\times 180°}{10} = \dfrac{1{,}440°}{10} = 144°$

Example 10.2-b

Verifying a Special Case of the Internal Angles Theorem

A trapezoid is any four-sided convex polygon with one pair of opposite sides that are parallel to each other (see diagram below). Use the properties of parallel lines and transversal angles to prove that the Internal Angles Theorem (IAT) - Part 1 holds true for all trapezoids.

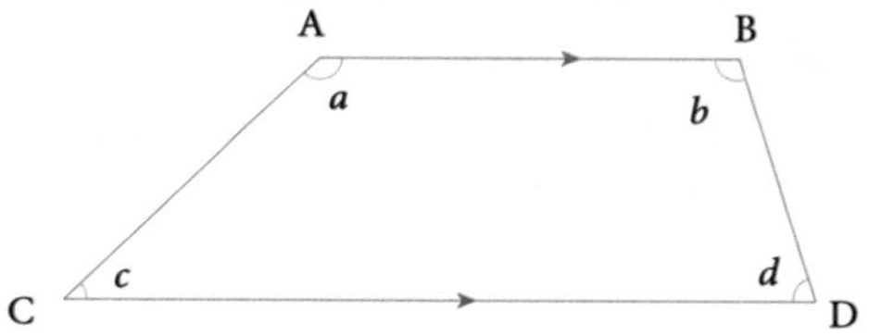

Solution

The IAT-Part 1 states that the sum of the internal angles of any 4-sided convex polygon is $(4 - 2) \times 180° = 360°$.

Since the line segment AB is parallel to the line segment CD, angles a and c are co-interior, transversal angles.

i.e., $\angle a + \angle c = 180°$ (1)

Similarly, b and d are also co-interior angles, hence supplementary.

i.e., $\angle b + \angle d = 180°$ (2)

Adding (1) and (2): $\angle a + \angle b + \angle c + \angle d = 360°$.

Therefore, the sum of all four angles in the trapezoid is 360°, which validates the result of the IAT - Part 1 formula. Hence, the formula is valid for all trapezoids.

An external angle of a simple polygon is the external angle obtained by extending one of the sides at a vertex where two line segments meet, and measuring the angle formed outside the simple polygon. For example, an n-sided polygon will have n external angles.

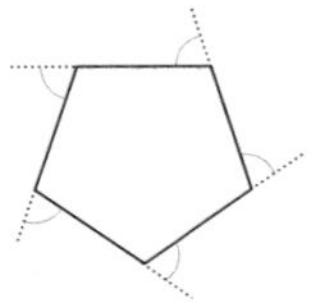

There are n vertices and the sum of the internal angle and the external angle at each vertex is supplementary, 180°; i.e., the sum of all interior and exterior angles of an n-sided polygon $= n \times 180°$. However, the sum of all the interior angles $= (n - 2) \times 180°$.

Therefore, the sum of all the exterior angles of an n sided polygon:

$$= n \times 180° - (n - 2)180°$$

$$= n \times 180° - n \times 180° + 2 \times 180°$$

$$= 360°$$

Therefore, the sum of the external angles formed by extending the sides of any n-sided, simple polygon = 360°. This is known as the **External Angles Theorem (EAT) – Part 1**.

Therefore, every external angle in a regular n-sided convex polygon $= \dfrac{360°}{n}$. This is known as the **External Angles Theorem (EAT) – Part 2.**

Example 10.2-c

External Angles of Regular Convex Polygons

Using the External Angles Theorem (EAT) - Part 2, calculate the measure of each external angle of the first eight, regular, convex polygons, listed in Exhibit 10.2-b.

Solution

Using $\theta = \dfrac{360°}{n}$

	Name of Polygon	Number of Sides (n)	Measure of Each External Angle
(i)	Triangle	3	$\theta = \dfrac{360°}{3} = 120°$
(ii)	Square	4	$\theta = \dfrac{360°}{4} = 90°$
(iii)	Pentagon	5	$\theta = \dfrac{360°}{5} = 72°$
(iv)	Hexagon	6	$\theta = \dfrac{360°}{6} = 60°$
(v)	Heptagon	7	$\theta = \dfrac{360°}{7} \approx 51.4°$

(vi)	Octagon	8	$\theta = \dfrac{360°}{8} = 45°$
(vii)	Nonagon	9	$\theta = \dfrac{360°}{9} = 40°$
(viii)	Decagon	10	$\theta = \dfrac{360°}{10} = 36°$

Note: The internal angle and the external angle at every vertex of a convex polygon are supplementary, as each pair of internal and external angles together form a straight line.

Example 10.2-d **An Application of the External Angles Theorem – Navigation**

A plane takes off, heading due west. Shortly after take-off, it turns 60° to the north (clockwise). Later on, it turns another 75° in the same (clockwise) direction. A few minutes later, it makes another turn of 80° in the same direction. Finally, it makes one last turn in the same direction and heads back to its take-off point, flying in to the airstrip bearing due south. Find the bearing change (change in angle) of the final turn.

Solution

Based on the given information, draw a picture of the situation:

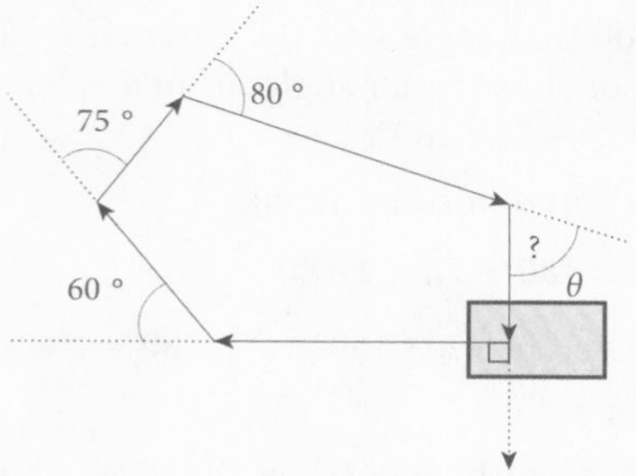

Using ETA – Part 1, the sum of all exterior angles = 360°.

Let the final external angle be θ.

i.e., $60° + 75° + 80° + \theta + 90° = 360°$

$\theta = 360° - 305° = 55°$

Therefore, the bearing change of the final turn is 55°.

Classification and Properties of Triangles

We will now examine one type of convex polygon – triangles. A **triangle** (literally meaning "three-angles") is any polygon with three sides and three internal angles. We will now look at the different sub-categories and classifications of triangles and the various properties of the figures.

Using the IAT - Part 1, the sum of the three internal angles of a triangle equals $(3 - 2) \times 180° = 1 \times 180° = 180°$. Therefore, since the sum of the internal angles equals 180°, each internal angle must be less than 180°, which means every triangle is a convex polygon.

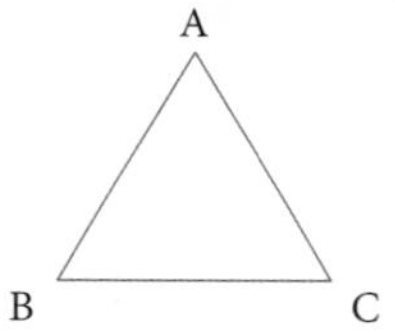

$\angle A + \angle B + \angle C = 180°$

There are two ways to classify triangles: by angle measure and by side length.

Classification of Triangles by Angle Measures

Acute triangle (three acute angles)	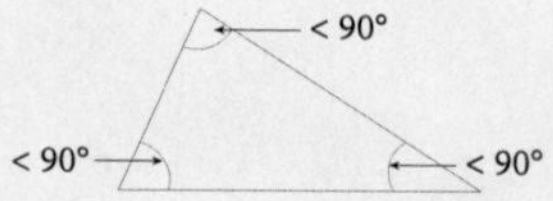	A triangle with all three angles less than 90° (acute angle) is called an **acute triangle**.
Right triangle (one right-angle)	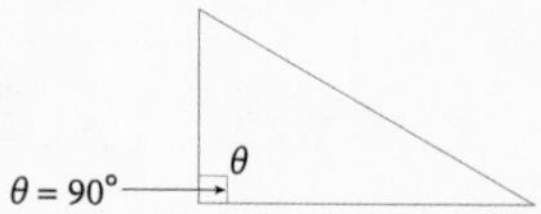	A triangle with one angle at 90° (right angle) is called a **right triangle**. Since the sum of the three angles is 180° and one angle is 90°, this means that the other two angles must add up to 90°; therefore, they are acute and complementary.

Obtuse triangle (one obtuse angle)	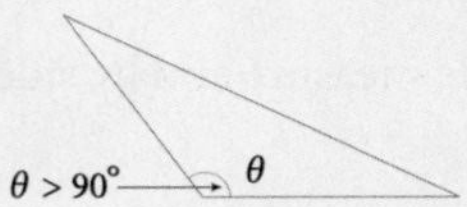	A triangle with one angle greater than 90° (obtuse angle) is called an **obtuse triangle.** Since the sum of the three angles is 180° and one angle is greater than 90°, this means that the other two angles must add up to less than 90°; therefore, they are acute.

Classification of Triangles by Side Measures

Equilateral triangle (three equal sides)	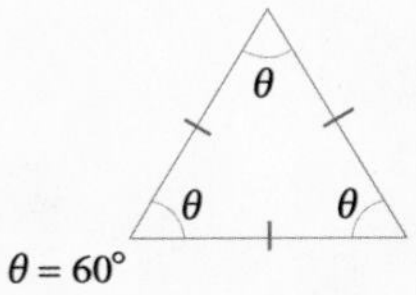	A triangle that has sides of equal lengths is called an **equilateral triangle.** Since an equilateral triangle is a regular polygon of three sides, by the IAT-Part 2, each angle is 60°. Therefore, every equilateral triangle is also an acute triangle.
Isosceles triangle (two equal sides)	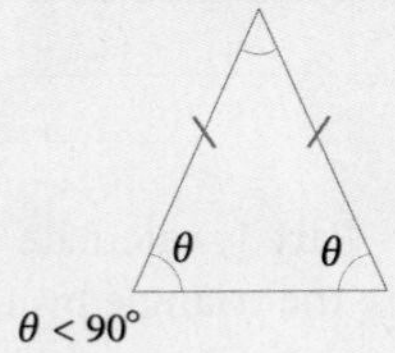	A triangle that has two sides of equal lengths is called an **isosceles triangle.** The angles opposite to the equal sides of an isosceles triangle will have equal measure. An isosceles triangle may be acute, right, or obtuse (but the equal angles will be acute).
Scalene triangle (no equal sides)		A triangle with sides of different lengths is called a **scalene triangle.** A scalene triangle may be acute, right, or obtuse.

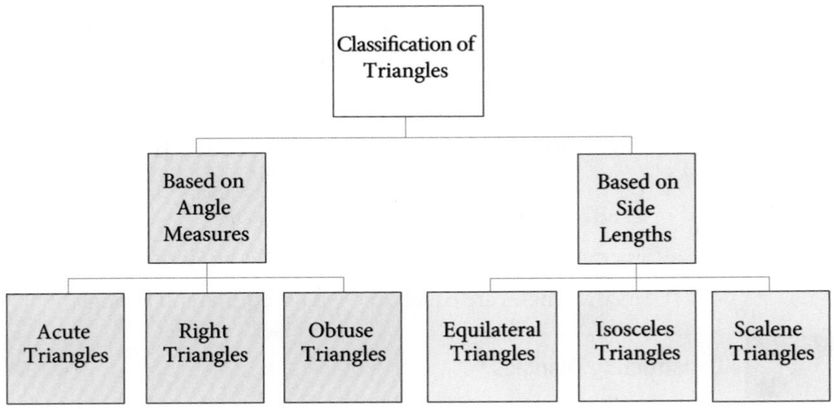

Exhibit 10.2-c Classification of Triangles

Note: It is common for the vertices to be labelled using capital letters, and the sides to be labelled as lower case letters, with the capitals and lower case letters corresponding to each other on opposite sides of the triangle as shown in the diagram.

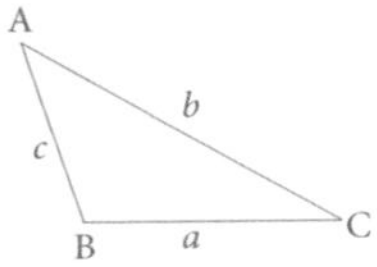

Example 10.2-e Classifying Triangles

Classify the following triangles by angle measure and by side length:

(i)

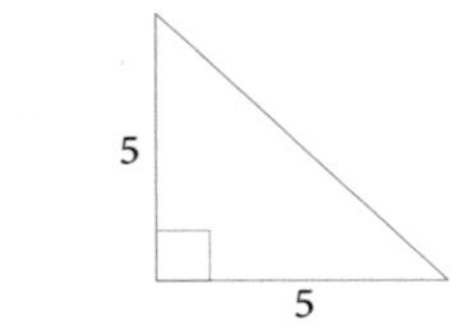

(ii)

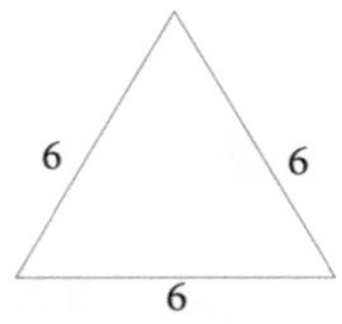

(iii)

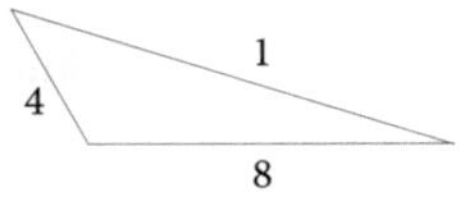

(iv)

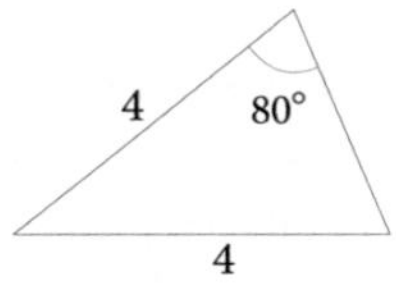

(v)

(vi)

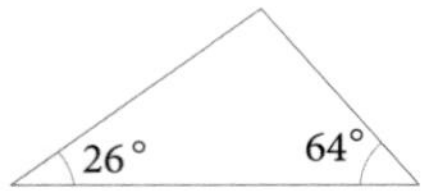

Solution

(i) Right and Isosceles triangle (ii) Acute and Equilateral triangle (iii) Obtuse and Scalene triangle

(iv) Acute and Isosceles triangle (v) Obtuse and Isosceles triangle (vi) Right and Scalene triangle

Example 10.2-f Calculating Unknown Angles in a Triangle

Using the Internal Angles Theorem (IAT) - Part 1, calculate the measure of the unknown angle in each of the following triangles. Then, classify the triangle by angle measure and by side length.

(i) ΔXYZ, $\angle YXZ = 30°$, $\angle XYZ = 120°$

(ii) ΔABC, $\angle BAC = 35°$, $\angle ACB = 55°$

(iii) ΔRST, $\angle RST = 60°$, $\angle STR = 60°$

Solution

(i) $\angle XZY = 180° - (30° + 120°) = 30°$

Since $\angle XYZ > 90°$, ΔXYZ is an **Obtuse triangle.**

Since $\angle YXZ = \angle XZY$, ΔXYZ is an **Isosceles triangle.**

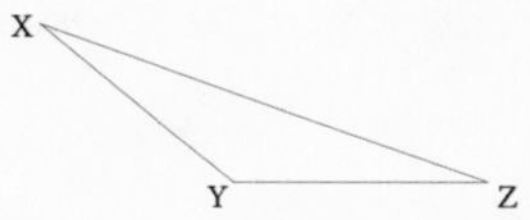

(ii) $\angle ABC = 180° - (35° + 55°) = 90°$

Since $\angle ABC = 90°$, ΔABC is a **Right triangle.**

Since no angles are equal, ΔABC is a **Scalene triangle.**

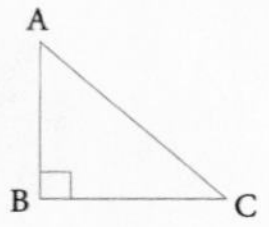

(iii) $\angle SRT = 180° - (60° + 60°) = 60°$

Since all angles are less than 90°, ΔRST is an **Acute triangle.**

Since all angles are equal, ΔRST is an **Equilateral triangle.**

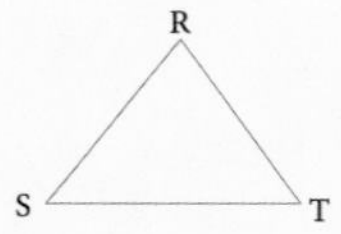

Example 10.2-g Constructing Triangles

Given that $\angle BAC = 37°$, a = 5 cm, and b = 8 cm, draw two different triangles, ΔABC, such that:

(i) ΔABC is an obtuse, isosceles triangle. (ii) ΔABC is an acute, scalene triangle.

Solution

(i)

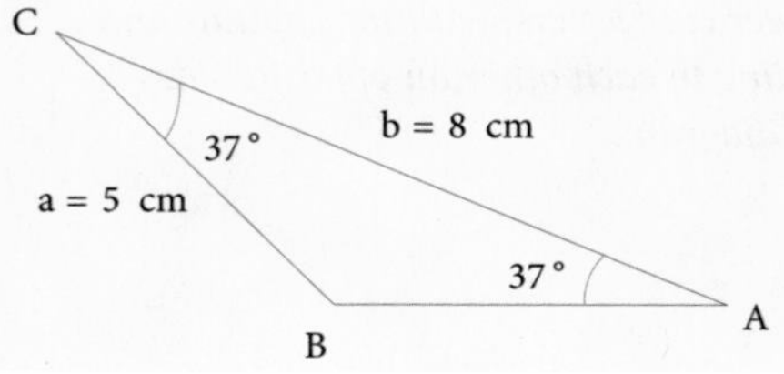

(ii)

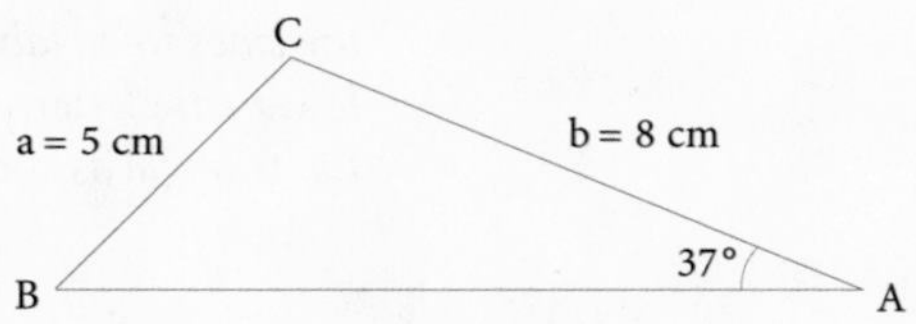

Example 10.2-h **Application of Triangles – Distances Between Cities**

The flying distance from Toronto to Sudbury is the same as that of Toronto to Ottawa, which is approximately 345 km. The angle from Toronto between Sudbury and Ottawa is 76°. What kind of triangle is created between the three cities?

Solution

Since the distance between Toronto and Sudbury is equal to the distance between Toronto and Ottawa, the angles opposite to these sides, are equal.

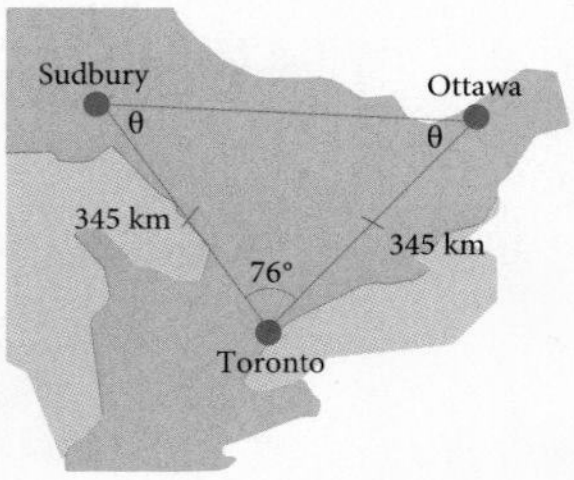

Let the equal angles be θ.

$$\theta + \theta + 76° = 180°$$

$$2\theta = 180° - 76° = 104°$$

$$\theta = \frac{104°}{2} = 52°$$

The angles are 52°, 52°, and 76°.

The two sides are equal and all three angles are less than 90°.

Therefore, the triangle created is an acute, isosceles triangle.

Classification and Properties of Quadrilaterals

We will now examine another class of convex polygons and their properties – **convex quadrilaterals**.

A **quadrilateral** (literally meaning "four-sided") is any polygon with four sides and four internal angles. In this section, we will examine **convex quadrilaterals** only, in which each of the internal angles is less than 180°.

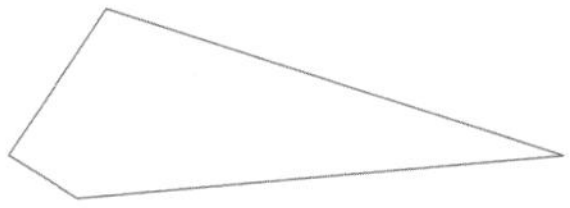

There are two main classes of quadrilaterals: **parallelograms**, which have special properties, and **non-parallelograms**.

A **parallelogram** is a quadrilateral with opposite sides that are parallel. As a result, in a parallelogram, the opposite sides are equal, the opposite angles are equal, and the adjacent angles are supplementary ($\theta + \varphi = 180°$).

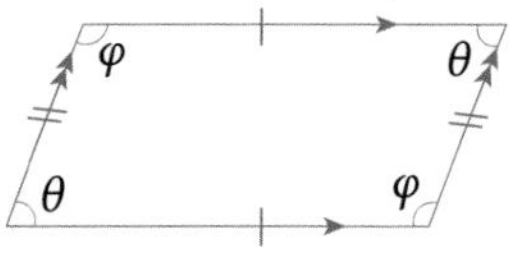

Classification of Quadrilaterals that are Parallelograms

Within the class of parallelograms, there are several sub-classes:

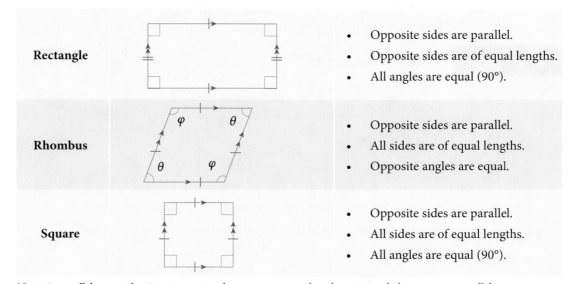

Rectangle	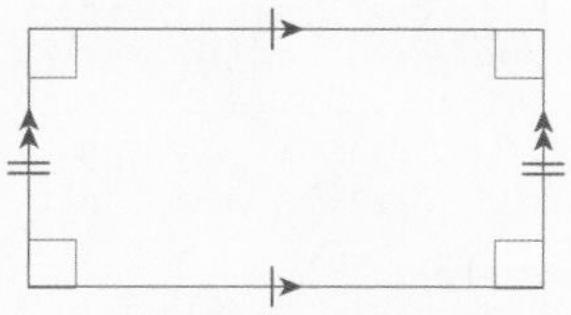	• Opposite sides are parallel. • Opposite sides are of equal lengths. • All angles are equal (90°).
Rhombus	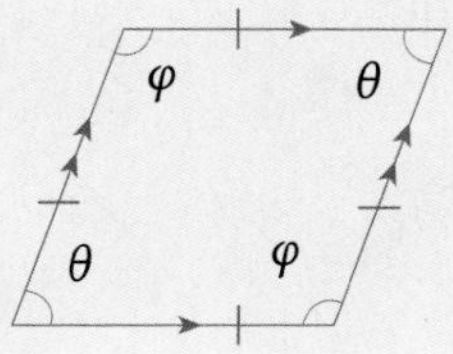	• Opposite sides are parallel. • All sides are of equal lengths. • Opposite angles are equal.
Square	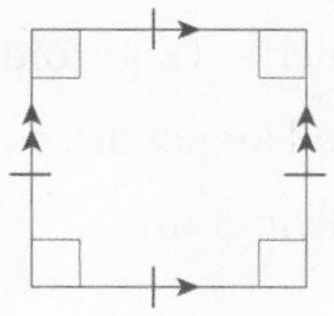	• Opposite sides are parallel. • All sides are of equal lengths. • All angles are equal (90°).

Note: A parallelogram that is not a rectangle, a square, or a rhombus, is simply known as a parallelogram.

Classification of Quadrilaterals that are Non-Parallelograms

Within the class of non-parallelograms, there are two sub-classes:

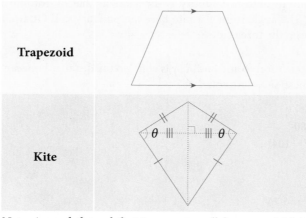

Trapezoid	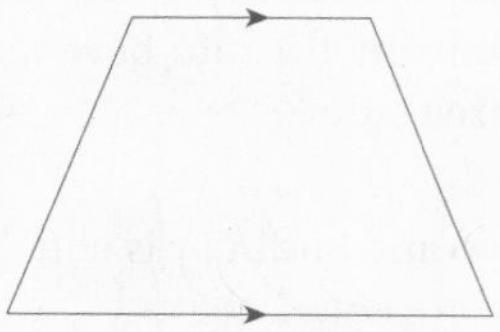	• One set of opposite sides are parallel. • Parallel sides are not of equal lengths.
Kite	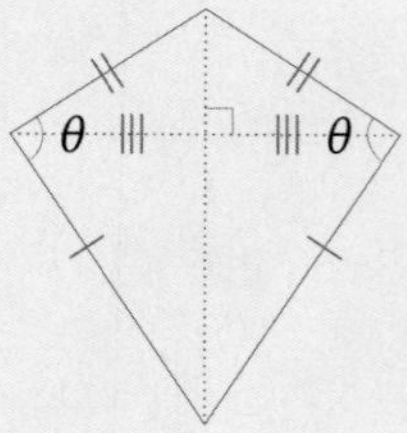	• Two sets of adjacent sides are of equal lengths. • One pair of opposite angles is equal. • Diagonals meet at right angles.

Note: A quadrilateral that is a non-parallelogram, which is neither a trapezoid nor a kite, is known as a general quadrilateral.

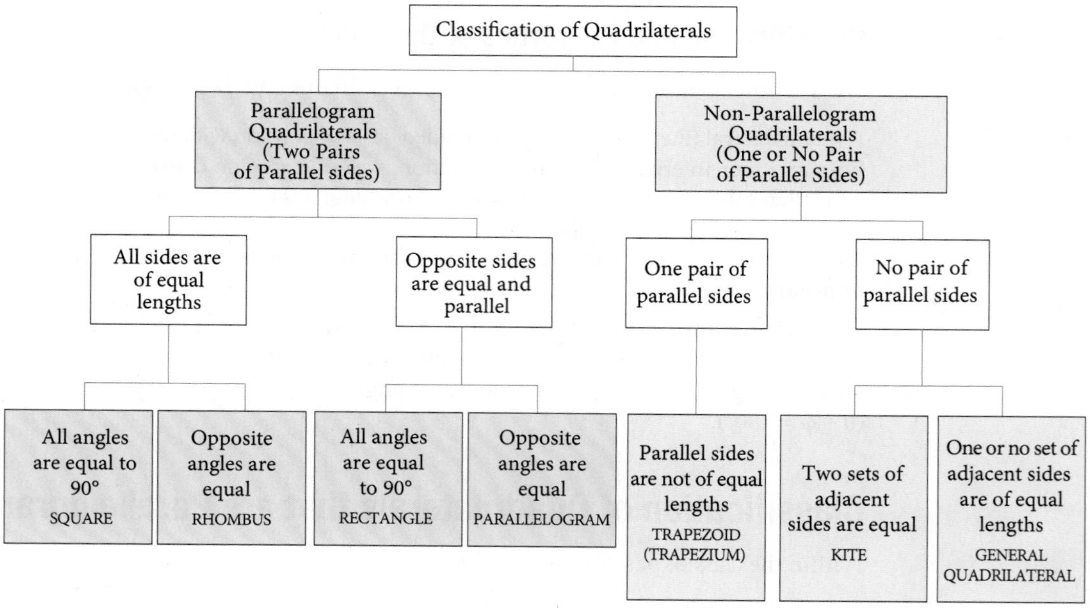

Exhibit 10.2-d Classification of Quadrilaterals

Example 10.2-i

Classifying Quadrilaterals

Classify the following quadrilaterals:

(i)

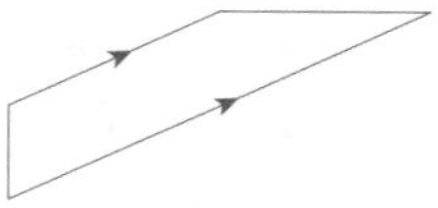

(ii)

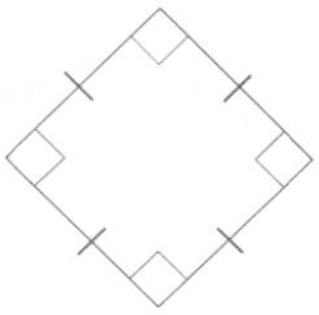

(iii)

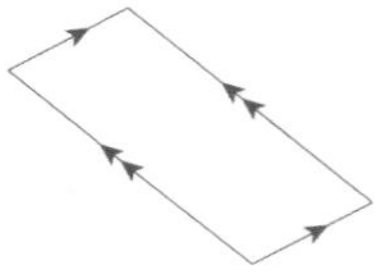

Solution

(i) One pair of opposite sides is parallel – Trapezoid

(ii) All sides are of equal lengths and all angles are equal (90°) – Square

(iii) Opposite sides are parallel – Parallelogram

Example 10.2-j Calculating Unknown Angles in a Quadrilateral

Using the Internal Angles Theorem (IAT)-Part 1, and the properties of various quadrilaterals, calculate the measure of the unknown angle(s) in each of the following:

(i) WXYZ is a general quadrilateral, $\angle XWZ = 72°$, $\angle WXY = 106°$, $\angle XYZ = 55°$.

(ii) ABCD is a parallelogram and $\angle ADC = 25°$.

(iii) QRST is a kite, where $\angle TQR = 80°$ and $\angle RST = 50°$.

Solution

Using the IAT - Part 1, the sum of all four angles of a quadrilateral equals $(4 - 2) \times 180° = 2 \times 180° = 360°$

(i) Since WXYZ is a quadrilateral, the four angles add up to 360°.

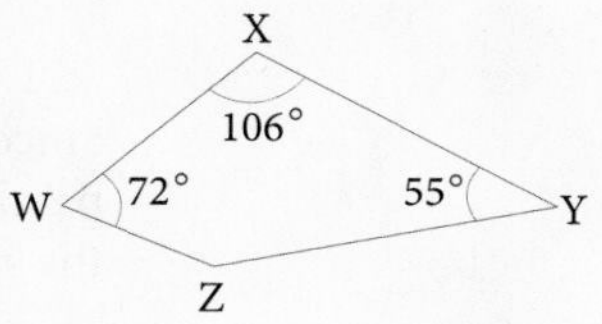

$\angle W + \angle X + \angle Y + \angle Z = 360°$ Substituting the known values and solving for $\angle Z$,

$\angle Z = 360° - (72° + 106° + 55°) = 360° - 233° = 127°$

(ii) Since ABCD is a parallelogram, the opposite angles are congruent and adjacent angles are supplementary.
Therefore,

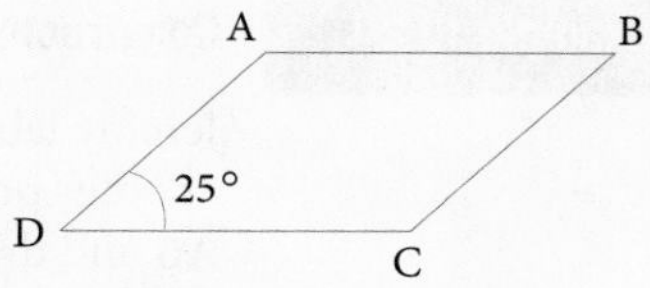

$\angle B = \angle D = 25°$ Opposite angles are equal.

$\angle A = \angle C = 180° - 25° = 155°$ Adjacent angles are supplementary.

(iii) Since QRST is a kite, one pair of opposite angles is equal, and since $\angle Q \neq \angle S$ then $\angle R = \angle T$.
Let θ represent the measure of each of the two equal angles:

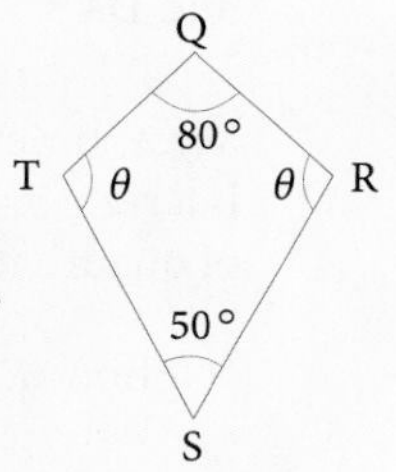

$\angle Q + \angle R + \angle S + \angle T = 360°$ Substituting the known values and solving for θ,

$$80° + \theta + 50° + \theta = 360°$$

$$2\theta = 360° - 130° = 230°$$

$$\theta = \frac{230°}{2} = 115°$$

Therefore, $\angle R = \angle T = 115°$.

Example 10.2-k Identifying Quadrilaterals Based on Angle Measures

For the following quadrilaterals, using the Internal Angles Theorem (IAT) - Part 1, find the missing angle measure, then classify the type of quadrilateral based on their angle measures:

(i) EFGH, given that $\angle E = 64°$, $\angle F = 116°$, and $\angle H = 90°$

(ii) MNOP, given that $\angle M = 112°$, $\angle N = 58°$, and $\angle O = 112°$

(iii) STUV, given that $\angle S = 45°$, $\angle U = 45°$, and $\angle V = 135°$

Solution

Using the IAT - Part 1, the the sum of all four angles of a quadrilateral is 360°.

(i) $\angle E + \angle F + \angle G + \angle H = 360°$ Substituting the known values and solving for $\angle G$,

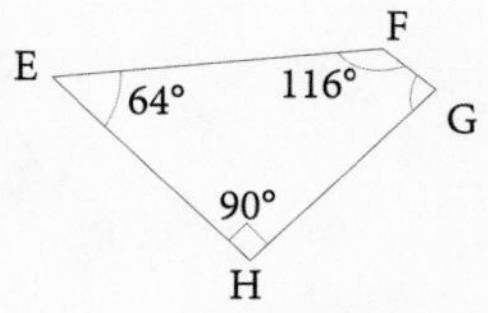

$\angle G = 360° - (64° + 116° + 90°) = 90°$

Therefore, $\angle G + \angle H = 180°$

$\angle E + \angle F = 180°$

Since adjacent angles are supplementary, one opposite pair of sides is parallel (i.e., $\overline{EH} \parallel \overline{FG}$).

Since opposite angles are not congruent, other opposite pair of sides, $\overline{EF}$ and $\overline{GH}$, are not parallel. Therefore, EFGH is a trapezoid.

Solution
continued

(ii) $\angle M + \angle N + \angle O + \angle P = 360°$ Substituting the known values and solving for $\angle P$,

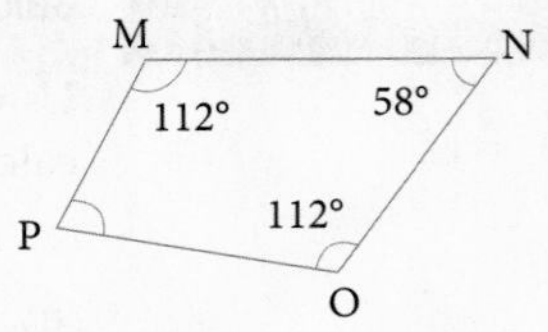

$\angle P = 360° - (112° + 58° + 112°) = 78°$

The fact that there is one pair of congruent, opposite angles does not give us enough information to determine the type of quadrilateral. However, we can narrow down the choices to two: a kite or a general quadrilateral.

(iii) $\angle S + \angle T + \angle U + \angle V = 360°$ Substituting the known values and solving for $\angle T$,

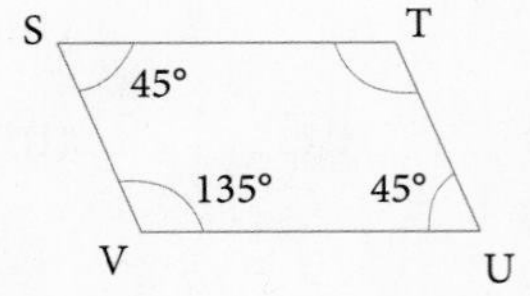

$\angle T = 360° - (45° + 45° + 135°) = 135°$

Since both pairs of opposite angles are congruent, STUV is either a parallelogram or a rhombus (we cannot tell which without knowing the side lengths).

Example 10.2-I **Constructing Quadrilaterals**

Jeremy labels a point A on his paper and draws a straight line 20 cm long to another point B. From there, he uses a compass to measure a 90° angle from $\overline{AB}$ and draws a line from point B to a third point C, that is perpendicular to $\overline{AB}$ and is 15 cm long. How many different types of quadrilaterals can Jeremy create by plotting a fourth point D and then connecting the line segments $\overline{CD}$ and $\overline{DA}$?

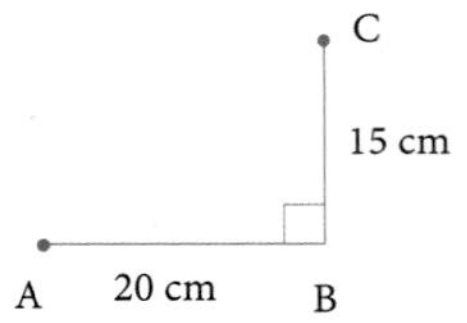

Solution

Since the lengths of two sides are different, Jeremy cannot create a square or a rhombus; since the angle is a right angle, he cannot create a general parallelogram, either. However, he can create 4 other kinds of quadrilaterals:

Option A: Jeremy can create a **rectangle** by measuring out another right angle from point C and drawing a line segment $\overline{CD}$ parallel to $\overline{AB}$, and 20 cm long.

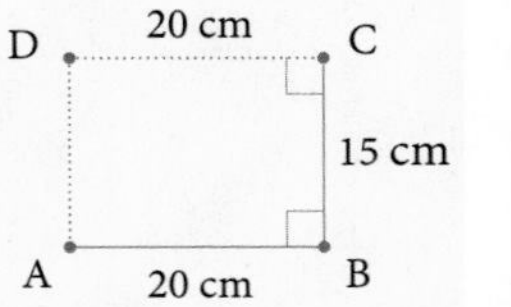

Option B: Jeremy can create a **trapezoid** by measuring out another right angle from point C and drawing a line segment $\overline{CD}$ parallel to $\overline{AB}$ but of a length other than 20 cm.

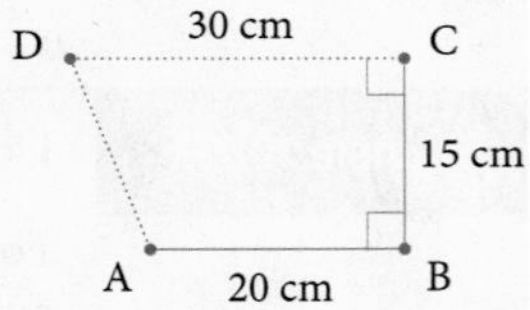

Option C: Jeremy can create a **kite** by drawing a dashed line from point A to point C, then drawing a line segment from point B to a fourth point D that is perpendicular to $\overline{AC}$ and twice the length from B to $\overline{AC}$.

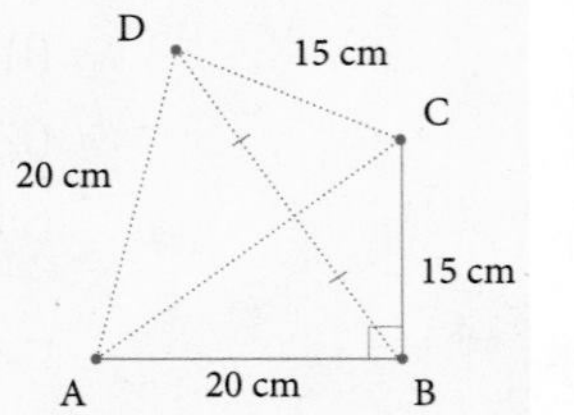

Option D: Jeremy can create a **general quadrilateral** by placing point D in any location that is any distance, other than 15 cm, away from point C and not parallel to $\overline{AB}$.

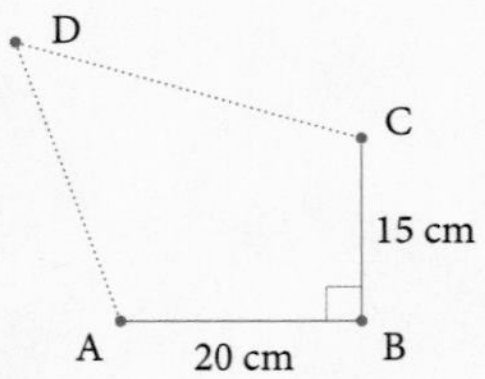

10.2 | Exercises

Answers to odd-numbered problems are available at the end of the textbook.

Using the Internal or External Angle Theorems (IAT or EAT), determine the measure of the unknown angle θ for the figures shown in Problems 1 to 4:

1.

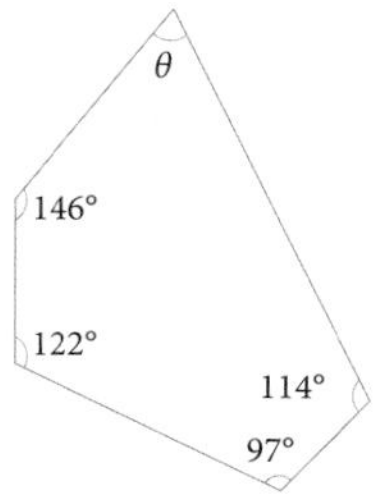

2.

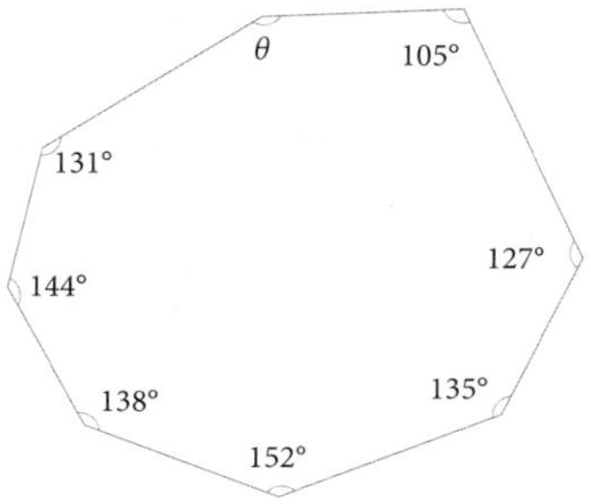

3.

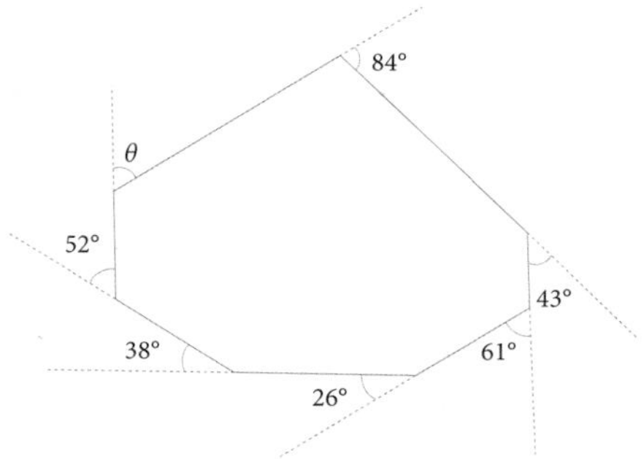

4.

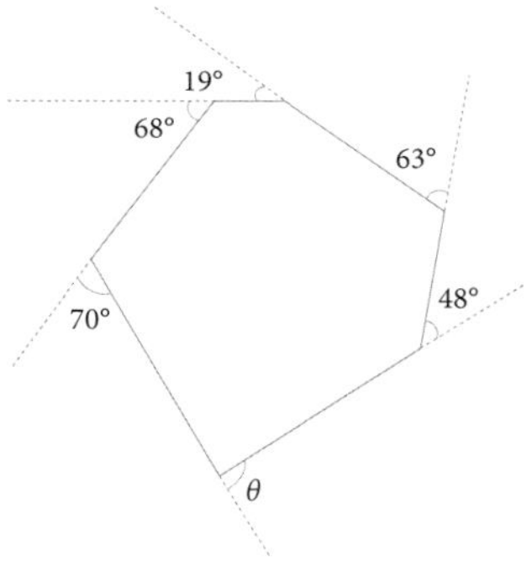

Using the Internal or External Angle Theorems (IAT or EAT) - Part 2, determine the measure of the internal and external angles for the figures in Problems 5 and 6:

5. a. Dodecagon (12 sides) b. Icosagon (20 sides)

6. a. Hexadecagon (16 sides) b. Hectogon (100 sides)

For Problems 7 and 8, the internal or external angle measure of a regular polygon is provided. Using the External Angle Theorem (EAT)- Part 2, determine the number of sides in the regular polygon.

7. a. External angle measure is 12° b. Internal angle measure is 175°
Hint: first find the measure of the external angle.

8. a. External angle measure is 15° b. Internal angle measure is 165°
Hint: first find the measure of the external angle.

9. A sailboat in a race heads west on the opening stretch of the race. At the first checkpoint, the boat makes a 66° turn to port (left) and sails towards the second checkpoint, where it then makes a 112° turn to port. It then continues toward the third checkpoint, makes a 75° turn to port and heads to the fourth and final checkpoint, where it makes a final turn to port until it faces due west again, and heads back toward the starting line to complete the circuit. Determine the degree measure of the final turn, knowing that the fourth check point forms an angle of 150° with the port (starting point).

10. The owners of a house with a backyard in the shape of an irregular hexagon (6 sides) are putting up a fence around their yard, except for one side of their yard which is tree-lined. Using a city survey, the owners have laid down guidelines and have determined the angles at each of the corners, except where the fence meets the trees. Use the diagram and measurements below to determine the unknown angle.

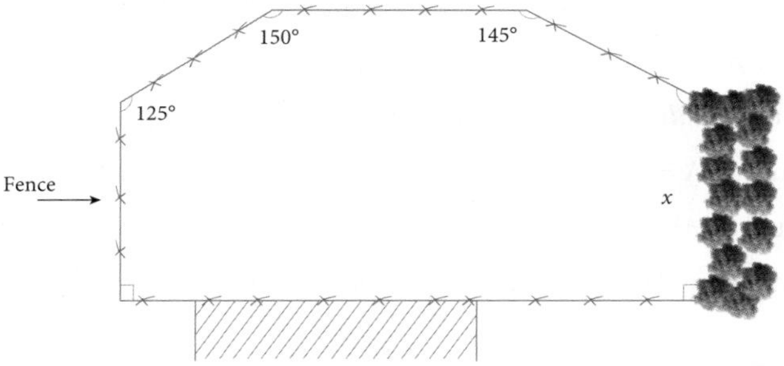

11. In an acute isosceles triangle, the measure of the unique angle is 2° less than three-fifths of the measures of each of the other two angles. Find the degree measures of all three internal angles.
12. In a parallelogram, the degree measure of the larger pair of congruent angles is 5° more than six times the degree measure of the smaller pair of congruent angles. Determine the degree measures of both pairs of congruent angles.
13. In an obtuse scalene triangle, the measure of the larger internal acute angle is 60°. The measure of the external angle to the obtuse angle is 6° greater than three times the measure of the smallest internal acute angle. Determine the measure of the internal obtuse angle.
14. Use the Internal Angle Theorem - Part 1 for triangles to show that any external angle of a triangle is equal to the sum of the two internal opposite angles.

Classify the triangles shown in Problems 15 and 16 by side length and by angle measure:

15. a.

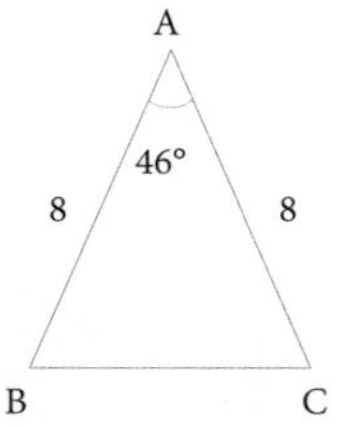

b.

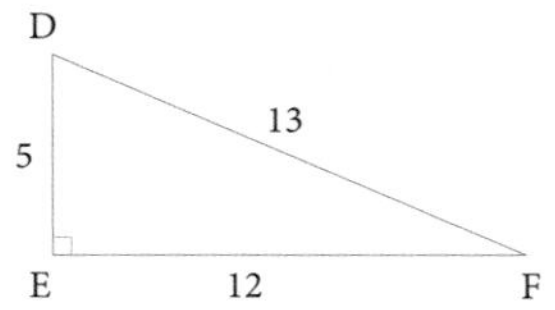

c.

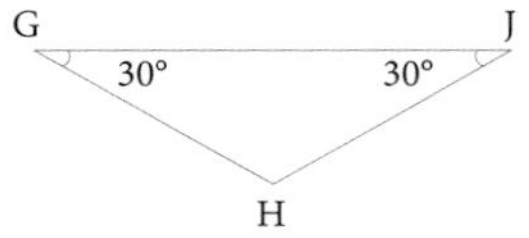

16. a.

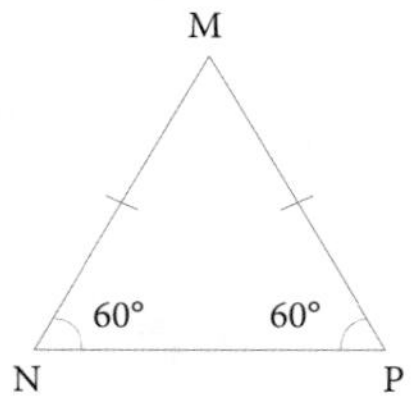

b.

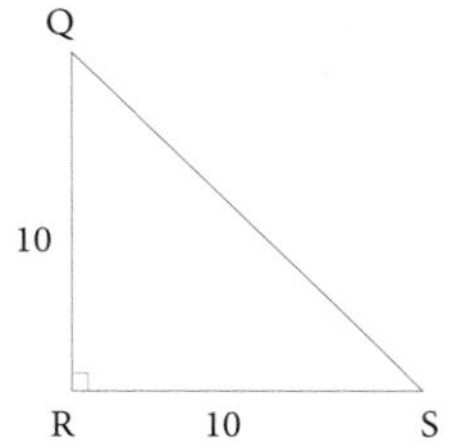

c.

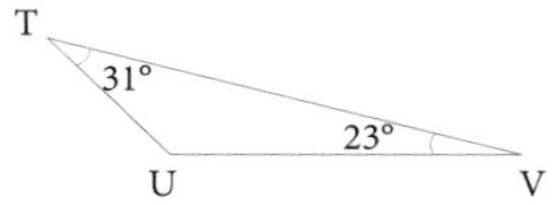

Classify the quadrilaterals shown in Problems 17 and 18:

17. a.

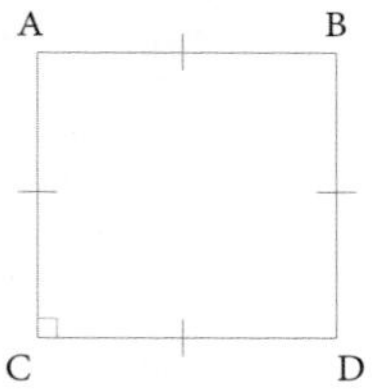

b.

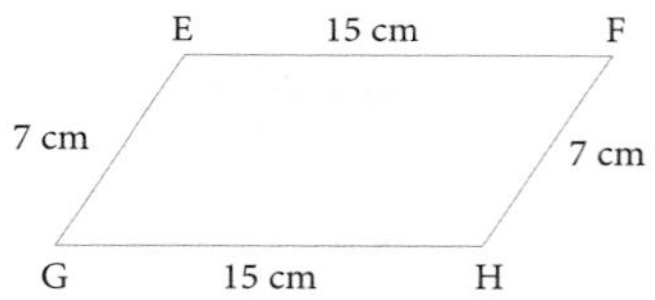

c.

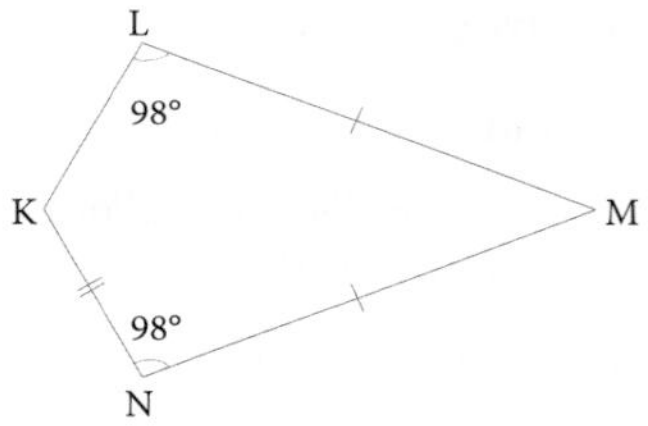

18. a.

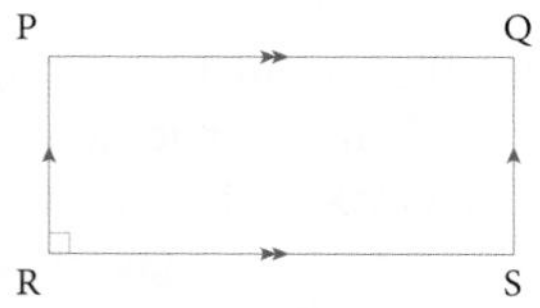

b.

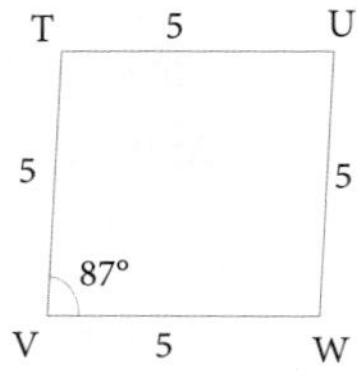

c.

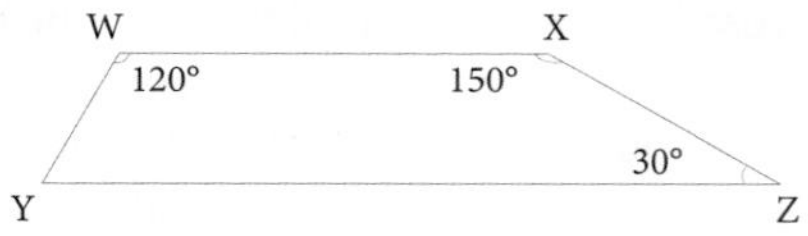

In Problems 19 to 22, determine the missing angle(s) for each quadrilateral ABCD:

19. ABCD is a rectangle
20. ABCD is a rhombus, with $\angle A = 77°$
21. ABCD is a kite, with $\overline{AB} = \overline{BC}$, $\overline{AD} = \overline{DC}$, $\angle A = 105°$, and $\angle D = 52°$
22. ABCD is a trapezoid, with $\overline{AB}$ parallel to $\overline{CD}$, $\angle A = 93°$, and $\angle B = 116°$

In Problems 23 to 26, classify the quadrilateral ABCD based on the properties given:

23. $\overline{AB} = \overline{BC} = \overline{CD} = \overline{DA}$ and $\angle A = 90°$
24. $\overline{AB} = \overline{CD}$, $\overline{BC} = \overline{DA}$, and $\angle A = 105°$
25. $\overline{AB} = \overline{BC} = \overline{CD} = 15$ cm, $\overline{DA} = 27$ cm, and $\overline{BC}$ is parallel to $\overline{DA}$
26. $\overline{AB} = \overline{BC} = 20$ cm, $\overline{AD} = \overline{DC} = 30$ cm, and $\angle A = \angle C$.

In Problems 27 to 30, state the names of all the possible quadrilaterals based on the given property.

27. a. 4 equal angles b. 4 equal sides
28. a. 4 right angles b. No equal sides
29. a. 2 pairs of parallel sides b. 2 pairs of equal angles
30. a. At least 1 pair of parallel sides b. At least 1 pair of equal angles

10.3 | Perimeters and Areas of Plane Geometric Figures

Introduction

In Section 10.2, we introduced the concept of **plane figures**; i.e., geometric objects that can be drawn in the 2-dimensional Cartesian plane. In this section we will introduce two important measurements - perimeter and area - of those figures, specifically of certain special convex polygons and circles.

The **perimeter** (P) of a plane figure is the total length of the boundary of the plane figure. In a polygon, the perimeter is the sum of the lengths of the line segments (sides) that form the boundary of the polygon.

The **area** (A) of a plane figure is the amount of 2-dimensional surface that is enclosed within the figure. Area is measured using square units – e.g., square centimetre (cm^2), square metre (m^2), square inch (in^2), or square foot (ft^2); that is, the amount of surface occupied by squares with the respective side lengths.

Squares and Rectangles

A **square** is a quadrilateral with sides of equal length and angles at right angles – this makes it a regular polygon. We denote the length of each side by the letter *s*.

A **rectangle** is a quadrilateral with angles at all right angles and opposite sides of equal in length. It is differentiated from a square by the property that the sides need not all be of the same length. We denote the longer side by the letter *l* (for **length**), and the shorter side by the letter *w* (for **width**).

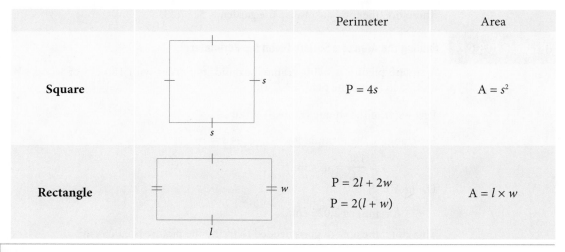

		Perimeter	Area
Square	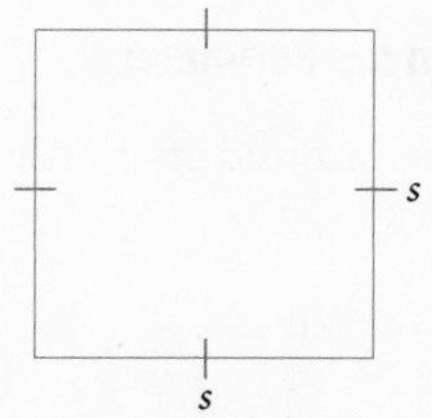	$P = 4s$	$A = s^2$
Rectangle	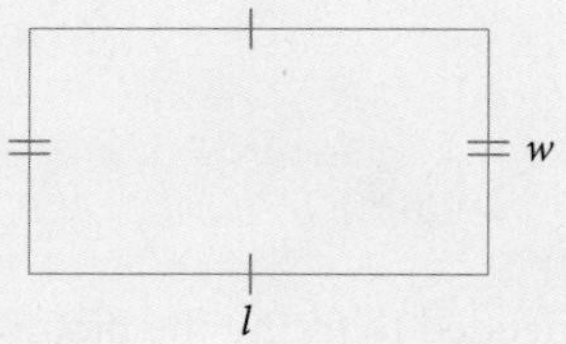	$P = 2l + 2w$ $P = 2(l + w)$	$A = l \times w$

Example 10.3-a **Calculating the Perimeter and Area of Squares and Rectangles**

Calculate the perimeter and area of the following figures:

(i)

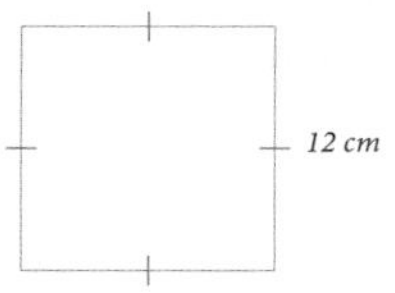

(ii)

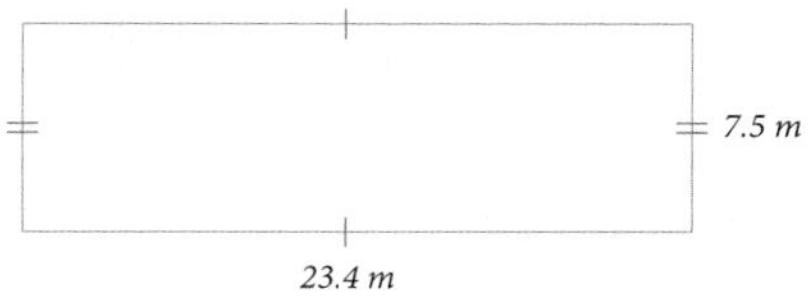

Solution

(i) The figure is a square.

Using $P = 4s$,

$$P = 4(12) = 48 \text{ cm}.$$

Using $A = s^2$,

$$A = (12)^2 = 144 \text{ cm}^2$$

Therefore, the perimeter is 48 cm and the area is 144 cm².

(ii) The figure is a rectangle.

Using $P = 2l + 2w$,

$$P = 2(23.4) + 2(7.5) = 61.8 \text{ m}.$$

Using $A = l \times w$,

$$A = (23.4)(7.5) = 175.5 \text{ m}^2$$

Therefore, the perimeter is 61.8 m and the area is 175.5 m².

Example 10.3-b **Determining the Cost to Lay a Rectangular Garden**

A rectangular garden is being built to be 6.5 m long and 3.2 m wide. The fencing for the garden costs \$2.95/m and the soil costs \$6.25/m². Calculate the cost to lay the garden.

Solution

Using $P = 2l + 2w$,

$$P = 2(6.5) + 2(3.2) = 19.4 \text{ m}$$

$$\text{Fencing cost} = \frac{\$2.95}{1\text{m}} \times 19.4\text{m} = \$57.23$$

Using $A = l \times w$,

$$A = (6.5)(3.2) = 20.8 \text{ m}^2$$

$$\text{Soil cost} = \frac{\$6.25}{1\text{m}^2} \times 20.8\text{m}^2 = \$130.00$$

Total cost = 57.23 + 130.00 = \$187.23

Therefore, the total cost to lay the garden is \$187.23.

Example 10.3-c **Finding the Area of a Square Given the Perimeter**

A square picture is being framed around its border with 180 cm of wood. What area of glass is needed to frame the picture?

Solution

Perimeter of the square frame, $P = 180$ cm.

Rearranging the formula $P = 4s$, we get $s = \frac{P}{4}$

$$s = \frac{180}{4} = 45 \text{ cm}$$

Using $A = s^2$,

$$A = (45)^2 = 2{,}025 \text{ cm}^2.$$

Therefore, the area of glass needed to frame the picture is 2,025 cm².

Rhombuses and Parallelograms

A **rhombus** is a quadrilateral with sides of equal in length. It is differentiated from a square by the property that the angles are not right angles. We denote the length of each side by the letter b, and the perpendicular height by the letter h.

Rhombuses, like squares, have four equal side lengths, which makes the calculation of the perimeter of a rhombus equal to that of a square.

The area of a rhombus is determined as follows:

Draw a perpendicular line from the top corner of the rhombus to its base. This is the "height", h, of the rhombus. "Cut" the resulting triangle that is created and "paste" it on the opposite side. The result is a rectangle with length b and width h, as shown in the diagram below:

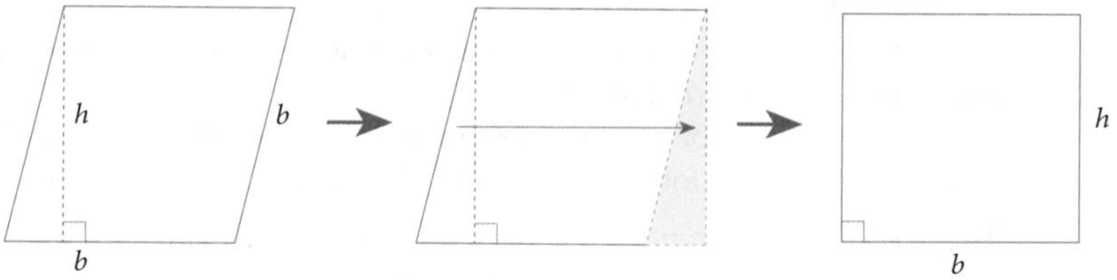

A **parallelogram** is a quadrilateral with opposite sides that are equal and parallel. It is differentiated from a rectangle by the property that the angles are not right angles. We denote the length of the **base** by the letter b, the length of the **slant** side by the letter a, and the perpendicular **height** by the letter h.

The calculation of the perimeter of a parallelogram is equal to that of a rectangle, replacing the letters l and w with a and b.

The area of a parallelogram is determined using the same procedure as that of a rhombus.

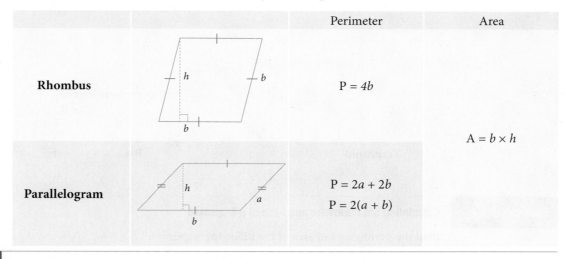

		Perimeter	Area
Rhombus	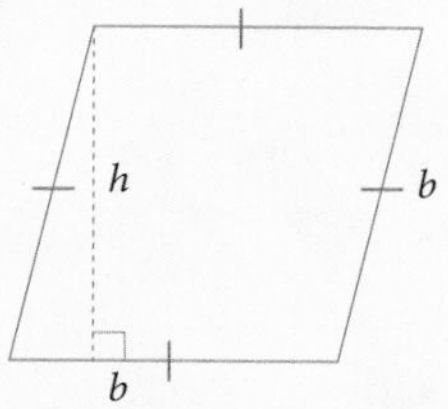	$P = 4b$	$A = b \times h$
Parallelogram	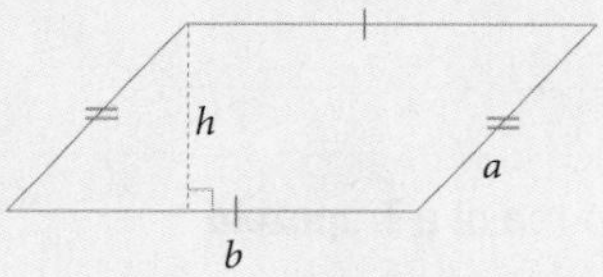	$P = 2a + 2b$ $P = 2(a + b)$	

Example 10.3-d

Calculating the Perimeter and Area of Rhombuses and Parallelograms

Find the perimeter and area of the following figures:

(i)

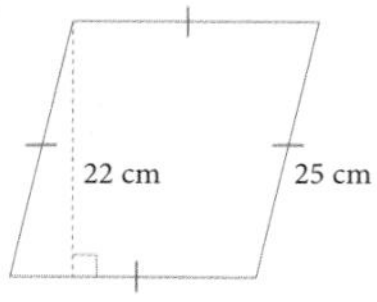

(ii)

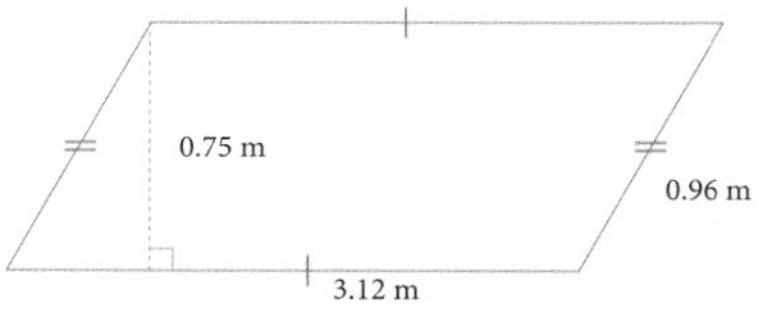

Solution

(i) The figure is a rhombus.

Using $P = 4b$ and $A = b \times h$,

$$P = 4(25) = 100 \text{ cm}$$

$$A = (25)(22) = 550 \text{ cm}^2$$

Therefore, the perimeter is 100 cm and the area is 550 cm^2.

(ii) The figure is a parallelogram.

Using $P = 2a + 2b$ and $A = b \times h$,

$$P = 2(3.12) + 2\,(0.96) = 8.16 \text{ m}$$

$$A = (3.12)(0.75) = 2.34 \text{ m}^2$$

Therefore, the perimeter is 8.16 m and the area is 2.34 m^2.

Trapezoids

A trapezoid is a quadrilateral with one pair of opposite sides that are parallel, It is differentiated from a parallelogram by the property that the other pair of opposite sides are not parallel. Since all four sides may have different lengths, we denote the length of the smaller, parallel side by the letter a, the length of the larger parallel side by the letter b, and the lengths of the other two sides by the letters c and d. Again, we denote the perpendicular height by the letter h.

The perimeter of a trapezoid is the sum of the four side lengths, a, b, c, and d.

To calculate the area of a trapezoid, "copy" the trapezoid, rotate the image by 180°, and paste it to the original trapezoid, as shown below. The result will be a parallelogram with an area of $(a + b) \times h$.

The area of the trapezoid is half the area of the parallelogram = $\frac{1}{2}(a+b)\times h$.

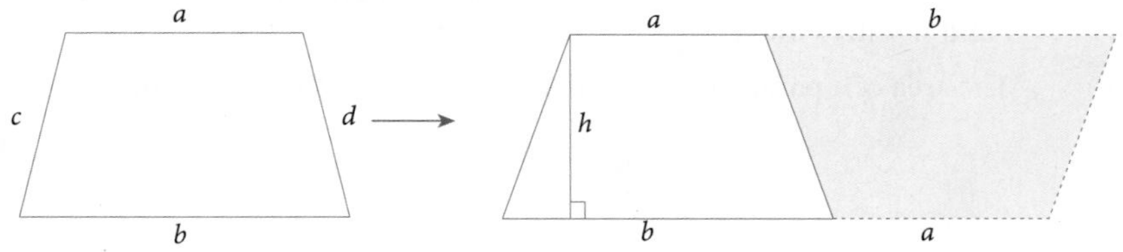

		Perimeter	Area
Trapezoid	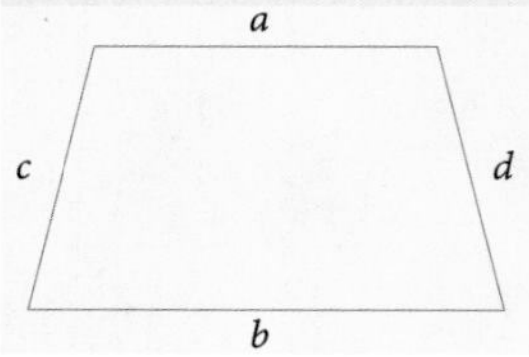	$P = a + b + c + d$	$A = \frac{1}{2}(a+b)\times h$

Example 10.3-e **Calculating the Perimeter and Area of a Trapezoid**

Find the perimeter and area of the following trapezoid:

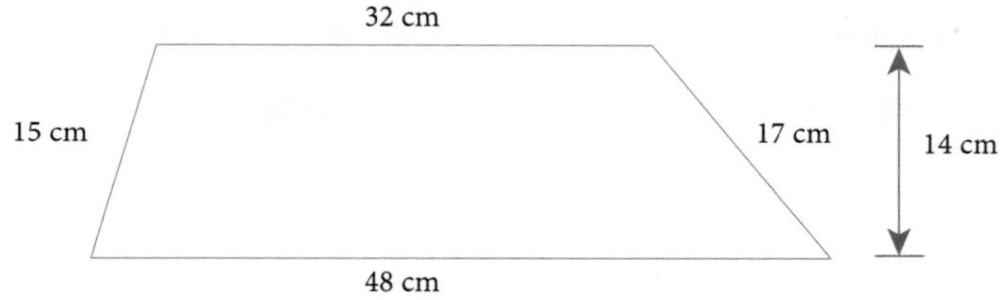

Solution

Using $P = a + b + c + d$,

$$P = 32 + 48 + 15 + 17 = 112 \text{ cm}$$

Using $A = \frac{1}{2}(a+b)\times h$,

$$A = \frac{32+48}{2}(14) = (40)(14) = 560 \text{cm}^2$$

Therefore, the perimeter of the trapezoid is 112 cm and the area of the trapezoid is 560 cm^2.

Example 10.3-f **Determining the Cost of Fencing and Sodding a Trapezoidal Lawn**

A house on the corner of a crescent has a backyard in the shape of a trapezoid, with the dimensions given on the figure below. If fencing costs $25.00 per linear foot and sod costs $0.40 per square foot, how much will it cost to fence and sod the backyard?

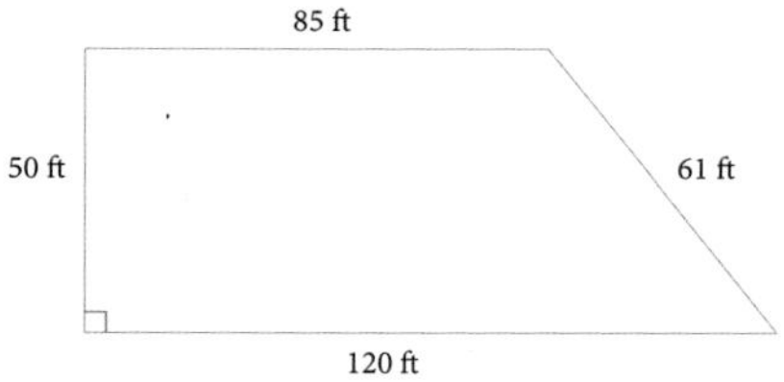

Solution

Using $P = a + b + c + d$,

$$P = 85 + 120 + 50 + 61 = 316 \text{ ft}$$

$$\text{Fencing Cost} = \frac{\$25.00}{1 \text{ ft}} \times 316 \text{ ft} = \$7{,}900.00$$

Using $A = \frac{1}{2}(a+b) \times h$,

$$A = \frac{1}{2}(85 + 120) \times 50 = 102.5 \times 50 = 5{,}125 \text{ ft}^2$$

$$\text{Sod cost} = \frac{\$0.40}{1 \text{ ft}^2} \times 5{,}125 \text{ ft}^2 = \$2{,}050.00$$

Total cost = 7,900.00 + 2,050.00 = $9,950.00

Therefore, it will cost $9,950 to fence and sod the backyard.

Triangles

A triangle is a closed figure formed by three sides and three internal angles. We use the letters a, b, and c to denote the side lengths, and h to denote the height.

The perimeter of a triangle (P), regardless of whether it is acute, right, or obtuse, is the sum of the three side lengths, a, b, and c.

$$P = a + b + c$$

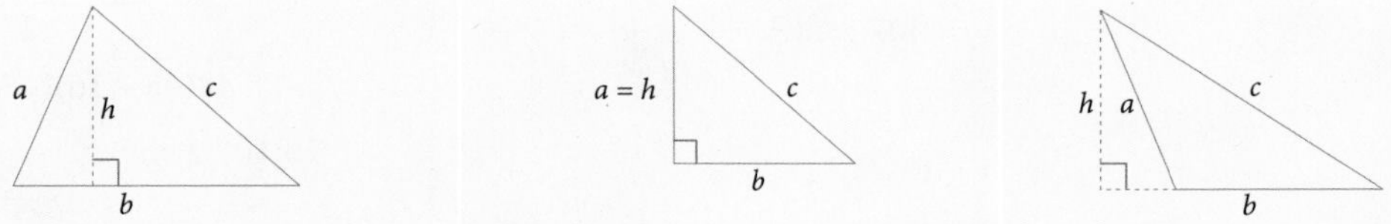

(i) Acute Triangle (ii) Right Triangle (iii) Obtuse Triangle

Calculating the area of a triangle (acute, right, or obtuse) when the length of the base and height are known.

To calculate the area of a triangle (regardless of whether it is acute, right, or obtuse), "copy" the triangle, rotate the image by 180°, and paste it to the original triangle, as shown below. The result in all three cases will be a parallelogram, with base b and height h.

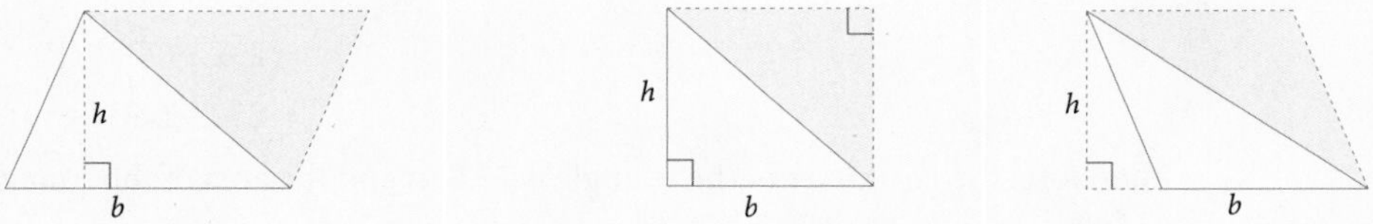

(i) (ii) (iii)

Thus, the area of a triangle is half that of a parallelogram:

$$A = \frac{1}{2}(b \times h)$$

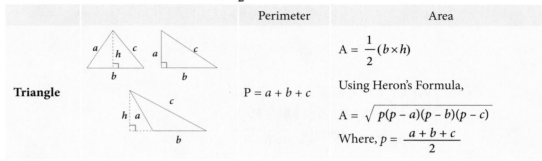

Calculating the area of a triangle (acute, right, or obtuse) when the length of all three sides are known (Using Heron's formula)

Heron's formula states that if a, b, c, are the lengths of the sides of the triangle, the area is given by:

$$A = \sqrt{p(p-a)(p-b)(p-c)}$$

Where p is half the perimeter (P), $p = \dfrac{a+b+c}{2}$

		Perimeter	Area
Triangle	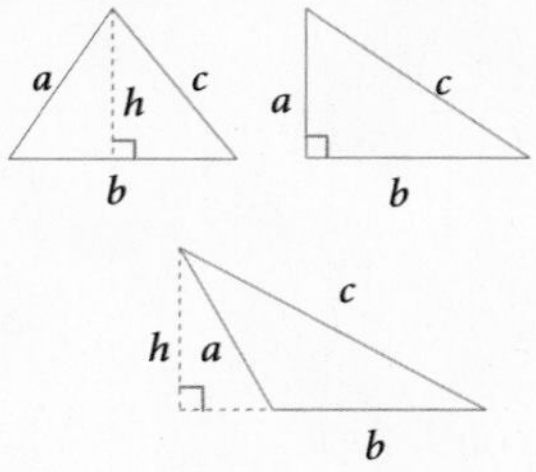	$P = a + b + c$	$A = \frac{1}{2}(b \times h)$ Using Heron's Formula, $A = \sqrt{p(p-a)(p-b)(p-c)}$ Where, $p = \frac{a+b+c}{2}$

Example 10.3-g

Calculating the Perimeter and Area of a Triangle

Find the perimeter and area of the following triangles:

(i)

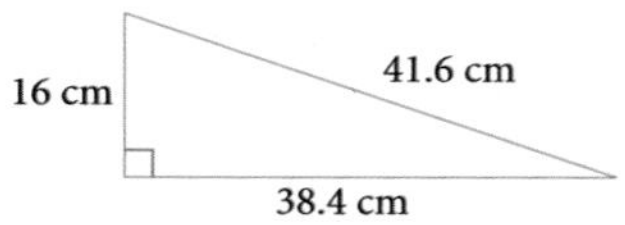

(ii)

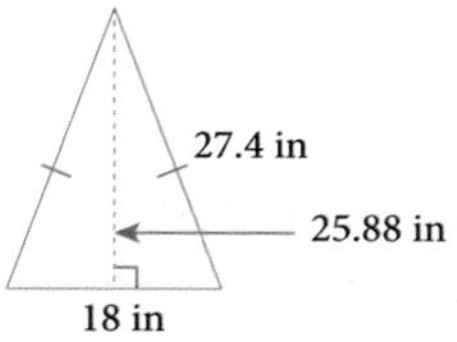

Solution

(i) Using $P = a + b + c$, $P = 16 + 38.4 + 41.6 = 96$ cm

Using, $A = \frac{1}{2}(b \times h)$

$A = \frac{1}{2}(38.4 \times 16)$

$= 307.2 \text{ cm}^2$

or

Using $A = \sqrt{p(p-a)(p-b)(p-c)}$,

where $p = \dfrac{a+b+c}{2}$

$p = \dfrac{16 + 38.4 + 41.6}{2} = 48$

$A = \sqrt{48(48-16)(48-38.4)(48-41.6)}$

$= 307.2 \text{ cm}^2$

Therefore, the perimeter of the triangle is 96 cm and the area is 307.2 cm^2.

(ii) $P = 27.4 + 18 + 27.4 = 72.8$ in

$A = \frac{1}{2}(18 \times 25.88)$

$= 232.92 \text{ in}^2$

or

$p = \dfrac{27.4 + 18 + 27.4}{2} = 36.4$

$A = \sqrt{36.4(36.4-27.4)(36.4-18)(36.4-27.4)}$

$= 232.917496...$

$= 232.92 \text{ in}^2$

Therefore, the perimeter of the triangle is 72.8 in and the area of the triangle is 232.92 in^2.

Example 10.3-h **Finding the Area of a Kite**

Calculate the area of the kite shown in the figure below:

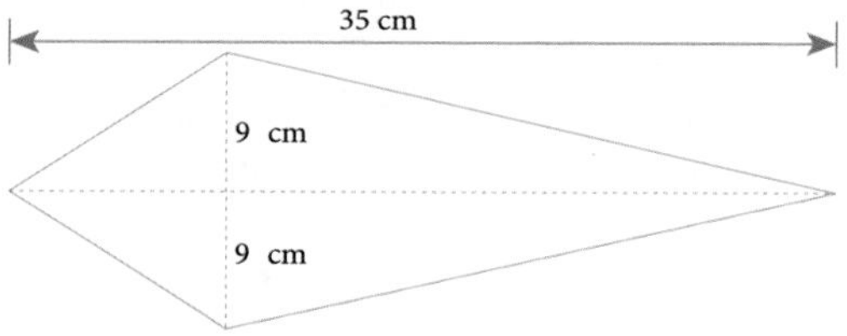

Solution

The kite consists of two identical triangles, each with a base of 35 cm and a height of 9 cm.

Using $A = \frac{1}{2}(b \times h)$

$$A = \frac{1}{2}\ (35 \times 9) = 157.5\ \text{cm}^2$$

Therefore, the area of the kite is $2 \times 157.5 = 315\ \text{cm}^2$.

Circles and Sectors

Circles

A **circle** is a closed plane curve such that any point on the curve lies within a fixed distance (the **radius**) from a fixed point (the centre).

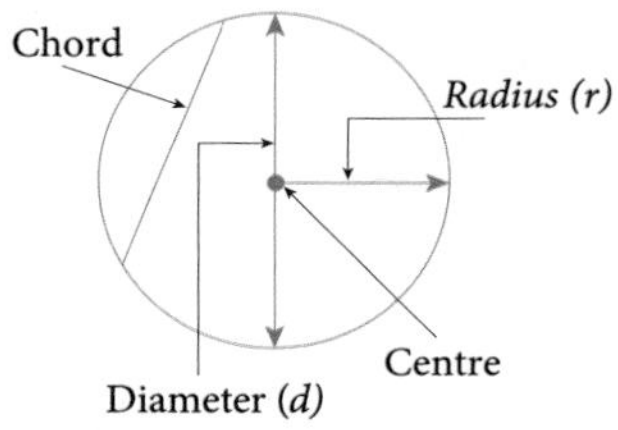

The **radius** ***(r)*** is the distance from the centre point of the circle to the boundary of the circle.

A **chord** is the line segment that connects any two points on the boundary of the circle.

The **diameter** ***(d)*** of the circle is the length of the largest chord on the circle – the one that passes through the centre point. Notice that the diameter is exactly twice the radius: $d = 2r$.

Exhibit 10.3-a A circle and its components

To describe the boundary length of the circle, the word **circumference**, rather than perimeter, is used. For any circle, the ratio of the circumference, C, to its diameter, d, is a constant special irrational number discovered by the ancient Greeks, known as π (*pi*, pronounced "pie").

i.e., $\frac{C}{d} = \pi$, and

$$C = \pi d$$
$$C = \pi(2r)$$
$$C = 2\pi r$$

Note: 'π' is an irrational number, which means that we cannot express its exact value as a decimal number, we can write down a decent approximation: $\pi \approx 3.14159$, or more simply, $\pi \approx 3.14$. However, in calculations involving 'π' in the examples and exercise questions within this chapter,we use the 'π' button in the calculator.

The area of a circle is calculated, as follows:

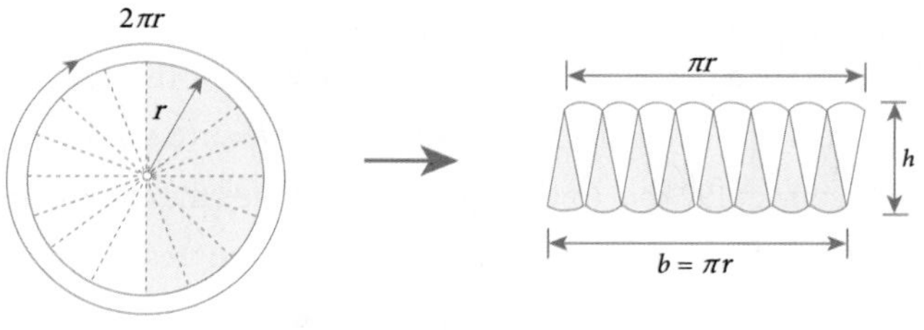

Step 1: Cut a circle into an even number of equal slices (for example, 16).

Step 2: Take half of the slices and arrange them end-to-end in the shape of "teeth". Do the same with the other half and place it on each end to make the interlocking shape symmetrical.

Step 3: The result is approximately a parallelogram. The length of the parallelogram is half of the circumference of the circle; i.e., $b = \frac{2\pi r}{2} = r\pi$. The height of the parallelogram is the distance from the boundary of the circle to the centre, which is the radius, r. The area of the circle, therefore, is approximately equal to the area of the parallelogram.

Note: The more slices used in the circle, the closer the approximation gets. Therefore, the formula in Step 3 is indeed the exact formula for the area of a circle:

$A \approx b \times h = (\pi r) \times r = \pi r^2$.

		Circumference	Area
Circle	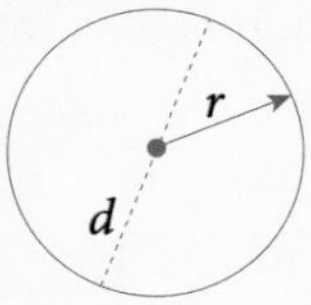	$C = \pi d$ $C = 2\pi r$	$A = \pi r^2$

Example 10.3-i

Calculating Circumference and Area of a Circle

Find the circumference and area of the following circles:

(i)

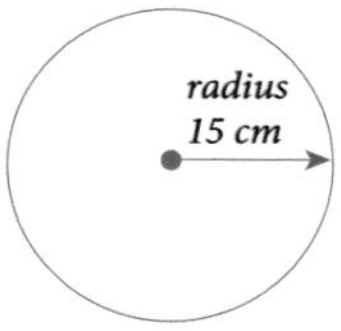

(ii)

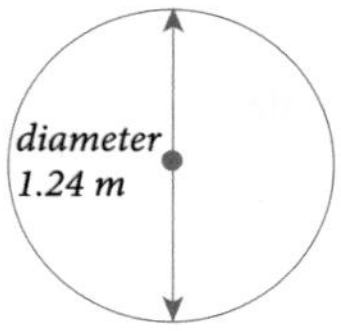

Solution

Using $C = 2\pi r$ and $A = \pi r^2$,

(i) $C = 2\pi r \approx 2\pi(15) = 94.247796... = 94.25$ cm

$A = \pi r^2 \approx \pi(15)^2 = 706.858347... = 706.86$ cm^2

Therefore, the circumference of the circle is 94.25 cm and the area is 706.86 cm^2.

(ii) $C = \pi d \approx \pi(1.24) = 3.895574... = 3.90$ m

$r = \frac{d}{2} = \frac{1.24}{2} = 0.62$ m

$A = \pi r^2 \approx \pi(0.62)^2 \approx 1.207628... = 1.21$ m^2

Therefore, the circumference of the circle is 3.90 m and the area is 1.21 m^2.

Example 10.3-j

Calculating the Distance Travelled on a Bicycle

A road bike has a wheel with a 622 mm diameter. If the wheel spins at 192 rpm (revolutions per minute), determine the distance the cyclist travels in 1 hour and 20 minutes, rounded to the nearest tenth of a km.

Solution

The distance travelled in one revolution of the wheel, is equivalent to the circumference of the wheel (since we are doing a large calculation, we will use the exact value of π).

Distance travelled in one revolution = $C = \pi d = \pi(622) = 1{,}954$ mm = 1.954 m

Since it spins at 192 rpm (revolution in one minute), the distance travelled in 1 minute = $192(1.954) \approx 375.2$ m.

The total distance travelled in 1 hour and 20 minutes (80 minutes) = $80(375.2) = 30{,}016$ m ≈ 30.0 km

Therefore, the cyclist travelled approximately 30.0 km in 1 hour and 20 minutes.

Example 10.3-k

Determining the Amount of Pizza Sauce Needed

An extra-large pizza is circular with a diameter of 16 inches. Pizza sauce is spread on the pizza dough at a rate of 1.5 mL of pizza sauce per square inch (in²) of crust. How much pizza sauce (rounded to the nearest 10 mL) is required to cover the entire pizza, if a 1-inch crust is to be left around the edge of the entire pizza?

Solution

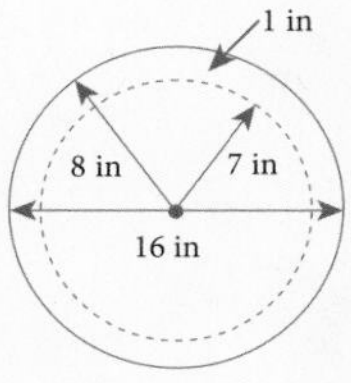

Radius of pizza dough surface $= r = \frac{d}{2} = \frac{16}{2} = 8$ in.

Since there is a 1-inch crust to be left at the edge of the pizza, the radius of the surface to be covered with pizza sauce is 7 inches.

The area of the pizza dough to be covered with the sauce is:
$A = \pi r^2 = \pi(7)^2 = \pi(49) \approx 154$ in²

The quantity of pizza sauce needed to cover the pizza = $(1.5)(154) \approx 230$ mL.

Therefore, approximately 230 mL of pizza sauce is needed to cover the pizza.

Sectors

A **sector** (denoted by a capital *S*) is a portion of a circle that is bounded by two radii from the centre of the circle to the boundary of the circle, as shown in the diagram below. The section of the circumference that bounds the sector is known as the **arc** (denoted by a capital *L*). The internal angle of the sector inscribed by the two radii is known as the **angle subtended by the arc** (denoted by the Greek letter θ).

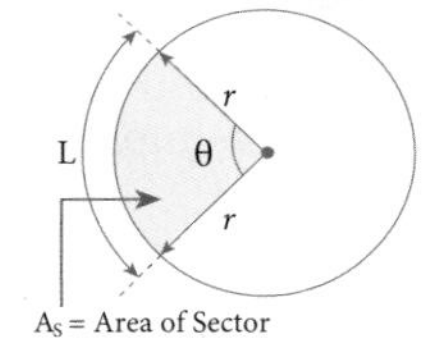

In a sector of a circle with sector angle θ:

(i) The arc length, L, of the sector is proportional to the circumference of the circle, πd, as θ is to 360°.

i.e., $\frac{\theta}{360°} = \frac{L}{\pi d} \longrightarrow L = \pi d \times \frac{\theta}{360°}$

Thus, the perimeter of the sector $P_S = r + r + L = 2r + L$

(ii) The area, AS, of the sector is proportional to the area of the circle, πr^2, as θ is to 360°.

$$\frac{\theta}{360°} = \frac{A_S}{\pi r^2} \longrightarrow A_S = \pi r^2 \times \frac{\theta}{360°}$$

		Arc length	Area
Sector	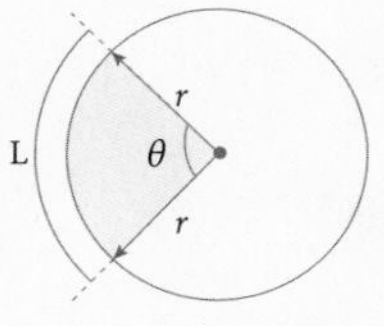	$L = \pi d \times \frac{\theta}{360°}$ Perimeter $P_S = 2r + L$	$A_S = \pi r^2 \times \frac{\theta}{360°}$

Example 10.3-l

Calculating the Perimeter and Area of a Sector

Calculate the perimeter and area (rounded to the nearest mm and mm², respectively) of a sector of a circle with a radius of 75 mm and an inscribed angle of 75°.

Solution

Using $P_S = 2r + L$ and $L = \pi d \times \frac{\theta}{360°}$,

$$P_S = 2(75) + \pi(2)(75)\left(\frac{75°}{360°}\right) \approx 150 + 98 = 248 \text{ mm}$$

Using $A_S = \pi r^2 \times \frac{\theta}{360°}$,

$$= \pi(75)^2\left(\frac{75°}{360°}\right) \approx 3{,}682 \text{ mm}^2$$

Example 10.3-m

Determining the Speed of a Gondola on a Ferris Wheel

The Niagara SkyWheel is a giant ferris wheel in Niagara Falls that has a diameter of 50.5 m. If the SkyWheel rotates at a maximum speed of 9° per second, determine the speed at which the gondolas on the rim of the wheel are moving (in km/h, rounded to the nearest tenth of a km).

Solution

Using $L = \pi d \times \frac{\theta}{360°}$,

$$\pi (50.5)\left(\frac{9°}{360°}\right) \approx 3.966\text{m}$$

Hence, the gondolas travel at a maximum speed of 3.966 m/s.

Converting this speed in km/h,

$$\text{Speed} = (3.966 \tfrac{\text{m}}{\text{s}})(60 \tfrac{\text{s}}{\text{min}})(60 \tfrac{\text{min}}{\text{hr}}) = 14{,}277.6 \tfrac{\text{m}}{\text{hr}} \approx 14.3 \tfrac{\text{km}}{\text{hr}}$$

Therefore, the gondolas travel at a maximum speed of approximately 14.3 km/h.

Composite Figures

It is quite common, when solving application problems, to see a complex geometric figure constructed out of two or more simple, geometric figures that have been previously described. Such figures are called **composite figures**.

To determine the perimeter of a composite figure, simply calculate the length of the boundary, by adding up all the straight lengths and sector lengths along the boundary.

To determine the area of a composite figure, break the figure up into simple figures and add up all the areas.

Example 10.3-n

Calculating the Perimeter and Area of a Parking Lot

A new parking lot is to be created around a commercial building (see image below). The edge of the parking lot is to be enclosed with concrete curbs and the surface of the parking lot is to be paved with asphalt. Determine how many linear metres of concrete curbing and square metres of asphalt are required to create the parking lot.

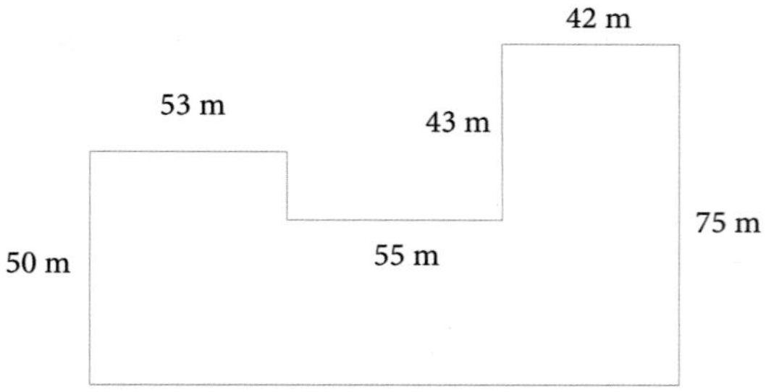

Solution

Let x, y, z be the unknown lengths as marked in the diagram.

$x = 53 + 55 + 42 = 150$ m

$y = 75 - 43 = 32$ m

$z = 50 - y = 50 - 32 = 18$ m

$P = 50 + 53 + z + 55 + 43 + 42 + 75 + x = 486$ m

To calculate the amount of asphalt needed, we calculate the area of the parking lot by breaking it up into three rectangular components, (1), (2) and (3):

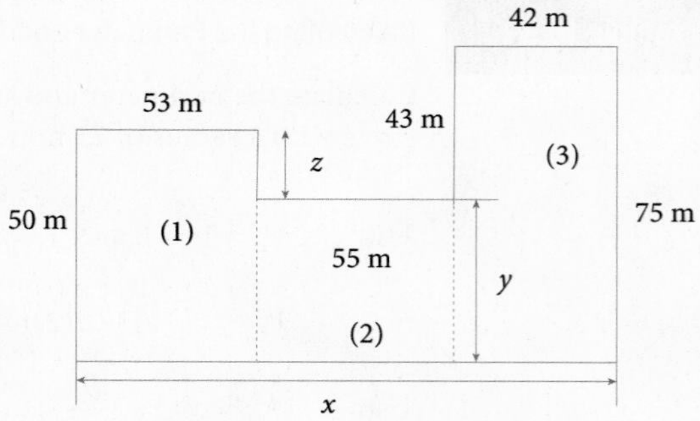

$A_1 = (50)(53) = 2{,}650 \text{ m}^2$

$A_2 = (y)(55) = (32)(55) = 1{,}760 \text{ m}^2$

$A_3 = (75)(42) = 3{,}150 \text{ m}^2$

$A = 2{,}650 + 1{,}760 + 3{,}150 = 7{,}560 \text{ m}^2$

Therefore, 486 m of concrete curbing and 7,560 m² of asphalt are needed to create the parking lot.

Example 10.3-o

Calculating the Perimeter and Area of a Hockey Rink

A hockey rink is created that is rectangular in shape with two semi-circular ends (see sketch below). Determine the surface area (rounded to the nearest square metre) of the rink ice if it is 60 m from end-to-end at its longest and 20 m wide.

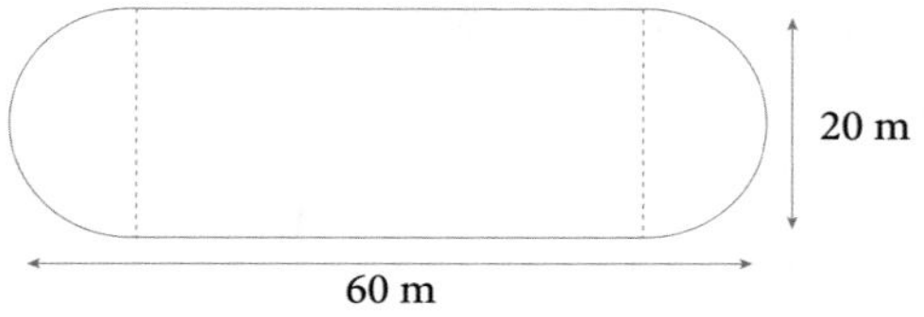

Solution

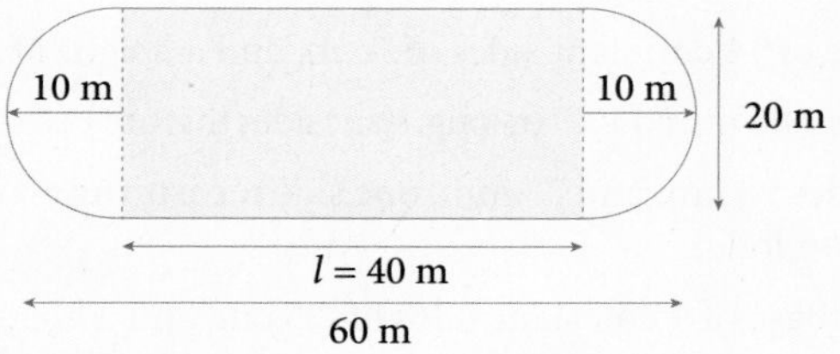

The width of the rectangle = 20 m.

Since the rink is 20 m wide, the diameters of each of the end semi-circles = 20 m; hence the radius = 10 m.

The length of the rectangle is the full length of the rink minus the radius of the two semi-circles at each end = 60 – 2(10) = 40 m.

$$A_{rectangle} = (40)(20) = 800 \text{ m}^2$$

$$A_{\text{semi-circle at both ends}} = 2\left[\frac{1}{2}\pi(10)^2\right] = 314 \text{ m}^2$$

Therefore, A ≈ 800 + 314 = 1,114 m^2.

In some cases, it may be easier to think of the composite figure as a "cut-out" shape; i.e., as a simple geometric figure with another simple geometric figure cut out of it. In such cases, subtraction may be necessary to calculate the perimeter or area of the composite figure.

Example 10.3-p

Calculating the Area of a "Cut-Out" Shape

Find the area of the following "cut-out" shape:

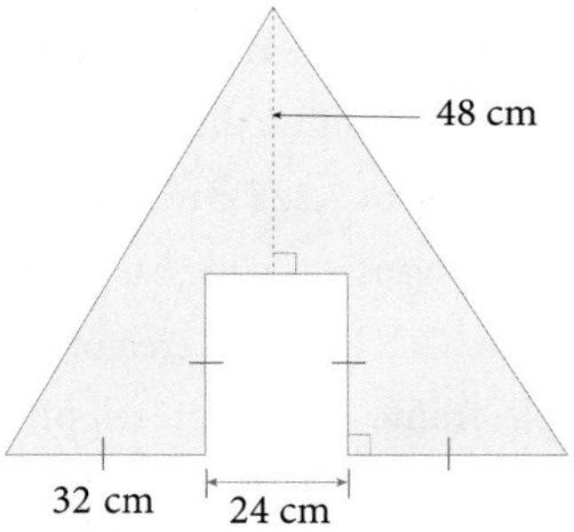

Solution

The shape is a triangle with a rectangle cut out of it. As with the previous question, we need the dimensions of both simple shapes:

The dimensions of the rectangle at the centre are l = 32 cm and w = 24 cm.

The height of the triangle is h = 48 + 32 = 80 cm

The base of the triangle is b = 2(32) + 24 = 88 cm

$$A_{triangle} = \frac{1}{2}(88)(80) = 3520 \text{ m}^2$$

$$A_{rectangle} = (32)(24) = 768 \text{ cm}^2$$

Therefore, the area of the 'cut-out' figure = 3520 – 768 = 2,752 cm^2

10.3 | Exercises

Answers to odd-numbered problems are available at the end of the textbook.

For Problems 1 to 10, calculate the perimeter and area of the plane figures:

1. a. A square with sides 8 mm long. b. A rectangle with sides of 6.4 m and 4.5 m.
2. a. A square with sides 22.5 cm long. b. A rectangle with sides of 15 m and 20 m.
3. A rhombus with sides of 16.25 cm and a height of 12.75 cm.
4. A rhombus with sides of 6.75 m and a height of 5.25 m.
5. A parallelogram with a base of 12 cm, slant sides of 4 cm, and a height of 3.5 cm.
6. A parallelogram with a base of 14 cm, slant sides of 7 cm, and a height of 5.5 cm.
7. A trapezoid with parallel sides 2.45 m and 1.55 m long, slant sides that are both 0.75 m long, and a perpendicular height of 0.6 m.
8. A trapezoid with parallel sides 98 mm and 73 mm, one side measuring 60 mm that is perpendicular to the parallel sides, and a slant side that is 65 mm long.
9. An isosceles triangle with a base of 9 cm, slant sides of 7.5 cm, and a height of 6 cm.
10. An equilateral triangle with sides 52.5 mm long and a height of 45.5 mm.

For Problems 11 to 14, calculate the circumference and area of the circles (rounded to the indicated place value):

11. A circle with a radius of 8 cm (to the nearest hundredth).
12. A circle with a radius of 25 cm (to the nearest tenth).
13. A circle with a diameter of 1.84 m (to the nearest thousandth).
14. A circle with a diameter of 95 mm (to the nearest whole number).

For Problems 15 to 18, calculate the perimeter and area of the given sectors (rounded to the indicated place value):

15. A sector of a circle with radius 72 cm, inscribed by an angle of 135° (to the nearest whole number).
16. A sector of a circle with radius 2.5 m, inscribed by an angle of 40° (to the nearest hundredth).
17. A sector of a circle with diameter 64 m, inscribed by an angle of 12° (to the nearest thousandth).
18. A sector of a circle with diameter 48 m, inscribed by an angle of 75° (to the nearest tenth).
19. A playground is being built on a rectangular piece of land, 35 m long by 28 m wide, at a local public park. If there is to be a 2 m wide walkway around the entire playground, determine the area available to build the playground.
20. A circular flower bed with diameter 3.5 m is built on a lawn 28 m long and 12.5 m wide. Calculate the remaining area of the lawn.
21. A circular pond has an area of 225 cm^2. Determine the diameter of the pond.
22. A square piece of window glass has an area of 7,225 cm^2. Determine the perimeter of the piece of glass.
23. A rectangular field that is three times as long as it is wide has a perimeter of 2.4 km. Determine the area of the field in km^2.
24. A square field has a perimeter of 144 m. Calculate the area of the field in m^2.
25. A kite is constructed using a simple frame of two pieces of bamboo, one long piece measuring 60 cm and one short piece measuring 32 cm, fashioned together in the shape of a perpendicular cross (see diagram to the right). A light-weight material is then fitted to the frame to make the kite. Determine the amount of material needed.

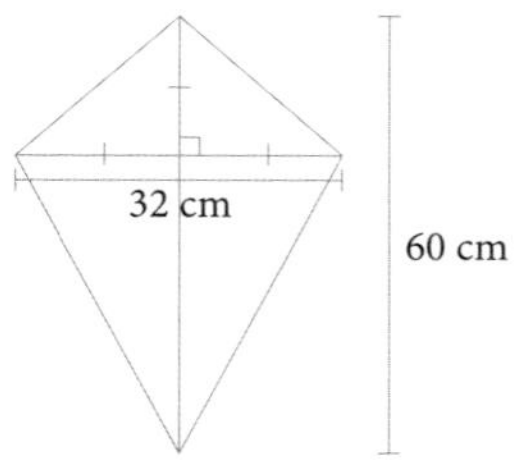

26. If the dimensions in Problem 25 were doubled, what would happen to the amount of material needed to construct the kite? What total amount of material would be required?
27. A garden is planted by a township on a right-triangular plot that is 6.5 m long and 6.5 m wide, at the corner of the main intersection coming into the town. If soil for the garden costs \$2.75 / m^2, determine the total cost to lay the soil in the garden.
28. A quilt for a new baby is constructed using triangular pieces of fabric, each 16 cm long at the base and 10 cm high. How many triangular pieces of fabric are needed to make a quilt that has an area of 1 m^2?

29. A ferris wheel with a diameter of 32 m makes a complete revolution in 40 seconds. Determine the speed of the passenger cars on the wheel, in km/h, rounded to the nearest tenth.

30. A car tire has a diameter of 68 cm and the car is travelling at a speed of 100 km/h. Determine the number of revolutions the tire makes in one minute (rpm), rounded to the nearest rpm.

For Problems 31 to 40, determine the perimeter and area of the composite plane figures.

31.

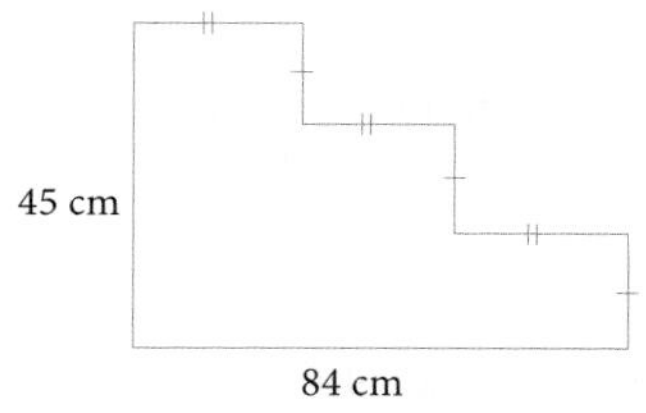

32.

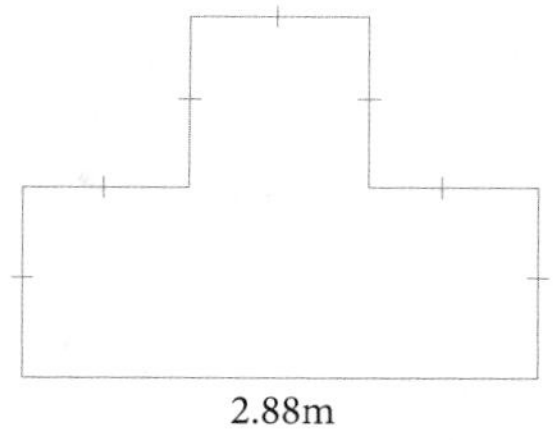

33.

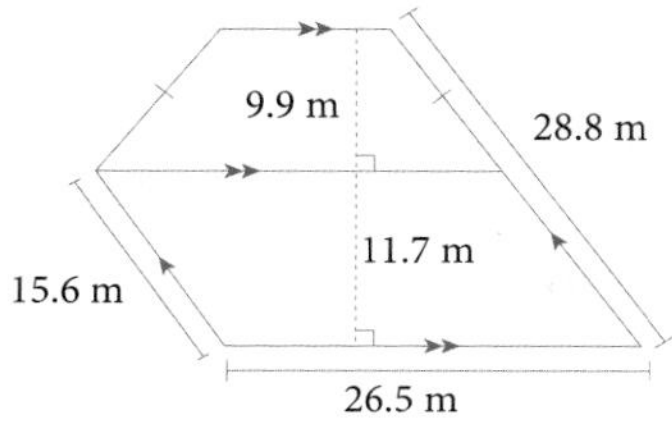

34.

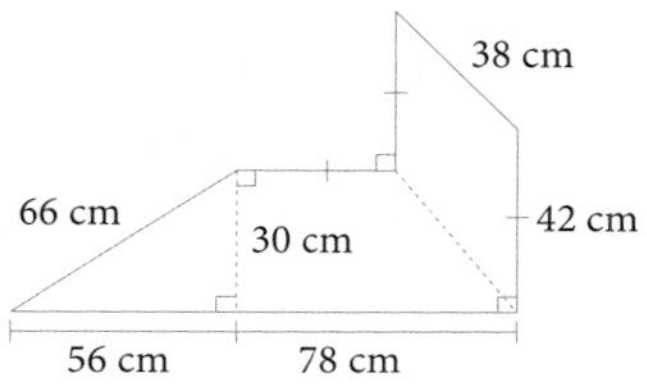

35.

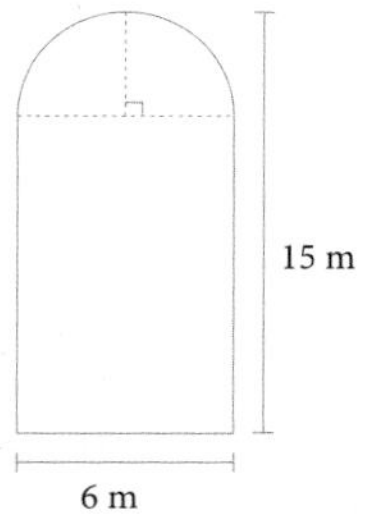

36.

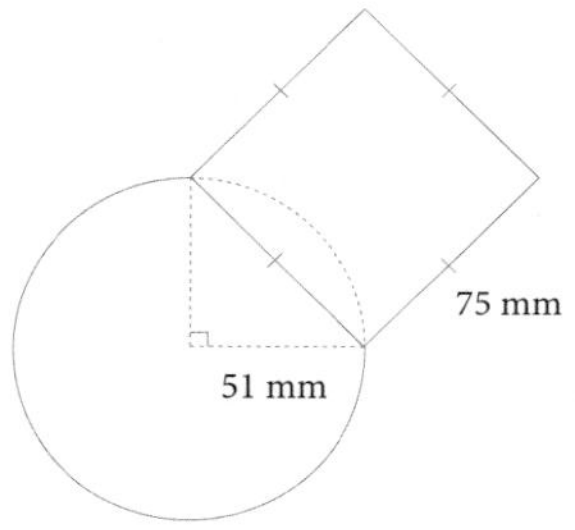

37.

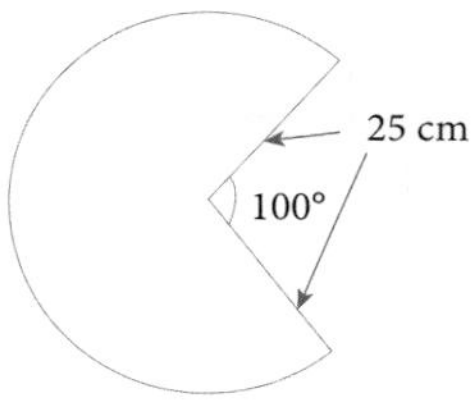

38.

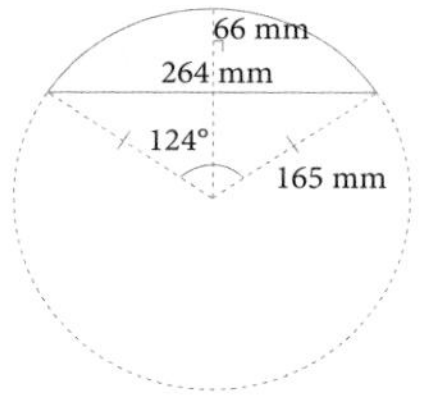

39.

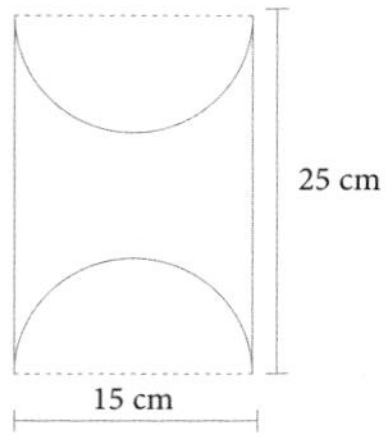

40.

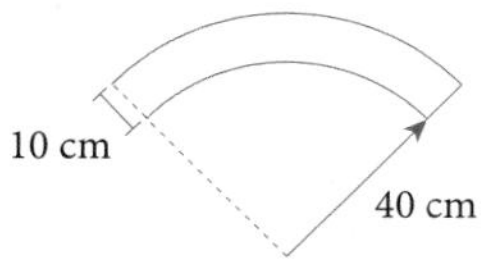

10.4 | Surface Areas and Volumes of Common Solid Objects

Introduction

All the shapes and figures outlined in the previous sections were 2-dimensional. In this section, the general classification of common solid objects that occupy 3-dimensions, and the two important measurements of these objects - surface area and volume will be discussed. The 3-dimensions are length (l), width (w), and height (h). Sometimes, these terms are interchanged with breadth, thickness, and depth.

The **surface area** of a solid is the total area of the surface of a solid including its ends and bases. The lateral area of a solid does not include the area of the base. It is measured in square units (cm^2, m^2, ft^2, etc.).

The **volume** of a solid is a measure of the space it occupies or encloses. It is measured in cubic units (cm^3, m^3, ft^3, etc.) or in the case of liquids, in litres, gallons etc.

The different types of common solid objects that are classified based on their shapes are shown in Exhibit 10.4-a.

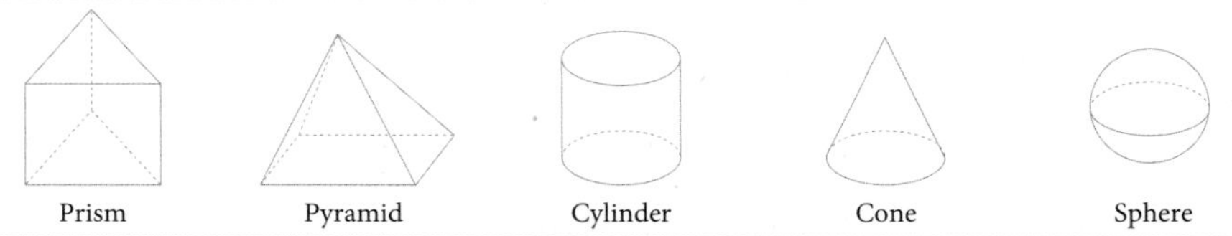

Exhibit 10.4-a The Different Types of Solid Objects

A **polyhedron** is a 3-dimensional object in which all the faces are polygons (flat surfaces). The sides of a polyhedron do not need to be the same polygon. Polyhedrons with congruent faces are known as **platonic solids**. For example, the Cube – all of its faces are congruent squares – and the Tetrahedron – all of its faces are congruent triangles – are platonic solids.

A **convex polyhedron** is a polyhedron with internal angles less than 180°. For example, prisms and pyramids are bounded by polygons (flat surfaces) and they are convex polyhedrons. However, cylinders, cones, and spheres are not polyhedrons because cylinders and cones have both curved and flat surfaces, whereas spheres only have curved surfaces.

Prisms

A prism is a polyhedron with two parallel and congruent end-faces (bases). The height of a prism is the perpendicular distance between its bases.

In an oblique prism, all lateral faces are parallelograms.

In a **right prism**, all the lateral faces are rectangles. The height of a rectangular prism is the length of a lateral edge.

Prisms are named according to the shape of the bases. For example, a prism with a rectangular base is a rectangular prism, while a prism with a triangular base is a triangular prism.

Lateral faces are faces in a solid object that are not bases (top or bottom).

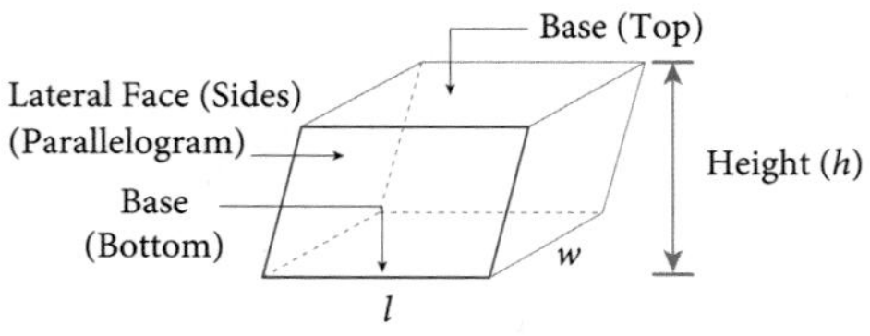

Oblique Rectangular Prism

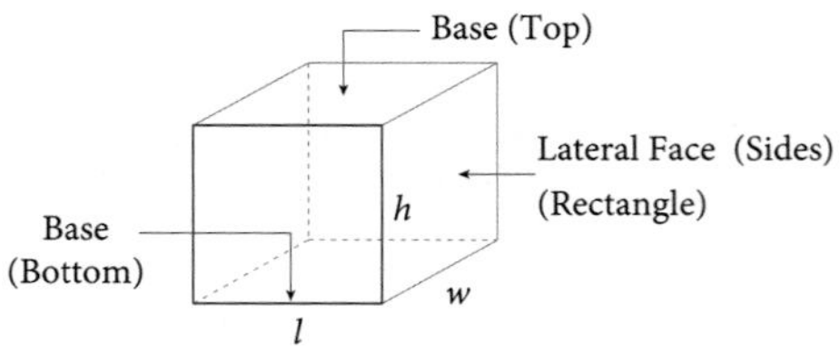

Right Rectangular Prism

Surface area of a prism = 2 × Base area + Sum of the area of all lateral faces

Volume of a prism = Base area × Height of the prism

Right Prisms

A Cube is a solid object with six congruent square faces.

A Rectangular Prism is a solid object with six rectangular faces. Opposite faces have the same area.

A Triangular Prism is a solid object with five faces. It has two triangle faces and three rectangular faces.

		Surface Area	Volume
Cube	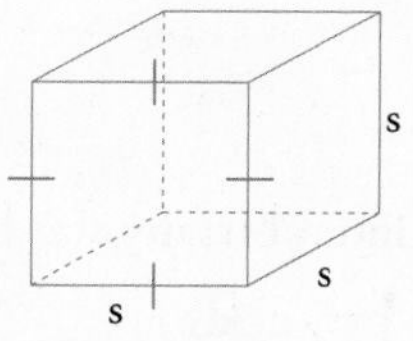	SA= $6s^2$	$V = s^3$
Rectangular Prism	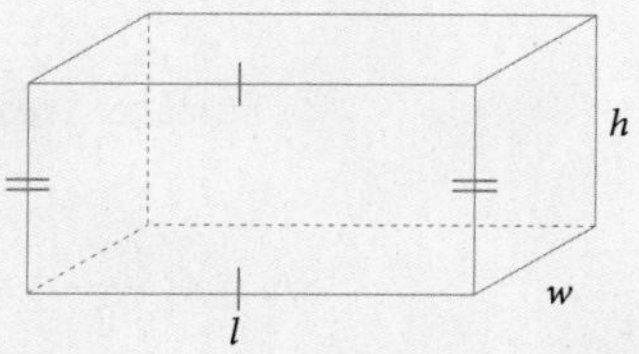	$SA = 2(l \times w) + 2(l \times h) + 2(w \times h)$ $= 2[(l \times w) + (l \times h) + (w \times h)]$	$V = l \times w \times h$
Triangular Prism	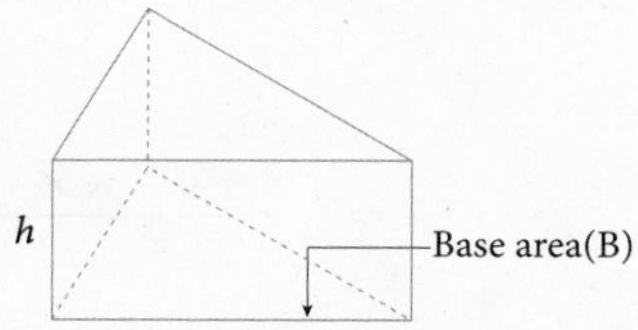	SA= 2 (B) + 3 rectangles	$V = B \times h$

Example 10.4-a | **Calculating the Surface Area and Volume of Rectangular Prisms**

The dimensions of a shipping box are 45 cm by 30 cm by 12 cm. Find the surface area and volume of the shipping box.

Solution

Using $SA = 2(l \times w) + 2(l \times h) + 2(w \times h)$,

$$SA = 2(45 \times 30) + 2(45 \times 12) + 2(30 \times 12)$$
$$= 2{,}700 + 1{,}080 + 720$$
$$= 4{,}500 \text{ cm}^2$$

Using $V = l \times w \times h$,

$$V = (45 \times 30 \times 12)$$
$$= 16{,}200 \text{ cm}^3$$

Therefore, the surface area of the shipping box is 4,500 cm^2 and the volume is 16,200 cm^3.

Pyramids

A pyramid is a polyhedron in which the base is a polygon and all lateral faces are triangles, meeting at a common point, known as the vertex (apex).

A regular right pyramid is a pyramid with is a regular, polygon base with all the lateral faces being congruent triangles. Also, the line connecting the apex to the centre of the base forms a right-angle with the base: this is the height of the regular pyramid.

A right rectangular pyramid is a pyramid with a rectangular base. If the base happens to be a square, then it is called a right **square pyramid.**

The slant heights of a right rectangular pyramid are usually denoted by s_1 for the slant height on the length side and s_2 for the slant height on the width side. In a right square pyramid, since all four triangular sides are identical, there is only one slant height, denoted by *s*.

The term **rectangular pyramid** is commonly used to describe a right rectangular pyramid, in which all triangular side faces are isosceles triangles and opposite side faces are congruent.

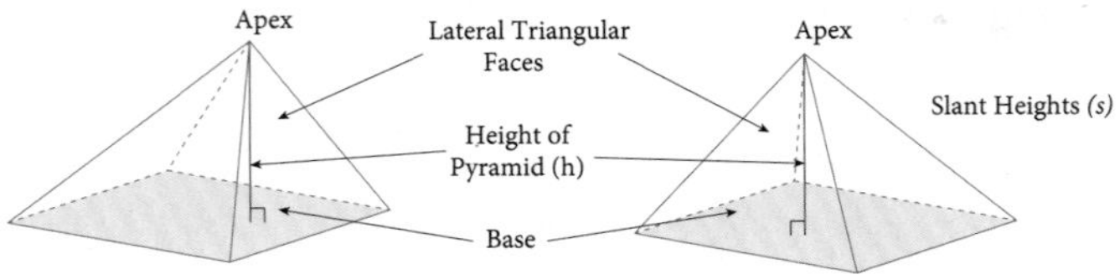

Oblique Rectangular Pyramid Right Rectangular Pyramid

Surface Area = (Sum of the area of all lateral triangular faces) + (Base area)

Volume = $\frac{1}{3}$(Base area × Height of the pyramid)

Right Pyramids

		Surface Area	Volume
Square Pyramid	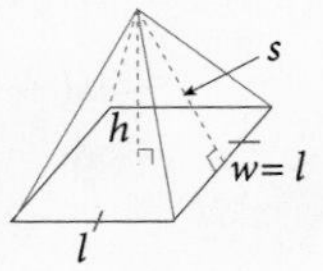	$SA = 4\left(\frac{l \times s}{2}\right) + l^2$ $SA = 2l \times s + l^2$	$V = \frac{1}{3}(l^2 \times h)$ $V = \frac{l^2 \times h}{3}$
Rectangular Pyramid	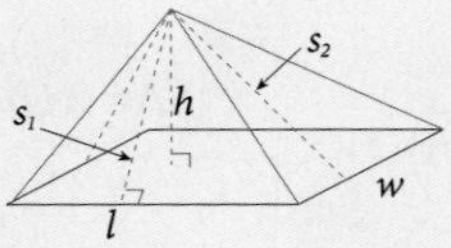	$SA = 2\left(\frac{l \times s_1}{2} + \frac{w \times s_2}{2}\right) + l \times w$ $SA = (l \times s_1 + w \times s_2) + l \times w$	$V = \frac{1}{3}(l \times w)h$ $V = \frac{l \times w \times h}{3}$
Triangular Pyramid	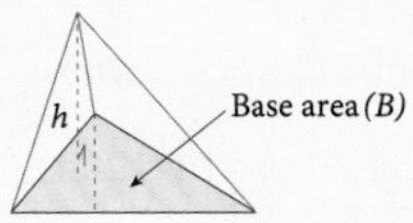	SA = Area of all 3 lateral faces + Base Area (B)	$V = \frac{1}{3}(B)h$ $V = \frac{B \times h}{3}$

Example 10.4-b **Calculating the Surface Area and Volume of Pyramids**

A tea bag is manufactured in the shape of a square-based pyramid, with side length 30 mm, height 20 mm, and slant height 25 mm. Find the following:

(i) The amount of mesh (in mm²) needed to manufacture the tea bag.

(ii) The volume of tea (in cm³) the bag can hold.

Solution

Since the tea bag has a square base, the slant heights are equal on all sides.

(i) Using $SA = 2l \times s + l^2$,

$$SA = 2(30 \times 25) + (30)^2$$
$$= 2{,}400 \text{ mm}^2$$

Therefore 2,400 mm² of mesh is needed to manufacture the tea bag.

(ii) The length is 30 mm = 3 cm, and the height is 20 mm = 2 cm.

Using $V = \frac{l^2 \times h}{3}$,

$$V = \frac{3^2 \times 2}{3}$$
$$= 6 \text{ cm}^3$$

Therefore, the tea bag can hold 6 cm³ of tea.

Cylinders

A **cylinder** is a prism with 2 parallel and congruent circular bases and a curved lateral surface connecting the two bases. The height (altitude), h, of the cylinder is the perpendicular distance between the two bases. The radius, r, of the cylinder is the radius of the base circle.

The term cylinder is commonly used to describe a circular cylinder.

In a right cylinder, the line joining the centre of the bases is perpendicular to the bases.

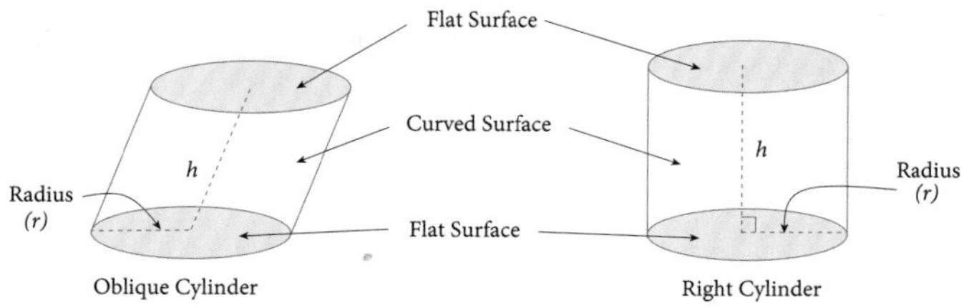

If the lateral side of a right circular cylinder is unwrapped, as in Exhibit 10.4-b, we see that it is a rectangle with a length equal to the circumference of the circular base ($C = 2\pi r$) and width equal to the height of the cylinder.

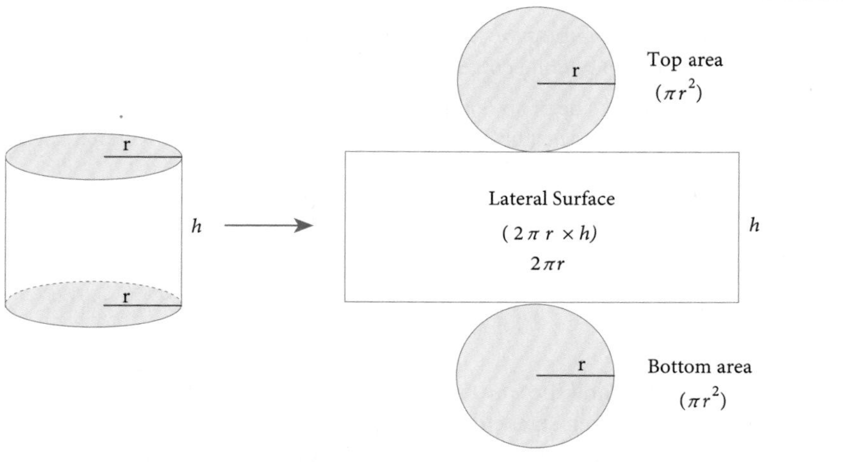

Exhibit 10.4-b Surface Area of a Cylinder

That is, we can take a rectangle and wrap it around to create a circular tube, which can then be "capped" at either or both ends with circles. This leads us to the following three definitions:

A **closed cylinder** (or **can**) is a cylinder that has a lateral face and two end-faces.

A **semi-closed cylinder** (or **cup**) is a cylinder that has a lateral face and one end-face.

An **open cylinder** (or **tube**) is a cylinder that only has a lateral face with no end-faces.

Surface area of a cylinder = 2 × Circular base area + Area of the curved lateral face

Volume of a cylinder = Base area × Height of the cylinder

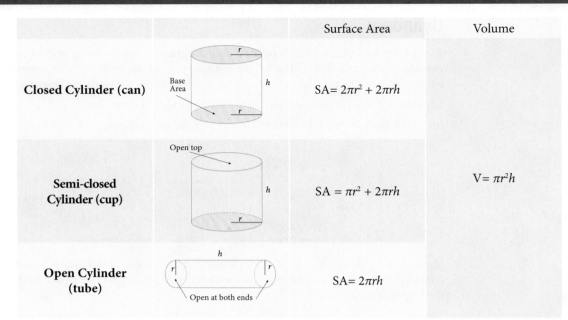

		Surface Area	Volume
Closed Cylinder (can)	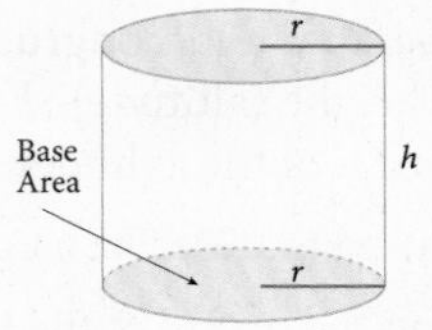	SA= $2\pi r^2 + 2\pi rh$	V= $\pi r^2 h$
Semi-closed Cylinder (cup)	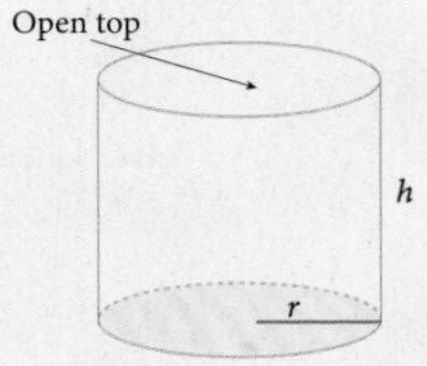	SA = $\pi r^2 + 2\pi rh$	
Open Cylinder (tube)	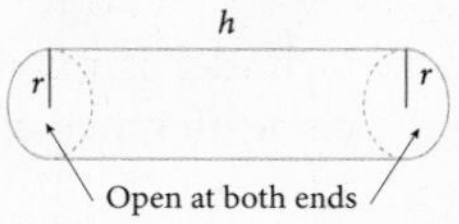	SA= $2\pi rh$	

Note: The formulas for surface area and volume of a right circular cylinder are exactly the same as those for an oblique circular cylinder.

If the lateral side of an oblique circular cylinder is "unwrapped", it becomes a parallelogram with the same base length and height (note: perpendicular height) as the rectangular, lateral side in a right circular cylinder.

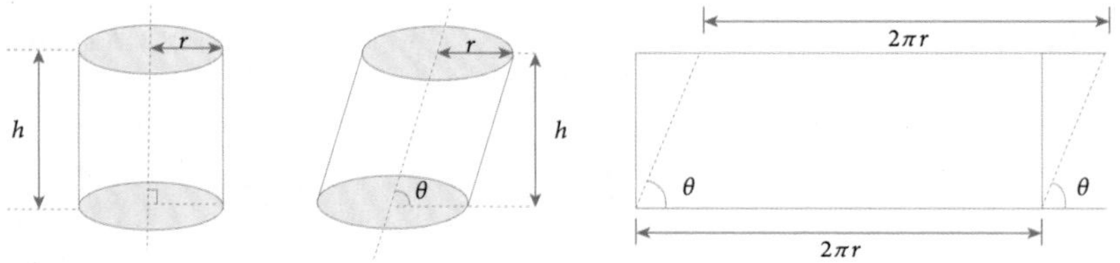

To understand the way the volume formula applies to an oblique circular cylinder, consider a stack of quarters; when stacked perfectly, they form a right cylinder. If this stack of quarters are pushed on a slant, they form an oblique cylinder; however, the volume of metal in the quarters has not changed.

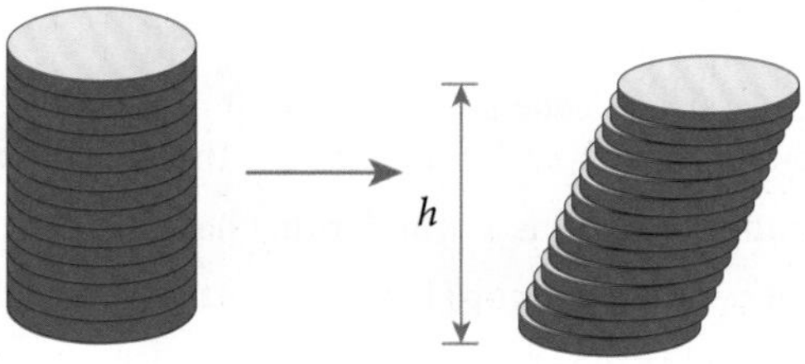

Example 10.4-c

Calculating the Surface Area and Volume of Cylinders

A cylindrical can of tomato soup has a diameter of 6 cm and a height of 10 cm. Find the following, rounded to the nearest whole number:

(i) The area of aluminum needed for the can, in cm^2.

(ii) The volume of soup the can is able to hold, in mL.

Solution

Since the can has both a top and a bottom face, it represents a closed cylinder. Also, since the diameter of the can is 6 cm, the radius is 3 cm.

(i) Using SA = $2\pi r^2 + 2\pi rh$,

$$SA = 2\pi(3)^2 + 2\pi(3)(10)$$

$$\approx 56.55 + 188.50$$

$$\approx 245 \text{ cm}^2$$

Therefore, the area of aluminum needed for the can is 245 cm^2.

Solution
continued

(ii) Using $V = \pi r^2 h$,

$$V \approx \pi(3)^2(10)$$
$$\approx 283 \text{ cm}^2$$

Recall that $1 \text{ cm}^3 = 1 \text{ mL}$; therefore, $V \approx 283 \text{ mL}$.

Therefore, the volume of soup that the can is able to hold is 283 cm^2.

Cones

A cone is a pyramid with a circular base and a curved lateral surface, which extends from the base to a point known as the vertex. The height (altitude), h, of the cone is the perpendicular distance from the vertex to the base. The radius, r, of the cylinder is the radius of the base circle. The slant height of the cone, s, is the distance from the vertex to any point on the edge of the base.

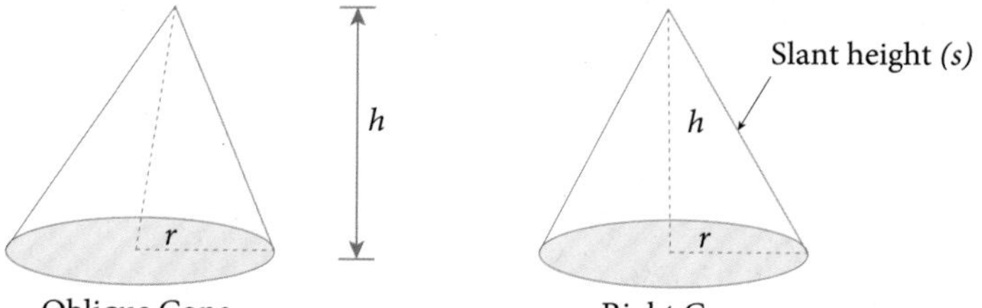

As with the cylinder, the formulas for surface area and volume of an oblique circular cone are exactly the same as that of the right circular cone.

The surface area of a closed cone is the sum of the area of the circular base and the area of the lateral face. The area of the lateral face is A = π × (radius) × (slant height); the explanation of this formula is beyond the scope of this textbook.

Surface Area = (Area of the circular base) + (Area of the lateral face)

Volume = $\frac{1}{3}$ **[(Area of circular base) × (Height of the cone)]**

As with cylinders, closed cones have "lids" while open cones do not. Therefore, the surface area of an open cone is simply the area of the lateral face

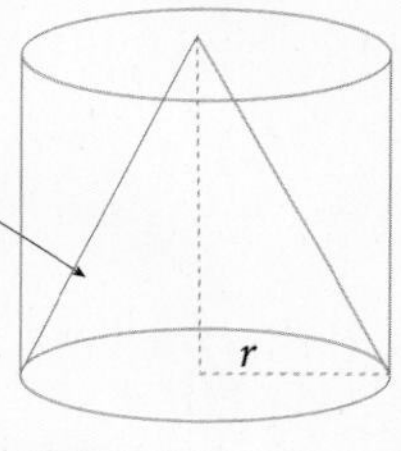

The volume of a cone is exactly one third that of the cylinder with the same base and height.

Right Cone

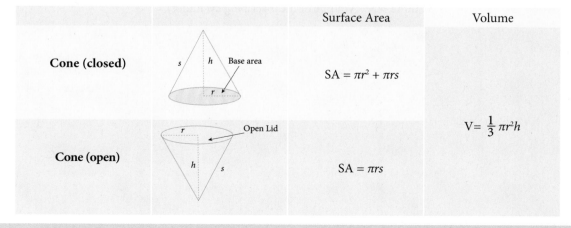

		Surface Area	Volume
Cone (closed)	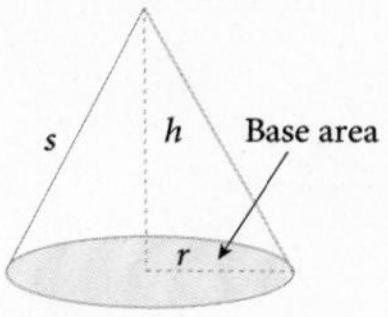	$SA = \pi r^2 + \pi rs$	$V = \frac{1}{3}\pi r^2 h$
Cone (open)	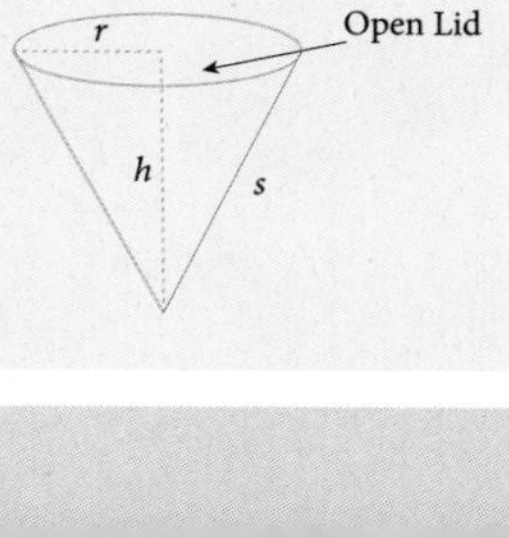	$SA = \pi rs$	

Example 10.4-d Calculating the Surface Area and Volume of Cones

A paper water cup used for a water cooler is in the shape of a cone, with a diameter of 6.4 cm, a height of 10.8 cm, and a slant height of 11.3 cm. Find the following:

(i) The area of the paper needed to make the cup (rounded to the nearest cm²).

(ii) The volume of water the cup can hold (rounded to the nearest mL).

Solution

Since the cup has no lid, we need the formula for an open cone. We also need the length of the radius, which is half of the diameter: $r = 3.2$ cm.

(i) Using $\text{SA} = \pi rs$,

$$\text{SA} = \pi(3.2)(11.3)$$
$$\approx 114 \text{ cm}^2$$

Therefore, the area of the paper needed to make the cup is 114 cm².

(ii) Using $\text{V} = \frac{\pi r^2 h}{3}$,

$$\text{V} = \frac{\pi(3.2)^2(10.8)}{3}$$
$$\approx 116 \text{ cm}^3$$
$$\approx 116 \text{ mL}$$

Therefore, the volume of water the cup can hold is 116mL.

Spheres

A sphere is a 3-dimensional object shaped like a ball. It is a solid, bounded by curved surfaces and every surface point is a fixed distance (the radius) away from a centrepoint.

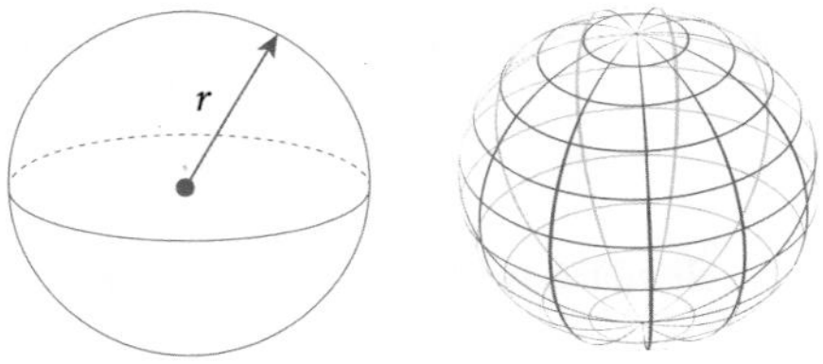

The surface area of a sphere is exactly equal to the area of the lateral face of the smallest cylinder that inscribes the sphere.

Surface Area = (Area of inscribing cylinder's lateral face)

$$\text{SA} = 2\pi rh$$
$$= 2\pi r(2r)$$
$$= 4\,\pi r^2$$

Volume = $\frac{2}{3}$ (Volume of the inscribing cyclinder)

$$\text{V} = \frac{2}{3}\pi r^2 h$$
$$= \frac{2}{3}\pi r^2(2r)$$
$$= \frac{4}{3}\pi r^3$$

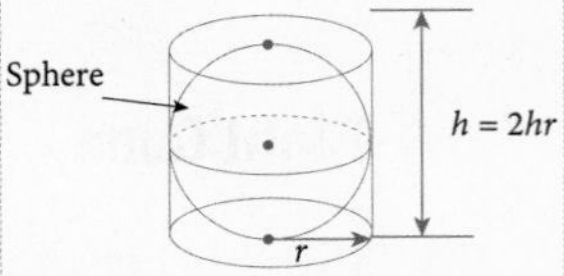

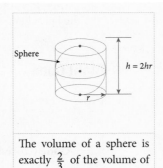

The volume of a sphere is exactly $\frac{2}{3}$ of the volume of the cylinder that inscribes it.

		Surface Area	Volume
Sphere	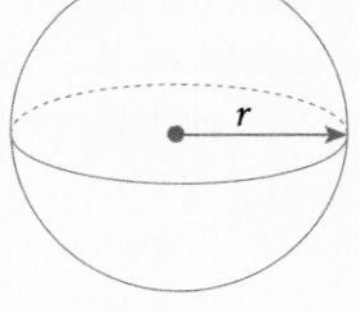	$SA = 4\pi r^2$	$V = \frac{4}{3}(\pi r^3)$
Half-sphere (solid)	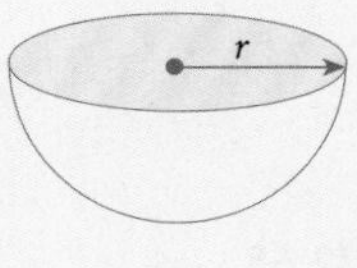	$SA = \frac{1}{2}(4\pi r^2) + \pi r^2$ $= 3\pi r^2$	$V = \frac{1}{2}\left(\frac{4}{3}\pi r^3\right)$ $= \frac{2}{3}\pi r^3$

Example 10.4-e **Calculating the Surface Area and Volume of Spheres**

A spherical yoga ball has a height of 75 cm. Find the following:

(i) The amount of rubber (in m^2, rounded to the nearest thousandth) needed to construct the ball.

(ii) The volume of air that the ball can hold when fully inflated (rounded to the nearest L).

Solution

The height of the yoga ball is the same as the diameter of the ball, which is twice the radius; therefore, $r = 37.5 \text{ cm} = 0.375 \text{ m}$.

(i) Using $SA = 4\pi r^2$,

$$SA = 4\pi(0.375)^2$$
$$\approx 1.767 \text{ m}^2$$

Therefore, the amount of rubber needed to construct the ball is 1.767 m^2.

(ii) Since 1 mL = 1 cm^3, 1 L = 1000 mL = 1000 cm^3.

Using $V = \frac{4}{3}\pi \times r^3$,

$$V = \frac{4}{3}\pi(37.5)^3 \approx 220{,}893 \text{ cm}^3$$
$$\approx 221 \text{ L}$$

Therefore, the volume of air that the ball can hold when fully inflated is 221 L.

Composite Figures

As in 2-dimensional plane geometry, there are many complex, 3-dimensional solids which are composed of simpler solids like prisms, cylinders, pyramids, cones, and spheres. A few example are outlined below:

Example 10.4-f **Calculating the Surface Area of a Composite Shape**

An aluminum shed is built 5.0 m long, 3.0 m wide, 2.55 m tall at the sides and 3.2 m tall in the middle, with a roof that has a slant height of 1.6 m, as per the following diagram:

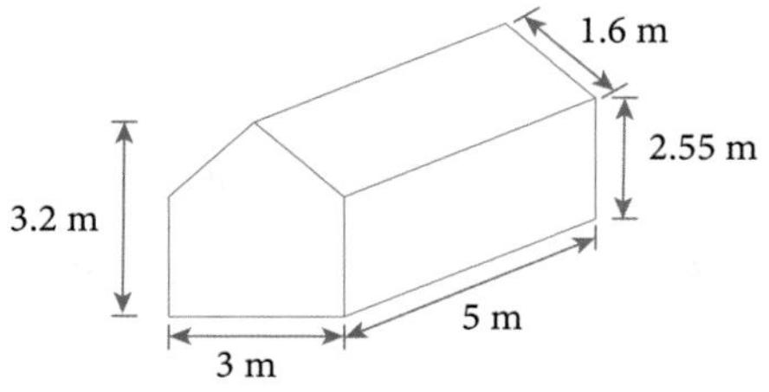

If aluminum costs \$3.96 / m^2, find the total cost of the aluminum needed to build the shed.

Solution

First, we need to determine the amount of aluminum needed to build the shed, in m², which is the surface area of the shed. This is a pentagonal prism, for which we do not have a formula. However, we can analyze the shape as a prism with 2 rectangular side faces, 2 rectangular roof faces, (no bottom face, since the floor is not constructed out of aluminum), and two end-faces that are each comprised of a rectangle and a triangle:

Using $SA = 2A_{side} + 2A_{roof} + 2(A_{end\ rectangle} + A_{end\ triangle})$

$$SA = 2(5.0)(2.55) + 2(5.0)(1.6) + 2\left((3.0)(2.55) + \frac{1}{2}(3.0)(3.2 - 2.55)\right)$$

$$= 25.5 + 16.0 + 2(8.625)$$

$$= 58.75\ m^2$$

$$\text{Cost} = \frac{\$3.96}{m^2} \times 58.75\ m^2 = \$232.65$$

Therefore, the total cost of the aluminum needed to build the shed is \$232.65.

Example 10.4-g

Calculating the Volume of a Composite Shape

An ice-cream waffle-cone has a diameter of 8.5 cm at the opening, a perpendicular height of 17.5 cm, and a slant height of 18 cm. Ice-cream is scooped and packed into the waffle-cone until it is completely filled with ice cream and an additional hemi-sphere of ice cream sits on top, as in the figure below:

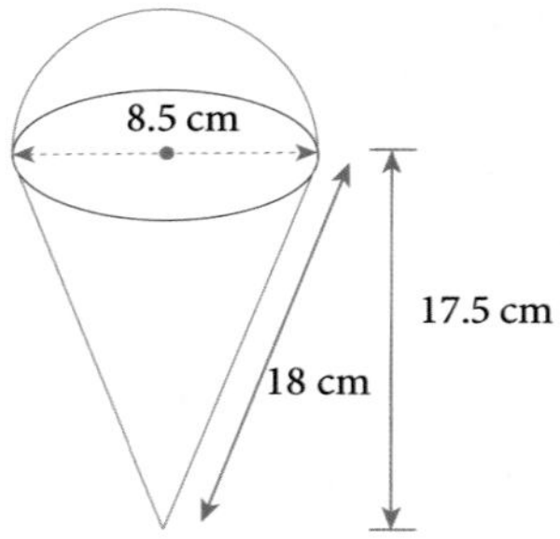

Find the following:

(i) The surface area of the waffle cone (rounded to the nearest cm²).

(ii) The volume of ice-cream the cone can hold, including the hemi-sphere on top (rounded to the nearest mL).

Solution

Since the cone does not have a lid, we use the formula for an open cone, and the radius is half of the diameter, so r = 4.25 cm:

(i) Using SA,

$$S = \pi rs$$
$$S = \pi(4.25)(18)$$
$$\approx 240\ cm^2$$

Therefore, the surface area of the waffle cone is 240 cm².

(ii) The volume of ice-cream is equal to the volume of the cone $\frac{\pi r^2 h}{3}$, plus half the volume of a sphere $\left(\frac{1}{2}\left[\frac{4}{3}\pi r^3\right] = \frac{2}{3}\pi r^3\right)$. Since the flat circular face of the hemisphere lines up with the open circular face of the cone, the radii of the two solids are equal (i.e., $r = 4.25$ cm for both).

$$V = \frac{\pi r^2 h}{3} + \frac{2}{3}\pi r^3$$

$$V = \frac{\pi(4.25)^2(17.5)}{3} + \frac{2}{3}\pi(4.25)^3$$

$$\approx 331.0 + 160.8$$

$$\approx 492\ mL$$

Therefore, the volume of ice-cream the cone can hold, including the hemi-sphere on top, is 492 mL.

10.4 | Exercises

Answers to odd-numbered problems are available at the end of the textbook.

For Problems 1 to 14, determine the surface area and volume of the given solids:

1. A cube with sides 25 mm long.
2. A cube with sides 8 cm long.
3. A rectangular prism with sides of 3 m, 6 m, and 12.5 m.
4. A rectangular prism with sides of 40 cm, 80 cm, and 150 cm.
5. A semi-open cylinder with a height of 15 cm and a base with a diameter of 12 cm.
6. An open cylinder with a height of 51 cm and a base with a radius of 5 cm.
7. A closed cylinder with a height of 85 mm and a base with a radius of 32 mm.
8. A semi-open cylinder with a height of 1.5 m and a base with a diameter of 64 cm.
9. An open cone with a perpendicular height of 22 cm, a slant height of 22.5 cm, and a base with a radius of 4.5 cm.
10. A closed cone with a perpendicular height of 94 mm, a slant height of 98 mm, and a base with a diameter of 56 mm.
11. A sphere with a radius of 22 cm.
12. A sphere with a radius of 8 mm.
13. A sphere with a diameter of 1.3 m.
14. A sphere with a diameter of 7.5 cm.
15. Find the volume of a cone with a base area of 140 cm^2 and a height of 40 cm.
16. Find the volume of a triangular pyramid with a base area of 270 m^2 and a height of 15 m.

For Problems 17 to 20, determine the volume of the given solids:

17. A square pyramid with sides 4.5 m long and a height of 2.8 m.
18. A rectangular pyramid with side lengths of 48 cm and 60 cm, and a height of 55 cm.
19. A triangular prism with a base area of 7 cm^2 and a height of 36 cm.
20. A triangular pyramid with a base area of 270 m^2 and a height of 15 m.

Solve the following application problems:

21. Calculate the volume of a rectangular box that measures 1.44 m by 1.25 m by 75 cm. How much cardboard is needed to construct the box?
22. Calculate the volume of a can of beans that has a base with a diameter of 7.4 cm and a height of 11 cm. How much aluminum is needed to create the can?
23. Determine the volume of air needed in a spherical basketball that has a surface area of 1,800 cm^2.
24. A puzzle cube has a surface area of 168.54 cm^2. Determine the volume of plastic needed to make the puzzle cube.
25. A rectangular box with a width that is twice its height and two-thirds its length has a volume of 93,750 cm^3. Determine the surface area of the box.
26. A cylindrical pipe with a height that is ten times its base diameter has a volume of 2.5 m^3. Determine the surface area of the (open) cylindrical pipe, rounded to the nearest tenth of a square metre.
27. A novelty megaphone sold at all home-games of a local football team is created from an open plastic cone that has a slant height of 70 cm and a base diameter of 25 cm. Determine the amount of plastic needed to create the megaphone.
28. The smallest of the three pyramids of Giza in Egypt has a square-base with side lengths of 108.6 m, a slant height of 85.8 m, and a perpendicular height of 66.4 m. The surface of the pyramid was originally covered in white limestone. Determine the amount of white limestone that would have been needed to complete this task.
29. The circumference of the Earth is approximately 40,075 km. Approximate the surface area (rounded to the nearest million km^2) and volume (rounded to the nearest billion km^3) of the Earth, assuming that it is a sphere.
30. A spherical bowling ball is made up of a polyurethane core and a reactive resin cover, and must have a circumference of 68 cm. Determine the cost to manufacture the ball if the polyurethane for the core costs \$0.0065/cm^3 and the reactive resin coating costs \$0.0105/cm^2. Round the answer to the nearest cent.

For Problems 31 to 34, determine the surface area and volume of the composite figures:

31. A child's playhouse consisting of a square prism base and a square-pyramid roof:

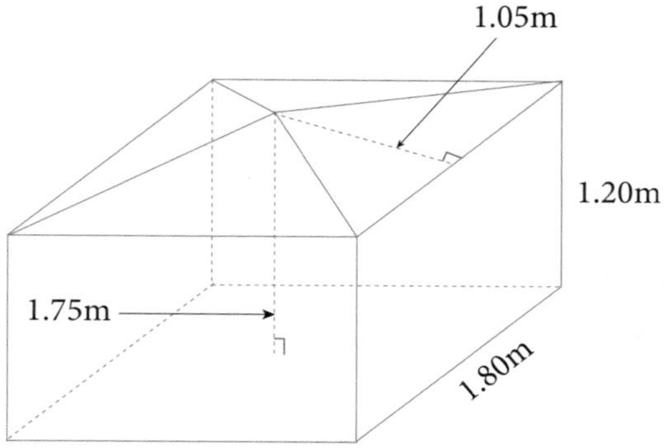

32. A greenhouse consisting of a rectangular base and a half-cylindrical roof:

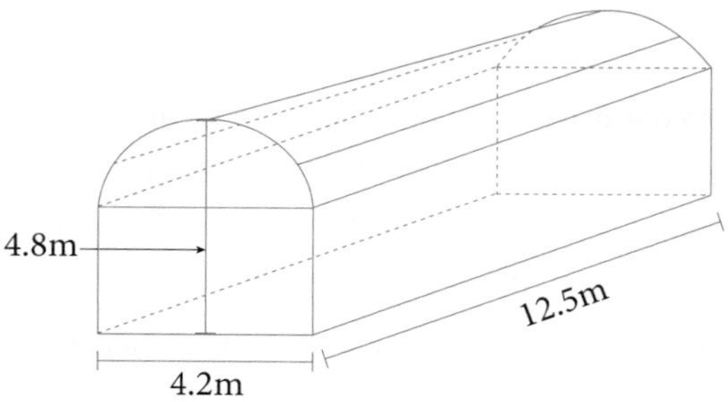

33. A silo consisting of a cylindrical base and a hemispherical roof:

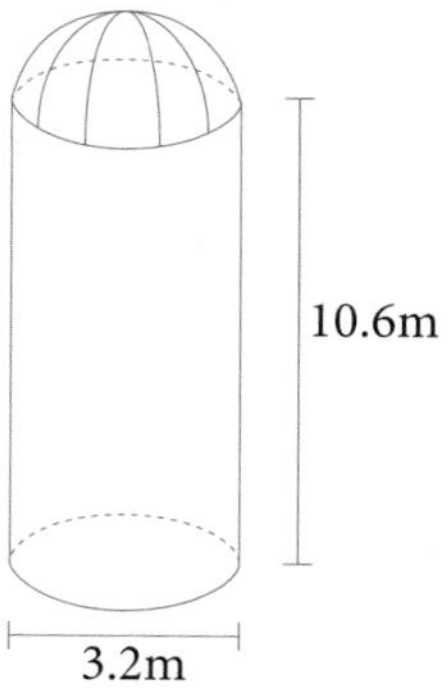

34. A gazebo consisting of a cylindrical base and a conical roof:

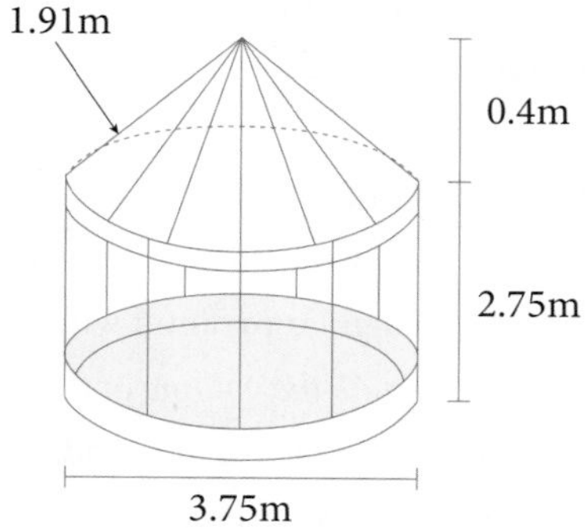

10 | Review Exercises

Answers to odd-numbered problems are available at the end of the textbook.

For Problems 1 and 2, determine (i) the measure of angle θ using a protractor and (ii) calculate the supplement and complement of the angle θ.

1. a.

b.

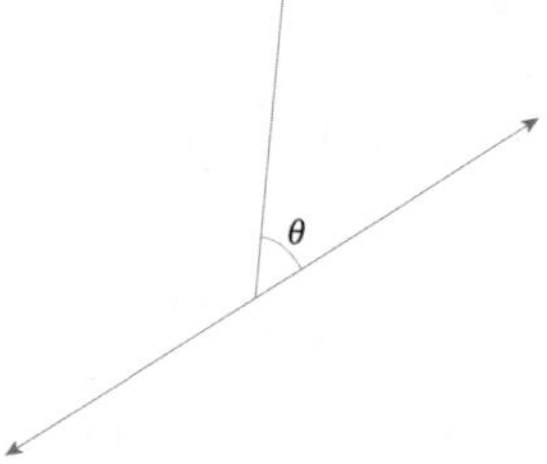

2. a.

b.

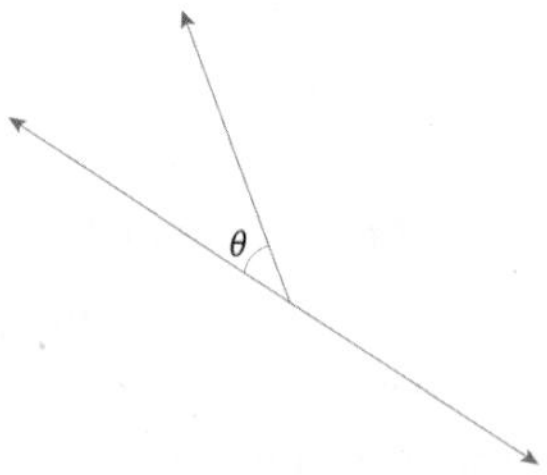

3. Given the following diagram:

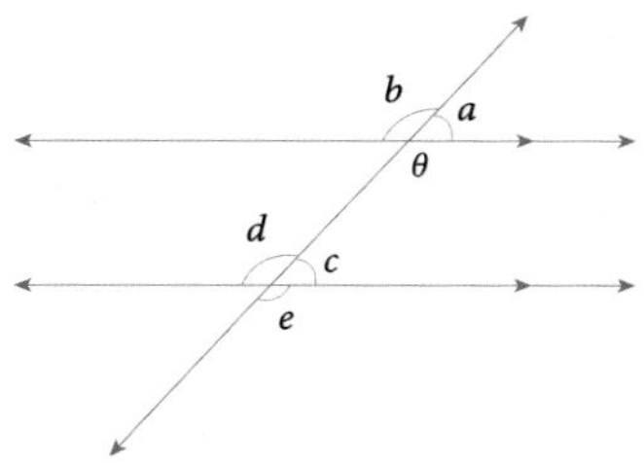

a. State the relationship of each of the unknowns, *a, b, c, d,* and *e.*

b. Calculate the angle measure of each of the unknown angles given that $\theta = 89\,°$.

4. Given the following diagram:

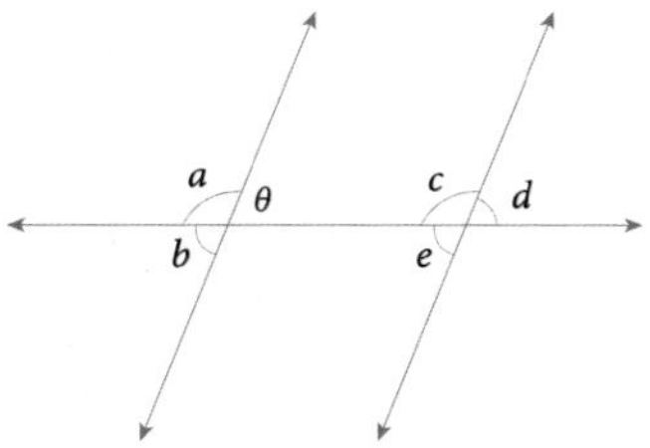

a. State the relationship of each of the unknowns, *a, b, c, d,* and *e.*

b. Calculate the angle measure of each of the unknown angles given that $\theta = 113\,°$.

In Problems 5 and 6, determine the unknown angles, a, b, and c, in each of the diagrams:

5. a.

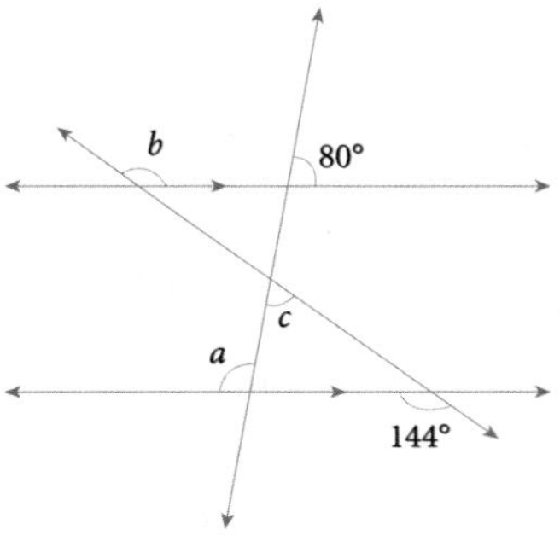

b.

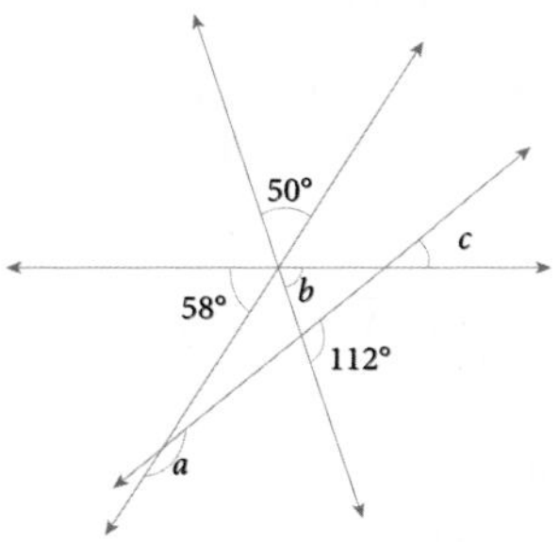

6. a.

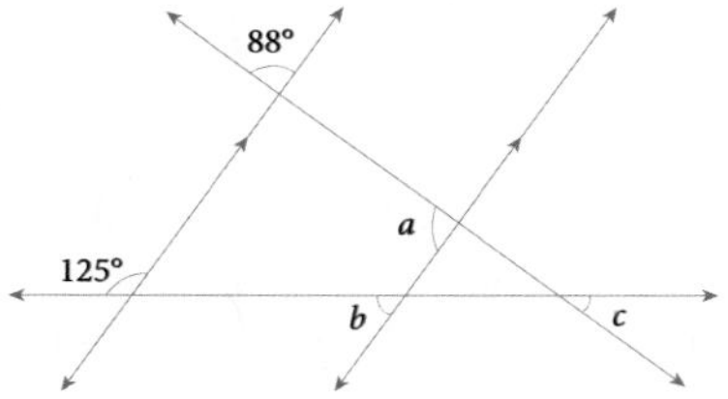

b.

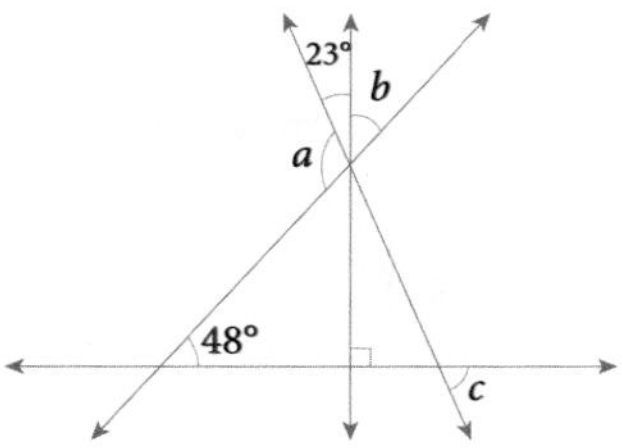

In Problems 7 and 8, classify the quadrilaterals:

7. a.

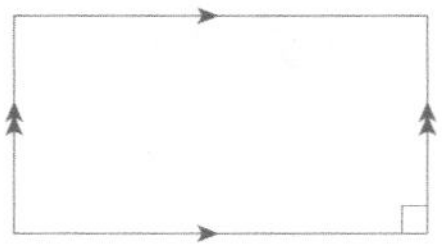

b.

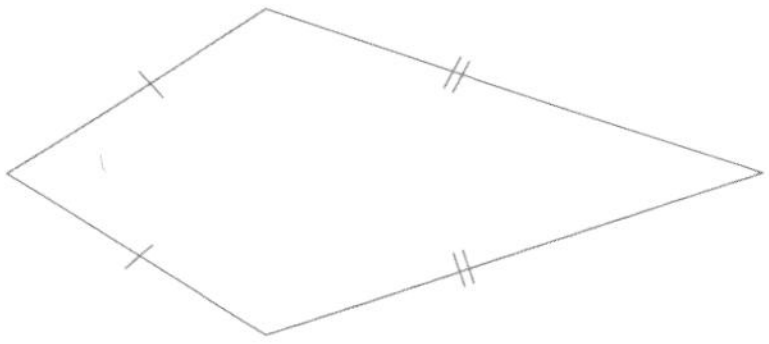

c.

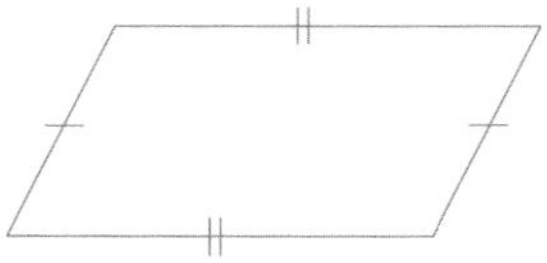

8. a.

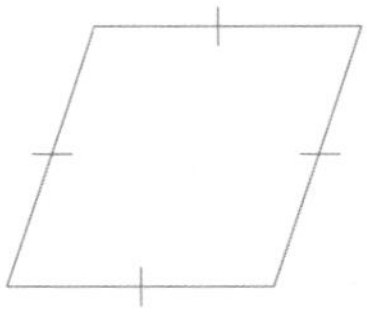

b.

c.

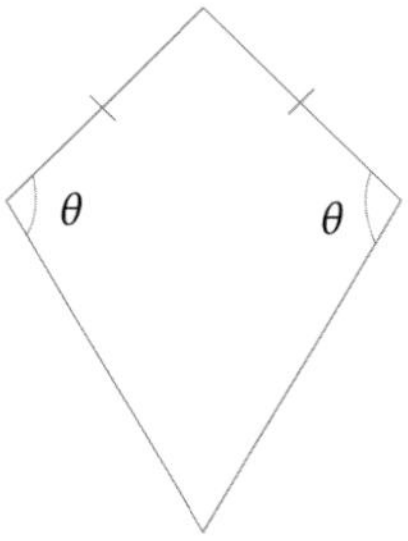

For Problems 9 and 10, use the Internal Angles Theorem (IAT) - Part 1 and the properties of various quadrilaterals to calculate the measure of the unknown angles:

9. a. ABCD is a rhombus, where $\angle DAB = 45°$.

   b. QRST is a general quadrilateral, where $\angle TQR = 112°$, $\angle RST = 68°$, $\angle STQ = 103°$.

   c. WXYZ is a trapezoid, where $\angle XYZ = 114°$, $\angle YZW = 76°$, $\angle ZWX = 68°$.

10. a. WXYZ is a parallelogram, where $\angle WXY = 63°$.

    b. ABCD is a general quadrilateral, where $\angle BAD = 128°$, $\angle ABC = 93°$, $\angle BCD = 52°$.

    c. QRST is a kite, where $\angle TQR = 93°$, $\angle SRQ = 87°$.

For the triangles in Problems 11 and 12:

i. Determine all the missing angles.

ii. Classify the triangle by side length and by angle.

11. a.

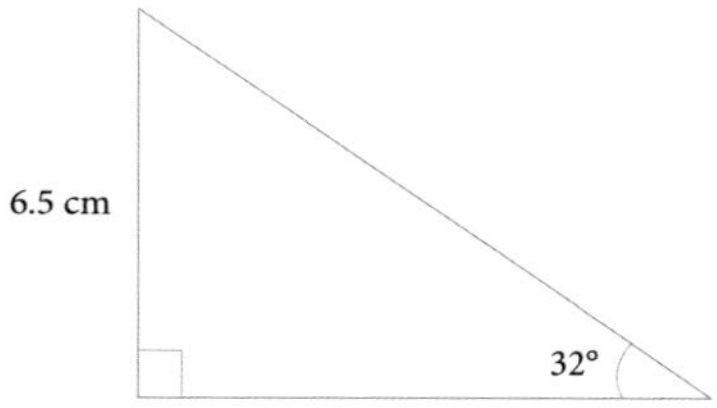

b.

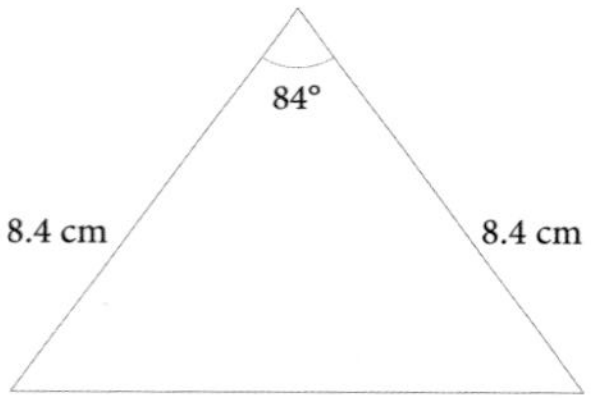

12. a.

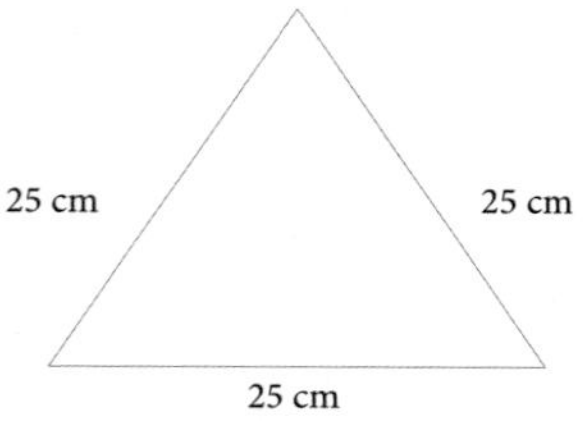

b.

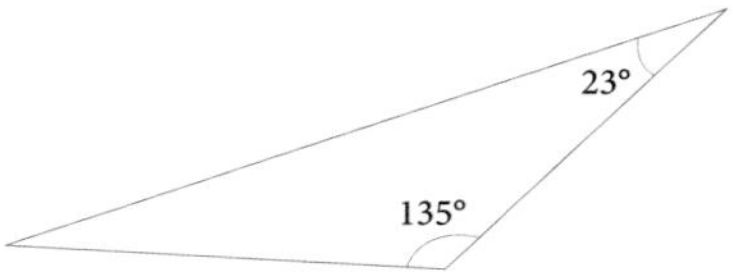

In Problems 13 and 14, calculate the perimeter and the area of the given triangles using the "half-base times height" method and Heron's formula:

13. a.

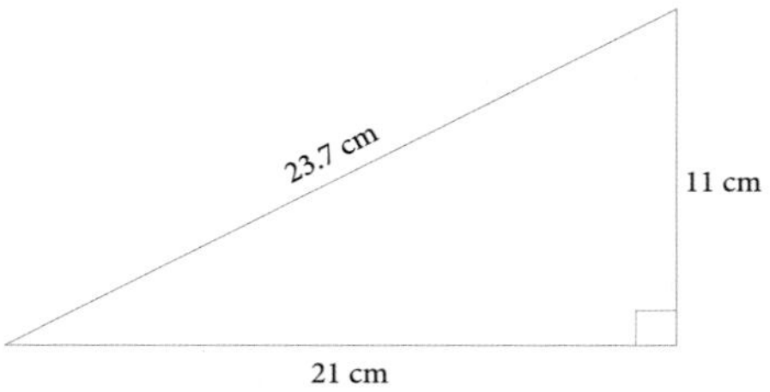

b.

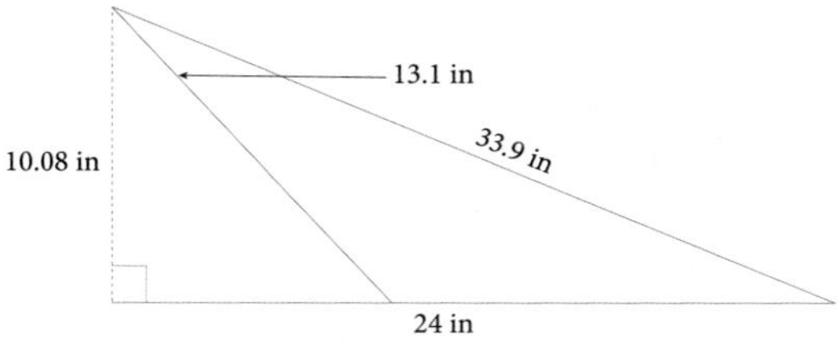

14. a.

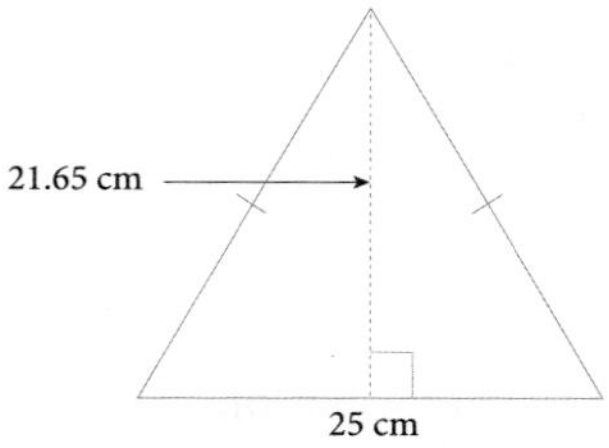

b.

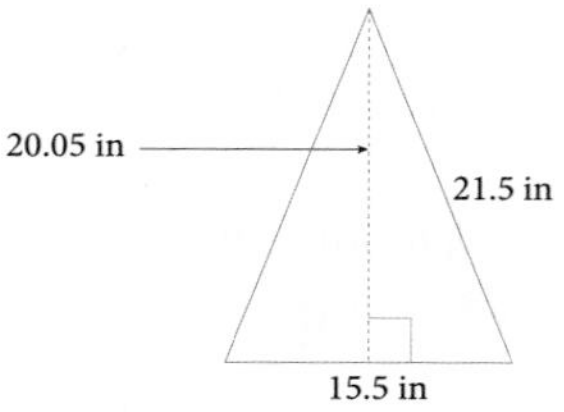

15. Calculate the perimeter of a rectangle with a length that is twice its width and an area of 392 cm^2.

16. Calculate the volume (to the nearest cm^3) of a sphere with a surface area of 452 cm^2.

In Problems 17 to 20, calculate the perimeter and area of the given shapes:

17. A parallelogram with a base of 32 cm, a perpendicular height of 15 cm, and a slant height of 18 cm.

18. A rhombus with a side length of 45 cm and a perpendicular height of 36 cm.

19. a. A circle with a radius of 23.6 m.

    b. A sector of a circle with a diameter of 125 cm and an inscribed angle of 30°.

20. a. A circle with a diameter of 3.5 m.

    b. A sector of a circle with a radius of 78 cm and an inscribed angle of 115°.

21. Calculate the surface area of a cylinder (to the nearest cm^2) that has a volume of 3,220 cm^3 and a height that is equal to its diameter.

22. A circular pane of glass is to be constructed to fit an attic window that has a diameter of 55 cm. Determine the amount of glass (in cm^2) needed to construct the window pane.

23. A medium pizza with a 10-inch diameter is cut into 8 unequal slices. The largest slice has a subtended angle of 65°, while the smallest slice has a subtended angle of 20°. Determine the difference in area between the two slices of pizza, to the nearest tenth of a square inch (in^2).

24. Sixteen spherical chocolates are stacked 4 chocolates long, 2 chocolates high, and 2 chocolates deep, and sold in a rectangular plastic box that perfectly fits the chocolates. Assuming that the box is 10 cm long, 5 cm high, and 5 cm deep, determine the volume of "wasted space" in the box (i.e., the space not occupied by the chocolates). What percent of the box does this represent? Does this seem surprising to you? Why or why not?

In Problems 25 to 28, determine the perimeter and area of the given composite shapes.

25.

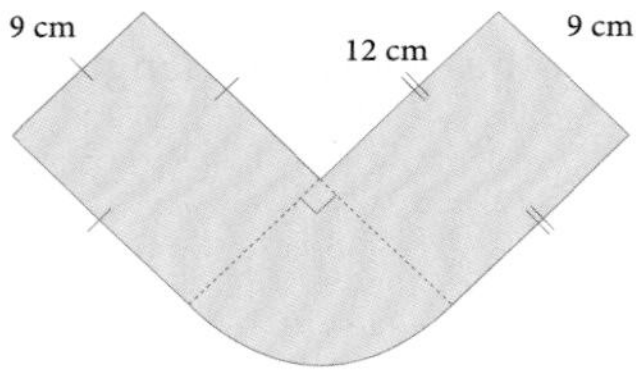

26.

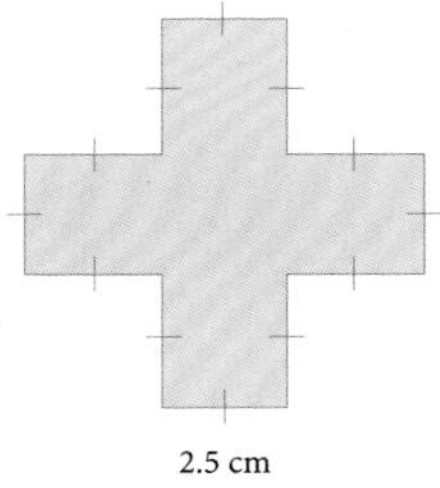

27.

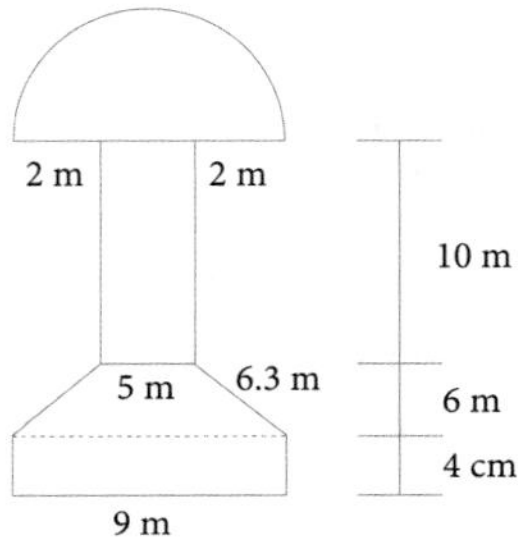

28.

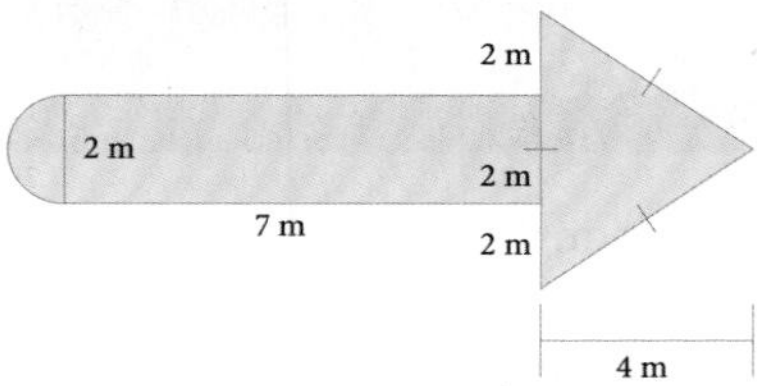

In Problems 29 to 32, determine the surface area and volume of the following 3-dimensional objects.

29. A cylindrical pop can with a radius of 32 mm and a height of 12 cm.

30. A cylindrical cardboard paper towel roll with a diameter of 38 mm and a length of 28 cm.

31. A cement monument in the shape of a square pyramid, with a base length of 4.2 m, a slant height of 3.5 m and a height of 2.8 m.

32. A tetrahedral (equilateral triangular prism) die for a board game, with side lengths of 22 mm each, and a height of 18 mm.

For the composite figures in Problems 33 and 34, determine the surface area and volume.

33.

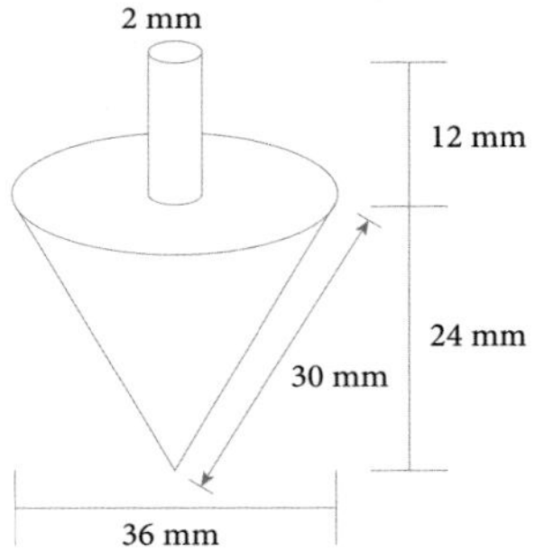

34.

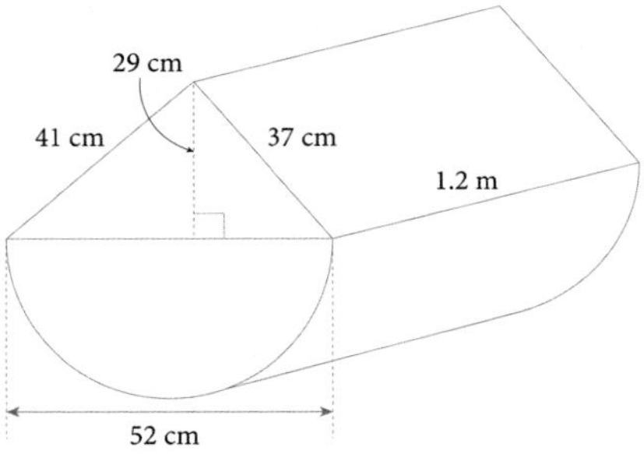

10 | Self-Test Exercises

Answers to all problems are available at the end of the textbook.

1. For the following angles:

   a. $\theta = 34°$ c. $\theta = 67°$

   b. $\theta = 116°$ d. $\theta = 90°$

   (i) Classify the angle as acute, right, or obtuse.

   (ii) Calculate the supplement of the angle.

   (iii) Calculate the complement of the angle (if applicable).

2. Determine the unknown angles for a, b, and c in the following figures:

   a.

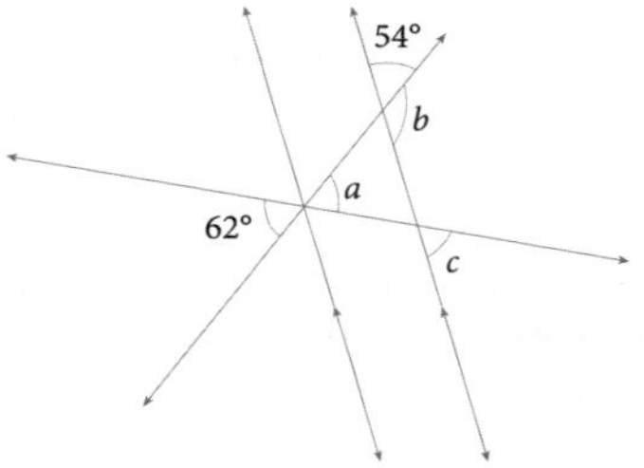

   b.

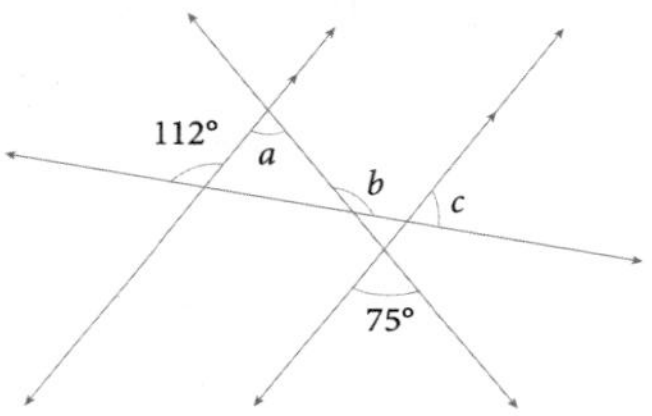

3. Classify the following triangles by angle measure and by side length:

   a.

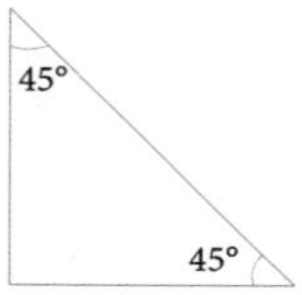

   b.

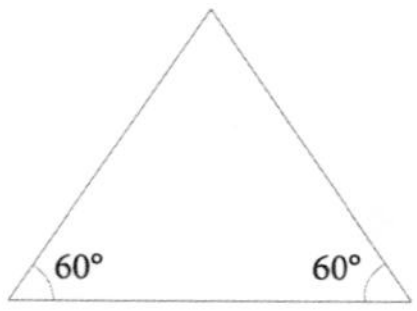

   c.

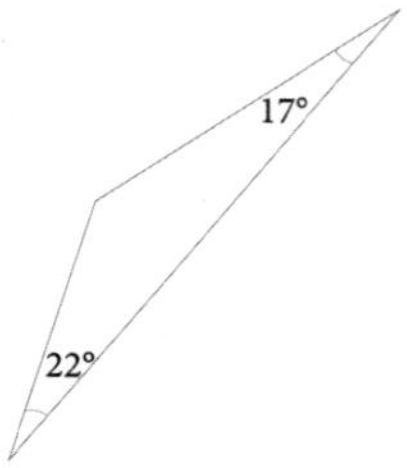

4. Classify the following quadrilaterals:

   a.

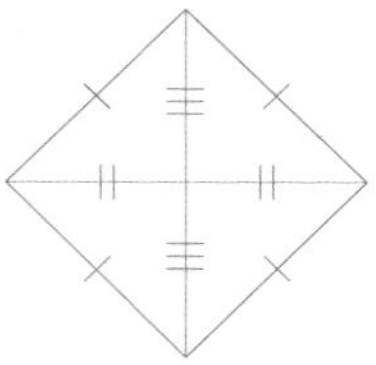

   b.

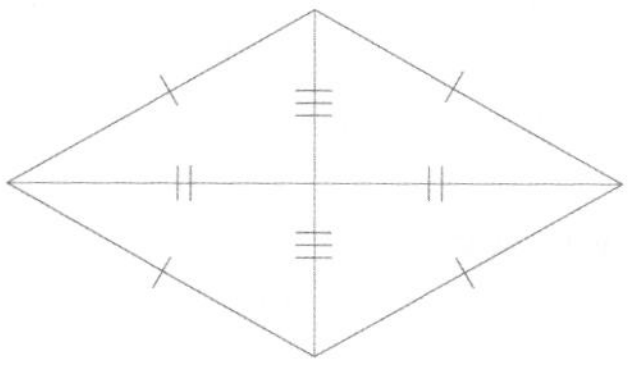

   c.

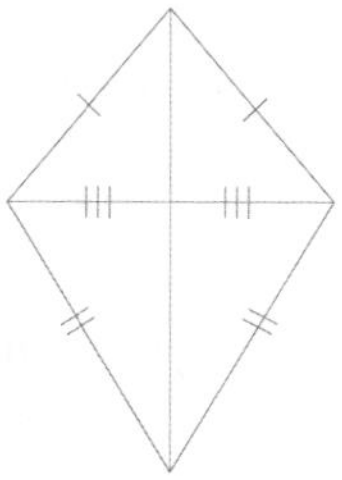

5. Calculate the area of the following triangles:

   a.

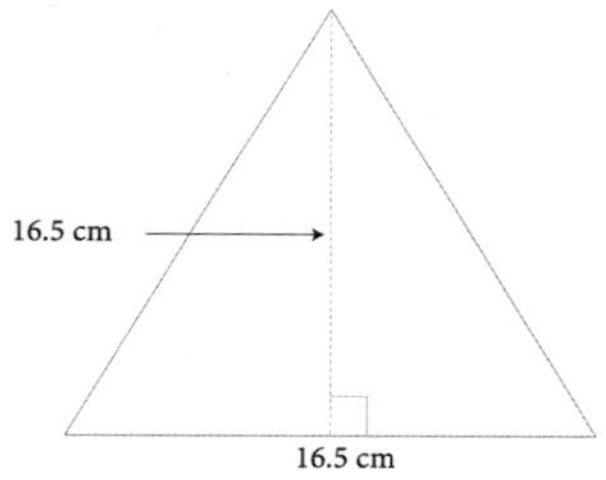

   b.

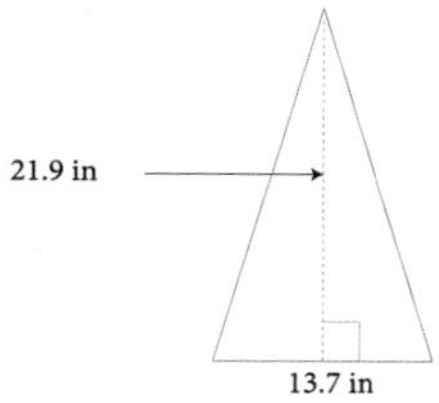

6. Find the area of the following figures:

   a. A rhombus with a side length of 8.5 cm and a perpendicular height of 7.2 cm.

   b. A parallelogram with a base of 1.75 m, a perpendicular height of 84 cm, and a slant height of 1.12 m.

7. Determine the circumference (or perimeter) and area of the following figures:

   a. A circle with a diameter of 2.5 m.

   b. A sector of a circle with a radius of 36 cm and an inscribed angle of 65°.

8. In order to calculate the speed to display on a vehicle's speedometer, the on-board computer must be programmed with the size of the car tire installed. Following this, it can compute the speed (in km/h) based on the number of revolutions per minute (rpm) at which the wheel turns. If the factory-installed tires on a new car have a diameter of 63 cm and the wheels are turning at a rate of 96 rpm, determine the speed displayed on the car's speedometer, in km/h.

9. Determine the area of the shaded regions in the following composite figures:

a.

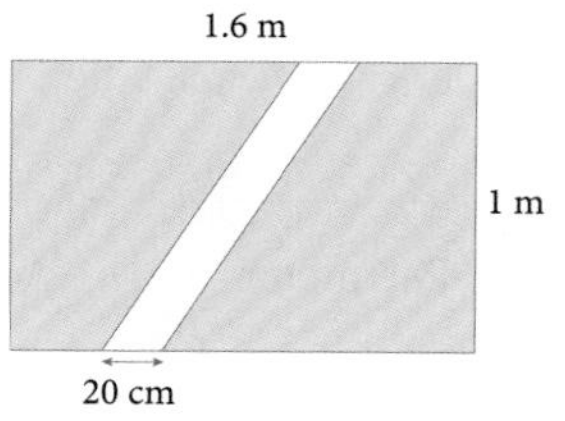

b.

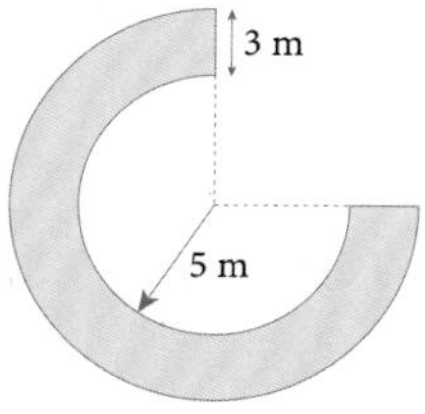

10. Calculate the volume of the following common household objects:

 a. A cylindrical pipe with a radius of 18 mm and a length of 175 mm.

 b. A cone-shaped paper cup with a diameter of 6.8 cm at the opening and a height of 9.2 cm.

 c. A spherical soccer ball with a circumference of 69 cm.

11. A cylinder with a height of 15 cm has a volume of 3,000 cm^3.

 a. Find its base radius, rounded to 2 decimal places.

 b. Find its surface area, rounded to the nearest cm^2.

12. A sphere has a surface area of 450 cm^2.

 a. Find its radius, rounded to 2 decimal places.

 b. Find its volume, rounded to the nearest cm^3.

13. A cylinder of a given volume has an optimal (minimal) surface area when its height is exactly the same as its diameter. Calculate the minimum possible surface area of a cylinder with a volume of 170 cm^3.

14. Calculate the surface area and volume of a swimming pool in the shape of a hexagonal prism, with a height of 1.5 m and six equal side lengths of 1.8 m each. *(Hint: to find the area of the hexagonal base, split it into two equal trapezoids.)*

15. A large coffee cup has a circular opening at the top and a circular base, tapering from top to bottom, with the opening at the top having a diameter of 9 cm, and the base having a diameter of 6 cm. If the cup is 14 cm tall, determine the volume of coffee the cup can hold. If the cup did not taper (i.e., the base also had a diameter of 9 cm), what would be the height of the cup that would accommodate the same volume of coffee? Why do you think coffee shops use cups that taper from top to bottom?

16. Calculate the volume of the following objects:

 a.

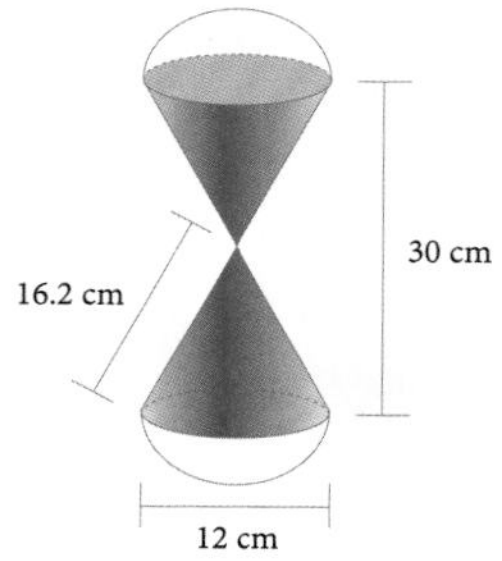

 b.

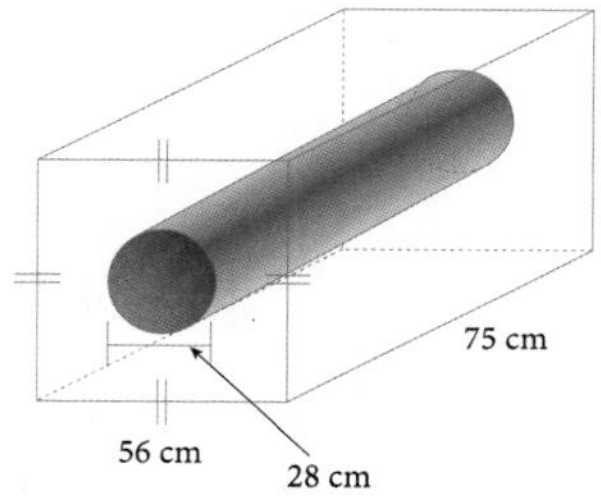

10 | Summary of Notation and Formulas

FORMULAS		COMMON PLANE FIGURES	NOTATION
Square:	$P = 4s$ $A = s^2$	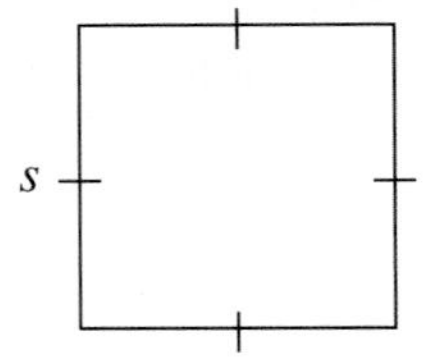	P = Perimeter A = Area s = length of each side
Rectangle:	$P = 2l + 2w = 2(l + w)$ $A = l \times w$	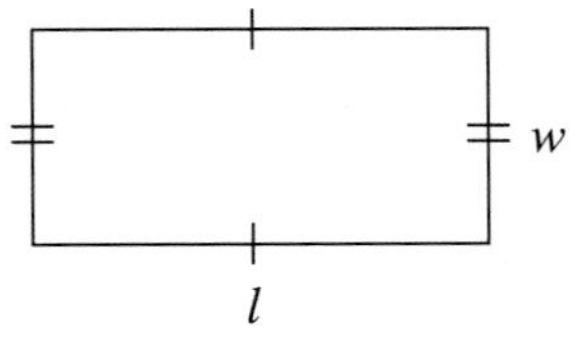	P = Perimeter A = Area l = length of the longer side w = width
Rhombus:	$P = 4b$ $A = b \times h$	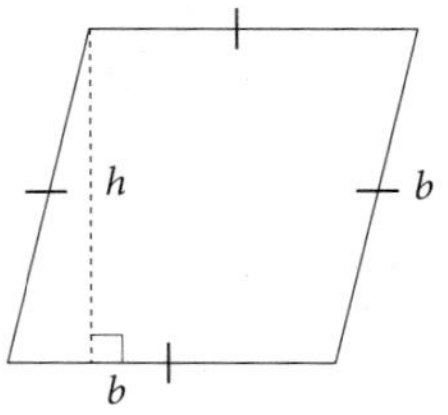	P = Perimeter A = Area b = length of each side h = perpendicular height
Parallelogram:	$P = 2a + 2b = 2\,(a + b)$ $A = b \times h$	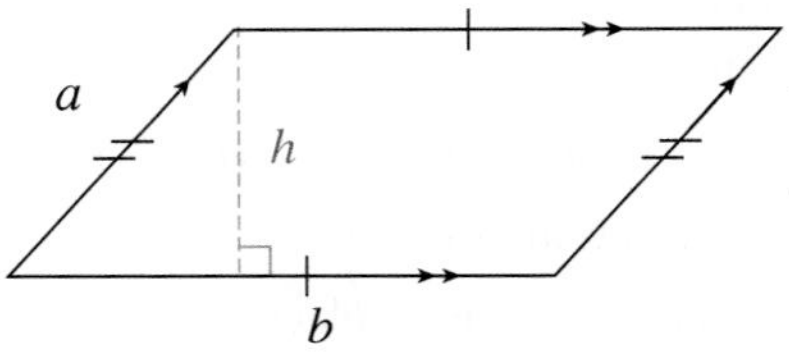	P = Perimeter A = Area a = length of the slant b = length of the base h = perpendicular height
Trapezoid:	$P = a + b + c + d$ $A = \frac{1}{2}(a + b) \times h$	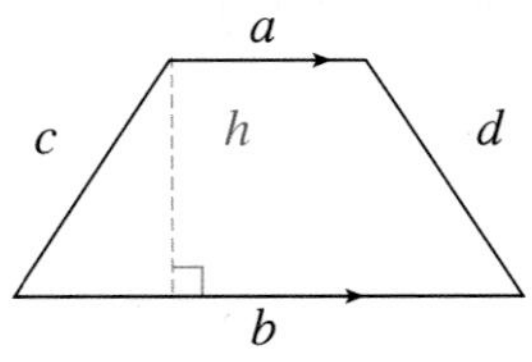	P = Perimeter A = Area a = length of the smaller side b = length of the larger, parallel side c, d = other sides h = perpendicular height

Triangle:

$P = a + b + c$

$A = \frac{1}{2}(b \times h)$

Heron's Formula:

$A = \sqrt{p(p-a)(p-b)(p-c)}$

Where, $p = \frac{a+b+c}{2}$

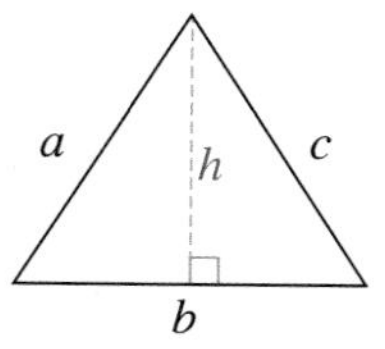

P = Perimeter

A = Area

a, b, c = side lengths

h = height

p = half of the Perimeter

Circle:

$P = C$

$C = \pi d$ or $2\pi r$

$A = \pi r^2$

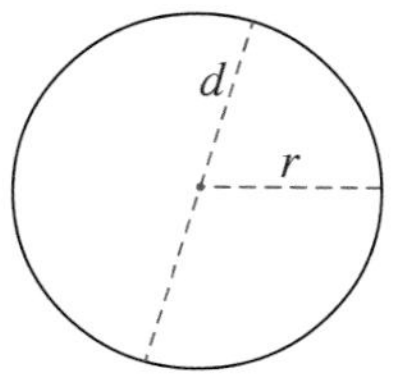

P = Perimeter

C = Circumference

A = Area

d = diameter

r = radius

Sector:

$L = \pi d \times \frac{\theta}{360°}$

$P_S = 2r + L$

$A_S = \pi r^2 \times \frac{\theta}{360°}$

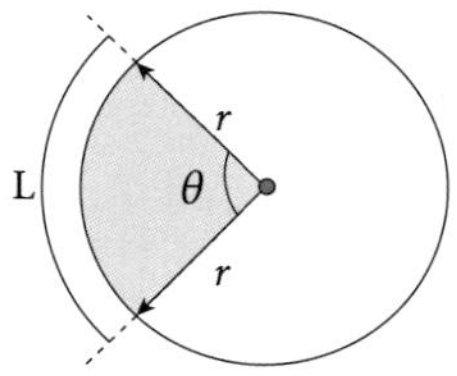

L = Arc length

P_S = Perimeter of sector

A_S = Area of sector

θ = angle subtended by the arc

d = diameter = $2r$

r = radius

FORMULAS	COMMON SOLID OBJECTS	NOTATION

Cube:

$SA = 6s^2$

$V = s^3$

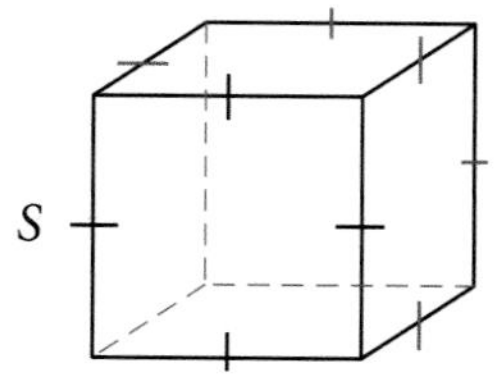

SA = Surface Area

V = Volume

s = side length

Rectangular Prism:

$SA = 2(l \times w) + 2(l \times h) + 2(w \times h)$

$= 2[(l \times w) + (l \times h) + (w \times h)]$

$V = l \times w \times h$

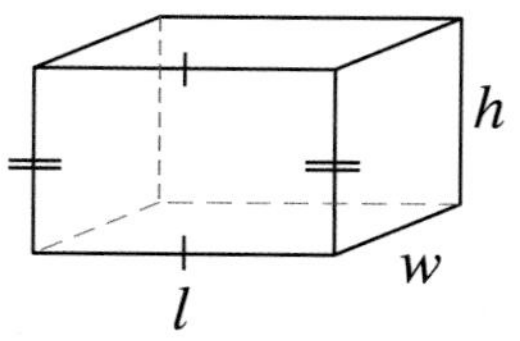

SA = Surface Area

V = Volume

l = length

w = width

h = height

Triangular Prism:

$SA = 2(B) + 3$ rectangles

$V = B \times h$

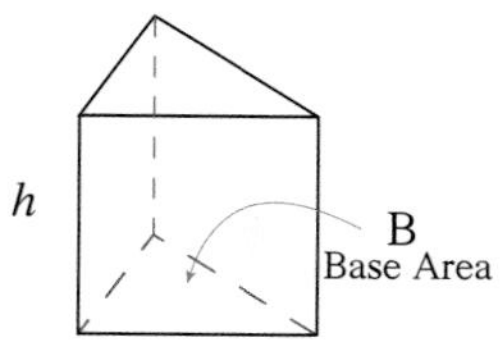

SA = Surface Area

V = Volume

B = Base Area

h = height

Square Pyramid:

$$SA = 4\left(\frac{l \times s}{2}\right) + l^2$$

$$SA = 2l \times s + l^2$$

$$V = \frac{1}{3}(l^2 \times h)$$

$$V = \frac{l^2 \times h}{3}$$

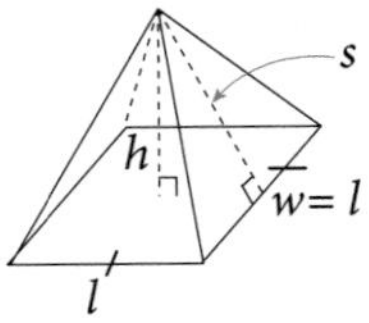

SA = Surface Area

V = Volume

s = slant height

h = height

l = length

w = width

Rectangular Pyramid:

$$SA = 2\left(\frac{l \times s_1}{2} + \frac{w \times s_2}{2}\right) + l \times w$$

$$SA = (l \times s_1 + w \times s_2) + l \times w$$

$$V = \frac{1}{3}(l \times w)h$$

$$V = \frac{l \times w \times h}{3}$$

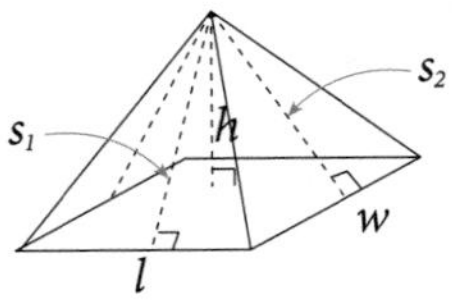

SA = Surface Area

V = Volume

B = Base Area

h = height

l = length

w = width

s_1 = slant height on the length side

s_2 = slant height on the width side

Triangular Pyramid:

SA = Area of all 3 lateral sides + Base Area (B)

$$V = \frac{1}{3}B \times h$$

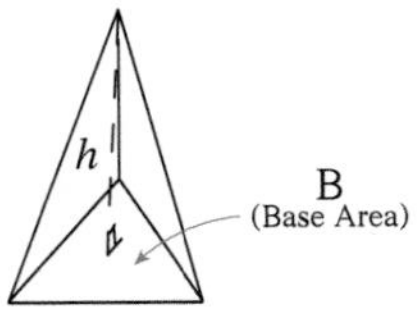

SA = Surface Area

V = Volume

B = Base Area

h = height

Cylinder:

$$SA = 2\pi r^2 + 2\pi rh \text{ (closed)}$$
$$= \pi r^2 + 2\pi rh \text{ (semi-closed)}$$
$$= 2\pi rh \text{ (open)}$$

$$V = \pi r^2 h$$

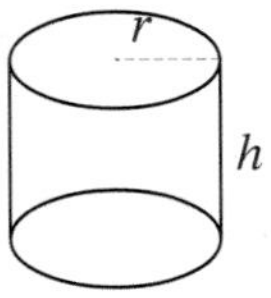

SA = Surface Area

V = Volume

r = radius

h = height

Cone:

$$SA = \pi r^2 + \pi rs \text{ (closed)}$$
$$= \pi rs \text{ (open)}$$

$$V = \frac{1}{3}\pi r^2 h$$

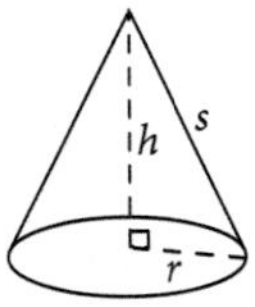

SA = Surface Area

V = Volume

r = radius

s = slant height

h = height

Sphere:

$$SA = 4\pi r^2$$

$$V = \frac{4}{3}\pi r^3$$

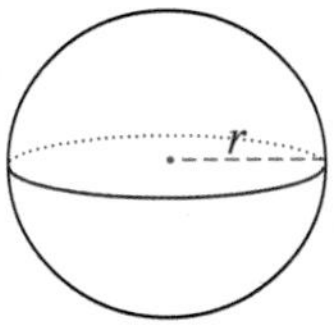

SA = Surface Area

V = Volume

r = radius

11 BASIC TRIGONOMETRY

The triangle is one of the most basic shapes in geometry because it is the simplest polygon. All triangles have three sides and three angles, but they come in many different shapes and sizes. In Chapter 10, you learned that triangles can be classified as acute, obtuse or right based on their angles. In this chapter, you will learn the characteristics of each of these types of triangles, and how the properties of the sides and angles can be used to solve for any missing part of a triangle, or to classify pairs of triangles. Since triangles are such a common and basic shape, understanding these characteristics will allow for real-world application problems, such as finding immeasurable distances, calculating the slope of a ramp or a road, or determining the magnitude and direction of a force, etc.

LEARNING OBJECTIVES

- Apply the properties of similar and congruent triangles in solving problems involving triangles.
- Use the Pythagorean Theorem to determine the length of the unknown side of a right triangle.
- Determine the basic trigonometric ratios of angles of right triangles.
- Evaluate the exact trigonometric ratios of special angles.
- Solve right triangles using the Pythagorean Theorem and trigonometric ratios.
- Solve triangles using the Sine Law and the Cosine Law.

CHAPTER OUTLINE

11.1 | Similar and Congruent Triangles

Introduction

Geometric shapes, also known as figures, are an important part of the study of geometry. Recognizing and using congruent and similar shapes make calculations and design work easier. For example, in most design work, rather than using different shapes, a few shapes are copied and used in different positions and/or produced in different sizes to complete the design.

When a shape is obtained from another figure by means of enlargement or reduction, its size will be different from the original one, but it remains the same shape as the original one.

Similar figures have the same shape and retain the same angle at corresponding vertices (congruent). They may or may not have the same size, but the lengths of the corresponding sides will be in proportion between the figures.

Congruent figures have sides with lengths that are in proportion and equal angle at corresponding vertices.

It is important to note that two figures can be similar, but not congruent; however, two figures cannot be congruent and not similar.

Similar Triangles

Similar figures must have the same shape, but their sizes may be different.

Two equal-sided polygons are said to be similar if all the corresponding angles are equal in measure and the corresponding sides are proportional in length.

The symbol for similar is "~".

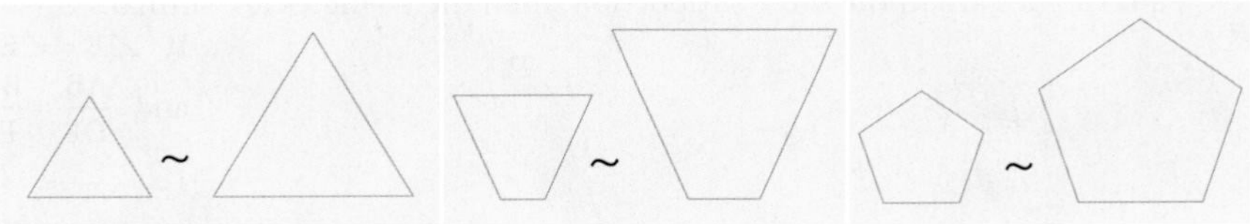

Each pair of polygons shown are similar.

When writing the similarity relationship, the order in which the letters are written to represent the similar figures is very important.

In similar figures, the measures of corresponding angles are equal and the ratio of the lengths of corresponding sides are equal. The length of ratio between the corresponding sides of similar figures are expressed as a fraction and is called the "scale" or scale factor.

For example, ΔABC is similar to ΔDEF,

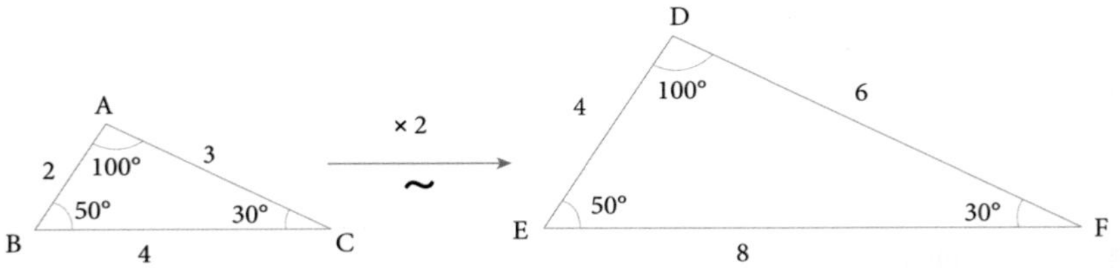

(i) $\Delta ABC \sim \Delta DEF$

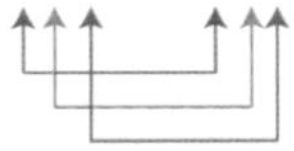

$\angle A = \angle D$, $\angle B = \angle E$, and $\angle C = \angle F$

(Corresponding angle measures of two triangles are equal.)

(ii)

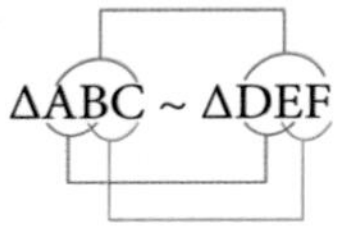

$$\frac{AB}{DE} = \frac{BC}{EF} = \frac{AC}{DF} = \frac{2}{1}$$

(Corresponding side lengths of two triangles are proportional.)

Any triangle is defined by six measures: three sides and three angles. However, it is not necessary to know all of the six measures to demonstrate that the two triangles are similar. If any one of the following four conditions are met, then the two triangles are similar:

1. AAA (angle, angle, angle)

   If all three pairs of corresponding angle measures of two triangles are equal, then the triangles are similar.

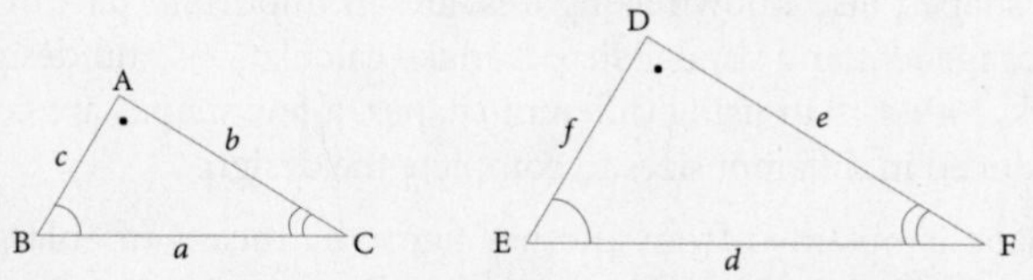

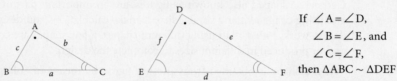

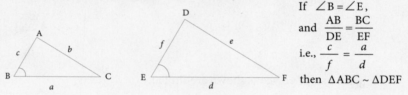

If $\angle A = \angle D$, $\angle B = \angle E$, and $\angle C = \angle F$, then $\Delta ABC \sim \Delta DEF$

   This is the same as AA (angle, angle) because if any two angles of the two triangles are equal, then the third angle must be equal.

2. SSS (side, side, side)

   If all three pairs of corresponding side lengths of two triangles are in the same proportion, then the triangles are similar.

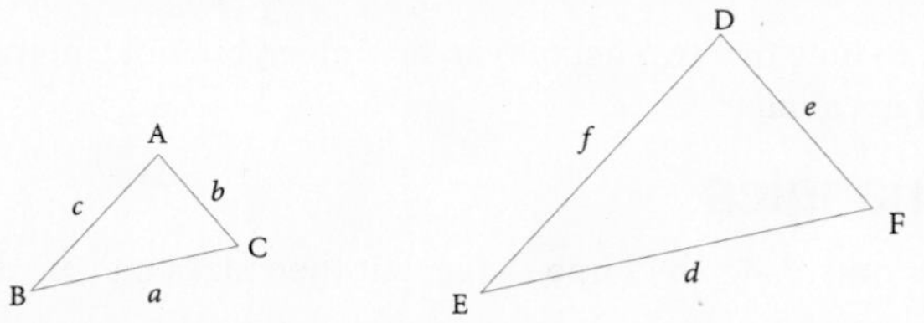

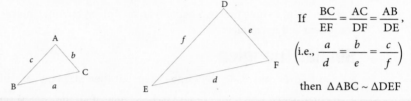

If $\frac{BC}{EF} = \frac{AC}{DF} = \frac{AB}{DE}$, $\left(\text{i.e., } \frac{a}{d} = \frac{b}{e} = \frac{c}{f}\right)$

then $\Delta ABC \sim \Delta DEF$

3. SAS (side, angle, side)

   If two triangles have a pair of equal angle measures and the corresponding sides containing the equal angles are in the same proportion, then the triangles are similar.

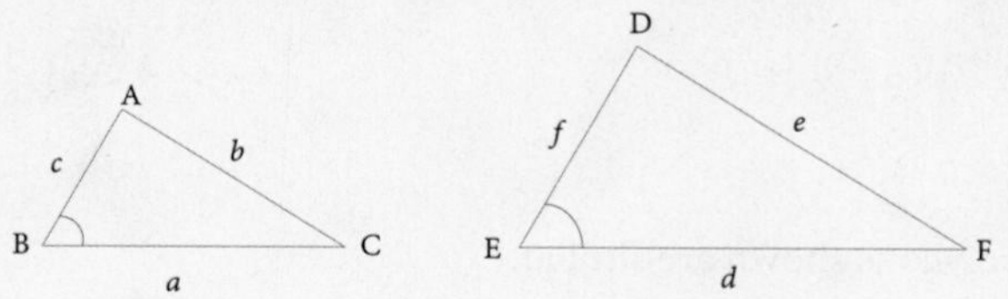

If $\angle B = \angle E$,

and $\frac{AB}{DE} = \frac{BC}{EF}$

i.e., $\frac{c}{f} = \frac{a}{d}$

then $\Delta ABC \sim \Delta DEF$

4. RHS (Right angle, hypotenuse, side)

   In right triangles, if the hypotenuses and lengths of one pair of corresponding sides are proportional, then the triangles are similar.

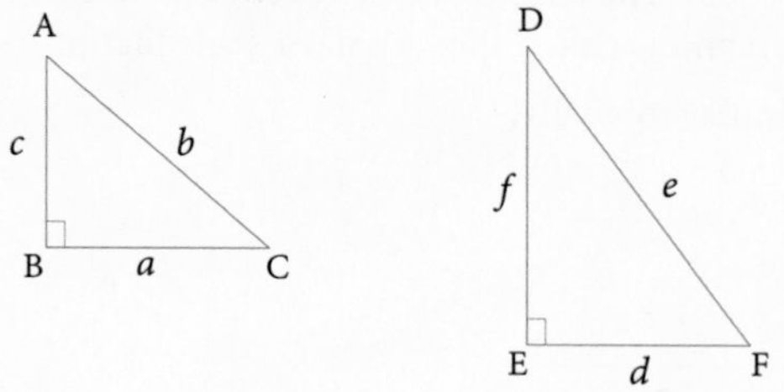

If $\angle B = \angle E = 90°$, and

and $\frac{AC}{DF} = \frac{BC}{EF}$, i.e., $\frac{b}{e} = \frac{a}{d}$

then $\Delta ABC \sim \Delta DEF$

Example 11.1-a **Rules for Similar Triangles**

Based on the information given in the following pairs of triangles, state the property that will prove that they are similar.

(i) (ii) (iii)

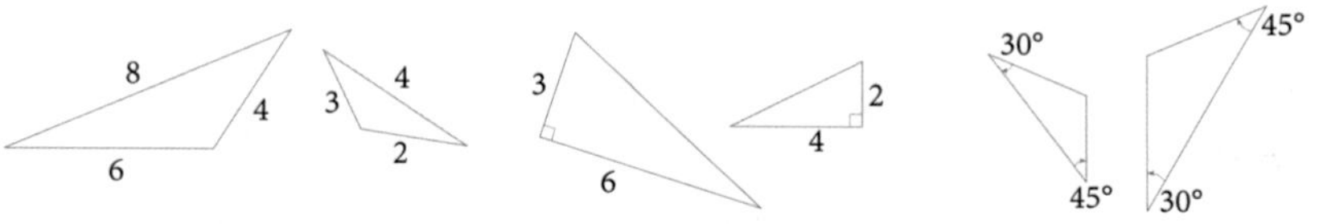

Solution (i) SSS Property (ii) SAS Property (iii) AAA Property

Example 11.1-b Using Similar Triangles to Find the Unknown Length

(i) If $\Delta PQR \sim \Delta XYZ$, find XY and XZ

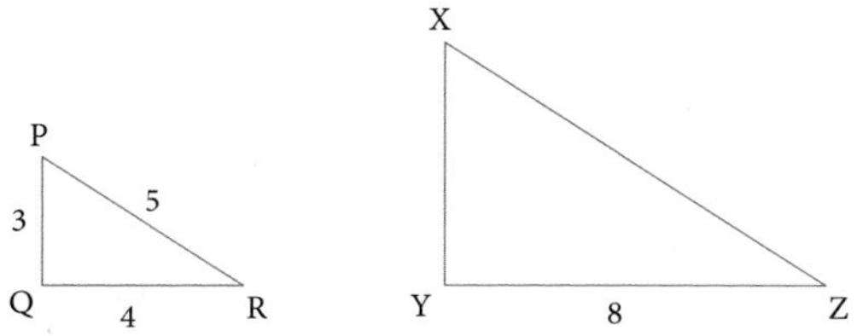

(ii) If $\Delta ABC \sim \Delta DEF$, find AB and DF

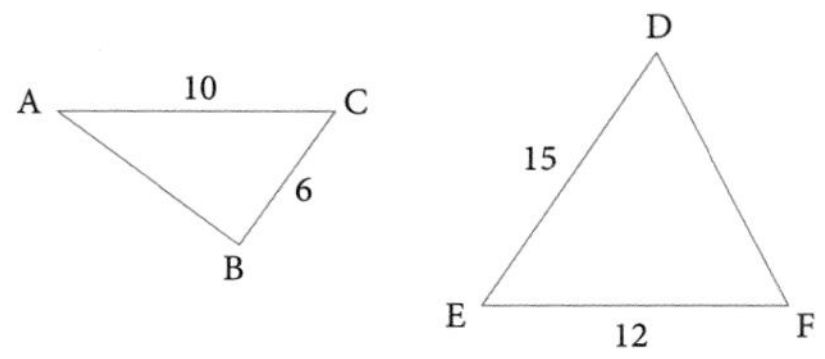

Solution

$\Delta PQR \sim \Delta XYZ$

Therefore, $\dfrac{PQ}{XY} = \dfrac{QR}{YZ} = \dfrac{PR}{XZ}$

$$\frac{3}{XY} = \frac{4}{8} = \frac{5}{XZ}$$

$$\frac{3}{XY} = \frac{4}{8}$$

$4(XY) = 3(8)$

$XY = \dfrac{3(8)}{4}$

$= 6$

$$\frac{4}{8} = \frac{5}{XZ}$$

$4(XZ) = 5(8)$

$XZ = \dfrac{5(8)}{4}$

$= 10$

Therefore, XY = 6 and XZ = 10.

(iii) $\Delta ABC \sim \Delta DEF$

Therefore, $\dfrac{AB}{DE} = \dfrac{BC}{EF} = \dfrac{AC}{DF}$

$$\frac{AB}{15} = \frac{6}{12} = \frac{10}{DF}$$

$$\frac{AB}{15} = \frac{6}{12}$$

$12(AB) = 6(15)$

$AB = \dfrac{6(15)}{12}$

$= 7.5$

$$\frac{6}{12} = \frac{10}{DF}$$

$6(DF) = 10(12)$

$DF = \dfrac{10(12)}{6}$

$= 20$

Therefore, AB = 7.5 and DF = 20.

Example 11.1-c Identifying Similar Triangles

Determine whether the following pairs of triangles are similar:

(i)

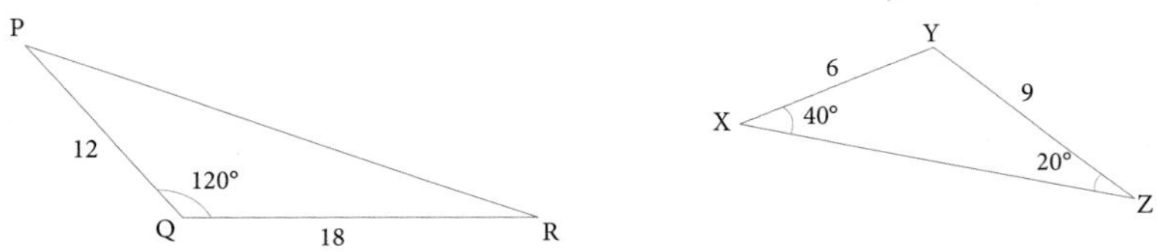

(ii)

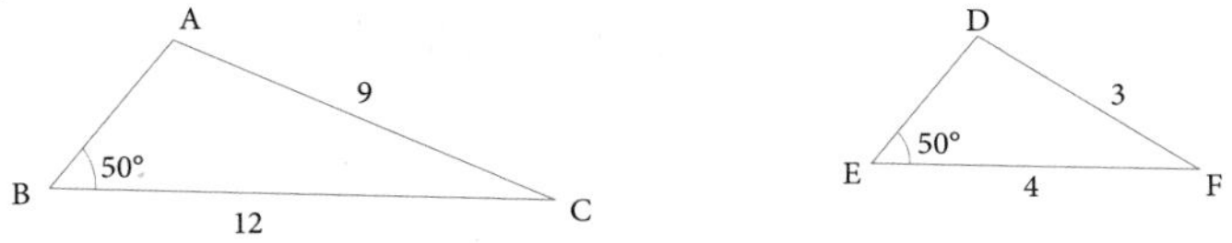

Solution

(i) $\angle Q = 120°$, $\angle Y = 180 - (40 + 20) = 120°$

$\angle Q = \angle Y$ (Equal angles)

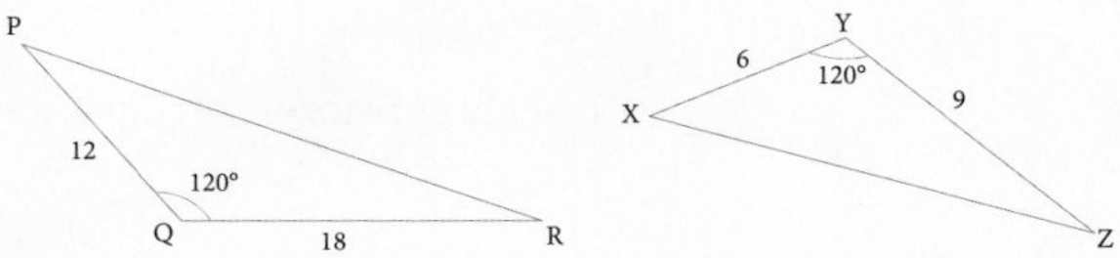

$\dfrac{PQ}{XY} = \dfrac{12}{6} = 2,$

$\dfrac{QR}{YZ} = \dfrac{18}{9} = 2$

i.e. $\dfrac{PQ}{YZ} = \dfrac{QR}{XY}$ (Corresponding sides containing the equal angles are in the same proportion)

$\Delta PQR \sim \Delta XYZ$ (SAS Property)

Solution
continued

(ii) $\angle B = \angle E$ (Equal angle measures)

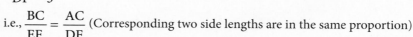

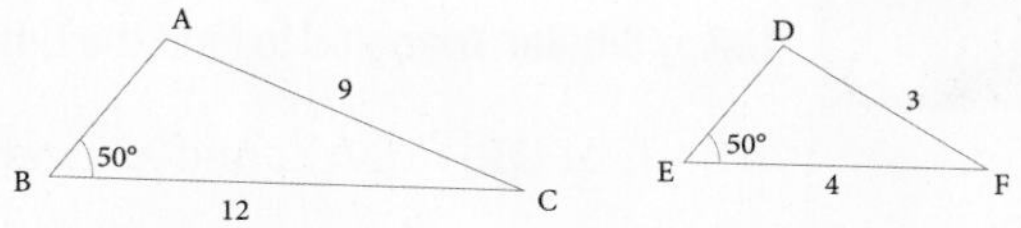

$$\frac{BC}{EF} = \frac{12}{4} = 3$$

$$\frac{AC}{DF} = \frac{9}{3} = 3$$

i.e., $\frac{BC}{EF} = \frac{AC}{DF}$ (Corresponding two side lengths are in the same proportion)

However, the sides that are proportional do not contain the equal angles. Therefore, we cannot conclude that ΔABC is similar to ΔDEF.

Note: SSA (side, side, angle) is not sufficient to conclude that two triangles are similar.

Congruent Triangles

Congruent figures must have the same shape and size.

Two equal-sided polygons are said to be **congruent** if all the corresponding angles are equal in measure and the corresponding sides are equal in length (i.e., the polygons are similar and they have equal side lengths).

The symbol for 'congruent' is '$\cong$'.

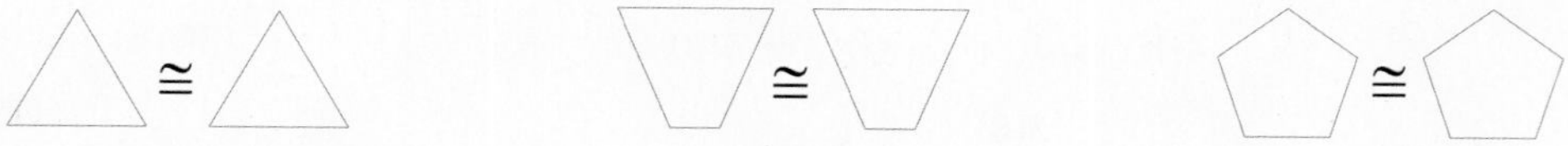

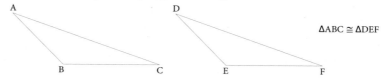

Each of the above pairs of polygons is congruent.

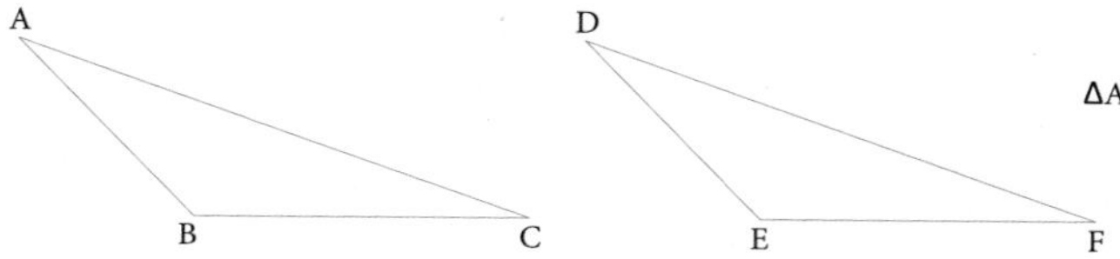

$\Delta ABC \cong \Delta DEF$

Once again, it is important to note that when the congruent relationship is written, the order of letters representing the figures must be consistent to illustrate the equal corresponding angle measures and side lengths. For example:

$\Delta ABC \cong \Delta DEF$

(i) $\angle A = \angle D$

(ii) $\angle B = \angle E$

(iii) $\angle C = \angle F$

$ABC \cong DEF$

(i) $AB = DE$

(ii) $BC = EF$

(iii) $AC = DF$

Corresponding angle measures and side lengths are equal (congruent).

If any of the following four conditions are met, then the two triangles are congruent.

The condition of congruence for triangles requires all three sides and all three angle measures to be congruent. However, it is not necessary to know all of the six measurements to demonstrate that the two triangles are congruent.

1. SSS (side, side, side)

   If all three pairs of corresponding side lengths of two triangles are equal, then the triangles are congruent.

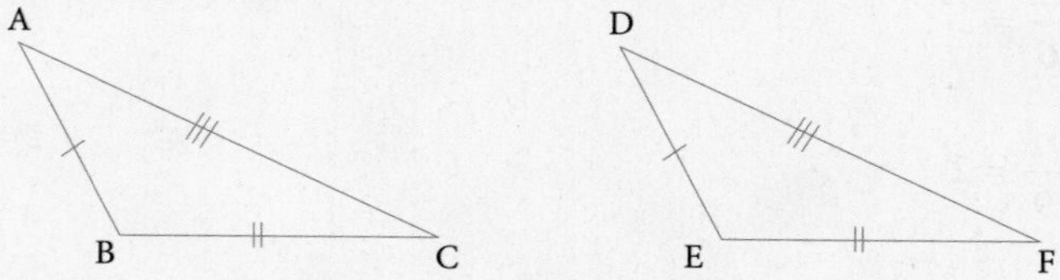

If $AB = DE$,

$BC = EF$, and

$AC = DF$,

then $\Delta ABC \cong \Delta DEF$

2. SAS (side, angle, side)

   If two side lengths and the contained angle measure of one triangle is correspondingly equal to two side lenghts and the contained angle measure of another triangle, then the triangles are congruent.

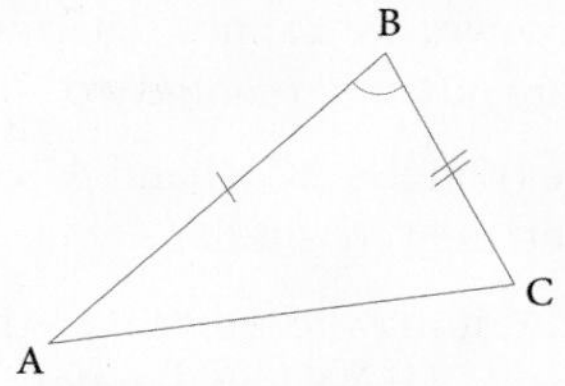

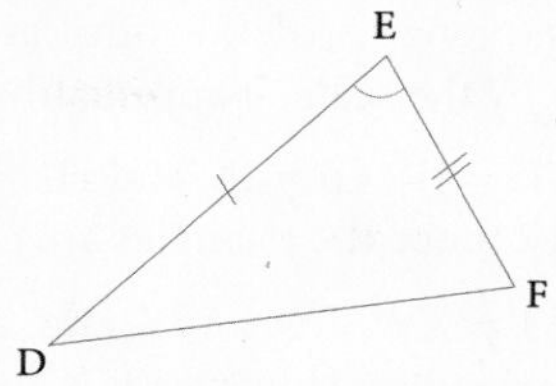

If $AB = DE$,
$BC = EF$, and
$\angle B = \angle E$,
then $\Delta ABC \cong \Delta DEF$

3. ASA (angle, side, angle)

   If two angle measures and the contained side length of one triangle is correspondingly equal to two angle measures and the contained side length of another triangle, then the triangles are congruent.

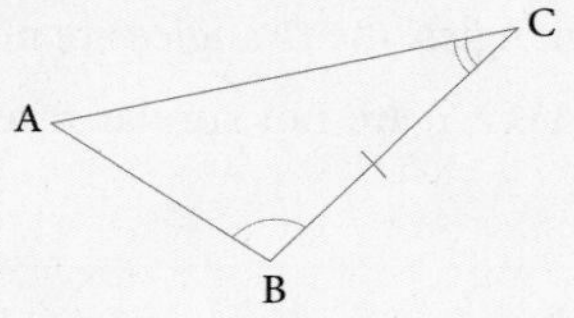

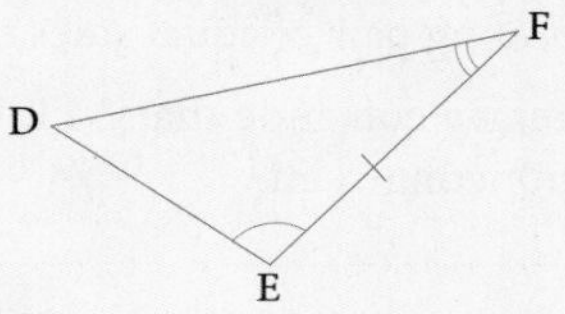

If $\angle B = \angle E$,
$\angle C = \angle F$, and
$BC = EF$,
then $\Delta ABC \cong \Delta DEF$

4. RHS (Right angle, hypotenuse, side)

   In a right triangle, if the hypotenuse and side length of one triangle is correspondingly equal to the hypotenuse and side length of another right triangle, then the triangles are congruent.

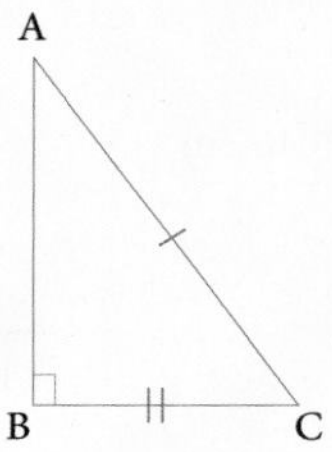

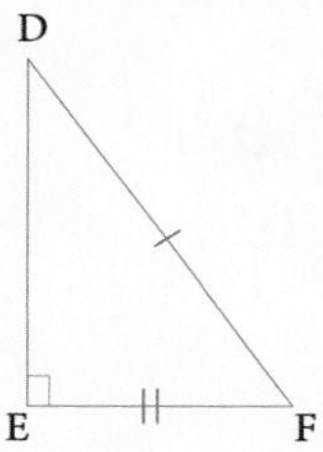

ΔABC and DEF are right triangle with $\angle B = \angle E = 90°$,
Therefore, if $AC = DF$, and
$BC = EF$,
then $\Delta ABC \cong \Delta DEF$

Example 11.1-d **Determining Similarity/Congruency of Triangles**

In the following examples, determine whether the pairs of triangles are similar, congruent, or neither:

(i)

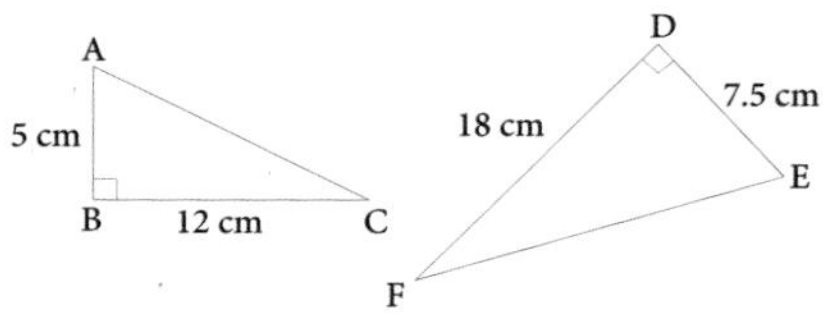

(ii)

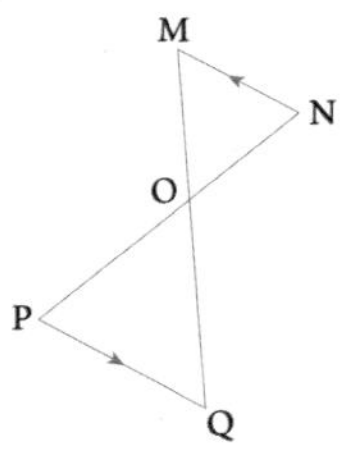

(iii)

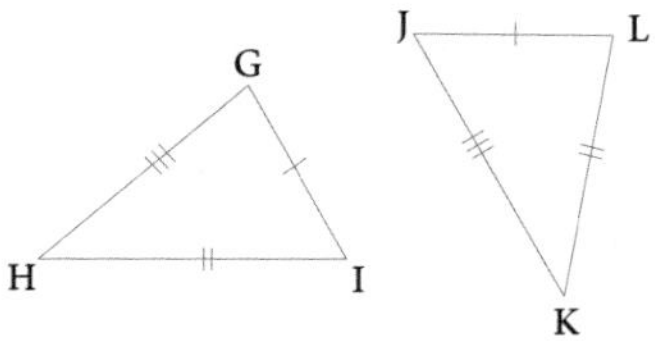

(iv)

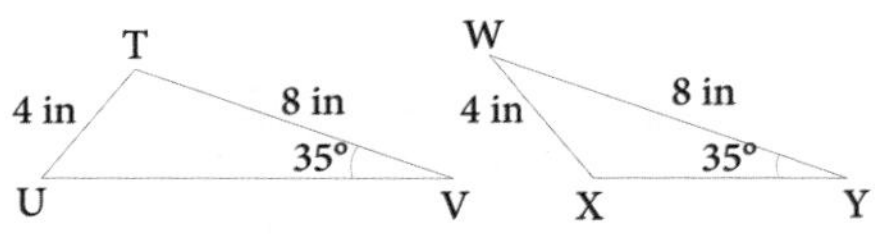

Solution

(i) Since $\frac{AB}{ED} = \frac{BC}{DF}$ and the angle measures between those two sides ($\angle B$ and $\angle D$) are equal, both right triangles, ΔABC and ΔEDF, are similar by the SAS Property (i.e., $\Delta ABC \sim \Delta EDF$). Since the corresponding lengths of the sides are different, the triangles are not congruent.

Solution *continued*

(ii) Since $\overline{MN}$ and $\overline{PQ}$ are parallel, we know that alternate angles are equal (i.e., $\angle N = \angle P$ and $\angle M = \angle Q$), and therefore, ΔMNO and ΔQPO are similar by the AA Property (i.e., $\Delta MNO \sim \Delta QPO$).

Since the lengths of the sides are not known, we cannot determine congruency. However, judging by the scale, it appears that they are **not** congruent.

(iii) Since GH = JK, GI = JL, and HI = KL, the triangles ΔGHI and ΔJKL are congruent by the SSS Property. Since the triangles are congruent, they are similar.

(iv) Since UT = XW, TV = WY, and $\angle V = \angle Y$, it may be tempting to label ΔTVU and ΔWYX as similar triangles. However, it is obvious that $UV \neq XY$, and therefore, they are not in proportion with the lengths of the other two sides; thus, the triangles are not similar (this is an example to demonstrate that the SSA criterion is not sufficient to demonstrate similarity).

Since the corresponding pair of equal angles ($\angle V = \angle Y = 35°$) is not contained by the corresponding pair of equal sides of the triangles, the tirangles are not congruent.

Therefore, we conclude that ΔTUV and ΔWXY are not similar triangles. They are neither similar nor congruent.

Example 11.1-e

Calculating Angle and Side Measures of Similar Triangles

Calculate the lengths of the unknown sides and unknown angle measures of the following pairs of similar triangles:

(i)

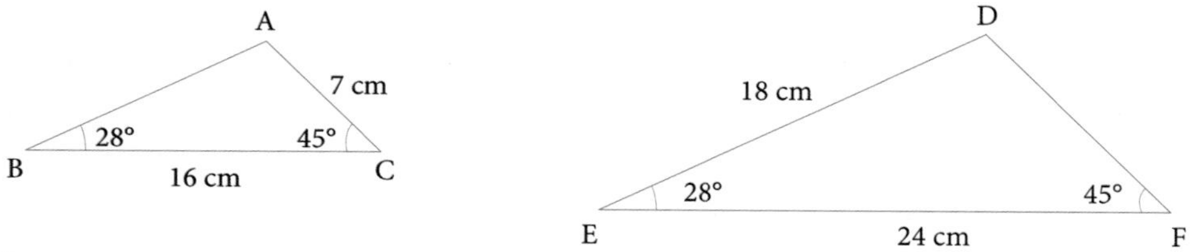

(ii)

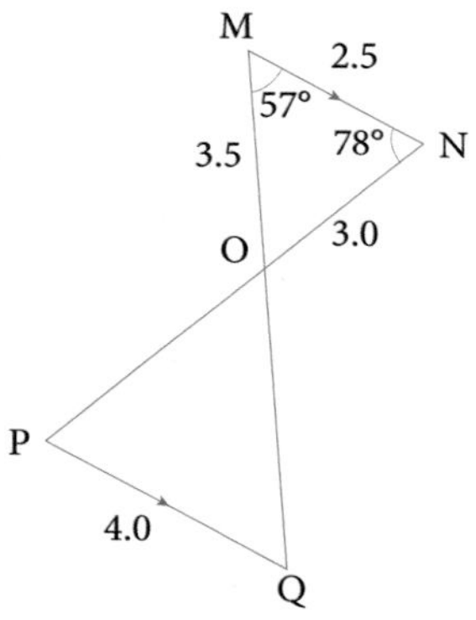

Solution

(i) Since $\Delta ABC \sim \Delta DEF$, the corresponding side lengths of the two triangles are proportional.

$$\frac{AB}{DE} = \frac{BC}{EF} = \frac{AC}{DF}$$

i.e., $\frac{AB}{18} = \frac{16}{24} = \frac{7}{DF}$

$\frac{AB}{18} = \frac{16}{24}$	$\frac{16}{24} = \frac{7}{DF}$
$AB = \frac{16(18)}{24}$	$DF = \frac{7(24)}{16}$
$= 12.0$ cm	$= 10.5$ cm

Solution *continued*

Since ΔABC ~ ΔDEF, the corresponding angles of the two triangles are equal.

$\angle C = \angle F = 45°$, $\angle E = \angle B = 28°$

Therefore, $\angle A = \angle D = 180° - 28° - 45° = 107°$.

(ii) Since $\overline{MN} \,//\, \overline{PQ}$, $\angle N = \angle P$ and $\angle M = \angle Q$, because they are alternate angles. $\angle P = 78°$ and $\angle Q = 57°$. Therefore, ΔMNO ~ ΔQPO by the AA Property.

Hence, the corresponding side lengths of the triangles are proportional:

$$\frac{MN}{QP} = \frac{NO}{PO} = \frac{MO}{QO}.$$

i.e., $\frac{2.5}{4.0} = \frac{3.0}{PO} = \frac{3.5}{QO}$

$$\frac{2.5}{4.0} = \frac{3.0}{PO}$$

$$PO = \frac{4.0(3.0)}{2.5} = 4.8 \text{ in}$$

$$\frac{2.5}{4.0} = \frac{3.5}{QO}$$

$$QO = \frac{4.0(3.5)}{2.5} = 5.6 \text{ in}$$

Since the corresponding two angles of the triangles are known, the third angle can be computed as follows: $\angle MON = \angle QOP = 180° - (78° + 57°) = 45°$. They are opposite angles as well (the angles cannot simply be referred as $\angle O$, as that creates ambiguity).

Solving Application Problems using Similar and Congruent Triangles

Similar and/or congruent triangles can be used to solve a variety of real-life application problems when it is difficult or impossible to calculate certain angles or lengths.

Example 11.1-f

Determining the Height of a Building using Similar Triangles

The new science building at a college is 6 stories tall. Arianna wishes to know the height of the building. She devises a method whereby, she and a friend measure the length of the shadow that the building casts at 3:00 in the afternoon. The length of this shadow is 6.24 m. She then has her friend measure her height - 165 cm - and the length of her shadow - 44 cm. Using this information, how can Arianna determine the height of the science building?

Solution

Since the sun meets all points on the ground in a close vicinity at the same angle at any given time, and it hits both the building and Arianna (standing vertically) at the same angle, the shadows created by the building and Arianna form similar triangles, as shown in the diagram.

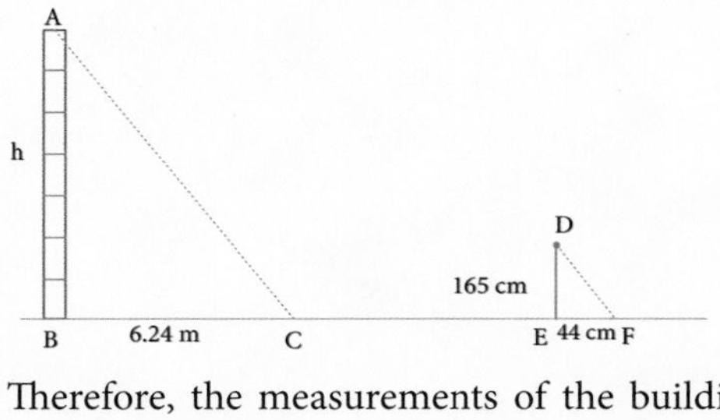

Therefore, the measurements of the building's height and length of its shadow are proportional to Arianna's respective measurements:

$$\frac{h}{6.24 \text{ m}} = \frac{165 \text{ cm}}{44 \text{ cm}}$$

Solving this ratio for h, $h = (6.24 \text{ m})\left(\frac{165 \text{ cm}}{44 \text{ cm}}\right) = 23.4 \text{ m}$.

Therefore, the science building has a height of approximately 23.4 m.

Example 11.1-g **Calculating the Distance across a Lake using Congruent Triangles**

A lake is situated on a property in the country. A couple looking to purchase the property wishes to know how long the lake is. How can they determine this (without getting wet)?

Solution

They can each mark a point on either end of the lake (denoted A and B on the diagram below), each a fixed distance away from the edge of the lake, and measure the distance to a common point on one of the adjacent sides of the lake (denoted C). They can then each continue to walk the same distance again in the same direction to another set of points on their property (denoted D and E respectively), creating congruent triangles (by SAS). Then, they can measure the distance from D to E, which will be the same distance as A to B, since the triangles are congruent. Finally, by subtracting the distance from each of A and B to the edge of the lake, they will have determined the length of the lake.

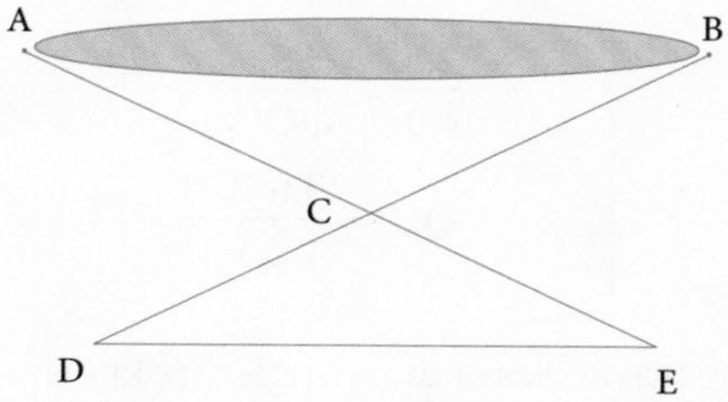

11.1 | Exercises

Answers to odd numbered problems are available at the end of the textbook.

In Problems 1 and 2, for each pair of similar triangles, name the proportional sides, and congruent angles.

1. a. ΔABC~ ΔDEF   b. ΔPQR ~ ΔRST

2. a. ΔUVW ~ ΔXYZ   b. ΔGHI ~ ΔJKL

In Problems 3 and 4, for each pair of congruent triangles, name the equal side, and equal angles.

3. a. ΔABC ≅ ΔXYZ   b. ΔDEF ≅ ΔRST

4. a. ΔUVW ≅ JKL   b. ΔXYZ ≅ ΔJKL

For Problems 5 to 10, identify the pairs of similar triangles and state the rule used to determine similarity.

5. a.
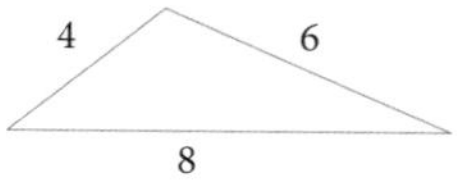

b.
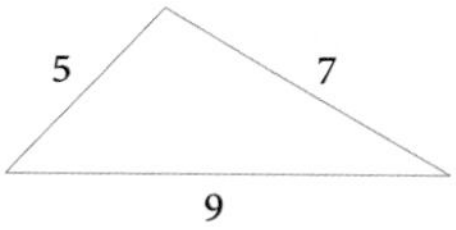

c.
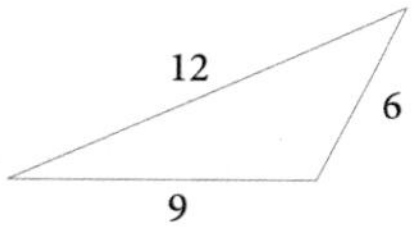

6. a.
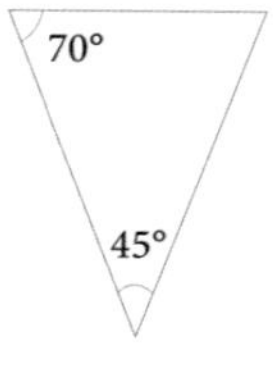

b.
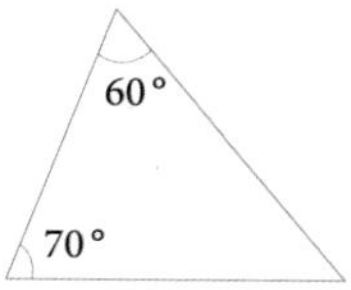

c.
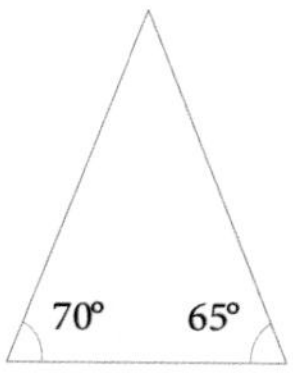

7. a.
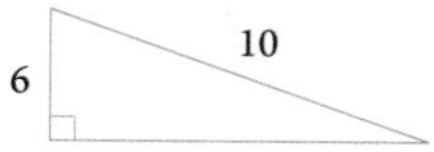

b.
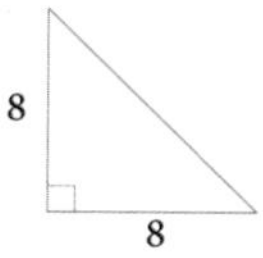

c.

8. a. 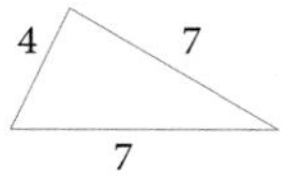

b. 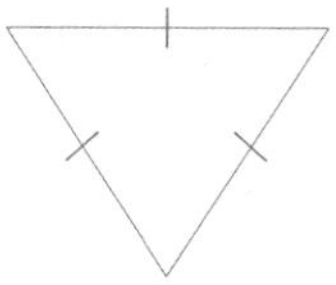

c. 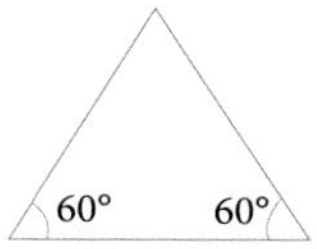

9. a. 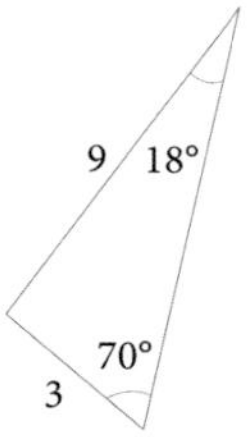

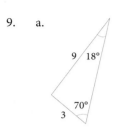

b. 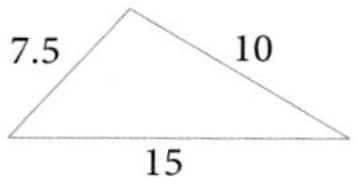

c. 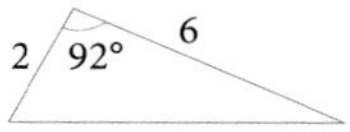

10. a. 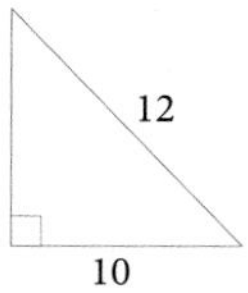

b. 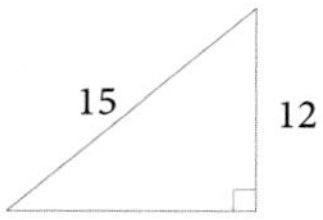

c. 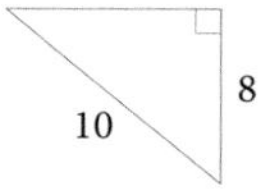

For Problems 11 to 16, identify the pair of congruent triangles and state the rule used to determine congruency.

11. a. 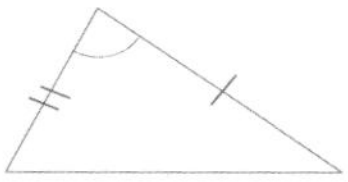

b. 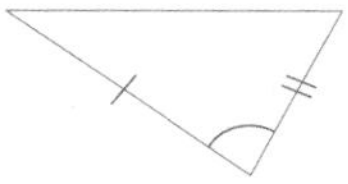

c. 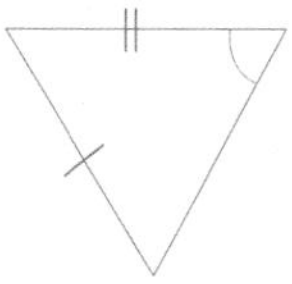

12. a. 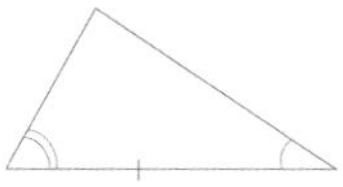

b. 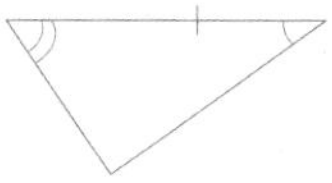

c. 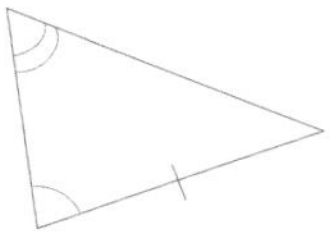

13. a. 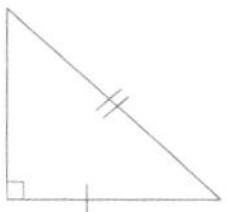

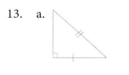

b. 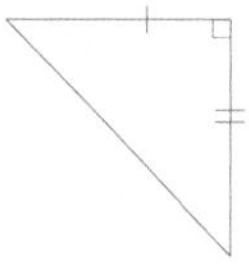

c. 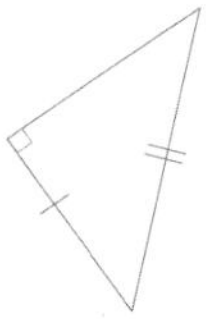

14. a. 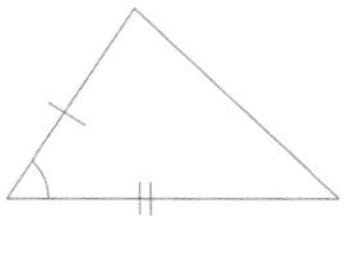

b. 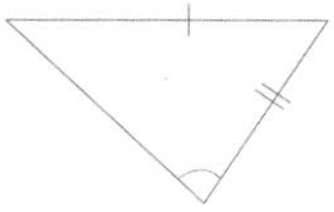

c. 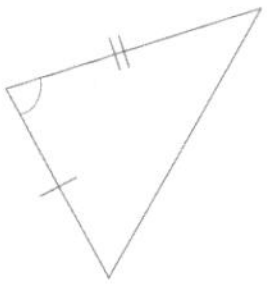

15. a. 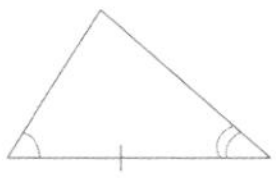

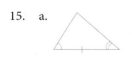

b. 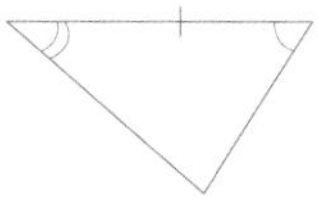

c. 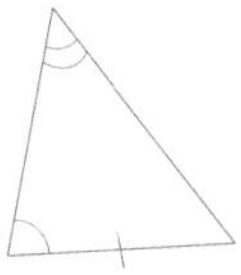

16. a. 

b. 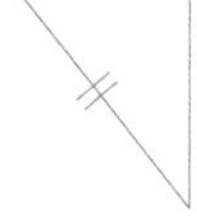

c. 

For Problems 17 to 22, determine whether each pair of triangles is congruent, similar, or neither:

17.

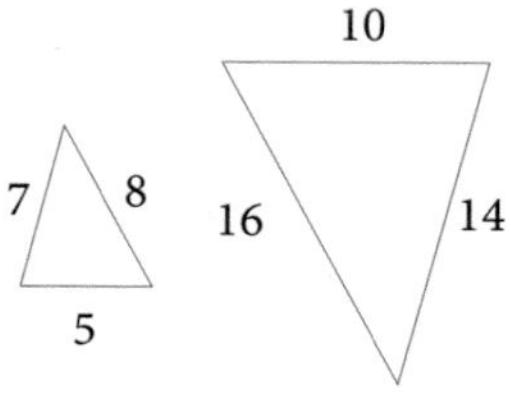

18.

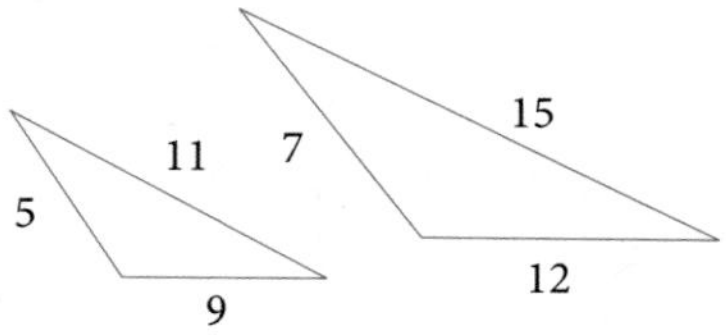

19.

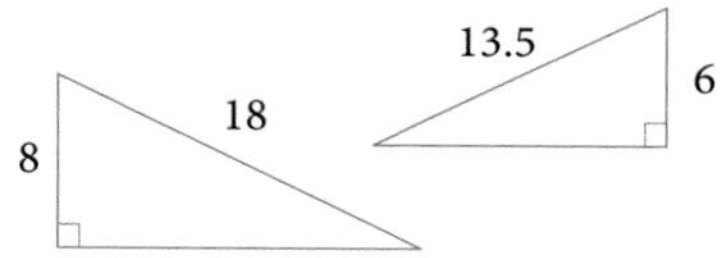

20.

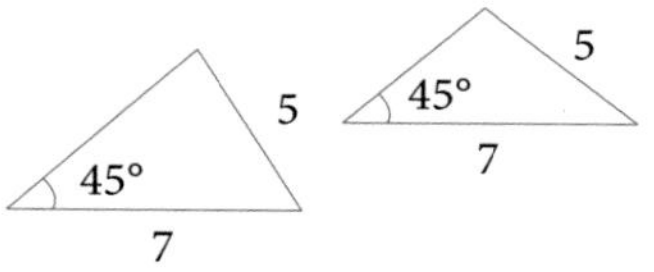

21.

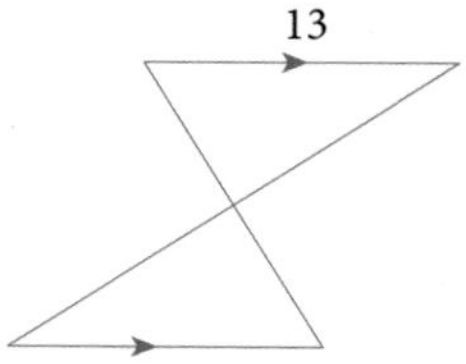

22.

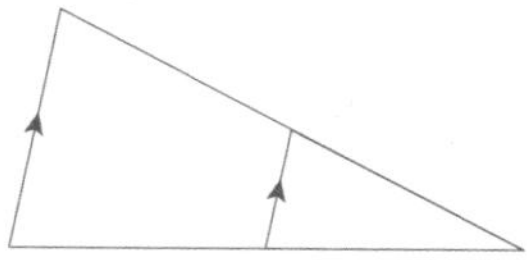

In Problems 23 to 26, triangles and quadrilaterals are divided into two triangular pieces. Determine if the resulting pieces are congruent, similar, or neither.

23.

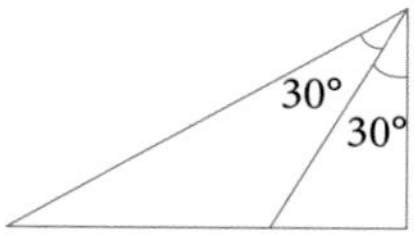

24.

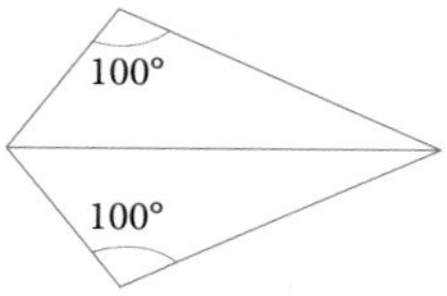

25.

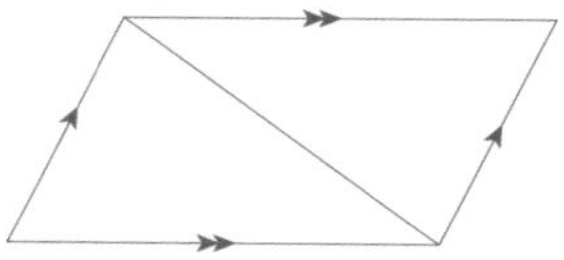

26.

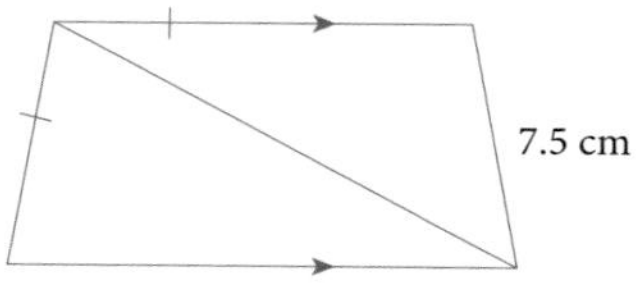

In Problems 27 to 30, solve each pair of similar triangles completely, calculating the unknown side lengths (rounded to the nearest tenth as necessary) and angle measures.

27.

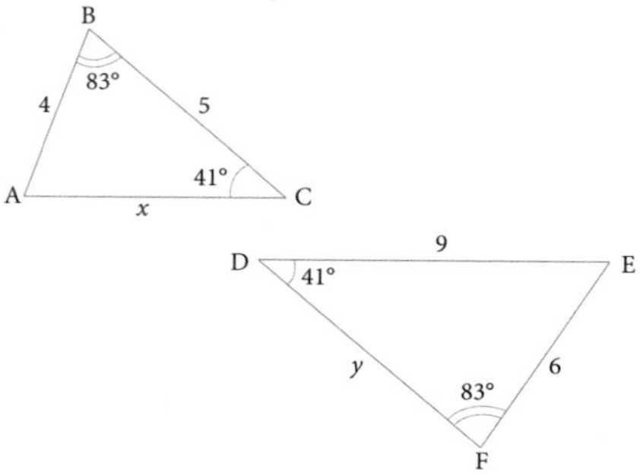

28.

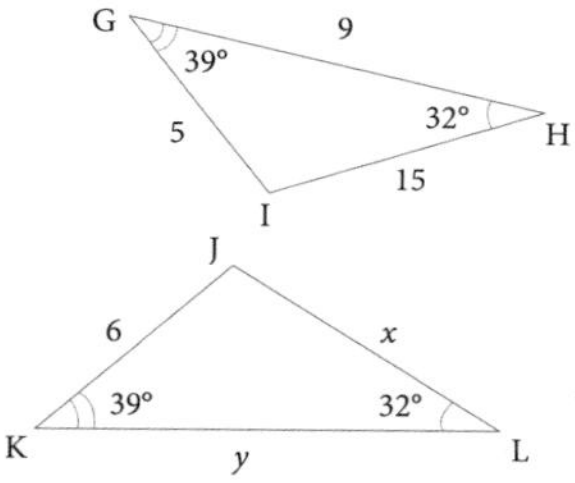

29.

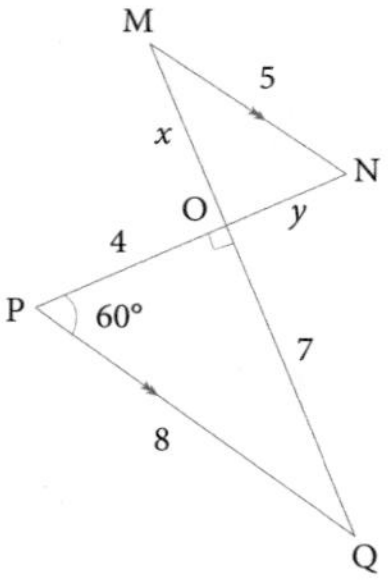

30.

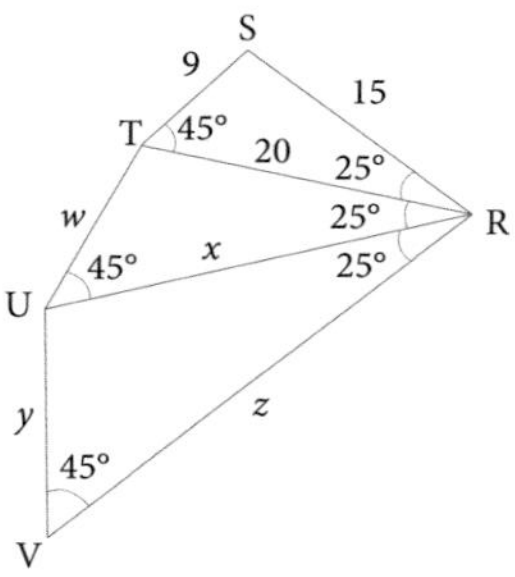

31. A flagpole casts a 3.4 m shadow. Melanie, who is 160 cm tall, stands beside the flagpole, and her shadow is 64 cm long. Draw a diagram and calculate the height of the flagpole.

32. A tree casts a 4.5m shadow. At the same time, a stick 55 cm long casts a shadow 90 cm long. Calculate the height of the tree in metres and centimeters.

33. In an outdoor theatre at night, a spotlight is placed 8 m behind a sheet that is 5.5 m high. As an actress, who is 1.65 m tall, walks from the sheet towards the spotlight, it casts her shadow onto the wall. How far away from the spotlight is the actress when her shadow is the entire height of the sheet?

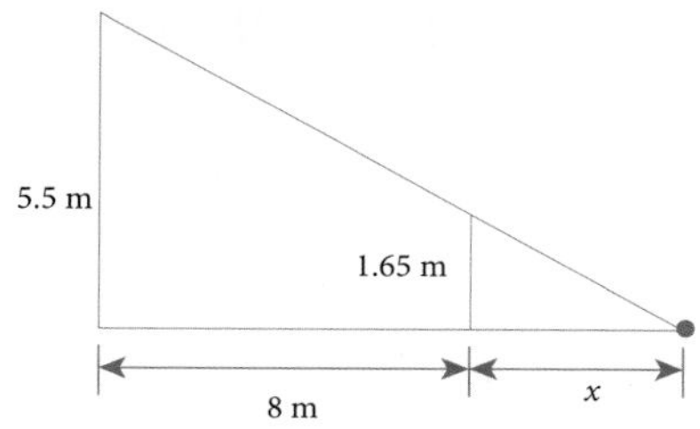

34. A streetlight situated 7.4 m above the street casts a shadow on a pedestrian, taking a late-night walk. If the pedestrian is 1.8 m tall, how long is his shadow when he is 7 m away from the streetlight?

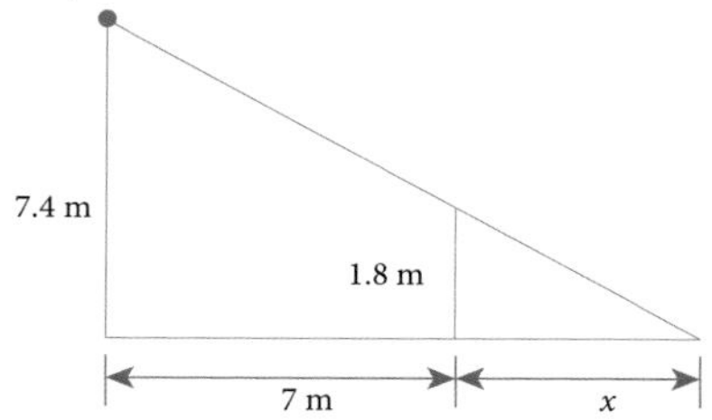

35. A man is standing 12 m away from a lamp post which is 10 m high. If his shadow is 2.2 m long, how tall is he?

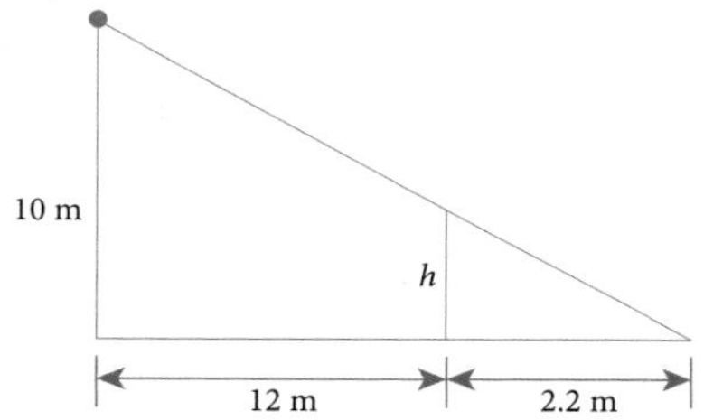

36. Two ladders of lengths 4 m and 9 m are leaning at the same angle against a wall. If the 4 m ladder reaches 3.2 m up the wall, how much further up the wall does the 9 m ladder reach?

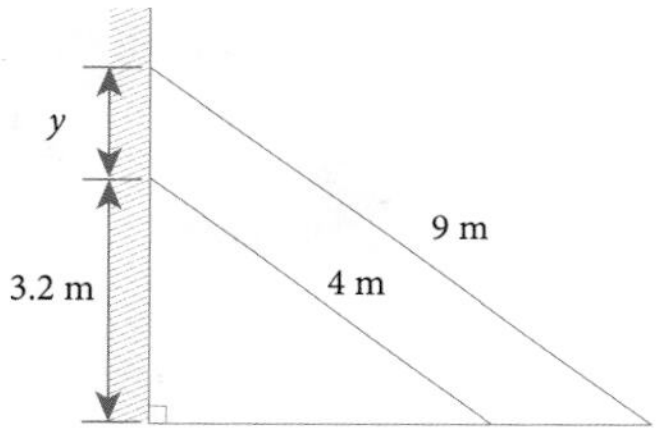

37. Calculate the height of "y" in the diagram below.

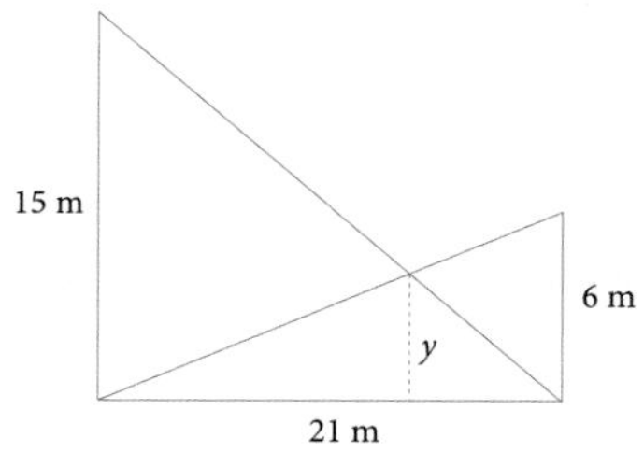

38. Calculate the length of "x" in the diagram below.

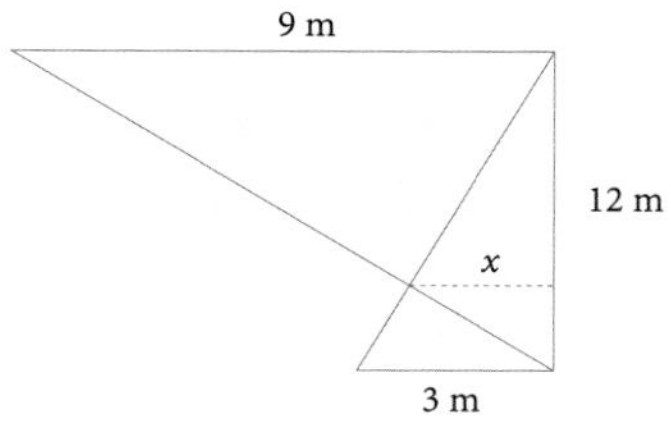

11.2 | Pythagorean Theorem

Introduction

The Pythagorean Theorem is a famous theorem in Mathematics. It is named after a Greek philosopher and mathematician, Pythagoras, who discovered[1] it thousands of years ago. It describes a special relationship between the lengths of the three sides of a right-angle triangle. The theorem states that the squares of the lengths of the two shorter sides that meet at the right-angle (called the **legs** of the right triangle) equal the square of the longest side opposite the right-angle (called the **hypotenuse** of the right triangle).

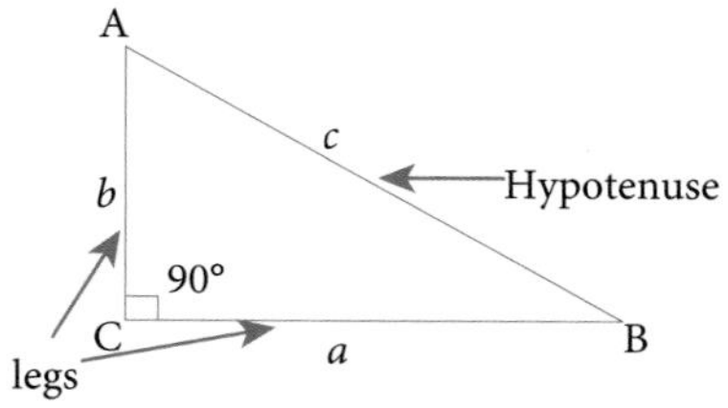

In a right-triangle, for example, ABC with the right angle at C, the Pythagorean Theorem is written as an equation relating the lengths of the sides of the right-triangle a, b, and c, where a and b represent the legs, and c represents the hypotenuse, as follows:

$$a^2 + b^2 = c^2$$

Using this equation, if the lengths of both legs (a and b) are known, then the hypotenuse (c) can be calculated as follows:

$$c = \sqrt{a^2 + b^2}$$

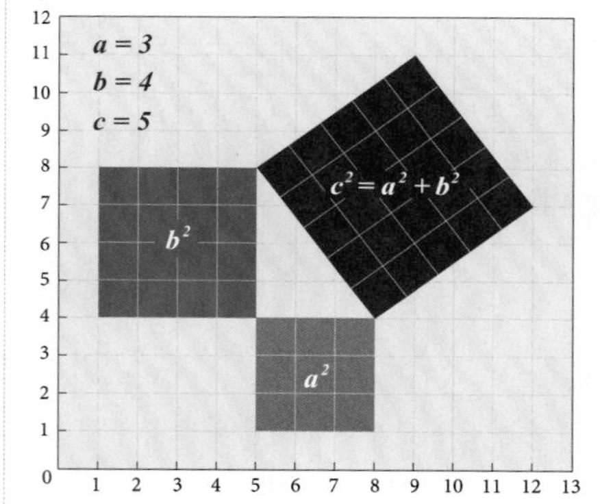

Exhibit 11.2-a Pythagorean Theorem

Similarly, if the lengths of the hypotenuse (c) and one leg (a or b) are known, then the length of the other leg can be calculated, as follows:

$$a = \sqrt{c^2 - b^2} \quad \text{or} \quad b = \sqrt{c^2 - a^2}$$

A set of positive integers that satisfies the Pythagorean Theorem are known as Pythagorean triples. For example, the integers 3, 4, and 5 are Pythagorean triples.

$3^2 + 4^2 = 5^2$

$(9 + 16 = 25)$

Some of the other Pythagorean triples are: (5, 12, 13), (7, 24, 25), (8, 15, 17), (9, 40, 41), (12, 35, 37), (20, 21, 28),...

Proofs of the Pythagorean Theorem

The theorem has numerous proofs. In this section, three proofs of the theorem will be discussed.

Proof Using Similar Triangles

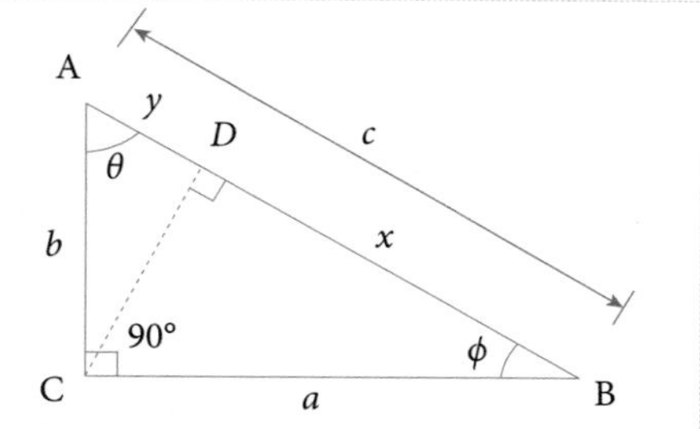

Exhibit 11.2-b Proof of Pythagorean Theorem using Similar Triangles

For this proof of the Pythagorean Theorem, start with a right-triangle, ABC, with legs, a and b, and hypotenuse, c.

Draw CD $\perp$ to AB

Let $\angle A = \theta$ and $\angle B = \phi$ [where $\theta + \phi = 90°$]

Let BD = x and AD = y [where $x + y = c$]

[1] Although Pythagoras is credited with the discovery of the theorem, there is evidence to suggest that it was known by the ancient Babylonians, over 1,000 years prior to Pythagoras.

As shown in Exhibit 11.2-b, ΔABC and ΔCBD are similar.

Therefore, $\frac{c}{a} = \frac{a}{x}$

i.e., $a^2 = cx$ ①

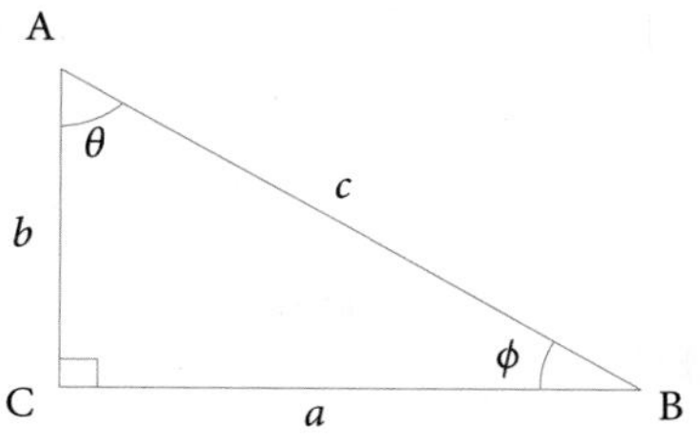

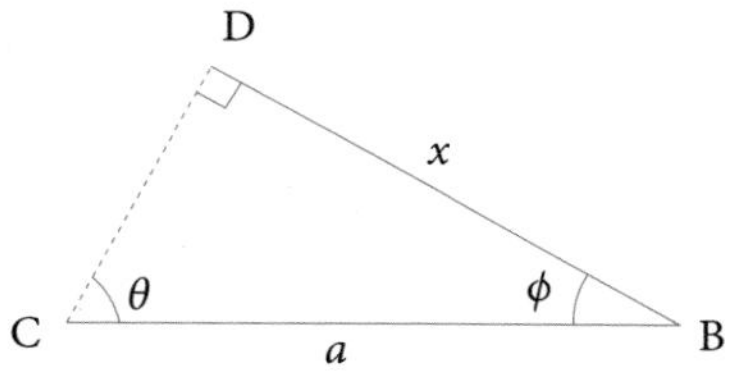

ΔABC and ΔACD are similar.

Therefore, $\frac{b}{c} = \frac{y}{b}$

i.e., $b^2 = cy$ ②

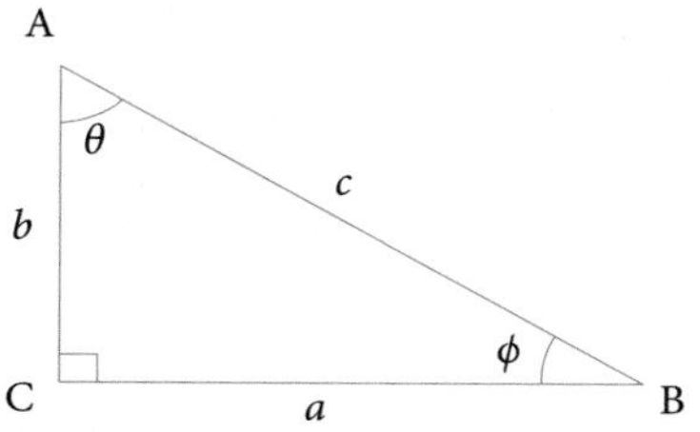

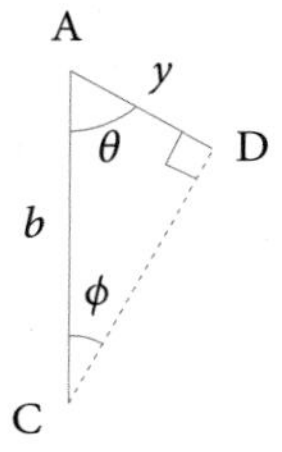

Adding ① and ②,

$a^2 + b^2 = cx + cy$

$a^2 + b^2 = c(x + y) = c(c) = c^2$

Therefore, $a^2 + b^2 = c^2$.

Proof Using a Geometric Construction

For this proof of the Pythagorean Theorem, start with a right triangle with legs, a and b, and hypotenuse, c. Then, three additional copies of the triangle are created and lined up tip-to-tip so that their boundary forms a square, as shown in Exhibit 11.2-c.

The outer boundary forms a square, as all angles are right-angles and all side lengths are equal to $(a + b)$.

Also, the inner boundary forms a square, as all angles are right-angles (by the IAT-Part 2 from Chapter 10) and all side lengths are equal to c.

Area of larger square = Area of smaller square + Area of each of the 4 triangles.

$$(a+b)^2 = c^2 + 4\left[\frac{a \times b}{2}\right]$$

$a^2 + 2ab + b^2 = c^2 + 2ab$

$a^2 + b^2 = c^2$

Therefore, $a^2 + b^2 = c^2$.

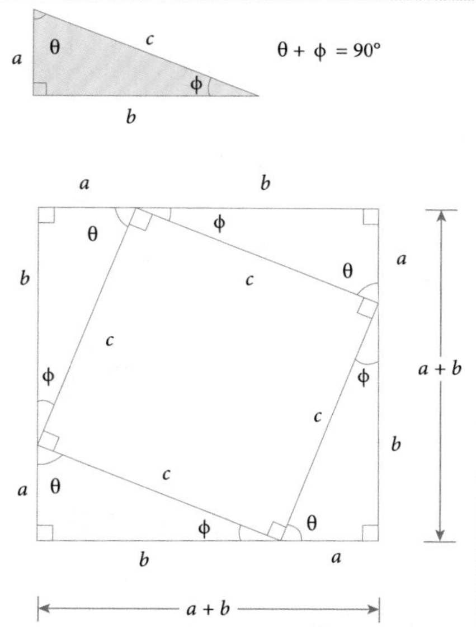

Exhibit 11.2-c Proof of Pythagorean Theorem using a Geometric Construction

Proof Using Congruent Triangles and Areas

For this proof of the Pythagorean Theorem, first draw ΔABC, so that point C is on the right-angle and label the opposite sides using the same, small-case letters, so that c is the hypotenuse and a and b represent the legs. Then, draw squares on each side of the triangle. Following this, draw a line from point C to the far side of the square on side c, perpendicular to AB, which intersects AB at 'K'. Label the diagram, as in Exhibit 11.2-d.

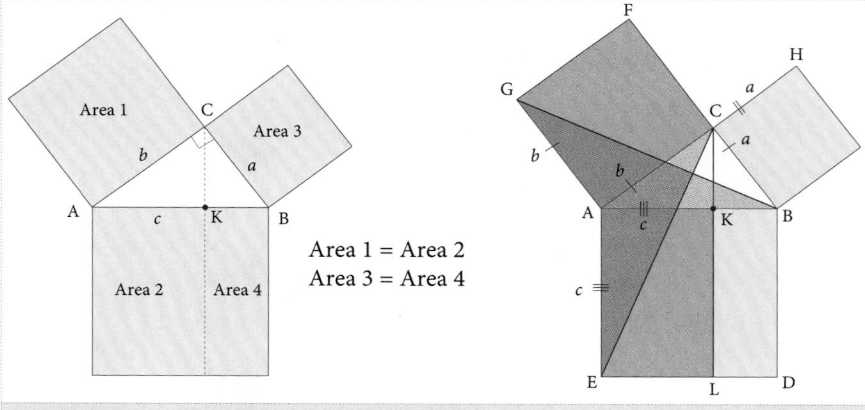

Exhibit 11.2-d Proof of Pythagorean Theorem using Congruent Triangles and Areas

Join BG and CE.

ΔABG and ΔACE are congruent, (SAS Property).

Area of ΔABG = Area of ΔACE using Area of $\Delta = \frac{1}{2}$ Base × Height,

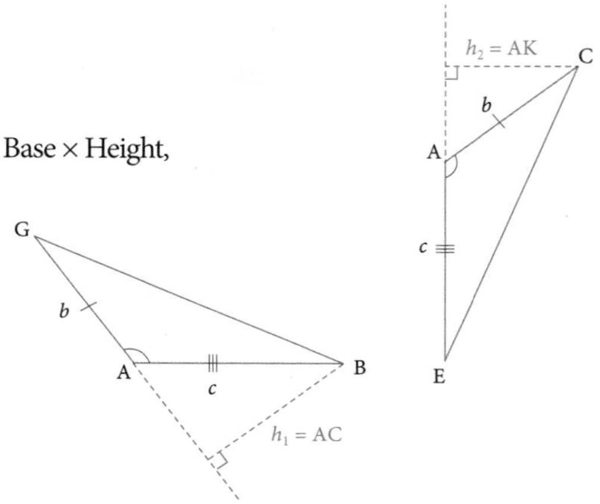

$$\frac{1}{2}\text{AG}\cdot h_1 = \frac{1}{2}\text{AE}\cdot h_2$$

$$\frac{1}{2}\text{AG}\cdot\text{AC} = \frac{1}{2}\text{AE}\cdot\text{AK}$$

$$\frac{1}{2}\text{Area 1} = \frac{1}{2}\text{Area 2}$$

Area 1 = Area 2. (1)

Similarly, it can be proven that **Area 3 = Area 4.** (2)

Adding (1) + (2), we get:

Area 1 + Area 3 = Area 2 + Area 4

i.e., $b^2 + a^2 = c^2$

Therefore, $a^2 + b^2 = c^2$.

Determining the Unknown Length of One Side of a Right Triangle

If the lengths of any two sides of a right triangle are given, the Pythagorean Theorem can be used to determine the length of the third side.

If the length of the hypotenuse is unknown, use the re-arrangement of the formula, $c^2 = a^2 + b^2$, and perform the square root on both sides to determine c.

Similarly, if the length of the hypotenuse is known, the formula can be rearranged from $a^2 + b^2 = c^2$ to $a^2 = c^2 - b^2$ (or $b^2 = c^2 - a^2$) and the square root can be performed on both sides to determine a or b.

Example 11.2-a **Calculating the Length of the Hypotenuse of a Right Triangle**

Using the Pythagorean Theorem, calculate the length (rounded to the nearest hundredth, as needed) of the hypotenuse, c, of the following right triangles, given the lengths of the two legs, a and b.

(i) a = 3 m and b = 4 m (ii) a = 10 cm and b = 12 cm

Solution

(i) Using $a^2 + b^2 = c^2$,

$c^2 = a^2 + b^2 = 3^2 + 4^2 = 9 + 16 = 25$

$c = \sqrt{25} = 5\text{m}$

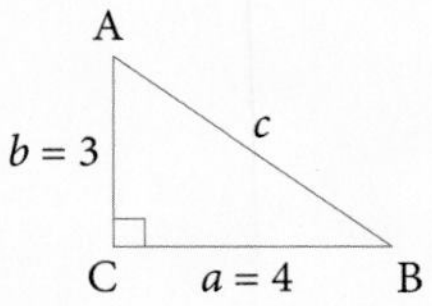

(ii) Using $a^2 + b^2 = c^2$,

$c^2 = a^2 + b^2 = 10^2 + 12^2 = 100 + 144 = 244$

$c = \sqrt{244} = 15.620499... \approx 15.62$ cm

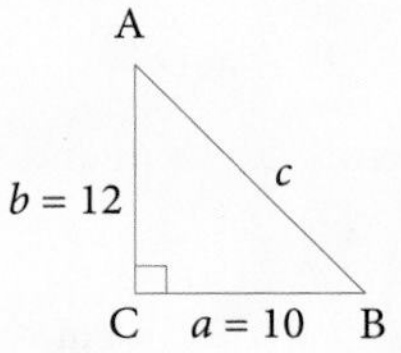

Example 11.2-b Calculating the Length of One of the Legs of a Right-Triangle

Using the Pythagorean Theorem, calculate the length (rounded to the nearest hundredth, as needed) of the missing leg, of the following right triangles, given the lengths of the hypotenuse, c, and one leg:

(i) $a = 5$ cm and $c = 13$ cm

(ii) $b = 8$ m and $c = 16$ m

Solution

(i) Using $a^2 + b^2 = c^2$

$b^2 = c^2 - a^2 = 13^2 - 5^2 = 169 - 25 = 144$

$b = \sqrt{144} = 12$ cm

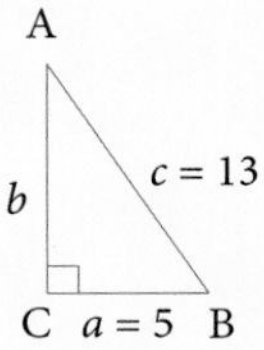

(ii) Using $a^2 + b^2 = c^2$

$a^2 = c^2 - b^2 = 16^2 - 8^2 = 256 - 64 = 192$

$a = \sqrt{192} = 13.856406... \approx 13.86$ m

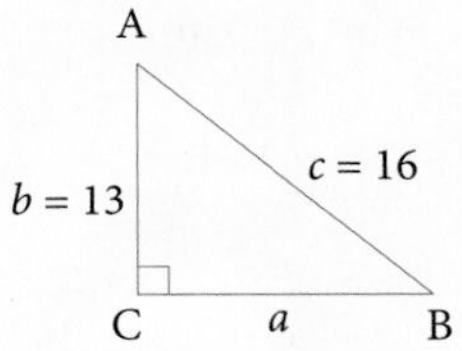

Example 11.2-c Calculate the Unknown Lengths (x and y) in the Following Diagrams

In the following figures, calculate the lengths of x and y (rounded to the nearest tenth, as needed):

(i)

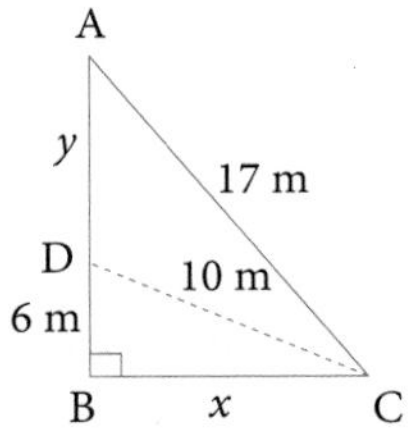

(ii)

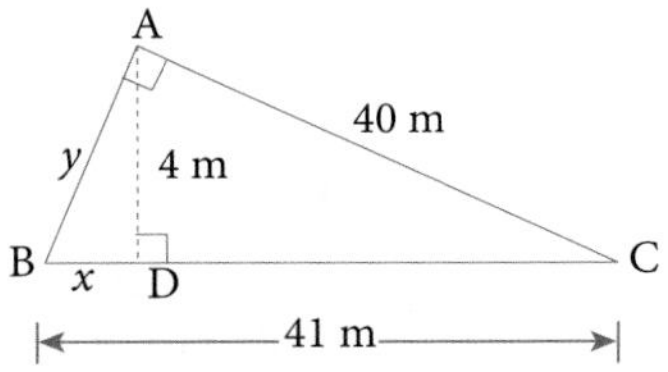

(iii)

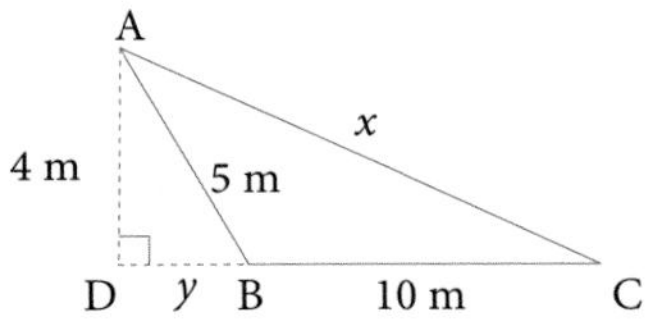

Solution

(i)

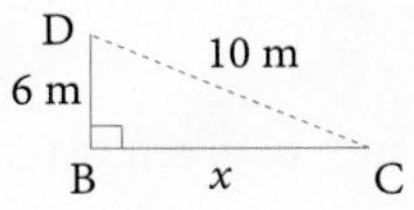

In the right triangle BCD, using the Pythagorean Theorem,

$x^2 + 6^2 = 10^2$

$x^2 = 10^2 - 6^2$

$= 100 - 36 = 64$

$x = \sqrt{64} = 8$ m

Solution
continued

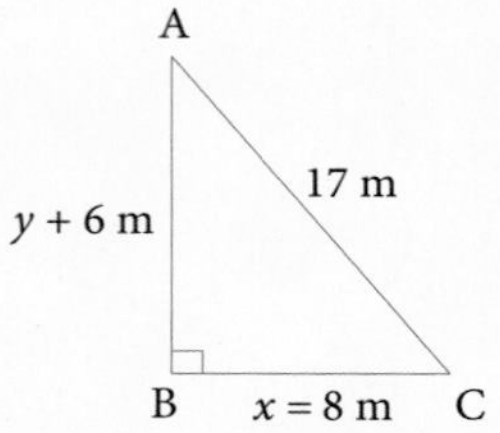

In the right triangle ABC, using the Pythagorean Theorem,

$(y + 6)^2 + x^2 = 17^2$

$(y + 6)^2 = 17^2 - 8^2$

$= 289 - 64 = 225$

$(y + 6) = \sqrt{225} = 15$

$y = 15 - 6 = 9$ m

Therefore, $x = 8$ m and $y = 9$ m.

(ii)

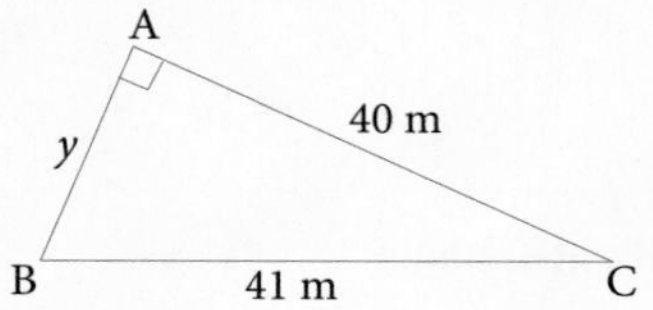

In the right triangle ABC, using the Pythagorean Theorem,

$y^2 + 40^2 = 41^2$

$y^2 = 41^2 - 40^2$

$= 1{,}681 - 1{,}600 = 81$

$y = \sqrt{81} = 9$ m

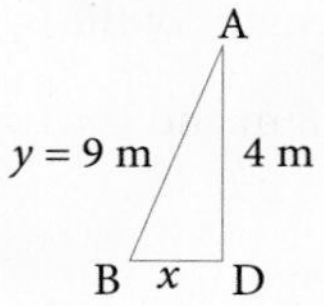

In the right triangle ABD, using the Pythagorean Theorem,

$x^2 + 4^2 = 9^2$

$x^2 = 9^2 - 4^2$

$= 81 - 16 = 65$

$x = \sqrt{65} = 8.062257... \approx 8.1$ m

Therefore, $x = 8.1$ m and $y = 9$ m.

(iii)

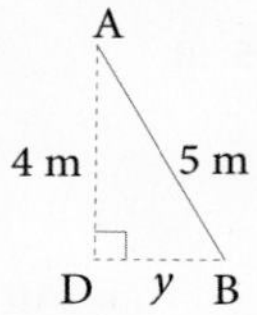

In the right triangle ADB, using the Pythagorean Theorem,

$y^2 + 4^2 = 5^2$

$y^2 = 5^2 - 4^2$

$= 25 - 16 = 9$

$y = \sqrt{9} = 3$ m

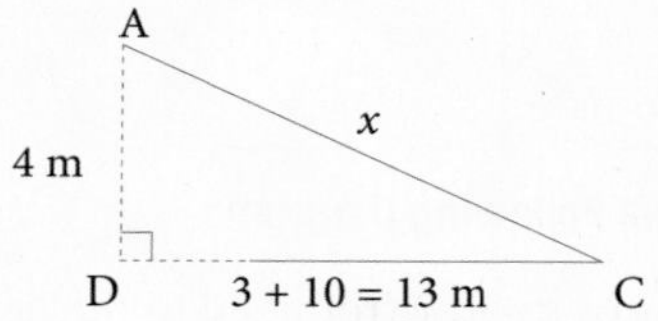

In the right triangle ADC, using the Pythagorean Theorem,

$4^2 + 13^2 = x^2$

$x^2 = 16 + 169 = 185$

$x = \sqrt{185} = 13.601470... \approx 13.6$ m

Therefore, $x = 13.6$ and $y = 3$ m.

Calculating the Distance Between Two Points

In Chapter 9, the concept of the distance between two points was introduced; however, it was limited to points that are on the same vertical line (sharing the same x-coordinate) or horizontal line (sharing the same y-coordinate). If the two points share neither the same x-coordinate nor y-coordinate, the calculation becomes more difficult. Certainly, the distance is at most, the sum of the horizontal and vertical distances between the two points, but there is a shorter distance – the line segment joining the two points.

In this section, the method to calculate the shortest distance between two points having coordinates $P(x_1, y_1)$ and $Q(x_2, y_2)$ will be demonstrated.

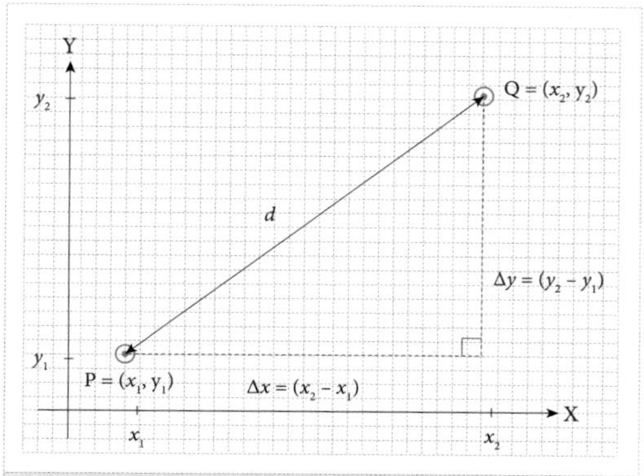

Exhibit 11.2-e Euclid's Proof of the Pythagorean Theorem using Congruent Triangles

Every horizontal line and every vertical line meet at a right-angle. Therefore, the shortest distance between two points is related to the horizontal and vertical distances between the points by the Pythagorean Theorem. This forms the equation for the shortest distance:

$$d^2 = (\Delta x)^2 + (\Delta y)^2,$$

where Δx is the horizontal distance between the two points and Δy is the vertical distance between the two points.

i.e., the equation for the shortest distance, d, between the two points $P(x_1, y_1)$ and $Q(x_2, y_2)$ is:

$$d^2 = (x_2 - x_1)^2 + (y_2 - y_1)^2$$

Performing the square root on both sides, the shortest distance, d, between the two points $P(x_1, y_1)$ and $Q(x_2, y_2)$ is:

$$d = \sqrt{(x_2 - x_1)^2 + (y_2 - y_1)^2}$$

Example 11.2-d **Calculating the Distance Between Two Points in the Cartesian Plane**

Calculate the distance (rounded to the nearest tenth of a unit, as needed) between the following points:

(i) A(2, 1) and B(7, 8)

(ii) P(−3, 7) and Q(3, −1)

(iii) X(4.5, −1.2) and Y(−7.3, 2.8)

Solution

Using $d^2 = (x_2 - x_1)^2 + (y_2 - y_1)^2$

(i) $d^2 = (7 - 2)^2 + (8 - 1)^2$

$= 5^2 + 7^2 = 25 + 49 = 74$

$d = \sqrt{74} = 8.602325... \approx 8.6$ units

(ii) $d^2 = [3 -(-3)]^2 + [(-1) - 7]^2$

$= 6^2 + (-8)^2 = 36 + 64 = 100$

$d = \sqrt{100} = 10$ units

(iii) $d^2 = [(-7.3) - 4.5]^2 + [2.8 -(-1.2)]^2$

$= (-11.8)^2 + (4.0)^2 = 139.24 + 16 = 155.24$

$d = \sqrt{155.24} = 12.459534... \approx 12.5$ units

Applications of the Pythagorean Theorem

Example 11.2-e **Calculating the Distance Between Two Cities**

Toronto is 45 km north and 26 km east of Hamilton. Find the shortest flying distance (rounded to the nearest kilometre) between the two cities.

Solution

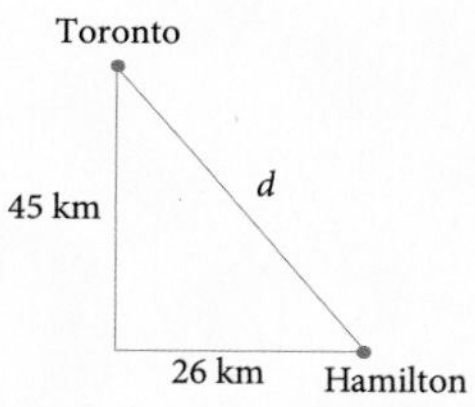

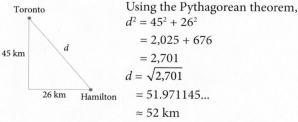

Using the Pythagorean theorem,

$d^2 = 45^2 + 26^2$

$= 2,025 + 676$

$= 2,701$

$d = \sqrt{2,701}$

$= 51.971145...$

≈ 52 km

Therefore, the shortest flying distance between the two cities is 52 km.

Example 11.2-f Calculating the Length of a Guy Wire

A guy wire is tied to an antenna tower 12 m above the ground and the other end of the guy wire is tied to the ground 15 m away. Determine the length of the guy wire, rounded to the nearest tenth of a metre.

Solution

Let ℓ be the length of the guy wire. Using the Pythagorean Theorem, $\ell^2 = 15^2 + 12^2$

$$= 225 + 144 = 369$$

$$\ell = \sqrt{369}$$

$$= 19.209372...$$

$$\approx 19.2 \text{ m}$$

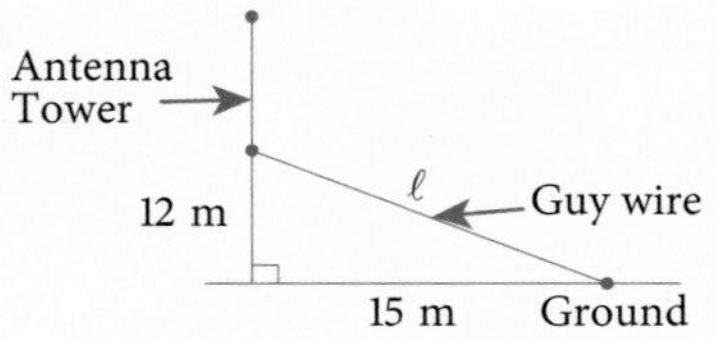

Therefore, the length of the guy wire is 19.2 m.

Example 11.2-g Determining the Dimensions of a Television

A 42″ television, with a length to height ratio 16 : 9, measures 42 inches across the diagonal. Find the length and the height of the TV, to the nearest tenth of an inch.

Solution

Since the ratio of the length of the TV to the height of the TV is 16 : 9, let $16x$ represent the length of the TV and $9x$ represent the height of the TV.

Using the Pythagorean Theorem,

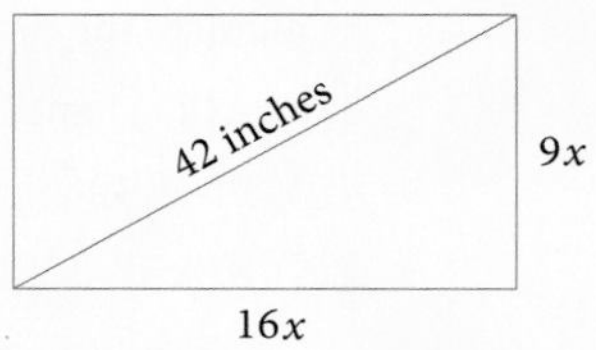

$$42^2 = (16x)^2 + (9x)^2$$

$$1{,}764 = 256x^2 + 81x^2$$

$$1{,}764 = 337x^2$$

$$x^2 = \frac{1{,}764}{337} = 5.234421...$$

$$x = \sqrt{5.234421...} = 2.287885...$$

Length of the TV = $16x = 16(2.287885...) = 36.606172... \approx 36.6$ inches

Height of the TV = $9x = 9(2.287885...) = 20.590972... \approx 20.6$ inches

Therefore, the length of the TV is 36.6 inches and the height is 20.6 inches.

Example 11.2-h Calculating the Height, Surface Area, and Volume of a Pyramid

The Great Pyramids of Giza in Egypt have certain special properties: the ratio of the slant height (S) of the pyramid to the semi-base (b_1) of the pyramid adheres to the "Golden Ratio," which is approximately 1.618 : 1.

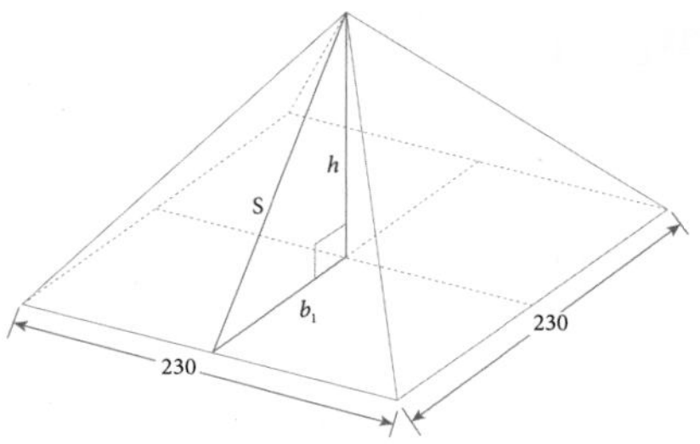

Jorge wishes to know the height (h) and volume (V) of the largest pyramid. If he measures the length of one side of the base to be 230 m, find the height of the pyramid, rounded to the nearest metre. Then, find the surface area and volume of the pyramid, rounded to the nearest square metre and cubic metre, respectively.

Solution

Since the base is 230 m, $b_1 = \frac{230}{2} = 115$ m.

Step 1: Calculate the slant height of the pyramid, s, using the Golden Ratio $\frac{S}{b_1} = 1.618$,

$$S = 1.618(115) = 186.07 \approx 186 \text{ m},$$

Therefore, the slant height of the pyramid is 186 m.

Step 2: Calculate the height of the pyramid using the Pythagorean Theorem.

$$S^2 = b_1^{\,2} + h^2$$

$$(186)^2 = (115)^2 + (h)^2$$

$$34{,}596 = 13{,}225 + h^2$$

$$h^2 = 21{,}371$$

$$h = \sqrt{21{,}371} = 146.188234... \approx 146 \text{ m}$$

Therefore, the height of the pyramid is 146 m.

Step 3: Calculate the surface area of the 4 equal triangular sides using slant height s = 186 m and b = 230 m.

$$SA = 4 \times \left[\frac{(230)(186)}{2}\right] = 85{,}560 \text{ m}^2$$

Step 4: Calculate the volume of the pyramid using the formula $V = \frac{b^2 \times h}{3}$ for a square-based pyramid.

$$V = \frac{(230)^2(146)}{3} = 2{,}574{,}466.667 \approx 2{,}574{,}467 \text{ m}^3$$

Therefore, the surface area of the pyramid is 85,560 m^2 and the volume of the pyramid is 2,574,467 m^3.

11.2 | Exercises

Answers to odd-numbered problems are available at the end of the textbook.

In Problems 1 to 4, use the Pythagorean Theorem to determine the length of the missing side in the given right-angled triangles, where a and b represent the legs of the triangle and c represents the hypotenuse of the triangle. Express the answers rounded to the nearest hundredth, wherever applicable.

1.

	a	*b*	*c*
a.	15 cm	20 cm	?
b.	2.5 cm	?	6.5 cm
c.	?	6 cm	6.25 cm

2.

	a	*b*	*c*
a.	7 cm	24 cm	?
b.	7.5 cm	?	12.5 cm
c.	?	20 cm	20.5 cm

3.

	a	*b*	*c*
a.	12 cm	15 cm	?
b.	8 cm	?	17 cm
c.	?	15 cm	16 cm

4.

	a	*b*	*c*
a.	16 cm	18 cm	?
b.	20 cm	?	29 cm
c.	?	17 cm	23 cm

In Problems 5 to 10, calculate the length of the missing side for each of the diagrams:

5.

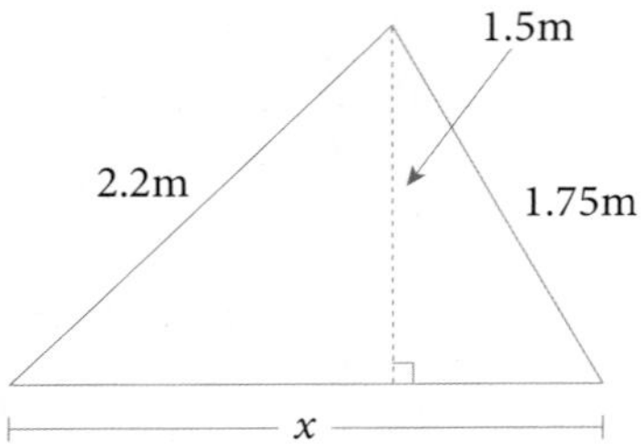

6.

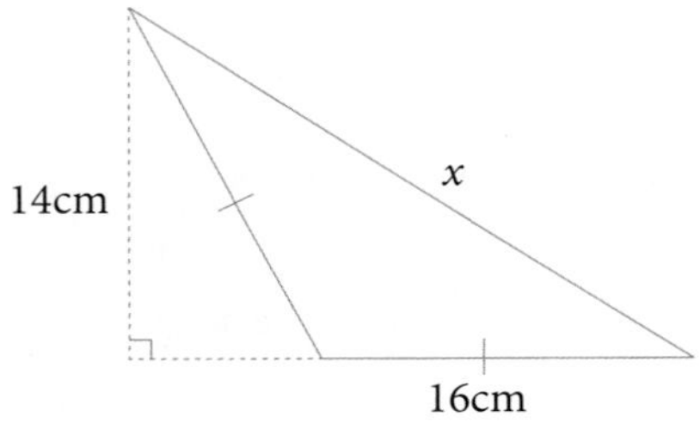

7.

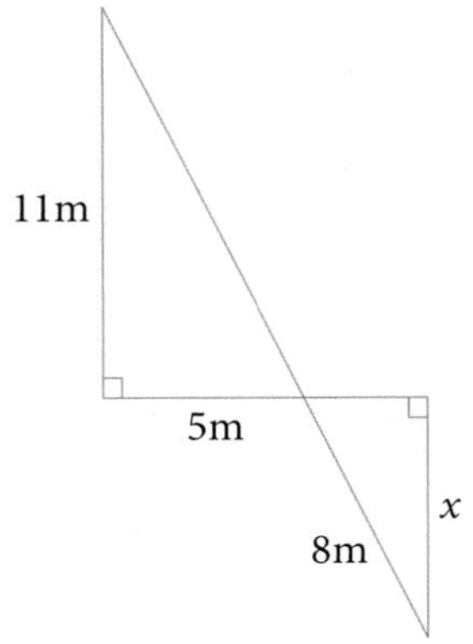

8.

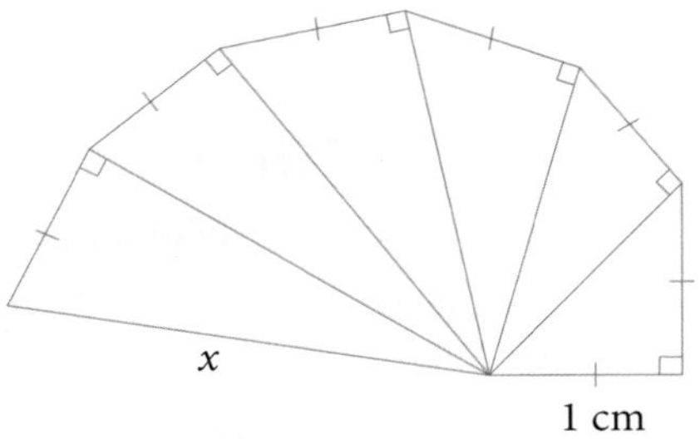

9.

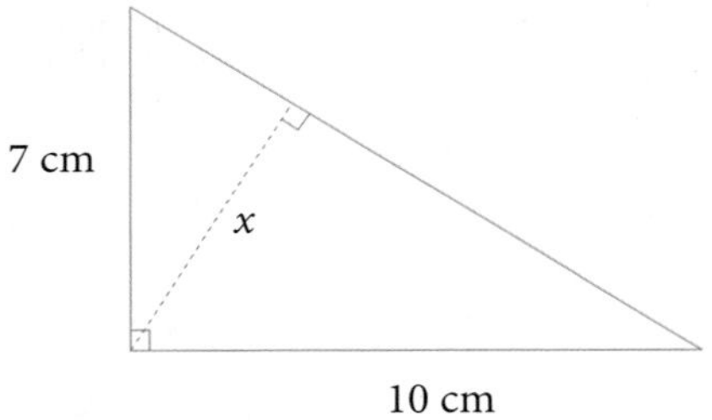

10.

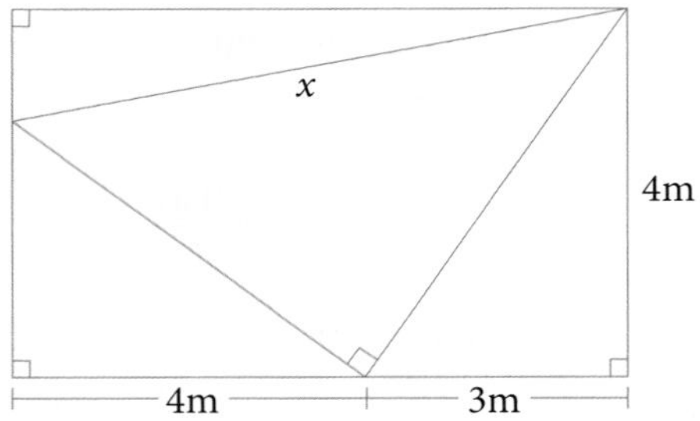

In Problems 11 to 14, calculate the perimeter and area of each of the given diagrams:

11.

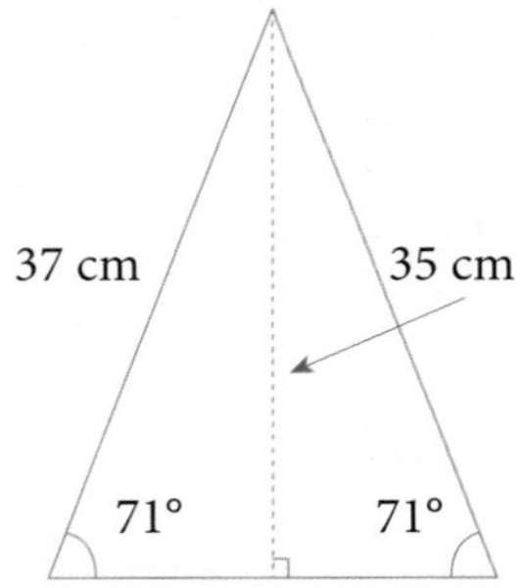

12.

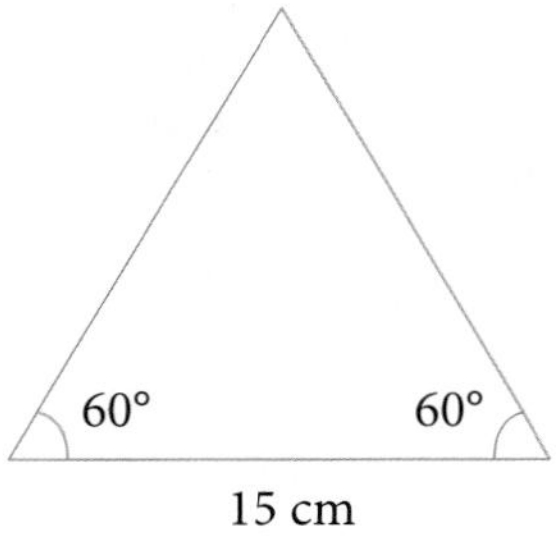

13.

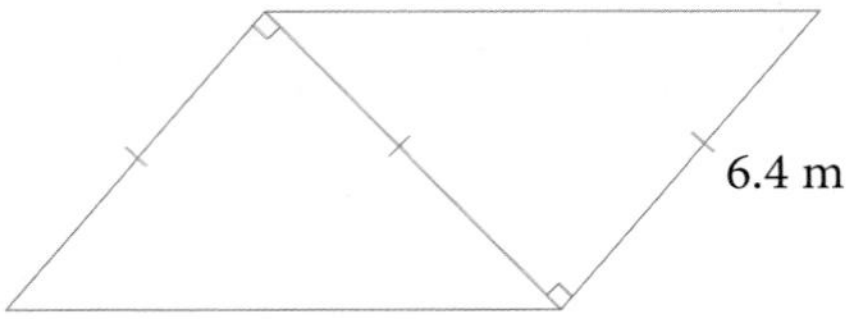

14.

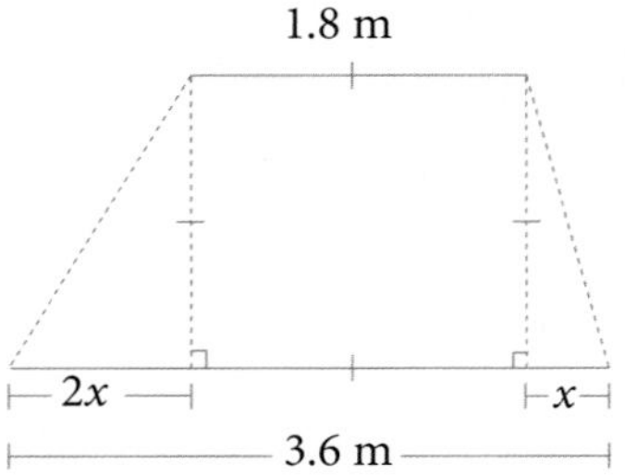

In Problems 15 to 22, calculate the length of the line segments joining the pairs of points.

15. $A(-2,5)$ and $B(4,7)$
16. $C(-6,1)$ and $D(2,5)$
17. $E(4,-3)$ and $F(-1,5)$
18. $G(1,-6)$ and $H(-4,3)$
19. $M(-3,-3)$ and $N(-7,2)$
20. $P(-4,-1)$ and $Q(3,-5)$
21. $S(0,4)$ and $T(-3,0)$
22. $U(2,0)$ and $V(0,-6)$

23. A laptop screen measures 31 cm long by 17.5 cm high. Determine the diagonal length of the computer screen, rounded to the nearest tenth of a cm.

24. From a point 'X', a person walked 850 m due west and then turned and walked for another 1.7 km due south to reach point 'Y'. Calculate the shortest distance between X and Y, rounded to the nearest hundredth of a km.

25. A 2.5 m tent pole is secured using a 4.3 m long guy rope from the top of the pole. How far away from the base of the pole will the rope need to be secured to the ground, assuming it is pulled taut?

26. A 5 m ladder is leaned up against a wall. If the base of the ladder is placed on the ground 1.7 m away from the wall, how high up against the wall will the ladder reach, rounded to the nearest tenth of a metre?

27. A skateboard ramp that is 3.5 m long is built with a slope of 3/5. Determine the maximum height of the ramp, rounded to the nearest cm.

28. A wheelchair ramp is to be constructed to the top of a set of stairs that is 1.75 m tall, with a maximum slope of 1/12. Determine the minimum ramp length required, in order for the ramp to be built according to specifications. Can you suggest a way to build the ramp that would save space?

29. A towel rack that is 1 m long is to be placed in a box measuring 75 cm × 60 cm × 45 cm. Will the towel rack fit along the diagonal at the bottom of the box? Will it fit in the box if placed on the 3-dimensional diagonal?

30. Will a 16-foot-long piece of lumber fit in a truck with interior cargo dimensions of 12.5 feet by 8 feet by 7.5 feet?

In Problems 31 to 36, calculate the perpendicular height (to the nearest tenth), surface area (to the nearest whole number), and volume (to the nearest whole number) of the solids.

31. A cone with a base diameter of 24 cm and a slant height of 30 cm.

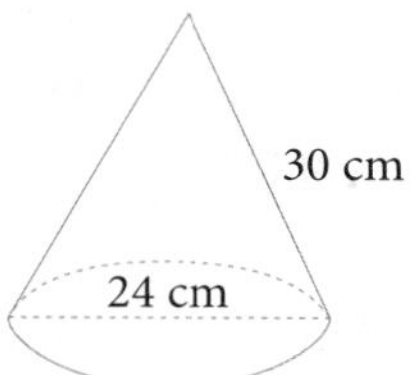

32. A cone with a base diameter of 64 mm and a slant height of 105 mm.

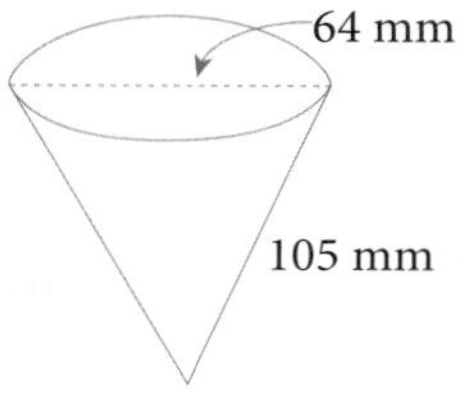

33. A square pyramid with a base length and corner edge length all equal to 98 m.

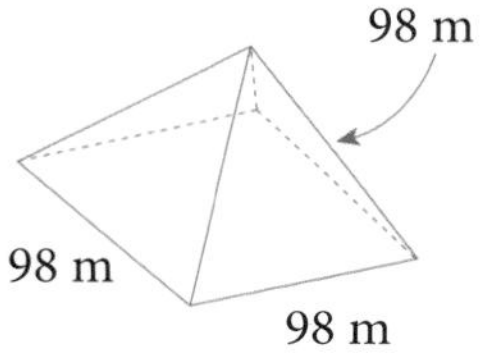

34. A pyramid with a rectangular base that has a length of 50 cm and a width of 36 cm, and a corner edge length of 45 cm.

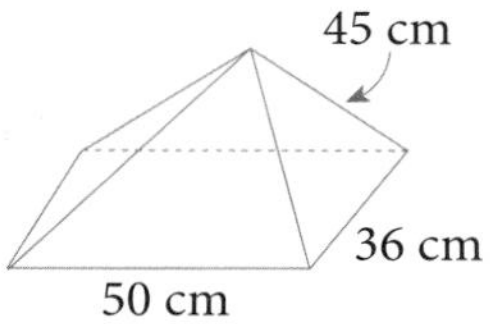

• 35. A truncated cone with a top diameter of 24 cm, a base diameter of 40 cm, and a slant height of 18 cm.

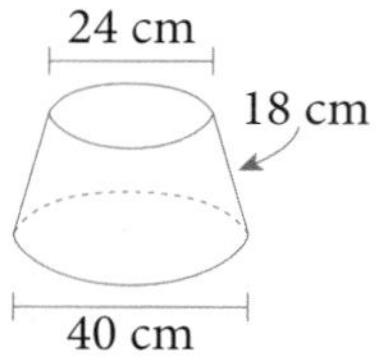

• 36. A truncated square pyramid with a top side length of 75 m, a base side length of 225 m, and a slant height of 120 m.

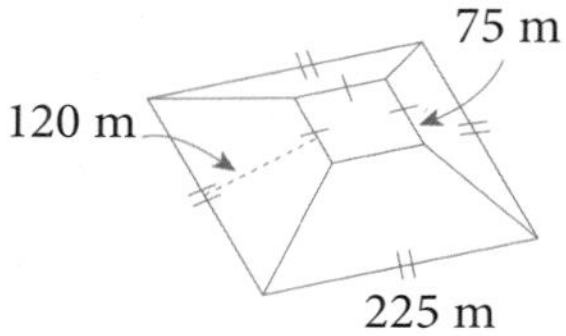

11.3 | Primary Trigonometric Ratios

Introduction

In the previous section, the relationship between the side lengths of the three sides of a right triangle was examined. In this section, we will study the relationship between the side lengths of a right triangle and its acute angle measures. The core concept behind this relationship is based on the fact that if one of the two acute angles of a right triangle is known, then all right triangles with that one angle measure will be similar; therefore, their side lengths will be in proportion.

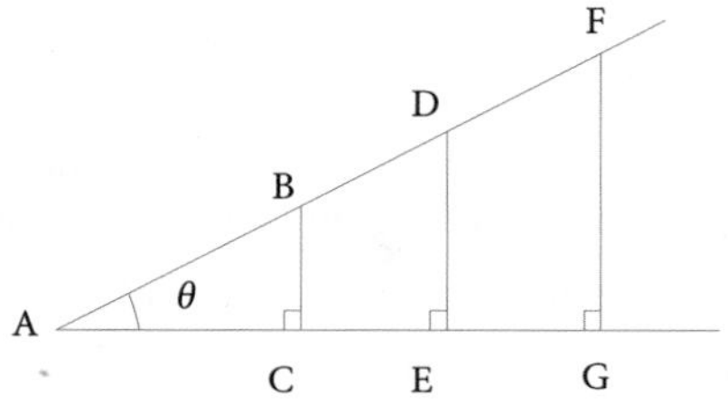

ΔABC, ΔADE, ΔAFG are similar and their side lengths are in proportion.

A **trigonometric ratio** is a ratio of the lengths of two sides of a right triangle. Mathematicians have given special names to the six ratios of the three side lengths, relative to one of the acute angles in the right triangle, known as θ. They are (1) the sine (sin) ratio, (2) the cosine (cos) ratio, (3) the tangent (tan) ratio, (4) the cosecant (csc) ratio, (5) the secant (sec) ratio, and (6) the cotangent (cot) ratio.

The first three ratios are known as the **primary trigonometric ratios**, and will be the focus of this section. The other three ratios, known as the **secondary** or **reciprocal trigonometric ratios**, are the reciprocal ratios of the three primary trigonometric ratios, respectively. They are not covered in this textbook.

Sine, Cosine, and Tangent Ratios of Angles in a Right Triangle

In a right triangle, recall that the hypotenuse, the longest side, is the side across from the right angle. In a right triangle with an acute angle θ (i.e., $0° < \theta < 90°$), the leg that forms the angle θ with the hypotenuse is known as the adjacent leg and the third side, across (opposite) from angle θ, is known as the opposite leg. The three primary trigonometric ratios of θ are shown in Exhibit 11.3-a:

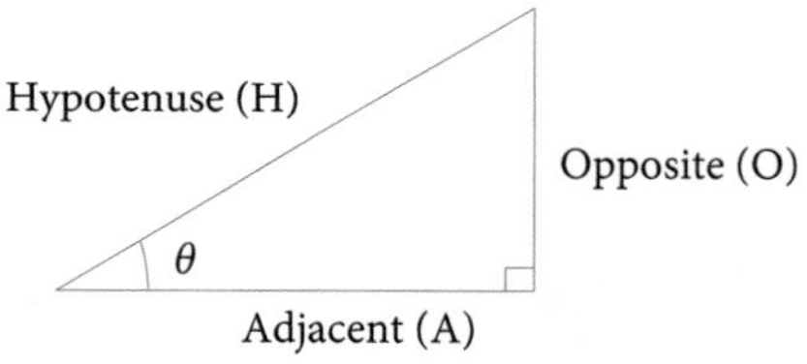

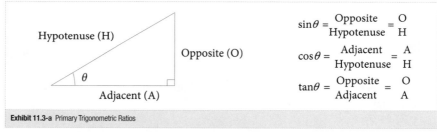

$$\sin\theta = \frac{\text{Opposite}}{\text{Hypotenuse}} = \frac{O}{H}$$

$$\cos\theta = \frac{\text{Adjacent}}{\text{Hypotenuse}} = \frac{A}{H}$$

$$\tan\theta = \frac{\text{Opposite}}{\text{Adjacent}} = \frac{O}{A}$$

Exhibit 11.3-a Primary Trigonometric Ratios

You may find it helpful to use the acronym **SOH-CAH-TOA** to remember the three primary trigonometric ratios:

SOH	Sin θ = **O**pposite/**H**ypotenuse
CAH	Cos θ = **A**djacent/**H**ypotenuse
TOA	Tan θ = **O**pposite/**A**djacent

In any acute angle,

$0 < \text{Sin}\ \theta < 1$

$0 < \text{Cos}\ \theta < 1$

$\text{Tan}\ \theta > 0$

Note: Since the lengths of the legs of a right triangle will be greater than 0 but always less than the hypotenuse, the sine and cosine ratios of any acute angle must be between 0 and 1. However, since there is no relationship between the opposite leg and the adjacent leg, except that they must both be greater than 0, the tangent ratio can be any positive number.

Example 11.3-a

Calculating Side Lengths Using the Sine Ratio

Calculate the unknown length in the following diagrams:

(i)

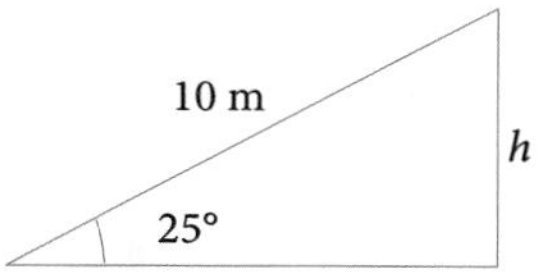

(ii)

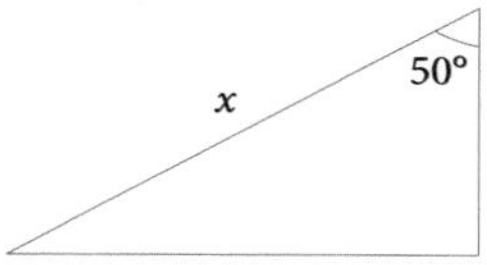

Solution

Using $\sin\theta = \frac{\text{O}}{\text{H}}$

(i) $\sin 25° = \frac{h}{10}$

$h = 10\ (\sin 25°)$

$= 4.226182... = 4.23\text{ m}$

(ii) $\sin 50° = \frac{8}{x}$

$x = \frac{8}{\sin 50°}$

$= 10.443258... = 10.44\text{ m}$

Example 11.3-b

Calculating Side Lengths Using the Cosine Ratio

Calculate the unknown length in the following diagrams:

(i)

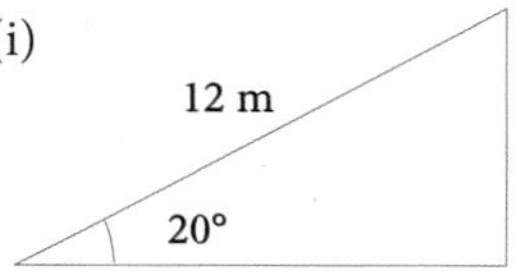

(ii)

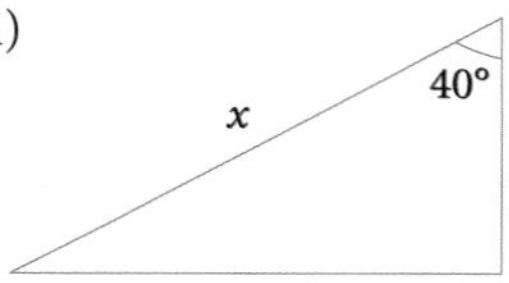

Solution

Using $\cos\theta = \frac{\text{A}}{\text{H}}$

(i) $\cos 20° = \frac{a}{12}$

$a = 12\ (\cos 20°)$

$= 11.276311... = 11.28\text{ m}$

(ii) $\cos 40° = \frac{6}{x}$

$x = \frac{6}{\cos 40°}$

$= 7.832443... = 7.83\text{ m}$

Example 11.3-c

Calculating Side Lengths Using the Tangent Ratio

Calculate the unknown length in the following diagrams:

(i)

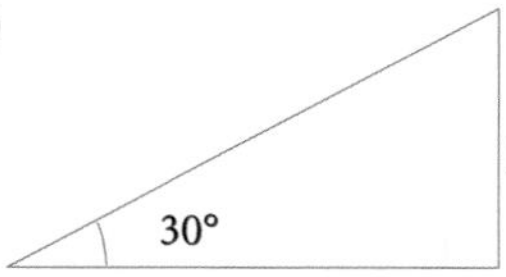

(ii)

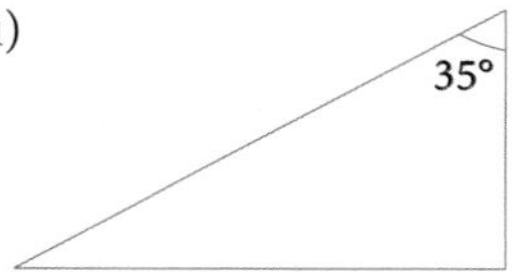

Solution

Using $\tan\theta = \frac{\text{O}}{\text{A}}$

(i) $\tan 30° = \frac{y}{7}$

$y = 7\ (\tan 30°)$

$= 4.041451... = 4.04\text{ m}$

(ii) $\tan 35° = \frac{5}{h}$

$h = \frac{5}{\tan 35°}$

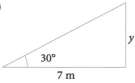

$= 7.140740... = 7.14\text{ m}$

Exact Trigonometric Ratios of Special Common Angles

There are trigonometric ratios of special common angles (30°, 45°, and 60°) that can be computed from special right triangles: the **30-60-90** triangle and **45-45-90** triangle.

30 - 60 - 90 Triangle

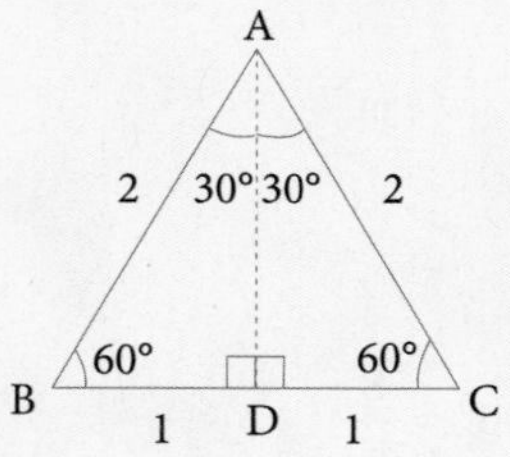

To calculate the trigonometric ratios of 30° and 60°, draw an equilateral triangle, ABC, with side lengths of 2 units each and draw AD ⊥ BC, as shown.

Since the angle measures are all 60°, the angle at the vertex A is bisected into 30° each and the base length 'BC' is bisected into 1 unit each.

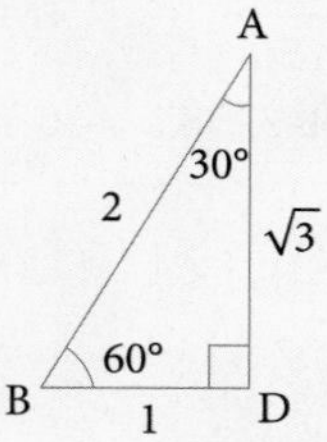

In the right triangle ABD (30 - 60 - 90), AB = 2 units, BD = 1 unit, and AD = $\sqrt{3}$ units (AD is calculated using the Pythagorean Theorem: $AD^2 = 2^2 - 1^2 = 4 - 1 = 3$, which gives AD = $\sqrt{3}$).

Using the above measures in the right triangle ABD, the sine, cosine, and tangent ratios of 30° and 60° can be calculated exactly:

$$\sin 30° = \frac{BD}{AB} = \frac{1}{2}, \qquad \sin 60° = \frac{AD}{AB} = \frac{\sqrt{3}}{2}$$

$$\cos 30° = \frac{AD}{AB} = \frac{\sqrt{3}}{2}, \qquad \cos 60° = \frac{BD}{AB} = \frac{1}{2}$$

$$\tan 30° = \frac{BD}{AB} = \frac{1}{\sqrt{3}}, \qquad \tan 60° = \frac{AD}{BD} = \frac{\sqrt{3}}{1} = \sqrt{3}$$

45 - 45 - 90 Triangle

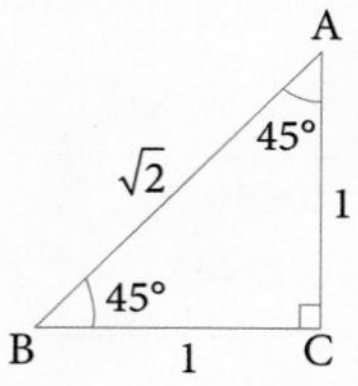

To calculate the trigonometric ratios of 45°, draw a right isosceles triangle, ABC, with leg side lengths of 1 unit each as shown.

Since the triangle is a right isosceles, the two acute angles must be equal. Therefore, the two acute angles are each 45°.

In the right isosceles triangle, ABC, (45 - 45 - 90), (AB is calculated using the Pythagorean Theorem: $AB^2 = 1^2 + 1^2 = 1 + 1 = 2$ which gives AB = $\sqrt{2}$)

Using the above measures in the right isosceles triangle ABC, the sine, cosine, and tangent ratios of 45° can be calculated exactly:

$$\sin 45° = \frac{AC}{AB} = \frac{1}{\sqrt{2}}, \qquad \cos 45° = \frac{BC}{AB} = \frac{1}{\sqrt{2}}$$

$$\tan 45° = \frac{AC}{BC} = \frac{1}{1} = 1$$

$\text{Sin } 30° = \text{Cos } 60° = \frac{1}{2}$

$\text{Sin } 60° = \text{Cos } 30° = \frac{\sqrt{3}}{2}$

$\text{Sin } 45° = \text{Cos } 45° = \frac{1}{\sqrt{2}}$

$\text{Tan } 30° = \frac{1}{\sqrt{3}}$

$\text{Tan } 45° = 1$

$\text{Tan } 60° = \sqrt{3}$

The primary trigonometric ratios of the special common angles are summarized in Exhibit 11.3-b. These are referred to as the special trig ratios.

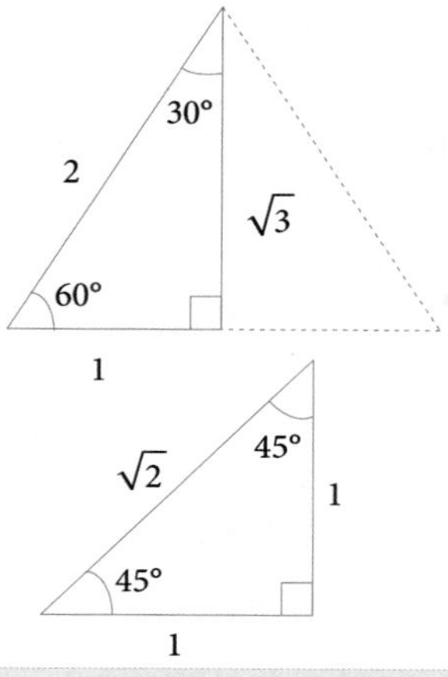

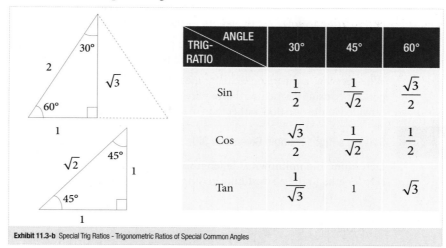

TRIG-RATIO \ ANGLE	30°	45°	60°
Sin	$\frac{1}{2}$	$\frac{1}{\sqrt{2}}$	$\frac{\sqrt{3}}{2}$
Cos	$\frac{\sqrt{3}}{2}$	$\frac{1}{\sqrt{2}}$	$\frac{1}{2}$
Tan	$\frac{1}{\sqrt{3}}$	1	$\sqrt{3}$

Exhibit 11.3-b Special Trig Ratios - Trigonometric Ratios of Special Common Angles

Using Calculators to Determine Trigonometric Ratios and Angles

A scientific calculator can be used to determine the trigonometric ratios of any other acute angle.

When using a calculator to determine the trigonometric ratios, ensure that it is in "degree" mode.

Note: Some calculators may yield trigonometric ratios as a decimal number. E.g. sin (60°) = 0.866025...

(which represents an equivalent ratio to $\frac{\sqrt{3}}{2}$ *).*

Example 11.3-d

Using a Calculator to Calculate sin, cos, and tan of Acute Angles

Using a calculator, calculate the sine, cosine, and tangent of the following acute angles, rounded to four decimal places as required:

(i) $\theta = 15°$ (ii) $\theta = 72°$ (iii) $\theta = 36.87°$

Solution

(i) sin 15° = 0.258819... = 0.2588
cos 15° = 0.965925... = 0.9659
tan 15° = 0.267949.... = 0.2679

(ii) sin 72° = 0.951056... = 0.9511
cos 72° = 0.309016... = 0.3090
tan 72° = 3.077683... = 3.0777

(iii) sin 36.87° = 0.600001... = 0.6000
cos 36.87° = 0.799998... = 0.8000
tan 36.87° = 0.750002... = 0.7500

Using Calculators to Calculate Angles

If we know the ratio of the lengths two sides of a right triangle, we can determine the angle related to that ratio using the **inverse trigonometric functions** of sine, cosine, and tangent, known as arcsine, arccosine, and arctangent, respectively. These functions often appear on scientific calculators as $\sin^{-1}$, $\cos^{-1}$, and $\tan^{-1}$.

Example 11.3-e

Using a Calculator to Calculate the Angle Given a Trig Ratio

Using a calculator, calculate the angle measure in degrees (rounded to the nearest tenth of a degree) for each of the following trigonometric ratios:

(i) $\sin \theta = 0.9063$ (ii) $\cos \theta = 0.6$ (iii) $\tan \theta = 0.1467$

Solution

(i) $\theta = \sin^{-1}(0.9063)$
$\theta = 64.998944... = 65.0°$

(ii) $\theta = \cos^{-1}(0.6)$
$\theta = 53.130102... = 53.1°$

(iii) $\theta = \tan^{-1}(0.1467)$
$\theta = 8.345761... = 8.3°$

Solving Right Triangles using Trigonometry

If one side length and one acute angle measure in a right triangle, are provided, trigonometric ratios may be used to solve for the lenght of the remaining side lengths.

Conversely, if any two side lengths of a right triangle are given, the inverse trigonometric functions and complementary angles may be used to solve for the two acute angles.

When solving right triangles, there are often several ways to proceed. However, calculations should be performed using the method that requires as fewer steps as possible, i.e., whenever convenient, measurements provided in the question, rather than measurements obtained from secondary calculations should be used.

Example 11.3-f **Solving a Right Triangle Given One Side Length and One Acute Angle**

Determine the unknown side lengths and missing angle of the following right triangles. Round all side lengths to the nearest hundredth and all angle measures to the nearest tenth.

(i)

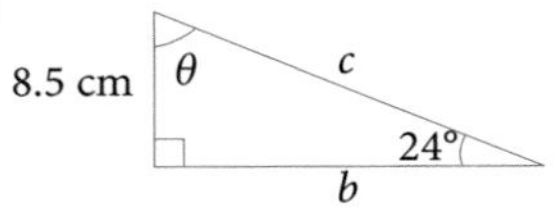

(ii)

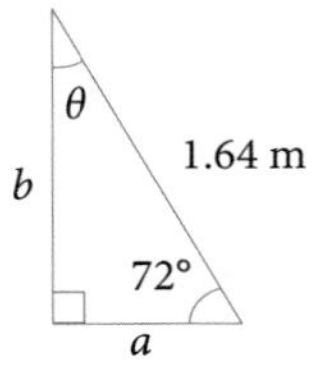

Solution

(i) First, calculate the length of one of the unknown sides using one of the primary trig ratios:

$$\tan 24° = \frac{\text{O}}{\text{A}} = \frac{8.5}{b}$$

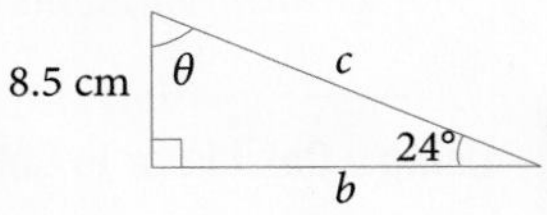

$$b \tan 24° = 8.5$$

$$b = \frac{8.5}{\tan 24°} = \frac{8.5}{0.445228...}$$

$$= 19.091312... \approx 19.1 \text{ cm}$$

Then, calculate the other unknown side length using another trig ratio or the Pythagorean Theorem.

Using trig ratio,

$$\sin 24° = \frac{\text{O}}{\text{H}} = \frac{8.5}{c}$$

$$c \sin 24° = 8.5$$

$$c = \frac{8.5}{\sin 24°} = \frac{8.5}{0.406736...}$$

$$= 20.898043... \approx 20.9 \text{ cm}$$

or

Using Pythagorean Theorem,

$$c^2 = 8.5^2 + 19.1^2$$

$$= 72.25 + 364.81 = 437.06$$

$$c = \sqrt{437.06} = 20.905980... \approx 20.9 \text{ cm}$$

> Using the Pythagorean Theorem to calculate the length of the hypotenuse, *c*, could have resulted in a rounding error or a compound calculation error had there been an error in calculating *b*.

Finally, since the acute angles in a right triangle are complimentary: $\theta = 90° - 24° = 66°$.

(ii) First, calculate the length of one of the unknown sides using one of the primary trig ratios:

$$\cos 72° = \frac{\text{A}}{\text{H}} = \frac{a}{1.64}$$

$$a = 1.64(\cos 72°)$$

$$= 1.64(0.309016...)$$

$$= 0.506787... \approx 0.51 \text{ m}$$

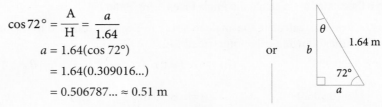

or

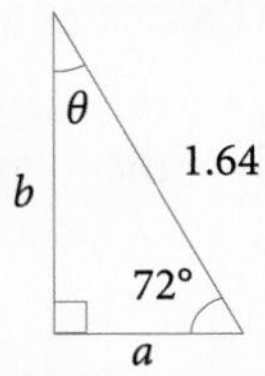

Then, calculate the other unknown side length using another trig ratio or the Pythagorean Theorem:

Solution *continued*

Using trig ratio,

$$\sin 72° = \frac{O}{H} = \frac{b}{1.64}$$

$$b = 1.64(\sin 72°)$$
$$= 1.64(0.951056...)$$
$$= 1.559732... \approx 1.56 \text{ m}$$

or

Using Pythagorean Theorem,

$$a^2 + b^2 = c^2$$
$$b^2 = 1.64^2 - 0.51^2$$
$$= 2.6986 - 0.260 = 2.4295$$
$$b = \sqrt{2.4295}$$
$$= 1.558685... \approx 1.56 \text{ m}$$

Using the Pythagorean Theorem to calculate the length of the unknown leg, b, could have resulted in a rounding error or a compound calculation error had there been an error in calculating a.

Finally, since the acute angles in a right triangle are complimentary: $\theta = 90° - 72° = 18°$.

Example 11.3-g **Solving a Right Triangle Given Two Side Lengths**

Determine the unknown side length and acute angles of the following right triangles (round all answers to the nearest tenth as required):

(i)

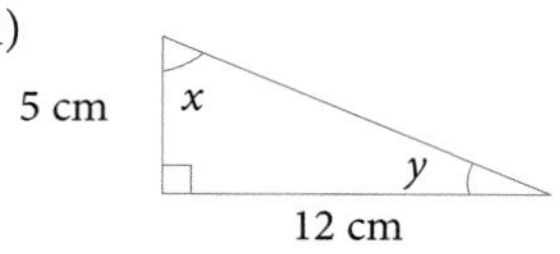

(ii)

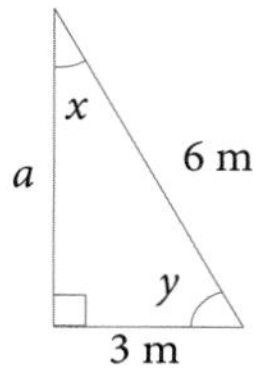

Solution

(i) First, calculate the length of the hypotenuse using the Pythagorean Theorem,

$$c^2 = 5^2 + 12^2 = 25 + 144 = 169$$
$$c = \sqrt{169} = 13$$

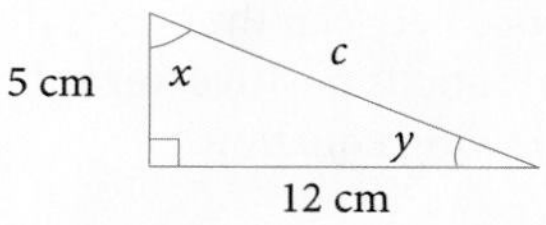

As the opposite and adjacent lengths are provided, use the inverse trig function for tan (i.e., $\tan^{-1}$) to determine the angle, x.

$$x = \tan^{-1}\left(\frac{12}{5}\right) = \tan^{-1}(2.4) = 67.380135... \approx 67.4°$$

Finally, since acute angles in a right triangle are complimentary: $y = 90° - 67.4° = 22.6°$.

(ii) First, calculate the length of the unknown leg using the Pythagorean Theorem,

$$a^2 = 6^2 - 3^2 = 36 - 9 = 27$$
$$a = \sqrt{27} = 5.196152... \approx 5.2 \text{ m}$$

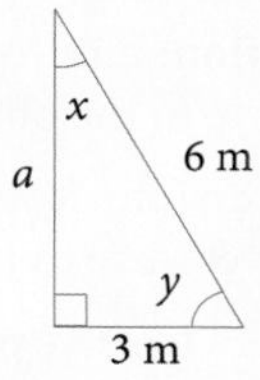

As the opposite and hypotenuse lengths are provided, use the inverse trig function for sin (i.e., $\sin^{-1}$) to determine the angle, x.

$$x = \sin^{-1}\left(\frac{3}{6}\right) = \sin^{-1}(0.5) = 30°$$

Finally, since acute angles in a right triangle are complimentary: $y = 90° - 30° = 60°$.

Slopes of Lines and Angles of Elevation and Depression

Slope of Lines

Recall from Section 9.2, that the definition of the slope of a line is the ratio of Rise to Run, or the ratio of the changes in the y-value to the changes in the x-value between two points, P and Q, on the line:

$$m = \frac{\text{Change in } y \text{ value}}{\text{Change in } x \text{ value}} = \frac{\Delta y}{\Delta x} = \frac{\text{Rise}}{\text{Run}}$$

Now, consider the right triangle that is created when the rise and run of a line are drawn between points P and Q on that line, as illustrated in Exhibits 11.3-c and 11.3-d

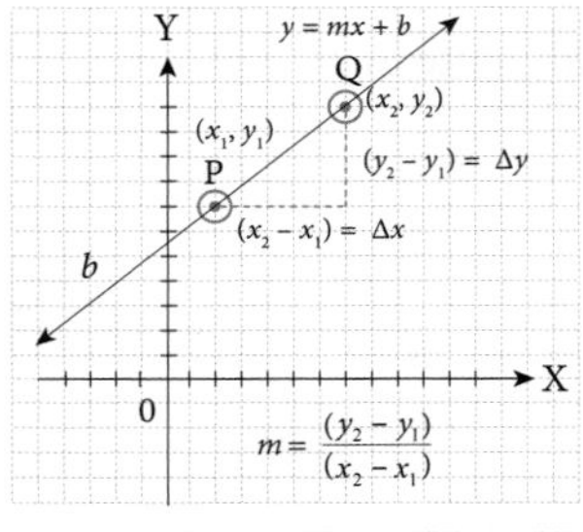

Exhibit 11.3-c Rise and Run Between Points *P* and *Q*

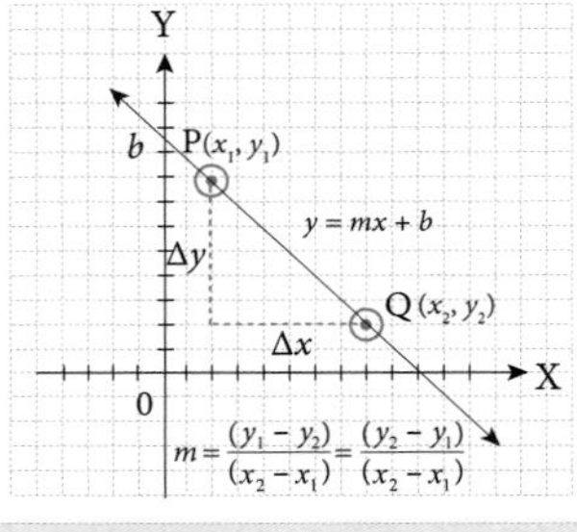

Exhibit 11.3-d Rise and Run Between Points *P* and *Q*

Notice that the tangent ratio of the angle θ is almost exactly the same as the slope of the line. The only difference between the two is that the tangent ratio is irrespective of the direction of the line (i.e., the tangent ratio is positive, regardless of whether the slope of the line is positive or negative). This yields the following equation:

$$\tan\theta = |m| = \frac{\text{Absolute Rise}}{\text{Absolute Run}} = \frac{|y_2 - y_1|}{|x_2 - x_1|}$$

Therefore, we can determine the angle, θ, of any line, by calculating the arc tangent of the slope of the line:

$$\theta = \tan^{-1}(|m|) = \tan^{-1}\left(\frac{|\Delta y|}{|\Delta x|}\right) = \tan^{-1}\left(\frac{|y_2 - y_1|}{|x_2 - x_1|}\right)$$

Angles of elevation and Depression

Angle of Elevation: It is the angle **above** the horizontal line from the observer's eye to the object, known as the angle of sight.

Angle of Depression: It is the angle **below** the horizontal line from the observer's eye to the object known as the line of sight.

Tangents are used to solve problems using angles of elevation and depression.

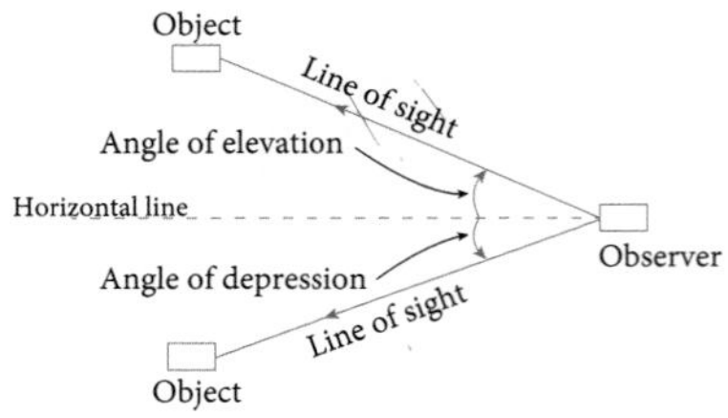

Example 11.3-h **Calculating the Angle of Elevation or Depression**

Determine the angle of elevation/depression of the following, rounded to the nearest tenth of a degree as required:

(i) A ramp with a rise of 1.2 m and a run of 15 m.

(ii) A road with a decline of 500 m over 8 km.

Solution

(i) The slope of the ramp is:

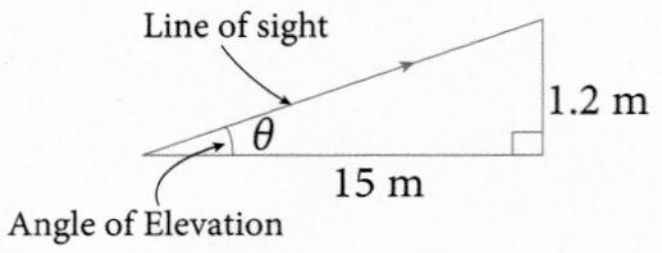

$$m \tan\theta = \frac{1.2}{15} = 0.08$$

$$\tan\theta = 0.08$$

Therefore, the angle of **elevation** is $\theta = \tan^{-1}(0.08) = 4.573921... \approx 4.6°$

(ii) Convert 8 km to 8000 m in order to compare.

The slope of the road (called the grade) is:

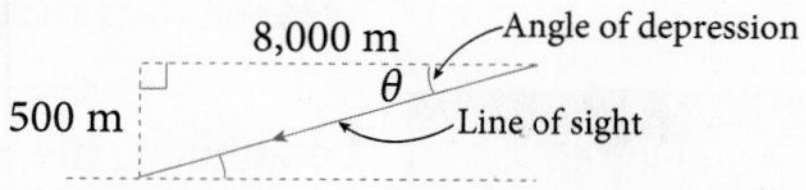

$$m \tan\theta = \frac{500}{8{,}000} = 0.0625$$

Therefore, the angle of **depression** is $\theta = \tan^{-1}(0.0625) = 3.576334... \approx 3.6°$.

Example 11.3-i **Determining the Slope Given the Angle of Elevation/Depression**

Determine the slope of the following, rounded to four decimal places as required:

(i) A skateboard ramp with an angle of elevation of 20°.

(ii) A ski hill with an angle of depression of 33.6°.

Solution

(i) The slope of the ramp is $m = \tan 20° = 0.363970... \approx 0.3640$.

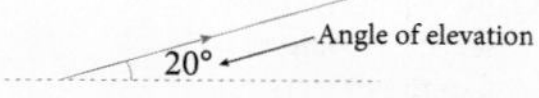

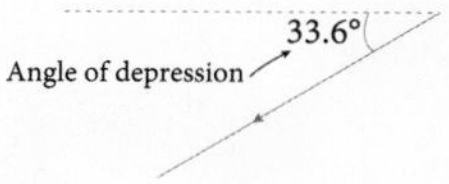

(ii) The slope of the ski hill is $m = \tan 33.6° = 0.664398... \approx 0.6644$.

Pythagorean Theorem and Trigonometric Ratios

The Pythagorean Theorem and primary trigonometric ratios can be combined to yield an important result in trigonometry, $\sin^2\theta + \cos^2\theta = 1$. This result is known as the **Fundamental Pythagorean Trigonometric Identity**.

Consider the following right triangle:

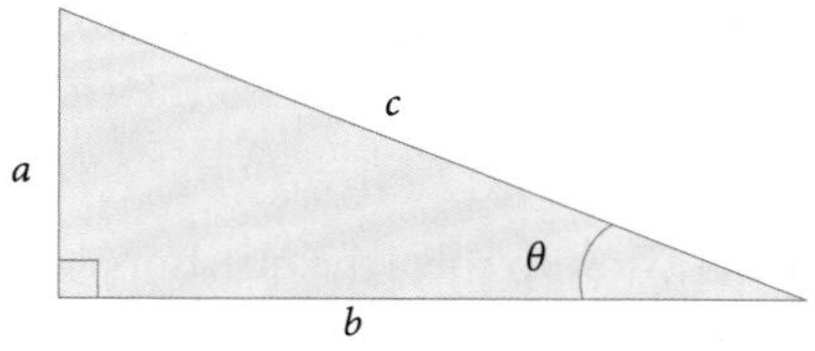

We know,

$$\sin\theta = \frac{a}{c},\ \cos\theta = \frac{b}{c}, \text{ and } a^2 + b^2 = c^2 \text{ (Pythagorean Theorem)}$$

Then $\sin^2\theta + \cos^2\theta = \left(\frac{a}{c}\right)^2 + \left(\frac{b}{c}\right)^2 = \frac{a^2}{c^2} + \frac{b^2}{c^2} = \frac{a^2+b^2}{c^2} = \frac{c^2}{c^2} = 1$

Therefore, $\mathbf{\sin^2\theta + \cos^2\theta = 1}$, regardless of what the value of θ is.

Example 11.3-j **Using the Fundamental Pythagorean Trigonometric Identity to Calculate Exact Trigonometric Ratios**

Using the Fundamental Pythagorean Trigonometric Identity, determine the exact value of $\cos\theta$, given that $\sin\theta = \frac{1}{3}$ (without using a calculator).

Solution

Using $\sin^2\theta + \cos^2\theta = 1$,

Substituting $\sin\theta = \frac{1}{3}$, and solving for θ,

$$\left(\frac{1}{3}\right)^2 + \cos^2\theta = 1$$

$$\cos^2\theta = 1 = \left(\frac{1}{3}\right)^2 = \cos^2\theta = 1 - \frac{1}{9} = \frac{8}{9}$$

$$\cos\theta = \sqrt{\frac{8}{9}} = \sqrt{\frac{4\times 2}{9}} = \frac{2\sqrt{2}}{3}$$

Therefore, $\cos\theta = \frac{2\sqrt{2}}{3}$.

Applications of the Trigonometric Ratios

Example 11.3-k

Determining the Height of the CN Tower

From a point 30 m away from the base of the CN Tower, the angle of elevation to the top of the tower is 83.5°. If the radius of the base is 33 m, determine the height of the tower, rounded to the nearest metre.

Solution

Angle of **elevation** is the angle between the horizontal line and the line from the observer's eye to the object (when the observer is **below** the level of the object).

First, draw a picture of this to better understand how to solve the question:

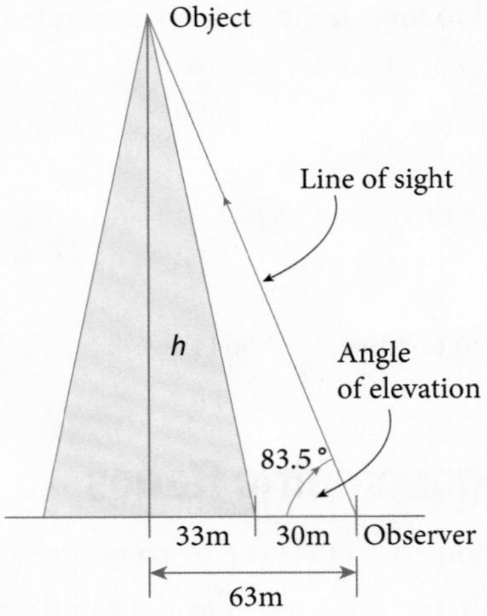

$$\tan 83.5° = \frac{h}{63}$$

$$h = 63\,(\tan 83.5°)$$
$$= 63\,(8.776887...)$$
$$= 552.943903...$$
$$\approx 553 \text{ m}$$

Therefore, the height of the tower is approximately 553 m.

Example 11.3-l

Determining the Distance Across a Lake

From a point 520 m above an elliptical (oval) lake, the angle of depression to one end of the lake is 40.6° and the angle of depression to the other end of the lake is 33.5°. Determine the length of the lake, to the nearest ten metres.

Solution

Angle of **depression** is the angle between the horizontal line and the line from the observer's eye to the object (when the object is **below** the level of the observer).

First draw a picture of this to better understand how to solve the question:

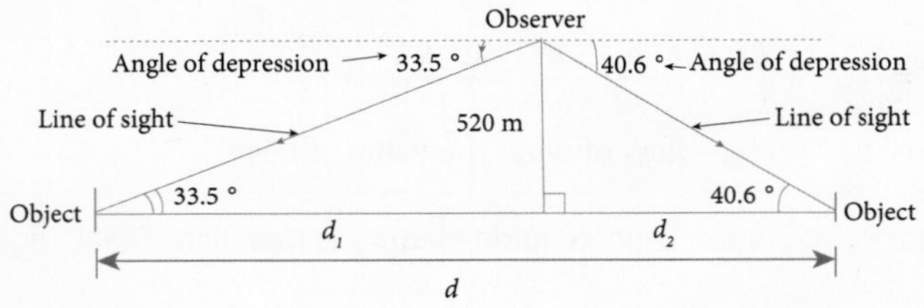

$$\tan 33.5° = \frac{520}{d_1}$$

$$d_1 = \frac{520}{\tan 33.5°} = \frac{520}{0.661885...} = 785.634300... \approx 785.6 \text{ m}$$

$$\tan 40.6° = \frac{520}{d_2}$$

$$d_2 = \frac{520}{\tan 40.6°} = \frac{520}{0.875103...} = 606.694410... \approx 606.7 \text{ m}$$

$d = d_1 + d_2 = 785.6 + 606.7 = 1392.3$ m.

Therefore, the length of the lake is approximately 1,392.3 m.

Example 11.3-m **Calculating the Heading and Groundspeed of a Plane**

An airplane is flying at a groundspeed of 880 km/h. The wind is blowing from due east at a speed of 132 km/h. If the airplane needs to travel due south, find the angle of its trajectory (the "heading") rounded to the nearest hundredth of a degree, and its resultant speed (the groundspeed), rounded to the nearest km/h.

Solution

If the plane were to head due south, the wind from the east would push it off course to the west. As such, the plane needs to fly into the wind (i.e., slightly east of south) in order to fly due south. First, draw a picture of this to better understand how to solve the question:

$$\sin\,\theta = \frac{132}{880} = 0.15$$

$$\theta = \sin^{-1}(0.15) = 8.626926... \approx 8.63°$$

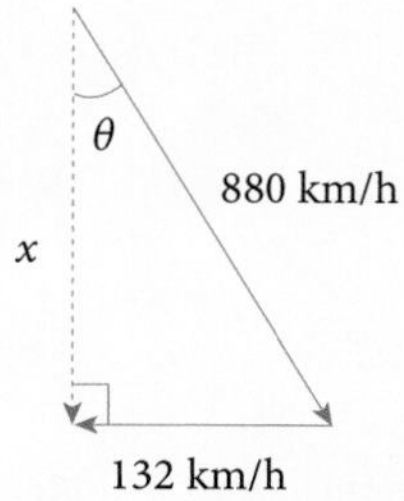

Using Pythagorean Theorem,

$$x^2 = 880^2 - 132^2 = 774,400 - 17,424 = 756,976$$

$$x = \sqrt{756,976} = 870.043677... \approx 870 \text{ km/h}$$

Therefore, the heading of the plane is 8.63°E and the groundspeed of the plane is 870 km/h.

11.3 | Exercises

Answers to odd-numbered problems are available at the end of the textbook.

Given the values of θ in Problems 1 and 2, determine the three, primary trigonometric ratios of θ, rounded to four decimal places.

1.

	θ	$\sin\theta$	$\cos\theta$	$\tan\theta$
a.	65°	?	?	?
b.	12.5°	?	?	?
c.	53.13°	?	?	?

2.

	θ	$\sin\theta$	$\cos\theta$	$\tan\theta$
a.	24°	?	?	?
b.	82.8°	?	?	?
c.	73.74°	?	?	?

Given one trigonometric ratio, in Problems 3 and 4, determine the corresponding angle θ, rounded to the nearest degree, and the other two, primary trigonometric ratios, rounded to four decimal places.

3.

	θ	$\sin\theta$	$\cos\theta$	$\tan\theta$
a.	?	0.4540	?	?
b.	?	?	0.2924	?
c.	?	?	?	0.3639

4.

	θ	$\sin\theta$	$\cos\theta$	$\tan\theta$
a.	?	0.5591	?	?
b.	?	?	0.9743	?
c.	?	?	?	8.1443

Given one trigonometric ratio, in Problems 5 and 6, determine the remaining trigonometric ratios exactly using the Pythagorean Theorem, and determine the corresponding angle, rounded to the nearest degree.

5.

	$\sin\theta$	$\cos\theta$	$\tan\theta$	θ
a.	$\frac{3}{5}$	?	?	?
b.	?	$\frac{24}{25}$	?	?
c.	?	?	$\frac{20}{21}$	?

6.

	$\sin\theta$	$\cos\theta$	$\tan\theta$	θ
a.	$\frac{5}{13}$	?	?	?
b.	?	$\frac{8}{17}$	?	?
c.	?	?	$\frac{12}{35}$	?

Use the special trig ratios in Exhibit 11.3-b to determine the exact value for Problems 7 to 12.

7. $\sin 60° \cdot \cos 45° - \sin 45° \cdot \cos 30°$

8. $\sin 60° \cdot \tan 30° - \sin 30° \cdot \tan 60°$

9. $\dfrac{\sin 45° \cdot \cos 45°}{2 \tan 45°}$

10. $\dfrac{\sin 60° - \sin 30°}{\cos 60° - \cos 30°}$

11. $\tan^2 60° - \sin^2 60° + \cos^2 60°$

12. $\sin^2 45° + \cos^2 30° - \tan^2 30°$

For Problems 13 to 18, determine the length of the unknown side, rounded to the nearest hundredths, for the given right triangles.

13.
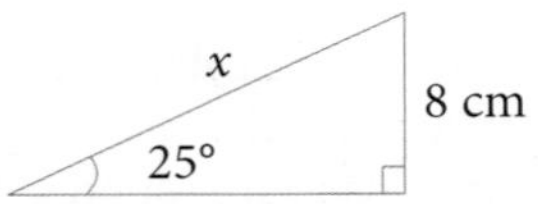

14.
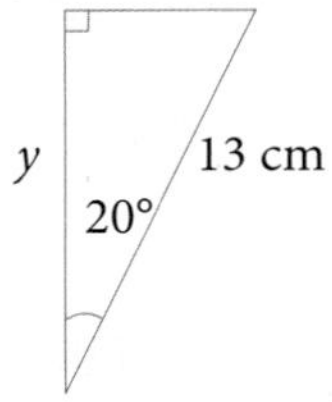

15.
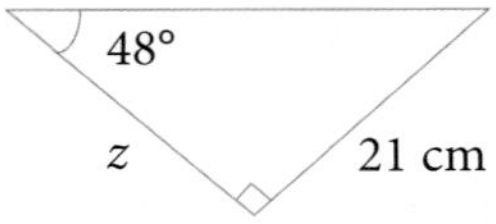

16.
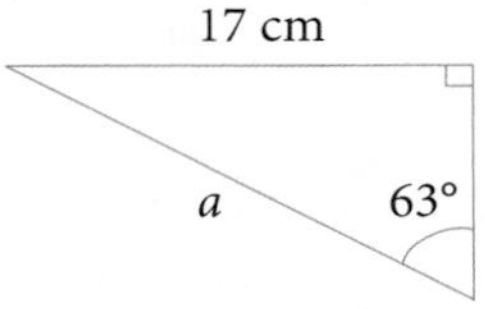

17.
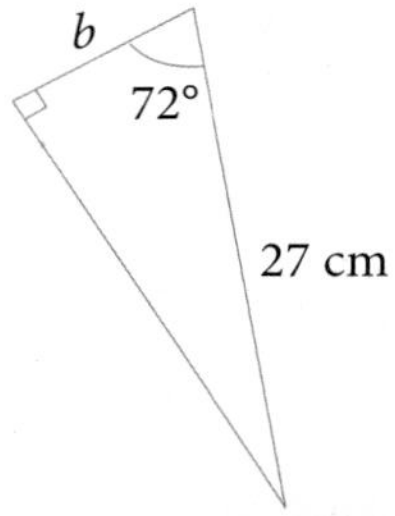

18.
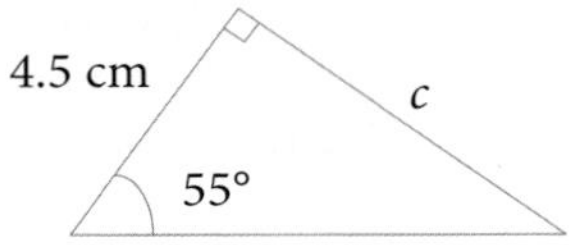

For Problems 19 to 24 determine the value of θ, rounded to the nearest hundredth of a degree, for the given right triangles.

19.
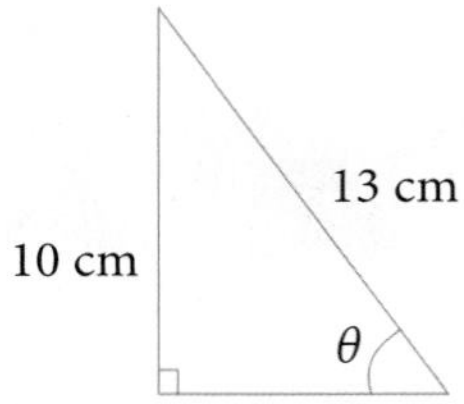

20.
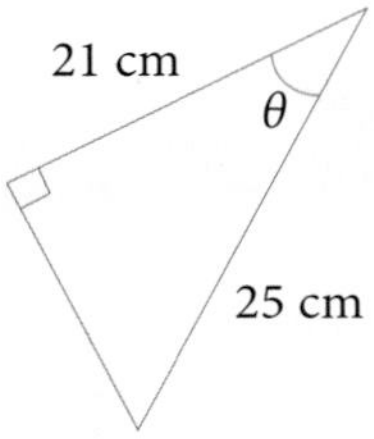

21.
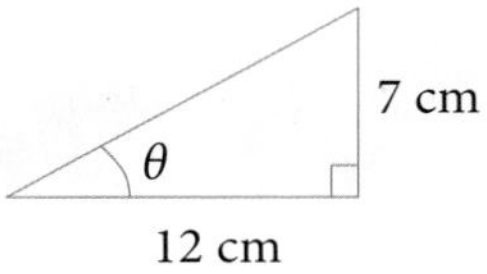

22.
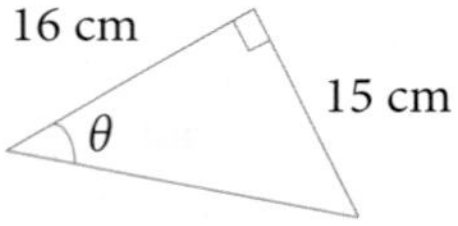

23.
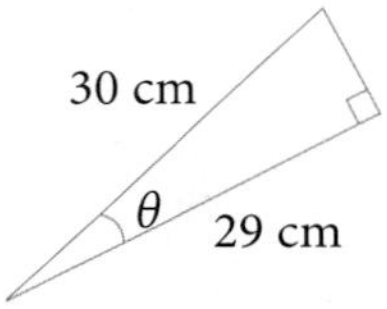

24.
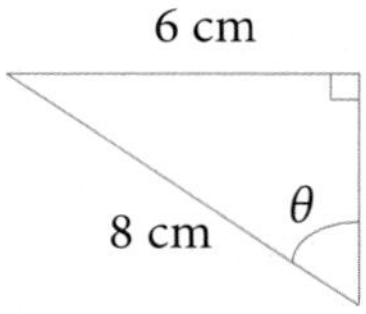

For Problems 25 to 30, solve the given right triangles fully (i.e., identify all missing side lengths and angle measures).

25.
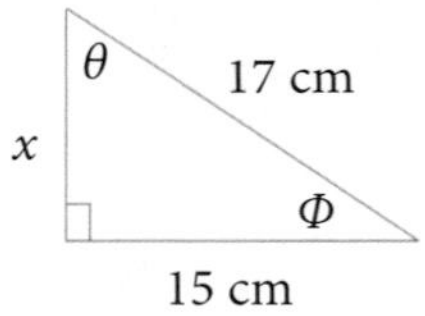

26.
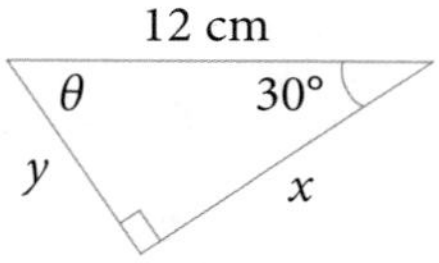

27.
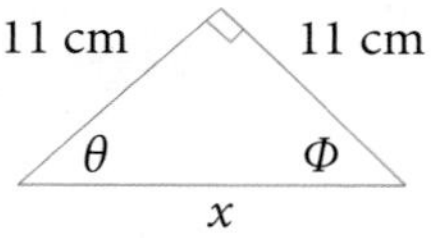

28.
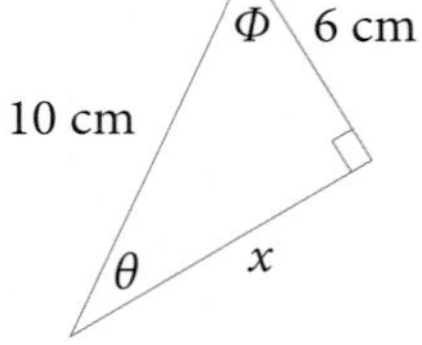

29.
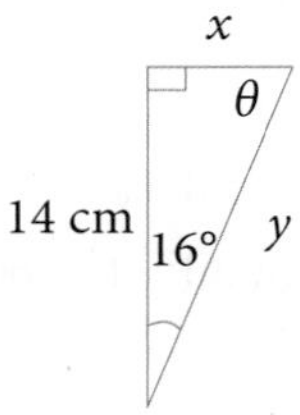

30.
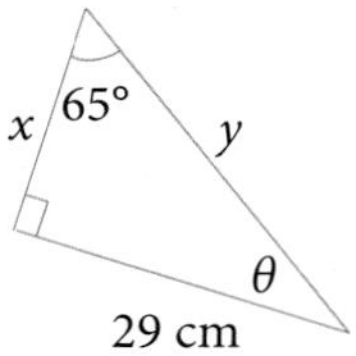

For Problems 31 to 34, determine the angle of elevation/depression, rounded to the nearest degree.

31. A wheelchair ramp that rises 1 inch for every 12 inches along the ground.
32. A bicycle ramp that rises 3 feet for every 8 feet along the ground.
33. A road that descends 500 m vertically for every 6 km horizontally.
34. A ski jump ramp that descends 7 m vertically for every 10 m horizontally.

For Problems 35 to 38, determine the slope, rounded to the nearest thousandth, that corresponds to the angles of elevation/descent.

35. A snowboard ramp with a 12.5° angle of elevation.
36. A mountain railroad with a steep 16.8° angle of elevation.
37. A skiing ramp with a 12.5° angle of descent.
38. A water slide with a 75° angle of descent.

Solve the following application problems:

39. The Burj Khalifa is the tallest building in the world, soaring over Dubai at a pinnacle height of approximately 830 m. From a point on the ground, an observer measures the angle of elevation to the aircraft beacon at the very top of the building to be 77.5°. He then measures the angle of elevation to the observation deck to be 67.85°. Determine the height of the observation deck, rounded to the nearest metre.
40. The distance between the CN Tower, the tallest free-standing building in Canada, and First Canadian Place, the tallest skyscraper in Canada, is 818 m (horizontally). From the top of First Canadian Place, the angle of depression to the bottom of the CN Tower is 20.0°, and the angle of elevation to the space-deck of the CN Tower is 10.4°.

    a. Determine the height of First Canadian Place, rounded to the nearest metre.

    b. Determine the height of the CN Tower space-deck, rounded to the nearest metre.
41. From the cockpit of a light aircraft 1,980 m above the ground, the angle of depression to the closer bank of a small lake is 52.5°, and the angle of depression to the farther bank of the same lake is 31.6°. Determine the distance across the lake, rounded to the nearest ten metres.
42. To measure the height of a hill, a surveyor records a 32.5° angle of elevation from the ground to the top of the hill. The surveyor moves 12 m closer on the flat ground and records a 43.5° angle of elevation to the top of the hill. Determine the height of the hill, rounded to the nearest tenth of a metre.
43. A goose is flying north at a groundspeed of 65 km/h. There is a cross wind coming from the west, blowing at a speed of 30 km/h. Determine the goose's resulting trajectory and groundspeed.
44. A swimmer is attempting to swim across a river. She wishes to land at a point on the opposite shore, directly across from the point she is starting. She swims at a speed of 4 km/h and the current is flowing at a speed of 2.4 km/h downstream.

    a. At what angle will she need to swim upstream in order to reach her desired point on the opposite shore?

    b. If the river is 400 m wide, how long will it take her to reach the other shore?
45. Determine the area of an isosceles triangle with base length of 32 cm and an opposite angle measuring 32°. Round the answer to the nearest tenth of a cm^2.
46. A segment of a circle is the area bounded between a chord and the boundary of the circle. Determine the area of a segment bounded by a chord of length 24 cm in a circle of radius 14 cm. Round the answer to the nearest hundredth of a cm^2.

11.4 | Laws of Sine and Cosine

Introduction

In the previous section, methods for solving right triangles using primary trigonometric ratios, sine, cosine, and tangent were outlined. However, if the triangle is oblique (acute or obtuse), which does not include a right angle, the primary trigonometric ratios do not apply.

In this section, the sine and cosine ratios will be used to develop two laws, namely the **Sine Law** and the **Cosine Law** for solving oblique triangles. One of the benefits of these laws is that they apply not only to oblique triangles, but also to right triangles.

As well, applications of these laws involving oblique triangles, will be discussed.

The Sine Law

The Sine Law provides a formula that relates the sides of a triangle to the sine of its angles.

It is developed as follows:

Draw an oblique triangle ABC and name the sides opposite to angles A, B, and C, as a, b, and c, respectively, as shown in the diagram.

Step 1: Draw a perpedincular line from the vertex B to the opposite side, AC, to meet at D.

(i.e., BD ⊥ AC). Let BD = h_1

In right ΔABD, $\text{Sin A} = \frac{h_1}{c} \Rightarrow h_1 = c \text{ Sin A}$

In right ΔBDC, $\text{Sin C} = \frac{h_1}{a} \Rightarrow h_1 = a \text{ Sin C}$

Equating h_1 from both equations,

$c \text{ Sin A} = a \text{ Sin C}$ Dividing both sides by 'ac',

$$\frac{\sin A}{a} = \frac{\sin C}{c} \quad (1)$$

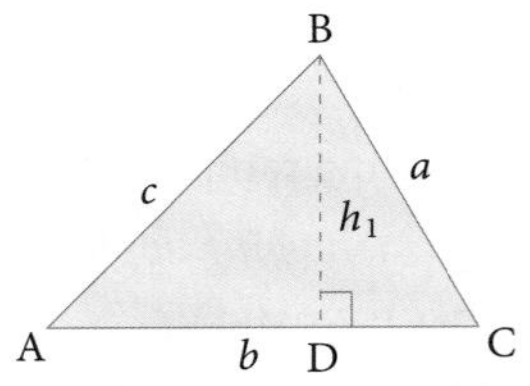

Step 2: Draw a perpendicular line from the vertex C to the opposite side, AB, to meet at E (i.e., CE ⊥ AB). Let CE = h_2.

In right ΔAEC, $\text{Sin A} = \frac{h_2}{b} \Rightarrow h_2 = b \text{ Sin A}$

In right ΔBEC, $\text{Sin B} = \frac{h_2}{a} \Rightarrow h_2 = a \text{ Sin B}$

Equating h_2 from both equations,

$b \text{ Sin A} = a \text{ Sin B}$ Dividing both sides by 'ab',

$$\frac{\sin A}{a} = \frac{\sin B}{b} \quad (2)$$

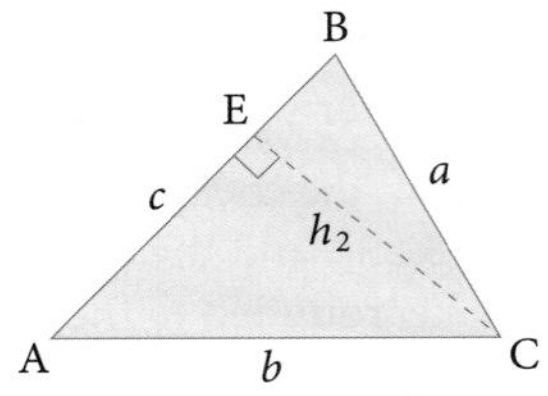

Step 3: Since $\frac{\sin A}{a} = \frac{\sin C}{c}$, from equation (1) and $\frac{\sin A}{a} = \frac{\sin B}{b}$, from equation (2),

We have, $\frac{\sin A}{a} = \frac{\sin B}{b} = \frac{\sin C}{c}$

This can be rearranged to:

$$\frac{a}{\sin A} = \frac{b}{\sin B} = \frac{c}{\sin C}$$

Sine Law for Sides	Sine Law for Angles
$\frac{a}{\sin A} = \frac{b}{\sin B} = \frac{c}{\sin C}$	$\frac{\sin A}{a} = \frac{\sin B}{b} = \frac{\sin C}{c}$

Sine Law is used to solve a triangle primarily in the following two situations:

- Two side lengths and an angle measure opposite to one of them are known (SSA).
- Two angle measures and any one side length are known (AAS or ASA).

  (The third angle measure is found by using IAT - Part 1: the sum of all angles in a triangle is 180°.)

Example 11.4-a **Calculating Side Lengths using the Sine Law, Given Two Angle Measures and a Side Length**

Given the following triangles, use the Sine Law to find the indicated side length. Round the answers to the nearest integer.

(i) In ΔXYZ, ∠X = 83°, ∠Z = 35°, and z = 10 cm. Find x.

(ii) In ΔABC, ∠A = 60°, ∠C = 54°, and b = 16 mm. Find a.

Solution

(i) Draw and label ΔXYZ.

Two angle measures and a side length opposite to one of them (AAS) are known.

Using the Sine Law for sides to find x,

$$\frac{x}{\sin X} = \frac{z}{\sin Z} \quad \text{Substituting the given values,}$$

$$\frac{x}{\sin 83°} = \frac{10}{\sin 35°} \quad \text{Solving for } x,$$

$$x = \frac{10 \sin 83°}{\sin 35°}$$

$$x = 17.304514... \approx 17 \text{ cm}$$

Therefore, $x \approx 17$ cm

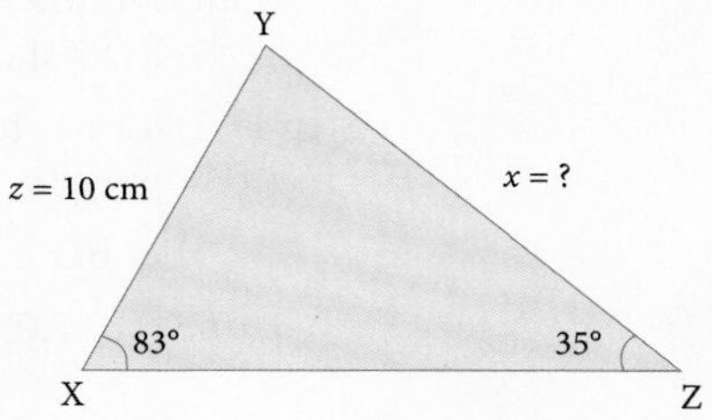

(ii) Draw and label ΔABC.

Two angle measures and a side length (AAS) are known. However, the side is not opposite to one of the known angles.

Therefore, first find the third angle using IAT - Part 1 and then use the Sine Law.

$$\angle A + \angle B + \angle C = 180°$$

$$\angle B = 180° - 54° - 60°$$

$$\angle B = 66°$$

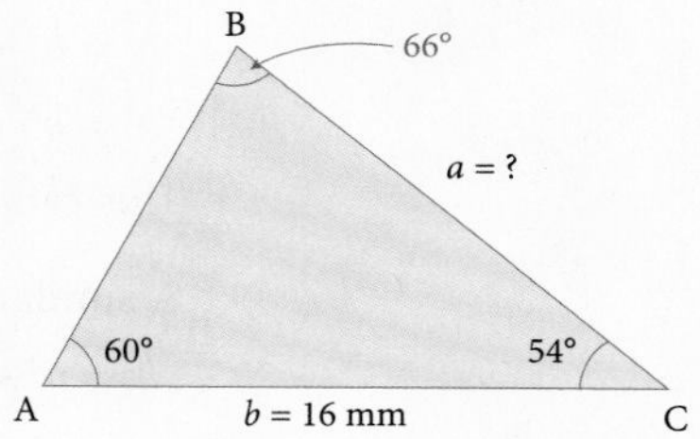

Now, using the Sine Law for sides to find a,

$$\frac{a}{\sin A} = \frac{b}{\sin B} \quad \text{Substituting the given values,}$$

$$\frac{a}{\sin 60°} = \frac{16}{\sin 66°} \quad \text{Solving for } a,$$

$$a = \frac{16 \sin 60°}{\sin 66°}$$

$$a = 15.167725... \approx 15 \text{ mm}$$

Therefore, $a \approx 15$ mm

Example 11.4-b **Calculating Angle Measure using the Sine Law, Given Two Side Lengths and an Angle Measure**

Given ΔSTU with $\angle U = 95°$, $u = 22$ cm, $t = 20$ cm, use the Sine Law to find $\angle T$. Round the answer to the nearest degree.

Solution

Draw and label ΔSTU.

Two side lengths and the angle measure opposite to one of them (SSA) are known.

Using the Sine Law for angles to find T,

$$\frac{\sin T}{t} = \frac{\sin U}{u} \quad \text{Substituting the given values,}$$

$$\frac{\sin T}{20} = \frac{\sin 95°}{22} \quad \text{Solving for T,}$$

$$\sin T = \frac{20 \sin 95°}{22}$$

$$T = \sin^{-1}\left(\frac{20 \sin 95°}{22}\right)$$

$$T = 64.908476... \approx 65°$$

Therefore, $T \approx 65°$

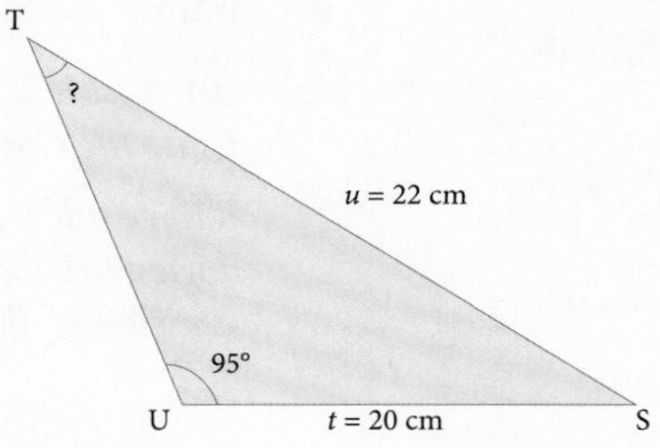

The Cosine Law

The Cosine Law provides a formula that relates the lengths of the sides of a triangle to the cosine of one of its angles. It is developed as follows:

Draw an oblique triangle ABC and name the sides opposite to angles A, B, and C as a, b, and c, respectively, as shown in the diagram.

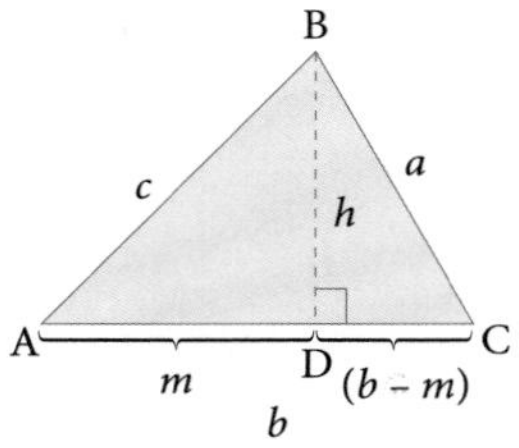

Step 1: Draw a perpendicular line from the vertex B to the opposite side, AC, to meet at D (i.e. BD ⊥ AC).

Let BD = h and AD = m

Since AC = b, DC = $(b - m)$

In right ΔADB, $\text{Cos A} = \dfrac{m}{c} \Rightarrow m = c \text{ Cos A}$ (1)

Step 2: In right ΔBDC, using the Pythagorean Theorem,

$a^2 = (b - m)^2 + h^2$ Expanding,

$a^2 = b^2 - 2bm + m^2 + h^2$ Regrouping,

$a^2 = b^2 + \underbrace{m^2 + h^2} - 2bm$ Using Pythagorean Property, $m^2 + h^2 = c^2$, in right ΔADB,

$a^2 = b^2 + c^2 - 2bm$ Substituting $m = c$ Cos A from (1)

$a^2 = b^2 + c^2 - 2bc \text{ Cos A}$

This can be rearranged to $\text{Cos A} = \dfrac{b^2 + c^2 - a^2}{2bc}$

A similar procedure can be used to obtain:

$b^2 = a^2 + c^2 - 2ac \text{ Cos B}$, and

$c^2 = a^2 + b^2 - 2ab \text{ Cos C}$

Cosine Law for Sides	Cosine Law for Angles
$a^2 = b^2 + c^2 - 2bc \text{ CosA}$	$\text{Cos A} = \dfrac{b^2 + c^2 - a^2}{2bc}$
$b^2 = a^2 + c^2 - 2ac \text{ Cos B}$	$\text{Cos B} = \dfrac{a^2 + c^2 - b^2}{2ac}$
$c^2 = a^2 + b^2 - 2ab \text{ Cos C}$	$\text{Cos C} = \dfrac{a^2 + b^2 - c^2}{2ab}$

Cosine Law is primarily used to solve triangles in the following two situations:

- Two side lengths and the contained (included) angle measure are known, (SAS).
- All three side lengths are known, (SSS).

Note: *If two side lengths and the contained angle measure are known, calculate the third side length using the Cosine Law and the other two angle measures can be calculated using the Sine Law.*

If three side lengths are known, calculate one of the angle measure using the Cosine Law and another angle can be calculated using the Sine Law. The third angle measure can be calculated using IAT - Part 1 (the sum of all angles in a triangle is 180°).

Example 11.4-c Calculating Side Length Using the Cosine Law, Given Two Side Lengths and the Contained Angle Measure

Given ΔQRS with ∠S=50°, q=5.8 m, and r=7.3 m, use the Cosine Law to find s. Round the answer to one decimal place.

Solution

Draw and label ΔQRS.

Two side lengths and the contained angle measure (SAS) are known.

Using the Cosine Law for Sides to find s,

$$s^2 = r^2 + q^2 - 2rq \cos S$$

Substituting the given values,

$$s^2 = 7.3^2 + 5.8^2 - 2(7.3)(5.8) \cos 50°$$

Solving for s,

$$s = \sqrt{7.3^2 + 5.8^2 - 2(7.3)(5.8) \cos 50°}$$

$$s = 5.700767... \approx 5.7 \text{ m}$$

Therefore, $s \approx 5.7$ m

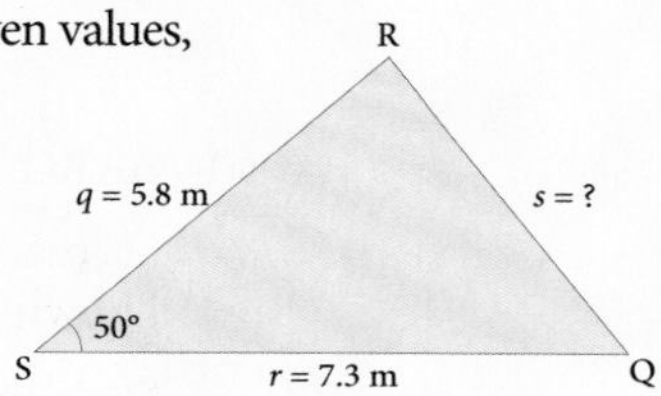

Example 11.4-d Calculating Angle Measure Using the Cosine Law, Given Three Side Lengths

Given ΔPQR with p = 9.1 mm, q = 10.5 mm, and r = 6.0 mm, use the Cosine Law to find ∠R. Round the answer to the nearest degree.

Solution

Draw and label ΔPQR.

Three side lengths (SSS) are known. Using the Cosine Law for Angles to find ∠R,

$$\cos R = \frac{p^2 + q^2 - r^2}{2pq}$$

Substituting the given values,

$$\cos R = \frac{9.1^2 + 10.5^2 - 6.0^2}{2(9.1)(10.5)}$$

Solving for R,

$$R = \cos^{-1}\left(\frac{9.1^2 + 10.5^2 - 6.0^2}{2(9.1)(10.5)}\right)$$

$$R = 34.727233... \approx 35°$$

Therefore, ∠R ≈ 35°

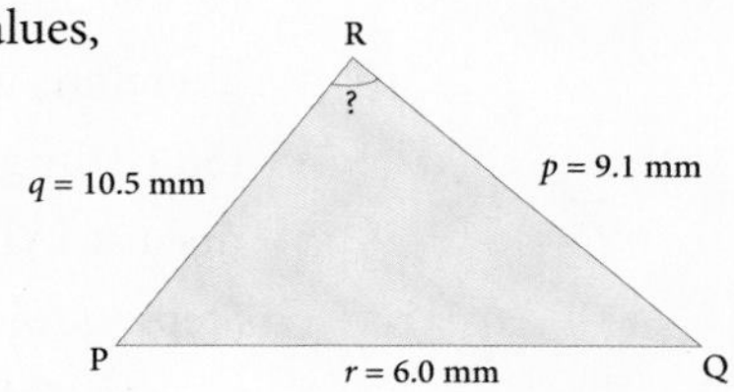

Solving Triangles using the Sine Law and the Cosine Law

Solving a triangle refers to finding the measurements of unknown sides and angles of that triangle.

A triangle has six measurements, three sides and three angles. To solve a triangle, the measure of at least one side and two other measures are necessary (it is not possible to solve a triangle with three angle measures only.).

As explained in the previous examples, different laws are used to solve for the measures of the unknown sides and angles of a triangle based on the given information. The following table summarizes these generalizations.

Given Information	Diagram	Law Required
Two angles and a side (AAS or ASA)		Sine Law
Two sides and an angle opposite to one of them (SSA)	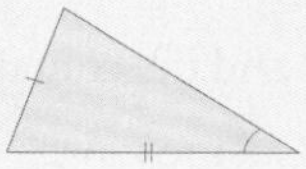	Sine Law
Two sides and the contained angle (SAS)	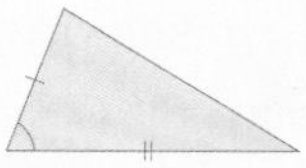	Cosine Law
Three sides (SSS)	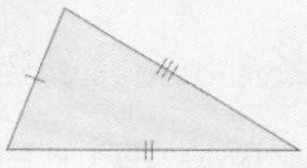	Cosine Law

Table 11.4 Use of Sine Law and Cosine Law in Different Situations

Example 11.4-e Identifying the Use of the Sine Law and the Cosine Law in Solving Triangles

For each of the following situations, determine whether to use the Sine Law or the Cosine Law to solve the triangles. Also, explain the steps required in solving for the unknown side lengths and angle measures.

(i) ΔABC, given b, c, and $\angle$C (ii) ΔABC, given $\angle$A, $\angle$B, and c (iii) ΔABC, given a, b, and c

(iv) ΔABC, given a, b, and $\angle$C (v) ΔABC, given $\angle$B, $\angle$C, and b

Solution

(i) ΔABC, given b, c, and $\angle$C

i.e. two side lengths and an angle measures opposite to one of them are known (SSA). Therefore, use the Sine Law.

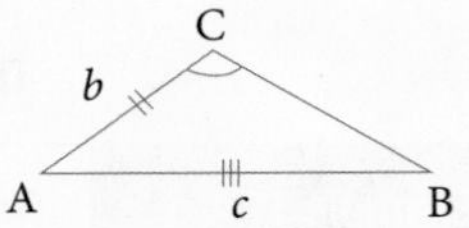

Steps to solve for the unknown measurements of the triangle:

Step 1: Solve for $\angle$B: use the Sine Law for Angles $\left(\frac{\sin B}{b} = \frac{\sin C}{c}\right)$

Step 2: Solve for $\angle$A: use IAT - Part 1 ($\angle A + \angle B + \angle C = 180°$)

Step 3: Solve for a: use the Sine Law for Sides $\left(\frac{a}{\sin A} = \frac{c}{\sin C}\right)$

(ii) ΔABC, given $\angle$A, $\angle$B, and c

i.e. two angle measures and a side lengths are known (ASA).

Therefore, use the Sine Law.

(Since the given side is not opposite to the known angle, first use IAT - Part 1 to find the third angle and then use the Sine Law).

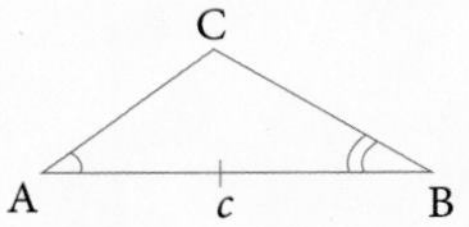

Steps to solve for the unknown measurements of the triangle:

Step 1: Solve for $\angle$C: use IAT - Part 1 ($\angle A + \angle B + \angle C = 180°$)

Step 2: Solve for a and b: use the Sine Law for Sides

$$\left(\frac{a}{\sin A} = \frac{b}{\sin B} = \frac{c}{\sin C}\right)$$

(iii) ΔABC, given a, b, and c

i.e. three side lengths are known (SSS)

Therefore, use the Cosine Law.

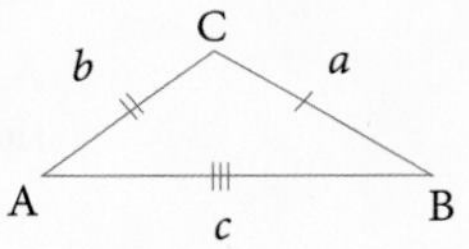

Steps to solve for the unknown measurements of the triangle:

Step 1: Solve for $\angle$A: use the Cosine Law for Angles

$$\left(\cos A = \frac{a^2 + b^2 - c^2}{2ab}\right)$$

Step 2: Solve for $\angle$B: Sine Law for Angles $\left(\frac{\sin A}{a} = \frac{\sin B}{b}\right)$

Step 3: Solve for $\angle$C: use IAT - Part 1 ($\angle A + \angle B + \angle C = 180°$)

(iv) ΔABC, given a, b, and $\angle$C

i.e. two side lengths and the contained angle measures are known (SAS)

Therefore, use the Cosine Law.

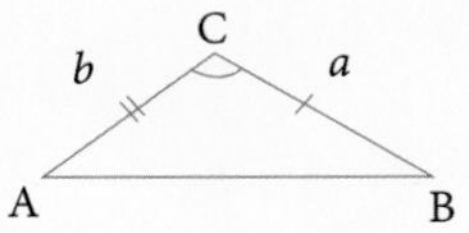

Steps to solve for the unknown measurements of the triangle:

Step 1: Solve for c: use the Cosine Law for Sides
($c^2 = a^2 + b^2 - 2ab$ Cos C)

Step 2: Solve for $\angle$A: use the Sine Law for Angles $\left(\frac{\sin A}{a} = \frac{\sin C}{c}\right)$

Step 3: Solve for $\angle$B: use IAT - Part 1 ($\angle A + \angle B + \angle C = 180°$)

Solution
continued

(v) ΔABC, given $\angle B$, $\angle C$, and b

i.e. two angle measures and a side lengths opposite to a given angle are known (AAS).

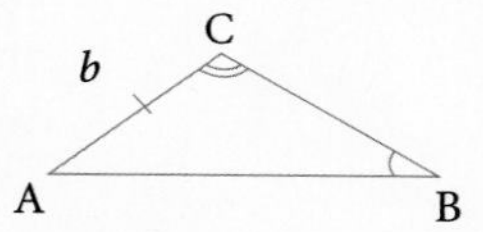

Therefore, use the Sine Law.

Steps to solve for the unknown measurements of the triangle:

Step 1: Solve for $\angle A$: use IAT - Part 1 ($\angle A + \angle B + \angle C = 180°$)

Step 2: Solve for a and c: use the Sine Law for Sides

$$\left(\frac{a}{\sin A} = \frac{b}{\sin B} = \frac{c}{\sin C}\right)$$

Identifying whether to use the Sine Law or the Cosine Law is the first step in the solution to solve the triangle. In each of the triangles listed in the above examples, there is enough information given to solve for all the unknown measures of the triangle.

These unknown measures can be determined using the Sine Law, the Cosine Law, or using IAT-Part 1 and applying the Sine and Cosine Laws repeatedly until all the unknown measures are solved.

Note: In the following examples and exercises, only acute angles will be used in calculating the solutions to angles using Sine values.

Example 11.4-f

Solving a Triangle Given SSA

In ΔSTU, t = 15 cm, u = 12 cm, and $\angle T = 65°$. Solve the triangle. Round angles to the nearest degree, and side lengths to one decimal place.

Solution

Using the Sine Law for Angles,

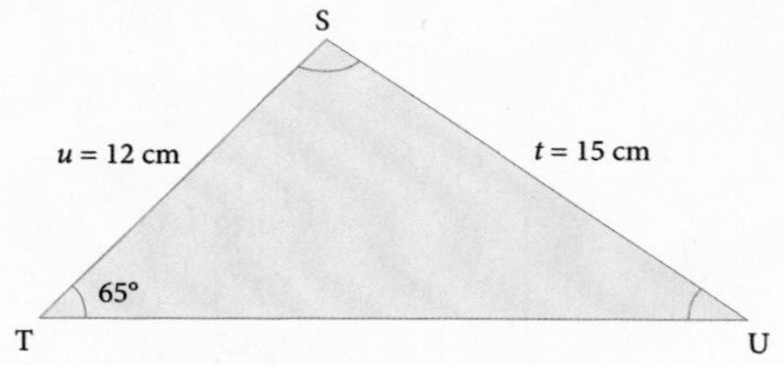

$$\frac{\sin T}{t} = \frac{\sin U}{u}$$ Substituting values,

$$\frac{\sin 65}{15} = \frac{\sin U}{12}$$ Solving for U,

$$\sin U = \frac{12 \cdot \sin 65}{15}$$

$$U = \sin^{-1}\left(\frac{12 \cdot \sin 65}{15}\right)$$

$$U = 46.4726937...$$

$$\angle U = 46°$$

To solve the triangle, we need to find $\angle S$ and s.

Using IAT-Part 1

$$\angle S + \angle T + \angle U = 180°$$

$$\angle S = 180° - 65° - 46°$$

$$\angle S = 69°$$

Method 1:

Using the Sine Law for Sides to find side s,

$$\frac{s}{\sin S} = \frac{t}{\sin T}$$

$$\frac{s}{\sin 69°} = \frac{15}{\sin 65°}$$

$$s = \frac{51 \sin 69°}{\sin 65°}$$

$$s = 15.451380...$$

$$s \approx 15.5 \text{ cm}$$

or

Method 2:

Using the Cosine Law for Sides to find side s,

$$s^2 = t^2 + u^2 - 2tu \cos S$$

$$s^2 = 15^2 + 12^2 - 2(15)(12) \cos 69°$$

$$s = \sqrt{15^2 + 12^2 - 2(15)(12) \cos 69°}$$

$$s = 15.495311...$$

$$s \approx 15.5 \text{ cm}$$

Example 11.4-g

Solving a Triangle Given SAS

In ΔXYZ, $x = 6.2$ m, $\angle Y = 50°$, and $z = 5.8$m. Solve the triangle. Round angles to the nearest degree, and side length to one decimal place.

Solution

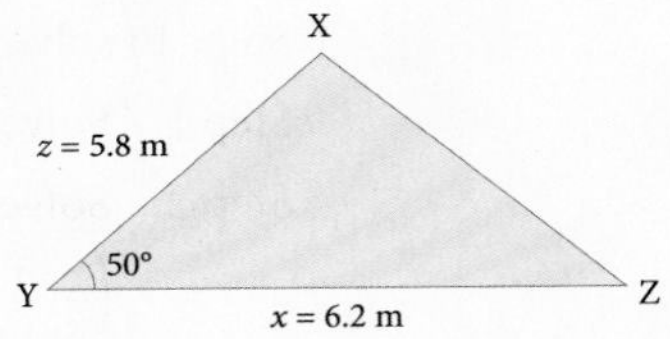

To solve the triangle, we need to find y, $\angle X$, and $\angle Z$,

Using the Cosine Law for Sides,

$$y^2 = x^2 + z^2 - 2xz \text{ Cos Y}$$

$$y^2 = (6.2)^2 + (5.8)^2 - 2(6.2)(5.8) \text{ Cos } 50°$$

$$y = \sqrt{(6.2)^2 + (5.8)^2 - 2(6.2)(5.8) \text{ Cos } 50°}$$

$$y = 5.084351...$$

$$y = 5.1 \text{ cm}$$

Method 1:

Using the Cosine Law for Angles to find $\angle Z$,

$$\cos Z = \frac{x^2 + y^2 - z^2}{2xy}$$

$$\cos Z = \frac{(6.2)^2 + (5.1)^2 - (5.8)^2}{2(6.2)(5.1)}$$

$$Z = \cos^{-1}\left(\frac{(6.2)^2 + (5.1)^2 - (5.8)^2}{2(6.2)(5.1)}\right)$$

$$Z = 60.843836...$$

$$\angle Z \approx 61°$$

Using IAT - Part 1, to find $\angle X$,

$$\angle X + \angle Y + \angle Z = 180°$$

$$\angle X = 180° - 50° - 61°$$

$$\angle X = 69°$$

or

Method 2:

Using the Sine Law for Angles to find $\angle X$,

$$\frac{\sin X}{x} = \frac{\sin Y}{y}$$

$$\frac{\sin X}{6.2} = \frac{\sin 50°}{5.1}$$

$$\sin X = \frac{6.2 \times \sin 50°}{5.1}$$

$$X = \sin^{-1}\left(\frac{6.2 \times \sin 50°}{5.1}\right)$$

$$X = 68.633613...$$

$$\angle X \approx 69°$$

Using IAT - Part 1, to find $\angle Z$,

$$\angle X + \angle Y + \angle Z = 180°$$

$$\angle Z = 180° - 69° - 50°$$

$$\angle Z = 61°$$

Applications of the Sine Law and the Cosine Law

Example 11.4-h

Calculating a Resultant Force

Two forces act on an object. One force acts due north with a magnitude of 81 N and the second acts N 38° E with a magnitude of 65 N. Determine the magnitude and direction of the resultant force. Round the answer to two decimal places.

Solution

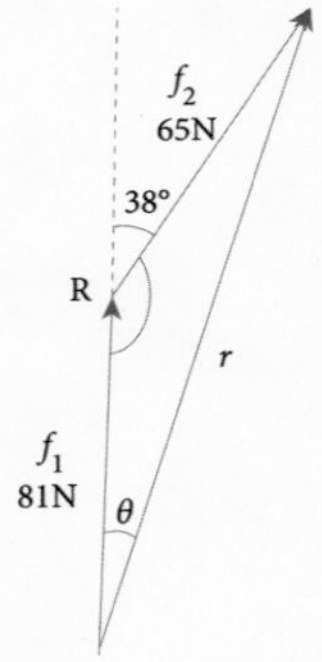

Draw a triangle to represent the magnitude and direction of the two forces, f_1 and f_2, and its resultant, r, as shown in the diagram.

In the triangle, we have known measures of two sides and the contained angle (SAS).

Therefore, use the Cosine Law for Sides in order to determine the magnitude of the resultant, r.

$$r^2 = f_1^2 + f_2^2 - 2f_1 f_2 \cos R$$

$$r^2 = 81^2 + 65^2 - 2(81)(65) \text{ Cos } 142°$$

$$r = \sqrt{81^2 + 65^2 - 2(81)(65) \text{ Cos } 142°}$$

$$r = 138.143958...$$

Note: $\angle$*R is the supplement of* N 38° E.

Solution *continued*

Now, use the Sine Law for Angles to determine the direction of the resultant, θ.

$$\frac{\sin\theta}{65} = \frac{\sin 142°}{138.14}$$

$$\sin\theta = \frac{65\sin 142°}{138.14}$$

$$\theta = \sin^{-1}\left(\frac{65\sin 142°}{138.14}\right)$$

$$\theta = 16.839492...°$$

$$\theta \approx 16.84°$$

Therefore, the resultant force has a magnitude of 138.14 N in a direction of N 16.84° E.

Example 11.4-i **Calculating the Length between the Tips of the Hands of a Clock**

A clock has a long hand of length 5 cm and a short hand of length 3 cm. What is the distance between the tips of the hands of the clock at 4 o'clock?

Solution

In the clock face, there are 12 equal divisions in a complete turn of 360°.

Therefore, the angle between each division at the center is equal to $\frac{360°}{12} = 30°$.

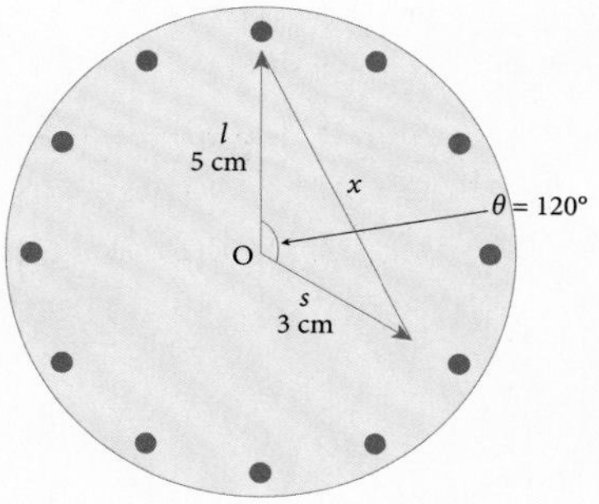

At 4 o'clock the hands are 4 divisions apart. That is, the angle between the hands of the clock at the center at 4 o'clock is 4 × 30° = 120°.

Using the Cosine Law for Sides to determine the length x,

$$x^2 = l^2 + s^2 - 2ls\text{ Cos }\theta$$

$$x^2 = 5^2 + 3^2 - 2(5)(3)\text{ Cos }120°$$

$$x = \sqrt{5^2 + 3^2 - 2(5)(3)\text{ Cos }120°}$$

$$x = 7\text{ cm}$$

Therefore, the length between the tips of the hands of the clock at 4 o'clock is 7 cm.

11.4 | Exercises

Answers to odd-numbered problems are available at the end of the textbook.

For the Problems in this exercise, express the distances rounded to one decimal place and the angles rounded to the nearest degree, wherever aplicable.

For Problems 1 to 8 use the Sine Law for Sides to find the length of the indicated side in each of the triangles.

1.
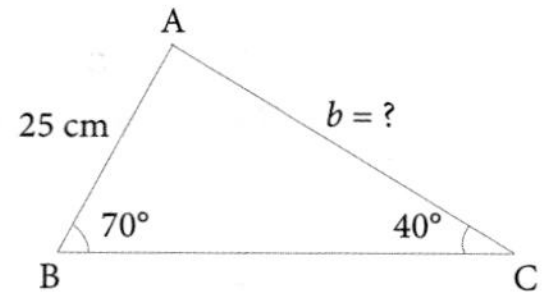

2.
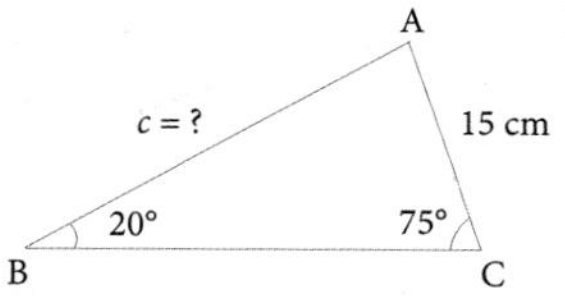

3.
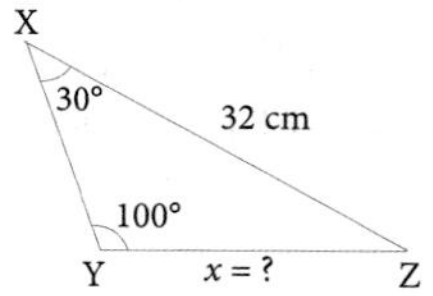

4.
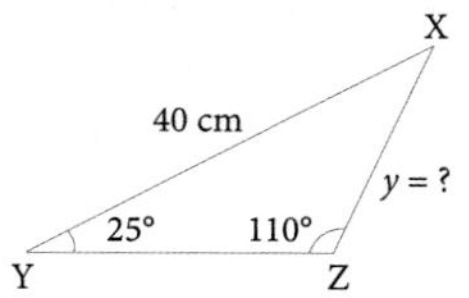

5.
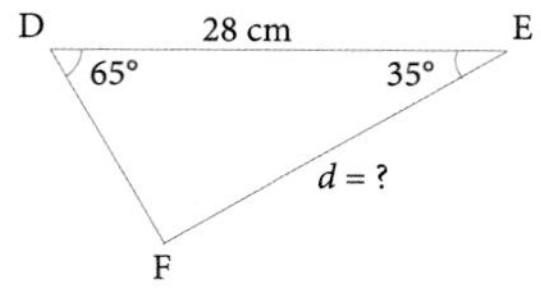

6.
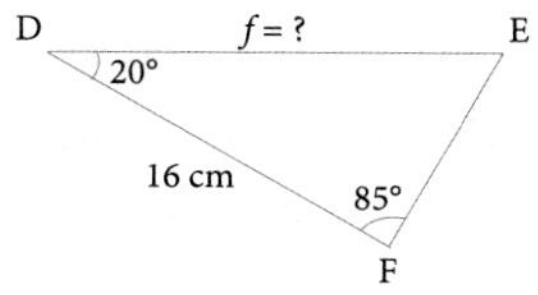

7.
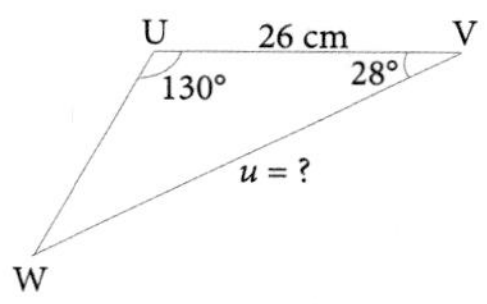

8.
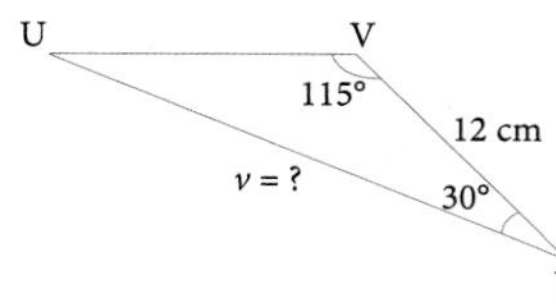

For Problems 9 to 16, use the Sine Law for Angles to find the measure of the indicated angle in each of the triangles.

9.
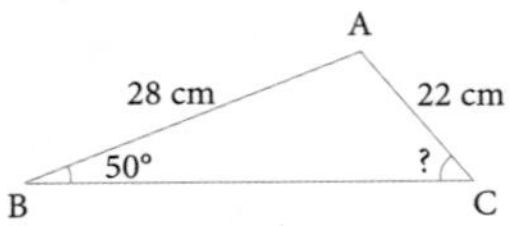

10.
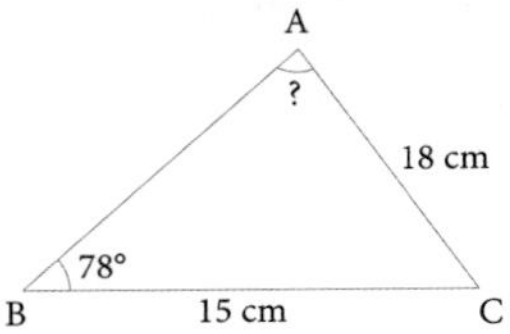

11.
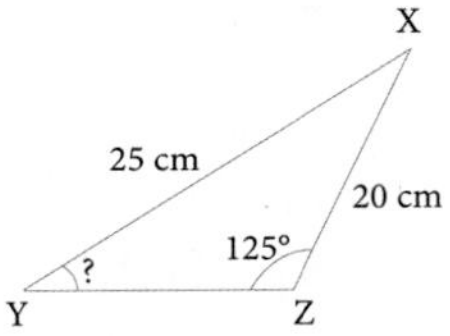

12.
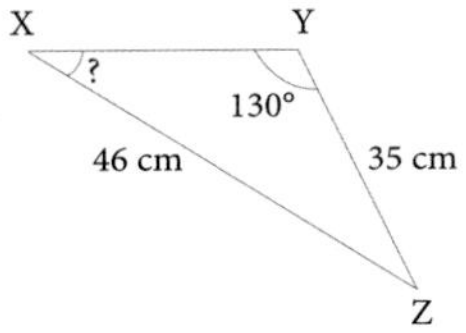

13.
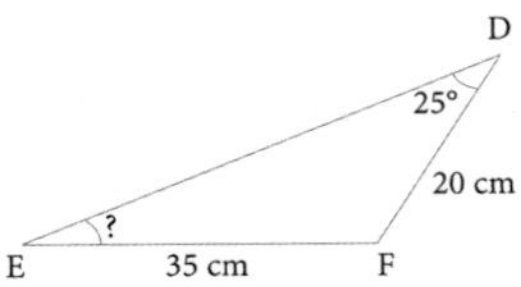

14.
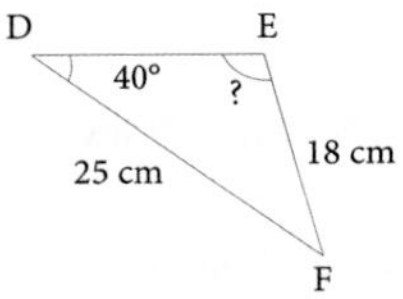

15.
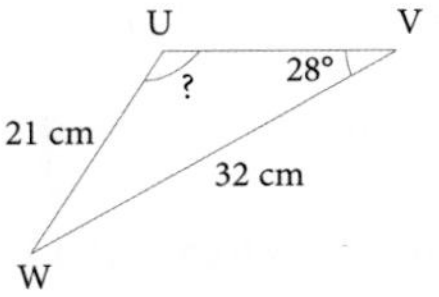

16.
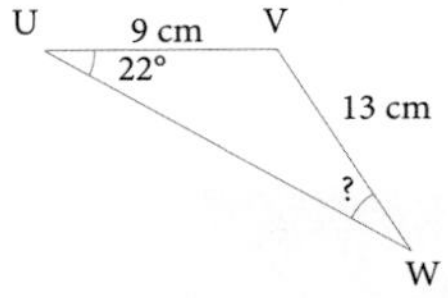

For Problems 17 to 24 use the Cosine Law for Sides to find the length of the indicated side in each of the triangles.

17.
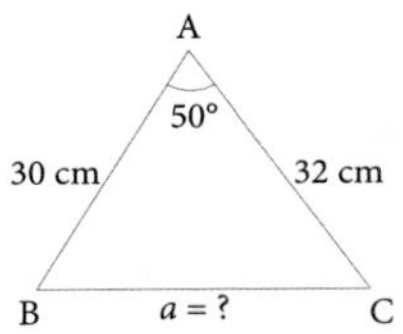

18.
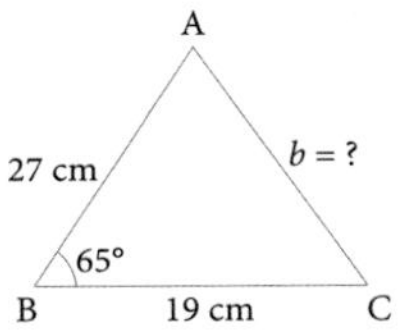

19.
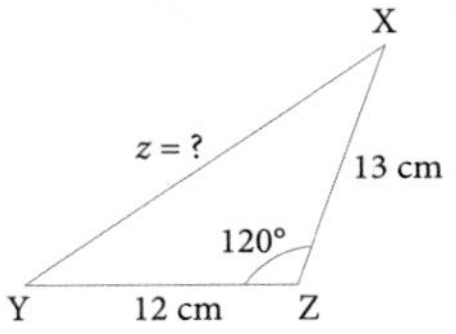

20.
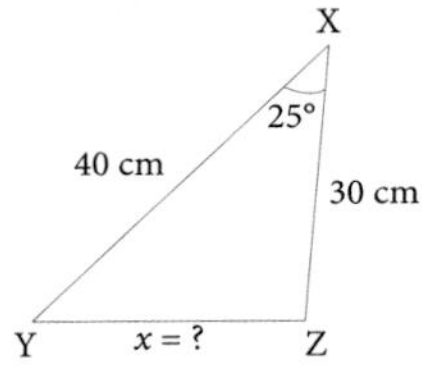

21.
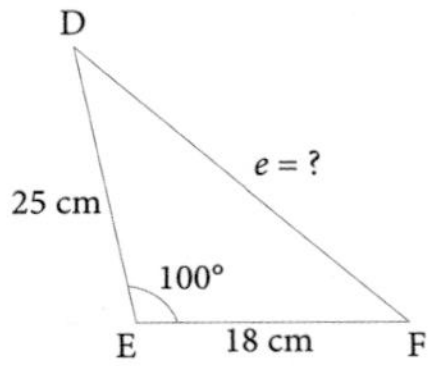

22.
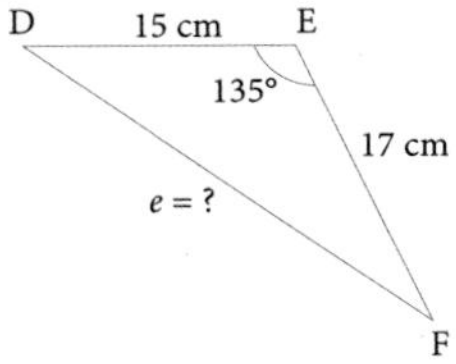

23.
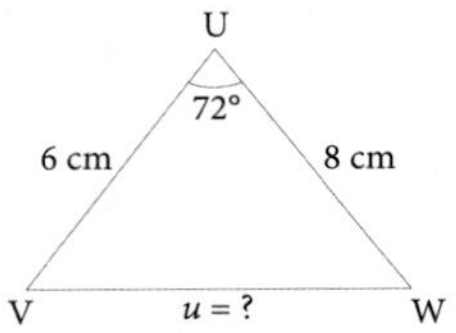

24.
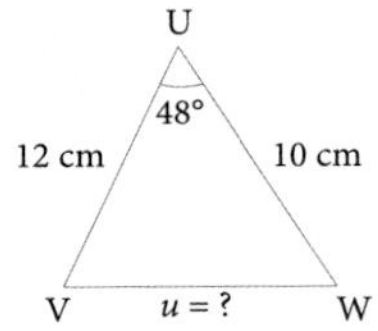

For Problems 25 to 32 use the Cosine Law for Angles to find the measure of the indicated angle in each of the triangles.

25.
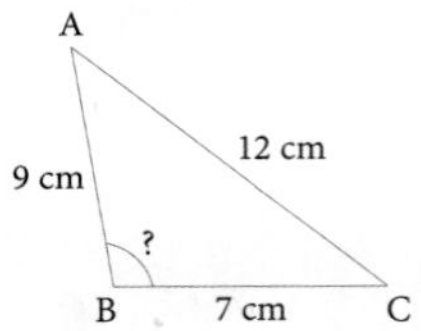

26.
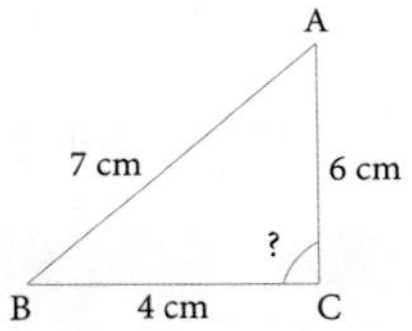

27.
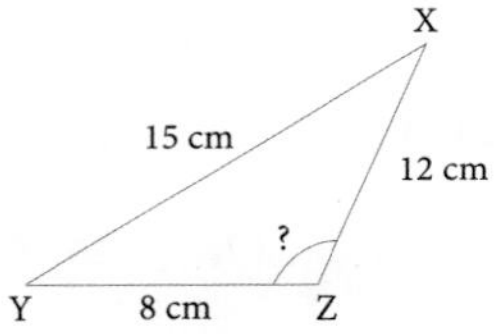

28.
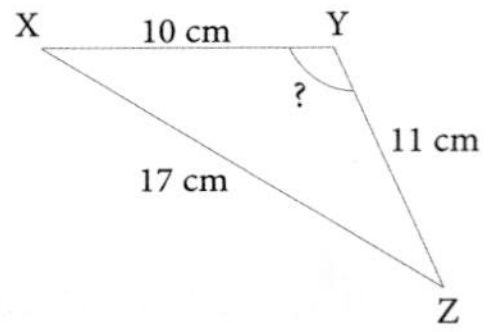

29.
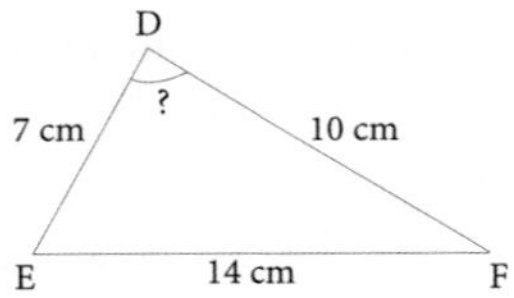

30.
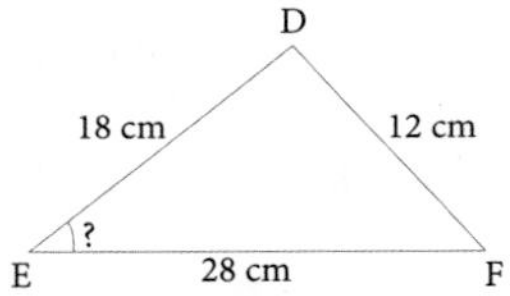

31.
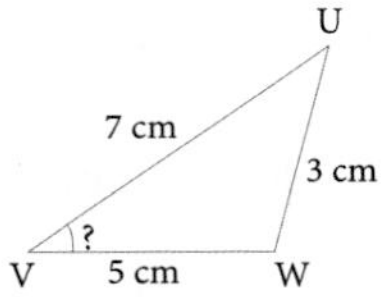

32.
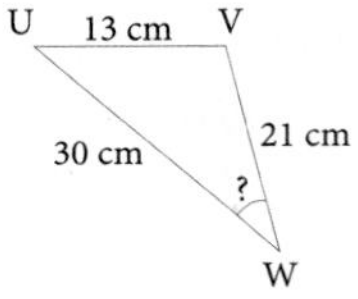

For Problems 33 to 42, state which formula, the Sine Law or the Cosine Law, would be required to begin in solving each of the triangles ABC.

33. Given ∠A, ∠B, and c
34. Given ∠B, ∠C, and b
35. Given ∠A, a, and b
36. Given ∠C, a, and b
37. Given b, ∠A, and c
38. Given ∠B, a, and b
39. Given a, b, and c
40. Given ∠B, ∠C, and a
41. Given ∠B, ∠C, and c
42. Given ∠B, a, and c

For Problems 43 to 54, solve the triangles fully (i.e., find all missing side lengths and angle measures). Round angles to the nearest degree and round sides to 2 decimal places.

	Angle (degrees)			Length (cm)		
	∠A	∠B	∠C	*a*	*b*	*c*
43.	35	120			12	
45.	22		81			50
47.			36	15	11.5	
49.		20		5		8
51.				13	9	6
53.	19	102				10

	Angle (degrees)			Length (cm)		
	∠A	∠B	∠C	*a*	*b*	*c*
44.		65	75			10
46.		115	45		18	
48.		85			15	25
50.			125	5	7.5	
52.				10	15	22.5
54.	25		60		16	

55. Lucy is leaving her house to go and run some errands. She needs to go to the grocery store and to the pet store. She knows that the grocery store is 5.6 km away and is situated N 18° E of her house, while the pet store is 3.4 km away at N 10° W of her home. What is the distance between the two stores?

56. Tabitha is sitting at one end of a soccer stadium, up in the top row of seats. She knows that the field is 110 m long, and from her seat, the angles of depression to the near and far ends of the field are 55° and 3°, respectively. How far is she from each end of the field?

57. A ship is traveling north at a speed of 10 knots in water with a current moving at 2 knots. The current flows S 60° E. What is the resultant speed and bearing of the ship?

58. Two unequal forces act on an object with an angle of 135° between them, and the resultant force has a magnitude of 62.1 N. If one of the original forces had a magnitude of 55.8 N, what was the magnitude of the other force?

59. From the base of a pyramid, the angle of elevation to the top of the pyramid is 47°. At a point 100 metres from the base, the angle of elevation to the top is 22°. Calculate the slant height of the pyramid.

60. From the base of a hill, the angle of elevation to the top of the hill is 65°. At a point 350 metres from the base, the angle of elevation to the top is 45°. Calculate the slant height of the hill.

11 | Review Exercises

Answers to odd-numbered problems are available at the end of the textbook.

In Problems 1 and 2, identify the two similar triangles and state the rule used to determine similarity.

1. a.

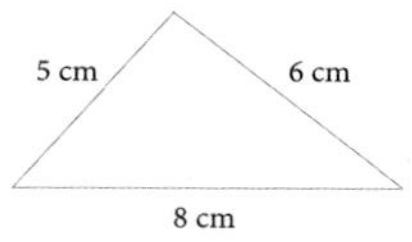

b.

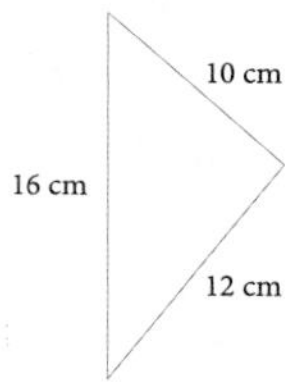

c.

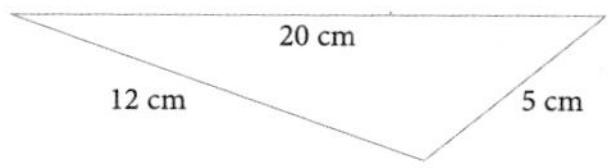

2. a.

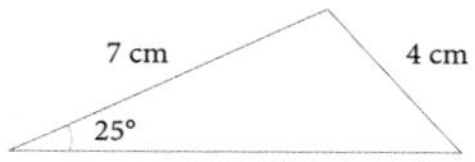

b.

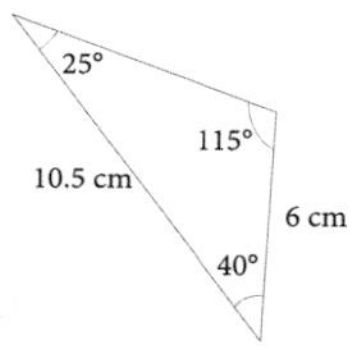

c.

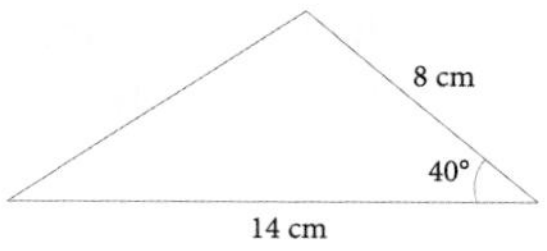

In Problems 3 and 4, identify the two congruent triangles and state the rule used to determine congruency.

3. a.

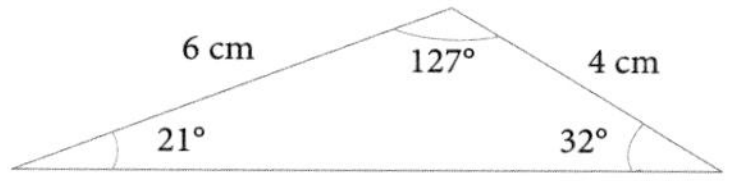

b.

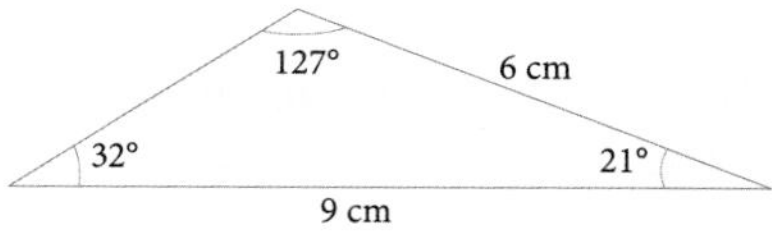

c.

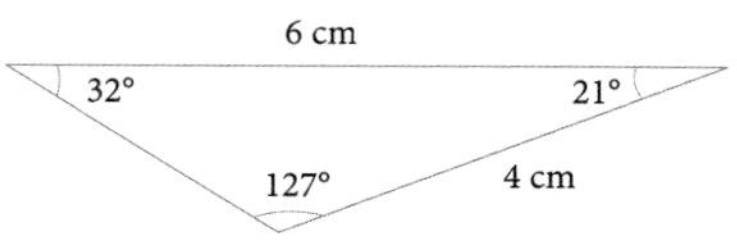

4. a.

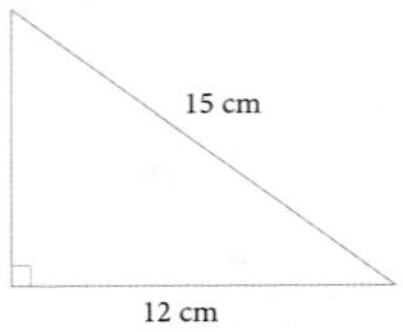

b.

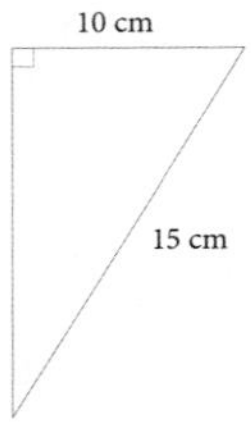

c.

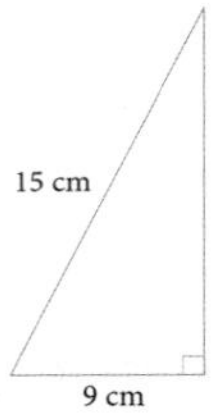

In Problems 5 and 6, determine the unknown side length of the given pairs of similar triangles.

5. a.

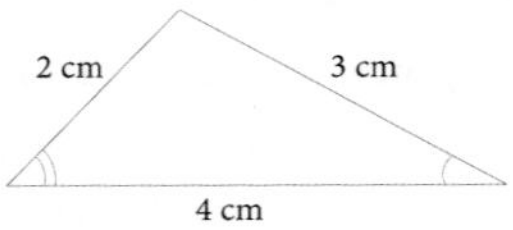

b.

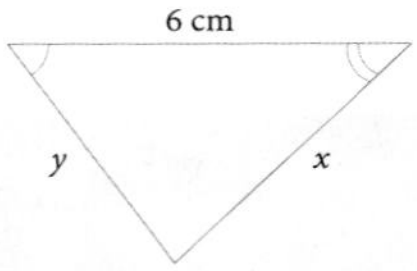

6. a.

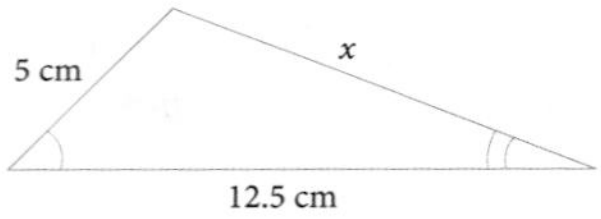

b.

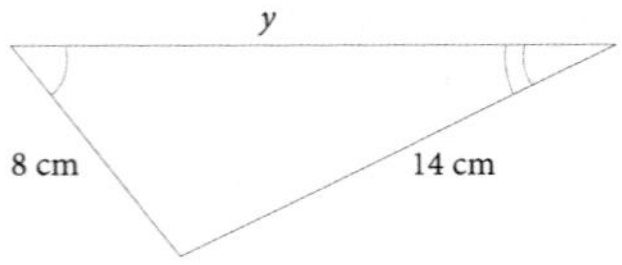

In Problems 7 and 8, calculate the unknown side lengths and angle(s) in the given figures.

7. a.

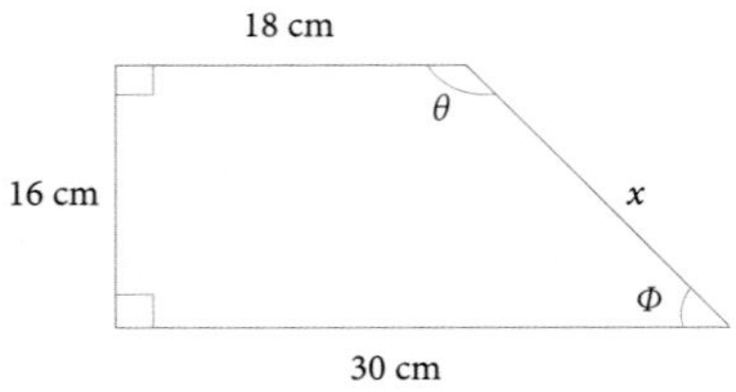

b.

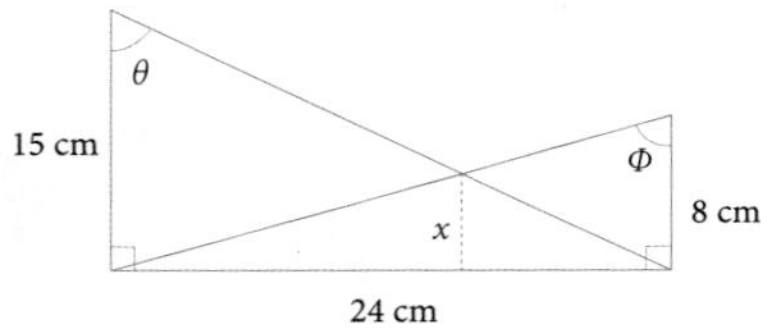

8. a.

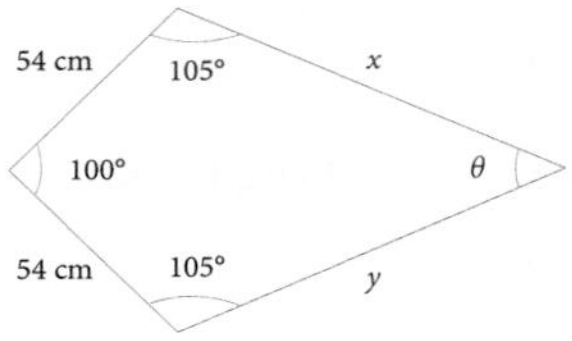

b.

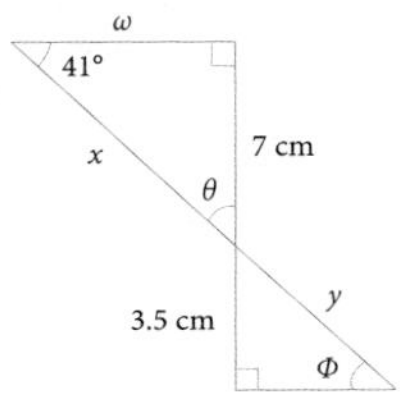

In problems 9 and 10, calculate the distance between the given Cartesian points:

9. a. $A\,(5, -1)$ and $B(-2, 6)$ b. $C\,(3, -2)$ and $D(0, -4)$

10. a. $M\,(-6, 8)$ and $N(3, -4)$ b. $P\,(1, -3)$ and $Q(4, 0)$

11. Use the Pythagorean Theorem to calculate the perimeter and area of a right trapezoid, with parallel sides that are 64 cm and 40 cm long, and a perpendicular height of 18 cm.

12. Use the Pythagorean Theorem to calculate the perimeter and area of an isosceles trapezoid, with parallel sides that are 6.5 m and 4.2 m long, and slant heights that are both 2.3 m long.

In Problems 13 and 14, determine the exact value of the given trigonometric expressions. Express the answers in simplified radical form.

13. a. $\sin 45° \cos 30° - \cos 45° \sin 30°$

b. $\dfrac{\sin^2 30° + \cos^2 30°}{\tan 30°}$

14. a. $\sin 30° \sin 60° + \cos 30° \cos 60° + \tan 30° \tan 60°$

b. $\dfrac{\tan^2 60° - \cos^2 30°}{\sin 60°}$

15. Calculate the degree measures of all angles in a kite, if the two equal angles are each 10° greater than twice the smaller remaining angle, and 10° less than twice the larger, remaining angle.

16. Calculate the degree measures of all five angles in a pentagon with four equal angles and the fifth angle twice the measure of the other four.

17. A radio mast is supported by a guy wire that runs from the top of the tower to a point on the ground 55 m away from the base of the mast.

a. If the angle that the guy wire makes with the ground is 63°, determine the height of the radio mast, rounded to the nearest metre.

b. For additional support, a second guy wire is attached from the same point on the ground to the mast, two-thirds of the way to the top. Determine the length needed for the additional guy wire and the angle it will make with the ground.

18. Standing on his balcony on the 17th floor, a man observes that the angle of elevation to the top of the building next to him is 35° and the angle of depression to the bottom of the same building is 45°. He then measures the ground distance between the buildings to be 60m.

    a. Determine the height of his balcony, in metres.

    b. Determine the height of the building next to him, rounded to the nearest metre.

19. On a hike, Cory and Nell walk 1.2 km west, then walk 500 m N20°W. How far are they from their original starting position, and at what bearing? Round your answers to the nearest integer.

20. The train routes between three cities form a triangle. The distance between City A and City B is 52 km, between City A and City C is 118 km, and between City B and City C is 74 km. Find the angle between the routes at City B, rounded to the nearest integer.

For Problems 21 to 30, solve the triangles fully (i.e., identify all missing side lengths and angle measures). Round angles to the nearest degree and round sides to two decimal places.

	Angles (degrees)			Length (cm)		
	∠A	∠B	∠C	*a*	*b*	*c*
21.		30		13.04		3.03
22.		32		43.23		53.29
23.		12	78		10.80	
24.		21	145		21.64	
25.	47			53.54	31.61	
26.	25			33.33	32.86	
27.	140				23	18
28.	50				30	28
29.				15	17	30
30.				12	18	28

11 | Self-Test Exercises

Answers to all problems are available at the end of the textbook.

1. Determine the unknown side length in the following similar triangles:

    a.

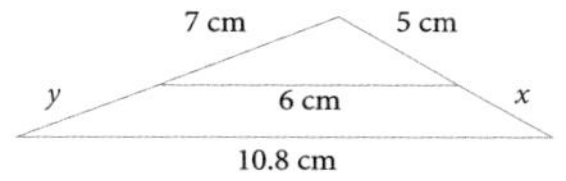

    b.

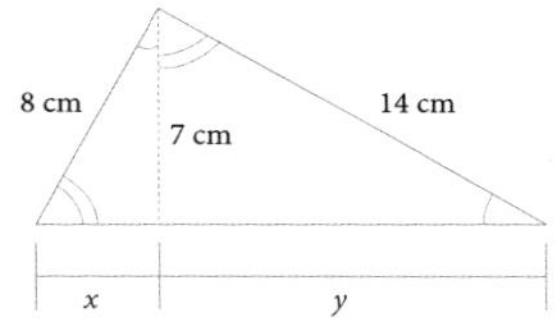

2. Determine the unknown side length of the following figures:

    a.

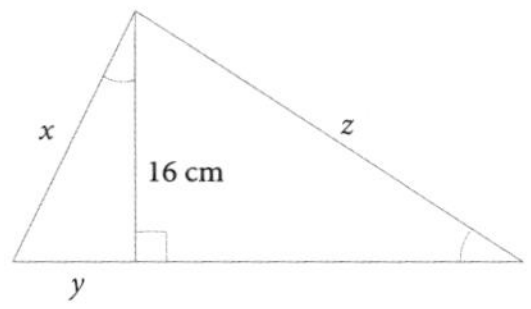

    b.

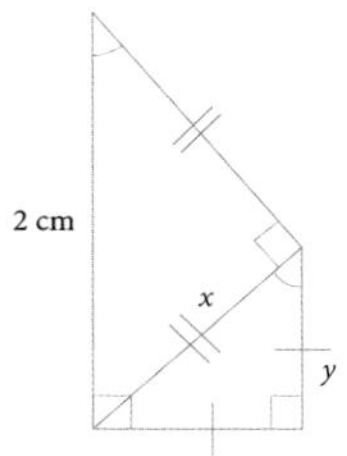

3. At 2:00 pm, a cliff with a vertical face casts a shadow 15 m long out onto the water. If, at the same time, a 72 cm buoy on the water casts a 45 cm shadow, how tall is the cliff?

4. Use the Pythagorean Theorem to find the perimeter and area of the following figures:

    a. A right trapezoid, with parallel sides that are 5.3 m and 9.7 m long, and a perpendicular height of 2.4 m.

    b. An isosceles triangle with a base length of 32 cm and slant heights that are each 34 cm.

5. Use the Pythagorean Theorem to determine the surface area and volume of the following 3-dimensional objects:

    a. An ice cream cone with a diameter of 4.4 cm and a height of 11.8 cm.

    b. A conical candy container with a radius of 15 cm and a height of 25 cm.

6. Find the distance between the following Cartesian points:

    a. $U(-4, -7)$ and $V(4, 8)$

    b. $W(7, -3)$ and $X(-1, 5)$

    c. $Y(0, -2.5)$ and $Z(6, 0)$

7. A house painter is using a 10 m ladder to paint the exterior wall of a house.

    a. How far back from the wall should the ladder be placed in order for it to reach a height of 8.5 m?

    b. If the maximum safe slope of the ladder is 4:1, what is the maximum safe height that the ladder can reach?

8. Solve the following triangles completely:

a.

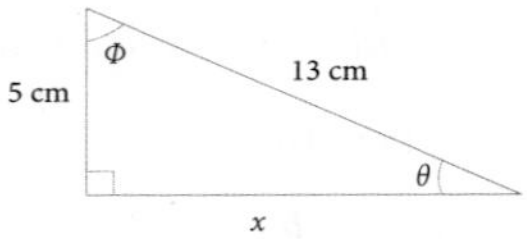

b.

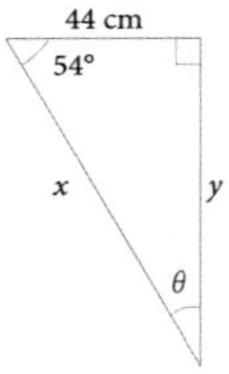

9. Solve the following triangles completely:

a.

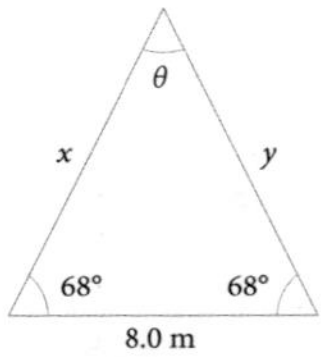

b.

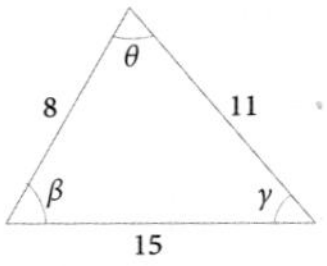

10. A mountain road has a 5° angle of descent for 7 km. How far down the mountain does the road descend? (Hint: the distance given represents the road length, not the horizontal distance travelled.)

11. A blimp is hovering over a Canadian football field, which is known to be approximately 100 m long. If the blimp measures an angle of depression of 42.6° to one end of the field and 38.8° to the other end, how high is the blimp above the field, to the nearest metre?

12. Using only the Cosine Law, solve ΔXYZ, with $x = 12.3$ mm, $y = 8.7$ mm, $\angle Z = 38°$. Round side lengths to one decimal place and angles to the nearest whole number.

13. Using only the Sine Law, solve ΔPQR with $\angle P = 50°$, $\angle Q = 30°$, and $q = 12$ cm. Round side lengths to one decimal place and angles to the nearest whole number.

14. In many parades, ropes are used to guide large balloon characters through the streets. One of these balloons has an 18 m rope attached to its top at an angle of elevation of 52° and another 3 m rope attached to its bottom at an angle of elevation of 10°. What is the height of the balloon?

15. Determine the following unknown values:

a.

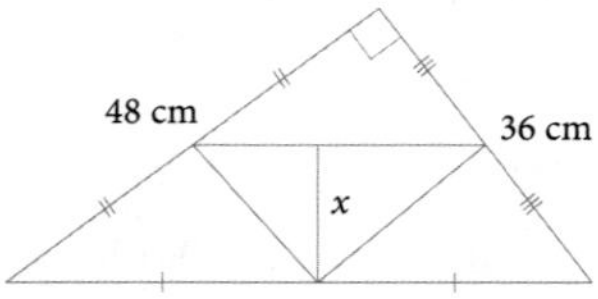

b.

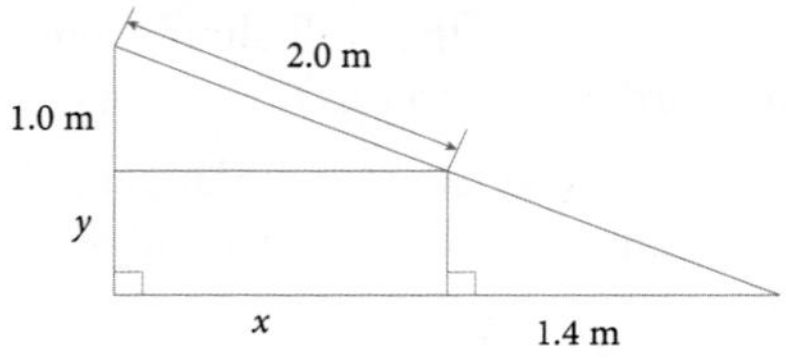

16. A family resort on a lake in Muskoka ropes off a small inlet of water at the beach to create a swimming area for children. Based on the diagram below, calculate the length of buoy rope needed for the swimming area.

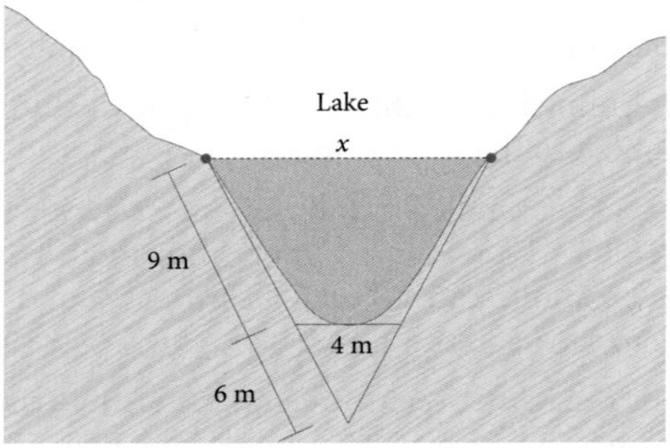

11 | Summary of Notation and Formulas

Pythagorean Theorem:

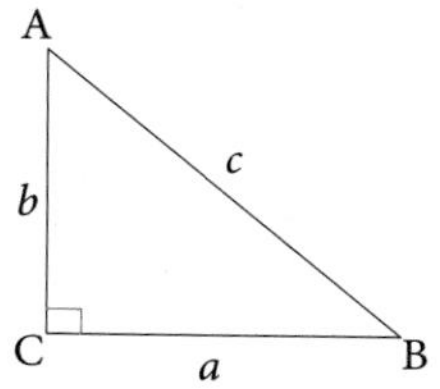

$a^2 + b^2 = c^2$

$c = \sqrt{a^2 + b^2}$

$a = \sqrt{c^2 - b^2}$

$b = \sqrt{c^2 - a^2}$

Distance (d) between two points P(x_1, y_1) and Q(x_2, y_2):

$$d = \sqrt{(x_2 - x_1)^2 + (y_2 - y_1)^2}$$

Primary Trigonometric Ratios:

$$\sin\theta = \frac{\text{Opposite}}{\text{Hypotenuse}} = \frac{\text{O}}{\text{H}}$$

$$\cos\theta = \frac{\text{Adjacent}}{\text{Hypotenuse}} = \frac{\text{A}}{\text{H}}$$

$$\tan\theta = \frac{\text{Opposite}}{\text{Adjacent}} = \frac{\text{O}}{\text{A}}$$

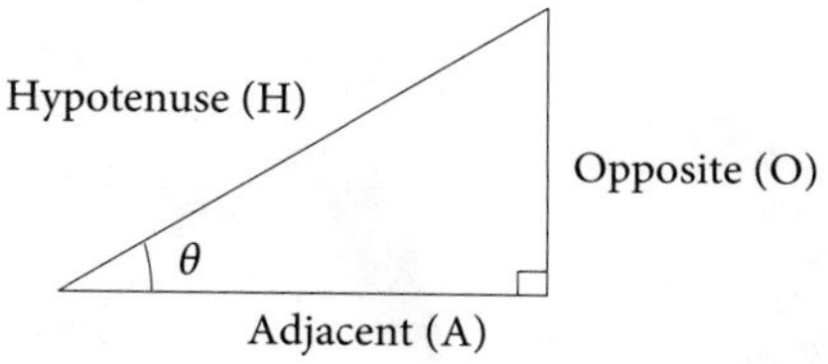

Exact Trigonometric Ratios of 30°, 45°, 60°:

$$\sin 30° = \cos 60° = \frac{1}{2}$$

$$\sin 45° = \cos 45° = \frac{1}{\sqrt{2}}$$

$$\sin 60° = \cos 30° = \frac{\sqrt{3}}{2}$$

$$\tan 30° = \frac{1}{\sqrt{3}}$$

$$\tan 45° = 1$$

$$\tan 60° = \sqrt{3}$$

Sine Laws:

Sine Law for Sides: $\dfrac{a}{\sin A} = \dfrac{b}{\sin B} = \dfrac{c}{\sin C}$

Sine Law for Angles: $\dfrac{\sin A}{a} = \dfrac{\sin B}{b} = \dfrac{\sin C}{c}$

Cosine Laws:

Cosine Law for Sides: $a^2 = b^2 + c^2 - 2bc \text{ Cos} A$

$b^2 = a^2 + c^2 - 2ac \text{ Cos B}$

$c^2 = a^2 + b^2 - 2ab \text{ Cos C}$

Cosine Law for Angles: $\text{Cos A} = \dfrac{b^2 + c^2 - a^2}{2bc}$

$\text{Cos B} = \dfrac{a^2 + c^2 - b^2}{2ac}$

$\text{Cos C} = \dfrac{a^2 + b^2 - c^2}{2ab}$

12 BASIC STATISTICS AND PROBABILITY

The applications of statistics are used by all in many ways in everyday life. Statistical information is presented daily in newspapers, magazines, radios, televisions, etc. Statistics is used in business, finance, economics, science, engineering, politics, and every other field. A basic knowledge in statistics is essential to understand, interpret, and make decisions based on information provided or collected. In this chapter, we will study descriptive statistics and learn techniques to organize and present data using graphs, charts, tables, etc., and learn to perform numerical analysis using measures of central tendency and dispersion to describe and summarize data in a meaningful way. Introduction to probability and probability calculation using the classical and empirical approach are also included in this chapter.

LEARNING OBJECTIVES

- Understand terminology used in statistics and distinguish between types of data and levels of measurement.
- Organize data using stem-and-leaf plot, tally chart, scatter plot, and line graphs.
- Summarize data using pie charts, bar charts, and histograms.
- Construct frequency polygons, frequency distribution, and cumulative frequency distribution.
- Perform calculations involving average, weighted average, arithmetic mean, and geometric mean.
- Calculate and interpret measures of central tendency using mean, median, and mode.
- Determine range, quartiles, inter-quartile range, and construct box-and-whisker plot.
- Calculate and interpret measures of dispersion using mean deviation, variance, and standard deviation.
- Identify properties of normal distribution, normal curve, and skewness of data.
- Define probability and calculate probabilities using the classical and empirical approach.

CHAPTER OUTLINE

12.1 | Organizing and Presenting Data

Introduction

Statistics is a branch of mathematics and procedures that involves collecting, organizing, presenting, analyzing, and interpreting data for the purpose of drawing conclusions and making a decision.

Statistics is divided into two categories:

- Descriptive statistics
- Inferential statistics

Descriptive statistics deals with the organizing, presenting, and summarizing of raw data to present meaningful information.

Inferential statistics deals with the analysis of a sample drawn from a larger population to develop meaningful inferences about the population based on sample results.

Population refers to all possible individuals, objects, or measurements of items of interest. This is usually of large or infinite quantity. For example, the ages of all college students.

Sample refers to a set of data drawn from the population. It is a subset of a population, meaning a portion or part of the population. For example, the ages of a representative sample of 200 college students.

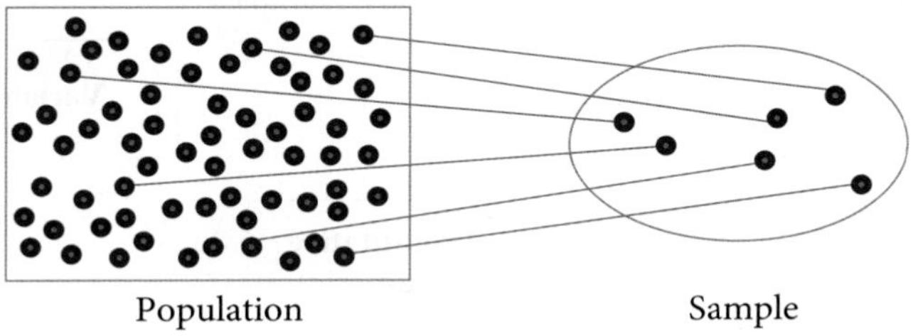

The descriptive values for a population are called parameters and that for a sample are called statistics. Parameters are usually represented by Greek letters (μ, σ) and statistics are usually represented by lowercase English letters ($\bar{x}$, s).

Normally, we may not have access to the whole population we are interested in investigating. Therefore, population parameters are often estimated from the sample statistics. Sample statistics are calculated from the actual data observed or measured from the sample.

For example, assume that there are 40 students in a particular math class of a college. If 80% of the students passed an exam, this 80% is referred to as a "parameter", because it includes the marks of all 40 students. However, if this class is selected as the representative math class of all the math classes in the college, then the 80% is referred to as a "statistic", because it represents a sample of the population.

In this section, the types of data, levels of measurement, and various methods for organizing and presenting data using tables and graphs will be outlined.

Types of Variables and Levels of Measurement

Types of Variables

A collection of facts and information obtained in a study is known as the data. The variables within a dataset may be numerical or non-numerical, and classified as:

- Quantitative variables
- Qualitative variables

Quantitative Variables

Quantitative variables are data that are expressed using numbers and are known as numeric data. These data are further classified as continuous variables or discrete variables.

Continuous variables are obtained by measuring. Measurements of length, weight, time, temperature, etc., are examples of continuous variables. These can be measured in whole units, approximated or rounded whole units, fractions, or decimal numbers (with any number of decimal places).

Discrete variables are obtained by counting, or are data that can only take on specific values. The number of students in a class, number of chapters in a book, position in a race, shoe size, etc., are examples of discrete variables. Also, any quantitative data that does not belong to the continuous variable classification, falls into the discrete variable classification.

Qualitative Variables

Qualitative variables are data that are expressed non-numerically and are known as non-numerical data. These data can be classified into categories and are also known as categorical data. Make and model of cars, colour, gender, etc., are examples of qualitative variables.

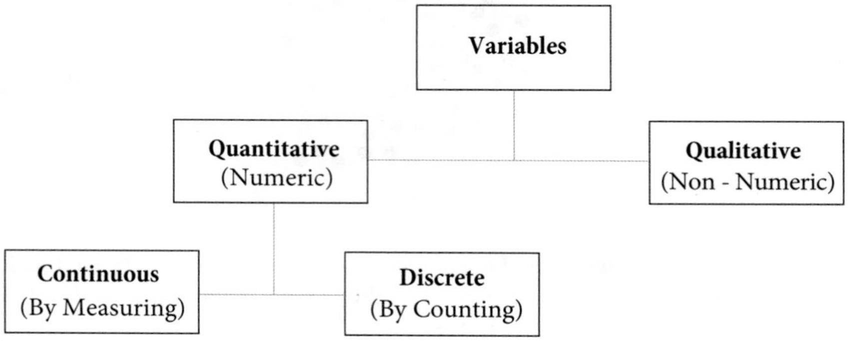

Levels of Measurement

Levels of measurement are rules that describe the properties of numbers that are measured and the way in which they can be used to provide additional information on the data. There are four levels of measurement: Nominal, Ordinal, Interval, and Ratio.

The properties used to classify these levels of measurement are: order (rank), meaningful difference (interval between measurements), and meaningful zero point.

Levels of Measurement	Order (Rank)	Meaningful Difference	Meaningful Zero
Nominal	No	No	No
Ordinal	Yes	No	No
Interval	Yes	Yes	No
Ratio	Yes	Yes	Yes

Levels of Measurement	Properties	Examples
Nominal	• Have no order, but numbers may be assigned for referencing and differentiating purposes using codes. • The interval between measurements is not meaningful. • No meaningful zero point. • Qualitative data and usually classified using letters, symbols, or names.	Gender, Religion, Country of birth, Colour, etc.
Ordinal	• Have order by their relative position. • The interval between measurements is not meaningful. • No meaningful zero point. • Qualitative data and usually classified using letters, symbols, or numbers.	High or low, Level of satisfaction, Rating of movies, GPA (A=4, B=3, C=2...), etc.
Interval	• Have order by their relative position. • Meaningful intervals between measurements. • No meaningful zero point. (The zero point is located arbitrarily.) • Quantitative data but measurements cannot be multiplied or divided.	Temperature, Dates, Years, Sea level, etc.
Ratio	• Have order by their relative position. • Meaningful intervals between measurements. • Meaningful zero point. • Quantitative data and measurements can be multiplied or divided.	Percent, Age, Weight, Speed, etc.

Statistical Representations of Data

Stem-and-Leaf Plot

A stem-and-leaf plot is one method of displaying data to show the spread of data and the location of where most of the data points lie. The method is simply a sorting technique to arrange the data from the lowest to the highest value, which is known as an **array**.

In this display, the set of numbers is re-written, so that the last digit (unit or ones digit) becomes the leaf and the other digits become the stem. The stems are written vertically and the leaves are written horizontally. A stem-and-leaf plot shows the exact values of individual data values.

For example, for a two digit number, 38, the stem is the tens digit number 3 (written on the left side), and the leaf is the unit digit number, 8 (written on the right side), as shown on the stem-and-leaf plot above.

For a three digit number, 156, the stem is 15 and the leaf is 6.

For a one digit number, 8, the stem is 0 and the leaf is 8.

For decimal numbers, all the digits including the decimal point will be the stem and all the decimal values will be the leaves.

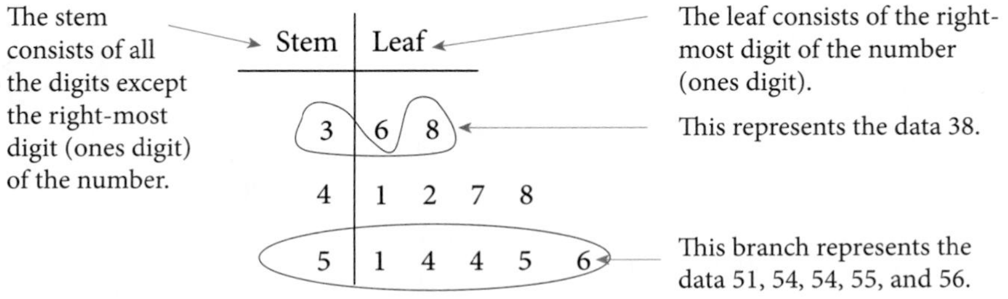
The stem consists of all the digits except the right-most digit (ones digit) of the number.
Stem
Leaf
3 | 6 8
4 | 1 2 7 8
5 | 1 4 4 5 6
The leaf consists of the right-most digit of the number (ones digit).
This represents the data 38.
This branch represents the data 51, 54, 54, 55, and 56.

The following example illustrates the procedure for constructing a stem-and-leaf plot.

Example 12.1-a

Constructing a Stem-and-Leaf Plot

The marks on a Statistics exam for a sample of 40 students are as follows:

63	74	42	65	51	54	36	56	68	57
62	64	76	67	79	61	81	77	59	38
84	68	71	94	71	86	69	75	97	55
48	82	83	54	79	62	68	58	41	47

(i) Construct a stem-and-leaf plot to display the data in an array.

(ii) Use the stem-and-leaf plot to determine the number of students who scored:

a. 70 marks or more

b. less than 50 marks.

Solution

(i) Construct a stem-and-leaf plot to display the data in an array.

Step 1: Identify the lowest and highest stem of the data.
Looking at the data, the lowest stem is 3 and the highest stem is 9.

Step 2: Use Step 1 to identify the range in the stem. The stem will have the digits 3, 4, 5, 6, 7, 8, and 9. Draw a vertical line and write out the stem in this order to the left of the line.

Step 3: Starting from the1[st] data, place each leaf of the number to the right of the vertical line on the corresponding stem, until the last data is recorded. There is no need to use commas on the leaf side.

For example,

- The first data value is 63. Therefore, the stem is 6 and the leaf is 3.
- The second data value is 74. Therefore, the stem is 7 and the leaf is 4.
- Continue until the last data, 47, where the stem is 4 and the leaf is 7.

	Stem	Leaf	# of data
	3	6 8	2
Last data, 47 →	4	2 8 1 7	4
	5	1 4 6 7 9 5 4 8	8
First data, 63 →	6	3 5 8 2 4 7 1 8 9 2 8	11
Second data, 74 →	7	4 6 9 7 1 1 5 9	8
	8	1 4 6 2 3	5
	9	4 7	2
			Total = 40

Step 4: Rearrange the leaves against each stem, from the smallest to the largest number, to have the numbers displayed in an array.

Stem	Leaf	# of data	
3	6 8	2	Number of data less than 50 is 2 + 4 = 6.
4	1 2 7 8	4	
5	1 4 4 5 6 7 8 9	8	
6	1 2 3 3 4 5 7 8 8 8 9	11	
7	1 1 4 5 6 7 9 9	8	Number of data 70 and above is 8 + 5 + 2 = 15.
8	1 2 3 4 6	5	
9	4 7	2	
		Total = 40	

Solution *continued*

(ii) a. Number of leaves against stem 7 = 8, against stem 8 = 5, and against stem 9 = 2.
Therefore, the number of students who scored 70 marks or more is 15.

b. Number of leaves against stem 4 = 4 and against stem 3 = 2.
Therefore, the number of students who scored less than 50 marks is 6.

Example 12.1-b **Interpreting Data in a Stem-and-Leaf Plot**

The following stem-and-leaf plot shows the number of CDs sold by a salesperson each day in the last 15 days.

Stem	Leaf
0	6 8
1	0 1 3 4
2	6 8 9
3	0 3 8 9
4	1 4

Calculate the following:

(i) Number of CDs sold in the last 15 days.

(ii) Highest and lowest sales in a day in the last 15 days.

(iii) Number of days 30 or more CDs were sold in the last 15 days.

Solution

(i) Add all the data values in each row of the stem and leaf plot,

Sum of 1st row data	$6 + 8$	=	14
Sum of 2nd row data	$10 + 11 + 13 + 14$	=	48
Sum of 3rd row data	$26 + 28 + 29$	=	83
Sum of 4th row data	$30 + 33 + 38 + 39$	=	140
Sum of 5th row data	$41 + 44$	=	85
	Total	=	370

Therefore, the number of CDs sold in the last 15 days = 370.

(ii) Highest data value is 44 and the lowest data value is 6.
Therefore, the highest sales in a day is 44 and the lowest sales in a day is 6.

(iii) Number of leaves against stem 3 = 4 and that against stem 4 = 2.
Therefore, the number of days 30 or more CDs were sold = 4 + 2 = 6.

Tally Chart

A tally chart is another method of collecting and organizing data. A tally chart is used to keep count of the number of times a particular event or data occurs.

For each count, a tally mark "|", a vertical line (or a slant line), in the row against that event or data is used. The fifth tally mark is marked "/", as a diagonal line (or as a horizontal line) across the four tally marks: "𝍸". This helps to count the data in multiples of five.

For example, 12 counts of the same item is shown as "𝍸 𝍸 ||" (two groups of five and two = 12). A tally chart helps to produce a frequency table. The number of times an event happens is known as the ***frequency (f)***. If the data is ranked using the stem-and-leaf method, then tallying may not be required to produce the frequency table.

Example 12.1-c Constructing a Frequency Table Using a Tally Chart

The ages of 35 students in a class were recorded as follows:

18	19	18	20	19	17	18	18	20	19
21	20	17	19	20	18	19	17	19	21
19	20	19	18	20	22	19	21	19	20
19	21	19	21	22					

Display the data using a tally chart to show the frequency distribution of ages of students in the class.

Solution

Step 1: Draw 3 columns to represent age, tally, and frequency (f).

Step 2: Identify the lowest and highest data.
17 is the lowest and 22 is the highest. Therefore, the first column will have 6 entries displaying ages from 17 to 22.

Step 3: Starting from the first data, use tally marks in Column 2 to count the frequency of the ages in the dataset.

Step 4: Total the tally marks in each row to get the frequency distribution of the ages and enter it in Column 3.

Age	Tally	Frequency (f)
17					3
18	𝍸		6
19	𝍸 𝍸 ||	12
20	𝍸 ||	7
21	𝍸	5
22				2
		Total = 35

Example 12.1-d Interpreting a Tally Chart

The tally chart below shows the height of students (in cm) in a class.

Height (cm)	Tally	Frequency (f)
140 to under 150	|||	
150 to under 160	𝍸 ||	
160 to under 170	𝍸 𝍸 𝍸	
170 to under 180	𝍸 |||	
180 to under 190	||	

(i) Complete the frequency column.

(ii) Identify the group with the highest frequency and the number of data in that group.

(iii) Calculate the total number of data above the group with the highest frequency and express it as a percent of the whole data.

Solution

(i)

Height (cm)	Tally	Frequency (f)
140 to under 150	|||	3
150 to under 160	𝍸 ||	7
160 to under 170	𝍸 𝍸 𝍸	15
170 to under 180	𝍸 |||	8
180 to under 190	||	2
		Total = 35

(ii) The group with the highest frequency is "160 to under 170" and the number of data in that group is 15.

(iii) The number of data above the group with the highest frequency = 8 + 2 = 10.

The percent of data above the group with the highest frequency = $\frac{10}{35}$ = 28.5%.

Scatter Plot

A scatter plot is a graph showing pairs of numerical data with the independent variable on a horizontal axis and the dependent variable on a vertical axis. The independent variable is the variable selected for the study and the dependent variable is the variable observed or measured. In a scatter plot, a dot or a small circle is used to represent a single data point for every pair of data measured to illustrate the relationship between the two sets of data. A scatter plot is especially useful when there is paired numerical data, where for a single independent variable, there may be multiple dependent variables.

The relationship between two variables is known as their correlation. If the variables are correlated, the data points will fall close to making a line. If the points are equally distributed on a horizontal plane in the scatter plot, the correlation is low, or zero.

A correlation is Positive when the slope is positive; i.e., as one variable increases the other variable increases and vice versa.

A correlation is Negative when the slope is negative; i.e., as one variable increases the other variable decreases, and vice versa.

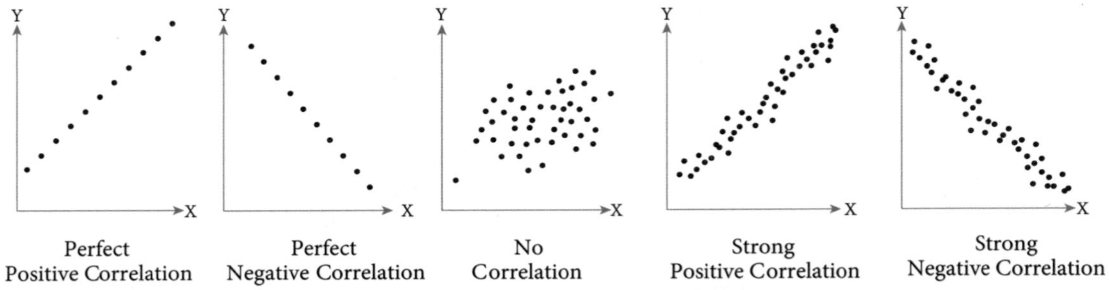

Example 12.1-e **Drawing a Scatter Plot of Weight (kg) vs. Height (cm)**

Construct a scatter plot for the following data and comment on the correlation between the heights and weights of 10 students.

Student	1	2	3	4	5	6	7	8	9	10
Height (cm)	164	145	169	162	181	155	191	151	172	176
Weight (kg)	60	43	62	57	77	55	82	50	64	75

Solution

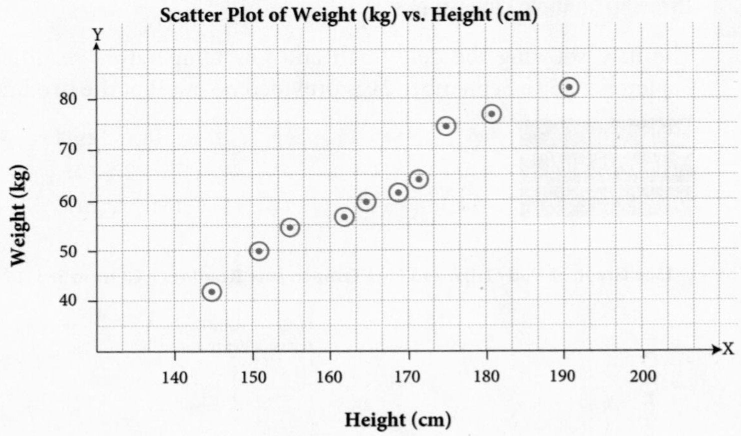

The scatter plot shows a strong positive correlation between the heights and the weights of the students; i.e., as the height increases, the weight increases.

Example 12.1-f

Drawing a Scatter Plot of Items Sold (numbers) vs. Price ($)

Construct a scatter plot for the following data and comment on the correlation between the price and the number of items sold.

Price ($)	15	18	20	25	27	30	35
Items Sold (numbers)	48	40	36	28	24	18	6

Solution

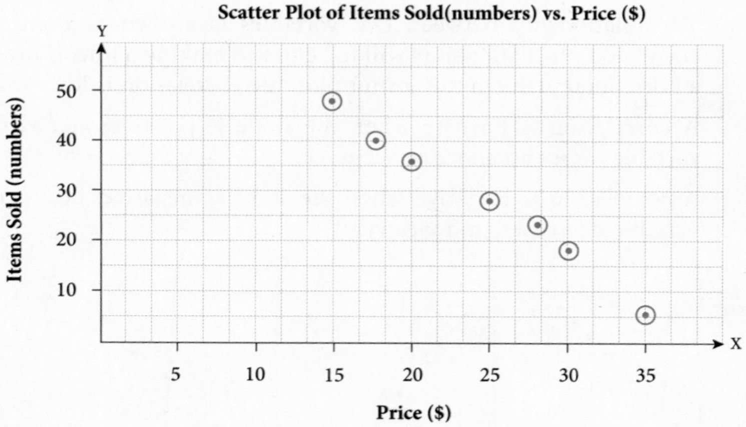

The scatter plot shows a strong negative correlation between the number of items sold and price; i.e., as the price increases, the number of items sold decreases.

Line Graphs

Line graphs are most often used for representing continuous data. Line graphs are an important feature of mathematics. This is similar to the topic discussed in Chapter 9.

The line graph should include the following:

- Title of the graph, describing the purpose.
- Labelled axes to show the variables and the units of measure used.
- Position of origin: (0, 0).

Example 12.1-g

Drawing Multiple Line Graphs

The data showing the daily high and low temperature readings in Toronto for the period from September 15 to September 21 is provided below. Plot the two line graphs for the data.

Date	Sep. 15	Sep. 16	Sep. 17	Sep.18	Sep. 19	Sep. 20	Sep. 21
Temp (°C) High	20	15	16	24	21	20	18
Temp (°C) Low	11	10	8	16	15	14	12

Solution

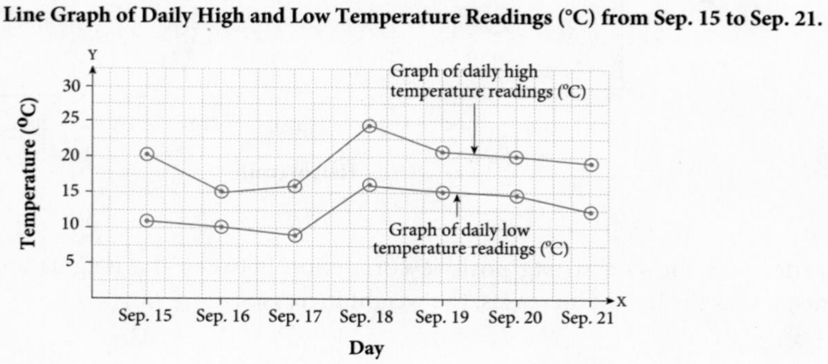

Example 12.1-h **Interpreting a Line Graph**

The line graph shown below illustrates the monthly sales (in millions of dollars) of a department store for the period from January to December 2014.

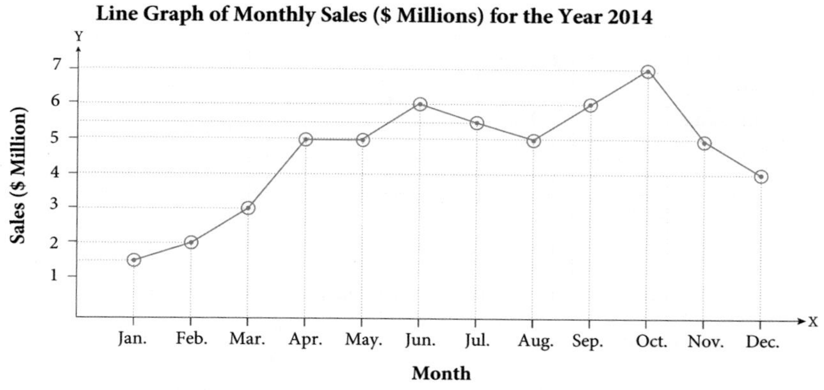

(i) Calculate the total sales for the months of May, June, July, and August.

(ii) Which month had the lowest sales and what is the amount of sales for that month?

(iii) Which month had the highest sales and what is the amount of sales for that month?

Solution

(i)

Sales in May	5	Million
Sales in June	6	Million
Sales in July	5.5	Million
Sales in August	5	Million
Total =	**21.5**	**Million**

Therefore, the total sales for the months of May, June, July, and August were 21.5 Million dollars.

(ii) The lowest sales amount was in January and the sales amount was 1.5 Million dollars.

(iii) The highest sales amount was in October and the sales amount was 7 Million dollars.

Pie Chart

Pie charts are usually used to summarize and show classes or groups of data in proportion to the whole dataset. The whole pie (circle) represents the total of all the values in the dataset which is 100% and is equal to 360 degrees.

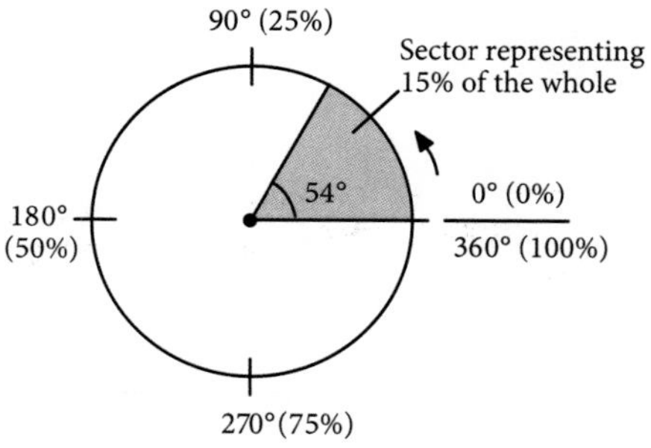

The size of each sector represents the percent portion (or fraction) of each category of data. Pie charts are very often used in presenting poll results, expenditures, etc.

The pie chart is constructed by first converting each category or group into a percent of the whole and then multiplying this by 360 degrees to determine the number of degrees for the sector of the category being represented in the pie chart.

For example, 15% of the data is represented by a sector with an angle of 54 degrees (15% of 360° = 54°).

The interpretation of a pie chart is based on the fact that the largest 'slice of pie' relates to the largest proportion of the data and the smallest 'slice' to the smallest proportion. It is therefore, easy to make comparisons between the relative sizes of data items.

Example 12.1-i

Drawing a Pie Chart for Given Data

Draw a pie chart representing the data using (i) percent and (ii) sector angles.

Item	Expense ($)
Housing	15,000
Meals	9,000
Transportation	8,000
Medicine	5,000
Miscellaneous	7,000
Savings	6,000
Total	**$50,000**

Solution

The expenses totalling $50,000 is 100% and represents 360° in a circle (pie chart).

Calculate the percent for each listed expense as a percent of the total.

For example, housing expense of $15,000 is $\frac{\$\ 15{,}000}{\$\ 50{,}000} \times 100\% = 30\%$.

Similarly, calculate the percent for all the remaining items and complete the 3rd column of the table, as shown below.

Calculate the angle that represents each sector in the pie chart by multiplying the calculated percent for each of the items by 360°.

For example, the sector angle for the housing expense is 30% of 360° = 108°.

Similarly, calculate the sector angle of all the remaining items and complete the 4th column of the table, as shown below.

Item	Expense	Percent	Sector Angle
Housing	$15,000	30%	108.0°
Meals	$9,000	18%	64.8°
Transportation	$8,000	16%	57.6°
Medicine	$5,000	10%	36.0°
Miscellaneous	$7,000	14%	50.4°
Savings	$6,000	12%	43.2°
Total	**$50,000**	**100%**	**360°**

(i) Construct the pie chart using the percent calculated for each of the items.

(ii) Construct the pie chart using the sector angle calculated for each of the items.

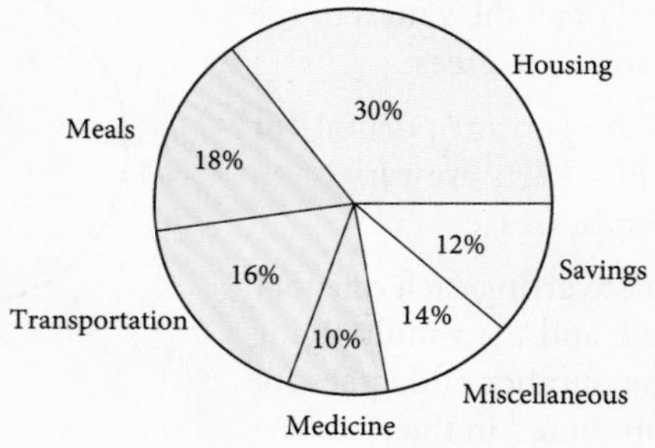

Pie Chart Using Percents

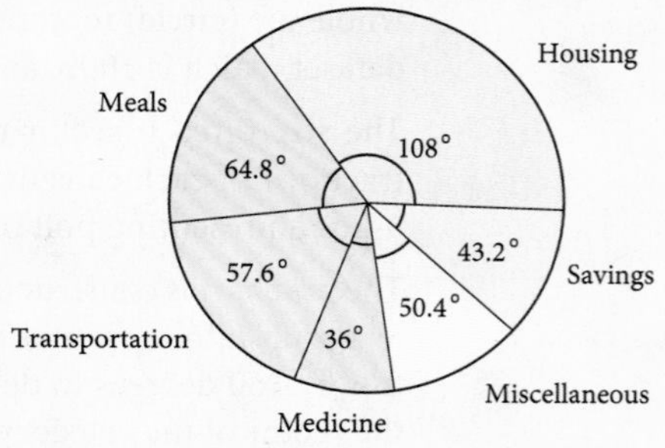

Pie Chart Using Sector Angles

Example 12.1-j

Interpreting a Pie Chart

The final grades of 40 students who passed a Math exam are represented in the pie chart below. Use the pie chart to complete the table.

Grade	Number of Students	Percent	Sector Angle
A+		20%	
A		25%	
B		30%	
C		10%	
D		15%	
Total	40	**100%**	360°

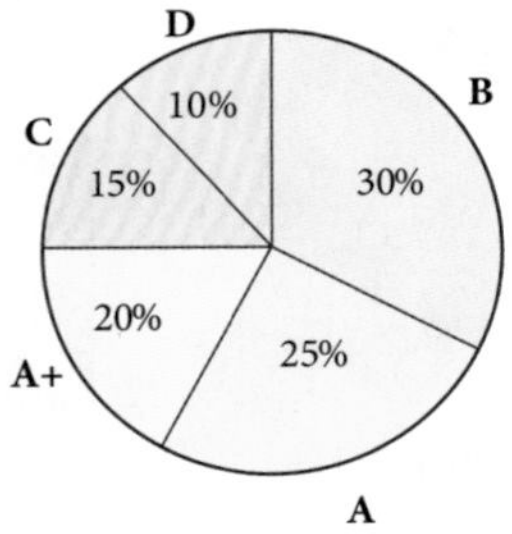

Solution

Grade	Number of Students	Percent	Sector Angle
A+	20% of 40 = 8	20%	20% of 360° = 72°
A	25% of 40 = 10	25%	25% of 360° = 90°
B	30% of 40 = 12	30%	30% of 360° = 108°
C	10% of 40 = 4	10%	10% of 360° = 36°
D	15% of 40 = 6	15%	15% of 360° = 54°
Total	**40**	**100%**	**360°**

Bar Chart

A bar chart is a graph that uses either horizontal or vertical bars to show comparisons among categories or class intervals of grouped data. The categories or class intervals are plotted on the X-axis. The distribution of the data in these categories or the frequencies associated with the class intervals is plotted on the Y-axis.

The width of the base of the rectangle for each category or class interval should be equal.

Classes should be set up without any overlap in the data.

Bar charts are easy to produce and easy to interpret. The lengths (or heights) of the bars show the quantity of the data in that category or the frequency of that class interval. These are represented by a rectangle with a base that corresponds to a category or class interval and a length (or height) that is proportional to the values that they represent.

A bar chart is also used to represent two or more sets of data having the same class interval, side-by-side, on one graph. This allows for the data values in these sets to be compared easily.

Example 12.1-k

Creating Bar Charts

Draw a vertical bar chart for the frequencies of grades obtained by students in a Math exam and use the chart to calculate the following:

(i) Total number of students graded.

(ii) Number of students obtaining a B grade or better.

Grade	Number of Students
A+	8
A	10
B	12
C	4
D	6

Solution

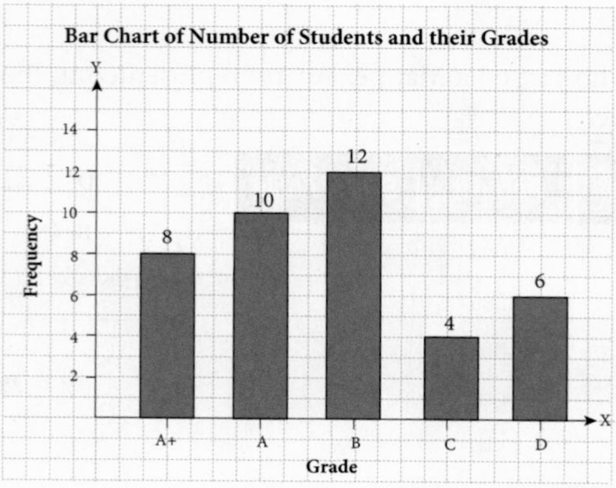

(i) Total number of students graded = 8 + 10 + 12 + 4 + 6 = 40

(ii) Number of students obtaining a B grade or better = 12 + 10 + 8 = 30

Example 12.1-I

Interpreting Bar Charts

The stacked bar chart below shows the number of cellphones sold by Store A and Store B from January to June.

Bar Chart of Number of Cellphones Sold from January to June by Stores A and B

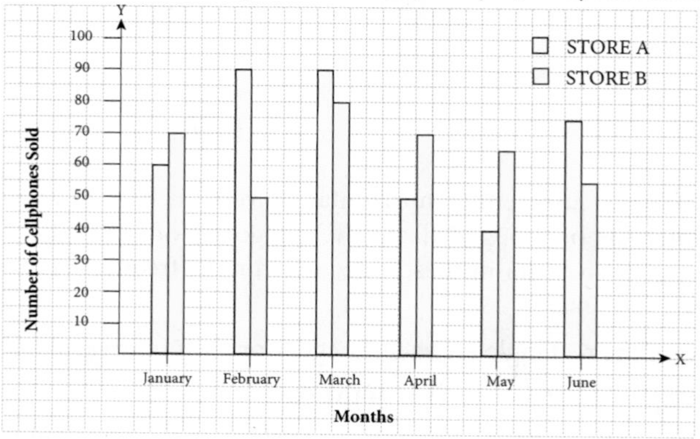

Use the bar chart to answer the following:

(i) What were the total cellphone sales by Stores A and B?

(ii) In which months did Store B sell more cellphones than Store A?

(iii) In which particular month did the sales in Store A exceed that of Store B by the greatest difference and by how much more?

Solution

(i) Total cellphone sales by Store A = 60 + 90 + 90 + 50 + 45 + 75 = 410
Total cellphone sales by Store B = 70 + 50 + 80 + 70 + 65 + 55 = 390

(ii) The months in which Store B sold more cellphones than Store A are January, April, and May.

(iii) The month in which there was the greatest difference was February. Store A sold = 90 – 50 = 40 more cellphones.

Histogram and Frequency Polygon

Histogram

A histogram is similar to a vertical bar chart in which the categories or class intervals are marked on a horizontal axis and the class frequencies are represented by the heights of the bars. However, in histograms, there should be no space between the rectangle of a class interval and the rectangle of an adjoining class interval. That is, the bars are drawn adjacent to each other.

Frequency Polygon

The frequency polygon is the line joining the midpoints of the bars of a histogram. An additional class interval on both ends of the histogram is created so that the frequency polygon starts and ends at the mid-points of the class intervals at the X-axis.

Example 12.1-m

Creating Histogram and Frequency Polygon

Draw a histogram and a frequency polygon for the distribution of age groups of 200 employees in a company group as shown below.

Age (Class Intervals)	Number of Employees (Frequency)
20 to under 30	35
30 to under 40	42
40 to under 50	64
50 to under 60	30
60 to under 70	24
70 to under 80	5
Total	**200**

Solution

Histogram and Frequency Polygon of Number of Employees vs. Age Group

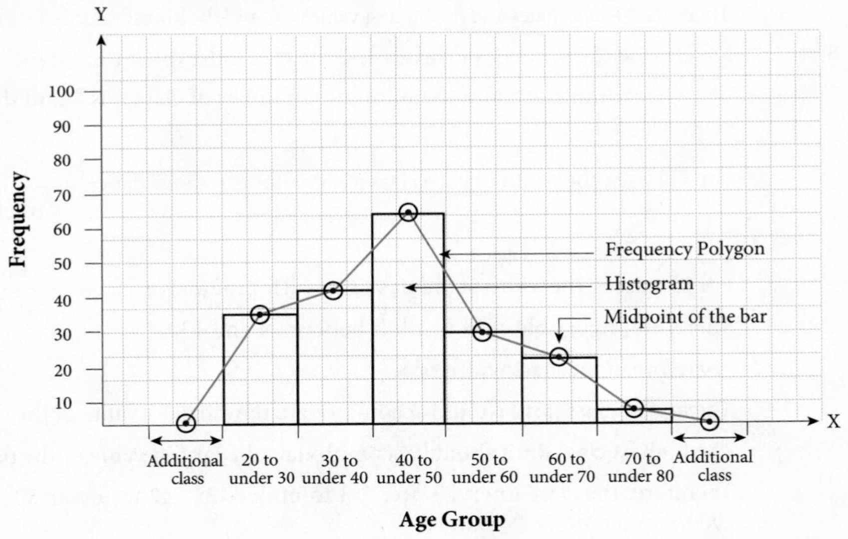

Note: Labels on X-axis representing the class interval can be in any of the following formats: 40-50, 50-60, 60-70…., or 40 to 50, 50 to 60…, or 40 to under 50, 50 to under 60…, or as mid-points of class intervals (45, 55, 65…).

Frequency Distributions

A frequency distribution is a method to summarize large amounts of data without displaying each value of the observation. It groups the data into different class intervals and indicates the number of observations that fall into the given class interval, known as the frequency, *f*. In a frequency distribution, the class widths of all intervals should be the same.

The smallest value that belongs to a class interval is called the lower class limit, and the largest value that belongs to the class interval is called the upper class limit. The class width refers to the difference between the upper class limit and the lower class limit.

For example, in the class interval "140 to under 150", the lower class limit is 140 and the upper class limit is below 150.

The class width = 150 – 140 = 10

Using the data from Example 12.1-a (shown below), the steps in constructing a frequency distribution table are as follows:

Data:										
	63	74	42	65	51	54	36	56	68	57
	62	64	76	67	79	61	81	77	59	38
	84	68	71	94	71	86	69	75	97	55
	48	82	83	54	79	62	68	58	41	47

The range is the difference between the highest and the lowest value in a dataset.

Step 1: First, array the data using the stem-and-leaf method and determine the number of data, highest value, lowest value, and the range.

Stem	Leaf	# of data
3	6 8	2
4	1 2 7 8	4
5	1 4 4 5 6 7 8 9	8
6	1 2 3 3 4 5 7 8 8 8 9	11
7	1 1 4 5 6 7 9 9	8
8	1 2 3 4 6	5
9	4 7	2
	Total =	**40**

There are 40 data values and the highest value is 97 and the lowest value is 36. The range is 97 – 36 = 61.

Step 2: Determine the number of classes and the class interval of each class.

(As a guideline, normally, the minimum number of classes is 5 and the highest number of classes is 15.)

For 5 classes, the width of each class interval for the above data = $\frac{\text{Range}}{\text{\# of classes}} = \frac{61}{5} = 12.20$

For 15 classes, the width of the class interval for the above data = $\frac{\text{Range}}{\text{\# of classes}} = \frac{61}{15} = 4.07$

Therefore, a possible class width is between 4 and 13.

Therefore, use a class width of 8.

The lowest class limit should accommodate the smallest value of the data, 36.

The highest class limit should accommodate the largest value of the data, 97.

Therefore, the class intervals are: "34 to under 42", "42 to under 50", "50 to under 58", ... "90 to under 98".

That is, there are 8 classes and each class interval is 8.

Step 3: Determine the class frequencies for each class using the stem-and-leaf plot and complete the frequency distribution.

Class Interval	Frequency
34 to under 42	3
42 to under 50	3
50 to under 58	6
58 to under 66	8
66 to under 74	7
74 to under 82	7
82 to under 90	4
90 to under 98	2
Total	**40**

Example 12.1-n

Creating a Frequency Distribution Table

The number of cars sold each month for the last 2 years by a car dealer is as follows:

44	58	68	27	21	55
39	15	19	16	33	25
51	52	10	26	37	48
70	75	84	73	65	80

Group the data into 5 classes and create a frequency distribution table.

Solution

Array the data using the stem-and-leaf method, as follows:

Stem-and-Leaf

Stem	Leaf
1	5 9 6 0
2	7 1 5 6
3	9 3 7
4	4 8
5	8 5 1 2
6	8 5
7	0 5 3
8	4 0

Data in Array

Stem	Leaf
1	0 5 6 9
2	1 5 6 7
3	3 7 9
4	4 8
5	1 2 5 8
6	5 8
7	0 3 5
8	0 4

Number of classes = 5 (given)

There are 24 data values. The highest value is 84 and the lowest value is 10.

Range = 84 – 10 = 74

Width of each class $= \frac{\text{Range}}{\text{\# of class}} = \frac{74}{5} = 14.8$ (use 15 for ease of presentation)

Therefore, the class interval = 15. Now, the lowest class interval will be "10 to under 25" and the highest class interval will be "70 to 85".

The following is the frequency distribution table:

Class Interval	Frequency
10 to under 25	5
25 to under 40	6
40 to under 55	4
55 to under 70	4
70 to under 85	5
Total	**24**

Relative Frequency Distribution and Percent Frequency Distribution

Relative Frequency Distribution

Relative frequency is the ratio of the frequency of a particular class interval to the total number of observations and is expressed in decimals or fractions. The sum of all relative frequency of a frequency distribution should be equal to one.

Percent Frequency Distribution

The percent frequency distribution is calculated by multiplying the relative frequencies of each class interval by 100 and expressing it as a percent. The sum of all relative frequencies of a frequency distribution should be equal to 100%.

Example 12.1-o

Creating Relative Frequency and Percent Frequency Distributions

Use the frequency distribution provided below to create the relative frequency distribution and the percent frequency distribution.

Class Interval	Frequency
30 to under 40	2
40 to under 50	4
50 to under 60	8
60 to under 70	11
70 to under 80	8
80 to under 90	5
90 to under 100	2
Total	**40**

Solution

Add two columns to the frequency table, one for the relative frequency distribution and one for the percent frequency distribution, as shown below.

Class Interval	Frequency	Relative Frequency	Percent Frequency
30 to under 40	2	0.05	5%
40 to under 50	4	0.10	10%
50 to under 60	8	0.20	20%
60 to under 70	11	0.275	27.5%
70 to under 80	8	0.20	20%
80 to under 90	5	0.125	12.5%
90 to under 100	2	0.05	5%
Total	**40**	**1**	**100%**

The relative frequency of any class is calculated by dividing the number of observations in that class by the total number of observations.

For example, the relative frequency of class "30 to under 40" is $\frac{2}{40} = 0.05$.

Similarly, calculate the relative frequency of the remaining class intervals and complete the "Relative Frequency" column.

The percent frequency distribution is calculated by multiplying the relative frequency by 100.

For example, the percent frequency of class "30 to under 40" is $0.05 \times 100\% = 5\%$.

Similarly, calculate the percent frequency of the remaining class intervals and complete the "Percent Frequency" column.

Cumulative Frequency Distribution and Cumulative Frequency Curve (or Polygon)

The cumulative frequency distribution at a given class interval is calculated by adding the frequency at that class interval to the preceding class intervals. That is, the sum of the frequencies of all the class intervals before the class interval in question and the particular class interval in question. Simply put, it is the running total of the frequencies.

A curve showing the cumulative frequency plotted against the upper class boundary of the class interval is called a cumulative frequency curve.

Example 12.1-p

Creating Cumulative Frequency Distribution

Use the frequency distribution in Example 12.1-o (also shown below) to create the relative cumulative frequency distribution and the cumulative percent frequency distribution. Also, draw the cumulative frequency curve.

Class Interval	Frequency
30 to under 40	2
40 to under 50	4
50 to under 60	8
60 to under 70	11
70 to under 80	8
80 to under 90	5
90 to under 100	2
Total	**40**

Solution

Add two columns to the frequency table, one for the cumulative frequency distribution and one for the cumulative percent frequency distribution, as shown below.

Class Interval	Frequency	Cumulative Frequency	Cumulative Percent Frequency
30 to under 40	2	2	5%
40 to under 50	4	6	15%
50 to under 60	8	14	35%
60 to under 70	11	25	62.5%
70 to under 80	8	33	82.5%
80 to under 90	5	38	95%
90 to under 100	2	40	100%
Total	**40**		

Compute the cumulative frequency of any class by using the total value of the frequency up to and including that class. For example, the cumulative frequency of class "50 to under 60" is $2 + 4 + 8 = 14$.

Compute the percent cumulative frequency by dividing the cumulative frequency distribution of that class by the total number of observations and convert the answer to a percent.

For example, the cumulative percent distribution of class "50 to under 60" is $\frac{14}{40} \times 100\% = 35\%$.

Solution
continued

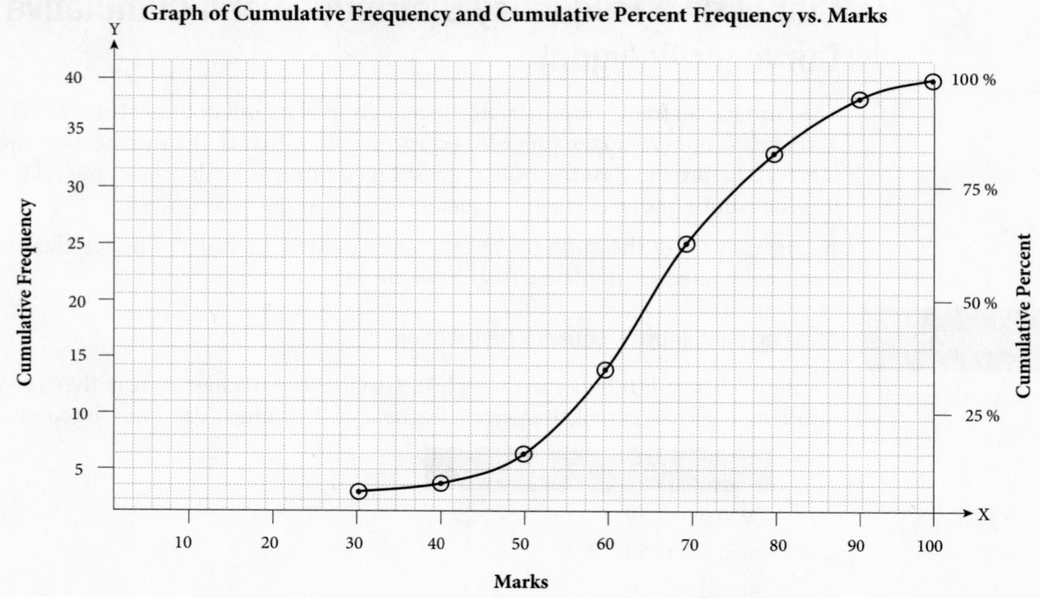

12.1 | Exercises

Answers to odd-numbered problems are available at the end of the textbook.

1. Identify the following variables as continuous or discrete:
   a. Height of students in a class b. Room temperature
   c. Net profit of a company d. Position in class
2. Identify the following variables as continuous or discrete:
   a. Number of seasons b. Weight of a person
   c. Time between the arrivals of two flights d. Air pressure
3. Identify the following variables as quantitative or qualitative:
   a. Marks on an exam b. Seasons of a year
   c. Amount of rainfall d. Mode
4. Identify the following variables as quantitative or qualitative:
   a. Height of a person b. Letter grade in an exam
   c. Median d. Model of a car
5. Identify the levels of measurements (nominal, ordinal, interval, or ratio) for the following measurements:
   a. Pant size b. Mean
   c. Annual salary of individuals d. Title of a person in a company
6. Identify the levels of measurements (nominal, ordinal, interval, or ratio) for the following measurements:
   a. Places of birth b. Ages of people
   c. Hours spent watching TV d. Temperature of ice in degrees C
7. Construct a stem-and-leaf plot to display the following data in an array:

39	32	44	13	29	38
31	18	19	37	25	27
34	31	19	43	21	28

8. Construct a stem-and-leaf plot to display the following data in an array:

7	16	19	5	37	25
22	18	26	20	32	11
17	31	9	16	13	35

9. Construct a stem-and-leaf plot to display the following data in an array:

65	77	81	55	51	45	85	82
75	78	48	92	52	69	84	70
95	80	73	81	59	88	64	97

10. Construct a stem-and-leaf plot to display the following data in an array:

76	95	77	75	78	66	97	71
72	84	88	62	58	52	92	91
89	83	85	59	97	87	80	65

11. The following data was collected from a sample survey of 40 first-year students who were asked to indicate their favourite subject among the four subjects, Statistics (*S*), Marketing (*M*), Accounting (*A*), and Finance Math (*F*).

A	*S*	*M*	*M*	*S*	*M*	*A*	*S*	*S*	*A*
M	*M*	*S*	*F*	*A*	*M*	*M*	*S*	*S*	*A*
S	*F*	*S*	*M*	*A*	*S*	*F*	*M*	*M*	*S*
M	*A*	*S*	*S*	*A*	*F*	*A*	*F*	*S*	*F*

Organize the data in a frequency table using a tally chart.

12. The following data was collected from a sample survey of 40 students who were asked to indicate the mode of transportation that they normally use to get to college during the summer term. Their choices were walking (*W*), bicycling (*B*), taking public transportation (*P*), and driving a car (*C*).

C	*B*	*C*	*B*	*C*	*B*	*P*	*W*	*P*	*C*
W	*B*	*P*	*P*	*B*	*P*	*C*	*W*	*W*	*P*
W	*W*	*P*	*C*	*B*	*W*	*W*	*C*	*C*	*B*
P	*C*	*P*	*W*	*B*	*W*	*B*	*C*	*P*	*B*

Organize the data in a frequency table using a tally chart.

13. The following are the letter grades obtained by 200 students in Finance Math, in the business program of a college:

Grade	Number of Students	Percent	Cumulative Percent	Angle	Cumulative Angle
A+	24				
A	30				
B	36				
C	52				
D	42				
F	16				
Total	**200**				

a. Complete the above table for percent, cumulative percent, angle, and cumulative angle.

b. Draw a pie chart using either the percent or the angle measure.

14. Victoria kept a record of the average number of hours she spent on different activities during the weekdays. The information is provided below:

Activity	Number of Hours	Percent	Cumulative Percent	Angle	Cumulative Angle
School	7.0				
Meals	1.0				
Homework	2.0				
Travel	2.5				
Sleep	8.0				
Other	3.5				
Total	**24**				

a. Complete the above table for percent, cumulative percent, angle, and cumulative angle.

b. Draw a pie chart using either the percent or the angle measure.

15. A store's monthly sales (in thousands of dollars) for last year were as follows:

Month	Jan.	Feb.	Mar.	Apr.	May	Jun.	Jul.	Aug.	Sep.	Oct.	Nov.	Dec.
Sales ($ Thousands)	45	52	74	78	70	95	98	120	105	89	80	92

Draw a line graph representing the data.

16. The number of houses sold by a developer for the period from 2006 to 2014 is provided below:

Year	2006	2007	2008	2009	2010	2011	2012	2013	2014
Number of houses sold	82	110	130	145	90	75	128	160	180

Draw a line graph representing the data.

17. Use a scatter plot to determine the relationship (if any) between the price of an item and the number of items sold:

Price ($)	60	61	62	64	66	68
Number of items sold	190	182	176	116	104	87

18. Use a scatter plot to determine the relationship (if any) between age and income:

Age (years)	21	27	35	41	46	52	56
Income ($ Thousands)	38	51	53	64	72	76	80

19. The frequency distribution below was constructed from data collected from a sample of 100 professors at a college. Construct a histogram and a frequency polygon for the data.

Years of Teaching	Frequency
0 to under 5	10
5 to under 10	14
10 to under 15	39
15 to under 20	24
20 to under 25	13

20. The frequency distribution below was constructed from data collected from a sample of 30 students at a college. Construct a histogram and a frequency polygon for the data.

Height (in cm)	Frequency
155 to under 160	2
160 to under 165	5
165to under 170	9
170 to under 175	7
175 to under 180	4
180 to under 185	3

21. Use the frequency distribution in Problem 19 to compute the following:
    a. Relative frequency distribution.
    b. Percent frequency distribution.
22. Use the frequency distribution in Problem 20 to compute the following:
    a. Relative frequency distribution.
    b. Percent frequency distribution.
23. Use the frequency distribution in Problem 19 to compute the following:
    a. Cumulative frequency distribution.
    b. Cumulative percent frequency distribution.
    c. Cumulative frequency and cumulative percent curve.
24. Use the frequency distribution in Problem 20 to compute the following:
    a. Cumulative frequency distribution.
    b. Cumulative percent frequency distribution.
    c. Cumulative frequency and cumulative percent curve.

12.2 | Measures of Central Tendency

Introduction

Central tendency is based on the concept that there is a single value that best summarizes an entire set of numeric data. Measures of central tendency are numerical values that are indicative of the central position (mean), the central location (median), or the greatest frequency (mode) concerning a set of data. That is, a single number that represents a "typical" value of a dataset is a measure of central tendency. This single value is useful to compare different datasets of the same type.

This section introduces these summarizing numbers (typical values) that describe the distribution of data. There are several common methods for selecting a typical value for a dataset. The most commonly used measures that describe this central position are the mean, median, and mode.

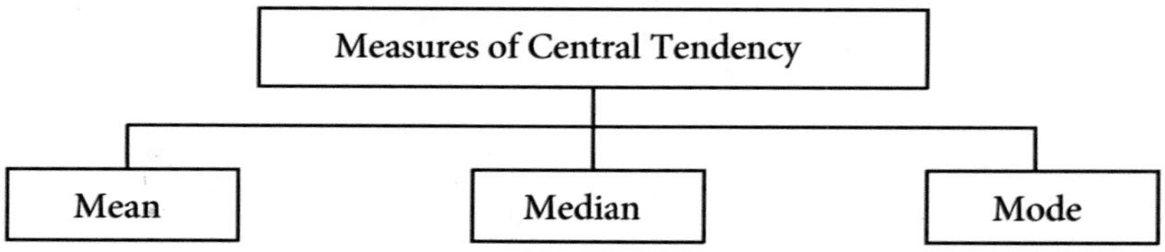

Mean

Mean is a measure of central tendency calculated by dividing the sum of the values of all the terms by the number of terms. The statistical mean of a set of data is the average of the values in that dataset.

Average or arithmetic mean has the exact same meaning as mean. The terms 'mean' and 'average' are used interchangeably. However, mean is used in more formal terms in statistics. The mean represents the expected value.

Arithmetic mean, or mean, is the ratio of the sum of all the terms to the number of terms, n.

Mean is the most commonly used measure of central tendency because of its mathematical qualities. It uses all the data and indicates the central position of the frequency distribution.

$$Mean = \frac{Sum\ of\ All\ the\ Values\ of\ the\ Terms}{Number\ of\ Terms}$$

The population mean is represented by μ.

The symbol used to describe a sample mean is $\overline{x}$. The 'bar' over the 'x' is a standard way of representing a mean and is read as x-bar.

The number of values or observations in a sample is represented by the variable 'n'.

Individual values are represented by 'x_i', where the subscript 'i' takes on a number to represent each individual value or measurement (i.e., i could take on any value from 1 to n).

The formula for the mean of any number of values is:

$$\overline{x} = \frac{\sum x_i}{n} \quad \begin{array}{l} \longleftarrow \text{Sum of values of '}n\text{' observations} \\ \longleftarrow \text{Number of observations} \end{array}$$

The symbol 'Σ' is the capital form of the Greek symbol *Sigma*, which means the summation of all the individual values.

This formula can be used to find the mean of any number of values by substituting the symbols x_1, x_2 and so on, up to x_n, with the actual data values:

$$\overline{x} = \frac{x_1 + x_2 + x_3 + \ldots x_n}{n}$$

Note: The arithmetic mean of a set of values is the number that satisfies,

$$x_1 + x_2 + x_3 + \ldots + x_n = \underbrace{\overline{x} + \overline{x} + \overline{x} + \ldots + \overline{x}}_{n \text{ times}} = n \cdot \overline{x}$$

Example 12.2-a Calculating the Mean

The number of cars sold by a sales person in the past 5 months is: {8, 15, 7, 11, 9}. Find the mean number of cars sold by the sales person. Explain on a number line what this number represents in relation to the above values.

Solution

{8, 15, 7, 11, 9} There are 5 terms.

To find the mean, first add all the terms to find their sum and then divide it by the number of terms.

$$Mean = \frac{Sum\ of\ All\ The\ Values\ of\ the\ Terms}{Number\ of\ Terms} = \frac{(8+15+7+11+9)}{5} = \frac{50}{5} = 10$$

Therefore, the mean or the average of the above five values is 10. If we plot these values on a number line, then the number 10 represents the center of these values.

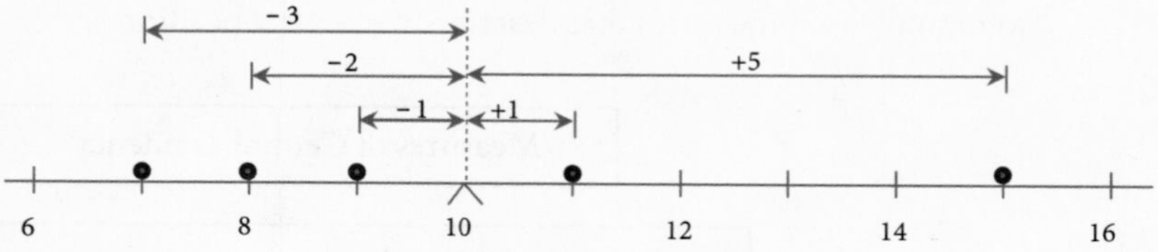

Example 12.2-b Calculating the Mean when New Data is Added to the Dataset

The mean of 6 observations is 70. If another observation with a value of 98 is added to the above data, calculate the mean of the 7 observations.

Solution

The mean of 6 observations (terms) is 70.

$$Mean = \frac{Sum\ of\ All\ The\ Values\ of\ the\ Terms}{Number\ of\ Terms}$$

$$70 = \frac{\text{The sum of 6 terms}}{6}$$

The sum of 6 terms = 70 × 6 = 420

When a new term with a value of 98 is added,

The sum of 7 terms = 420 + 98 = 518

The mean of 7 terms $\frac{518}{7} = 74$

Therefore, the mean of 7 terms (observations) is 74.

Example 12.2-c Solving for an Unknown Term when the Mean is Given

The mean of 4 terms is 12. Three of the terms are 9, 11, and 13. Find the 4th term.

Solution

Let the 4th term be x.

$$\text{Using } \bar{x} = \frac{\sum x_i}{n}$$

$$12 = \frac{(9+11+13+x)}{4}$$

$$9 + 11 + 13 + x = 12 \times 4$$

$$33 + x = 48$$

$$x = 48 - 33 = 15$$

Therefore, the 4th term is 15.

Outlier

An outlier is a number that is very different from the rest of the group. We usually remove the outliers from the dataset before calculating the mean of a dataset as it affects the mean value. If the dataset includes outlier/s, then the value of the mean may be misleading.

Example 12.2-d **Showing the Effect of Extreme Values (Outliers) in the Mean**

Calculate the mean (i) using all values and (ii) after removing the outlier/s in the dataset: {3, 40, 45, 52, 60, 66, 70}.

Solution

(i) Mean of all the 7 values in the dataset:

Using $\bar{x} = \frac{\sum x_i}{n} = \frac{3+40+45+52+60+66+70}{7} = \frac{336}{7} = 48$

(ii) Except for the value 3, the other values are reasonably close to each other. Therefore, 3 is an outlier. After removing the value 3 from this dataset, the mean of the remaining 6 values of the dataset:

$$\bar{x} = \frac{\sum x_i}{n} = \frac{40+45+52+60+66+70}{6} = \frac{333}{6} = 55.5$$

Therefore, the mean is greatly affected by extreme values, numbers that are very different from the rest of the group, known as outliers.

Example 12.2-e **Calculating the Mean after Removing the Outlier/s**

Calculate the mean for the dataset {2,22,25,26,34,23,29,30,75} after removing the outlier/s.

Solution

Except for the values 2 and 75 in the dataset, the remaining values are close to each other.

Therefore, 2 and 75 are outliers of the dataset.

The mean of the dataset after removing the outliers:

$$\bar{x} = \frac{\sum x_i}{n} = \frac{22+25+26+34+23+29+30}{7} = \frac{189}{7} = 27$$

Therefore, the mean of the dataset after removing the outliers is 27.

Weighted Mean

The weighted mean is also known as the weighted average. It is similar to the mean, but instead of each term contributing an equal weight in the average calculation, now each of the terms may contribute a different weight compared to the other terms.

When all the values of the terms are not equal, each value to be averaged is assigned a different weight. The weightings determine the relative importance of each value. If all the weightings are equal, then the weighted mean is the same as the mean.

The weighted mean is calculated as follows: $\bar{x} = \frac{\sum x_i \cdot w_i}{\sum w_i}$

That is, each value in the group (x) is multiplied by the weight factor (w) and the products are then summed and divided by the sum of the weights.

In the Weighted Mean formula, x_i represents each data value (x_1, x_2, x_3........x_n)

and w_i represents its weight or frequency (w_1, w_2, w_3......w_n)

i.e., $\sum x_i \cdot w_i$ is the sum of the weighted values, and

$\sum w_i$ is the sum of the weighting factors or the cumulative frequency.

We can also use the formula for weighted mean whenever values are repeated. We multiply the value x by the number of times it is repeated, add the products, and divide by the total number of values.

Example 12.2-f

Calculating the Weighted Mean

For a Math course, the final mark is computed using a weighted average, based on the following factors (weights):

Quizzes:	1 Point
Online homework:	2 Points
Midterm test:	3 Points
Final exam:	4 Points

If a student received 80% for the quizzes, 70% for the online homework, 75% for the midterm test, and 65% for the final exam, calculate the student's final mark for the Math course.

Solution

Evaluation Component	Score (x_i)	Factor (Weights, w_i)	$x_i \cdot w_i$
Quizzes	80%	1	$0.80 \times 1 = 0.80$
Online homework	70%	2	$0.70 \times 2 = 1.40$
Midterm test	75%	3	$0.75 \times 3 = 2.25$
Final exam	65%	4	$0.65 \times 4 = 2.60$
		$\sum w_i = 10$	$\sum x_i \cdot w_i = 7.05$

$$\textit{Weighted Mean} = \frac{\sum x_i \cdot w_i}{\sum w_i} = \frac{7.05}{10} \times 100\% = 70.50\%$$

Therefore, the student's final mark for the Math course is 70.50%.

Geometric Mean

The geometric mean indicates the central tendency of a dataset by using the product of their values. Whereas, the arithmetic mean uses the sum of the numbers in the dataset to find the central tendency.

When it comes to finding the average rate at which a quantity grows over a time period, the arithmetic mean is not a good measure. The geometric mean is a better measure which allows estimating the average rate of change of growth over that period of time. It is a very useful measure in accounting and finance. It is used often in financial analysis, when analysts look at processes with compound interest.

The geometric mean is calculated by multiplying all the values of the terms together and then taking the nth root of the result (this is the same as raising the result to the power $\frac{1}{n}$), where n is the number of terms in the dataset.

If there are n terms ($x_1, x_2, x_3, x_4, x_4 .... x_n$), then the geometric mean, G, is:

Geometric mean is the nth root of the product of n terms.

$$G = \sqrt[n]{x_1 \cdot x_2 \cdot x_3 \cdot x_4 \cdot x_5 \cdots \cdot x_n}$$

$$\text{i.e., } G = \left(x_1 \cdot x_2 \cdot x_3 \cdot x_4 \cdot x_5 \cdots \cdot x_n\right)^{\frac{1}{n}}$$

Note: Geometric mean, 'G', of a set of values is the number G that satisfies:

$$x_1 \cdot x_2 \cdot x_3 \cdots \cdot x_n = \underbrace{G \times G \times G \times G \ldots.}_{\text{n times}} = G^n$$

Example 12.2-g

Finding the Geometric Mean

Find the geometric mean of the following 5 terms: 3, 4, 6, 9, 14.

Solution

Using, $G = \left(x_1 \cdot x_2 \cdot x_3 \cdot x_4 \cdot x_5 \cdots \cdot x_n\right)^{\frac{1}{n}}$

$$= [3 \times 4 \times 6 \times 9 \times 14]^{\frac{1}{5}} = 6.187661... = 6.19$$

Therefore, the geometric mean is 6.19.

Example 12.2-h **Finding the Average Annual Growth Rate**

Sam invested $100 for four years. If the growth rate for each year was 10%, 14%, 17%, and 18%, what was the average annual growth rate.

Solution

The average growth rate using arithmetic mean = $\left[\frac{(10\%+14\%+17\%+18\%)}{4}\right]=14.75\%$

However, this is not the correct calculation in this case. The correct calculation is to determine the geometric mean, as explained below:

End of the first year, the value = 100(1 + 0.10)

End of the second year, the value = 100(1 + 0.10)(1 + 0.14)

End of the third year, the value = 100(1 + 0.10)(1 + 0.14)(1 + 0.17)

End of the fourth year, the value = 100(1 + 0.10)(1 + 0.14)(1 + 0.17)(1 + 0.18)

If 'G' is the average annual growth rate over the 4-year period, then,

$$100(1+G)^4 = 100(1+0.10)(1+0.14)(1+0.17)(1+0.18)$$

$$= 100(1.10)(1.14)(1.17)(1.18)$$

$$(1+G) = [(1.10)\,(1.14)\,(1.17)\,(1.18)]^{\frac{1}{4}} = 1.147073...$$

$$G = 0.147073... = 14.71\%$$

Therefore, the annual average growth rate was 14.71%.

Median

The median is the value of the middle term when the terms are in an array, arranged in an ascending order (lowest to highest value) or in a descending order (highest to lowest). That is, half of the values are below the median and the other half of the values are above the median.The median is not affected by extreme values (outliers).

Median is the middle value when the data is in an array.

The median is also called the 50th percentile (denoted by P_{50}) or the 2nd quartile (denoted by Q_2) of the dataset.

The position of the median in an array is determined by $\frac{n+1}{2}$, where n is the number of terms in the dataset.

When some values in the measurements are not representative of the general value of the dataset or when the measurements contain extreme values (outliers), the median is the most preferred measure of central tendency.

If the number of terms is odd, the median is the value of the term in the middle, when the data is in an array.

If the number of terms is even, the median is the average of the value of the two terms in the middle, when the data is in an array.

Example 12.2-i **Finding the Median When There Is an Odd Number of Terms in a Dataset**

The heights (cm) of a sample group of students are:

{182, 168, 175, 180, 171, 179, 177}

Calculate the median height for this group of students.

Solution

Arrange the data in ascending order as follows:

168, 171, 175, **177**, 179, 180, 182

There are 7 terms in the dataset.

Median position = $\frac{n+1}{2}=\frac{7+1}{2}=\frac{8}{2}=4$

The 4th term in the array is 177.

Therefore, the median height for this group of students is 177 cm.

Example 12.2-j

Finding the Median When There is an Even Number of Terms in a Data Set

The monthly rent ($) for a sample group of two-bedroom condominium units in downtown are:

{2,550, 2,700, 2,650, 2,925, 3,050, 2,850}

Calculate the median rent for this group of two-bedroom condominium units.

Solution

Arrange the data in ascending order as follows:

2,550, 2,650, 2,700, 2,850, 2,925, 3,050

There are 6 terms in the dataset.

Median position $= \frac{n+1}{2} = \frac{6+1}{2} = \frac{7}{2} = 3.5$

Therefore, the median is located between the 3rd and 4th terms.

3rd term = 2,700

4th term = 2,850

Average of 3rd and 4th terms $= \frac{2{,}700 + 2{,}850}{2} = \$2{,}775$

Therefore, the median rent for this group of two-bedroom condominium units is $2,775.

Mode

Mode is the most frequently observed value in a data set.

The mode of a set of observations is the specific value that occurs with the most frequency (occurs most often). For non-numeric data (e.g., colour) or when the frequency is more important than the value (e.g., shirt size), the mode is used as the central tendency.

If all the observations occur with the same frequency (i.e., there is no "most frequent" measurement in the dataset), then there is no mode.

There may be more than one mode in a set of observations if there are several values that all occur with the greatest frequency.

A dataset with two modes is described as bi-modal and a dataset with more than two modes is described as multimodal.

For example,

- In the dataset: [1, 3, 6, 7, 12, 15,17], there is no mode.
- In the dataset: [11, 13, **16, 16, 16,** 17, 17, 22, 22, 27], the mode is unique and is 16.
- In the dataset: [10, **11, 11,** 12, 13, 14, **15, 15**], the mode is not unique. There are two modes, 11 and 15. This data is said to be bi-modal.

The following table provides a summary of the measures of central tendency and their use.

Measures of Central Tendency	Summary
Mean	Use the mean when the data is symmetrical or after outliers have been removed.
Median	Use the median when the data is skewed (left or right) or when there are outliers in the data.
Mode	Use the mode when the frequency of observations is more important than the value of the observations.

Example 12.2-k

Calculating Measures of Central Tendency

Given the following set of data, calculate (i) mean, (ii) median, and (iii) mode.

14 28 17 40 26 21 36 26 27 31

Solution

The mean, median, and mode are computed as follows:

Arrange the data in ascending order as follows:

14 17 21 26 26 27 28 31 36 40

(i) Using $Mean = \frac{\sum x_i}{n}$,

$$Mean = \frac{(14+17+21+26+26+27+28+31+36+40)}{10} = \frac{266}{10} = 26.6$$

Therefore, the mean is 26.6.

(ii) Median position is determined by $\frac{(n+1)}{2}$.

There are 10 terms. The median position is $\frac{(10+1)}{2} = 5.5$

Therefore, the median is located between the 5th and 6th terms.

$$Median = \frac{\left(5^{\text{th}} \text{ term} + 6^{\text{th}} \text{ term}\right)}{2} = \frac{(26+27)}{2} = 26.5$$

Therefore, the median is 26.5.

(iii) The value that occurs most frequently is 26. It occurs two times in the dataset.
Therefore, the mode is 26.

The mid-range is another measure of central location that is occasionally used. It is computed as the average of the smallest and largest values in a dataset.

For example, in the dataset in Example 12.2-k, the mid-range is $\frac{14+40}{2} = \frac{54}{2} = 27$.

Example 12.2-l

Calculating the Mean, Median, and Mode in a Frequency Distribution

The hourly wages of 30 employees are provided in the frequency distribution table below:

Hourly Wages ($) (Class)	15	20	25	30	35	40
Number of Employees (Frequency)	5	8	6	5	4	2

Calculate the (i) mean, (ii) median, and (iii) mode of the hourly wages of the employees.

Solution

(i) The table indicates that the number of employees earning $15 per hour is 5, $20 per hour is 8, ...$40 per hour is 2.

Therefore, the mean of all the values of the term can be computed using the weighted average formula,

$$\bar{x} = \frac{\sum x_i \cdot w_i}{\sum w_i}$$

$$\bar{x} = \frac{[(15\times5)+(20\times8)+(25\times6)+(30\times5)+(35\times4)+(40\times2)]}{(5+8+6+5+4+2)} = \frac{755}{30} = 25.17$$

Therefore, the mean hourly wage is $25.17.

(ii) Median position $= \frac{n+1}{2} = \frac{30+1}{2} = 15.5$

$$Median = \frac{15^{\text{th}} \text{ term} + 16^{\text{th}} \text{ term}}{2}$$

(There are 5 terms with $15, 8 terms with $20, 6 terms with $25, etc.)

Therefore, the 14th term to the 19th term will have a value of $25.

Solution
continued

i.e., 15th term = 25, 16th term = 25.

$$Median = \frac{25+25}{2} = 25$$

Therefore, the median hourly wage is $25.

(iii) The value that occurs most frequently is $20. There are 8 data with $20.

Therefore, the mode of the hourly wage is $20.

Mean, Median, and Mode for Grouped Data

The calculation of mean, median, and mode for grouped data is different from that used for ungrouped data. In grouped data, the data is organised into a frequency table with class intervals and frequencies.

In grouped data, we usually do not have access to each value of the data (raw data) that lie within each class interval. Therefore, we calculate the approximate values of mean, median, and mode as follows:

Calculation of Mean for Grouped Data

Mean is defined as the arithmetic average of the values of all the terms in the dataset. Since we do not have the raw data, the midpoint of each class interval is used as an approximation of all values within that class interval. The class midpoint is represented by the symbol 'x' and the observed frequency within the class interval is represented by 'f'.

Therefore, the formula for calculating the mean for grouped data is:

$$\overline{x} = \frac{\sum f \cdot x}{n}$$

This formula indicates that the mean for the grouped data is determined by first multiplying the mid-point of each class interval by its respective class frequency, adding the products, and finally, dividing by the total number of data. This formula is similar to the calculation of weighted mean.

Example 12.2-m **Calculating the Mean for Grouped Data**

The distribution of marks (out of 100) following a statistics exam for a sample of 50 students grouped in a frequency distribution is provided below. Calculate the mean mark on the statistics exam.

Class interval (Exam marks)	Frequency (f) (Number of students)
40 to under 50	4
50 to under 60	5
60 to under 70	18
70 to under 80	10
80 to under 90	6
90 to under 100	7

Solution

Class interval	Frequency (f)	Class Midpoint (x)	Weighted Class MidPoint $(f \cdot x)$
40 to under 50	4	45	180
50 to under 60	5	55	275
60 to under 70	18	65	1,170
70 to under 80	10	75	750
80 to under 90	6	85	510
90 to under 100	7	95	665
Totals	$n = 50$		$\Sigma f \cdot x = 3{,}550$

The class midpoint is represented by x (the 3rd column) and the value of x for each class is computed by finding the average of the lowest and highest class limit in each class interval.

Solution *continued*

For the 1st class interval, the class midpoint is $\frac{40+50}{2} = 45$.

The last column $(f \cdot x)$ represents the weighted class midpoint.

For example, for the 1st class interval, $f \cdot x = 4 \times 45 = 180$

$$\bar{x} = \frac{\sum f \cdot x}{n} = \frac{3{,}550}{50} = 71$$

Therefore, the mean mark is 71.

Calculation of Median for Grouped Data

Median is defined as the value of the middle term. When the raw data is not available, it is not possible to calculate the median exactly. Therefore, we calculate an approximated median value.

First, identify the class interval which contains the median, known as the 'median class'. This is the class which has the cumulative frequency greater or equal to one-half of the total number of data.

Once the median class is identified, we may use the midpoint of that class interval as the approximate median value.

We may also use the method of interpolation to estimate the median to a higher level of approximation, using the following formula:

$$\text{Median} = \ell + \left[\left(\frac{n}{2} - m\right)\right] \times \left(\frac{c}{f}\right)$$

$\ell =$ lower limit of the median class

$n =$ total number of frequency

$m =$ cumulative frequency in the class one above the median class

$c =$ class width

$f =$ frequency in the median class

Note: In the examples and exercises, we will use the midpoint of the median class as the approximate median value.

Example 12.2-n **Calculating the Median of Grouped Data (using the Data in Example 12.2-m)**

For the distribution of marks (out of 100) following a statistics exam for a sample of 50 students grouped in a frequency distribution given in Example 12.2-m, calculate the median mark on the statistics exam.

Solution

Class interval	Frequency (f)	Class Midpoint (x)	Cumulative Frequency (f_c)	
40 to under 50	4	45	4	
50 to under 60	5	55	9	
60 to under 70	18	65	27	← Median Class
70 to under 80	10	75	37	
80 to under 90	6	85	43	
90 to under 100	7	95	50	
	$n = 50$			

Compute the cumulative frequency (f_c):

There are 50 terms.

$$\text{Median Position} = \frac{n+1}{2} = \frac{50+1}{2} = 25.5$$

$$\text{Median} = \frac{25^{th}\text{ term} + 26^{th}\text{ term}}{2}$$

Solution *continued*

From the cumulative frequency, (f_c), the 25th + 26th term will fall in the class interval '60 to under 70'. This is the median class.

Using the midpoint value of that class, the median for the data is 65.

Therefore, the median mark is 65.

Calculation of Mode for Grouped Data

Mode is defined as the value that occurs most often. When the raw data is not available, it is not possible to calculate the mode exactly. Therefore, we calculate an approximated modal value.

First, identify the class interval which contains the highest frequency, known as the "modal class".

Once the modal class is identified, use the mid-point of that class interval as the modal value.

Example 12.2-o **Calculating the Mode of Grouped Data (using the Data in Example 12.2-m)**

For the distribution of marks (out of 100) for the statistics exam for a sample of 50 students grouped in a frequency distribution given in Example 12.2-m, calculate the mode for the statistics exam marks.

Solution

Class interval (Exam marks)	Frequency (f) (Number of students)	
40 to under 50	4	
50 to under 60	5	
60 to under 70	18	⟵ Modal Class
70 to under 80	10	
80 to under 90	6	
90 to under 100	7	

Modal class is the class interval with the highest frequency.

The class having the class interval '60 to under 70' contains the highest frequency of 18. Therefore, it is the modal class.

The midpoint of the class is $\frac{60+70}{2} = 65$.

Therefore, the mode is 65.

Empirical Relationship among Mean, Median, and Mode

There is a relationship among mean, median, and mode that is empirically based (from observations of these values calculated for many sets of data).

The relationship observed most of the time is that the difference between the mean and the mode is 3 times the difference between the mean and the median.

$$\textit{Mean} - \textit{Mode} = 3(\textit{Mean} - \textit{Median})$$

Example 12.2-p **Calculating the Median, Given the Mean and the Mode**

The average height of the students in a college class was 172 cm and the most frequently observed height (mode) was 163 cm. What is the median height of this group of students?

Solution

Using the empirical relationship among mean, mode and the median,

Let the median be x.

Solution *continued*

$$Mean - Mode = 3(Mean - Median)$$

$$172 - 163 = 3(172 - x)$$

$$9 = 516 - 3x$$

$$3x = 507$$

$$x = 169$$

Therefore, the median height is 169 cm.

Symmetry and Skewness

For symmetrically distributed data (zero skewness), the mean, median, and mode will be equal.

When Mean = Median = Mode,
Data is Symmetrically Distributed.

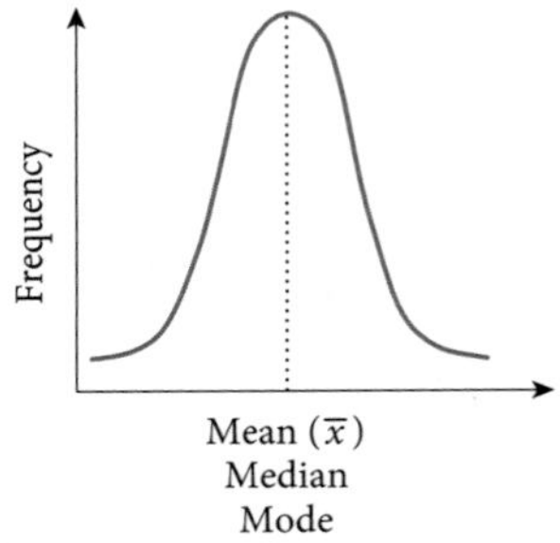

For **non-symmetrically distributed data,** mean, median, and mode will differ. In this case, the mean is drawn toward a long tail by extreme values. The symmetry of a frequency distribution is indicated by the sign of the value of the mean minus the median.

When the mean minus the median is positive (i.e., mean > median), the distribution is skewed to the right, and the distribution has a long right tail (positively skewed).

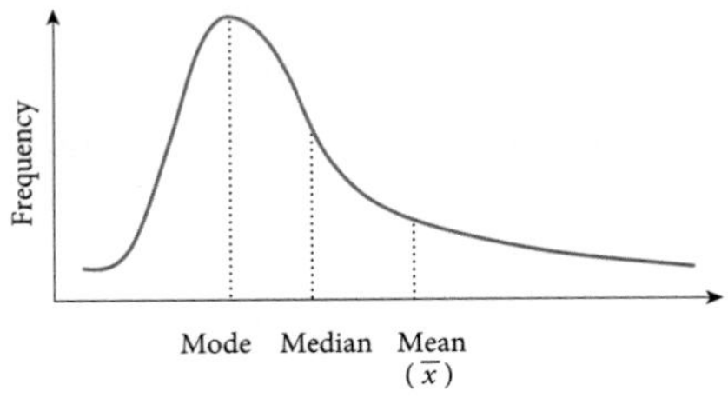

When Mean > Median,
Positively Skewed (skewed to the right).

When the mean minus the median is negative (i.e., mean < median), the distribution is skewed to the left, and the distribution has a long left tail (negatively skewed).

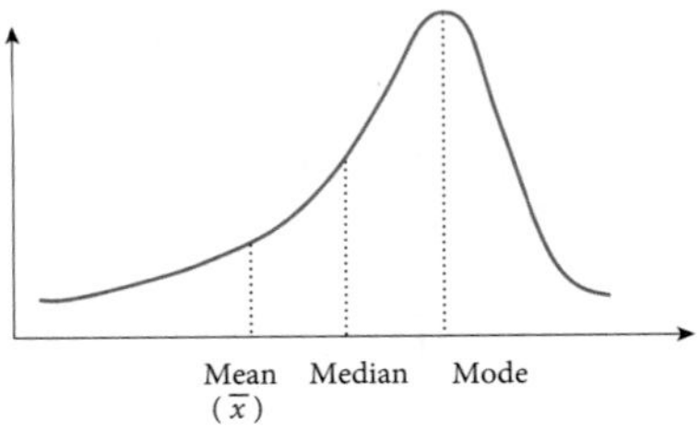

When Mean < Median,
Negatively Skewed (skewed to the left).

When the data is positively skewed or negatively skewed, then the median best represents the central tendency.

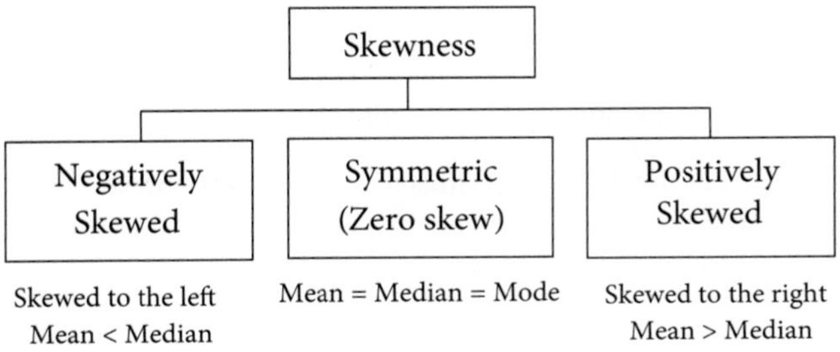

Example 12.2-q

Determining the Shape of the Distribution (Using data in Example 12.2-k)

Determine the shape of the distribution of the data presented in example 12.2-k.

Solution

In example 12.2-k we determined that mean is 26.6, median is 26.5, and mode is 26.

The mean, median, and mode of the set of data are close to each other. This suggests that the data is symmetrically distributed, as shown below.

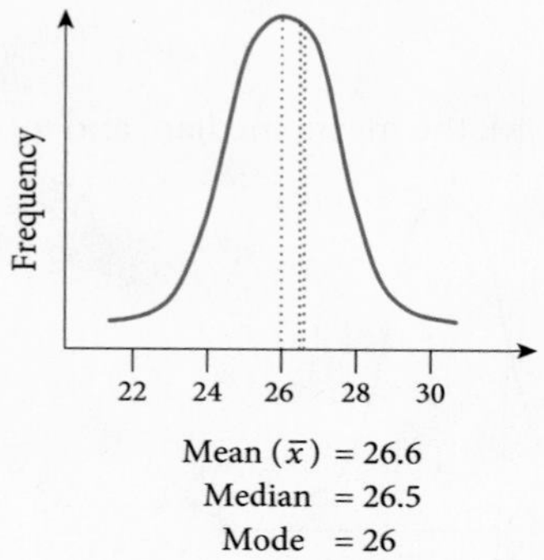

Example 12.2-r

Determining the Shape of the Distribution

For a given group of students working together on a project, the average age is 22 years old, the median is 19, and the mode is 18. Based on the given measures of central tendency, determine the shape of the distribution of the students' ages.

Solution

Mean = 22

Median = 19

Mode = 18

The difference between the Mean and the Median is positive (i.e., Mean > Median), which suggests that there are unusually high values (i.e., outliers) in the dataset that have destroyed the symmetry.

Therefore, the distribution is skewed to the right, and the distribution has a long right tail (distribution is positively skewed).

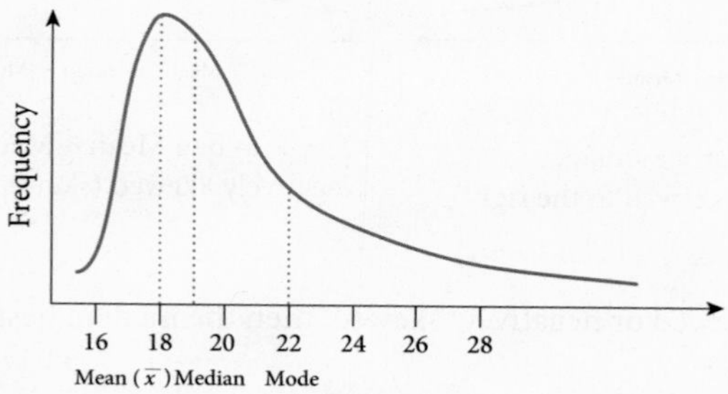

Example 12.2-s

Determining the Shape of the Distribution

The average mark on a statistics test for a class of 35 students was 60, the median mark was 70, and the mode was 80. Based on these measures of central tendency, determine the shape of the distribution of the students' marks.

Solution

Mean = 60

Median = 70

Mode = 80

The difference between the Mean and the Median is negative (i.e., Mean < Median), which suggests that there are unusually low values (i.e., outliers) in the dataset that have destroyed the symmetry.

Therefore, the distribution is skewed to the left, and the distribution has a long left tail (distribution is negatively skewed).

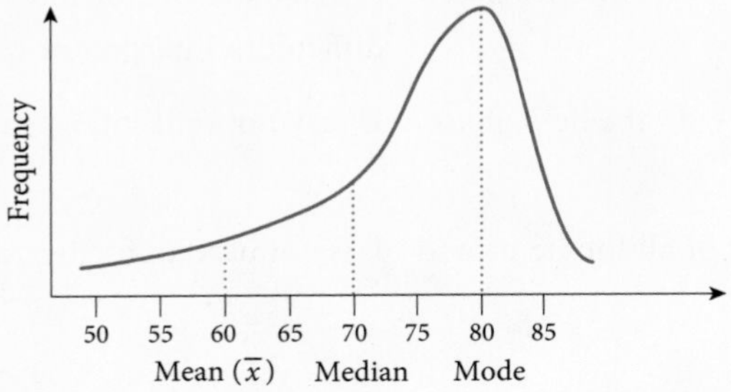

Advantages and Disadvantages of Mean, Median, and Mode

Mean	
Advantages	**Disadvantages**
It is defined by an algebraic formula.	It cannot be determined by inspecting the data.
It is based on all values of the given data.	It cannot be computed for qualitative data.
It has a unique value and is useful in comparing sets of data.	Its value may not exist in the data.
It is used algebraically in further statistical calculations.	It is affected by extremely large or small values in the data.
It is used in calculating the sum of the values of the data by multiplying with the number of items.	It cannot be computed when class intervals have open ends.

Median	
Advantages	**Disadvantages**
It is easy to identify by knowing the number of items and the middle item in the data.	It is not a representative measure when the values of the data are wide apart from each other.
It can be estimated through the graphic presentation of the data.	It is not based on all the items in the data.
It is not affected by extremely large or small values in the data.	It is an approximate measure when located between the two middle values.
It has a unique value and is useful in comparing sets of data.	It is not used in further statistical calculations.
It is a good measure of central tendency for data with skewed distribution.	It is not useful to calculate the sum of the values of the data.

Mode	
Advantages	**Disadvantages**
It is easy to locate knowing the items with the highest frequency in the data set.	It is not a representative value of all the items in the data.
It is not affected by extremely large or small values in the data.	It is not possible to identify when frequencies of all items are identical.
It is a very popular measure for qualitative data.	It may have one or more values and may be difficult to interpret or compare.
It can be located graphically with the help of histograms.	It may not reflect the centre of the distribution.
It does not require the value of all the items and frequencies of a distribution.	It is not used in further statistical calculations.

12.2 | Exercises

Answers to odd-numbered problems are available at the end of the textbook.

1. The final marks of a student in 6 subjects were 89, 95, 68, 86, 91, and 78. Calculate the average (arithmetic mean) mark.
2. The weights (in kilograms) of 7 students were 62 68, 65, 69, 73, 58, and 64. Calculate the average (arithmetic mean) weight.
3. Henry received the following marks on his first three Math tests: 85, 94, and 89. What mark must he receive on his 4th test to have an average of exactly 90 on the four tests?
4. Giang received the following marks on her first four Math tests: 87, 93, 89 and 88. What mark must she receive on her 5th test to have an average of exactly 90 on the five tests?
5. The mean of 10 observations is 20 and that of another 15 observations is 16. Find the mean of all 25 observations.
6. A class of 25 students took a Science test. Ten students had an average (arithmetic mean) score of 80. The other students had an average score of 60. What is the average score of the whole class?
7. The mean of 6 numbers is 50. If one of the numbers is excluded, the mean gets reduced by 5. Determine the excluded number.
8. The mean of 5 numbers is 27. If one of the numbers is excluded, the mean gets reduced by 2. Determine the excluded number.
9. The average monthly salary of 50 people was $4,220. The average monthly salary of 42 of them was $3,500. Calculate the average monthly salary of the remaining 8 people.
10. The average mark for a class of 40 students was 74. The 15 male students in the class had an average mark of 70. Calculate the average mark of the female students in the class.
11. In a survey, 10 people were found to have an average weight of 72 kg. When another person joined the survey, the average of the 11 people dropped by 2 kg. Find the weight of the 11th person.
12. The average mark of 14 students in a class was 75. Another student took a make-up test and the class average dropped by 1 mark. What was the mark of the 15th student?
13. Find the median for the following datasets:

    a. 51, 56, 63, 46, 48

    b. 26, 24, 29, 24, 25, 28, 23

    c. 28, 24, 22, 24, 26, 26, 22, 28, 27
14. Find the median for the following datasets:

    a. 14, 11, 19, 17, 15

    b. 30, 27, 29, 24, 22, 31, 25

    c. 93, 90, 62, 44, 75, 89, 74, 78, 72

15. Find the median for the following datasets:

a. 41, 44, 37, 39, 27, 35, 42, 40

b. 18, 13, 5, 14, 18, 14, 19, 17, 15, 10

c. 74, 100, 78, 61, 78, 81, 67, 93, 90, 62, 75, 89

16. Find the median for the following datasets:

a. 75, 78, 92, 69, 84, 70, 75, 89

b. 74, 99, 78, 61, 78, 81, 67, 93, 90, 62

c. 52, 57, 61, 64, 70, 72, 78, 79, 79, 80, 80, 81

17. The results on a recent class test out of 30 are: {30, 27, 19, 24, 22, 31, 25, 28, and 26}.

a. Find the median mark.

b. If a mark of 24, achieved by another student, is included in the test score, find the new median mark.

18. The test results on a recent exam out of 100 were: {67, 62, 70, 68, 90, 84, 94}.

a. Find the median mark.

b. If a mark of 75, achieved by another student, is included in the exam scores, find the new median mark.

19. Find the mode for the following datasets:

a. 5, 6, 7, 10, 11, 12, 13, 15, 16

b. 14, 16, 16, 27, 31, 31, 31, 35, 37

c. 34, 36, 36, 36, 37, 41, 41, 41, 42

20. Find the mode for the following datasets:

a. 6, 7, 8, 11, 13, 14, 16, 17

b. 15, 15, 17, 25,28, 29, 32, 34, 35

c. 29, 30, 32, 34, 35, 37, 42, 42, 42

21. A class is given a quiz with 5 questions. Twenty percent of the students got all 5 correct, 30% got 4 correct, 25% got 3 correct, 10% got 2 correct, 5% got 1 correct, and the others got them all wrong. If there are 40 students in the class, what is the mean mark on the quiz?

22. A class is given a test with 5 questions. Fifteen percent of the students got all 5 correct, 25% got 4 correct, 40% got 3 correct, 5% got 2 correct, 10% got 1 correct, and the others got them all wrong. If there are 40 students in the class, what is the mean mark on the test?

23. A student obtained marks of 75, 85, 60, 65, and 50 in the subjects of Finance, Statistics, Accounting, Marketing, and English, respectively. Assuming weights of 5, 4, 3, 2, and 1, respectively, for the above subjects, find the weighted arithmetic mean mark for the subjects.

24. In a survey of 100 people, 75 of them have an average salary of $2,500 a month. Twenty-five of them earn an average salary of $8,000 a month .What is the average monthly salary of the 100 people surveyed?

25. Calculate the geometric mean for the following datasets:

a. 4, 36 b. 2, 4, 8 c. 1.10, 1.16, 1.13, 1.18

26. Calculate the geometric mean for the following sets of data:

a. 9, 25 b. 4, 6, 8 c. 1.08, 1.09, 1.05, 1.12

27. Calculate the mean, median, and mode for the following datasets:

a. 8, 4, 6, 4, 10, 4, 10

b. 72, 68, 56, 65, 72, 56, 56, 68

c. 125, 132, 120, 118, 120, 128, 126, 120, 132

28. Calculate the mean, median, and mode for the following datasets:

a. 6, 2, 4, 7, 6, 3, 8

b. 18, 10, 21, 17, 12, 5, 9, 12

c. 47, 50, 64, 85, 50, 47, 36, 24, 61, 48, 50, 73

29. Six employees in a restaurant earn the following weekly wages:

$140, $220, $90, $180, $140, $200

a. Find the average weekly income of the six employees.

b. What is the median wage?

c. Find the mode.

30. Ten employees of a department store earn the following weekly wages:

$200, $150, $160, $125, $160, $150, $180, $130, $170, $150

a. Find the average weekly income of the ten employees.

b. What is the median wage?

c. Find the mode.

31. Using the empirical relationship among mean, median, and mode, calculate the mode if the mean is 17 and the median is 16 for a given statistical observation, and comment on the skewness of the distribution.

32. Using the empirical relationship among mean, median, and mode, calculate the mean if the median is 22 and the mode is 30 for a given statistical observation, and comment on the skewness of the distribution.

33. The hourly wages for a sample of 45 students during their summer employment were grouped into the following frequency distribution. Compute the mean, the median, and the mode.

Hourly Wages	Number (f)
$10 up to $12	3
$12 up to $14	6
$14 up to $16	12
$16 up to $18	15
$18 up to $20	7
$20 up to $22	2

34. The ages of a sample of 40 applicants for a training program are grouped into the following frequency distribution. Compute the mean, the median, and the mode.

Age	Number (f)
20 up to 22	4
22 up to 24	7
24 up to 26	10
26 up to 28	14
28 up to 30	3
30 up to 32	2

35. The following table shows the number of TVs per household in a sample of 50 households. Compute the mean, median, and mode.

Number of TVs in household	0	1	2	3	4	5	6
Number of households	0	5	19	16	6	3	1

36. The following table shows the number of hours per day a sample of 60 people spend watching TV. Compute the mean, median, and mode.

Number of hours	0	1	2	3	4	5	6	7
Number of people	0	1	8	16	14	12	5	4

12.3 | Measures of Dispersion

Introduction

In the previous section, Measures of Central Tendency, calculation of a central number (mean, median, and mode) in order to summarize an entire set of numeric data was discussed. However, these values give no information on the spread or dispersion of data.

For example, consider the following two datasets, A and B:

Dataset A: {40, 45, **50**, 55, 60}

Dataset B: {10, 20, 30, 40, **50**, 60, 70, 80, 90}

You will notice that the central value, both the mean and the median, in sets A and B is the same and is equal to 50. However, the spread of data in set A (varies from 40 to 60) versus set B (varies from 10 to 90) is very different.

Similarly, the mean mark of students in a class may be 70 out of 100. However, not all students will have scored the mean mark. In fact, their marks will be spread out, with some having marks lower than the mean and others higher.

To describe this spread, there are other numerical measures, known as Measures of Dispersion (variability), which provides information on the way the other measurements are spread from the central number. There are four measures of dispersion: the range, deviation from the mean, variance, and standard deviation.

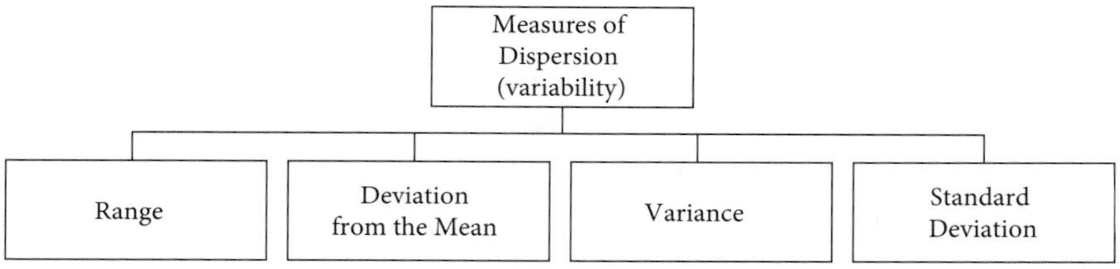

In this section, calculations of these measures of dispersion for ungrouped data will be discussed.

Range

The first measure of dispersion is the 'Range' of a dataset. The **range *(R)*** is the difference between the highest *(H)* and the lowest (*L*) value in a dataset. It is the simplest measure of dispersion or spread and is easy to compute.

$$Range = Highest\ value - Lowest\ value$$

$$R = H - L$$

For example, a dataset {5, 18, 19, 20, 22, 35} has a range of 5 to 35, which is equal to 30 (R = 35 – 5).

The range provides information on the number of units between the highest and lowest data. The range does not provide information about the dispersion of values between the lowest and the highest values. The range, as in the case of the mean, is influenced by extreme values because only two values are used in the calculation.

Example 12.3-a **Finding the Range**

The following dataset provides the ages of 10 students in a class {17, 17, 18, 18, 19, 19, 20, 21, 21, 36}.

(i) Calculate the range of the dataset.

(ii) Calculate the range if the extreme value, the age of the 36-year-old student, is dropped.

(iii) Comment on the result.

Solution $\{17, 17, 18, 18, 19, 19, 20, 21, 21, 36\}$

(i) Range in age of the 10 students:

$$R = H - L$$

$$R = 36 - 17 = 19 \text{ years}$$

Therefore, in age of 10 students in the data are spread over a range of 19 years.

(ii) Range in age of 9 students (after dropping the age of the 10th student):

$$R = H - L$$

$$R = 21 - 17 = 4 \text{ years}$$

Therefore, the ages of the 9 students, after dropping the age of the 10th student (the extreme value), are spread over 4 years.

(iii) The range of the ages of students decreased from 19 years to 4 years after dropping the extreme value. Therefore, the range is not a good measure of dispersion when the dataset contains outliers (extreme values).

Inter-Quartile Range

We learned in the previous section that the median is the point below which one-half of the ranked data values lie. In a similar way, we define the First Quartile (Q_1) as the point below which the first one-fourth (0 - 25%) of the ranked data values lie and the Third Quartile (Q_3) as the point above which the last one-fourth (75 - 100%) of the ranked data values lie.

Quartiles are specific percentiles. Q_1 is the 25th percentile, Q_2 (median) is the 50th percentile, and Q_3 is the 75th percentile.

The difference between the third quartile (Q_3) and the first quartile (Q_1) is another measurement of variability, known as the **inter-quartile range** or ***IQR***. The inter-quartile range includes the middle 50% (half) of the data. It is not affected by the extreme values of the data.

$$IQR = Q_3 - Q_1$$

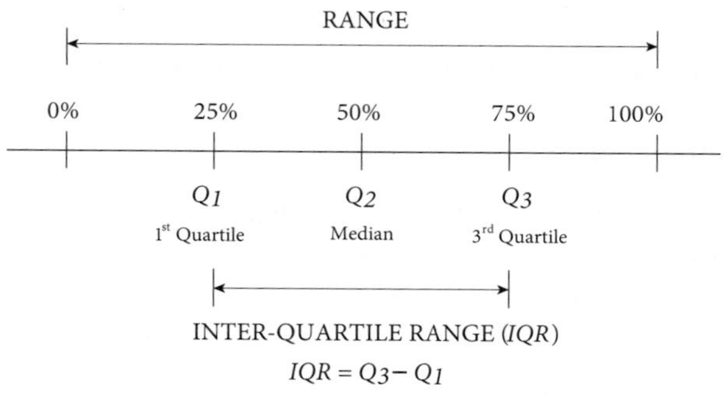

Note: When a quartile or median falls between two values of a dataset, we average the two values to estimate the values for the quartile or median.

Calculating Quartiles when there are Even Numbers of Data

Step 1: Find the median.

Step 2: Divide the data into low-value and high-value groups.

Step 3: Find the median in the two separate groups to determine the first quartile (Q_1) and the third quartile (Q_3).

Example 12.3-b

Calculating the Inter-Quartile Range when there are Even Numbers of Data

Calculate the Inter-Quartile Range of the dataset: {77, 65, 60, 68, 64, 80, 75, 70, 62, 68, 60, 63}

Solution

First, array the data as follows:

60, 60, 62, 63, 64, 65, 68, 68, 70, 75, 77, 80

There are 12 data (even number).

Divide the dataset into two groups, each with 6 data.

Find Q_1 and Q_3 by finding the median in the low-value and high-value groups of the data.

Low-values group:

60, 60, **62**, **63**, 64, 65

↑ Q_1

Q_1 = Median of this group

$$Q_1 \text{ Position} = \frac{6+1}{2} = 3.5$$

$$Q_1 = \frac{3^{rd}\text{ data} + 4^{th}\text{ data}}{2}$$

$$Q_1 = \frac{62 + 63}{2} = 62.5$$

High-values group:

68, 68, **70**, **75**, 77, 80

↑ Q_3

Q_3 = Median of this group

$$Q_3 \text{ Position} = \frac{6+1}{2} = 3.5$$

$$Q_3 = \frac{3^{rd}\text{ data} + 4^{th}\text{ data}}{2}$$

$$Q_3 = \frac{70+75}{2} = 72.5$$

Therefore, $Q_1 = 62.5$ and $Q_3 = 72.5$

Inter-quartile range, $IQR = Q_3 - Q_1 = 72.5 - 62.5 = 10$

Therefore, the inter-quartile range is 10.

Calculating Quartiles when there are Odd Numbers of Data

Step 1: Find the median.

Step 2: Divide the data into low-value and high-value groups, excluding the middle value from both groups.

Step 3: Find the median in the two separate groups to determine the first quartile (Q_1) and the third quartile (Q_3).

Example 12.3-c

Calculating the Inter-Quartile Range when there are Odd Numbers of Data

Calculate the inter-quartile range of the dataset: {30, 28, 38, 35, 42, 26, 40, 32, 21, 23, 33}

Solution

First, array the data:

21, 23, 26, 28, 30, 32, 33, 35, 38, 40, 42

There are 11 data (odd number), Median Position $= \frac{n+1}{2}$

Median Position is $\frac{11+1}{2} = 6$

Median = 32

Exclude the median and divide the dataset into two groups, each with 5 data.

Find Q_1 and Q_3 by finding the median in the low-value and high-value groups of the data.

Solution
continued

Low-values group:

21, 23, **26**, 28, 30

↑

$Q1$

$Q1$ = Median of this group

$$Q1 \text{ Position} = \frac{5+1}{2} = \frac{6}{2} = 3$$

$Q1 = 3^{rd}$ data

$= 26$

High-values group:

33, 35, **38**, 40, 42

↑

$Q3$

$Q3$ = Median of this group

$$Q3 \text{ Position} = \frac{5+1}{2} = \frac{6}{2} = 3$$

$Q3 = 3^{rd}$ data

$= 38$

Therefore, $Q1 = 26$ and $Q3 = 38$

Inter-Quartile, $IQR = Q3 - Q1 = 38 - 26 = 12$

Therefore, the Inter-Quartile Range is 12.

Box-and-Whisker Plot

A box-and-whisker plot is a graph that visually illustrates the full range of variation of the data from minimum to maximum, the common range of variation from first quartile to third quartile, and the median; i.e., a box-and-whisker plot demonstrates the following five points:

1. Lowest data point
2. First quartile ($Q1$ or lower quartile)
3. Median ($Q2$ or second quartile)
4. Third quartile ($Q3$ or upper quartile)
5. Highest data point

A box with closed ends through the first and third quartile points is drawn to show the inter-quartile range, as shown below.

Example 12.3-d

Graphing a Box-and-Whisker Plot

For the dataset in Example 12.3-c, {21, 23, 26, 28, 30, 32, 33, 38, 40, 42}, graph the box-and-whisker plot.

Solution

Using the solution from Example 12.3-c for the dataset

{21, 23, **26**, 28, 30, **32**, 33, 35, **38**, 40, 42}

↑ $Q1$ ↑ $Q2$ ↑ $Q3$

Lowest Data:	$L = 21$
1st Quartile:	$Q1 = 26$
Median:	$Q2 = 32$
3rd Quartile:	$Q3 = 38$
Highest Data:	$H = 42$

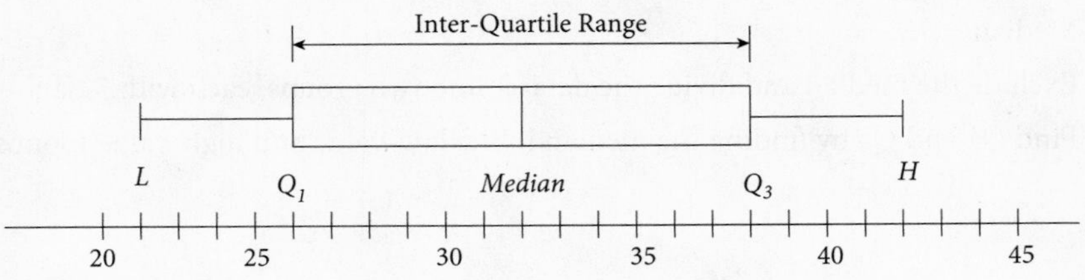

Identifying Outliers

Outliers are points that lie more than 1.5 times the inter-quartile range above $Q3$ or below $Q1$.

Step 1: Find $Q1$ and $Q3$.

Step 2: Calculate the inter-quartile range (IQR) using $IQR = Q3 - Q1$.

Step 3: Multiply the IQR by 1.5.

Step 4: Identify the points that are more than 1.5 times the IQR below $Q1$ or above $Q3$ as outliers.

Example 12.3-e **Identifying Outliers and Drawing the Box and Whisker Plot**

Identify the outlier/s of the following dataset and draw the box-and-whisker plot.

{7, 8, 13, 16, 16, 17, 17, 18, 18, 19, 19, 20, 20, 21, 26, 30, 32}

Solution

There are 17 data (odd number of data), already arranged in an array.

Median Position $= \dfrac{17+1}{2} = 9.$

Median $Q2 = 18$.

Divide the data into 2 groups of 8 data, excluding the median data.

Find $Q1$ and $Q3$ by finding the median in the low-value and high-value groups of the data.

Low-values group:

7, 8, 13, 16, 16, 17, 17, 18

$Q1$ = Median of this group

$$Q1 \text{ Position} = \frac{8+1}{2} = \frac{9}{2} = 4.5$$

$$Q1 = \frac{4^{\text{th}} \text{ data} + 5^{\text{th}} \text{ data}}{2}$$

$$Q1 = \frac{16+16}{2} = 16$$

High-values group:

19, 19, 20, 20, 21, 26, 30, 32

$Q3$ = Median of this group

$$Q3 \text{ Position} = \frac{8+1}{2} = \frac{9}{2} = 4.5$$

$$Q3 = \frac{4^{\text{th}} \text{ data} + 5^{\text{th}} \text{ data}}{2}$$

$$Q3 = \frac{20+21}{2} = 20.5$$

$IQR = Q3 - Q1 = 20.5 - 16 = 4.5$

$1.5 \times IQR = 1.5 \times 4.5 = 6.75$

Outliers are data below ($Q1 - 1.5 \times IQR$) or above ($Q3 + 1.5 \times IQR$)

Outliers are data below (16 – 6.75) or above (20.5 + 6.75), i.e., below 9.25 or above 27.25.

Therefore, in the dataset {(7),(8), 13, 16, 16, 17, 17, 18, 18, 19, 19, 20, 20, 21, 26, (30),(32)}

7, 8, 30, and 32 are outliers.

After removing the outliers, the lowest value (L) in the dataset is 13 and the highest value (H) in the dataset is 26.

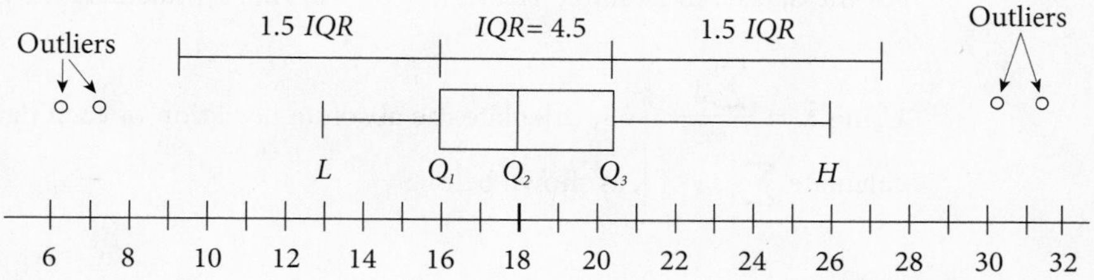

Deviation from the Mean

Different sets of data can produce the same mean. The second measure of dispersion (variability) is the **deviation from the mean.** It shows the amount by which each value or measurement in the dataset deviates from the mean. It indicates the spread of data from the mean of the data.

The deviation from mean is calculated by subtracting the mean from each value in the dataset.

$$\textit{Deviation from mean} = x - \overline{x}$$

Example 12.3-f **Calculating the Deviation from the Mean**

Calculate the deviation from the mean in the sample dataset {55, 65, 70, 72, 78}.

Solution

First, find the mean.

$$\text{Mean, } \overline{x} = \frac{(55 + 65 + 70 + 72 + 78)}{5} = \frac{340}{5} = 68$$

The deviation of the 1st data in the dataset from the mean $= x - \overline{x} = 55 - 68 = -13$

Therefore, the 1st data in the dataset is 13 units below the mean.

Now, find the deviation of each data from the mean by subtracting the mean from each data and tabulate as follows:

x	$\overline{x}$	$(x - \overline{x})$
55	68	-13
65	68	-3
70	68	+2
72	68	+4
78	68	+10

$$\sum x - \overline{x} = 0$$

Average (Mean) Deviation from the Mean

The sum of the deviation from the mean will be zero. Therefore, to find the average deviation from the mean, we find the sum of the absolute value of each difference and divide it by the number of values.

$$\textit{Mean deviation} = \frac{\sum |x - \overline{x}|}{n}$$

Example 12.3-g **Calculating the Mean Deviation from the Mean**

For the dataset in Example 12.3-f, {55, 65, 70, 72, 78}, calculate the mean deviation from the mean.

Solution

Using $\overline{x} = \frac{\sum x}{n} = 68$, calculate the absolute deviation of each data from the mean, $|(x - \overline{x})|$, then calculate $\sum |x - \overline{x}|$, as shown below:

Solution
continued

x	$\overline{x}$	$(x - \overline{x})$	$\lvert(x - \overline{x})\rvert$
55	68	−13	13
65	68	−3	3
70	68	2	2
72	68	4	4
78	68	10	10
$n = 5$		$\sum x - \overline{x} = 0$	$\sum \lvert x - \overline{x} \rvert = 32$

$$\text{Mean deviation from mean} = \frac{\sum \lvert x - \overline{x} \rvert}{n} = \frac{32}{5} = 6.40$$

Therefore, the mean deviation of the data from the mean is 6.40.

Variance

The third measure of dispersion (variability) is the **variance**. The variance is used as a measure to describe the spread of numbers from each other, in a dataset. Variance is the mean of the squared difference between each data value and the average (mean).

In calculating the deviation of the mean, we noticed that some of the values are negative and others positive, resulting in the sum of all the values being zero. Therefore, the distance of the data values from the mean is squared, in variance calculation, because squaring makes all the values positive and is a convenient way of overcoming this.

Variance is a better measure than range because the calculation of variance involves every data item in the set, whereas the calculation of range involves two data items, the lowest and highest values in the dataset.

The greater the scatter of the data values, the larger the variance.

The method of calculating variance depends on whether the dataset constitutes a population or is a sample. The variance of a population is represented by the symbol σ^2 (lower case Greek letter sigma, squared), and that of a sample by the symbol s^2 (lower case S, squared).

For a Population, $\sigma^2 = \dfrac{\sum (x - \mu)^2}{N}$ where μ is the population mean and N is the number of data in the population.

For a Sample, $s^2 = \dfrac{\sum (x - \overline{x})^2}{n - 1}$ where $\overline{x}$ is the sample mean and n is the number of data in the sample.

Note: For sample variance (s^2), the sum of squares of the deviations is divided by (n – 1), whereas for the population variance, (σ^2), it is divided by N. The reason for dividing by (n – 1) for the sample variance is beyond the scope of this Introduction to Statistics chapter.

In the examples and exercises in this chapter, we will use the dataset of a sample for the calculation of variance.

Follow these steps to calculate the variance of a sample:

Step 1: Find the deviation of the data from the mean by subtracting the mean from each data item: $(x - \overline{x})$

(The sum of deviations from the mean, $\sum (x - \overline{x})$, will be equal to zero.)

Step 2: Square each deviation: $(x - \overline{x})^2$

(The values are squared because the square of any value is positive and the squared sum of the deviations from the mean will not be zero.)

Step 3: Find the sum of the squared-deviations: $\sum (x - \overline{x})^2$

Step 4: Divide the sum of the squared deviations by the number of data minus 1: $(n - 1)$

The result is the variance: $s^2 = \dfrac{\sum (x - \overline{x})^2}{n - 1}$

Sample variance (s^2) is divided by (n – 1) because it loses a degree of freedom as it is a sample.

Example 12.3-h **Calculating the Variance of a Sample Data**

Calculate the variance of the sample dataset in Example 12.3-f, {55, 65, 70, 72, 78}.

Solution

#	x	$\overline{x}$	$(x - \overline{x})$	$(x - \overline{x})^2$
1	55	68	-13	169
2	65	68	-3	9
3	70	68	+2	4
4	72	68	+4	16
5	78	68	+10	100
$n = 5$	$\sum x = 340$		$\sum (x - \overline{x}) = 0$	$\sum (x - \overline{x})^2 = 298$

$$\text{Mean, } \overline{x} = \frac{\sum x}{n} = \frac{340}{5} = 68$$

$$\text{Variance, } s^2 = \frac{\sum (x - \overline{x})^2}{n - 1} = \frac{298}{4} = 74.50$$

Therefore, the variance of the sample data is 74.50.

Standard Deviation

The fourth measure of variation is the **standard deviation**. It is the most common statistical measure of dispersion. The standard deviation measures the extent to which scores deviate from the mean. The standard deviation is calculated by taking the positive square root of the variance (the mean of the differences between each data value and the average). Taking the square root of the variance will have the same units as the original data, not 'square units'.

$$\textit{Population Standard Deviation} = +\sqrt{\sigma^2} = \sigma = \sqrt{\frac{\sum (x - \mu)^2}{N}}$$

$$\textit{Sample Standard Deviation} = +\sqrt{s^2} = s = \sqrt{\frac{\sum (x - \overline{x})^2}{n - 1}}$$

The smaller the standard deviation, the closer the data values are to each other. This also indicates that the data is more uniform and consistent. The frequency distribution curve will be narrower for smaller standard deviations and wider for larger standard deviations.

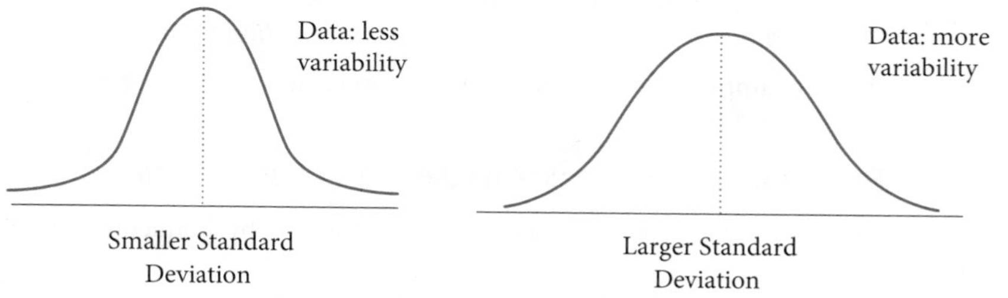

Example 12.3-i **Calculating the Standard Deviation of a Sample**

Calculate the standard deviation of the sample dataset in Example 12.3-h {55, 65, 70, 72, 78}.

Solution

{55, 65, 70, 72, 78}

The variance of the sample set as calculated in Example 12.3-h is 74.50.

Solution *continued*

i.e., $s^2 = 74.50$

$s = +\sqrt{74.50} = 8.63$

Therefore, the standard deviation of the sample dataset is 8.63.

Example 12.3-j

Comparing the Mean and Standard Deviation of Two Datasets

Calculate the mean and standard deviation of the following datasets and state which set is more uniform and consistent.

Dataset A = {10, 30, 50, 70}

Dataset B = {25, 38, 47, 58}

Solution

Dataset A

x	$\bar{x}$	$(x-\bar{x})$	$(x-\bar{x})^2$
10	40	−30	900
30	40	−10	100
50	40	+10	100
70	40	+30	900
$\sum x = 160$			$\sum(x-\bar{x})^2 = 2000$

Dataset B

x	$\bar{x}$	$(x-\bar{x})$	$(x-\bar{x})^2$
25	42	−22	484
38	42	-9	81
47	42	0	0
58	42	11	121
$\sum x = 168$			$\sum(x-\bar{x})^2 = 686$

Dataset A:

Mean, $\bar{x} = \dfrac{\sum x}{n}$

$\bar{x} = \dfrac{160}{4} = 40$

Std. Deviation, $s = \sqrt{\dfrac{(x-\bar{x})^2}{n-1}}$

$s = \sqrt{\dfrac{2000}{3}} = 25.82$

Dataset B:

Mean, $\bar{x} = \dfrac{\sum x}{n}$

$\bar{x} = \dfrac{168}{4} = 42$

Std. Deviation, $s = \sqrt{\dfrac{(x-\bar{x})^2}{n-1}}$

$s = \sqrt{\dfrac{686}{3}} = 15.12$

Sample Statistic	Dataset A	Dataset B
Mean, $\bar{x}$	40	42
Standard Deviation, s	25.82	15.12

Dataset B has a lower standard deviation compared to Dataset A.

Therefore, Dataset B is more uniform and consistent. That is, the data in set B is closer to the mean.

Normal Distribution

As outlined in Section 12.2, the frequency distribution can be symmetrical, positively skewed, or negatively skewed. However, most scientific and business data, and natural relationships, such as weight, height etc., when displayed using a histogram frequency curve are bell shaped, and symmetrical, known as a normal distribution.

This graphical representation in statistics is called a normal curve.

Properties of a Normal Curve

- Bell shaped
- Symmetrical at the mean
- Mean = Median = Mode
- 50% of the data is above the mean and 50% of the data is below
- The curve approaches the X-axis but never touches it.

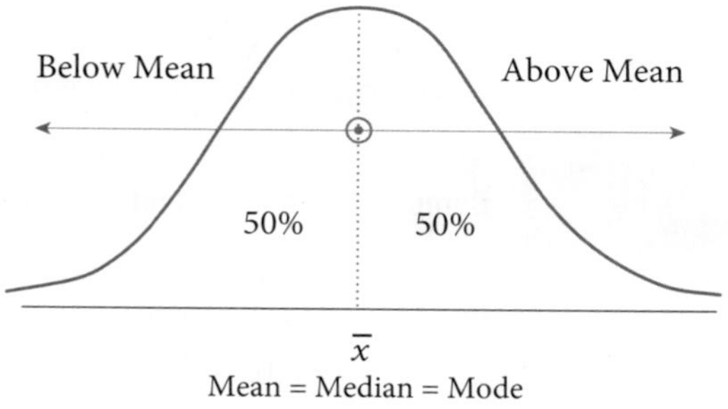

Normal Curve (Bell Shaped)

Empirical Rule for Normal Distribution

There is a relationship among the mean, standard deviation, and the number of data of a normal distribution. It is known as the Empirical Rule for normal distribution and is outlined below:

- Approximately 68% (68.27%) of the data is within ± 1 standard deviation from the mean.
- Approximately 95% (95.45%) of the data is within ± 2 standard deviations from the mean.
- Almost all (99.70%) of the data is within ± 3 standard deviations from the mean.

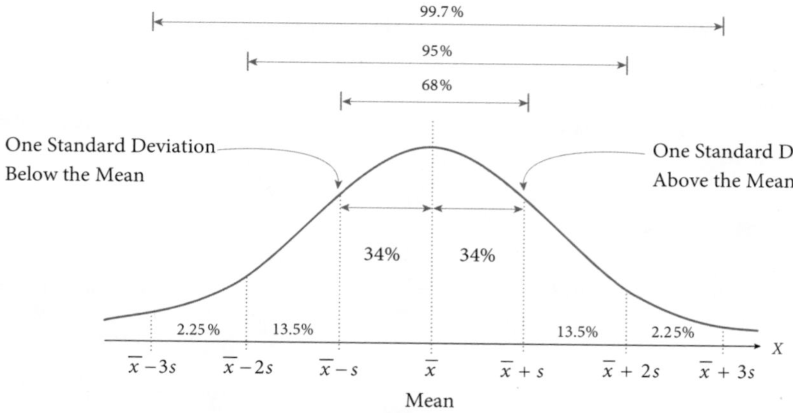

Normal Curve

For example, for a normal distribution, if the mean of a dataset is 40 and the standard deviation is 12 units, then,

- 68% of the data will fall within 40 ± 12 units (i.e., 28 to 52 units).
- 95% of the data will fall within 40 ± 2(12) units (i.e., 40 ± 24 equals to 16 to 64).
- Almost all of the data will fall within 40 ± 3(12) units (i.e., 40 ± 36 equals to 4 to 76 units).

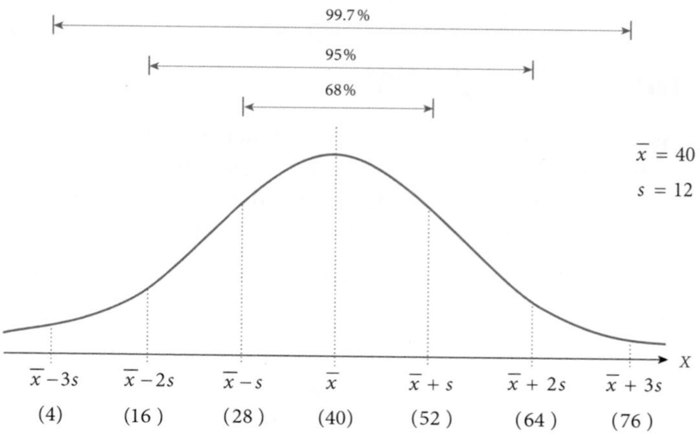

- Approximately 80% of the data is within ± 1.28 standard deviation from the mean.
- Approximately 90% of the data is within ± 1.64 standard deviation from the mean.

Because of its mathematical properties, the normal curve is often used in statistics with the assumption that the mean and standard deviation of a set of measurements define the distribution.

When the data is "normally distributed" there is an empirical relationship between the mean deviation and the standard deviation. The relationship is:

$$\textit{Mean Deviation} = 0.80 \times \textit{Standard Deviation}$$

Example 12.3-k

Calculating the Range of Values for a Percent of Normal Distribution, Given the Mean and Standard Deviation

Based on records, the average flight time from Toronto to Ottawa is 85 minutes with a standard deviation of 15 minutes. Using the Empirical Rule, estimate the maximum and minimum time for:

(i) 95% of the flights from Toronto to Ottawa.

(ii) 90% of the flights from Toronto to Ottawa.

Assume that 95% of data is within ± 2 standard deviation from the mean, and 90% of the data is within ± 1.64 standard deviation from the mean.

Solution

(i) $\bar{x} = 85$ minutes
$s = 15$ minutes

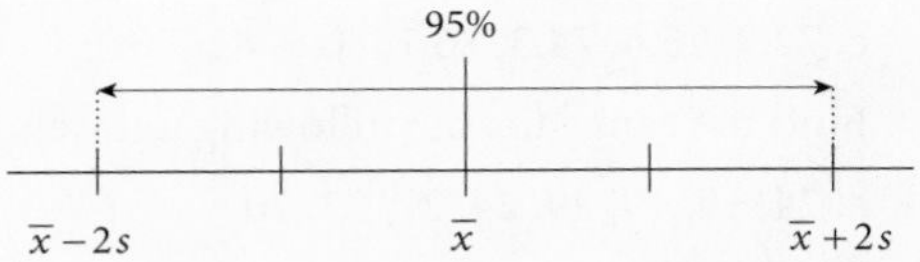

95% of the flights will be within $\bar{x} \pm 2s$ minutes.

Maximum time = $\bar{x} + 2s = 85 + 2(15) = 115$ minutes

Minimum time = $\bar{x} - 2s = 85 - 2(15) = 55$ minutes

Therefore, 95% of the flights from Toronto to Ottawa will take between 55 to 115 minutes, approximately.

(ii) $\bar{x} = 85$ minutes
$s = 15$ minutes

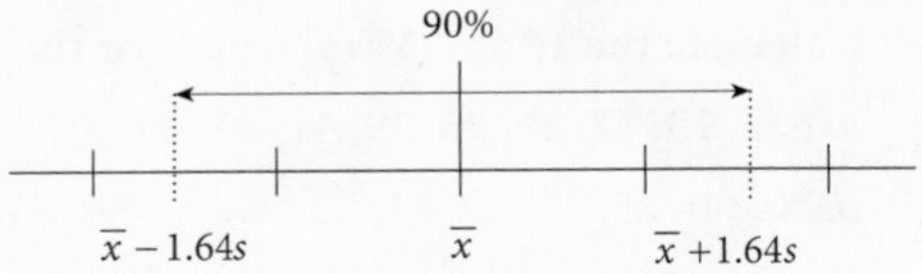

90% of the flights will be within $\bar{x} \pm 1.64s$ minutes.

Maximum time = $\bar{x} + 1.64s = 85 + 1.64(15) = 109.6$ minutes

Minimum time = $\bar{x} - 1.64s = 85 - 1.64(15) = 60.4$ minutes

Therefore, 90% of the flights from Toronto to Ottawa will take between 60 to 110 minutes, approximately.

Example 12.3-l

Calculating Percent of Normal Distribution, Given the Mean and Range of Values

150 students took a test and the test scores have a bell-shaped distribution with a mean mark of 70 and standard deviation of 10 marks. Determine:

(i) The percent of students who scored between 60 and 80 marks.

(ii) The number of students who scored between 50 and 90 marks.

Solution

$\bar{x} = 70$

$s = 10$

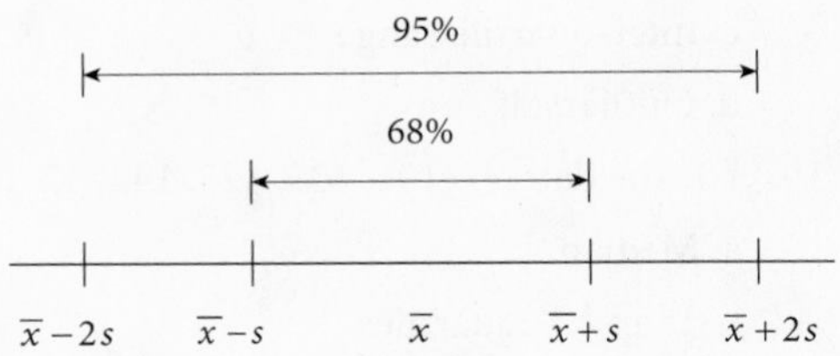

(i)

60 marks is $\bar{x} - s$

80 marks is $\bar{x} + s$

Solution
continued

i.e., 60 and 80 marks fall within $x \pm s$.

Therefore, 68% of the students scored between 60 and 80 marks.

(ii)

50 marks is $\bar{x} - 2s$

90 marks is $\bar{x} + 2s$

i.e., 50 and 90 marks fall within $\bar{x} \pm 2s$.

Therefore, 95% of the students scored between 50 and 90 marks.

Number of students = 95% × 150 = 142

Therefore, 142 students scored between 50 and 90 marks.

12.3 | Exercises

Answers to odd-numbered problems are available at the end of the textbook.

1. Find the range for the following datasets:
   a. 56, 72, 98, 64, 87, 91, 22, 45
   b. 3, 13, 6, 12, 9, 8, 16, 15, 11, 10
   c. 72.9, 75.6, 74.3, 86.1, 80.5, 82.7
2. Find the range for the following datasets:
   a. 24, 15, 19, 29, 24, 22, 23, 20
   b. 113, 98, 107, 102, 123, 110
   c. 0.8, 1.3, 1.7, 2.1, 2.5, 2.8, 3.2, 3.5
3. Calculate the 1st and 3rd quartiles for the following datasets:
   a. 2, 3, 5, 7, 9, 13, 15, 18, 19, 20, 22, 23
   b. 98, 109, 123, 126, 127, 139, 139, 143, 147, 151, 175
4. Calculate the 1st and 3rd quartiles for the following datasets:
   a. 6, 7, 13, 17, 20, 25, 39, 41, 43, 49, 51, 62
   b. 50, 60, 73, 77, 80, 81, 82, 83, 84, 84, 84, 85, 88, 95, 100
5. Determine the inter-quartile range and identify the outliers, if any, for the datasets in Problem 3.
6. Determine the inter-quartile range and identify the outliers, if any, for the datasets in Problem 4.
7. In a dataset, Q_1=44, median=48, and Q_3=58.
   a. A value greater than what number would be an outlier?
   b. A value less than what number would be an outlier?
8. In a dataset, Q_1=75, median=80, and Q_3=85.
   a. A value greater than what number would be an outlier?
   b. A value less than what number would be an outlier?
9. For the dataset {76, 98, 102, 104, 76, 96, 57, 97, 99}, compute the following:
   a. Median
   b. 1st and 3rd quartiles
   c. Inter-quartile range
   d. Outliers, if any.
10. For the dataset {104, 139, 123, 142, 57, 104, 153, 105, 139}, compute the following:
    a. Median
    b. 1st and 3rd quartiles
    c. Inter-quartile range
    d. Outliers, if any.

11. Draw a box-and-whisker plot for the data in Problem 9.
12. Draw a box-and-whisker plot for the data in Problem 10.
13. Given the following information for a dataset, draw a box-and-whisker plot:

Lowest value	82
1st quartile	94
Median	95
3rd quartile	102
Highest value	110

14. Given the following information for a dataset, draw a box-and-whisker plot:

Lowest value	2
1st quartile	6
Median	11.5
3rd quartile	16
Highest value	30

15. Find the mean absolute deviation for the dataset: {92, 75, 95, 90, and 98}.
16. Find the mean absolute deviation for the dataset: {26, 87, 34, 21, 67, 92, 74}.
17. Which of the following datasets has the bigger mean absolute deviation?

    a. 1, 2, 3, 4, 5 b. 1, 4, 9, 12, 15
18. Which of the following datasets has the bigger mean absolute deviation?

    a. 3, 9, 15, 21, 27 b. 3, 5, 9, 12, 18
19. Calculate the variance and standard deviation of the datasets in Problem 17.
20. Calculate the variance and standard deviation of the datasets in Problem 18.
21. Given the following information of a sample data, calculate the variance and standard deviation:

    n = 10, sum of the squared deviation = 40, and the sum of the data = 610.
22. Given the following information of a sample data, calculate the variance and standard deviation:

    n = 5, sum of the squared deviation = 46, and the sum of the data = 40.
23. The weights (in kilograms) of a group of ten randomly selected men are as follows:

    82 79 80 80 72 74 88 82 92 83

    Calculate: a. mean b. standard deviation
24. The marks of a group of ten students are as follows:

    77 82 43 63 59 61 66 61 76 54

    Calculate: a. mean b. standard deviation
25. The following are the annual incomes of five, randomly selected professors of a college:

    \$75,000, \$78,000, \$72,000, \$83,000, and \$90,000. Compute the following:

    a. Mean b. Mean absolute deviation

    c. Variance d. Standard deviation
26. The following are the weekly incomes for a group of seven, randomly selected employees:

    \$875, \$945, \$905, \$885, \$910, \$820, \$841. Compute the following:

    a. Mean b. Mean absolute deviation

    c. Variance d. Standard deviation
27. An aptitude test is normally distributed with a mean of 500 and a standard deviation of 100. Use the empirical rule to answer the following:

    a. Approximately, what percent of the students will have a score between 400 and 600?

    b. Randomly selected students will have a 95 percent chance of having scores fall between what values?

    c. Randomly selected students will have a 90 percent chance of having scores fall between what values?

28. A bell shaped distribution has a mean of 550 and a standard deviation of 150. Use the empirical rule to answer the following:

    a. What percent of the data will fall between 400 and 700?

    b. Randomly selected data will have a 95 percent chance of falling between what values?

    c. Randomly selected data will have a 90 percent chance of falling between what values?

29. Out of a sample of 100 boxes of cereal, 95 boxes weigh between 780 and 820 grams. Use the empirical rule to estimate the average weight of the cereal box and the standard deviation in weight of the sample.

30. Out of a sample of 100 juice bottles, 68 bottles contain between 975 and 1,025 litres of juice. Use the empirical rule to estimate the average quantity (in litres) in the juice bottles and the standard deviation in volume of the sample.

31. On average, a college test center can accommodate 350 students per day with a standard deviation of 75 students. Use the empirical rule to estimate the maximum and the minimum number of students the test center can expect in a day.

32. On average, a flight reservation center can handle 200 customer calls per day with a standard deviation of 35 calls. Use the empirical rule to estimate the maximum and the minimum number of calls the flight reservation center can handle in a day.

12.4 | Probability

Introduction

In the previous sections of this chapter, the methods for presenting data using charts, diagrams, tables, graphs, and summarizing data using mean, median, mode, range, variance, standard deviation, etc., were outlined.

The next step is to analyze the data of the sample taken from the population and use the sample evidence to make inferences about the population. This is known as **inferential statistics**. Statistical inference involves making generalizations or inferences about population parameters, based on observations in the sample statistic.

Probability theory is the basis for statistical inference. Therefore, the knowledge of probability is essential to make decisions about the population based on sample statistics. Probability involves the use of mathematics to describe the level of certainty (likelihood, chance, or possibility) that an event will occur. We hear about probabilities in everyday situations.

For example, weather forecasts (probability of rain or snow), lottery (probability of winning), etc.

Measures of Probability

The probability of an event cannot be negative or greater than 1.

All probabilities describing the possibility of an event lie between 0 (0%) and 1 (100%), inclusive.

The probability of an event which cannot (or will never) occur is 0 and the probability of an event which certainly (or will definitely) occur is 1.

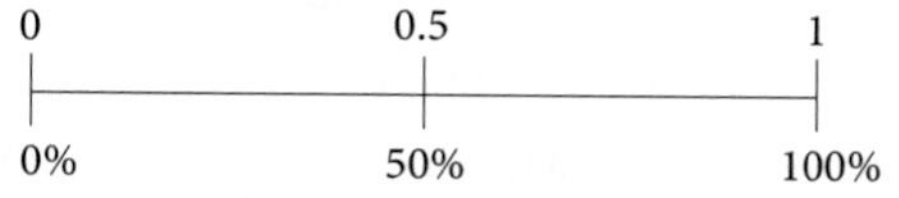

The probability can also be expressed as a fraction, a decimal, or a percent. A probability of $\frac{1}{2}$ (or 0.5 or 50%) means that there is an equal chance that a particular event may or may not occur.

Approaches to Probability

There are two major approaches to the probability theory: subjective and objective approaches.

Subjective Probability

The probability of an event, based on judgment, belief, experience, knowledge of known facts, or interpretation is known as **subjective probability**.

This approach is mostly applicable in business, finance, marketing, etc., in making quick decisions or statements without performing any formal calculations. The disadvantage of subjective probability is that two or more persons may state different probabilities for the same event based on their judgment, knowledge on the subject, etc. For example, the probability that the mortgage rate will increase next year is 90%.

Objective Probability

The probability of an event, using theoretical methods or calculations, based on observation or actual measurements, rather than personal judgment is known as **objective probability**.

In this section, the basics of probability and the methods to solve simple probability problems using objective probability will be discussed. This will help to develop a better understanding of probability in statistics to make inferences about a population, based on sample evidence.

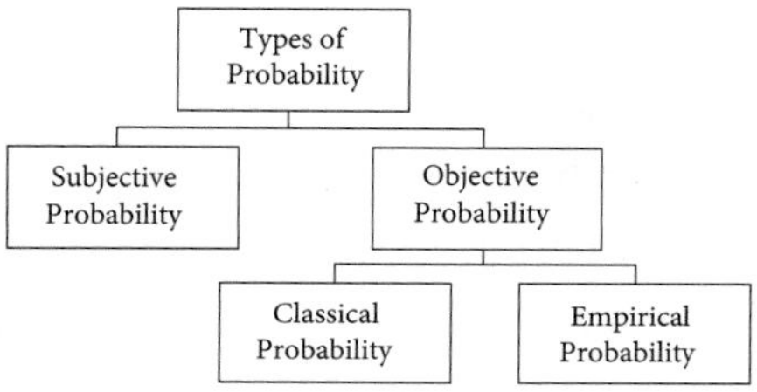

Objective probabilities are more accurate than subjective probabilities. In objective probability, there are two approaches for finding the probabilities of events, using classical probability or empirical probability.

Classical Probability

Classical probability, also known as theoretical probability, is based on mathematical analysis and on the assumption that the outcomes of an experiment are equally likely.

For example, if there are "n" possible outcomes of an experiment and if all the outcomes are equally likely, then we assign a probability of $\frac{1}{n}$ for each outcome. The classical probability of an event (E), $P(E)$, is calculated as follows:

$$P(E) = \frac{\text{Number of favourable outcomes of event "E"}}{\text{Total number of possible outcomes}}$$

$$P(E) = \frac{n(E)}{n(S)}$$

For example, if you toss a coin once, there are two possible outcomes: Heads (H) or Tails (T). The probability of getting Heads (H) is calculated as follows:

Number of possible outcomes in the event, i.e., getting an H, is one: $n(E) = 1$.

Total outcome in the sample space, $S = \{H, T\}$: $n(S) = 2$.

Using $P(E) = \frac{n(E)}{n(S)}$ $\qquad P(H) = \frac{1}{2}$

Empirical Probability

Empirical probability is also known as the relative frequency approach and is more applicable to situations where the outcomes of an experiment are not equally likely. The empirical probability is based on results from direct observation or past results.

For example, if you conduct an experiment repeatedly, for "n" times, and observed that a particular event "E" occurs "f" times, then the empirical probability of the event (E), $P(E)$, is calculated as follows:

$$P(E) = \frac{Number\ of\ times\ (frequency)\ that\ event\ \text{“}E\text{”}\ occurs}{Number\ of\ trials}$$

$$P(E) = \frac{f}{n}$$

The empirical probability of event "E" is the relative frequency of event "E".

For example, if a coin is tossed 20 times and the frequency of Heads (H) is observed 7 times, then the relative frequency of obtaining Heads (H) is calculated as follows:

Number of times (frequency) of event, $f = 7$
Number of trials, $n = 20$

Using $P(E) = \frac{f}{n}$ $\qquad$ $P(H) = \frac{7}{20}$

Note: The result from empirical probability may differ from classical probability, when only a few trials are carried out. If more trials are carried out, then the result will approximate or equal that calculated from classical (theoretical) probability.

Example 12.4-a Classical Approach to Probability

A six-sided die is rolled once. Find the probability of the following events:

(i) Rolling the number 3.

(ii) Rolling any number less than 4.

(iii) Rolling a number 5 or more.

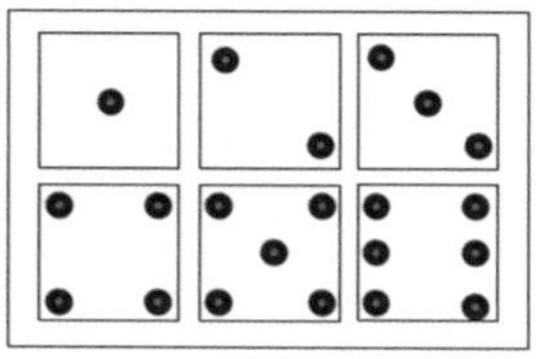

Solution

Using $P(E) = \frac{n(E)}{n(S)}$, where $n(S) = 6$

(i) The probability of rolling the number 3:
There is only one favourable outcome for this event.
$P(3) = \frac{1}{6}$
Therefore, the probability of rolling the number 3 is $\frac{1}{6}$.

(ii) The probability of rolling any number less than 4:
There are three favourable outcomes for this event: {1, 2, 3}.
$P(<4) = \frac{3}{6} = \frac{1}{2}$
Therefore, the probability of rolling any number less than 4 is $\frac{1}{2}$.

(iii) The probability of rolling a number 5 or more:
There are two favourable outcomes for this event: {5, 6}.
$P(\geq 5) = \frac{2}{6} = \frac{1}{3}$
Therefore, the probability of rolling a number 5 or more is $\frac{1}{3}$.

Example 12.4-b Empirical Approach to Probability

Out of 150 LED bulbs tested, 15 of them were defective. Based on this, what is the probability that an LED bulb that you purchase will be defective?

Solution

$P(E) = \frac{f}{n}$

$P(defective) = \frac{15}{150} = \frac{1}{10}$

Therefore, the probability of purchasing a defective bulb is $\frac{1}{10}$.

Basic Concept of Probability

The basic concept of probability deals with experiment, outcome, event, and sample space.

An **experiment** is a process or action that leads to one and only one well-defined result of several possible results (i.e., the action performed).

An **outcome** is the particular result of a single trial of an experiment (i.e., what is observed and recorded from the experiment).

An **event** is the specific outcome of an experiment. It may be one or more outcomes of an experiment (i.e., what is being looked for from the experiment). Usually, events are denoted by capital letters. For example, *A, B, E*, etc.

n event is a subset of e sample space.

The **sample space** is the set of all possible outcomes in an experiment (i.e., all possible events that can be expected from the experiment). The symbol used for sample space is "*S*".

Example 12.4-c

Tossing a Coin and Identifying the Experiment, Outcome, Event, and Sample Space

A coin is tossed once and you are looking for the result to be Heads *(H)*. Identify the experiment, outcome, event, and sample space.

Solution

Experiment: Tossing a coin.

Outcome: Either *H* or *T*.

Event, $E = \{H\}$, since you are looking for the result to be *H* from the experiment.

Sample space, $S = \{H, T\}$, all the possible outcomes of the experiment.

Example 12.4-d

Tossing Two Coins and Identifying the Experiment, Outcome, Event, and Sample Space

Two coins are tossed once and you are looking for the results to be *H* and *H*. Identify the experiment, outcome, event, and sample space.

Solution

Experiment: Tossing two coins.

Outcome: Any one of *(H, H), (H, T), (T, H), (T, T)*.

Event, $E = \{H, H\}$, since you are looking for the result to be $\{H, H\}$ from the experiment.

Sample space, $S = \{(H, H), (H, T), (T, H), (T, T)\}$, all the possible outcomes of the experiment.

Example 12.4-e

Rolling a Die Once and Identifying the Experiment, Outcome, Event, and Sample Space

A die is rolled once and you are looking for the result to be a face with an even number. Identify the experiment, outcome, event, and sample space.

Solution

Experiment: Rolling the die once.

Outcome: The face with any of the numbers 1, 2, 3, 4, 5, or 6.

Event, $E = \{2, 4, 6\}$, you are looking for the face with an even number from the experiment.

Sample space, $S = \{1, 2, 3, 4, 5, 6\}$, all the possible outcomes of the experiment.

Tree Diagram

The sample space for an experiment can be described easily by a tree diagram. In a tree diagram, each outcome is represented by a branch of a tree. Below is a tree diagram to demonstrate the possible outcomes of tossing a coin twice.

Step 1: When the coin is tossed once, there are two possible outcomes, *H* and *T*. Therefore, start drawing two branches from a point and mark one end of the branch as *H* and the other end as *T*.

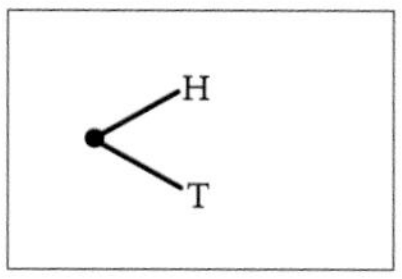

Step 2: When the coin is tossed a second time, there are two possible outcomes, *H* and *T*, as in the first toss. Draw two branches from the end point *H* (from Step 1) and mark one end of the new branch as *H* and the other as *T*. This is to show the possible outcome of a second toss when the outcome from the first toss is *H*.

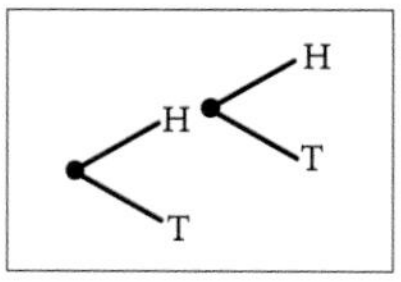

Step 3: Similarly, draw two branches from the end point *T* (from Step 1) and mark one end of the new branch as *H* and the other as *T*. This is to show the possible outcome of a second toss when the outcome from the first toss is *T*.

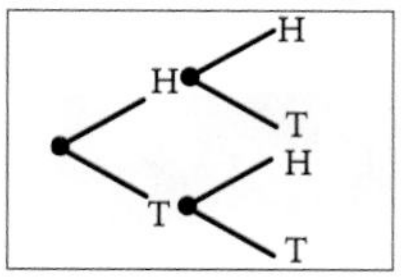

Step 4: There are 4 end points marked *H*, *T*, *H*, and *T*. Starting from each end point of the branch, trace through the branches to the starting point to identify all the possible outcomes, as shown in the diagram below.

All the possible outcomes are *HH, TH, HT, TT.*

Therefore, the sample space, $S = \{HH, HT, TH, TT\}$.

Example 12.4-f **Drawing a Tree Diagram for Tossing Three Coins**

Three coins are tossed. Draw a tree diagram and list the sample space.

Solution

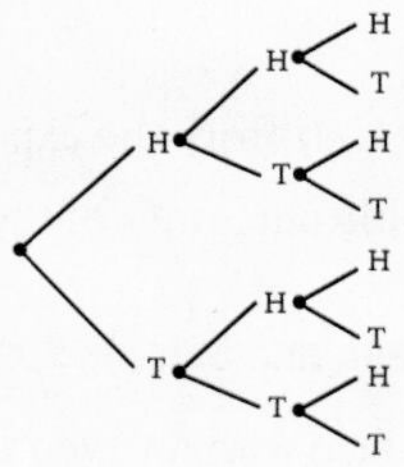

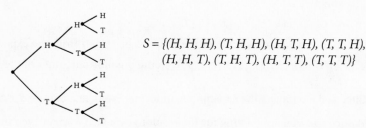

$S = \{(H, H, H), (T, H, H), (H, T, H), (T, T, H),$
$(H, H, T), (T, H, T), (H, T, T), (T, T, T)\}$

Example 12.4-g **Drawing a Tree Diagram for Rolling Two Dice**

Two dice are rolled simultaneously. Draw a tree diagram and list the sample space.

Solution

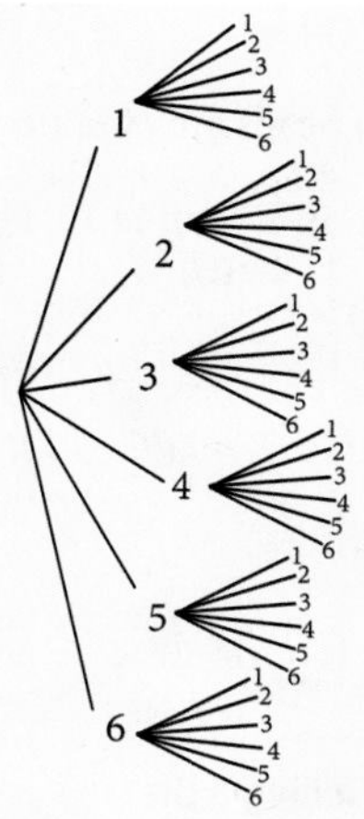

$$S = \{(1,1), (2,1), (3,1), (4,1), (5,1), (6,1)$$
$$(1,2), (2,2), (3,2), (4,2), (5,2), (6,2)$$
$$(1,3), (2,3), (3,3), (4,3), (5,3), (6,3)$$
$$(1,4), (2,4), (3,4), (4,4), (5,4), (6,4)$$
$$(1,5), (2,5), (3,5), (4,5), (5,5), (6,5)$$
$$(1,6), (2,6), (3,6), (4,6), (5,6)\ (6,6)\}$$

Note: Read from branch to tree.

Example 12.4-h **Identifying Events when Three Coins are Tossed**

Three coins are tossed. Using the sample space in Example 12.4-f, list all the possible outcomes for the following events, *E*:

(i) At least two *H*. (ii) Two *T* and one *H*.

Solution

(i) At least two *H*: *(H, H, H), (T, H, H), (H, T, H), (H, H, T)*

(ii) Two *T* and one *H*: *(T, T, H),(T, H, T),(H, T, T)*

Example 12.4-i **Identifying Events when Two Dice are Rolled**

Two dice are rolled. Using the sample space in Example 12.4-g, list all the possible outcomes for the following events, *E*:

(i) Numbers on the faces of the dice are equal.

(ii) The sum of numbers on the faces of the dice is equal to 5.

(iii) The sum of numbers on the faces of the dice is less than 5.

(iv) The sum of numbers on the faces of the dice is more than 9.

Solution

(i) Numbers on the faces of the dice are equal:
(1,1), (2,2), (3,3), (4,4), (5,5), (6,6)

(ii) The sum of numbers on the faces of the dice is equal to 5:
(1,4), (2,3), (3,2), (4,1)

(iii) The sum of numbers on the faces of the dice is less than 5:
(1,1), (2,1), (3,1), (1,2), (2,2), (1,3)

(iv) The sum of numbers on the faces of the dice is more than 9:
(6,4), (5,5), (6,5), (4,6), (5,6), (6,6)

Example 12.4-j **Calculating the Probability of an Event**

Find the probability of getting an odd number when a die is rolled once.

Solution

The event is getting an odd number.

Event, $E = \{1, 3, 5\}$, the odd numbers on a die. $n(E) = 3$

The sample space $S = \{1, 2, 3, 4, 5, 6\}$. $n(S) = 6$

Using $P(E) = \dfrac{n(E)}{n(S)}$,

$$P(\textit{odd number}) = \frac{3}{6} = \frac{1}{2}$$

Therefore, the probability of getting an odd number, when a die is rolled once is $\frac{1}{2}$ or 50%.

Example 12.4-k Calculating the Probability of an Event from Tossing Three Coins Once

Three coins are tossed once. Find the probability that at least two heads are obtained.

Solution

The event is obtaining at least two H (refer to the tree diagram in Example 12.4-f).

Event, $E = \{(H, H, H), (T, H, H), (H, T, H), (H, H, T)\}$. $n(E) = 4$.

The sample space:

$S = \{(H, H, H), (T, H, H), (H, T, H), (T, T, H), (H, H, T), (T, H, T), (H, T, T), (T, T, T)\}$

$n(S) = 8$

$P(\text{at least } 2H) = \frac{4}{8} = \frac{1}{2}$

Therefore, the probability that at least two heads are obtained is $\frac{1}{2}$ or 50%.

Example 12.4-l Calculating the Probability of an Event from Tossing a Coin and Rolling a Die

A coin is tossed and a die is rolled.

(i) List the sample space using a Tree diagram.

(ii) Using the sample space from (i), find the probability of the following:

a. The coin shows a tail (T) and the die shows a number less than 5.

b. The coin shows a head (H) and the die shows an even number.

(i)

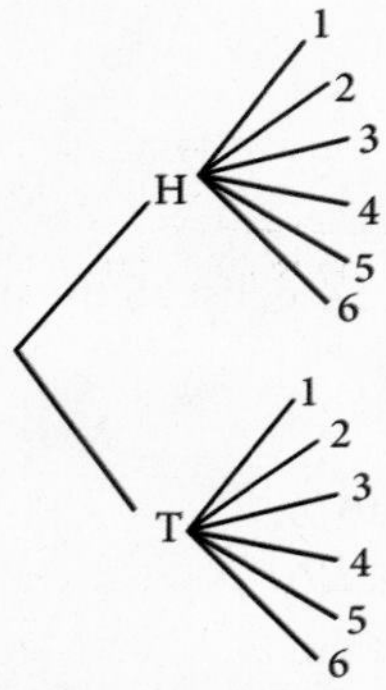

Let S = the sample space

$S = \{(1, H), (2, H), (3, H), (4, H), (5, H), (6, H), (1, T), (2, T), (3, T), (4, T), (5, T), (6, T)\}$

$n(S) = 12$

(ii) a. Let E be the event where E is the coin that shows a tail (T) and the die shows a number less than 5.

$E = \{(1, T), (2, T), (3, T), (4, T)\}$

$n(E) = 4$

$P(E) = \frac{n(E)}{n(S)} = \frac{4}{12} = \frac{1}{3}$

b. Let E be the event where E is the coin that shows a head (H) and the die shows an even number.

$E = \{(2, H), (4, H), (6, H)\}$

$n(E) = 3$

$P(E) = \frac{n(E)}{n(S)} = \frac{3}{12} = \frac{1}{4}$

Example 12.4-m Calculating the Probability of an Event in a Game Involving a Spinning Wheel

A game of chance involves spinning a wheel that has 10 equal sectors marked $S, T, A, T, I, S, T, I, C$, and S as shown in the diagram.

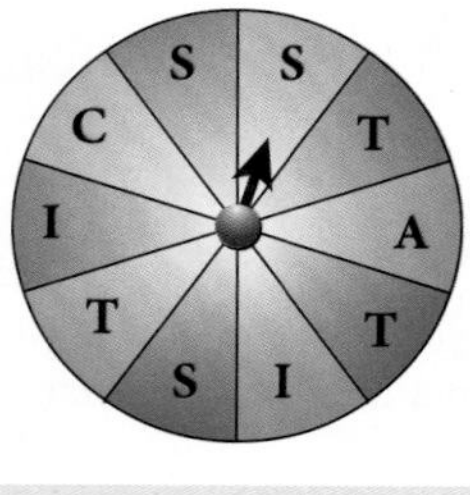

If you spin the wheel, determine the chances of landing on:

(i) S

(ii) I

(ii) Either I or S

(iv) Either S or T

Solution

Number of equal sectors = 10. $n(S) = 10$

Number of sectors of $S = 3$

Number of sectors of $T = 3$

Number of sectors of $A = 1$

Number of sectors of $I = 2$

Number of sectors of $C = 1$

$$P(E) = \frac{n(E)}{n(S)}$$

(i) Let E be the event where E = landing on S

$n(E) = 3$

$P(E) = \frac{3}{10} = 0.30 = 30\%$

(ii) Let E be the event where E = landing on I

$n(E) = 2$

$P(E) = \frac{2}{10} = 0.20 = 20\%$

(iii) Let E be the event where E = landing on I or S

$n(E) = 2 + 3 = 5$

$P(E) = \frac{5}{10} = 0.5 = 50\%$

(iv) Let E be the event where E = landing on S or T

$n(E) = 3 + 3 = 6$

$P(E) = \frac{6}{10} = 0.6 = 60\%$

To solve probability problems involving cards, there are a few basic facts about a deck of cards that need to be remembered:

1. A standard deck of playing cards consists of 52 cards.
2. Two suits, the spades and clubs, are black; i.e., there are 26 black cards.

Spades	♠	Diamonds	♦
Clubs	♣	Hearts	♥

3. Two suits, the diamonds and hearts, are red; i.e., there are 26 red cards.
4. Each suit has 13 cards $\left(\frac{52}{4}\right)$: Ace, 2, 3, 4, 5, 6, 7, 8, 9, 10, Jack, Queen, King.
5. The Jack, Queen, and King cards from each suit are called the face (or picture) cards; i.e., there are 12 face cards (3×4).

"Ace" is not a face (or picture) card.

Example 12.4-n Probability of an Event Involving a Deck of Cards

A card is drawn at random from a standard deck of cards. Find the probability of getting the following (assume the drawn card is put back into the deck after each draw):

(i) Red card (ii) Face card (iii) King card

Solution

$$P(E) = \frac{n(E)}{n(S)}$$

$n(S) = 52$

(i) Let E be the event where E = red card

$n(E) = 13 + 13 = 26$

$P(red\ card) = \frac{26}{52} = \frac{1}{2}$

(ii) Let E be the event where E = face card

$n(E) = 4 \times 3 = 12$

$P(face\ card) = \frac{12}{52} = \frac{3}{13}$

(iii) Let E be the event where E = King card

$n(E) = 1 \times 4 = 4$

$P(King\ card) = \frac{4}{52} = \frac{1}{13}$

Example 12.4-o **Calculating the Probability of an Event Involving Marbles in a Box**

A box contains 4 red marbles, 5 green marbles, 6 blue marbles, and 10 yellow marbles.

If a marble is drawn from the box at random, find the probability of getting the following:

(i) A green marble.

(ii) A marble, either blue or yellow.

(iii) A marble, other than red.

Solution

(i) Let E be the event where E = Green marbles
$n(E) = 5$
$P(E) = \frac{5}{25} = \frac{1}{5}$

(ii) Let E be the event where E = either Blue or Yellow marbles
$n(E) = 6 + 10 = 16$
$P(E) = \frac{16}{25}$

Marbles	
Red	4
Green	5
Blue	6
Yellow	10
Total : $n(S)$	**25**

(iii) Let E be the event where E = Green, Blue, or Yellow marbles
$n(E) = 5 + 6 + 10 = 21$
$P(E) = \frac{21}{25}$

Definitions Used in the Rules of Probability

Complement of an event: The set of all outcomes that are not contained in an event.

Mutually exclusive (or disjoint) event: Two or more events that have no outcomes in common.

Mutually non-exclusive (or joint) event: Two or more events that have common outcomes.

Independent event: The outcome of one event is not affected by the outcome of another event.

Dependent event: The outcome of one event is affected by the outcome of another event.

Conditional probability: The probability of an event occuring given that another event has already occured.

ODDS: The ratio of the number of ways an event can occur to the number of ways it cannot occur.

Basic Rules of Probability

Probability rules simplify the computations of the probability of an event from the known probabilities of other events.

Basic probability rules include the Complement Rule, Addition Rule, Multiplication Rule, and Conditional Probability Rule.

Complement Rule

When all the probabilities of all the outcomes of an experiment are added, the answer will be one.

An event A will either happen or not happen. Therefore, the two probabilities of happening and not happening always add to 1.

The complement of event A is that event A does not happen.

The complement is usually represented by the symbol with a mark (') such as A' (or represented by $\bar{A}$). $P(A')$ wil be used to represent the probability of the complement of event A.

$P(A) + P(A') = 1$

Therefore, $P(A) = 1 - P(A')$

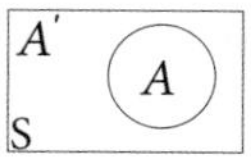

If the probability of an event's complement is known, then it can be subtracted from 1 to find the probability of the event.

Also $P(A') = 1 - P(A)$

Similarly, if the probability of an event is known, then it can be subtracted from 1 to find the probability of the event's complement.

Sometimes it is easier to find the probability of the complement of an event than the probability of the event itself.

For example, when a die is rolled, to calculate the probability of not getting the number 2, we may find the probability of getting the number 2 and then subtracting it from 1.

That is, the event is getting any of the numbers 1, 3, 4, 5, 6.

This is the same as getting the complement of number 2.

Let A be the event of getting a number 2; i.e., $P(A)$ is the probability of getting the number 2.

$n(A) = 1$ and $n(S) = 6$

$$P(A) = \frac{n(A')}{n(S)} = \frac{1}{6}$$

Also, $P(A') = 1 - P(A) = 1 - \frac{1}{6} = \frac{5}{6}$

Therefore, the probability of rolling a die and not getting the number 2 is $\frac{5}{6}$.

Example 12.4-p **Calculating the Probability Using the Complement of an Event**

A card is drawn from a standard deck of cards. Find the probability that the card is neither a red card nor a face card.

Solution

Let A be the event that the card is neither a red card nor a face card.

Then A' is the event that the card is a red card or a face card.

$n(A') = 26 + 6 = 32$ (There are 26 red cards which include 6 face cards in red. Also, there are 6 face cards in black.)

$n(S) = 52$

$$P(A') = \frac{n(A')}{n(S)} = \frac{32}{52} = \frac{8}{13}$$

$$P(A) = 1 - P(A') = 1 - \frac{8}{13} = \frac{5}{13}$$

Therefore, the probability that the card is neither a red nor a face card is $\frac{5}{13}$.

Addition Rule

Addition Rule helps to solve problems that involve two or more events in performing one task (rolling dice, drawing cards, etc.), and finding the probability of two or more events without tasks.

Addition Rule for Mutually Exclusive Events

If two events, A and B, are **mutually exclusive** (i.e., A and B cannot occur at the same time or there is no common outcome), then the probability of A or B occurring is the sum of their individual probability.

$$P(A \text{ or } B) = P(A) + P(B)$$

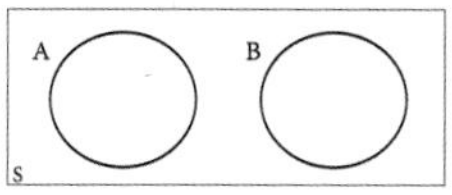

In general, the word "or" in a probability calculation means addition.

For example, the probability of selecting a black card or a diamond card from a deck of playing cards is:

$P(Black \text{ or } Diamond) = P(Black) + P(Diamond)$

$$= \frac{26}{52} + \frac{13}{52}$$

$$= \frac{39}{52} = \frac{3}{4}$$

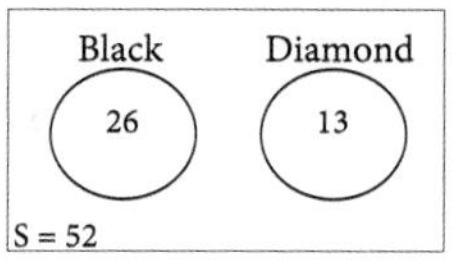

Addition Rule for Mutually Non-Exclusive Events

If two events (A and B) are **mutually non-exclusive** (i.e., A and B occur at the same time or there is a common outcome), then the probability of A or B occurring is the sum of their individual probability minus the probability of both A and B occurring.

$$P(A \text{ or } B) = P(A) + P(B) - P(A \text{ and } B)$$

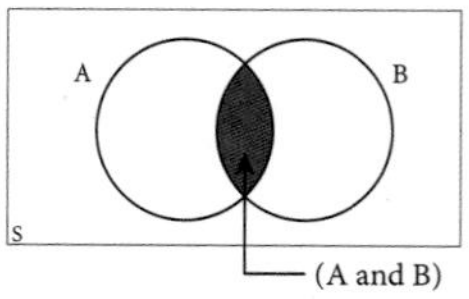

For example, the probability of selecting a red card or a queen card from a deck of playing cards is:

$P(\text{Red or Queen}) = P(\text{Red}) + P(\text{Queen}) - P(\text{Red and Queen})$

$$= \frac{26}{52} + \frac{4}{52} - \frac{2}{52}$$

$$= \frac{28}{52} = \frac{7}{13}$$

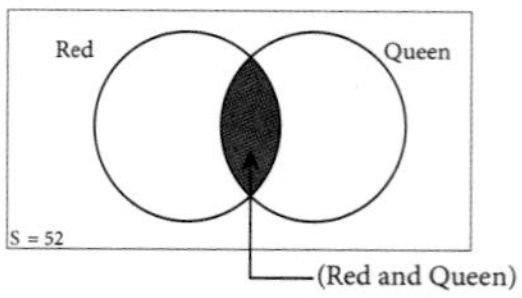

Note: There are 26 red cards, which include 2 Queen cards that are red.

Example 12.4-q

Mutually Exclusive or Mutually Non-Exclusive Events

A die is rolled once. Identify which of the following events are mutually exclusive and which are mutually non-exclusive, and find the probability of the events.

(i) Getting a number less than 3 or more than 4.

(ii) Getting an even number or a number less than 4.

(iii) Getting an odd number or the number 6.

Solution

(i) Event A: Number less than 3 $A = 1, 2$

Event B: Number more than 4 $B = 5, 6$

There is no common outcome in both events.

Therefore, the events are mutually exclusive.

Using Addition Rule for Mutually Exclusive Events,

$$P(A \text{ or } B) = P(A) + P(B)$$

$$= \frac{2}{6} + \frac{2}{6}$$

$$= \frac{4}{6} = \frac{2}{3}$$

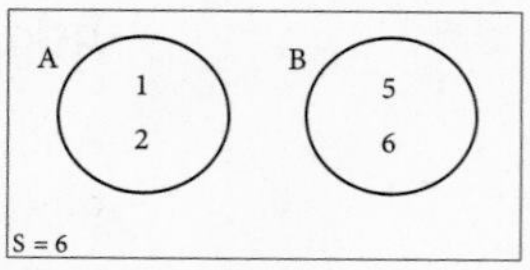

Therefore, the probability of getting a number less than 3 or greater than 4 is $\frac{2}{3}$.

(ii) Event A: Even number $A = 2, 4, 6$

Event B: Less than 4 $B = 1, 2, 3$

2 is a common outcome to both events

Therefore, the events are mutually non-exclusive

Using Addition Rule for Multiply Non-Exclusive Events,

$$P(A \text{ or } B) = P(A) + P(B) - P(A \text{ and } B)$$

$$= \frac{3}{6} + \frac{3}{6} - \frac{1}{6}$$

$$= \frac{5}{6}$$

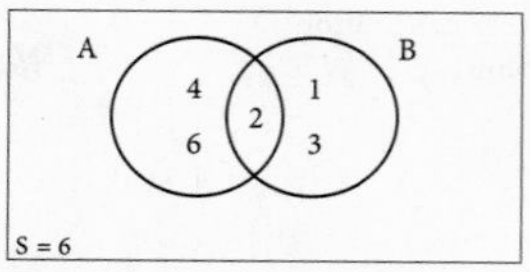

Therefore, the probability of getting an even number or a number less than 4 is $\frac{5}{6}$.

Solution *continued*

(iii) Event A: Odd number $A = 1, 3, 5$

Event B: 6 $B = 6$

There is no common outcome in both events.

Therefore, the events are mutually exclusive.

Using Addition Rule for Mutually Exclusive Events,

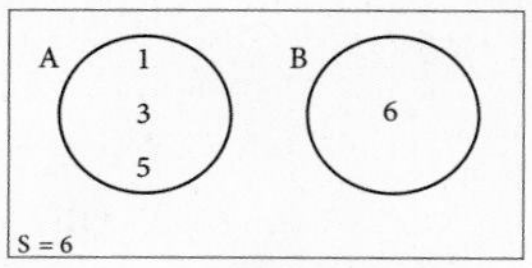

$$P(A \text{ or } B) = P(A) + P(B)$$
$$= \frac{3}{6} + \frac{1}{6}$$
$$= \frac{4}{6} = \frac{2}{3}$$

Therefore, the probability of getting an odd number or the number 6 is $\frac{2}{3}$.

Multiplication Rule

Multiplication Rule helps to find the probability of two or more events that occur in a sequence of tasks.

Multiplication Rule for Independent Events

If two events A and B are **independent** events (i.e., the occurrence of one event has no effect on the occurrence of the other event), then the probability of A and B occurring simultaneously is the product of the probability of each event.

$$P(A \text{ and } B) = P(A) \times P(B)$$

In general, the word "and" in probability calculations means multiplication.

For example, if a coin is tossed and a die is rolled, the probability of getting a "Heads" and a "number 4" is

$$P(H \text{ and } 4) = P(H) \times P(4)$$
$$= \frac{1}{2} \times \frac{1}{6}$$
$$= \frac{1}{12}$$

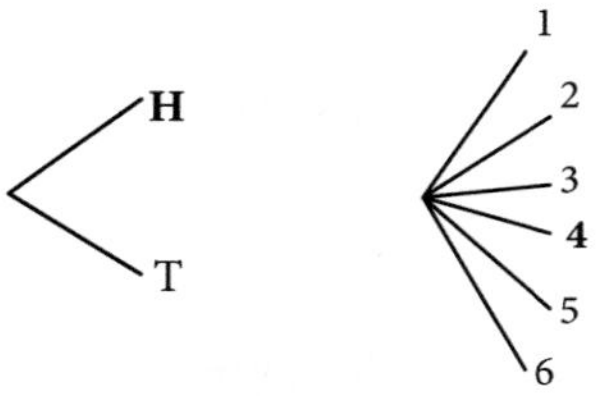

Example 12.4-r

Probability of Independent Events

If 2 cards are selected from a standard deck of cards, and the first card is placed back in the deck before the second card is selected, find the probability of the following:

(i) Getting a King card and a Spade card.

(ii) Getting a red card and a Jack card.

(iii) Getting an Ace and a black Queen.

Solution

All the events are independet events since the first card is placed back in the deck before the second card is selected. (i.e., the probability of the second event is not affected by the first event).

Using the Multiplication Rule for independent events,

$P(A \text{ and } B) = P(A) \times P(B)$

(i) Event A: King card 4 cards

Event B: Spade card 13 cards

$$P(A \text{ and } B) = \frac{4}{52} \times \frac{13}{52}$$
$$= \frac{1}{52}$$

Therefore, the probability of getting a King card and Spade card is $\frac{1}{52}$.

Solution *continued*

(ii) Event A: Red card 26 cards

Event B: Jack card 4 cards

$$P(A\ and\ B) = \frac{26}{52} \times \frac{4}{52}$$
$$= \frac{1}{26}$$

Therefore, the probability of getting a red card and a Jack card is $\frac{1}{26}$.

(iii) Event A: Ace card 4 cards

Event B: Black queen 2 cards

$$P(A\ and\ B) = \frac{4}{52} \times \frac{2}{52}$$
$$= \frac{1}{338}$$

Therefore, the probability of getting an Ace card and a black Queen card is $\frac{1}{338}$.

Multiplication Rule for Dependent Events

If two events A and B are **dependent events** (i.e., the possible outcome of one event depends on the outcome of the other event), then the probability of obtaining both events, $P(A\ and\ B)$, is the product of the probability of event A, $P(A)$, and the probability of event B, given that event A has occurred, which is denoted by $P(B|A)$ and read as "Probability of B given A".

$$P(A\ and\ B) = P(A) \times \underbrace{P(B|A)}_{\text{Probability of } B \text{ given that event } A \text{ has occurred.}}$$

For example, the probability of selecting a red marble then a white marble (without replacing the red marble) from a box containing 6 red marbles and 3 white marbles, is a dependent event.

6 red	After selecting one red marble →	5 red
3 white		3 white
9 marbles		**8 marbles**
$P(R) = \frac{6}{9}$		$P(W|R) = \frac{3}{8}$

$$P(R\ and\ W) = P(R) \times P(W|R)$$
$$= \frac{6}{9} \times \frac{3}{8}$$
$$= \frac{1}{4}$$

The probability of choosing the red marble is 6 out of 9. The probability of choosing the white marble is 3 out of 8 (because the red marble is not replaced and the white marble is chosen only from the remaining 8 marbles).

That is, the outcome of choosing the first marble has affected the outcome of choosing the second marble, making these events dependent.

Conditional Probability Rule

The probability of an event occuring given that another event has occured is a **conditional probability** (i.e., the second event is conditional on the first event).

The formula for conditional probability can be derived from the multiplication rule for dependent events as follows:

$$P(A\ and\ B) = P(A) \times P(B|A)$$ Interchanging left side and right side,

$$P(A) \times P(B|A) = P(A\ and\ B)$$ Dividing both sides by $P(A)$,

$$\mathbf{P(B|A) = \frac{P(A\ and\ B)}{P(A)}}$$

Similarly, $$\mathbf{P(A|B) = \frac{P(A\ and\ B)}{P(B)}}$$ Note that $P(A|B)$ is not the same as $P(B|A)$.

Example 12.4-s **Probability of Dependent Events**

There are 5 defective CDs in a collection of 20 CDs. If 2 CDs are selected, find the probability of the following:

(i) Both CDs are defective.

(ii) Both CDs are non-defective.

(iii) One of the CDs is defective.

Solution

$$20 \text{ Cds} \left\} \begin{array}{l} 5 \text{ Defective} \\ 15 \text{ Non-defective} \end{array} \right.$$

The events are dependent because the outcome of the 2nd selection is dependent on the outcome of the first.

Let A: 1st selection

and B: 2nd selection

Using the Multiplication Rule for dependent event,

$$P(A \text{ and } B) = P(A) \times P(B|A)$$

(i) $P(\text{Both defective}) = P(1^{st} \text{ defective}) \times P(2^{nd} \text{ defective})$

$$= \frac{5}{20} \times \frac{4}{19}$$

$$= \frac{1}{19}$$

Therefore, the probability of selecting both defective CDs is $\frac{1}{19}$.

(ii) $P(\text{Both non-defective}) = P(1^{st} \text{ non-defective}) \times P(2^{nd} \text{ non-defective})$

$$= \frac{15}{20} \times \frac{14}{19}$$

$$= \frac{21}{38}$$

Therefore, the probability of selecting both non-defective CDs is $\frac{21}{38}$.

(iii) $P(\text{One of them defective}) = P(1^{st} \text{ defective}) \times P(2^{nd} \text{ non-defective}) + P(1^{st} \text{ non-defective}) \times P(2^{nd} \text{ defective})$

$$= \frac{5}{20} \times \frac{15}{19} + \frac{15}{20} \times \frac{5}{19}$$

$$= \frac{15}{76} + \frac{15}{76}$$

$$= \frac{15}{38}$$

Therefore, the probability of one of them being defective is $\frac{15}{38}$.

Example 12.4-t **Conditional Probability and Complementary Event**

The probability that a student passes Finance Math is 0.85, and the probability that a student passes Statistics is 0.70. The probability that a student passes both subjects is 0.55.

If a student is selected in random, calculate the following:

(i) Probability that the student passes Statistics given that the student passed Finance Math.

(ii) Probability that the student passes Finance Math given that the student passed Statistics.

(iii) Probability that the student fails both subjects.

Solution

(i) and (ii) are conditional probability.

We know $P(A|B) = \dfrac{P(A \text{ and } B)}{P(B)}$ and $P(B|A) = \dfrac{P(A \text{ and } B)}{P(A)}$

$P(A) = P(Passing\ Finance\ Math) = 0.85$

$P(B) = P(Passing\ Statistics) = 0.70$

$P(A \text{ and } B) = P(Passing\ both\ subjects) = 0.55$

(i) Using $P(B|A) = \dfrac{P(A \text{ and } B)}{P(A)}$

$= \dfrac{0.55}{0.85}$

$= 0.647058...$

$= 0.65$

Therefore, the probability that the student passes Statistics given that the student passed Finance Math is 0.65.

(ii) Using $P(A|B) = \dfrac{P(A \text{ and } B)}{P(B)}$

$= \dfrac{0.55}{0.70}$

$= 0.785714...$

$= 0.79$

Therefore, the probability that the student passes Finance Math given that the student passed Statistics is 0.79.

(iii) This is the complementary of the event that the student passes both subjects.

Using $P(A') = 1 - P(A)$

$= 1 - P(A \text{ and } B)$

$= 1 - 0.55$

$= 0.45$

Therefore, the probability of the student failing both subjects is 0.45.

Odds In Favour and Odds Against an Event

Odds are another way to express outcomes. Odds are relative probabilities. Odds are used on outcomes when the probability of an event and its complement is of interest.

Most probabilities in the media are stated in terms of odds. It helps to compare the size of one probability relative to another. An event with a probability of 80% has odds of 80 to 20. This is the same as 4 to 1. This means that the event is four times more likely to occur than not occur.

Odds In Favour of an Event

The odds in favour of an event, A, is the ratio of the probability that event A will happen to the probability that event A will not happen(A').

If the possible number of outcomes is $n(S)$ and the number of favourable events, A, is $n(A)$, then the probability of a favourable event, A, is $P(A) = \dfrac{n(A)}{n(S)}$.

If the number of possible outcomes is $n(S)$, then there are $[n(S) - n(A)]$ unfavourable events.

The probability of an unfavourable event, A, is: $P(A') = \dfrac{[n(S) - n(A)]}{n(S)}$

Odds in favour of an event $= \dfrac{P(A)}{P(A')} = \dfrac{n(A)}{n(S) - n(A)}$

This can also be expressed as a ratio, $n(A) : \{n(S) - n(A)\}$

Note: Odds in favour of an event is the ratio of the number of favourable choices (successes) to the number of unfavourable choices (failures).

Example 12.4-u

Calculating the Odds in Favour of an Event

Professors of a college reviewed the "Business and Finance Mathematics" textbook and 15 members voted for the adoption of the textbook and 3 members voted against it. What are the odds in favour of adopting the textbook?

Solution

$n(S) = 15 + 3 = 18$

Let A be the favourable event to adopt the book; $n(A) = 15$.

Therefore, $n(A') = 3$.

Method 1: $P(A) = \frac{n(A)}{n(S)} = \frac{15}{18} = \frac{5}{6}$

Therefore, $P(A') = \frac{n(A')}{n(S)} = \frac{3}{18} = \frac{1}{6}$

Odds in favour of adopting the book $= \frac{P(A)}{P(A')} = \frac{\frac{5}{6}}{\frac{1}{6}} = \frac{5}{6} \times \frac{6}{1} = \frac{5}{1}$

Therefore, the odds in favour of adopting the book is 5 : 1.

Method 2: Odds in favour of adopting the book $= \frac{n(A)}{n(A')} = \frac{15}{3} = \frac{5}{1}$

Therefore, the odds in favour of adopting the book is 5 : 1.

Odds Against an Event

Sometimes odds are quoted as odds against an event, rather than as odds in favour.

The odds against an event A is the ratio of the probability that the event, A, will not happen to the probability that the event, A, will happen.

Odds against an event $= \frac{P(A')}{P(A)} = \frac{n(S) - n(A)}{n(A)}$

This can also be expressed as a ratio, $\{n(S) - n(A)\} : n(A)$

Therefore, the odds against an event is the ratio of the number of unfavourable choices (failures) to the number of favourable choices (successes).

In Example 12.4-u, the odds against adopting the textbook are 1 : 5.

Example 12.4-v

Odds Versus Probability

If the odds against an event is 4 : 5, calculate the probability for the event and the probability against the event.

Solution

The odds against an event is 4 : 5.

i.e., the outcomes against the event = 4

The outcomes for the event = 5

Total number of outcomes = 4 + 5 = 9

Therefore, the probability for the event is $\frac{5}{9}$ and the probability against the event is $\frac{4}{9}$.

12.4 | Exercises

Answers to odd-numbered problems are available at the end of the textbook.

1. Last semester, Ann-Marie taught Finance Math and out of 120 students, 96 students passed the subject. What is the probability that a student will pass Finance Math in Ann-Marie's class this semester?
2. Based on past records, Kaspar established that on average, 32 out of 36 students in a Finance Math class will register for the online lessons and labs. What is the probability that a student in a Finance Math class will register for the online lessons and labs next semester?
3. Out of the past 12 visits to a restaurant, Vera ordered fried rice 9 times. What is the probability that she will order fried rice in her next visit to the restaurant?
4. In the last 15 times that Lily had driven to the college, she was able to find a space in car park "A" 12 times. Estimate the probability that there will be an empty space in car park "A" the next time she drives to the college.
5. There are 3 different models of study tables (T1, T2, and T3) and 2 different models of chairs (C1, C2) available in a furniture store. Draw a tree diagram to show all the possible choices for purchasing a table and a chair.
6. A first-year student at a college is required to choose one of the 2 Math subjects (M1, M2) and one of the 4 General Education subjects (G1, G2, G3, G4) being offered. Draw a tree diagram to show all the possible choices for choosing a Math and General Education subject.
7. What is the probability of choosing an odd number from the set of numbers: {1, 2, 3, 4, 5, 6, 7, 8, 9}.
8. What is the probability of choosing an even number from the set of numbers: {11, 12, 13, 14, 15, 16, 17, 18, 19}.
9. If you choose a two-digit number, what is the probability that the number you choose is:

   a. Divisible by 5? b. More than 50? c. Not divisible by 5?
10. If you choose a two-digit number, what is the probability that the number you choose is:

    a. Divisible by 6? b. Between 60 and 90? c. Not divisible by 6?
11. A die is rolled once. Find the probability that the number rolled is:

    a. Less than 3. b. Greater or equal to 2. c. Even or less than 3.
12. A die is rolled once. Find the probability that the number rolled is:

    a. Greater than 2. b. Less than or equal to 3. c. Odd or greater than 4.
13. A card is drawn from a well shuffled, standard, 52-card deck of cards. Find the probability that it is:

    a. A red card. b. A Face card.
14. A card is drawn from a well shuffled, standard, 52-card deck of cards. Find the probability that it is:

    a. An Ace card. b. A numbered card.
15. A card is drawn from a well shuffled, standard, 52-card deck of cards. Find the probability that it is:

    a. A number 5 card or a red card. b. An odd numbered card.
16. A card is drawn from a well shuffled, standard, 52-card deck of cards. Find the probability that it is:

    a. A Jack or a black card. b. An even numbered card.
17. A spinning wheel is divided into 9 equal sectors and numbered 1 to 9. Find the probability of spinning:

    a. A number divisible by 3. b. A number less than 6. c. An odd number.
18. A spinning wheel is divided into 8 equal sectors and numbered 1 to 8. Find the probability of spinning:

    a. A number divisible by 3. b. A number greater than 5. c. An even number.
19. A pair of 6-sided dice, one white and the other red, is rolled simultaneously.

    a. Find the probability that the sum of the two dice is 5.

    b. Find the probability that the sum of the two dice is not 5.
20. A pair of 6-sided dice, one black and the other white, is rolled simultaneously.

    a. Find the probability that the sum of the two dice is 7.

    b. Find the probability that the sum of the two dice is not 7.

21. Find the probability of selecting a face card in each of two consecutive draws from a well shuffled, standard, 52-card deck of cards if the first card is:

    a. Replaced before the second draw. b. Not replaced before the second draw.

22. Find the probability of selecting a red card in each of two consecutive draws from a well shuffled, standard, 52-card deck of cards if the first card is:

    a. Replaced before the second draw. b. Not replaced before the second draw.

23. The probability that a student takes Math is 0.70, English is 0.65, and both Math and English is 0.50. Find the probability that a student selected at random takes Math or English.

24. The probability that a student learns Music is 0.75, Dance is 0.60, and both Music and Dance is 0.45. Find the probability that a student selected at random takes Music or Dance.

25. A card is drawn from a well shuffled, standard, 52-card deck of cards.

    a. What are the odds in favour of selecting a face card?

    b. What are the odds against selecting an Ace card?

26. A card is drawn from a well shuffled, standard, 52-card deck of cards.

    a. What are the odds in favour of selecting a numbered card?

    b. What are the odds against selecting a heart card?

27. A bag contains 8 quarters, 6 dimes, and 4 nickels. Two coins are selected (without replacement) from the bag. What is the probability that:

    a. Both coins are dimes?

    b. The first coin is a quarter and the second coin is a nickel?

28. A bag contains 12 red marbles, 8 black marbles, and 5 white marbles. Two marbles are drawn (without replacement) from the bag. What is the probability that:

    a. Both of the marbles are red?

    b. The first marble is red and the second marble is white?

29. In a group of 50 students, 25 take Math, 20 take English, and 15 take both Math and English.

    Find the probability that a student selected at random:

    a. Takes Math, but not English. b. Takes English, but not Math.

    c. Takes neither Math nor English. d. Takes Math or English.

30. In a group of 40 families, 21 own a dog, 20 own a cat, and 6 own both a dog and a cat.

    If a family is selected at random, what is the probability that the family:

    a. Owns a dog, but not a cat? b. Owns a cat, but not a dog?

    c. Owns neither a dog nor a cat? d. Owns a dog or a cat?

31. In a class of 40 students, 15 are males. If two students are selected at random to represent the class, what is the probability that:

    a. Both are males? b. Both are females? c. One is male and the other is female?

32. A box contains 20 bulbs, out of which, 5 are defective. If two bulbs are selected at random at the same time, what is the probability that:

    a. Both are defective? b. Both are not defective? c. One is defective and the other is not?

12 | Review Exercises

Answers to odd-numbered problems are available at the end of the textbook.

1. a. State the difference between discrete and continuous variables.

   b. State the difference between the classifications of interval and ratio in the levels of measurement.

2. a. State the difference between a quantitative and qualitative variable.

   b. State the difference between the classifications of nominal and ordinal in levels of measurement.

3. For each of the following, identify the data type (as quantitative or qualitative - if quantitative, identify as discrete or continuous) and specify the appropriate measurement scale (as nominal, ordinal, interval or ratio):

   a. Gender

   b. Year of birth

   c. Volume of a container

   d. Number of correct answers

   e. Time to complete homework

4. For each of the following, identify the data type (as quantitative or qualitative - if quantitative, identify as discrete or continuous) and specify the appropriate measurement scale (as nominal, ordinal, interval or ratio):

   a. Nationality

   b. Ranking of favourite food

   c. Average marks on an exam

   d. Number of trees in a park

   e. Distance between two cities

5. The grades on a math exam for a sample of 40 students are provided below:

69	83	66	72	88	52	60	71	40	62
49	58	78	74	56	45	81	65	68	91
59	61	73	67	76	45	79	80	51	76
96	65	55	84	44	51	63	53	65	54

   a. Construct a stem-and-leaf plot to display the data in an array.

   b. Group the above data using a class interval of 10.

6. The ages of a sample of 40 students in a college are provided below:

24	26	26	20	22	19	28	21	25	24
19	23	21	21	20	21	23	23	27	21
19	19	19	22	29	30	18	18	21	26
26	25	21	22	22	20	24	26	29	23

   a. Construct a stem-and-leaf plot to display the above data in an array.

   b. Group the above data using a class interval of 2.

7. The five departments of a company had the following net profits last year:

Department	Profit ($ Thousands)
Dept. A	750
Dept. B	325
Dept. C	475
Dept. D	275
Dept. E	625

   Represent the above information using:

   a. A horizontal bar chart.

   b. A line graph.

   c. A pie chart.

8. The survey results of a sample of 50 students on their favourite sport is provided below:

Favourite Sport	Number of students
Swimming	10
Tennis	18
Basketball	12
Badminton	6
Volleyball	4

   Represent the above information using:

   a. A horizontal bar chart.

   b. A line graph.

   c. A pie chart.

9. The following table shows the starting salaries of a sample of recent business graduates:

Income ($ Thousands)	Number of Graduates
15 - 19	40
20 - 24	60
25 - 29	80
30 - 34	18
35 – 39	2

Calculate the percent of graduates who earn the following starting salaries:

a. At least $30,000.

b. Less than $25,000.

c. At least $20,000.

10. The following table shows the number of years of service of a group of employees at a college:

Years	Frequency
0 to under 5	10
5 to under 10	14
10 to under 15	39
15 to under 20	24
20 to under 25	13

Calculate the percent of employees with the following years of service:

a. Less than 10 years of service.

b. More than 20 years of service.

c. Between 10 and 20 years of service.

11. The following frequency distribution shows scores earned by a sample of 100 students on an Aptitude Examination marked out of 200:

Marks out of 200	Number of students
25 to under 50	5
50 to under 75	18
75 to under 100	28
100 to under 125	32
125 to under 150	8
150 to under 175	6
175 to under 200	3

Construct the following for the above data:

a. Histogram and frequency polygon.

b. Relative frequency and percent frequency distribution.

c. Relative cumulative frequency and cumulative percent frequency distribution.

d. Cumulative frequency and cumulative percent curve.

12. The following frequency distribution shows the ages of 50 employees in an organization:

Age	Number of employees
30 to under 40	3
40 to under 50	5
50 to under 60	7
60 to under 70	12
70 to under 80	16
80 to under 90	5
90 to under 100	2

Construct the following for the above data:

a. Histogram and frequency polygon.

b. Relative frequency and percent frequency distribution.

c. Relative cumulative frequency and cumulative percent frequency distribution.

d. Cumulative frequency and cumulative percent curve.

13. For the following data in ascending order {84, 89, 91, 92, 93, 93, 95, 96, 97, 98, 100}:

a. Determine the mean, median, and mode.

b. Determine the 1st and 3rd quartile.

c. Determine the inter-quartile range.

d. Draw a box-and-whisker plot for the data.

e. Identify outliers, if any.

14. For the data given in ascending order {10, 16, 18, 20, 20, 20, 22, 22, 24, 25, 26, 29}:

a. Determine the mean, median, and mode.

b. Determine the 1st and 3rd quartile.

c. Determine the inter-quartile range.

d. Draw a box-and-whisker plot for the data.

e. Identify outliers, if any.

15. Monthly rent (in dollars) for a sample of 18, two-bedroom condominium units in downtown Toronto are provided in the table below:

Rental amount ($)	Number of units
2400	1
2600	2
2700	7
2800	5
2900	3

Find the mean, median, and mode of the rent for the two-bedroom condominium units at the above location, and determine the shape of the distribution.

16. The market values of 15, four-bedroom houses in Toronto are provided in the table below:

Value of house ($)	Number of houses
550,000	1
600,000	4
650,000	3
700,000	5
850,000	2

Find the mean, median, and mode of the market values for the four-bedroom houses at the above location, and determine the shape of the distribution.

17. For the grouped data in Problem 11:

a. Find the mean.

b. Find the modal class and the mode.

c. Find the interval that contains the median and find the median.

18. For the grouped data in Problem 12:

a. Find the mean.

b. Find the modal class and the mode.

c. Find the interval that contains the median and find the median.

19. For the data in Problem 13, compute the following:

a. Average (mean) deviation from the mean.

b. Variance.

c. Standard deviation.

20. For the data in Problem 14, compute the following:

a. Average (mean) deviation from the mean.

b. Variance.

c. Standard deviation.

21. In a frequency distribution, the mean is 32 and the mode is 56. Using the Empirical formula: (mean – mode) = 3(mean – median), calculate the median and comment on the nature of the distribution.

22. In a frequency distribution, the median is 19 and the mode is 23. Using the Empirical formula: (mean – mode) = 3(mean – median), calculate the mean and comment on the nature of the distribution.

23. The evaluation components of a subject are as follows: tests 20%, midterm 25%, final exam 30%, online labs 15%, and homework 10%. A student obtained the following marks: 86% (tests), 96% (midterm), 82% (final exam), 98% (online labs), and 100% (homework). Organize the scores and weights in a table and find the weighted mean of the scores.

24. The evaluation components of a subject are as follows: tests 40%, weekly assignments 10%, book reviews 15%, in-class exercises 5%, and final exam 30%. A student obtained the following marks: 75% (tests), 85% (weekly assignments), 98% (book reviews), 90% (in-class exercises), and 80% (final exam). Organize the scores and weights in a table and find the weighted mean of the scores.

25. Calculate the mean deviation from the mean of the following datasets:

a. {3, 9, 15, 21, 27}

b. {24, 37, 21, 32, 25, 36, 22, 28}

26. Calculate the mean deviation from the mean of the following datasets:

a. {7, 10, 19, 15, 28]

b. {98, 102, 107, 110, 113, 123}

27. In a normal distribution, if the mean is 35 and the standard deviation is 6, what percent of the data falls between 23 and 47?

28. In a normal distribution, if the mean is 115 and the standard deviation is 25 what percent of the data falls between 90 and 140?

29. The mean of a normally distributed group of employee income is $975 with a standard deviation of $125. Approximately, what percent of employees will have an income between $850 and $1100?

30. The scores on an IQ test are normally distributed with a mean of 200 and standard deviation of 17.5. If data is selected randomly, the value of that data has a ninety-five percent chance of falling between what scores?

31. Compute the mean, median, variance, and standard deviation of the following dataset: {17, 22, 20, 18, 23}.

32. Compute the mean, median, variance, and standard deviation of the following dataset: {30, 28, 35, 40, 25}.

33. A baseball team played 162 games and won 72 times. What is the probability that the team will win the next game?

34. Last month, a car salesman sold 30 cars out of the 125 cars sold in the dealership. Estimate the probability that the next car sale is by the same salesman.

35. A pair of fair, 6-sided, dice is rolled. Find the probability that the roll:

a. Has a sum of 5.

b. Has a sum less than 7.

36. A pair of fair, 6-sided dice, is rolled. Find the probability that the roll:

a. Has a sum of 7.

b. Has a sum more than 10.

37. A card is drawn from a well shuffled, standard, 52-card deck. Find the probability that it is:

    a. A Jack card or a black Queen card.

    b. A red card or a face card.

    c. An Ace card or a heart card.

38. A card is drawn from a well shuffled, standard, 52-card deck. Find the probability that it is:

    a. A number 10 card or a black card.

    b. A King card or a diamond card.

    c. A spade card or a face card.

39. A card is drawn from a well shuffled, standard, 52-card deck.

    a. What are the odds in favour of selecting a face card?

    b. What are the odds against selecting a heart card?

40. A card is drawn from a well shuffled, standard, 52-card deck.

    a. What are the odds in favour of selecting a numbered card?

    b. What are the odds against selecting an Ace card?

41. What is the probability that a two-digit number that you choose is not divisible by 7?

42. What is the probability that a two-digit number that you choose is not divisible by 11?

43. A survey revealed that 85% of drivers wear the seatbelt while driving. If two drivers are chosen at random, what is the probability that they will not be wearing a seatbelt?

44. A survey revealed that 75% of all children like fast food. If 3 children are chosen at random, what is the probability that all three dislike fast food?

45. A box contains 7 white balls, 5 black balls, and 9 yellow balls. Two balls are chosen. What is the probability that both balls are black (a) with replacement or (b) without replacement?

46. Three cards are chosen at random from a deck of 52 cards. What is the probability of getting three face cards (a) with replacement or (b) without replacement?

47. Nine boys and five girls apply for 3 scholarships. Find the probability that:

    a. All 3 scholarships go to boys.

    b. At least 1 scholarship goes to a girl.

48. The probability that I leave for college on time is 0.60. The probability that I arrive at college on time is 0.80. What is the probability that I leave on time and arrive at college on time?

12 | Self-Test Exercises

Answers to all problems are available at the end of the textbook.

1. For each of the following, identify the data type (as quantitative or qualitative - if quantitative as discrete or continuous) and specify the appropriate measurement scale (as nominal, ordinal, interval, or ratio):

    a. Marital status.

    b. Number of cars in a parking lot.

    c. Travel time from home to college.

    d. Letter grades in a final exam.

    e. Annual salary.

2. The grades on a math exam for a sample of 40 students are provided below:

63	74	42	65	51	54	36	56	68	57
62	64	76	67	79	61	81	77	59	38
84	68	71	94	71	86	69	75	91	55
48	82	83	54	79	62	68	58	41	47

    a. Construct a stem-and-leaf display for the data.

    b. Construct a frequency distribution and relative frequency distribution for the data, using seven class intervals of 10.

3. The Consumer Price Index for the years 2007 to 2014 is provided below:

Year	CPI
2007	111.5
2008	114.4
2009	114.4
2010	116.5
2011	119.9
2012	121.7
2013	122.8
2014	125.2

Represent the above information using:

a. A horizontal bar chart. b. A line graph.

4. Draw a pie chart to represent the following investment funds of a corporation:

Fund	Amount ($ Thousands)
GIC	270
Bond	216
Equity	108
Fixed Income	162
Money Market	144

5. The following frequency distribution shows the hourly wages earned by a sample of 50 students during their summer employment:

Hourly wages ($)	Number of students
15 to under 20	4
20 to under 25	8
25 to under 30	12
30 to under 35	16
35 to under 40	5
40 to under 45	3
45 to under 50	2

Construct the following for the above data:

a. Histogram and frequency polygon.

b. Relative frequency and percent frequency distribution.

c. Relative cumulative frequency and cumulative percent frequency distribution.

d. Cumulative frequency and cumulative percent curve.

6. For the following data in ascending order {40, 46, 47, 48, 49, 49, 50, 51, 52, 53, 58}:

a. Determine the mean, median, and mode.

b. Determine the 1st and 3rd quartiles.

c. Determine the inter-quartile range.

d. Identify outliers, if any.

e. Draw a box-and-whisker plot for the data.

7. For the grouped data in Problem 5:

a. Find the mean.

b. Find the modal class and the mode.

c. Find the interval that contains the median and find the median.

8. For the data in Problem 6 compute the following:

a. Average (mean) deviation from the mean.

b. Variance.

c. Standard deviation.

9. In a frequency distribution the mode is 65, and the median is 122. Using the Empirical formula: (mean – mode) = 3(mean – median), calculate the mean and comment on the nature of the distribution.

10. The following are the number of students who took Finance Math and the percent of students who passed the course at a college in Windsor last year:

Semester	Percent Passed	# of students enrolled
Fall	82%	1200
Summer	70%	750
Winter	76%	300

What percent of the students who took Finance Math last year passed?

11. Calculate the deviation from the mean of the following datasets:

a. {1, 5, 3, 7, 6, 9} b. {80, 85, 81, 0, 85, 90, 87, 92}

12. Compute the mean, median, variance, and standard deviation of the following dataset:

{23,45, 49, 25, 34, 31, 19, 20, 59, 31, 21}

13. The quartiles for a distribution are Q1 = 67 and Q3 = 85.

a. A value greater than what number is considered as a high outlier?

b. A value lower than what number is considered as a low outlier?

14. In a normal distribution, if the mean is 180 and the standard deviation is 15, what percent of the data falls:

a. Between 150 and 210? b. Between 135 and 225?

c. Below 150? d. Above 225?

15. A number between 0 and 15 is chosen. Find the probability of choosing an odd number.

16. A single letter is chosen at random from the word "Professor". What is the probability that the letter chosen is 's' or 'r'?

17. An urn contains 6 red marbles and 4 black marbles. Two marbles are drawn without replacement from the urn. What is the probability that both of the marbles are black?

18. If a fair die is rolled once, what is the probability that the roll will result in:

a. 2 or 5? b. An odd number?

19. If a card is drawn from a well shuffled, standard, 52-card deck of cards, find the probability that the card is neither a spade card nor a face card.

20. Two cards are drawn from a well shuffled, standard, 52-card deck without replacement. Find the probability of drawing:

a. Two face cards.

b. A King and a Queen.

c. A face card (Jack, Queen, or King) and an Ace card.

d. Two spade cards.

21. There are 20 male students and 15 female students in a class. If a student is selected at random:

a. What are the odds in favour of selecting a female student?

b. What are the odds against selecting a male student?

12 | Summary of Notation and Formulas

MEASURES OF CENTRAL TENDENCY

Mean (ungrouped data):

$$\bar{x} = \frac{\sum x_i}{n}$$

$\sum x_i$ ← Sum of all the values of the terms

n ← Number of terms

Mean (grouped data):

$$\bar{x} = \frac{\sum f \cdot x}{n}$$

$\sum f \cdot x$ ← Sum of the product of class frequency (f) and class midpoint (x)

n ← Number of terms

Weighted Mean:

$$\bar{x} = \frac{\sum x_i \cdot w_i}{\sum w_i}$$

$\sum x_i \cdot w_i$ ← Sum of the weighted values of the terms

$\sum w_i$ ← Sum of the weighted factors

Geometric Mean:

$$G = \sqrt[n]{x_1 \cdot x_2 \cdot x_3 \cdot x_4 \cdot x_5 \cdots\cdots x_n}$$

n^{th} root of the product of all values of the data

Median (ungrouped data):

$$Median = \textit{The value of term in the position} \left(\frac{n+1}{2}\right)$$

Median (grouped data):

$$Median = \ell + \left[\left(\frac{n}{2} - m\right)\right] \times \left(\frac{c}{f}\right)$$

ℓ = lower limit of the median class

n = total number of frequency

m = cumulative frequency in the class one above the median class

c = class width

f = frequency in the median class

Mode (ungrouped data):

Mode = The most frequent value in the data

Mode (grouped data):

Mode = Mid-point of the class interval containing the highest frequency modal class

Empirical Relationship for Mean, Median and Mode:

Mean – Mode = 3 (Mean – Median)

MEASURES OF DISPERSION

Range:

Range = Highest value – Lowest value

$$R = H - L$$

Mean Devation:

$$\text{Mean deviation} = \frac{\sum |x - \bar{x}|}{n}$$

$\sum |x - \bar{x}|$ ← Sum of absolute deviation of terms from the mean

n ← Number of terms

Variance (Population):

$$\sigma^2 = \frac{\sum (x - \mu)^2}{N}$$

Variance (Sample):

$$s^2 = \frac{\sum (x - \bar{x})^2}{n - 1}$$

Standard deviation (Population):

$$\sigma = \sqrt{\frac{\sum (x - \mu)^2}{N}}$$

μ = Population Mean

N = Number of data in population

Standard deviation (Sample):

$$s = \sqrt{\frac{\sum (x - \bar{x})^2}{n - 1}}$$

$\bar{x}$ = Sample Mean

n = Number of data in sample

PROBABILITY

Probability of an event:

$$P(E) = \frac{\text{Number of favourable outcomes of event "E"}}{\text{Total number of possible outcomes}} = \frac{n(E)}{n(S)}$$

Complement Rule:

$P(A) + P(A') = 1$

Probability of Mutually Exclusive Events:

$P(A \text{ or } B) = P(A) + P(B)$

Probability of Independent Events:

$P(A \text{ and } B) = P(A) \times P(B)$

Probability of Mutually Non-Exclusive Events:

$P(A \text{ or } B) = P(A) + P(B) - P(A \text{ and } B)$

Probability of Dependent Events:

$P(A \text{ and } B) = P(A) \times P(B|A)$

Conditional Probability:

$$P(A|B) = \frac{P(A \text{ and } B)}{P(B)}$$

Answer Key

Chapter 1

Exercises 1.1

1. **a.** (i) Tens (ii) 90
   b. (i) Hundreds (ii) 300
   c. (i) Hundreds (ii) 700
3. **a.** (i) Ten thousands (ii) 10,000
   b. (i) Ten thousands (ii) 20,000
   c. (i) Millions (ii) 6,000,000
5. **a.** (i) Expanded form: 400 + 7
   (ii) Word form: Four hundred seven
   b. (i) Expanded form: 2,000 + 50 + 6
   (ii) Word form: Two thousand, fifty-six
7. **a.** (i) Expanded form: 20,000 + 9,000 + 100 + 80 + 6
   (ii) Word form: Twenty-nine thousand, one hundred eighty-six
   b. (i) Expanded form: 400,000 + 60,000 + 4,000 + 400 + 40 + 8
   (ii) Word form: Four hundred sixty-four thousand, four hundred fourty-eight
9. **a.** (i) Expanded form: 2,000,000 + 600,000 + 4,000 + 300 + 20 + 5
   (ii) Word form: Two million, six hundred four thousand, three hundred twenty-five
   b. (i) Expanded form: 10,000,000, 5,000,000 + 300,000 + 600 + 4
   (ii) Word form: Fifteen million, three hundred thousand, six hundred four
11. **a.** (i) Standard form: 679
   (ii) Word form: Six hundred seventy-nine
   b. (i) Standard form: 3,147
   (ii) Word form: Three thousand, one hundred fourty-seven
13. **a.** (i) Standard form: 2,605
   (ii) Word form: Two thousand, six hundred five
   b. (i) Standard form: 9,024
   (ii) Word form: Nine thousand, twenty-four
15. **a.** (i) Standard form: 40,990
   (ii) Word form: Forty thousand, nine hundred ninety
   b. (i) Standard form: 10,053
   (ii) Word form: Ten thousand, fifty-three
17. **a.** (i) Standard form: 570
   (ii) Expanded form: 500 + 70
   b. (i) Standard form: 803
   (ii) Expanded form: 800 + 3
19. **a.** (i) Standard form: 80,630
   (ii) Expanded form: 80,000 + 600 + 30
   b. (i) Standard form: 75,025
   (ii) Expanded form: 70,000 + 5,000 + 20 + 5
21. **a.** (i) Standard form: 12,452,832
   (ii) Expanded form: 10,000,000 + 2,000,000 + 400,000 + 50,000 + 2,000 + 800 + 30 + 2
   b. (i) Standard form: 32,684,256
   (ii) Expanded form: 30,000,000 + 2,000,000 + 600,000 + 80,000 + 4,000 + 200 + 50 + 6
23. **a.** (i) Standard form: 125,000
   (ii) Expanded form: 100,000 + 20,000 + 5,000
   b. (i) Standard form: 750,000
   (ii) Expanded form: 700,000 + 50,000
25. **a.**

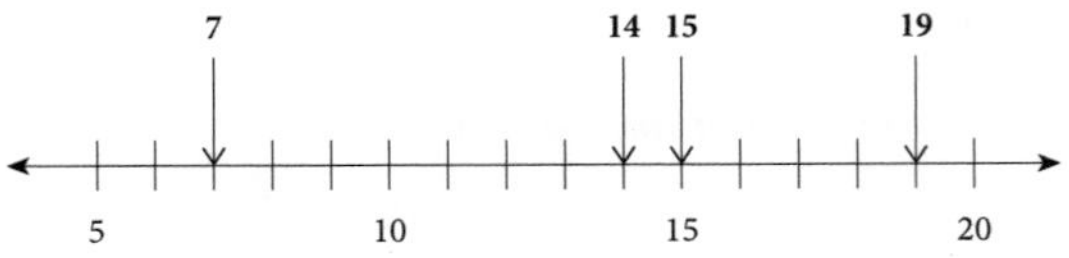

   b.

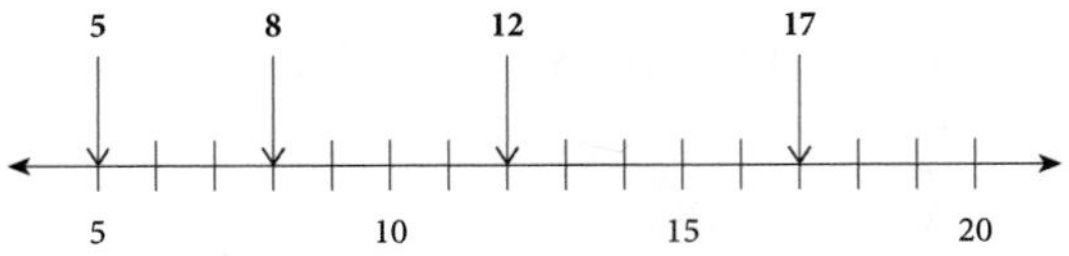

27. **a.** 7 < 15 **b.** 19 > 14 **c.** 0 < 5 **d.** 19 > 14
29. **a.** (i) 6 is less than 9 (ii) 9 is greater than 6
   b. (i) 11 is less than 18 (ii) 18 is greater than 11
   c. (i) 5 is less than 11 (ii) 11 is greater than 5
   d. (i) 0 is less than 11 (ii) 11 is greater than 0
31. **a.** 87, 96, 99, 103, 108
   b. 108, 139, 141, 159, 167
33. **a.** 2,040, 2,067, 2,533, 2,638
   b. 78,812, 79,468, 79,487, 79,543
35. **a.** (i) 259 (ii) 952
   b. (i) 1,789 (ii) 9,871
   c. (i) 3,458 (ii) 8,543
37. **a.** (i) 430 (ii) 400 (iii) 1,000
   b. (i) 1,650 (ii) 1,600 (iii) 2,000
   c. (i) 53,560 (ii) 53,600 (iii) 54,000
   d. (i) 235,360 (ii) 235,400 (iii) 235,000
39. **a.** (i) 880,000 (ii) 900,000 (iii) 1,000,000
   b. (i) 1,660,000 (ii) 1,700,000 (iii) 2,000,000
   b. (i) 3,370,000 (ii) 3,400,000 (iii) 3,000,000
   d. (i) 4,570,000 (ii) 4,600,000 (iii) 5,000,000

Exercises 1.2

1. **a.** (i) 80 (ii) 77 **b.** (i) 140 (ii) 133
3. **a.** (i) 930 (ii) 923 **b.** (i) 650 (ii) 653
5. **a.** (i) 420 (ii) 410 **b.** (i) 1,520 (ii) 1,511
7. **a.** (i) 670 (ii) 662 **b.** (i) 1,830 (ii) 1,818
9. **a.** (i) 1,400 (ii) 1,413 **b.** (i) 600 (ii) 652
11. **a.** (i) 7,400 (ii) 7,349 **b.** (i) 5,700 (ii) 5,616
13. **a.** (i) 4,500 (ii) 4,531 **b.** (i) 3,800 (ii) 3,732
15. **a.** (i) 30 (ii) 37 **b.** (i) 10 (ii) 15
17. **a.** (i) 130 (ii) 129 **b.** (i) 270 (ii) 268
19. **a.** (i) 610 (ii) 608 **b.** (i) 490 (ii) 496
21. **a.** (i) 1,060 (ii) 1,058 **b.** (i) 2,040 (ii) 2,039
23. **a.** (i) 400 (ii) 494 **b.** (i) 600 (ii) 604
25. **a.** (i) 700 (ii) 675 **b.** (i) 2,200 (ii) 2,128
27. **a.** (i) 700 (ii) 667 **b.** (i) 2,300 (ii) 2,324
29. **a.** (i) 4,800 (ii) 4,350 **b.** (i) 3,600 (ii) 3,717
31. **a.** (i) 38,000 (ii) 40,492
    b. (i) 56,000 (ii) 54,332
33. **a.** (i) 80,000 (ii) 73,815
    b. (i) 129,000 (ii) 126,850
35. **a.** (i) 8 (ii) Quotient: 15 Remainder: 3
    b. (i) 4 (ii) Quotient: 4 Remainder: 4
37. **a.** (i) 3 (ii) Quotient: 3 Remainder: 5
    b. (i) 4 (ii) Quotient: 4 Remainder: 2
39. **a.** (i) 65 (ii) Quotient: 46 Remainder: 10
    b. (i) 20 (ii) Quotient: 16 Remainder: 12
41. **a.** (i) 129 (ii) Quotient: 143 Remainder: 4
    b. (i) 41 (ii) Quotient: 43 Remainder: 21
43. **a.** (i) 15 (ii) Quotient: 14 Remainder: 148
    b. (i) 13 (ii) Quotient: 13 Remainder: 27
45. **a.** \$719 **b.** \$133
47. **a.** \$1,362 **b.** \$620
49. **a.** 360 pens **b.** 12 pieces
51. **a.** 45 weeks **b.** 352 chairs
53. \$53
55. \$2,130
57. \$450
59. 42 weeks
61. 762 students
63. 125
65. \$163
67. **a.** 24 **b.** 17

Exercises 1.3

1. 2, 3, 5, 7, 11, 13, 17, and 19
3. 12, 14, 15, 16, 18, 20, 21, 22, 24, 25, 26, 27, and 28
5. **a.** 13, 19, and 47 **b.** 11, 29, and 43
7. **a.** (i) Factors: 1, 3, 5, and 15
   (ii) Prime factors: 3 and 5
   b. (i) Factors: 1, 2, 17, and 34
   (ii) Prime factors: 2 and 17
9. **a.** (i) Factors: 1, 2, 4, 8, 16, 32, and 64
   (ii) Prime factor: 2
   b. (i) Factors: 1, 2, 3, 6, 9, 18, 27, and 54
   (ii) Prime factors: 2 and 3
11. **a.** (i) Factors: 1, 3, 7, and 21
    (ii) Prime factors: 3 and 7
    b. (i) Factors: 1, 5, and 25
    (ii) Prime fator: 5
13. **a.** (i) Factors: 1, 2, 3, 4, 6, 9, 12, 18, and 36
    (ii) Prime factors: 2 and 3
    b. (i) Factors: 1, 5, 13, and 65
    (ii) Prime factors: 5 and 13
15. **a.** 6, 12, 18, 24, 30, 36
    b. 8, 16, 24, 32, 40, 48
17. **a.** 9, 18, 27, 36, 45, 54
    b. 10, 20, 30, 40, 50, 60
19. **a.** 30 **b.** 90
21. **a.** 72 **b.** 315
23. **a.** 64 **b.** 120
25. **a.** 24 **b.** 180
27. **a.** 150 **b.** 108
29. **a.** 84 **b.** 54
31. **a.** 72 **b.** 90
33. **a.** (i) Factors of 15: 1, 3, 5, and 15
    Factors of 25: 1, 5, and 25
    (ii) Common factor: 5
    (iii) HCF: 5
    b. (i) Factors of 18 : 1, 2, 3, 6, 9, and 18
    Factors of 32: 1, 2, 4, 8, 16 and 32
    (ii) Common factor: 2
    (iii) HCF: 2
35. **a.** (i) Factors of 18: 1, 2, 3, 6, 9, and 18
    Factors of 48: 1, 2, 3, 4, 6, 8, 12, 16, 24, and 48
    (ii) Common factors: 2, 3, and 6
    (iii) HCF: 6
    b. (i) Factors of 32: 1, 2, 4, 8, 16, and 32
    Factors of 60: 1, 2, 3, 4, 5, 6, 10, 12, 15, 20, 30, and 60
    (ii) Common factors: 2 and 4
    (iii) HCF is: 4
37. **a.** (i) Factors of 25: 1, 5, and 25
    Factors of 80: 1, 2, 4, 5, 8, 10, 16, 20, 40, and 80
    (ii) Common factor: 5
    (iii) HCF: 5

b. (i) Factors of 40: 1, 2, 4, 5, 8, 10, 20, and 40
Factors of 120: 1, 2, 3, 4, 5, 6, 8, 10, 12, 15, 20, 24, 30, 40, 60, and 120
(ii) Common factors: 2, 4, 5, 8, 10, 20, and 40
(iii) HCF: 40

39. a. (i) Factors of 8: 1, 2, 4, and 8
Factors of 12: 1, 2, 3, 4, 6, and 12
Factors of 15: 1, 3, 5, and 15
(ii) Common factor: 1
(iii) HCF: 1
b. (i) Factors of 6: 1, 2, 3, and 6
Factors of 15: 1, 3, 5, and 15
Factors of 20: 1, 2, 4, 5, 10, and 20
(ii) Common factor: 1
(iii) HCF: 1

41. a. (i) Factors of 12: 1, 2, 3, 4, 6, and 12
Factors of 18: 1, 2, 3, 6, 9, and 18
Factors of 24: 1, 2, 3, 4, 6, 8, 12, and 24
(ii) Common factors: 2, 3, and 6
(iii) HCF: 6
b. (i) Factors of 12: 1, 2, 3, 4, 6, and 12
Factors of 30: 1, 2, 3, 5, 6, 10, 15, and 30
Factors of 42: 1, 2, 3, 6, 7, 14, 21, and 42
(ii) Common factors: 2, 3, and 6
(iii) HCF: 6

43. a. (i) Factors of 40: 1, 2, 4, 5, 8, 10, 20, and 40
Factors of 50: 1, 2, 5, 10, 25, and 50
Factors of 80: 1, 2, 4, 5, 8, 10, 16, 20, 40, and 80
(ii) Common factors: 2, 5 and 10
(iii) HCF: 10
b. (i) Factors of 30: 1, 2, 3, 5, 6, 10, 15, and 30
Factors of 75: 1, 3, 5, 15, 25, and 75
Factors of 90: 1, 2, 3, 5, 6, 9, 10, 15, 18, 30, 45, and 90
(ii) Common factors: 3, 5, and 15
(iii) HCF: 15

45. 32 cm **47.** March 1st
49. 9 metres **51.** 6 minutes

Exercises 1.4

1. a. 6^4 b. 12^2 **3.** a. 3^6 b. 9^4
5. a. Base: 2 Exponent: 9 b. Base: 5 Exponent: 7
7. a. Base: 1 Exponent: 20 b. Base: 5 Exponent: 7
9. a. $10 \times 10 \times 10 \times 10 \times 10 \times 10 = 1{,}000{,}000$
b. $3 \times 3 \times 3 \times 3 \times 3 = 243$
11. a. $3^9 = 19{,}683$ b. $3^{11} = 177{,}147$
13. a. 256 b. 72 **15.** a. 9 b. 125
17. a. 35 b. 9 **19.** a. 70 b. 25
21. a. 15 b. 5 **23.** a. 12 b. 42
25. a. 4 b. 8 **27.** a. 5 b. 12
29. a. 2 b. 7 **31.** a. 8 b. 20
33. a. 21 b. 16 **35.** a. 16 b. 32
37. a. 16 b. 20 **39.** a. 108 b. 10
41. a. 32 b. 28 **43.** a. 126 b. 36
45. a. 407 b. 10 **47.** a. 4 b. 14
49. 148

Review Exercises 1

1. a. (i) Expanded form: 7,000 + 500 + 2
(ii) Word form: Seven thousand, five hundred two
b. (i) Expanded form: 20,000 + 5,000 + 40 + 7
(ii) Word form: Twenty-five thousand, forty-seven
c. (i) Expanded form: 600,000 + 20,000 + 20 + 5
(ii) Word form: Six hundred twenty thousand, twenty-five
d. (i) Expanded form: 3,000,000 + 50,000 + 4,000 + 700 + 5
(ii) Word form: Three million, fifty-four thousand, seven hundred five

3. a. (i) Standard form: 5,607
(ii) Expanded form: 5,000 + 600 + 7
b. (i) Standard form: 37,040
(ii) Expanded form: 30,000 + 7,000 + 40
c. (i) Standard form: 408,105
(ii) Expanded form: 400,000 + 8,000 + 100 + 5
d. (i) Standard form: 1,070,055
(ii) Expanded form: 1,000,000 + 70,000 + 50 + 5

5. a. $167 < 176$ b. $2{,}067 < 2{,}097$
c. $79{,}084 < 79{,}087$ d. $162{,}555 > 162{,}507$

7. a. (i) 3,900 (ii) 3,856
b. (i) 5,900 (ii) 5,772
c. (i) 7,100 (ii) 7,181
d. (i) 3,600 (ii) 3,636

9. a. 10,696 b. 8,760
c. Quotient: 62, Remainder: 4
d. Quotient: 210, Remainder: 4

11. a. 60
b. 144
c. 1,584

13. a. 4
b. 6
c. 2

15. a. 11 b. 14 **17.** a. 13 b. 7
19. a. 89 b. 4 **21.** a. 27 b. 27
23. a. 3 b. 10 **25.** a. 9 b. 25
27. a. 130 b. 14
29. 873 stamps **31.** 850 tickets **33.** $52,725
35. Allan: $1,675, Babar: $875
37. 16 boxes **39.** 12 metres **41.** 42 days

Self-Test Exercises 1

1. a. (i) 7,300 (ii) 7,264 b. (i) 6,900 (ii) 6,864
c. (i) 520,000 (ii) 445,900
d. (i) 67 (ii) Quotient: 59 Remainder: 42
2. a. 24 b. 34 c. 3 d. 2
3. a. 6 b. 56 c. 36 d. 2
4. a. 54 b. 4 c. 108 d. 40

5. a. 18 b. 2 c. 20 d. 9
6. Bob: $6,375 Hari: $1,275
7. a. 37,278 b. 884
8. 25,995 kg
9. $1,212
10. $937.50
11. 394 cars
12. a. 707 b. 582
13. 320
14. 217
15. 16 min 48 sec
16. 6 metres

Chapter 2

Exercises 2.1

1. a. proper fraction b. mixed number
3. a. improper fraction b. mixed number
5. a. mixed number b. complex fraction
7. a. $\frac{16}{7}$ b. $\frac{25}{8}$
9. a. $\frac{29}{5}$ b. $\frac{27}{4}$
11. a. $2\frac{5}{7}$ b. $5\frac{5}{8}$
13. a. $7\frac{2}{3}$ b. $5\frac{1}{6}$
15. Equal
17. Not equal
19. Equal
21. Equal
23. Not equal
25. Equal
27. Equal
29. Equal
31. a. (i) $\frac{8}{5}$ (ii) $\frac{5}{8}$ b. (i) $\frac{4}{7}$ (ii) $\frac{7}{4}$
33. a. (i) $\frac{7}{6}$ (ii) $\frac{6}{7}$ b. (i) $\frac{4}{1}$ (ii) $\frac{1}{4}$
35. a. (i) $\frac{4}{7}$ (ii) $\frac{7}{4}$ b. (i) $\frac{5}{8}$ (ii) $\frac{8}{5}$
37. Equal
39. Not equal
41. Not equal
43. Equal
45. a. 12 b. 45
47. a. 24 b. 3
49. a. 8 b. 18
51. $\frac{1}{3}$
53. $\frac{3}{4}$
55. $\frac{3}{4}$
57. $\frac{149}{240}$

Exercises 2.2

1. $\frac{2}{5}$
3. $\frac{12}{15}$
5. $\frac{8}{7}$
7. $\frac{8}{9}$
9. $\frac{5}{8}$ and $\frac{3}{5}$
11. a. $1\frac{1}{2}$ b. $1\frac{1}{3}$
13. a. $1\frac{2}{5}$ b. $1\frac{143}{200}$
15. a. $2\frac{1}{6}$ b. $18\frac{2}{3}$
17. a. $15\frac{11}{12}$ b. $14\frac{5}{12}$
19. a. $\frac{5}{9}$ b. $\frac{3}{20}$
21. a. $1\frac{7}{24}$ b. $14\frac{5}{8}$
23. a. $3\frac{1}{2}$ b. $2\frac{1}{10}$
25. a. 4 b. $2\frac{1}{3}$
27. a. $\frac{15}{88}$ b. $12\frac{1}{2}$
29. a. $\frac{1}{14}$ b. $3\frac{1}{3}$
31. a. $1\frac{1}{2}$ b. $\frac{3}{32}$
33. a. $1\frac{5}{9}$ b. $2\frac{2}{3}$
35. a. $\frac{2}{5}$ b. $3\frac{3}{4}$
37. a. $\frac{309}{1,000}$ b. $1\frac{9}{10}$
39. a. $\frac{39}{125}$ b. $\frac{11}{16}$
41. a. $\frac{2}{3}$ b. $1\frac{41}{44}$
43. a. $3\frac{91}{100}$ b. $33\frac{29}{70}$
45. $\frac{2}{3}$
47. $5\frac{7}{15}$
49. a. $\frac{7}{8}$
51. $\frac{13}{28}$ kg
53. $\frac{1}{10}$
55. 1,350
57. $3\frac{1}{2}$ km
59. 14
61. 200
63. 304
65. $2\frac{2}{5}$

Exercises 2.3

1. a. 0.6 b. 0.007
3. a. 0.12 b. 0.029
5. a. 7.5 b. 9.503
7. a. 3.67 b. 2.567
9. (i) 87.2 (ii) $87\frac{2}{10}$
11. (i) 3.04 (ii) $3\frac{4}{100}$
13. (i) 0.0401 (ii) $\frac{401}{10,000}$
15. (i) 89.0625 (ii) $89\frac{625}{10,000}$
17. (i) 1,787.025 (ii) $1,787\frac{25}{1,000}$
19. (i) 412.65 (ii) $412\frac{65}{100}$
21. (i) 1,600,000.02 (ii) $1,600,000\frac{2}{100}$
23. (i) 23.5 (ii) $23\frac{5}{10}$
25. a. Forty-two and fifty-five hundredths
 b. Seven hundred thirty-four and one hundred twenty-five thousandths
27. a. Twenty-five hundredths
 b. Nine and five tenths
29. a. Seven and seven hundredths
 b. Fifteen and two thousandths
31. a. Sixty-two thousandths
 b. Fifty-four thousandths
33. 0.403
35. 415.2
37. 264.2
39. 24.2
41. 10.4
43. 14.36
45. 181.13
47. $16.78
49. $9.99

Exercises 2.4

1. 1,716.045
3. 869.593
5. 479.444
7. 964.571
9. 240.922
11. 238.192
13. 15.88
15. 281.283
17. 229.668
19. 415.01
21. 744.606
23. 259.5571
25. 0.344
27. 319.4598
29. Quotient: $7.53\overline{1}$ Remainder: 1
31. Quotient: 91.575 Remainder: 0
33. Quotient: $24.\overline{3}$ Remainder: 2
35. Quotient: 12.4 Remainder: 0

37. 627.40 – 248.76 = $378.64

39. 30.75 – 15.89 = $14.86

41. 52.43 + 23.95 = $76.38

43. 25.67 + 38.89 = $64.56

45. $1.54 47. $1,281.85 49. $187.86

51. $86.46 53. $44.21 55. $3,469.09

57. $54.45 59. 14 61. $2.55

Exercises 2.5

1. **a.** $\frac{1}{5}$ **b.** 0.75 **c.** $\frac{3}{50}$
3. **a.** 0.36 **b.** $\frac{1}{250}$ **c.** 0.14
5. **a.** 0.5 **b.** $\frac{2}{5}$ **c.** 0.06
7. **a.** $\frac{1}{200}$ **b.** 0.36 **c.** $\frac{1}{100}$
9. **a.** $\frac{7}{2}$ **b.** 1.6 **c.** $\frac{28}{5}$
11. **a.** 5.05 **b.** $\frac{34}{5}$ **c.** 2.75
13. **a.** $2\frac{1}{4}$ **b.** 1.75 **c.** $4\frac{1}{50}$
15. **a.** 8.35 **b.** $16\frac{1}{200}$ **c.** 15.5
17. **a.** $\frac{2}{3}$ **b.** $0.2\overline{5}$ **c.** $\frac{25}{99}$
19. **a.** $0.\overline{6}$ **b.** $\frac{2}{9}$ **c.** $0.\overline{72}$
21. **a.** $\frac{9}{25}$ **b.** $\frac{36}{49}$ 23. **a.** $\frac{27}{64}$ **b.** $\frac{625}{81}$
25. **a.** $1\frac{7}{9}$ **b.** $42\frac{7}{8}$ 27. **a.** $\frac{8}{75}$ **b.** $\frac{3}{256}$
29. **a.** 4 **b.** $2\frac{1}{4}$ 31. **a.** $\frac{1}{3}$ **b.** $\frac{1}{7}$
33. **a.** $\frac{2}{5}$ **b.** $\frac{9}{4}$ 35. **a.** $\frac{10}{11}$ **b.** $\frac{1}{10}$
37. **a.** 1 **b.** $\frac{4}{5}$ 39. **a.** $1\frac{3}{4}$ **b.** $2\frac{1}{2}$
41. **a.** 0.001 **b.** 0.09 43. **a.** 0.16 **b.** 0.000008
45. **a.** $\frac{1}{2}$ **b.** $\frac{7}{10}$ 47. **a.** $1\frac{1}{10}$ **b.** $1\frac{3}{10}$
49. **a.** $\frac{1}{10}$ **b.** $\frac{7}{100}$ 51. **a.** $14\frac{19}{25}$ **b.** $3\frac{107}{200}$
53. **a.** $6\frac{1}{9}$ **b.** 4 55. **a.** 0.338 **b.** 0.01
57. **a.** $2\frac{1}{3}$ 59. $1\frac{5}{7}$ 61. **a.** 0.1 63. 0.6

Review Exercises 2

1. **a.** 3, 48 **b.** 4, 60 **c.** 4, 15 **d.** 27, 24
3. **a.** $\frac{24}{21} < \frac{11}{5}$ **b.** $\frac{20}{44} > \frac{6}{15}$ **c.** $\frac{18}{45} < \frac{16}{4}$ **d.** $\frac{15}{25} = \frac{63}{105}$
5. **a.** $1\frac{1}{2}$ **b.** $1\frac{1}{2}$ **c.** $7\frac{1}{3}$ **d.** $11\frac{1}{3}$
7. **a.** $\frac{5}{23}$ **b.** $\frac{31}{12}$ **c.** $\frac{14}{3}$ **d.** $\frac{4}{5}$
9. **a.** Five tenths **b.** Seven thousandths
   c. Twelve hundredths **d.** Twenty-nine thousandths
11. **a.** Thirty-two and four hundredths
    b. Two hundred and two tenths
    c. Forty-five thousand five and one thousandths
    d. One million five thousand seventy-one and twenty-five hundredths
13. **a.** 564.667 **b.** 40.103
    c. 79.3802 **d.** Quotient: 9.63625
    Remainder: 0
15. 0.189 17. 1.996
19. **a.** $\frac{1}{40}$ **b.** 0.625 **c.** $\frac{2}{25}$
    d. 0.28 **e.** $\frac{1}{500}$ **f.** 0.78
21. $13\frac{13}{24}$ kg 23. $5\frac{5}{6}$ 25. $376\frac{1}{5}$
27. Alisha: $360, Beyonce: $220
29. $2,201.40 31. $870.89 33. 96
35. $15\frac{27}{125}$ 37. $1\frac{3}{4}$ 39. $\frac{21}{625}$
41. $\frac{5}{108}$ 43. $\frac{3}{4}$ 45. $1\frac{19}{25}$

Self-Test Exercises 2

1. **a.** 32, 15 **b.** 11, 30 **c.** 18, 96 **d.** 66, 24
2. **a.** $\frac{15}{2}$ **b.** $\frac{26}{3}$ **c.** $\frac{16}{9}$ **d.** $\frac{9}{55}$
3. **a.** $14\frac{1}{4}$ **b.** $1\frac{13}{15}$ **c.** $\frac{1}{2}$ **d.** 6
4. **a.** 27.9028 **b.** 8.133
   c. 2.13792 **d.** Quotient: 2.297
   Remainder: 2
5. **a.** Four thousandths
   b. Six and five hundredths
   c. Three hundred and two hundredths
   d. Seven and seventy-one thousandths
6. **a.** $\frac{5}{8}$ **b.** $\frac{16}{5}$ **c.** $\frac{17}{5}$
   d. $\frac{8}{11}$ **e.** $2\frac{1}{3}$ **f.** $\frac{107}{200}$
7. **a.** 0.35 **b.** 2.2 **c.** 1.8
   d. $0.\overline{8}$ **e.** $1.0\overline{6}$ **f.** $2.\overline{3}$
8. 593.75 km, 37.8 cm 9. 13
10. $1,500 11. $\frac{1}{3}$, $120

12. \$26.67 **13.** \$33.76 **14.** \$242.69 **15.** $9\frac{1}{8}$ km

16. $-1\frac{27}{50}$ **17.** $25\frac{13}{40}$ **18.** $\frac{2}{9}$ **19.** $8\frac{3}{4}$

20. $12\frac{17}{24}$ **21.** $8\frac{16}{19}$ **22.** $3\frac{91}{100}$ **23.** $4\frac{11}{270}$

24. $-1\frac{97}{120}$

Chapter 3

Exercises 3.1

1. **a.** Base: 7
Exponent: 4
Power: 7^4

b. Repeated multiplication:
$9 \times 9 \times 9 \times 9 \times 9$
Base: 9
Exponent: 5

c. Repeated multiplication:
$3 \times 3 \times 3 \times 3$
Power: 3^4

d. Base: $\left(\frac{2}{5}\right)$
Exponent: 6
Power: $\left(\frac{2}{5}\right)^6$

e. Repeated multiplication:
$\frac{5}{7} \times \frac{5}{7} \times \frac{5}{7} \times \frac{5}{7} \times \frac{5}{7}$
Base: $\frac{5}{7}$
Exponent: 5

f. Repeated multiplication:
$\frac{4}{7} \times \frac{4}{7} \times \frac{4}{7}$
Power: $\left(\frac{4}{7}\right)^3$

g. Base: (1.15)
Exponent: 4
Power: $(1.15)^4$

h. Repeated multiplication:
$(1.6) \times (1.6) \times (1.6)$
Base: (1.6)
Exponent: 3

i. Repeated multiplication:
$(1.25) \times (1.25) \times (1.25) \times (1.25) \times (1.25)$
Power: $(1.25)^5$

3. $4^9 = 262{,}144$ **5.** $\left(\frac{1}{2}\right)^7 = 0.01$

7. $\left(\frac{5}{2}\right)^5 = 97.66$ **9.** $(3.25)^6 = 1{,}178.42$

11. $6^5 = 7{,}776$ **13.** $\left(\frac{2}{5}\right)^2 = 0.16$

15. $(1.4)^3 = 2.74$ **17.** $6^6 = 46{,}656$

19. $\left(\frac{2}{3}\right)^{12} = 0.01$ **21.** $(2.5)^6 = 244.14$

23. 2^{10} **25.** 3^8 **27.** 3^6 **29.** 2^8

31. 10^6 **33.** 2^6 **35.** 150 **37.** 609

39. 240 **41.** 58 **43.** 368 **45.** 7

47. 609 **49.** 257 **51.** 8,000 **53.** 625

55. 13,168.72 **57.** 91 **59.** 96 **61.** 1.38

63. 5.14 **65.** 5,184 **67.** 2.07 **69.** 104,976

Exercises 3.2

1. **a.** $\sqrt{64} = 8$ **b.** $\sqrt[2]{\frac{25}{16}} = 1.25$

3. **a.** $\sqrt[3]{8} = 2$ **b.** $\sqrt[3]{\frac{27}{64}} = 0.75$

5. **a.** $144^{\frac{1}{2}} = 12$ **b.** $64^{\frac{1}{3}} = 4$

7. **a.** $2^{\frac{6}{2}} = 8$ **b.** $40^{\frac{1}{2}} = 6.32$

9. **a.** $8^{\frac{1}{2}} \times 12^{\frac{1}{2}} = 9.80$ **b.** $7^{\frac{1}{2}} \times 14^{\frac{1}{2}} = 9.90$

11. **a.** $25^{\frac{2}{4}} \times 25^{\frac{2}{4}} = 25$ **b.** $5^{\frac{2}{4}} \times 25^{\frac{3}{4}} = 25$

13. **a.** $\left(\frac{25}{49}\right)^{\frac{1}{2}} = 0.71$ **b.** $\left(\frac{64}{9}\right)^{\frac{1}{2}} = 2.67$

15. **a.** $5^{\frac{5}{4}} = 7.48$ **b.** $3^{\frac{103}{72}} = 4.81$

17. **a.** $8^{\frac{7}{5}} = 18.38$ **b.** $5^{\frac{5}{6}} = 3.82$

19. **a.** $8^2 = 64$ **b.** $3^{-\frac{2}{3}} = 0.48$

21. **a.** $4^{\frac{3}{7}} = 1.81$ **b.** $3^{\frac{2}{3}} = 2.08$

23. **a.** $12^2 = 144$ **b.** $7 = 49$

25. **a.** 4.88 **b.** 1 **27.** **a.** 10.07 **b.** 7.56

29. **a.** 8.49 **b.** 51.96 **31.** **a.** 1.17 **b.** 0.19

33. **a.** 0.41 **b.** 3.66

35. **a.** 0.63 **b.** 2

37. **a.** 1.49 **b.** 20.08

39. **a.** 0.01 **b.** 216

41. **a.** 4,096 **b.** 0.002

43. **a.** 0.67 **b.** 0.83 **45.** **a.** 0.33 **b.** 8

47. **a.** 0.91 **b.** 2.25

Exercises 3.3

1. **a.** $-5 < 0$ **b.** $-2 < +6$ **3.** **a.** $+8 > -3$ **b.** $+1 > -2$

5. **a.** $-6 > -8$ **b.** $-5 < -2$

7. **a.** −8, −6, −5, 2, 5, 8 **b.** −9, −8, −6, 3, 4, 7

9 **a.** −8, −5, 3, 7, 9, 10 **b.** −13, −8, −3, 2, 12, 15

11. **a.** 16 **b.** −3 **13.** **a.** −5 **b.** 9

15. **a.** −3 **b.** −5 **17.** **a.** 50 **b.** 5

19. **a.** −18 **b.** −4 **21.** **a.** −20 **b.** 6

23. **a.** 12 **b.** 14 **25.** **a.** 7 **b.** −3

27. **a.** 30 **b.** −24 **29.** **a.** 8 **b.** −9

31. **a.** 2 **b.** 17 **33.** **a.** 70 **b.** −72

35. **a.** 265 **b.** 30 **37.** **a.** 110 **b.** −101.77

39. **a.** $(-6)^8 = 1{,}679{,}616$ **b.** $8^3 = 512$

41. **a.** $(-4)^2 = 16$ **b.** $5^2 = 25$

43. **a.** $-\left(\frac{1}{2}\right)^{-1} = -2$ **b.** $\left(-\frac{3}{5}\right)^{-2} = 0.36$

45. **a.** $(-2)^1 = -2$ **b.** $3^{-4} = 0.01$

47. **a.** −23 **b.** 17

49. **a.** −18 **b.** −15

Exercises 3.4

1. **a.** 1 **b.** 3
3. **a.** 3 **b.** 4
5. **a.** 4 **b.** 6
7. **a.** 4 **b.** 5
9. **a.** 1 **b.** 3
11. **a.** (i) 5,060 (ii) 5,100 **b.** (i) 1,980 (ii) $2,\tilde{0}00$
13. **a.** (i) 589 (ii) 590 **b.** (i) 57.4 (ii) 57
15. **a.** (i) 48.5 (ii) 48 **b.** (i) 25.9 (ii) 26
17. **a.** (i) 0.785 (ii) 0.78 **b.** (i) 6.07 (ii) 6.1
19. **a.** (i) 0.989 (ii) 0.99 **b.** (i) 6.67 (ii) 6.7
21. **a.** 151.26 **b.** 353.2
23. **a.** 281.24 **b.** 412.1
25. **a.** 26.3 **b.** 42.4
27. **a.** 660 **b.** 6,960
29. **a.** 9.94 **b.** 8.83
31. **a.** 290,000 **b.** 760
33. **a.** 2.35×10^2 **b.** 4.23×10^4
35. **a.** 1.275×10^1 **b.** 7.891×10^1
37. **a.** 5.8×10^{-1} **b.** 4.8×10^{-2}
39. **a.** 3.8×10^{-3} **b.** 2×10^{-4}
41. **a.** 6×10^6 **b.** 2.5×10^{-12}
43. **a.** 46,000 **b.** 2.9
45. **a.** 3,090,00 **b.** 46,540
47. **a.** 0.89 **b.** 0.000216
49. **a.** 0.00315 **b.** 0.0000615
51. **a.** 5.6 **b.** 0.0004065
53. **a.** 8.884×10^5
55. 9.978×10^{-3}
57. **a.** 2.84×10^9
59. 7.215×10^{-2}
61. **a.** 2.439×10^4
63. 1.72×10^{14}
65. **a.** 3.15×10^{-6}
67. 3.2×10^{-3}
69. **a.** 5×10^{-3}
71. 1.4×10^3

Review Exercises 3

1. **a.** 7
3. $3^5 = 27$
5. **a.** 2^2 **b.** 5^3
7. **a.** $3^3 = 9$ **b.** $6^1 = 6$
9. **a.** 27 **b.** 125
11. **a.** 400 **b.** −10,000,000
13. **a.** 0.2 **b.** 0.14 **c.** 0.89
15. **a.** 49 **b.** 0.83 **c.** 1.2
17. **a.** $3\frac{34}{35}$ **b.** 50
19. **a.** 96.57 **b.** 24
21. **a.** −19 **b.** 27
23. **a.** 7,180.08 **b.** 1,817.28
25. 164,593.54
27. 11,341.04
29. **a.** 0 **b.** −7
31. **a.** 13 **b.** −28
33. **a.** 5 **b.** 5 **c.** 2
35. **a.** 890 **b.** 0.056 **c.** 0.000964
37. **a.** 4.7495×10^{14} **b.** 7.715×10^{-2}
39. **a.** 3.9744×10^6 **b.** 2.759×10^{-3}
41. **a.** 2.4×10^{12} **b.** 4.5×10^{-10}
43. **a.** 5×10^{-4} **b.** 2.5×10^{-7}

Self-Test Exercises 3

1. **a.** 5^4 **b.** 3^6 **c.** 2^7
2. **a.** 3^3 **b.** 2^3
3. **a.** 3^{10} **b.** 10^9
4. **a.** 3.80 **b.** 18
5. **a.** 0.08 **b.** 1
6. **a.** $2\frac{5}{8}$ **b.** $3\frac{1}{5}$ **c.** $5\frac{4}{5}$
7. **a.** $13\frac{3}{5}$ **b.** $4\frac{1}{8}$ **c.** 1
8. **a.** 32 **b.** 12.8
9. **a.** 81 **b.** 13.92
10. **a.** 1, 953,125 **b.** 100, 000,000
11. **a.** 3 **b.** 12
12. **a.** −26 **b.** 42 **c.** 1,240.75
13. **a.** −61 **b.** −16 **c.** 5,468.75
14. **a.** 342.76 **b.** 424.17
15. **a.** 1,376.18 **b.** 3,762.75
16. **a.** 20,293.53
17. 65,460.89
18. **a.** −3 **b.** 16 **c.** 0
19. **a.** $2\frac{2}{3}$ **b.** $\frac{3}{16}$
20. **a.** 1.009×10^1 **b.** 5×10^{-3} **c.** 6.02×10^4
21. **a.** 2,700 **b.** 0.00415 **c.** 0.030405
22. **a.** 4.1099×10^4 **b.** 2.899×10^{-4}
23. **a.** 2.7888×10^6 **b.** -9.534×10^{-7}
24. **a.** 5.2×10^{-1} **b.** 1.4×10^{19}

Chapter 4

Exercises 4.1

1. **a.** 3 : 8 **b.** 1 : 4 **c.** 2 : 5
3. **a.** (i) 3 : 8 : 5 (ii) 1 : 2.67 : 1.67
   b. (i) 7 : 2 : 5 (ii) 3.5 : 1 : 2.5
   c. (i) 9 : 20 : 40 (ii) 1 : 2.22 : 4.44
5. **a.** (i) 10 : 3 (ii) 3.33 : 1
   b. (i) 36 : 5: 9 (ii) 7.2 : 1: 1.81
   c. (i) 3 : 15 : 20 (ii) 1 : 5 : 6.67
7. b and d
9. c
11. 75 km/hr
13. 11 km/L
15. 75 words/min
17. 29 pages/min
19. 2 kg of flour for $3.30
21. 8 pencils for $2.88
23. 0.8 litres for $1.40
25. 11 : 20
27. 540 km/hr
29. A's
31. **a.** Kate: $28.00, Susan: $27.75
    b. Kate's, by $0.25
33. **a.** 12 : 2 : 1: 4 **b.** 24 : 4 : 1: 8
35. Mike: $40, Sarah: $50
37. Amy's share: $2,500, Gary's share: $4,000, Andrew's share: $1,000
39. Alex: $800, Brooks: $1,200
41. $16,875
43. A : B : C = 8 : 6 : 5

Exercises 4.2

1. a and c
3. **a.** $x = 3$ **b.** $x = 36$ **c.** $x = 1.67$ **d.** $x = 10$
5. **a.** $x = 12.43$ **b.** $x = 3.87$ **c.** $x = 0.61$ **d.** $x = 2.63$
7. 180 L
9. $2,290.91
11. 11.63 km
13. GIC: $13,625 Fixed deposit: $8,175

15. a. $15,000
b. B's profit: $24,000
C's profits: $18,000
c. A's investment: $56,250
B's investment: $45,000
C's investment: $33,750

17. A's investment: $15,000, B's investment: $18,000, C's investment: $12,000

19. 29 : 37 : 53 21. $496 23. $881.67
25. $1,730.77 27. $45,000
29. a. 26 b. 20 : 13 31. 360

Review Exercises 4

1. 1 : 20
3. a. $x = 6$ b. $x = 18$ c. $x = 0.06$
5. a and c 7. $1,057.69
9. $165.50 11. $3.75 per 480 grams
13. a. $0.70 b. $0.21
15. a. 36 km/hr b. 54 km
17. Offer c 19. Gina, by $0.75 per hour
21. sugar : flour : eggs = 9 : 15 : 5
23. $13,625
25. Khan: $1,000, Thomas: $2,500
27. 17: 20 : 23
29. Anton: $1,200
Cheryl: $2,250
Ellen: $1,800

Self-Test Exercises 4

1. 360 grams for $4.89 2. 600 grams for $3.72
3. 74.07 km/hr 4. 9 hours and 20 minutes
5. a. $x = 12$ b. $x = 40.5$ 6. a. $x = 7.5$ b. $x = 7.2$
7. 212.5 km 8. $6,035.59
9. $2,668.90 10. 22.5 L
11. Offer c 12. 6 : 10 : 15
13. $2,700 14. $208.33
15. A's investment: $1,500, B's investment: $2,500, C's investment: $2,000
16. 11: 21
17. Alice's share: $18,000, Bill's investment: $12,000, Carol's investment: $28,800

Chapter 5

Exercises 5.1

1. a. 0.75, $\frac{3}{4}$ b. 30%, $\frac{3}{10}$ c. 25%, 0.25
3. a. 0.05, $\frac{1}{20}$ b. 20%, $\frac{1}{5}$ c. 60%, 0.60
5. a. 1.50, $1\frac{1}{2}$ b. 17.50%, $\frac{7}{40}$ c. 48%, 0.48
7. a. 0.125, $2\frac{1}{4}$ b. 5%, $\frac{1}{20}$ c. 450%, 4.5
9. a. 0.006, $\frac{3}{500}$ b. 0.5%, $\frac{1}{200}$ c. 460%, 4.6
11. a. 0.0005, $\frac{1}{2,000}$ b. 0.25%, $\frac{1}{400}$ c. 112.50%, 1.125
13. a. 0.006, $\frac{3}{500}$ b. 108%, $1\frac{2}{25}$ c. 3.75%, 0.0375
15. a. 0.0125, $\frac{1}{80}$ b. 202.5%, $2\frac{1}{40}$ c. 0.25%, 0.0025
17. a. 0.065, $\frac{13}{200}$ b. 250%, $2\frac{1}{2}$ c. 16%, 0.16
19. a. 70 b. 100 21. a. 0.19 b. 50 km
23. a. 52 b. 55 25. 2 27. $16.50
29. $45 31. 7.5 33. 40% 35. 400%
37. 45.45% 39. 28% 41. 800 43. $186
45. 130 47. $2,200 49. $32.50
51. $25,000 53. 74% 55. $700,000
57. $315,723.08 59. 13% 61. $89,400

Exercises 5.2

1. a. $391.50 b. $10,687.50 c. $480
d. $620.69 e. 50.00% f. 170.59%
3. a. $79.75 b. $159.38 c. $550
d. $4,459.02 e. 45.95% f. 69.23%
5. $2,110 7. $280,000 9. 20%
11. $45.00 13. $30.53 15. 10.34%
17. $29,706.75 19. $721.78 21. 22.02%
23. $30.94 25. $60,800 27. 22.22%
29. 16.67% 31. 4.76% 33. 13.33%
35. –11.86% 37. 25% less 39. 4.17% increase
41. First year: 13.51% decrease
Second year: 21.56% decrease
Over the two-year period: 32.16% decrease
43. $450.00 45. Tudor

Review Exercises 5

1. a. 0.8, $\frac{4}{5}$ b. 25%, $\frac{1}{4}$ c. 150%, 1.5
d. 0.065, $\frac{13}{200}$ e. 4.8%, $\frac{6}{125}$ f. 8%, 0.08
3. a. 36 b. 20% c. $0.23
5. $460,000.00 7. 75%
9. $1,153,153.15 11. a. 36,750 b. 33,846,154
13. a. 306 b. $9.00 c. $11,250.00 d. 680 kg
15. a. $530.00 b. 7.38 c. 75% d. 25%
17. $49.00 19. 20% 21. 12.5%
23. $250,000.00 25. $41,643.84 27. $180,200.00
29. 13.04% 31. a. 33.33% b. 22.54%
33. 5.80% increase

Self Test Exercises 5

1. a. 0.106, $\frac{53}{500}$ b. 225%, $\frac{9}{4}$ c. 0.25%, 0.0025
d. 0.005, $\frac{1}{200}$ e. 0.2%, $\frac{1}{500}$ f. 26.58%, 0.2658

2. a. 12.50% b. $337.50 c. 500
3. $71,080.80
4. a. 60% b. 10%
5. a. 56.25% b. $819.25 c. $4.73
6. a. 25% b. $90.40 c. $310.00
7. $800.00
8. $1,300.00
9. 15%
10. 21
11. 85%
12. $150.54
13. $27,984.00
14. $85.00
15. 28% decrease
16. $468,000.00
17. $4.16
18. a. $18.20 b. 9% decrease
19. a. First year: 7.67% decrease
    Second year: 16.61% decrease
    b. 23.01% decrease
20. Depreciated by 4%

Chapter 6

Exercises 6.1

1. $123.75, 25%
3. $437.50, 12%
5. $45.50, 87.5%
7. $88.20, $340.20
9. $1,400.00, $1,575.00
11. $160.00, 59.26%
13. $950.00, 52%
15. $15.50, $54.25
17. $432.00, 25%
19. $60.00, $84.00
21. $630.00, $2,430.00
23. $37.80, 36.00%
25. $50.00, $57.50
27. $20.25, 78.63%
29. $30.60, $105.40
31. $80.00, 42.50%
33. $7.50, 30%
35. $126.84, $95.13
37. $175.00, 30%
39. $28.50, $161.50
41. $48.00, 37.50%
43. $40.80, 32%
45. $475.00, $308.75
47. $83.88, 12%
49. $25.00, $3.00
51. $33.75, 10%
53. $329.00, $49.35

Exercises 6.2

1. I = $135.00, S = $1,035.00
3. I = $99.90, S = $1,579.90
5. I = $72.00, S =$5,912.00
7. $182.00
9. $126.00
11. I = $40.00, S = $1,500.00
13. I = $558.00, S = $4,158.00
15. I = $180.00, r= 8% p.a.
17. t = 2 years and 2 months, S = $5,500.00
19. P = $2,540.00, r = 3.15% p.a.
21. I = $192.00, t = 3 years
23. P = $1,825.00, S = $1,861.00
25. r = 5% p.a.
27. 4 years
29. $2,500.00
31. 7% p.a.
33. P = $4,155.28, I = $304.72
35. I = $220.00, r = 13.94%
37. t = 852 days
39. r = 4.32%

Exercises 6.3

1. $4,062.50, $2,031.25, $1,875.00, $937.50
3. $40,560.00, $1,690.00, $1,560.00, $780.00
5. $42,900.00, $3,575.00, $1,650.00, $825.00
7. $35,100.00, $2,925.00, $1,462.50, $675.00
9. $35,022.00, $2,918.50, $1,459.25, $1,347.00
11. Bi-weeklyPay: $1,400.00, Monthly Pay: $3,033.33
13. Annual Salary: $49,725.00, Monthly Pay: $4,143.75
15. Annual Salary: $49,725.00, Weekly Pay: $956.25
17. $2,145.00
19. Bi-weekly Pay: $2,640.00, Semi-Monthly Pay: $2,860.00
21. $1,100.00, $27.50, $41.25
23. $38,870.00, $23.00, 1.5
25. $26,702.00, 32.6, $48.90
27. $33,540.00, $645.00, $38.70
29. a. $1,307.69 b. $56.04 c. $336.24
31. Hourly Rate: $39.00, Annual Salary: $65,910.00
33. Weekly Pay: $829.50, Annual Salary: $43,134.00
35. $2,047.50
37. $58,500.00
39. 3%
41. $2,612.50
43. $51,500.00
45. 6.5%

Exercises 6.4

1. £102.73
3. €4,651.60
5. €1,833.11
7. US$26.71
9. a. C$1,950.17 b. C$47.57
11. C$5,694.22
13. a. C$1,268.65
15. C$39.39
17. C$1,710.71
19. 1.03%

Exercises 6.5

1. 2012: 111.76, 2014: 117.65
3. Adults: 135.44, Students: 129.73
5. Year 5: $2,558.14, Year 7: $2,790.70
7. Year 2: $1,909.09, Year 3: $1,954.55
9. $63,111.15
11. 7.47%
13. $3,502.08
15. 2013 : 81.43% : 2014, 79.87%
17. $30,975.48
19. $41,242.46

Review Exercises 6

1. $225.00, 52.94%
3. $750.00, $2,000.00
5. $225.00, 50%
7. $100.00, 20%
9. $59.85, $339.15
11. $50.00, 25%
13. $225.00
15. $3,125.00
17. 5.5% p.a.
19. Annual Salary: $45,500.00, Monthly Pay: $3,791.67
21. Hourly Rate: $22.50, Overtime Rate: $45.00
23. Annual Salary: $28,275.00,
    Semi-monthly Pay: $1,178.13
25. Annual Salary: $53,913.60, Bi-weekly Pay: $2,073.60
27. $36,000.00
29. £770.50
31. €916.56
33. C$3,777.12
35. $26,351.93
37. $4,612.36
39. 85.84%

Self-Test Exercises 6

1. $8.69; $28.44
2. $31,075.00; 13%
3. $44.55; 90%
4. $55.00; 40%
5. $187.25; 25%
6. $360.00; 12.5%
7. $19.20; $76.80
8. 4.8% p.a.
9. $4,500.00
10. $45.36
11. Annual Salary: $42,120.00, Monthly Pay: $3,510.00
12. a. $1,344.00 b. $19.20
13. $2,535.00
14. 7.5%
15. C$1,468.39
16. C$2,832.83

17. 0.48% **18.** $33,936.61 **19.** $73,797.64
20. $9,720.45

Chapter 7

Exercises 7.1

1. **a.** 240 cm, 2,400 mm **b.** 8.60 m, 8,600 mm **c.** 3,442 cm, 34.42 m
3. **a.** 25 cm, 250 mm **b.** 0.58 m, 580 mm **c.** 847 cm, 8.47 m
5. **a.** 1,620 m, 162,000 cm **b.** 2.39 km, 239,000 cm **c.** 223.20 m, 0.0232 km
7. **a.** 650 m, 65,000 cm **b.** 0.154 km, 15,400 cm **c.** 17.70 m, 0.0177 km
9. **a.** 2,321 cm **b.** 167 mm **c.** 5,252 m
11. **a.** 3 m 35 cm **b.** 60 cm 3 mm **c.** 1 km 487 m
13. 0.15 km < 150,800 mm < 15,200 cm < 155 m
15. 775 m **17.** 178 cm
19. **a.** 2,620 g **b.** 6.75 kg
21. 840 g, 0.58 kg
23. **a.** 1,650 g, 1,650,000 mg **b.** 4.95 kg, 4,950,000 mg **c.** 6.44 g, 0.00644 kg
25. **a.** 760 g, 760,000 mg **b.** 35.76 kg, 35,760,000 mg **c.** 50.3 g, 0.0503 kg
27. **a.** 18,079 g **b.** 2,000, 116 mg **c.** 3,074 kg
29. **a.** 5 kg 903 g **b.** 2 g 884 mg **c.** 9 t 704 kg
31. 850,250 mg < 0.075 t < 123,200 g < 125 kg
33. 200 **35.** 175 g **37.** $16.25
39. **a.** 3,250 mL **b.** 5.06 L
41. **a.** 45 mL **b.** 0.22 L
43. **a.** 5.085 L **b.** 2.005 L
45. **a.** 2 L 708 mL **b.** 12 L 80 mL
47. **a.** 4.5 L **49.** 790 mL

Exercises 7.2

1. **a.** 126 ft.; 1,512 in. **b.** 16 yd.; 576 in. **c.** 54 ft.; 18 yd.
3. **a.** 139.5 ft.; 1,674 in. **b.** 7.5 yd.; 270 in. **c.** 240 ft.; 80 yd.
5. **a.** 15,840 ft.; 5,280 yd. **b.** 18,480 ft.; 3.5 mi. **c.** 2 mi.; 3,520 yd.
7. **a.** 11,880 ft.; 3,960 yd. **b.** 6,600 ft.; 1.25 mi. **c.** 1.17 mi.; 2,064 yd.
9. **a.** 37.5 ft. **b.** 142 in. **c.** 1,881 yd.
11. **a.** 26 yd. **b.** 47 ft. 6 in. **c.** 3 mi 425 yd.
13. 15 in. **15.** 4.5 ft. **17.** 7.5 mi.
19. **a.** 18 lb **b.** 128 lb
21. **a.** 14.5 lb **b.** 404 oz
23. **a.** 70,000 lb **b.** 7.25 ton
25. **a.** 25,500 lb **b.** 32.5 ton
27. **a.** 186 oz **b.** 5,250 lb
29. **a.** 27 ton 1,825 lb **b.** 9 lb 6 oz
31. 1.2 ton > 2,250 lb.> 34,400 oz
33. 5 oz **35.** 1,000
37. **a.** 44 pt.; 88 c **b.** 19 qt.; 76 c **c.** 34 pt.; 17 qt.
39. **a.** 65 pt.; 130 c **b.** 22.5 qt.; 90 c **c.** 47 pt.; 23.5 qt.
41. **a.** 48 qt.; 96 pt. **b.** 4.5 gal; 36 pt. **c.** 28 qt.; 7 gal
43. **a.** 30 qt.; 60 pt. **b.** 3.5 gal; 28 pt. **c.** 25 qt.; 6.25 gal
45. **a.** 19 pt. **b.** 33 c **c.** 49 qt.
47. **a.** 9 qt. 1 pt. **b.** 19 pt. 1 c **c.** 3,565 yd
49. **a.** 6 qt. < 14 pt. < 29 < c < 2 gal.
51. 3.75 gal **53.** 9 c

Exercises 7.3

1. **a.** 155.38 mi **b.** 193.08 km **3.** **a.** 19.14 yd **b.** 20.12 m
5. **a.** 820.21 ft **b.** 22.86 m **7.** **a.** 39.37 in **b.** 8.89 cm
9. **a.** 155.38 mi **b.** 402.25 km **11.** **a.** 19.14 yd **b.** 20.12 m
13. 4,250 cm > 28 yd > 82.5 ft > 24 m > 900 in.
15. 2.45 m **17.** 159.1 m
19. **a.** 3.86 ton **b.** 2,268 kg **21.** **a.** 34.14 lb **b.** 20.43 kg
23. **a.** 2.64 lb **b.** 2,951 g **25.** **a.** 7.05 oz **b.** 113.4 g
27. 5.7 lb > 2.5 kg > 2,450 g > 80 oz.
29. 158 g **31.** 68.65 kg.
33. **a.** 13.21 gal **b.** 39.74 L **35.** **a.** 15.86 qt **b.** 13.24 L
37. **a.** 15.85 pt **b.** 6.62 L **39.** **a.** 19.02 c **b.** 3.31 L
41. **a.** 0.27 fl oz **b.** 606.19 mL
43. 10.5 pt > 4.8 qt > 1 gal > 3.5 L.
45. 9.51 gal **47.** 1,13 L **49.** 69.8°F **51.** 37°C
53. 284°F **55.** 44.44°C
57. –26.11°C **59.** 6.85°C
61. 292.15 K **63.** 300.37°F
65. 26.85°C **67.** –99.67°F
69. 253.15 K **71.** 211.48°F

Review Exercises 7

1. **a.** 705 cm **b.** 15,050 m **c.** 7 cm 5 mm **d.** 9 m 5 cm
3. **a.** 118 ft **b.** 55 in **c.** 9 ft 6 in **d.** 3 mi 10 yd
5. **a.** 10,032 g **b.** 45,052 mg **c.** 3 kg 620 g **d.** 42 g 7 mg
7. **a.** 103 oz **b.** 29 g 5 mg **c.** 16 ton 0 lb **d.** 7 lb 8 oz
9. **a.** 6,049 mL **b.** 9 L 6 mL **c.** 38 qt **d.** 37 qt 1 pt
11. **a.** 210°C **b.** 176°F **c.** 51.67°C **d.** 86°F
13. **a.** –33.15°C **b.** 294.15 K **c.** 278.71 **d.** 80.33°F
15. **a.** 40.40 mi **b.** 29.53 ft **c.** 228.6 cm **d.** 5,148.8 m
17. **a.** 11.01 lb **b.** 44.09 oz **c.** 113.5 g **d.** 9.07 kg
19. **a.** 9.25 gal **b.** 0.88 fl oz **c.** 64.35 L **d.** 1.24 L
21. 5.35 mi > 9,200 yd > 7.5 km.
23. 115 oz > 7 lb > 3 kg.
25. 75 qt > 70 L > 18 gal.
27. **a.** 224.13 km **b.** 139.29 mi
29. **a.** 200.01 lb. **b.** 90.81 kg.
31. **a.** 2.73 gal **b.** 10.33 L
33. 176.67°C

Self-Test Exercises 7

1. a. 273 mm b. 1,250 cm
   c. 8 km 105 m d. 106 cm 5 mm
2. a. 47 ft b. 62 in
   c. 35 ft 10 in d. 3 mi 420 yd
3. a. 53,107 g b. 6,223 mg
   c. 5 g 519 mg d. 84 kg 176 g
4. a. 127 oz b. 8,030 lb c. 20 ton 0 lb d. 9 lb 5 oz
5. a. 5,007 mL b. 9 L 60 mL
   c. 105 qt d. 41 qt 1 pt
6. a. −9.44°C b. 14°F
   c. 76.85°C d. 276.59 K
7. a. 155.38 mi b. 147.64 ft
   c. 800.1 cm d. 4,022.5 m
8. a. 5.51 lb b. 14.11 oz c. 794.5 g d. 6.38 kg
9. a. 15.85 gal b. 14.37 fl oz
   c. 9.46 L d. 0.89 L
10. 215 ft > 65 m > 2,500 in.
11. 2.5 lb < 1,200 g < 45 oz.
12. 84 L > 22 gal > 175 pt.
13. a. 1,005.91 ft. b. 306.6 m
14. a. 92.83 oz. b. 2,631.73g
15. a. 0.42 gal b. 1,588.75 mL
16. 20°C

Chapter 8

Exercises 8.1

1. a. $2x - 3$ b. $\frac{2x}{5}$ c. $25 + 3x$
3. a. 2nd term: $7xy$, Coefficient: 7,
   3rd term: $-4y$, Coefficient: −4
   b. 3rd term: $-y$, Coefficient: −1, 4th term: 3
   c. 1st term: $9xy$, Coefficient: 9, and the 3rd term: $-6y$, Coefficient: −6
5. a. Constant: 5
   Coefficient of the 1st term: 5
   Coefficient of the 2nd term: −3
   b. Constant: 1
   Coefficient of the 1st term: −2
   Coefficient of the 2nd term: 3
   c. Constant: 7
   Coefficient of the 1st term: −2
   Coefficient of the 2nd term: −2
7. a. $5A + 3B$ b. $x + 5y + 7$
9. a. $-6x + 12y$ b. $8xy^2 - 1x^2y + 2x^2 + 4$
11. a. 30 b. 56
13. a. −18 b. 6,750
15. $2a + 14b - 12c + 2$; 24
17. $3x^2 - 2x$; 65
19. a. $2\frac{5}{9}$ b. 24
21. a. 30 b. 22
23. a. $11x^2 + 17x$ b. $-7y^2 + y$
25. a. $3x + 3y^2$ b. $xy^2 + x^2y^2$
27. a. $1\frac{3}{5}$ b. $1\frac{1}{2}$
29. a. 4 b. $1\frac{1}{2}$
31. $-75x - 3$
33. −38
35. $-5x + 7$
37. $2x - 4$
39. $-10y + 30x - 90$
41. $-14y - 144$
43. $-7y^2 - 12y + 6$
45. $4x + 25$
47. $-17x^2 - 58x - 36$
49. $10x^2 - 16x - 14$
51. $-8x^2 - 16y + 15$
53. $-x - y$
55. $5x - 3y + 1$
57. $\frac{x^2}{2y}$
59. $\frac{3x + 9}{2}$
61. $\frac{3x - 15}{8}$
63. $\frac{15}{16}y$
65. a. $x^2 + 10x + 25$ b. $4x^2 + 12xy + 9x^2$
67. a. $9 - 6x + x^2$ b. $9x^2 - 12xy + 4y^2$
69. a. $1 - 6x + 9x^2$ b. $9 - 12x + 4x^2$
71. a. $x^2 - 25$ b. $1 - 49x^2$
73. $2x^2 + 2x + 13$
75. $8x + 25$
77. $13x^2 - 12x - 13$
79. $4x^2 - 16x - y^2 - 16y + 7$
81. $3y(2x^2 - x - 3)$
83. $3(5y^2 - 4y - 1)$
85. $b(6a - 5c) + 7ac$
87. $3y(2x - 3z)$
89. $2x^2(5x - 2)$
91. $-40y(3y - 1)$
93. $(y + 2)(5x + 3)$
95. $(x - 5)(4y - x)$
97. $(x - 2)(y + 5)$
99. $(x + 1)(x - y)$
101. $(x + 4)(x - y)$

Exercises 8.2

1. $x + 6 = 10$; 4
3. $6x = 72$; 12
5. $\frac{x}{5} = 4$; 20
7. $\frac{2}{3}x = 12$; 18
9. 30
11. 18
13. −17
15. 6
17. 1.18
19. $1\frac{2}{5}$
21. 2
23. $-\frac{3}{20}$
25. 4
27. 24
29. 16
31. 1.72
33. 4
35. 1.8
37. −2
39. −2.2
41. 4.33
43. 0.41
45. 16
47. 42
49. 52.60
51. 11
53. −5
55. 5
57. 9 m, 16 m
59. Becky's share: $325.00, Andy's share: $175.00
61. Adult tickets: $10.00, Children tickets: $7.00
63. 182 m²
65. $12.50
67. $26.00
69. 30°, 70°, and 80°
71. 15 cm, 25 cm, and 30 cm

Exercises 8.3

1. x^{10}
3. $8x^5$
5. $15x^8$
7. $-6x^8$
9. x^{14}
11. $24x^6$
13. x^3
15. $3x^4$
17. x^3
19. x^{23}
21. 256
23. $\frac{8x^{12}}{125y^6}$
25. $\frac{4x^6}{25y^4}$
27. 1
29. $\frac{1}{16x^8}$
31. $\frac{x^5y}{2}$
33. $\frac{x^6}{9y^6}$
35. $\frac{8x^6}{y^{12}}$
37. $\left(\frac{x}{y}\right)$
39. $\left(\frac{x}{y}\right)$

41. x^9 **43.** $-8x^4$ **45.** $\frac{25}{16y^6}$ **47.** x^4

49. $-8x^4y^7$ **51.** $\frac{3x^2}{y^4}$ **53.** x^3y^5 **55.** x^8y^2

57. $x^{\frac{1}{5}}$ **59.** $\frac{1}{x^{\frac{3}{2}}}$ **61.** $x^{\frac{5}{6}}$ **63.** $\frac{1}{x^{\frac{4}{3}}}$

65. x^6 **67.** $\frac{1}{(2x)^{\frac{1}{3}}}$ **69.** x^4 **71.** x^3y^4

73. x^5 **75.** $3x^2$ **77.** x^2 **79.** $-x^2$

Exercises 8.4

1. **a.** $\log_{10} 100{,}000 = 5$ **b.** $\log_4 1{,}024 = 5$

3. **a.** $\log_2 64 = 6$ **b.** $\log_6 7{,}776 = 5$

5. **a.** $\log_3 9 = 2$ **b.** $\log_9 6{,}561 = 4$

7. **a.** $10^2 = 100$ **b.** $4^3 = 64$

9. **a.** $2^5 = 32$ **b.** $5^4 = 625$

11. **a.** $3^6 = 729$ **b.** $6^3 = 216$

13. **a.** 2.3521 **b.** 0.1875

15. **a.** 1.5441 **b.** −0.6021

17. **a.** 2.3076 **b.** 0.0050

19. **a.** −1.8018 **b.** 0.0198

21. 1.62 **23.** 5.53 **25.** 2.33 **27.** 8.83

29. $\ln 3 - \ln 7$ **31.** $\ln 4 + \ln 9$

33. $\ln A + \ln B - \ln C$ **35.** $\ln X - \ln Y + \ln Z$

37. $\ln 3 + \ln x - \ln 2 + \ln y + \ln z$ **39.** $\ln x + \ln y - \frac{1}{2}\ln z$

41. $M - N$ **43.** $M + 2N$ **45.** $2M - N$ **47.** $-\frac{1}{2}(M-N)$

49. $\frac{4}{5}M$ **51.** $-\frac{1}{3}(M+N)$ **53.** $\ln 40$ **55.** $\ln 5$

57. $\ln 675$ **59.** $\ln\left(\frac{32}{9}\right)$ **61.** $\ln 25$ **63.** $\ln 216$

65. $\ln\left(\frac{x}{y}\right)^2$ **67.** $\ln (ab)^4$ **69.** $\ln\left(\frac{a^3b^2}{c^5}\right)$ **71.** $\ln\left(\frac{81}{2}\right)$

73. 1.5 **75.** 0.78 **77.** 0.48 **79.** 0.64

81. 0.07 **83.** 0.52 **85.** 42.33 **87.** 31.00

Exercises 8.5

1. $x = \frac{y-5}{4}$ **3.** $x = \frac{7+y}{3}$

5. $C = S - M$ **7.** $L = \frac{N}{1-d}$

9. $E = S - C - P$ **11.** $x = \frac{y+6}{3}$

13. $a = \frac{b}{b-c}$ **15.** $b = \frac{a-c}{c}$

17. $a = \frac{c+2b}{b-c}$ **19.** $b = \frac{c(4+a)}{a-1}$

21. $x = \frac{y-6a}{6}$ **23.** $x = \frac{-3a}{2}$

25. $u = \sqrt{V^2 + 2as}$ **27.** $y = \sqrt{r^2 - x^2}$

29. $x = -15.5$ **31.** $x = \frac{y}{1-y}$

33. $x = \frac{5y+5}{y-1}$ **35.** $x = \frac{y^2-5}{2}$

37. $x = (8-y)^2$ **39.** $A = 4\pi r^2$

41. $y = \frac{x}{x-5}$ **43.** $a = \frac{2a-bh}{h}$

45. $x = \sqrt{y+16}$

47. **a.** $S = \sqrt{A}$ **b.** 21cm **49.** **a.** $r = \sqrt{\frac{A}{4\pi}}$ **b.** 7.98cm

Review Exercises 8

1. **a.** 12 **b.** −12 **3.** **a.** −32 **b.** 10

5. **a.** −24 **b.** 91 **7.** **a.** 2 **b.** −72

9. **a.** 28 **b.** 198 **11.** **a.** $12 + 3x$ **b.** $x - 5$

13. **a.** $x(x+3)$ **b.** $10x + 15$

15. **a.** $5x + 17 = 42; x = 5$ **b.** $\frac{x}{15} = 45; x = 675$

17. **a.** $x - 10 = 10; x = 20$ **b.** $3(4x) = 36; x = 3$

19. **a.** $x = 3$ **b.** $x = 18$ **21.** **a.** $x = -9$ **b.** $x = 2$

23. **a.** $\frac{1}{x^2}$ **b.** $-\frac{1}{x^3}$ **25.** **a.** x^4 **b.** $\frac{1}{x^2}$

27. **a.** $\left(\frac{y}{x}\right)^{\frac{1}{2}}$ **b.** $6^{\frac{1}{3}}$ **29.** **a.** x^2 **b.** 1

31. **a.** $3x^7$ **b.** x^4 **33.** **a.** $\frac{x^8}{4y^7}$ **b.** $\frac{2y^{10}}{x^8}$

35. **a.** $\frac{8x^9}{y^6}$ **b.** $2x^2$ **37.** **a.** x^{14} **b.** $\frac{y^{24}}{4x^5}$

39. **a.** 26.25 **b.** 1,691.63 **41.** **a.** 7 **b.** 4

43. **a.** 28.36 **b.** 55.48 **45.** **a.** 8.97 **b.** 14.21

47. **a.** $r = 11.94$ **b.** $A = 447.65\ \text{cm}^2$

49. **a.** $h = \frac{3V}{\pi r^2}$ **b.** $h = 35.99$ cm

Self-Test Exercises 8

1. **a.** 5 **b.** 19 **2.** **a.** −15 **b.** 4

3. 31 **4.** 45 **5.** **a.** 96 **b.** 30

6. **a.** −112 **b.** 14 **7.** **a.** $3x - 25$ **b.** $x + 18$

8. **a.** $2x - 6$ **b.** $\frac{x}{3}$

9. **a.** $2x - 9 = 21; x = 15$ **b.** $5x - 3 = 22; x = 5$

10. **a.** $4 \times 8 = 16x; x = 2$ **b.** $30 = 6x; x = 5$

11. **a.** $x = 4$ **b.** $x = 18$ **12.** **a.** $x = -0.57$ **b.** $x = 4.67$

13. **a.** $(-x)^7$ **b.** y^{18} **14.** **a.** $(-x)^3$ **b.** $\frac{1}{(-x)^4}$

15. **a.** $\frac{1}{x^2}$ **b.** $\frac{1}{x^9}$ **16.** **a.** x^2 **b.** x^{17}

17. **a.** $9x^6$ **b.** $16x^4y^6$ **18.** **a.** $4y^2$ **b.** $\frac{-2y^4}{x^2}$

19. **a.** $\frac{1}{x^2}$ **b.** $\frac{y^2}{x^6}$ **20.** **a.** 1 **b.** $\frac{-y^5}{2x^3}$

21. **a.** $n = 15.45$ **b.** $n = 3.17$ **22.** **a.** $n = 7.75$ **b.** $n = 17.59$

23. **a.** 13.33 **b.** 102.70

24. **a.** $F = \dfrac{9C}{5} + 32$ **b.** $F = 86°$

25. **a.** $h = \dfrac{A}{2\pi r} - r$ **b.** $h = 9.10$

Chapter 9

Exercises 9.1

1.

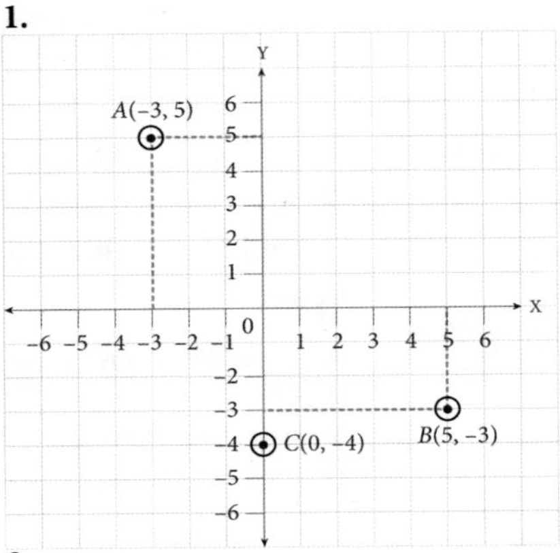

3.

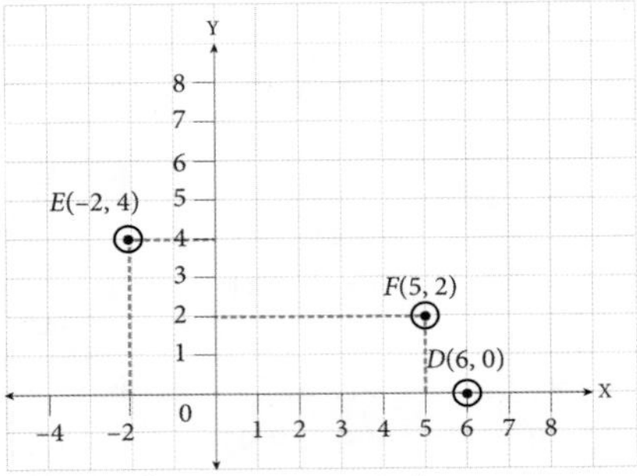

5. **a.** 2nd **b.** 4th **c.** 1st

7. **a.** X-Axis **b.** 3rd **c.** Y-Axis

9. **a.**

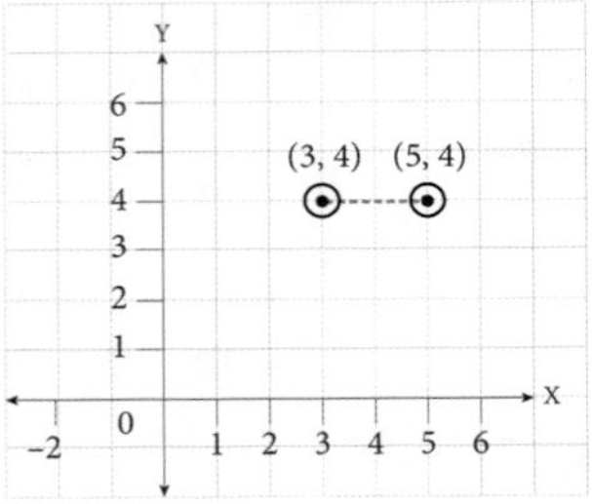

length = 2 units

b.

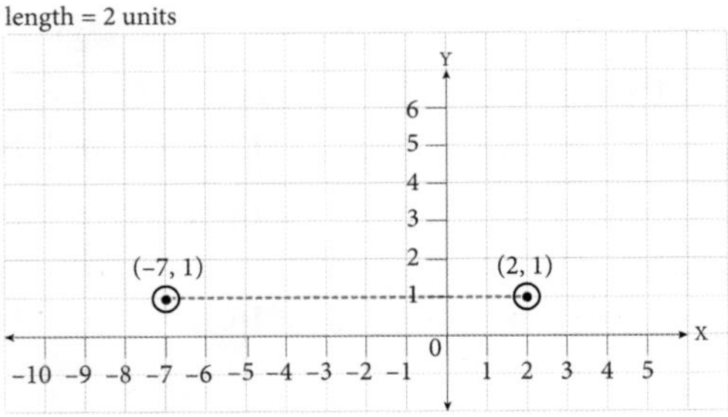

length = 9 units

11. **a.**

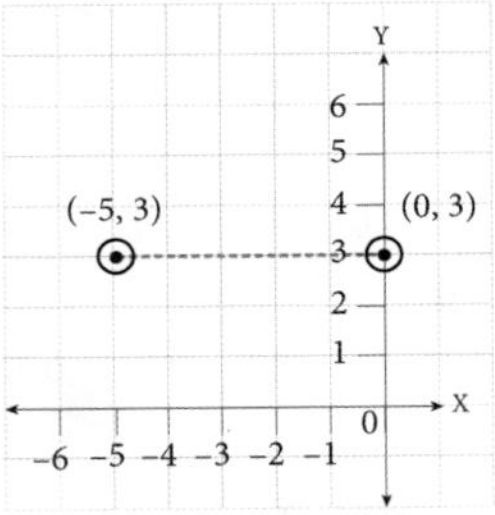

length = 5 units

b.

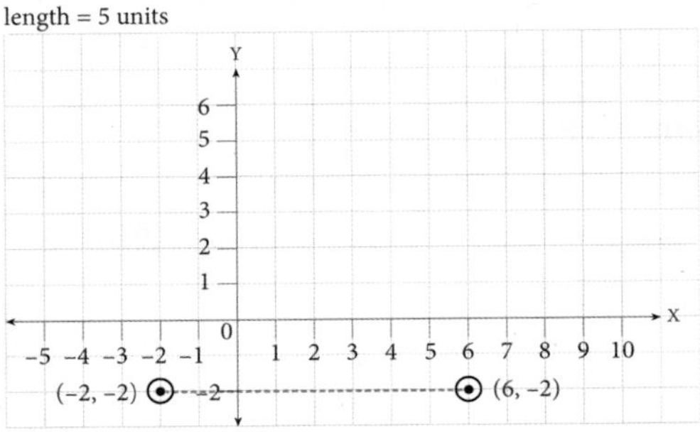

length = 8 units

13. **a.**

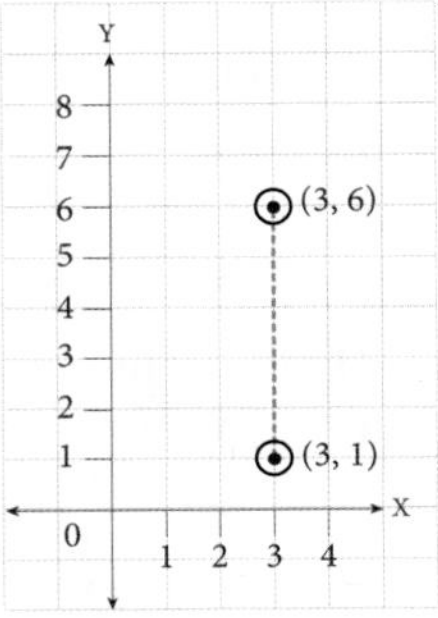

length = 5 units

b.

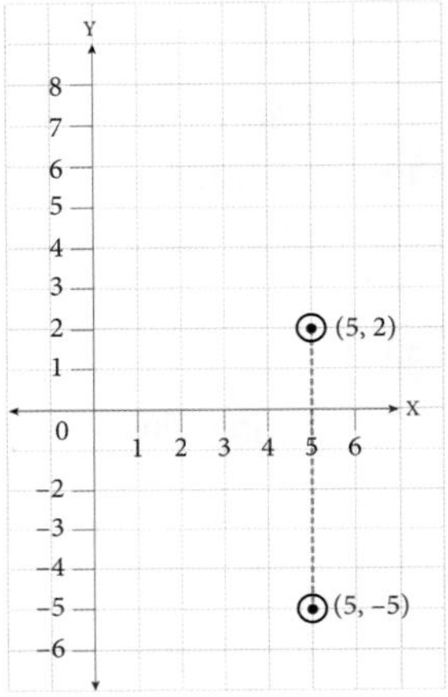

length = 7 units

15. **a.**

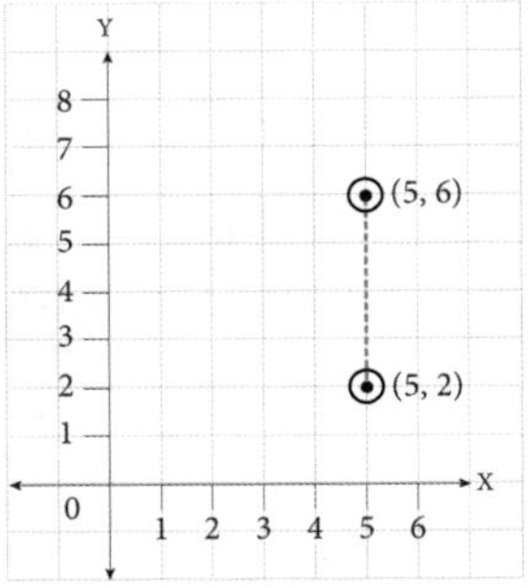

length = 4 units

b.

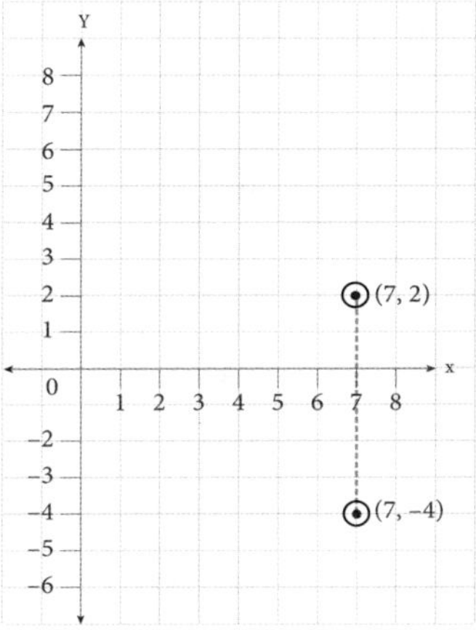

length = 6 units

17. D(−3, −1) **19.** S(−3, −1)

21. (1, 12) and (1, −2) **23.** (5, 3) and (−7, 3)

Exercises 9.2

1. **a.** 4 **b.** 10 **c.** 6 **d.** 9 **e.** 15 **f.** 6

3. **a.** −3 **b.** 3 **c.** 1 **d.** $\frac{3}{2}$ **e.** 6 **f.** −6

5. $y = -\frac{3}{2}x - \frac{3}{4}$ **7.** $y = \frac{2}{3}x + 3$

9. $y = -\frac{3x}{2} + 3$ **11.** $5x - 2y = -2$

13. $3x + 4y = -12$ **15.** $-x + 2y = 3$

17.

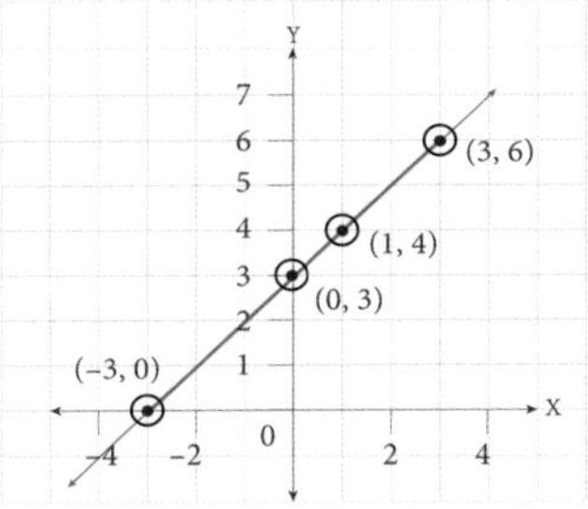

19.

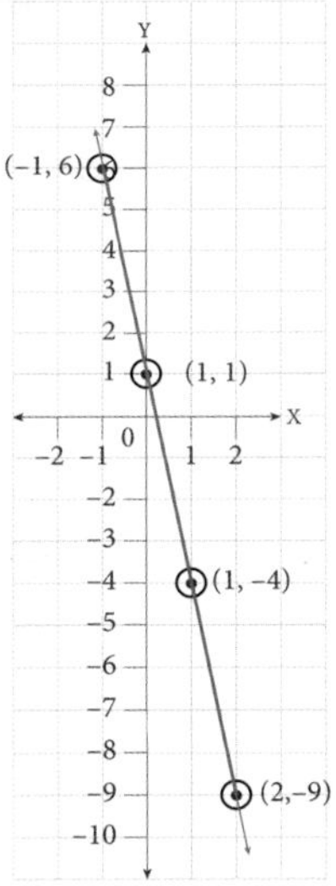

21.

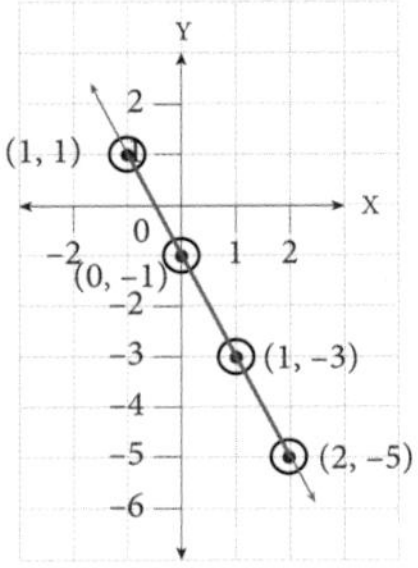

23.

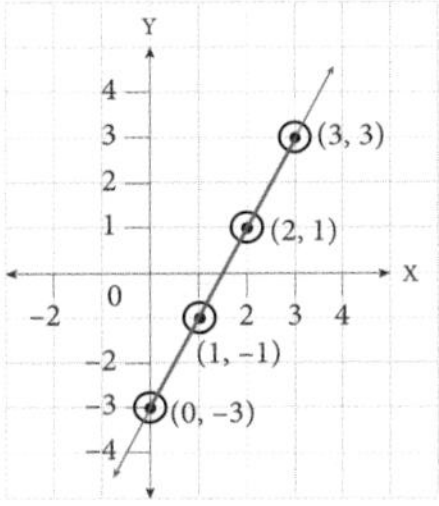

25. $(-\frac{2}{0}, 0)$; (0, −2)

27. (7, 0); (0, 7)

29. (−2, 0); (0, 4)

31. Positive

33. $\frac{2}{3}$; (0,-6)

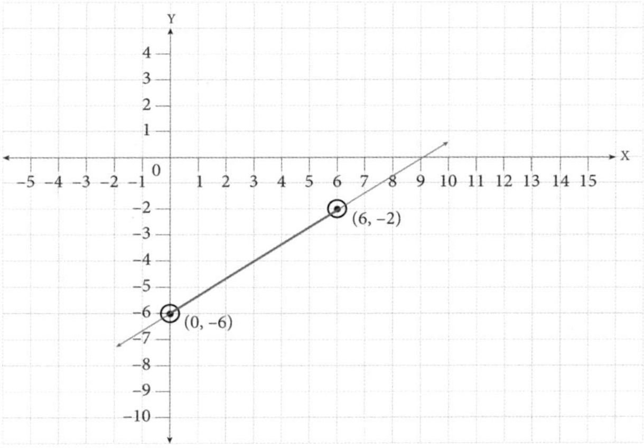

35. $\frac{4}{7}$; (0, 3)

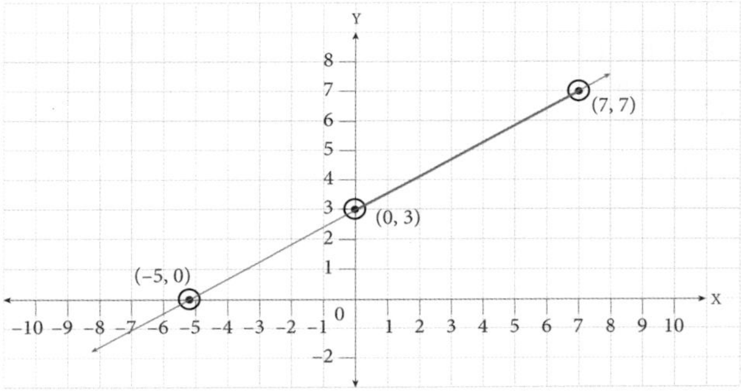

37. $y = 2$ **39.** $y = x - 2$ **41.** $y = x + 4$

43. $y = 2x$ **45.** $y = \frac{5}{4}x - 5$ **47.** 0

49. $-\frac{5}{8}$ **51.** $y = 2$ **53.** $y = 7$

55. $y = -\frac{5}{3} + 5$ **57.** $y = -2x + 1$

59. $y = \frac{2}{3}x - \frac{13}{3}$ **61.** $y = \frac{1}{3}x - 20$

63. $y = x + 7$ **65.** $y = -\frac{1}{2}x + 1$

Exercises 9.3

1. Perpendicular **3.** Parallel **5.** Perpendicular

7. Parallel **9.** One Solution **11.** One Solution

13. No Solution **15.** No Solution **17.** 4 **19.** 6

21. (1,1); consistent and independent

23. no solution; inconsistent and independent

25. infinite (many) solutions; consistent and dependent

27. no solution; inconsistent and independent

29. (2, 1); consistent and independent

31. (−2, 1); consistent and independent

33. infinite (many) solutions; consistent and dependent

35. no solution; inconsistent and independent

37. (3, −3); consistent and independent

39. $(-\frac{8}{3}, \frac{1}{3})$; consistent and independent

Exercises 9.4

1. (2, -2)	**3.** $\left(\frac{54}{11}, \frac{37}{11}\right)$	**5.** (3, −3)
7. (2, 1)	**9.** (6, −1)	**11.** (1, 2)
13. (9, 2)	**15.** (2, 3)	**17.** (−1, −2)
19. (1, −2)	**21.** (2, 4)	**23.** (3, −2)
25. (−3, −1)	**27.** (3, −2)	**29.** (10, 6)
31. $\left(\frac{9}{7}, \frac{27}{7}\right)$	**33.** (1, 3)	**35.** (3, −2)
37. $12	**39.** 32; 60	

41. slope = 15 and y-intercept = 5

43. $15,000 at 5% , $10,000 at 4%

45. 98 quarters, 32 dimes

47. 129° , 51° **49.** 5 litres; 5 litres

Review Exercises 9

1. a. 4th **b.** 2nd **c.** X-axis
d. 4th **e.** X-axis **f.** Y-axis

3.

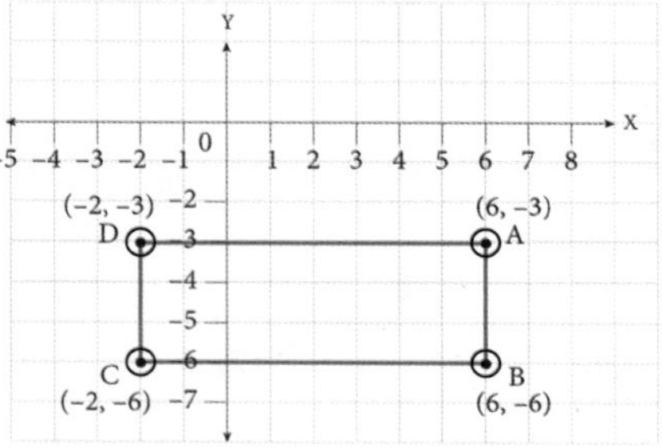

rectangle;
Area = 24 square units
Perimeter = 22 units

5.

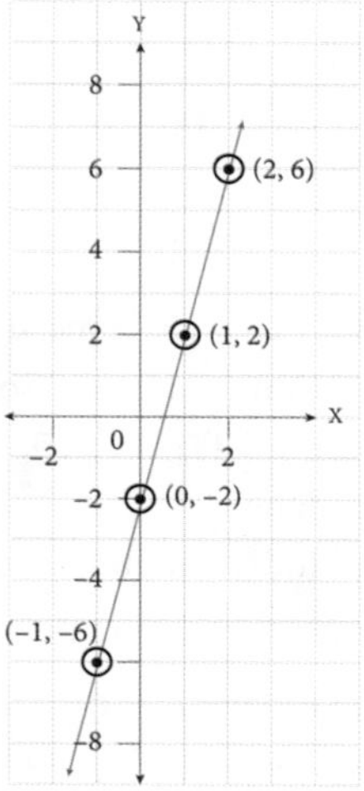

7.

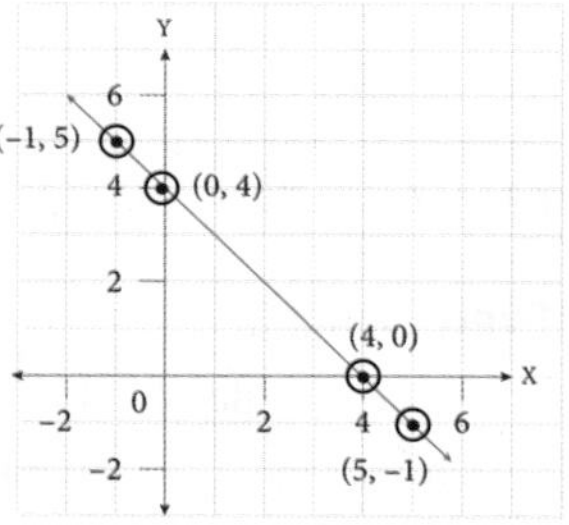

9.

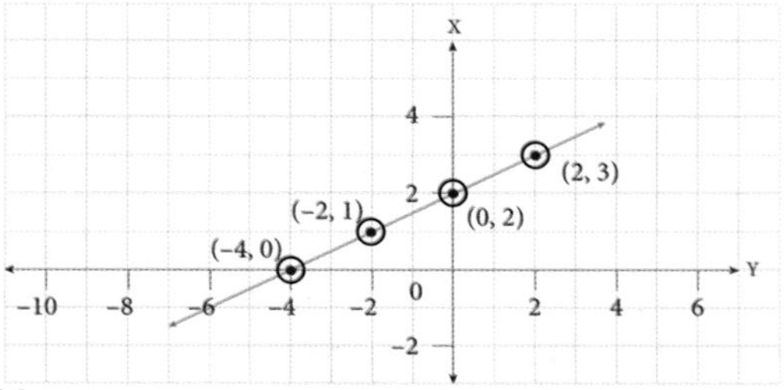

11.

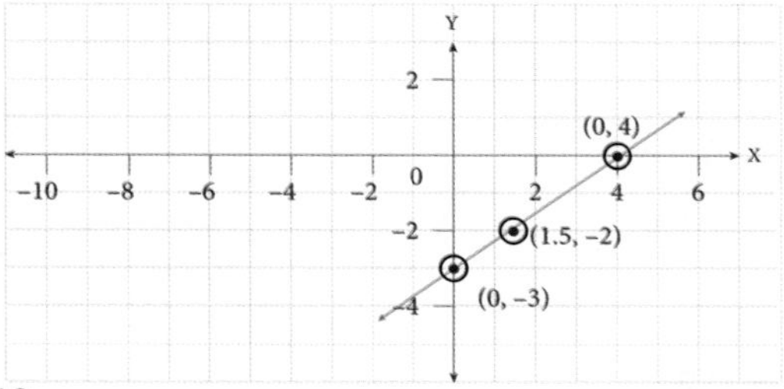

13.

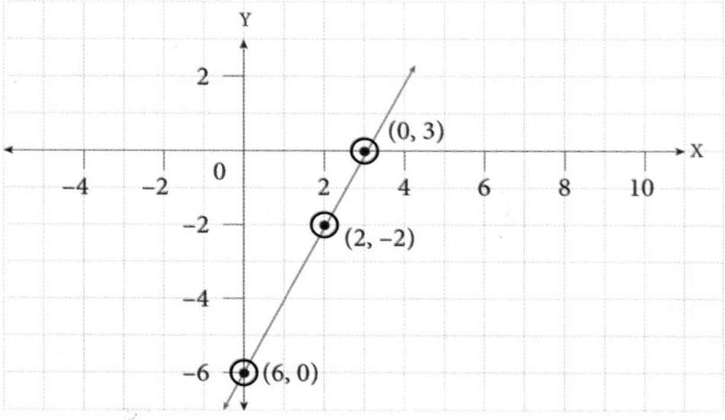

15.

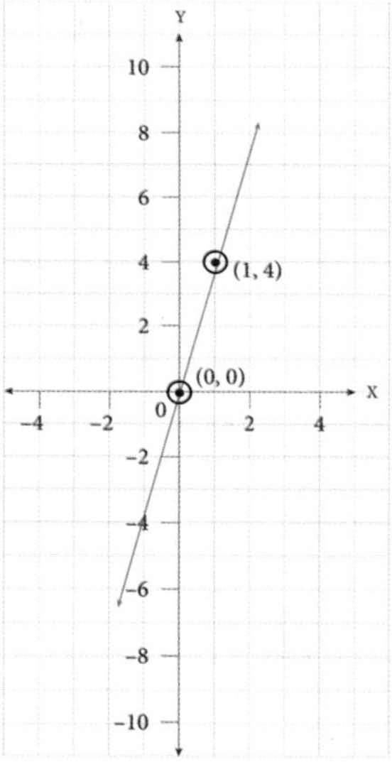

17.

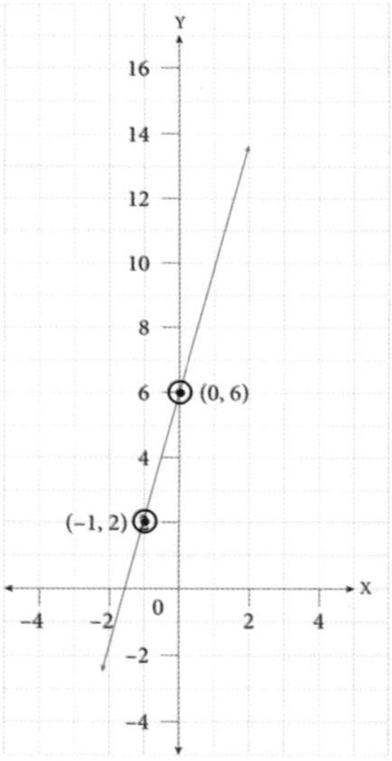

19.

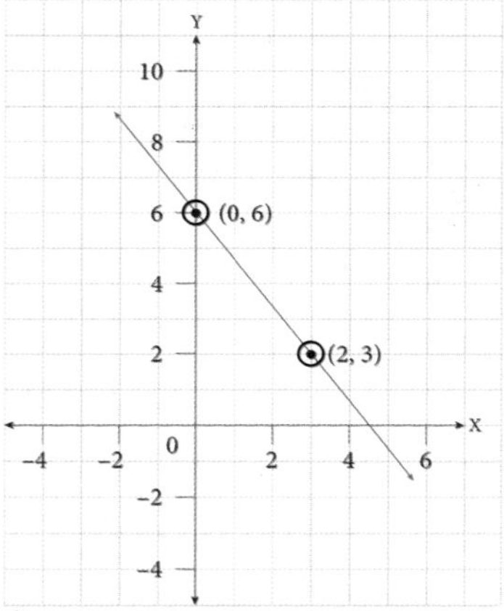

21.

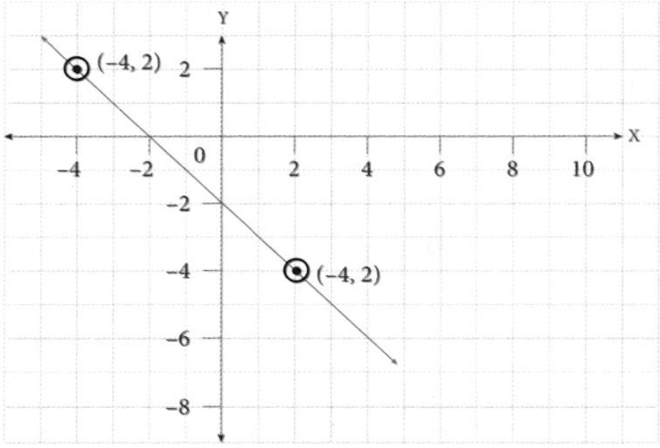

23. $y = \frac{3}{4}x - \frac{1}{4}$ **25.** $y = \frac{4}{3}x + \frac{8}{3}$

27. $y = 3x - 5$ **29.** $3x - 4y + 18 = 0$

31. $2x + y - 1 = 0$ **33.** one solution

35. no solution **37.** many solutions

39. (2, −5) **41.** (6, 2)

43. (2, 1) **45.** (4, 1)

47. $\left(\frac{52}{19}, -\frac{70}{19}\right)$ **49.** (1, 1)

51. (2, 1) **53.** (−4, −2) **55.** (3, 0) **57.** (3, 4)

59. (15, 12) **61.** $(\frac{29}{7}, -\frac{13}{7})$

63. 65 and 30 **65.** 210 adults and 90 children

Self-Test Exercises 9

1. a. $2x - 3y = 6$ **b.** $2x - 6y = \frac{1}{4}$

2. D(−3, −1); A = 40 square units

3. a. $m = \frac{2}{3}, b = 2$ **b.** $m = -\frac{3}{4}, b = \frac{5}{4}$

4. $4x + 5y - 9 = 0$

5.

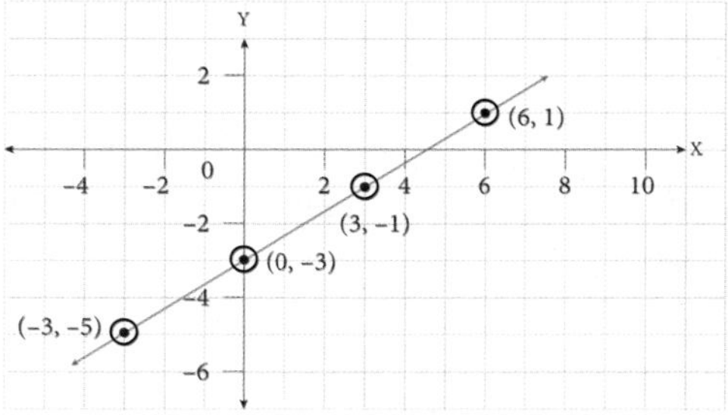

6. a. parallel **b.** not parallel

7. $3x - 2y + 12 = 0$

8.

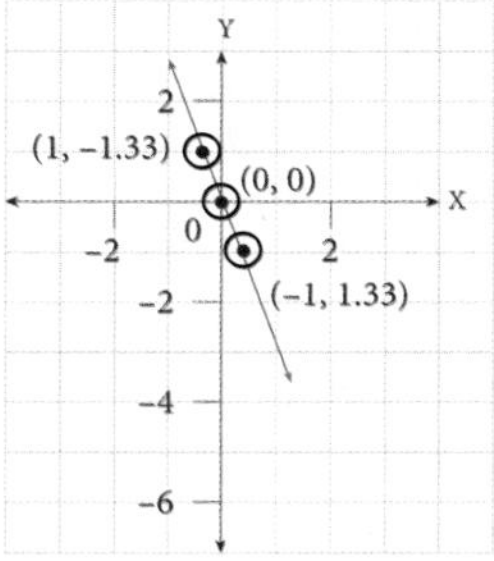

9. a. $x + 2y + 8 = 0$ **b.** $2x - 3y - 6 = 0$

10.

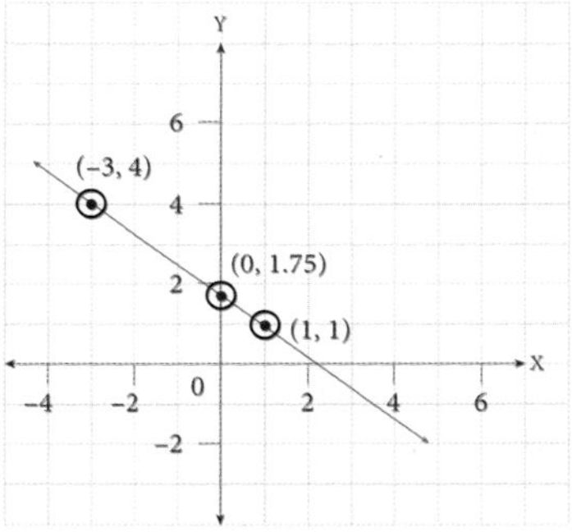

11. $2x + 3y + 15 = 0$ **12.** $x + 5y - 11 = 0$

13. $3x + 4y - 11 = 0$ **14.** $4x - 3y = 0$

15. $3x - 5y - 15 = 0$ **16.** $y = 5x$

17. one solution **18.** no solution

19. no solution

20. infinite (many) solution

21. $\left(-\frac{25}{11}, \frac{2}{11}\right)$

22. $\left(\frac{15}{7}, -\frac{18}{7}\right)$ **23.** (−4, 4) **24.** $(-\frac{3}{2}, -\frac{3}{2})$

25. $\left(-\frac{17}{31}, \frac{128}{31}\right)$ **26.** 35 and 30

27. 75 quarters and 25 dimes **28.** 325

29. a. \$13,500 **b.** \$25,500 **30. a.** \$5,450 **b.** 108,750

Chapter 10

Exercises 10.1

1.

a. 

b. 

c. 

3. **a.** Ray $\overrightarrow{AB}$ **b.** Line segment $\overline{LM}$ **c.** Line $\overleftrightarrow{YZ}$

5. **a.** (i) $\angle$DPC (ii) Acute
(iii) 60° (iv) Supplement =120°
Complement = 30°

b. (i) $\angle$AQB (ii) Acute
(iii) 80° (iv) Supplement = 100°
Complement = 10°

7. **a.** (i) $\angle$ZXY (ii) Right
(iii) 90° (iv) Supplement = 90°

b. (i) $\angle$RPQ (ii) Acute
(iii) 52° (iv) Supplement = 128°
Complement = 38°

9. **a.** 57.5° **b.** 72° **11.** **a.** 56.6° **b.** 91°

13. **a.** $\angle$AOB = $\angle$COD; $\angle$AOC = $\angle$BOD
b. $\angle$q = $\angle$t; $\angle$r = $\angle$s

15. $\angle$a = $\angle$c; $\angle$e= $\angle$g;
$\angle$b = $\angle$d; $\angle$d = $\angle$f;
$\angle$c = $\angle$e

17. **a.** $\angle$a = $\angle\theta$ = 132°
$\angle$b = 48°
$\angle$c = $\angle\theta$ = 132°
$\angle$d = 48°

b. $\angle$a = $\angle\theta$ = 120°
$\angle$b = 60°
$\angle$c = $\angle\Phi$ = 70°

19. **a.** $\angle$a = 63°
$\angle$b = 59°
$\angle$c = 63°
$\angle$d = 58°

b. $\angle$a = 50°
$\angle$b = 30°
$\angle$c = 130°

21. Φ = 32°

23. **a.** θ = 48°
b. $\angle a$ = 70°
$\angle b$ = 60°
$\angle c$ = 50°

Exercises 10.2

1. θ = 61° **3.** θ = 56°

5. **a.** Internal angles, θ = 150°, external angles, θ = 30°
b. Internal angles, θ = 162°, external angles, θ = 18°

7. **a.** n = 30 **b.** n = 72

9. θ = 137°

11. two angles θ = 70°, unique angle α = 40°

13. smaller pair = 25°, larger pair: 155°

15. **a.** Isosceles, acute triangle
b. Scalene, right triangle
c. Isosceles, obtuse triangle

17. **a.** Square **b.** Parallelogram **c.** Kite

19. $\angle$A = $\angle$B = $\angle$C = $\angle$D = 90°

21. $\angle$B = 98°, $\angle$C = 105°

23. Square **25.** Trapezoid

27. **a.** Square or rectangle **b.** Square or rhombus

29. **a.** Trapezoid, parallelogram, rhombus, rectangle, square
b. Isosceles trapezoid, parallelogram, kite, rhombus, rectangle, square

Exercises 10.3

1. **a.** P = 32 mm; A = 64 mm^2
b. P = 21.8 m; A = 28.8m^2

3. P = 65 cm; A = 207.19 cm^2

5. P = 32 m; A = 42 m^2

7. P = 5.5 m; A = 1.2 m^2

9. P = 24 cm; A = 27 cm^2

11. C = 50.27 cm; A = 201.06 cm^2

13. C = 5.781 m; A = 2.659 m^2

15. P = 314 cm; A = 6,107 cm^2

17. P = 70.702 m; A = 107.233 m^2

19. A = 744 m^2 **21.** d = 16.92 m

23. A = 0.27 km^2 **25.** A = 960 cm^2

27. $58.09 **29.** 9 km/h

31. P = 258 cm; A = 2,520 cm^2

33. A = 839.28 m^2

35. P = 39.42 m; A = 86.13 m^2

37. P = 163.45 cm, A = 1,418.08 cm^2

39. P = 97.12 cm, A = 198 cm^2

Exercises 10.4

1. SA = 3,750 mm^2, V = 15,625 mm^3

3. SA = 261 m^2, V = 225 m^3

5. SA = 678.58 cm^2, V = 1,696.46 cm^3

7. SA = 23,524.25 cm^2, V = 273,444.22 mm^3

9. SA = 318.09 cm^2, V = 466.53 cm^3

11. SA = 6,082.12 cm^2, V = 44,602.23 cm^3

13. SA = 5.31 m^2, V = 1.15 m^3

15. V = 1.866.67 m^3 **17.** V = 18.90 m^3 **19.** V = 252 m^3

21. V = 1.35 m^3, SA = 7.64 m^3

23. V = 7,180.96 m^3 **25.** SA = 13,750 cm^3

27. SA = 2,748.89 cm^2

29. SA = 511 mil. km^2, V = 1,086 bil. km^3

31. SA = 12.42 m^2, V = 1.38 m^3

33. SA = 122.54 m^2, V = 93.83 m^3

Review Exercises 10

1. **a.** (i) 35° (ii) Supplement = 145°
Complement = 55°

b. (i) 40° (ii) Supplement = 140°
Complement = 50°

3. **a.** a is adjacent to angle θ.
b is opposite to angle θ.
c is co-interior to angle θ.
d is alternate to angle θ.
e is corresponding to angle θ.

b. $b = d = e$ = 89°, $a = c$ = 91°

5. (i) $a = 100°$, $b = 144°$, $c = 64°$
(ii) $a = 162°$, $b = 72°$, $c = 40°$

7. Rectangle **b.** Kite **c.** Parallelogram

9. **a.** $\angle C = 45°$
$\angle B = \angle D = 135°$
b. $\angle R = 77°$
c. $\angle X = 102°$

11. **a.** 58°; Right, scalene triangle
b. 48°; Acute, Isosceles triangle

13. **a.** $P = 55.7$cm; $A = 115.5$ cm^2
b. $P = 71$ cm; $A = 120.96$ cm^2

15. $P = 84$ cm **17.** $P = 100$ cm, $A = 480$ cm^2

19. **a.** $C = 148.28$ cm, $A = 1{,}749.74$ cm^2
b. $C = 157.72$ cm, $A = 1{,}022.65$ cm^2

21. $SA = 644$ cm^2 **23.** 9.82 in^2

25. $P = 74.14$ cm, $A = 252.83$ cm^2

27. $P = 58.74$ m, $A = 159.81$ m^2

29. $SA = 305.61$ cm^2, $V = 386.04$ cm^3

31. $SA = 23.52$ cm^2, $V = 10.88$ cm^3

33. $SA = 2{,}789.73$ mm^2, $V = 8{,}180.71$ mm^3

Self-Test Exercises 10

1. **a.** (i) acute (ii) 146° (iii) 56°
b. (i) obtuse (ii) 64° (iii) n/a
c. (i) acute (ii) 113° (iii) 23°
d. (i) right (ii) 90° (iii) n/a

2. **a.** $a = 62°$, $b = 64°$, $c = 64°$,
b. $a = 75°$, $b = 143°$, $c = 68°$,

3. **a.** Right - isosceles triangle
b. Acute - equilateral triangle
c. Obtuse - scalene triangle

4. Square **b.** Rhombus **c.** Kite

5. **a.** $A = 13.61$ cm^2 **b.** $A = 150.02$ in^2

6. **a.** $A = 61.2$ cm^2 **b.** $A = 1.47$ m^2

7. **a.** $P = 7.85$ m, $A = 4.91$ m^2
b. $P = 112.84$ m, $A = 735.13$ m^2

8. 114 km/h

9. **a.** $A = 1.4$ m^2 **b.** $A = 91.89$ m^2

10. **a.** $V = 178{,}128.30$ mm^3
b. $V = 111.37$ cm^3
c. $V = 5{,}544.92$ cm^3

11. **a.** 7.98 cm **b.** $SA = 1{,}152$ cm^3

12. **a.** $r = 5.98$ cm **b.** $SA = 896$ cm^3

13. $SA = 113.18$ cm^3

14. **a.** $SA = 32.94$ m^2 **b.** $V = 12.56$ cm^3

15. $V = 626.74$ cm^3, $SA = 7.38$ cm^2

16. **a.** $V = 2{,}035.75$ cm^3 **b.** $V = 189{,}018.59$ cm^2

Chapter 11

Exercises 11.1

1. **a.** $\frac{AB}{DE} = \frac{BC}{EF} = \frac{AC}{DF}$; $\angle A = \angle D$; $\angle B = \angle E$; $\angle C = \angle F$;
b. $\frac{PQ}{RS} = \frac{QR}{ST} = \frac{PR}{RT}$; $\angle P = \angle R$; $\angle Q = \angle S$; $\angle R = \angle T$;

3. **a.** $AB = XY$; $BC = YZ$; $AC = XZ$;
$\angle A = \angle X$; $\angle B = \angle Y$; $\angle C = \angle Z$;
b. $DE = RS$; $EF = ST$; $DF = RT$;
$\angle D = \angle R$; $\angle E = \angle S$; $\angle F = \angle T$

5. a and c; SSS **7.** a and c; RHS

9. a and c; SAS **11.** a and b; SAS

13. a and c; RHS **15.** a and b; ASA

17. Similar **19.** Similar

21. Similar

23. Neither **25.** Congruent

27. $\angle A = \angle E = 56°$; $x = 6$; $y = 7.5$

29. $\angle N = \angle P = 60°$; $\angle M = \angle Q = 30°$; $x = 4.4$; $y = 2.5$

31. 8.5 m **33.** 3.44 m **35.** 1.55 m **37.** 7.5 m

Exercises 11.2

1. **a.** $c = 25$ cm **b.** $b = 6$ cm **c.** $a = 1.75$ cm

3. **a.** $c = 19.21$ cm **b.** $b = 15$ cm **c.** $a = 5.57$ cm

5. 2.5 cm **7.** 7.28 m **9.** 5.74 cm

11. P = 96 cm; A = 420 cm^2

13. P = 30.9 cm; A = 40.96 cm^2

15. $d = 6.32$ **17.** $d = 9.43$ **19.** $d = 6.40$

21. $d = 5$ **23.** 35.6 cm **25.** $d = 3.5$ m

27. 300 cm **29.** Yes, No

31. $h = 27.50$ cm; SA = 1,583.36 cm^2; V = 4,145.39 cm^3

33. $h = 84.87$ cm; SA = 26,238.52 cm^2; V = 219,867.57 cm^3

35. $h = 16.12$ cm; SA = 3,518.57 cm^2; V = 13,234.57 cm^3

Exercises 11.3

1. **a.** $\sin\theta = 0.9063$, $\cos\theta = 0.4226$, $\tan\theta = 2.1445$
b. $\sin\theta = 0.2164$, $\cos\theta = 0.9763$, $\tan\theta = 0.2217$
c. $\sin\theta = 0.7999$, $\cos\theta = 0.6000$, $\tan\theta = 1.3333$

3. **a.** $\theta = 27°$, $\cos\theta = 0.8910$, $\tan\theta = 0.5095$
b. $\theta = 72.99°$, $\sin\theta = 0.9562$, $\tan\theta = 3.2688$
c. $\theta = 19.99°$, $\sin\theta = 0.3418$, $\cos\theta = 0.9379$

5. **a.** $\cos\theta = \frac{4}{5}$, $\tan\theta = \frac{3}{4}$, $\theta = 37°$
b. $\sin\theta = \frac{7}{25}$, $\tan\theta = \frac{7}{24}$, $\tan\theta = 16°$
c. $\sin\theta = \frac{20}{29}$, $\cos\theta = \frac{21}{29}$, $\tan\theta = 44°$

7. 0 **9.** 0.25 **11.** 2.5

13. 18.93 cm **15.** 18.91 cm **17.** 8.34 cm

19. 50.29° **21.** 30.26° **23.** 14.83°

25. $\theta = 19.99°$, $\varphi = 28.07°$, $x = 8$ cm

27. $x = 15.56$ cm, $\theta = 45°$

29. $\theta = 74°$, $\sin \theta = 14.56$ cm, $x = 4.01$ cm

31. 5° **33.** 5° **35.** $m = 0.22$

37. $m = -0.22$ **39.** 452 m **41.** 1,700 m

43. 28.3°, 73.82 km/h **45.** $A = 892.7\ \text{cm}^2$

Exercises 11.4

1. $b = 36.5$ cm **3.** $x = 16.2$ cm **5.** $d = 25.7$ cm

7. u = 53.2 cm **9.** C = 77° **11.** Y = 41°

13. E = 14° **15.** U = 46 ° **17.** a = 26.3 cm

19. $z = 21.7$ cm **21.** $e = 33.2$ cm **23.** $u = 8.4$ cm

25. B = 94° **27.** Z= 95° **29.** D= 110°

31. V= 38° **33.** Sine Law **35.** Sine Law

37. Cosine Law **39.** Cosine Law **41.** Sine Law

43. ∠C = 25°, $a = 8.8$cm, $c = 18$cm

45. ∠B = 77°, $a = 51$cm, $b = 19$ cm

47. ∠ A= 72°, ∠C= 117°, $c = 23$ cm

49. ∠A= 148°, ∠C = 12°, $b = 13$ cm

51. ∠A = 34°, ∠B = 54°, ∠C = 91.470

53. ∠C = 19°, $a = 10$ cm, $b = 3.8$ cm

55. 6.3 km **57.** 9.17 knots at N 11° E

59. 74.4 m

Review Exercises 11

1. a and b, SSS **3.** a and b, ASA

5. $x = 3$ cm, $y = 4.5$ cm

7. **a.** $x = 20$ cm, $\varphi = 53.13°$, $\theta = 126.86°$
b. $x = 5.21$ cm, $\theta = 58°$, $\varphi = 71.56°$

9. **a.** $d = 9.9$ **b.** $d = 3.6$

11. **a.** $P = 152$ cm **b.** $A = 1{,}872\ \text{cm}^2$

13. $\frac{\sqrt{2}}{4}(\sqrt{3} - 1)$ **b.** $\sqrt{3}$

15. $\alpha = 120°$, $\beta = 55°$, $\gamma = 65°$

17. **a.** $h = 108$ m **b.** $x = 72$ m, $\theta = 52.62°$

19. 1,825 m

21. ∠A = 142°, ∠C = 8°, $b = 10.52$ cm

23. ∠A = 90°, $a = 51.95$ cm, $c = 50.81$ cm

25. ∠B = 26°, $a = 53.54$ cm, $c = 70.01$ cm

27. ∠B = 21°, ∠C = 19°, $a = 54.51$ cm

29. ∠A = 19°, ∠B = 22°, ∠C = 139°

Self-Test Exercises 11

1. **a.** $x = 5.6$ cm, $y = 4$ cm **b.** $y = 12.25$ cm, $x = 4$ cm

2. **a.** $x = 13.85$ cm, $y = 8$ cm, $z = 27.71$ cm
b. $x = 1.41$ cm, $y = 1$ cm

3. 24 cm

4. **a.** $P = 22.41$ m, $A = 18\ \text{m}^2$
b. $P = 100$ cm, $A = 480\ \text{cm}^2$

5. **a.** $SA = 81.55\ \text{cm}^2$, $V = 59.80\ \text{cm}^3$
b. $SA = 1{,}178.09\ \text{cm}^2$, $V = 5{,}890.48\ \text{cm}^3$

6. **a.** $d = 17$ **b.** $d = 11.31$ **c.** $d = 6.5$

7. **a.** 15.26 m **b.** 9.70 m

8. **a.** $x = 12$ cm, $\theta = 22.61°$, $\varphi = 67.39°$,
b. $x = 25.86$ cm, $\theta = 36°$, $y = 60.56$ cm

9. **a.** $\theta = 44°$, $y = 4.31$ cm, $x = 4.31$ cm,
b. $\theta = 103°$, $\beta = 47°$, $\gamma = 30°$,

10. 80.45 km **11.** 43 m

12. X = 98°, Y = 44°, $z = 7.6$ cm

13. R = 100°, $p = 18.4$ cm, $r = 23.6$ cm

14. 15.90 m

15. **a.** $x = 14.4$ cm **b.** $x = 1.73$ m, $y = 0.80$ m

16. 10 m

Chapter 12

Exercises 12.1

1. **a.** Continuous **b.** Continuous
c. Discrete **d.** Discrete

3. **a.** Quantitative **b.** Qualitative
c. Quantitative **d.** Quantitative

5. **a.** Ratio **b.** Ratio
c. Ratio **d.** Ordinal

7.

Stem	Leaf
1	3 8 9 9
2	1 5 7 8 9
3	1 1 2 4 7 8 9
4	3 4

9.

Stem	Leaf
4	5 8
5	1 2 5 9
6	4 5 9
7	0 3 5 7 8
8	0 1 1 2 4 5 8
9	2 5 7

11.

Subject	Tally	Frequency (f)
S	𝍸 𝍸 ||||	14
M	𝍸 𝍸 |	11
A	𝍸 ||||	9
F	𝍸 |	6

13. **a.**

Grade	# of students	Percent	Cumulative Percent	Angle	Cumulative angle
A+	24	12%	12%	43.2°	43.2°
A	30	15%	27%	54°	97.2°
B	36	18%	45%	64.8°	162°
C	52	26%	71%	93.6°	255.6°
D	42	21%	92%	75.6°	331.2°
F	16	8%	100%	28.8°	360°
Total	200				

b.

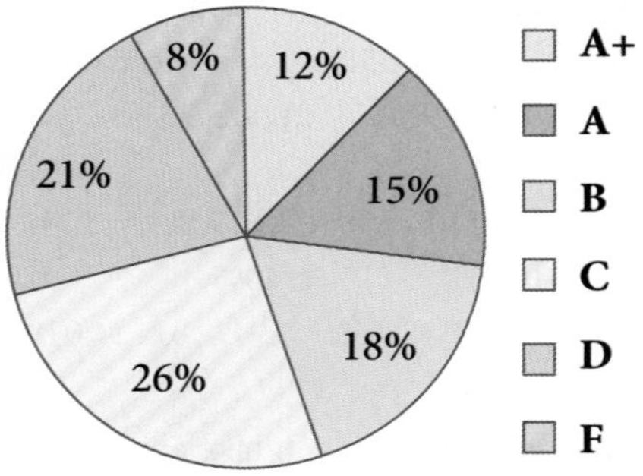

15.

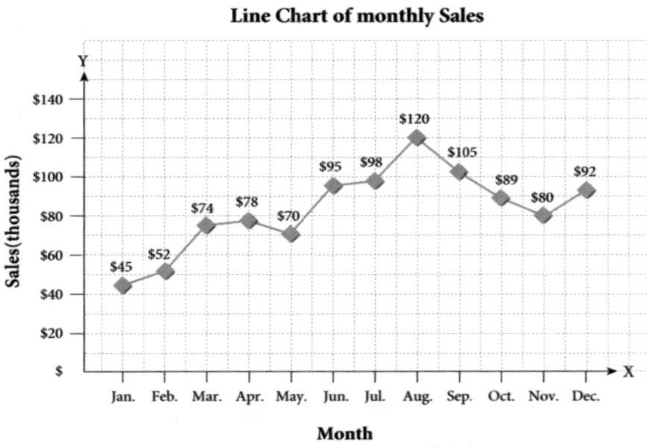

17.

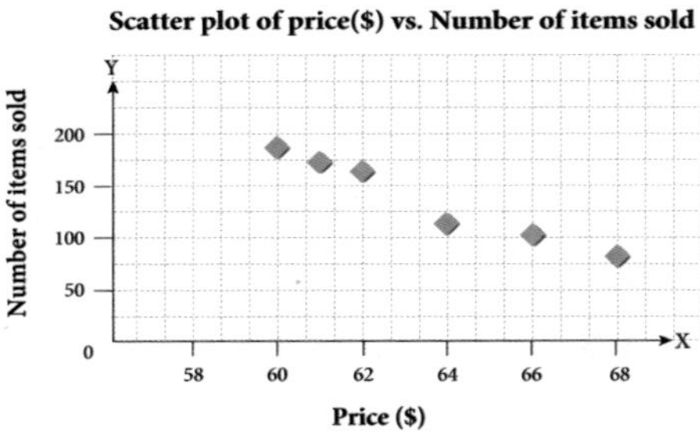

Negative correlation.

19.

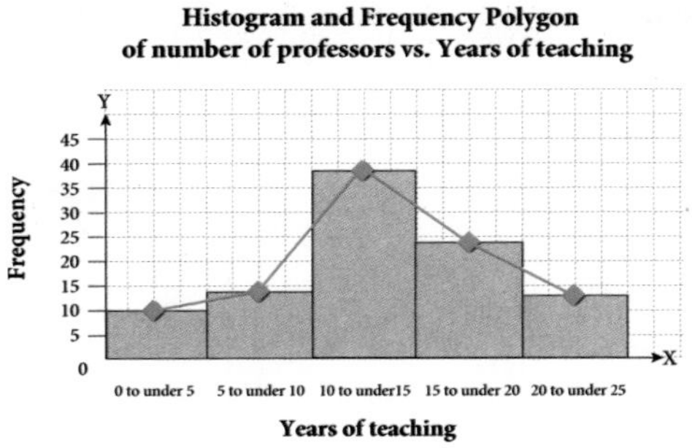

19.

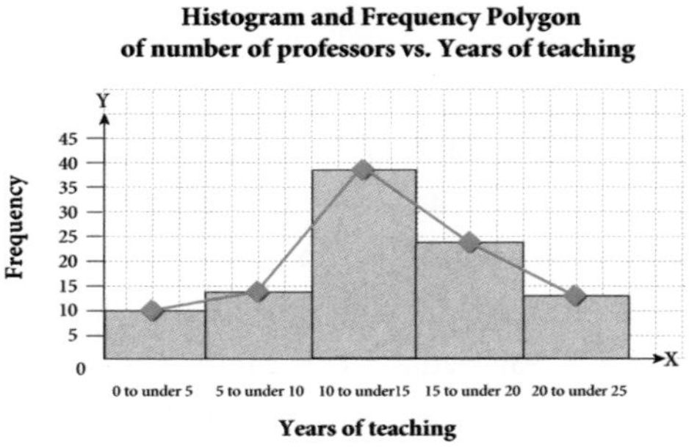

21.

Years	Number of students	Percent	Cumulative Percent
0 to under 5	10	0.10	10%
5 to under 10	14	0.14	14%
10 to under 15	39	0.39	39%
15 to under 20	24	0.24	24%
20 to under 25	13	0.13	13%
Total	100	1	100%

23. a. and **b.**

Years	Number of students	Cumulative frequency distribution	Cumulative Percent Frequency
0 to under 5	10	10	10%
5 to under 10	14	24	24%
10 to under 15	39	63	63%
15 to under 20	24	87	87%
20 to under 25	13	100	100%

c.

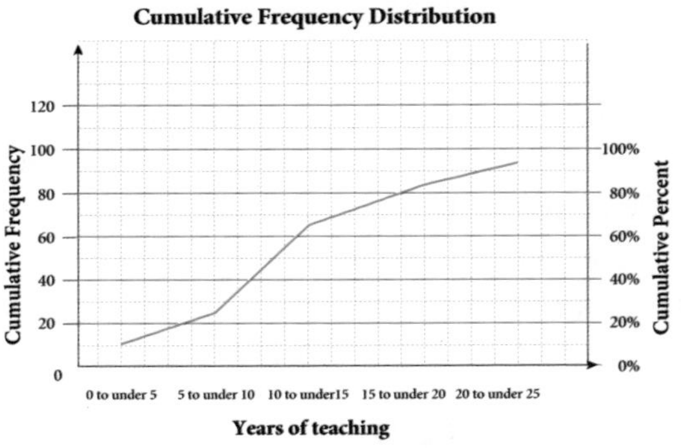

Exercises 12.2

1. 84.5 **3.** 92 **5.** 17.6

7. 75 **9.** $8,000 **11.** 50 kg

13. a. 51 **b.** 25 **c.** 26

15. a. 39.5 **b.** 14.5 **c.** 78

17. a. 26 **b.** 25.5

19. **a.** the data has no mode

b. 31

c. 36 and 41

21. 3.2 **23.** 71.67

25. **a.** 12 **b.** 4 **c.** 1.14

27. **a.** Mean: 6.57, Median: 6, Mode: 4

b. Mean: 64.13, Median: 66.5, Mode: 56

c. Mean: 124.56, Median: 125, Mode: 120

29. **a.** \$161.67 **b.** \$160 **c.** \$140

31. Mode:14; positively skewed.

33. Mean: \$16.02, Median: \$17.00, Mode: \$17.00

35. Mean: 2.72, Median: 3, Mode: 2

Exercises 12.3

1. **a.** 76 **b.** 13 **c.** 13.2

3. **a.** Q_1: 6, Q_3: 19.5 **b.** Q_1: 123, Q_3: 147

5. **a.** IQR = 13.5 **b.** IQR = 24

7. **a.** Greater than 79 **b.** Less than 23

9. **a.** Median: 97 **b.** Q_1: 76, Q_3: 100.5

c. IQR = 24.5 **d.** no outliers

11.

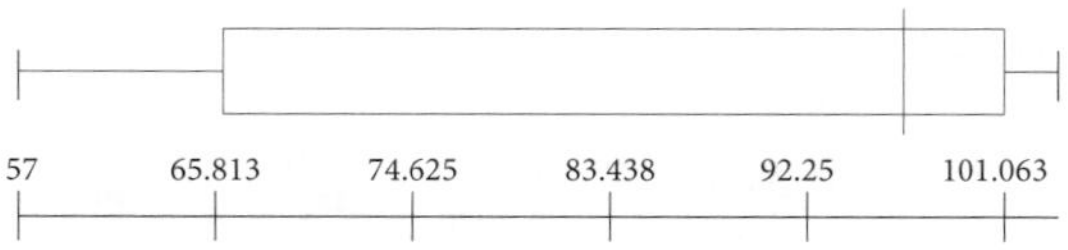

13.

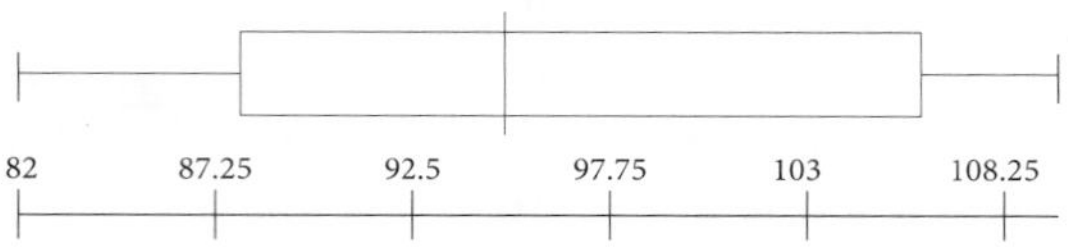

15. 6 **17.** **a.** 1.2 **b.** 4.56

19. **a.** $s^2 = 2.5$, $s = 1.58$ **b.** $s^2 = 32.7$, $s = 5.71$

21. $s^2 = 4.44$, $s = 2.11$

23. **a.** 81.2 **b.** 5.88

25. **a.** \$79,600 **b.** \$5,520

c. \$50,300,000 **d.** \$7,092.25

27. **a.** 68% **b.** 300 and 700 **c.** 336 and 664

29. $\bar{x} = 800$ g, $s = 20$

31. Maximum: 575, Minimum: 125

Exercises 12.4

1. 80% **3.** 75%

5.

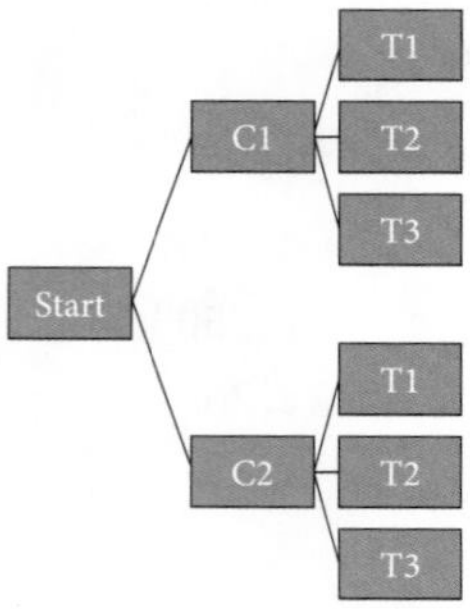

7. 55.56%

9. **a.** 20% **b.** 54.44% **c.** 80%

11. **a.** 33.33% **b.** 83.33% **c.** 66.67%

13. **a.** 50% **b.** 23.08% **15.** **a.** 53.84% **b.** 30.77%

17. **a.** 33.33% **b.** 55.56% **c.** 55.56%

19. **a.** 11.11% **b.** 88.89% **21.** **a.** 5.33% **b.** 4.98%

23. 85%

25. **a.** 3 : 1.0 **b.** 12 : 1 **27.** **a.** 9.8% **b.** 10.46%

29. **a.** 20% **b.** 10% **c.** 40% **d.** 60%

31. **a.** 21.54% 38.46% **c.** 24.01%

Review Exercises 12

1. **a.** **Continuous variables** can take any value within certain intervals, while discrete variables can only take certain values. Continuous variables are obtained by measurement, while **discrete variables** are given by counting.

b. **Ratio** measurements have a meaningful zero point and can be used in multiplying or dividing operations, while **interval** measurements have an arbitrary zero point and although they can be denoted by numbers, no meaningful multiplying or dividing operations can be performed with these.

3. **a.** Qualitative, discrete, nominal.

b. Quantitative, discrete, interval.

c. Quantitative, continuous, ratio.

d. Quantitative, discrete, ordinal.

e. Quantitative, continuous, ratio.

5.

Stem	Leaf
4	0 4 5 5 9
5	1 1 2 3 4 5 6 7 8 9
6	0 1 2 3 5 5 5 6 7 8 9
7	1 2 3 4 6 6 8 9
8	0 1 3 4 8
9	1 6

Class Interval	Frequency
40 to under 50	5
50 to under 60	9
60 to under 70	11
70 to under 80	8
80 to under 90	5
90 to under 100	2
Total	**40**

7. a.

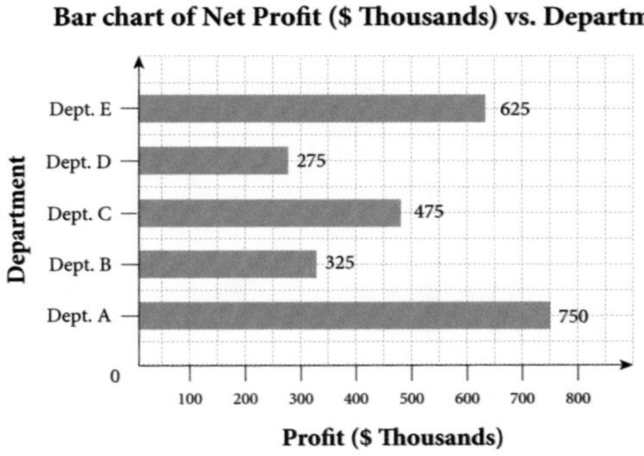

b.

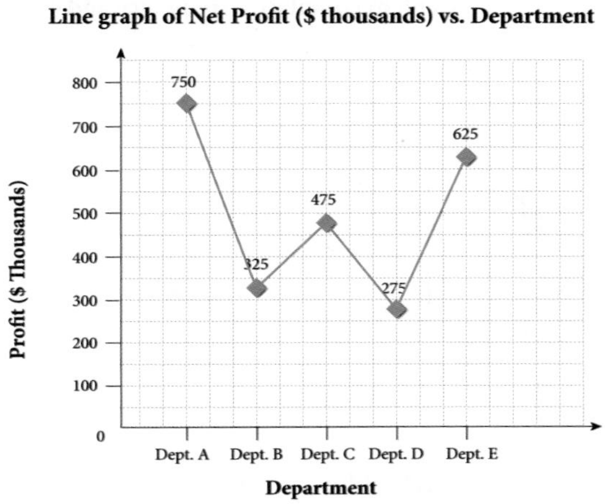

c. Pie chart of Profit ($ thousands) vs. Department

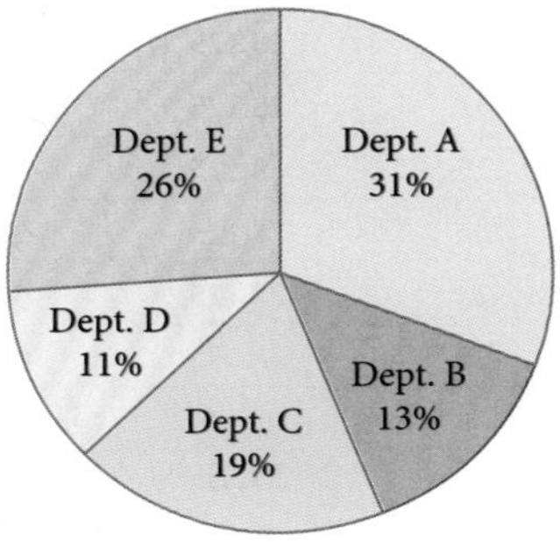

9. **a.** 10% **b.** 50% **c.** 80%

11. a.

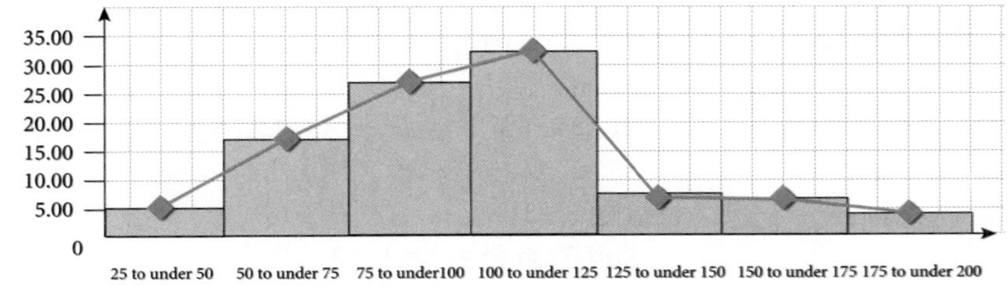

b and **c**

Marks out of 200	Frequency	Relative Frequency	Percent Frequency	Cumulative Frequency Distribution	Cumulative Percent Frequency
25 to under 50	5	0.05	5%	0.05	5%
50 to under 75	18	0.18	18%	0.23	23%
75 to under 100	28	0.28	28%	0.51	51%
100 to under 125	32	0.32	32%	0.83	83%
125 to under 150	8	0.08	8%	0.91	91%
150 to under 175	6	0.06	6%	0.97	97%
175 to under 200	3	0.03	3%	1	100%

d. **Graph of cumulative frequency and cumulative percent frequency vs. Marks**

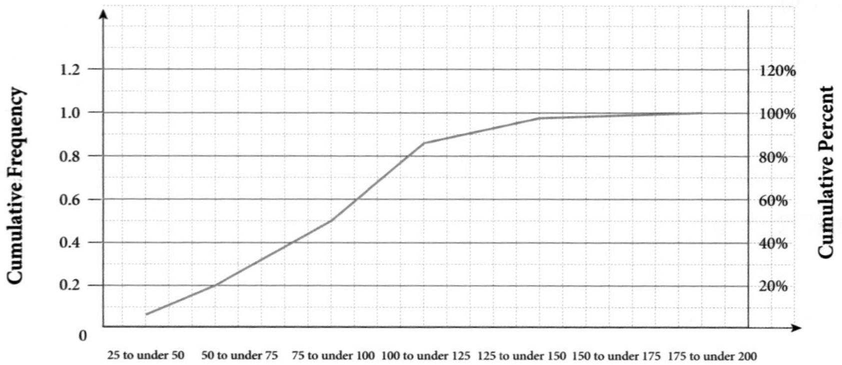

13. **a.** Mean: 93.45, Median: 93, Mode: 93

b. $Q_1 = 91$, $Q_3 = 97$

c. $IQR = 6$

d.

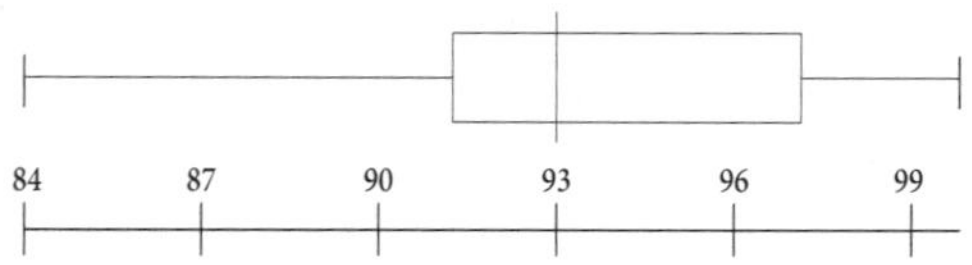

e. no outliers

15. Mean: 2,733.33, Median: 2,700, Mode: 2,700, Distribution: positively skewed.

17. **a.** Mean: 100

b. Modal class: '100 to under 125', mode: 112.5

c. Median is 87.5 and it falls in '75 to under 100' class.

19. **a.** 3.40 **b.** 11.34 **c.** 3.37

21. Median: 40, distribution: negatively skewed

23.

Evaluation	Percent w_i	Mark x_i	Weight $x_i\, w_i$
Test	20%	86	17.2
Midterm	25%	96	24
Final exam	30%	82	24.6
Online labs	15%	98	14.7
Homework	10%	100	10
	$\sum w_i = 100$		$\sum x_i\, w_i = 90.5$

25. **a.**

x	$\bar{x}$	$(x - \bar{x})$	$(x - \bar{x})$
3	15	−12	−12
9	15	−6	−6
15	15	0	0
21	15	6	6
27	15	12	12
$n = 5$		$\Sigma x - \bar{x} = 0$	$\Sigma\lvert x - \bar{x}\rvert = 36$

b.

x	$\bar{x}$	$(x - \bar{x})$	$(x - \bar{x})$
24	28.125	−4.125	4.125
37	28.125	8.875	8.875
21	28.125	-7.125	7.125
32	28.125	3.875	3.875
25	28.125	−3.125	3.125
36	28.125	7.875	7.875
22	28.125	−6.125	6.125
28	28.125	−0.125	0.125
	$n = 8$	$\Sigma x - \bar{x} = 0$	$\Sigma\lvert x - \bar{x}\rvert = 41.25$

27. 95% **29.** 68%

31. Mean: 20, Variance: 6.5, Standard deviation: 2.55

33. 44.44%

35. **a.** 11.11% **b.** 41.67%

37. **a.** 9.61% **b.** 61.54% **c.** 30.77%

39. **a.** 3 : 10 **b.** 3 : 1

41. 85.56% **43.** 2.25%

45. **a.** 5.67% **b.** 4.76%

47. **a.** 23.08% **b.** 76.92%

Self-Test Exercises 12

1. **a.** Qualitative, discrete, nominal.

b. Quantitative, discrete, ratio.

c. Quantitative, continuous, ratio.

d. Qualitative, discrete, ordinal.

e. Quantitative, continuous, ratio.

2.

a.

Stem	Leaf
3	6 8
4	1 2 7 8
5	1 4 4 5 6 7 8 9
6	1 2 2 3 4 5 7 8 8 8 9
7	1 1 4 6 5 7 9 9
8	1 2 3 4 6
9	1 4

b.

Class Interval	Frequency
30 to under 40	2
40 to under 50	4
50 to under 60	8
60 to under 70	11
70 to under 80	8
80 to under 90	5
90 to under 100	2
Total	**40**

3. a.

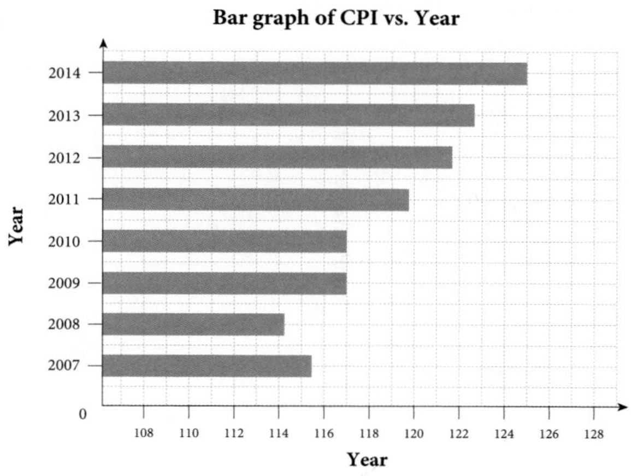

b.

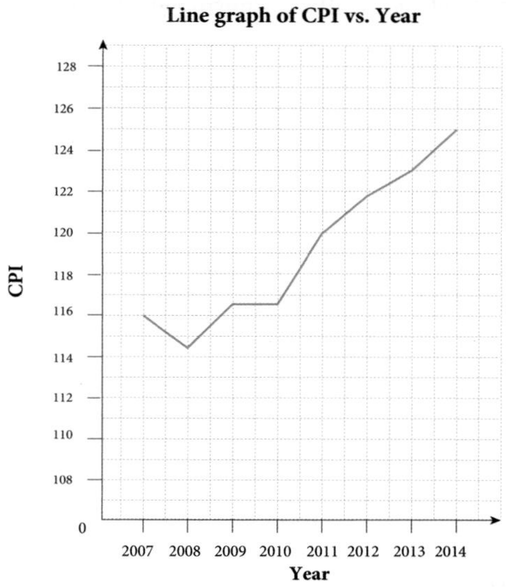

4.

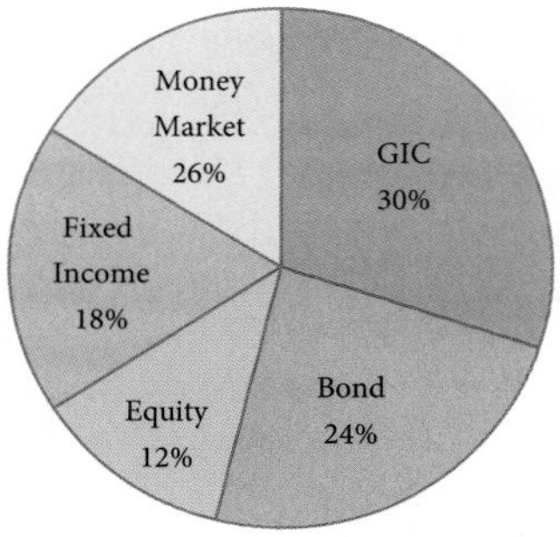

5. a.

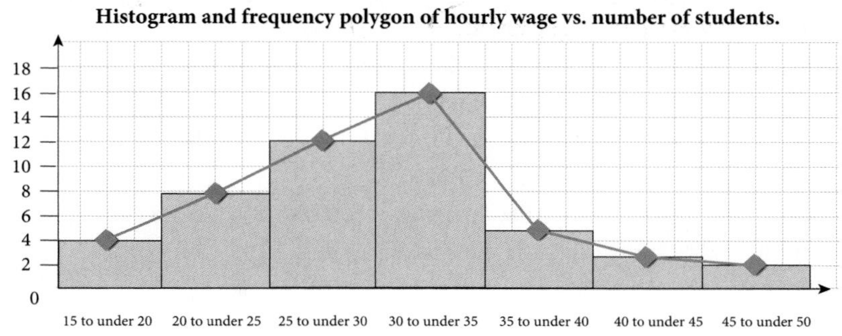

b and c

Hourly wages ($)	Students	Relative Frequency	Percent Frequency	Cumulative Frequency Distribution	Cumulative Percent Frequency
15 to under 20	4	0.08	8%	0.08	8%
20 to under 25	8	0.16	16%	0.24	24%
25 to under 30	12	0.24	24%	0.48	48%
30 to under 35	16	0.32	32%	0.8	80%
35 to under 40	5	0.1	10%	0.9	90%
40 to under 45	3	0.06	6%	0.96	96%
45 to under 50	2	0.04	4%	1	100%

d. Graph of Cumulative Frequency and Cumulative Percent Frequency vs. Hourly Wage

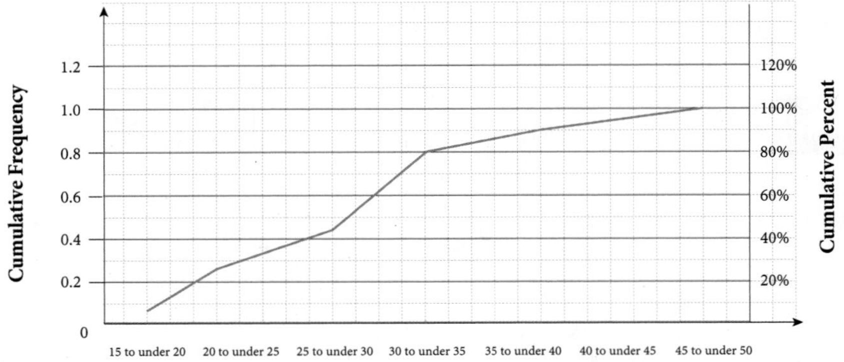

6. **a.** Mean: 49.36, Median: 49, Mode: 49

b. $Q_1 = 47, Q_3 = 52$

c. $IQR = 5$

d. No outliers

e.

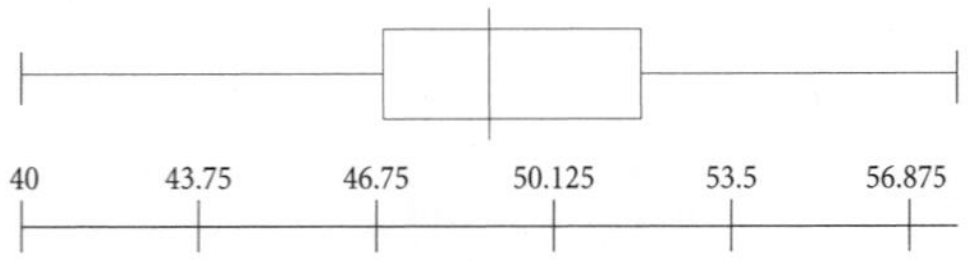

7. **a.** Mode: 30.2

b. Modal class: '30 to under 35', Mode: 32.5

c. '30 to under 35'

8. **a.** 3.12 **b.** 20.45 **c.** 4.52

9. Mean: 150.5, distribution: positively skewed.

10. 77.2%

11. **a.**

x	$\bar{x}$	$(x - \bar{x})$	$(x - \bar{x})$
1	5.17	−4.17	4.17
5	5.17	−0.17	0.17
3	5.17	−2.17	2.17
7	5.17	1.83	1.83
6	5.17	0.83	0.83
9	5.17	3.83	3.83
	$n = 5$	$\Sigma x - \bar{x} = 0$	$\Sigma\lvert x - \bar{x}\rvert = 13$

b.

x	$\bar{x}$	$(x - \bar{x})$	$(x - \bar{x})$
80	75	5	5
85	75	10	10
81	75	6	6
0	75	−75	75
85	75	10	10
90	75	15	15
87	75	12	12
92	75	17	17
	$n = 8$	$\Sigma x - \bar{x} = 0$	$\Sigma\lvert x - \bar{x}\rvert = 150$

12. Mean: 32.45

Median: 31

Variance: 175.7

Standard deviation: 13.25

13. **a.** Greater than 112 **b.** Lower than 40

14. **a.** 95% **b.** 99.7% **c.** 2.5% **d.** 2.5%

15. 50% **16.** 44.44%

17. 13.33%

18. **a.** 33.33% **b.** 50%

19. 43.31%

20. **a.** 4.98% **b.** 0.6% **c.** 1.81% **d.** 5.88%

21. **a.** 3 : 4 **b.** 3 : 4

Glossary

Absolute value of a number is its distance from the origin '0' on the number line. Since it is a distance, it is always positive and the direction does not matter.

Addend represents each of the numbers being added.

Addition refers to combining (finding the total or sum of) numbers.

Algebra is a branch of mathematics that is used to analyze and solve day-to-day business and finance problems. It deals with different relations and operations by using letters and symbols to represent numbers, values, etc.

Algebraic expression consists of one or more terms, with a combination of variables, numbers, and operation sign.

Alternate angles are formed on the opposite sides of the transversal on the interior of the parallel lines.

Angle is formed when two rays intersect at their endpoints.

Area(A) of a plane figure is the amount of 2-dimensional surface that is enclosed within the figure.

Annual salary is the amount that an employee will be paid for service over a period of one year.

Bar chart is a graph that uses either horizontal or vertical bars to show comparisons among categories or class intervals of grouped data.

Base(B) refers to the whole quantity or value (100%). It is usually followed by the word 'of', or 'percent of'.

Bi-weekly pay period refers to payment received once in two weeks. An employee will receive 26 bi-weekly payments through the year.

Billions group is the fourth group of three digits starting from the right of a whole number.

Binomial is a polynomial with two terms.

Buying rate (buy rate) is the rate at which the financial institution buys a particular foreign currency from the customers.

Celsius scale (°C) is part of the metric system. It has a basis in which water freezes at 0°C and boils at 100°C.

Central tendency is based on the concept that there is a single value that best summarizes the entire set of numeric data.

Co-interior angles are formed on the same side of the transversal and on the interior of the parallel lines.

Coefficient is the numerical factor in front of the variable in a term.

Commission is the payment that an employee receives for selling a product or service.

Commission rate is used to calculate the commission payment that an employee receives for selling a product or service.

Common factor is a factor that is common to two or more numbers.

Common logarithm is a logarithm to the base 10.

Complex fraction is a fraction in which one or more fractions are found in the numerator or denominator.

Complex number is a number that consists of real numbers and imaginary numbers.

Composite number is a whole number that has at least one factor other than 1 and the number itself.

Conditional equations are equations whose left side and right side are equal only for a certain value of the variable.

Consistent linear system is a linear system of two equations that has one or many solutions.

Constant is a term that has only a number, without any variables.

Consumer Price Index (CPI) is an indicator of changes in consumer prices experienced by Canadians.

Continuous variables is obtained by measuring.

Contradiction is an equation that is not true for any value of the variable.

Corresponding angles are formed on the same corner of the intersection between the transversal and each of the parallel lines.

Cosine Law provides a formula that relates the lengths of the sides of a triangle to the cosine of one of its angles.

Currency cross-rate table is used to display the currency exchange rates for quick reference.

Decimal numbers represent a part or a portion of a whole number.

Denominator represents the total number of equal parts into which the whole unit is divided.

Dependent system of equations is a system of equations that has an infinite number of solutions.

Descriptive Statistics deals with the organizing, presenting, and summarizing of raw data to present meaningful information.

Difference refers to the result of subtracting two or more numbers.

Discrete variables are obtained by counting, or are data that can only take on specific values.

Dividend refers to the number that is being divided.

Division can be thought of as repeated subtractions.

Divisor is the number by which the dividend is divided.

Elimination method is a method of solving systems of linear equations, when none of the equations in the system has a variable with a coefficient of 1 or −1.

Equivalent equations are equations that have the same solution.

Equivalent ratio is obtained when all the terms of the ratio are multiplied by the same number or divided by the same number.

Event is the specific outcome of an experiment.

Exchange rates also called the foreign exchange rate or forex rate, are used for converting currencies between countries.

Experiment is a process or action that leads to one and only one well-defined result of several possible results.

Exponent represents the number of times the base of an exponential notation is multiplied.

Exponential notation is used to represent a number that is multiplied by itself repeatedly.

Expression is a combination of terms. It usually refers to a statement of relations among variables.

Factor refers to each of the combinations of variables and/or numbers multiplied together in a term.

Factor of a number is a whole number that can divide the number with no remainder.

Factor tree helps to find all the prime factors of a number.

Fahrenheit scale (°F) is primarily used in the USA. It has a basis in which water freezes at 32°F and boils at 212°F.

Formula is similar to an equation. In a formula, the relationship among many variables is written as a rule for performing calculations.

Fraction in lowest terms is a fraction in which the numerator and denominator have no factors in common (other than 1).

Fraction is a method of representing numbers, where one non-zero integer is divided by another non-zero integer.

Fraction bar represents the division sign.

Fractional exponent is when the exponent of a number or variable is a fraction.

Frequency(*f*) is the number of times an event happens.

Frequency distribution is a method to summarize large amounts of data without displaying each value of the observation.

Geometry is a branch of Mathematics that deals with the study of relative positions, properties, and relations of geometric objects.

Highest Common Factor (HCF) of two or more numbers is the largest common number that divides the numbers with no remainder. HCF is also known as the Greatest Common Divisor (GCD).

Histogram is similar to a vertical bar chart in which the categories or class intervals are marked on a horizontal axis and the class frequencies are represented by the heights of the bars .

Hourly rate of pay refers to payments received per hour for service provided.

Hypotenuse is the longest side of a right-triangle opposite the right-angle.

Identity is an equation which is true for any value of the variable.

Imaginary Number is a number, which when raised to the power of 2, results in a negative real number.

Improper fraction is a fraction in which the numerator is greater than the denominator; i.e., the value of the entire fraction is more than 1.

Inconsistent linear system is a linear system of two equations that has no solutions.

Independent events refers to an event the occurrence of which has no effect on the occurrence of the other event.

Independent system of equations is a system of equations that has one or no solutions.

Index number is used to express the relative value of an item compared to a base value.

Inferential Statistics deals with the analysis of a sample drawn from a larger population to develop meaningful inferences about the population based on sample results.

Inflation is a rise on the general level of prices of goods and services in an economy over time.

Interest is a fee that borrowers pay to lenders for using their money temporarily for a period of time.

Interest percent (%) is the product of the interest rate (*r*) and the time.

Irrational number is a number that cannot be expressed as a fraction.

Levels of measurement are rules that describe the properties of numbers that are measured and the way in which they can be used to provide additional information on the data.

Like terms are terms that have the same variables and exponents.

Line is an object that has only one dimension: length.

Line segment is the portion of a line bound between two points.

Linear equation is an algebraic equation with one or two variables (each to the power of one), which produces a straight line when plotted on a graph.

Logarithm is a faster method of solving for an unknown exponent. It is the exponent to which the base is raised to get the number.

Lowest Common Denominator (LCD) of a set of two or more fractions is the smallest whole number that is divisible by each of the denominators.

Lowest Common Multiple (LCM) of two or more numbers is the smallest multiple that is common to those numbers.

Markdown is the amount by which the selling price of a product is reduced in determining the sale price.

Markup is the amount that a business adds to the cost of the product to arrive at the selling price of the product.

Maturity value (S) is the sum of the accumulated value of interest over time and the principal amount of the loan or investment.

Metric system of measurement uses meter (m), gram (g), and liter (L) as the base units for the measurements of length, mass, and capacity, respectively. The Celsius (°C) scale is used for temperature.

Millions group is the third group of three digits starting from the right of a whole number.

Minuend is the number from which another number is subtracted.

Mixed number consists of both a whole number and a proper fraction, written side-by-side, which implies that the whole number and proper fraction are added.

Monomial is an algebraic expression that has only one term.

Monthly pay period refers to payment received once a month. An employee will receive 12 monthly payments through the year.

Multiple of a number is a whole number that can be divided by the number with no remainder.

Multiplicand is the number that indicates the number of times a number is multiplied.

Multiplication can be thought of as repeated additions.

Multiplier is the number that is multiplied.

Mutually exclusive refers to events that cannot occur at the same time or there is no common outcome.

Mutually non-exclusive refers to events that occur at the same time or there is a common outcome.

Natural logarithm is a logarithm to the base '*e*', where the constant $e = 2.718282....$

Number line is used to represent numbers graphically as points on a horizontal line.

Numerator represents the number of equal parts in a fractional number.

Opposite angles are formed by any intersecting lines that are opposite to the same vertex.

Order of a ratio is the order in which a ratio is presented.

Order of operations is the order in which arithmetic operations are carried out in an equation. The order that is followed is: Brackets, Exponents, Division, Multiplication, Addition, and Subtraction (BEDMAS).

Ordered pair is used to locate a point in the coordinate system. The ordered pair (x, y) describes a point in the plane by its x- and y-coordinates.

Outcome is the particular result of a single trial of an experiment (i.e., what we observe and record from the experiment).

Outlier is a number that is very different from the rest of the group.

Overtime payment refers to additional payment eligible to be received for working more than the specified number of hours in a week.

Overtime rate of pay refers to the rate used to calculate the overtime payment for working more than the specified number of hours in a week.

Parallel lines are lines that have the same slope. All vertical lines are parallel to each other and all horizontal lines are parallel to each other.

Pay period refers to the frequency of payments (how often payments are being made).

Payroll is a record of the payment made to every employee of an organization.

Percent (per cent or per hundred in the literal meaning) is used to express a quantity out of 100 units and is represented by the symbol '%'.

Percent change is often used to express the amount of change to the initial (original) value; i.e., the amount of change (increase or decrease) is calculated as a percent change (%*C*) of its initial value.

Perfect root is a whole number whose root is also a whole number.

Perfect square is any whole number base with an exponent of 2; i.e., a whole number multiplied by itself results in a perfect square.

Perimeter (P) of a plane figure is the total length of the boundary of the plane figure.

Perpendicular lines are lines that have a slope of −1. The lines are also perpendicular if one of them is vertical and the other is horizontal.

Pie chart is usually used to summarize and show classes or groups of data in proportion to the whole dataset.

Place value is the position of each digit in a number.

Plane Geometry is the study of the properties and relations of plane figures such as triangles, quadrilaterals, circles, etc.

Polynomial is an algebraic expression that has two or more terms.

Population refers to all possible individuals, objects, or measurements of items of interest.

Portion (*P*) refers to the portion of the whole quantity or value (portion of the base).I

Prime number is a whole number that has only two factors: 1 and the number itself.

Principal (*P*) is the initial amount of money invested or borrowed.

Principal root is the positive root of a number.

Pro-ration is defined as sharing or allocating the quantities, usually the amounts, on a proportionate basis.

Product refers to the result from multiplying numbers.

Proper fraction is a fraction in which the numerator is less than the denominator.

Proportion is used to describe two sets of ratios that are equal.

Purchasing power of money is the number of goods/services that can be purchased with a unit of currency.

Pythagorean Theorem is a famous theorem in Mathematics that states that the squares of the lengths of the two shorter sides that meet at the right-angle equals the square of the longest side opposite the right-angle.

Quadrant is one of the four regions that is formed by the X- and Y-axes in the rectangular coordinate system. They are numbered counter-clockwise from one (I) to four (IV).

Qualitative variables are data that are expressed non-numerically and are known as non-numerical data.

Quantitative variables are data that are expressed using numbers and are known as numeric data.

Quotient refers to the result of dividing numbers.

Range(*R*) is the difference between the highest and the lowest value in a dataset.

Rate is a special ratio that is used to compare two quantities or amounts having different units of measure.

Rate (R) refers to the percent relationship between the base and portion. It usually carries the percent sign (%) or the word 'percent'.

Ratio is a comparison or relationship between two or more quantities with the same unit.

Rational number is a fraction where one integer is divided by another non-zero integer.

Ray is the portion of a line bound in one direction by a point.

Real income is the income after adjusting for inflation.

Real number includes rational and non-rational numbers.

Reciprocal is the fraction that is obtained by inverting the original fraction.

Remainder refers to the number left over when the dividend cannot be divided evenly by the divisor.

Repeating decimal is a decimal that does not end but shows a repeating pattern.

Root is the inverse of exponents.

Rounding numbers makes them easier to work with and easier to remember. Rounding changes some of the digits in a number but keeps its value close to the original.

Rules of Logarithms can be used to combine two or more logarithmic expressions into a single logarithmic expression.

Rules or Laws of Exponents are used to simplify expressions that involve exponents.

S&P/TSX is an index of stock prices of the largest companies on the Toronto Stock Exchange.

Sale Price of an item refers to the reduced (or discounted) selling price; i.e., the price after markdown (D).

Sample refers to a set of data drawn from the population.

Sample space is the set of all possible outcomes in an experiment.

Scatter Plot is a graph showing pairs of numerical data with the independent variable on a horizontal axis and the dependent variable on a vertical axis.

Scientific notation is a method of expressing numbers using decimal numbers with one non-zero digit to the left of the decimal point multiplied by the power of 10.

Selling price (S) of an item refers to the regular (or normal) selling price; i.e., the price before markdown (D).

Selling rate (sell rate) is the rate at which the financial institution sells a particular foreign currency to the customers.

Semi-monthly pay period refers to payment received twice a month. An employee will receive 24 semi-monthly payments through the year.

Sharing quantities refers to the allocation or distribution of a quantity into two or more portions (or units) based on a given ratio.

Short ton is the US customary unit for ton and is represented by 'ton'.

Significant digits are used to determine the accuracy of a number.

Simplifying fractions is when you divide both the numerator and denominator of a fraction by the same number, which results in an equivalent fraction.

Sine Law provides a formula that relates the sides of a triangle to the sine of its angles.

Slope (m) is the steepness of the line relative to the X-axis. It is the ratio of the change in the value of y (called 'rise') to the corresponding change in the value of x (called 'run').

Statistics is a branch of Mathematics and procedures that involves collecting, organizing, presenting, analyzing, and interpreting data for the purpose of drawing conclusions and making a decision.

Stem-and-Leaf Plot is one method of displaying data to show the spread of data and the location of where most of the data points lie.

Stock index is an application of index numbers and is used to measure the performance of stock markets.

Substitution method is a method of solving systems of linear equations, when one of the equations in the system has a variable with a coefficient of 1 or −1.

Subtraction refers to finding the difference between numbers.

Subtrahend is the number that is being subtracted from another number.

Sum refers to the result from adding two or more numbers.

System of equations refers to two or more equations analyzed together.

Tally Chart is a method of collecting and organizing data, used to keep count of the number of times a particular event or data occurs.

Term is a number, variable, or a combination of numbers and variables that are multiplied and/or divided together.

Term of a ratio is the quantity in a ratio.

Terminating decimal is a decimal that ends.

Thousands group is the second group of three digits starting from the right of a whole number.

Time period (t) is the time taken to settle a loan or an investment.

Trigonometric ratio is a ratio of the lengths of two sides of a right-triangle.

Trigonometry is a branch of Mathematics that studies relationships involving lengths and angles of triangles.

Trillions group is the fifth group of three digits starting from the right of a whole number.

Trinomial is a polynomial with three terms.

Unit price is the unit rate when it is expressed in unit currency (dollars, cents, etc.).

Unit rate represents the number of units of the first quantity (or measurement) that corresponds to one unit of the second quantity.

Units group is the first group of three digits starting from the right of a whole number.

Unlike terms are terms that have different variables or the same variables with different exponents.

US Customary system of measurement uses the yard (yd), the pound (lb), and the gallon (gal) as the base units for the measurements of length, mass, and capacity, respectively. The Fahrenheit (°F) scale is used for temperature.

Variable is a letter that represents one or more numbers.

Variance is used as a measure to describe the spread of numbers from each other, in a dataset.

Vertex of an angle is the point of intersection of two rays.

Weekly pay period refers to payment received once a week. An employee will receive 52 weekly payments through the year.

Whole number is any counting number (0, 1, 2, 3, 4…), including zero (0) and any natural number or positive integer (1, 2, 3, 4...).

Workweek is the standard working hours per week specified by the organization.

x-intercept is the point at which the line crosses the X-axis and where the y-coordinate is zero.

y-intercept is the point at which the line crosses the Y-axis and where the x-coordinate is zero.

Zero is the smallest whole number.

Index

P

Q

R

S